# *Warman's* AMERICANA & COLLECTIBLES

## Volumes in the Encyclopedia of Antiques and Collectibles

Harry L. Rinker, Series Editor

*Warman's Americana & Collectibles,* 6th Edition,
edited by Harry L. Rinker

*Warman's Country Antiques & Collectibles,*
by Dana Gehman Morykan and Harry L. Rinker

*Warman's English & Continental Pottery & Porcelain,* 2nd Edition,
by Susan and Al Bagdade

*Warman's Furniture,*
edited by Harry L. Rinker

*Warman's Glass,*
by Ellen Tischbein Schroy

*Warman's Oriental Antiques,*
by Gloria and Robert Mascarelli

*Warman's*

# AMERICANA & COLLECTIBLES

## 6th EDITION

Edited by
HARRY L. RINKER

Wallace-Homestead Book Company
Radnor, Pennsylvania

Sixth edition 

ISBN: 0-87069-684-X
ISSN: 0739-6457
Library of Congress Catalog Card No.: 84-643834
Manufactured in the United States of America

2 3 4 5 6 7 8 9 0    2 1 0 9 8 7 6 5 4

Additional copies of this book may be obtained from your bookstore or directly from the publisher, Wallace-Homestead Book Company, Radnor, PA 19089. Enclose $15.95 plus $2.50 for postage and handling for the 1st book, 50¢ for each additional book. Pennsylvania residents please add 96¢ state sales tax per book.

## EDITORIAL STAFF

HARRY L. RINKER
*Editor*

ELLEN T. SCHROY
*Senior Editor*

TERESE J. OSWALD
*Associate Editor*

DANA N. MORYKAN
*Associate Editor*

NANCY M. BUTT
*Research Librarian*

HARRY L. RINKER, JR.
*Art Director*

JOCELYN C. MOUSLEY, RICHARD SCHMELTZLE, DIANE L. STERNER
*Support Staff*

## BOARD OF ADVISORS

Franklin Arnall
The Collector
P. O. Box 253
Claremont, CA 91711
(714) 621-2461
*Padlocks*

Arthur R. Bink
Zeppelin
P. O. Box 2502
Cinnaminson, NJ 08077
(609) 829-3959
*Dirigibles*

Dick Bitterman
1701 West Chase Ave.
Chicago, IL 60626
(312) 743-3330
*Flag Collectibles; Pens and Pencils; Pin-Up Art*

Bob Block
42 Bassett St.
Milford, CT 06460
*Marbles*

Stanley A. Block
P. O. Box 222
Trumball, CT 06611
(203) 261-3223
*Marbles*

Rick Botts
2545 SE 60th Ct.
Des Moines, IA 50317
(515) 265-8324
*Jukeboxes*

Lorie Cairns
Cairns Antiques
P. O. Box 44026
Lemoncove, CA 93244
(209) 564-2158
*Labels*

Leonard Calabrese
3065 Rumsey Dr.
Ann Arbor, MI 48105
(313) 662-0140
*Planter's Peanuts*

Tina M. Carter
882 So. Mollison Ave.
El Cajon, CA 92020
(619) 440-5043
*Teapots*

Kathie Diehl
P. O. Box 5672
Baltimore, MD 21210
(301) 243-3747
*Little Golden Books*

Craig Dinner
P. O. Box 4399
Sunnyside, NY 11104
(718) 729-3850
*Figural, Bottle Openers*

Marilyn Dipboye
33161 Wendy Dr.
Sterling Hts., MI 48315
(313) 264-0285
*Cat Collectibles*

Doug Flynn and Al Bolton
Holloway House
P. O. Box 547
Mesilloc, NM 88046-0547
(505) 527-4555
*British Royalty Commemoratives*

M. D. Fountain
201 Alvena
Wichita, KS 67203
(316) 943-1925
*Swankyswigs*

Jerry Gallagher
420 First Avenue N.W.
Plainview, MN 55964
(507) 534-3511
*Morgantown Glass*

Roselyn Gerson
P. O. Box Letter S
Lynbrook, NY 11563
*Compacts*

Ted Hake
Hake's Americana & Collectibles
P. O. Box 1444
York, PA 17405
(717) 848-1333
*Disneyana, Political Items*

Doris & Burdell Hall
B & B Antiques
P. O. Box 1501
Fairfield Bay, AR 72088
(501) 884-6571
*Morton Potteries*

Mrs. Mary Hamburg
20 Cedar St.
Danville, IL 61832
(217) 446-2323
*Pig Collectibles*

Todd Holmes
12411 Wornall Rd.
Kansas City, MO 64145
(816) 941-3100
*Boyd Crystal Art Glass, Business and Office Equipment, Typewriters*

Tim Hughes
Hughes'
P. O. Box 3636
Williamsport, PA 17701
(717) 326-1045
*Newspapers, Headline Editions*

Joan Hull
1376 Nevada
Huron, SD 57350
(605) 352-1685
*Hull Pottery*

David and Sue Irons
Irons Antiques
R. D. #4, Box 101
Northampton, PA 18067
(215) 262-9335
*Irons*

Ron Lieberman
The Family Album
R. D. #1, Box 42
Glen Rock, PA 17327
(717) 235-2134
*Books, Limited Editions Club*

Wray Martin
221 Upper Paradise
Hamilton, Ontario
Canada, L9C 5C1
(416) 383-0454
*Matchcovers*

Richard W. Massiglia
380 Medford St.
Somerville, MA 02145
(617) 625-4067
*Elephant Collectibles*

Patricia McDaniel
Old Storefront Antiques
P. O. Box 357
Dublin, IN 47335
(317) 478-4809
*Drugstore Collectibles, Veterinary Collectibles*

Joyce Magee
7219 Auld Rd.
Bradford, OH 45308
(513) 447-7134
*Children's Books*

Nancy McMichael
P. O. Box 53132
Washington, D. C., 20009
*Snowdomes*

Gary L. Miller and K. M. Scotty Mitchell
Millchell
2112 Lipscomb
Ft. Worth, TX 76110
(817) 923-3274
*Electrical Appliances*

Jocelyn C. Mousley
137 South Main St.
Quakertown, PA 18951
(215) 536-9211
*Dog Collectibles*

Susan Brown Nicholson
P. O. Box 595
Lislie, IL 60532
(312) 964-5240
*Post Cards*

Joan Collett Oates
685 S. Washington
Constantine, MI 49042
(313) 887-5677
*Phoenix Bird Pattern*

Clark Phelps
Amusement Sales
127 North Main
Midvale, UT 84047
(801) 255-4731
*Punchboards*

Ferill J. Rice
302 Pheasant Run
Kaukauna, WI 54130
*Fenton*

Harry L. Rinker
P. O. Box 248
Zionsville, PA 18092
(215) 965-1122
*Canal Collectibles, Puzzles*

Harry L. Rinker, Jr.
6730 Geissinger Rd. Extended
Zionsville, PA 18092
(215) 966-3939
*World War II*

Christie Romero
P. O. Box 1904
Hawaiian Gardens, CA 90716
(310) 425-4373
*Jewelry, Costume*

Jim and Nancy Schaut
Box 10781
Glendale, AZ 85318
(602) 878-4293
*Horse Collectibles*

Virginia R. Scott
275 Milledge Terrace
Athens, GA 30606
(404) 548-5966
*Candlewick*

George Theofiles
Miscellaneous Man
Box 1776
New Freedom, PA 17349
(717) 235-4766
*Posters*

John S. Waldsmith
Antique Graphics
P. O. Box 191
Sycamore, OH 44882
(419) 927-2930
*Bookmarks; Stereo Viewers; Stereographs; Viewmasters*

Lewis S. Walters
2640 Washington St.
Allentown, PA 18104
(215) 820-5088
*Radios*

Fred L. Wilhelm
828 Hermes Ave.
Leucadia, CA 92024
(619) 753-8264
*Soldiers, Dimestore*

Kathy Wojciechowski
P. O. Box 230
Peotone, IL 60468
*Nippon*

Estelle Zalkin
7524 West Treasure Dr.
Miami Beach, FL 33141
(305) 864-3012
*Thimbles*

# Introduction

Welcome to *Warman's Americana & Collectibles,* the cornerstone of the Warman's Encyclopedia of Antiques and Collectibles. In 1983, the first edition of *Warman's Americana & Collectibles* introduced the collecting community to the Warman format—category introductions featuring collecting hints, history, references, periodicals, and reproduction and copycat information complemented by detailed, accurate listings and values. As a result of the enthusiastic acceptance of this format, it was extended to *Warman's Antiques and Their Prices* and ultimately to subsequent volumes of Warman's Encyclopedia of Antiques and Collectibles.

*Warman's Americana and Collectibles* was a pioneering work, the first general price guide to mass–produced, twentieth century objects. It helped define and solidify the modern collectibles market. As the collectibles market has matured, so has *Warman's Americana and Collectibles.* If you have a copy of the first edition, compare the categories listed in it to those found in this sixth edition. Times *have* changed. Perhaps this is why so many individuals find the collectibles market so exciting.

*Collectibles* are the things your parents, you, and your children have played and lived with. The things that belonged to your grandparents are now *antiques.* The evolution of an object from new to desirable to collectible to antique within one's lifetime, i.e., an approximate fifty year span, is difficult for some to accept. However, it is reality.

*Warman's Americana & Collectibles* takes you on a nostalgic trip down memory lane. Do not get angry about the things you or your parents discarded. Be thrilled by the value of the things that were saved. Do not hesitate to buy back the things from your childhood that evoke pleasant memories. As you do, you will find that the real value of objects is not monetary, but the joy that comes from collecting, owning, and, most importantly, playing and living with them once again.

Finally, do not ever be embarrassed by what you collect. *Warman's Americana & Collectibles* is based on the premise that it is acceptable to collect anything you wish. Remember one simple fact. All of today's antiques were collectibles in the past.

## WHAT IS A COLLECTIBLE?

As the twentieth century nears its end, the definition of what constitutes an antique is becoming clearer and what is a collectible more confusing. Part of the confusion rests with myself. I am not yet ready to admit that I am an antique.

An antique is anything made before 1945. A great many individuals in the antiques and collectibles field disagree with this definition, but with each passing year it becomes harder and harder to deny this fact. The key is the war years of 1942–1945. During this period, production switched from domestic to wartime products. When the war ended, things were different. American life and expectations were very different in 1948 than in 1938, partially due to the new technologies developed during the war. However, the most telling fact of all is that well over half the population living in America today was born after 1945 and approximately two–thirds grew up in the post–1945 era.

Keeping this in mind and seeking technical definitions, a collectible then becomes an object made between 1945 and 1962 and a desirable object is one made after 1962. The difference between a collectible and a desirable is that a collectible has a clearly established secondary market while desirables exist in a market rampant with speculation.

Actually the post–1945 era is breaking down into three distinct collecting periods: 1945–62, 1962–80, and post–1980. Goods in the 1962 to 1980 period are moving out of their speculative mode to one of price stability.

As a pre–babyboomer, I am not ready to admit that I am antique. As a writer in the trade, I am still trying to get the majority of antiques dealers to admit that the twentieth century exists, although a number are now willing to mumble "1915" under their breath.

Within the Warman's Encyclopedia of Antiques and Collectibles, *Warman's Americana & Collectibles* is the volume designed to deal with objects from the twentieth century. Three criteria help define what objects appear: (1) massed produced, (2) made in the twentieth century, preferably after 1945, and (3) the majority of the items in each category must sell between a few pennies and two hundred dollars. The ideal collectible fits all three qualifications.

There is a fourth factor: attitude. I collect things relating to the American canal movement. As a result, I own a number of pieces of dark blue English Staffordshire which were made when the Erie Canal was completed in the mid–1820s. Staffordshire of this type is considered a blue chip antique, but I collect it primarily for its "canal related" value. Does this make it a collectible rather than an antique? In my eyes and mind it does.

Since collecting antiques became fashionable in the early twentieth century, there have been attempts to define certain groups of objects as "true" antiques, worthy of sophisticated collectors, and to ignore the remaining items. Most museums clearly demonstrate this attitude. Where do early twentieth century tin toys, toy soldiers, or dolls fit? Those made before 1915 are antique. No one argues this any longer. Those made between 1920 and 1940 are in transition. We designate them "prestige" collectibles, objects changing in people's minds from collectible to antique.

In reality these divisions are artificial and deserve to be broken down. Today's Star Wars items, if properly preserved, will someday be over one hundred years old. They may be a much better key to interpreting life in the twentieth century than the Knoll furniture now found on pedestals in leading museums in the United States.

In summary, collectibles are the objects you and your children have played and lived with. As mentioned previously, your grandparents' things are antiques. Your parents' objects are in transition—a few already in the antiques category, about one–third classified as prestige collectibles, and the remainder still collectibles.

## INTERNATIONAL MARKET

Collectibles began to draw worldwide interest at the end of the 1980s. All of a sudden American buyers found themselves competing with buyers from Europe and Japan on their home turf. In head to head competition, the American buyers frequently lost. How can this be explained?

The most dominant portion of the 1990s collectibles market is post–World War II material. During this period, the youth of the world were influenced by American movies, music, and television. As the children of the 1950s, 1960s, and even 1970s reach adulthood and start buying back their childhood, many of the things they remember and want have American associations.

America is the great motherlode of post–war collectibles. At the moment it is packages and boxes of American collectibles that are being sent abroad. It will not be too much longer before the volume reaches container loads.

American collectors also are expanding their horizons. They recognize that many objects within their favorite collectible category were licensed abroad. They view their collections as incomplete without such examples. Objects are obtained by either traveling abroad or by purchasing through mail or auction from foreign sources.

## PRICE NOTES

Prices in the collectibles field are not as firmly established as in the antiques area. Nevertheless, we do not use ranges unless we feel they are absolutely necessary.

Our pricing is based on an object being in very good condition. If otherwise, we note this in our description. It would be ideal to suggest that mint, or unused, examples of all objects do exist. Objects from the past were used, whether they be glass, china, dolls, or toys. Because of this use, some normal wear must be expected. Furthermore, if the original box is important in establishing a price, it is assumed that the box is present with the article.

The biggest problem in the collectibles field is that an object may have more than one price. A George Eastman bubble gum card may be worth one dollar to a bubble gum card collector, but thirty–five dollars to a collector of photographic memorabilia. I saw the same card marked both ways. In preparing prices for this guide we have looked at the object within the category being considered. Hence, a "girly" matchcover sells for twenty–five to fifty cents to a matchcover collector and two to five dollars to a pin–up art collector. However, if all you can find are matchcover collectors, best take the quarter and move on.

Some collectibles do have regional interest. However, a national price consensus has formed as a result of the publication of specialized price guides, collectors' club newsletters, and magazines and newspapers. This guide also has contributed to breaking down regional pricing.

## ORGANIZATION OF THE BOOK

**Listings:** We have attempted to make the listings descriptive enough so the specific object can be identified. Most guides limit their descriptions to one line, but not *Warman's*. We have placed emphasis on those items which are actively being sold in the marketplace. Nevertheless, some harder–to–find objects are included in order to demonstrate the market spread. A few categories in this book also appear in *Warman's Antiques and Their Prices*. The individual listings, however, seldom overlap except for a few minor instances. It is our intention to show the low to middle price range of a category in *Warman's Americana & Collectibles* and the middle to upper range in our main antiques guide, *Warman's Antiques and Their Prices*, thus creating two true companion lists for the general dealer or collector.

**Collecting Hints:** This section calls attention to specific hints as they relate to the category. We note where cross category collecting and nostalgia are critical in pricing. Clues are given to spotting reproductions. In most cases, we just scratch the surface. We encourage collectors to consult specialized publications.

**History:** Here we discuss the category, describe how the object was made, who are or were the leading manufacturers, and the variations of form and style. In many instances a chronology for the objects is established. Finally, we place the object in a social context—how it was used, for what purposes, etc.

**References:** A few general references are listed to encourage collectors to learn more about their objects. Included are author, title, most recent edition, publisher (if published by a small firm or individual, we have indicated "published by author"), and a date of publication.

Finding these books may present a problem. The antiques and collectibles field is blessed with a dedicated core of book dealers who stock these specialized publications. You may find them at flea markets, antiques shows, and through their advertisements in leading publications in the field. Many dealers publish annual or semi–annual catalogs. Ask to be put on their mailing lists. Books go out–of–print quickly, yet many books printed over twenty–five years ago remain the standard work in a field. Also, haunt used book dealers for collectible reference material.

**Collectors' Clubs:** The large number of collectors' clubs adds vitality to the collectibles field. Their publications and conventions produce knowledge which often cannot be found anywhere else. Many of these clubs are short lived; others are so strong that they have regional and local chapters.

**Periodicals:** In respect to the collectibles field, there are certain general monthly periodicals to which the general collector should subscribe:

*Antiques & Collecting Hobbies*, 1006 South Michigan Avenue, Chicago, IL 60605.

*Collectors' Showcase*, 7130 South Lewis, Suite 210, Tulsa, OK 74136.

*The Inside Collector*, P.O. Box 98, Elmont, NY 11003.

There are also a number of specialized collectible periodicals, e.g., *Antique Toy World* (P.O. Box 34509, Chicago, IL 60634). Special attention is directed toward the publications of Krause Publications, Inc., (700 East State Street, Iola, WI 54945), especially *Toy Shop*.

Although no weekly publication is devoted exclusively to collectibles, *The Antique Trader Weekly* (Box 1050, Dubuque, IA 52001) and *Antique Week* (P.O. Box 90, Knightstown, IN 46148) extensively cover the range of items listed in this book. Specialized auctions of prestige collectibles are regularly reported in depth in the *Maine Antique Digest* (Box 358, Waldoboro, ME 04572).

**Museums:** The best way to study a specific field is to see as many documented examples as possible. For this reason, we have listed museums where significant collections of collectibles are on display. Special attention must be directed to the Margaret Woodbury Strong Museum in Rochester, New York, and the Smithsonian Institution's Museum of American History in Washington, D.C.

**Reproduction Alert:** Reproductions are a major concern, especially with any item related to advertising. Most reproductions are unmarked; the newness of their appearance is often the best clue to uncovering them. Where "Reproduction Alert" appears, a watchful eye should be kept within the entire category.

Reproductions are only one aspect of the problem; outright fakes are another. Unscrupulous manufacturers make fantasy items which never existed, e.g., Hopalong Cassidy guitar from the non–existent Jefferson Musical Toys.

## RESEARCH

Collectors of the categories found in this book deserve credit for their attention to scholarship and the skill by which they have assembled their collections. This book attests to how strong and encompassing the collectibles market has become through their efforts.

We obtain our prices from many key sources—dealers, publications, auctions, collectors, and field work. The generosity with which dealers have given advice is a credit to the field. Everyone recognizes the need for a guide that is specific and has accurate prices. We study newspapers, magazines, newsletters, and other publications in the collectibles and antiques field. All of them are critical in understanding what is available in the market. Special recognition must be given to those collectors' club newsletters and magazines which discuss prices.

Our staff is constantly in the field—from Massachusetts to Florida, Pennsylvania to California. Our Board of Advisors provides regional as well as specialized information. Over one hundred specialized auctions are held annually, and their results are provided to our office. Finally, private collectors have worked closely with us, sharing their knowledge of price trends and developments unique to their specialties.

## BUYER'S GUIDE, NOT SELLER'S GUIDE

*Warman's Americana & Collectibles* is designed to be a buyer's guide, a guide to what you would have to pay to purchase an object on the open market from a dealer or collector. **It is not a seller's guide to prices.** People frequently make this mistake and are deceiving themselves by doing so.

If you have an object in this book and wish to sell it, you should expect to receive approximately 35% to 40% of the value listed. If the object cannot be resold quickly, expect to receive even less. The truth is simple. Knowing to whom to sell an object is worth 50% or more of its value. Buyers are very specialized; dealers work for years to assemble a list of collectors who will pay top dollar for an item.

Examine your piece as objectively as possible. If it is something from your childhood, try to step back from the personal memories in evaluating its condition. As an antiques appraiser, I spend a great deal of my time telling people their treasures are not "gold," but items readily available in the marketplace.

In respect to buying and selling, a simple philosophy is that a good purchase occurs when both the buyer and seller are happy with the price. Don't look back. Hindsight has little value in the collectibles field. Given time, things tend to balance out.

## WHERE TO BUY COLLECTIBLES

The collectible has become standard auction house fare in the 1990s. Christie's East (219 East 67th Street, New York, NY 10021) and Sotheby's (1334 York Avenue, New York, NY 10021) conduct collectibles sales several times each year. Specialized auction firms, e.g., Lloyd Ralston Toys (447 Stratfield Road, Fairfield, CT 06432) in toys and Greenberg's (7566 Main Street, Sykesville, MD 21784) in trains, have proven the viability of the collectible as a focal point.

The major collectibles marketing thrust continues to be the mail auction, either with material on consignment or directly owned. Hake's Americana & Collectibles (P.O. Box 1444, York, PA 17405) is the leading mail auction. Hake's is being challenged by Debby and Marty Krim's New England Auction Gallery (P.O. Box 2273, Peabody, MA 01960), Smith House Toy Sales (P.O. Box 336, Eliot, ME 03903), and a host of others. A recent development is the mail auction conducted through classified and display advertising in trade periodicals.

Direct sale catalogs abound. Most major categories have one or more. These dealers and many more advertise in periodicals and collectors' clubs' newsletters. Most require an annual fee to receive their catalogs.

Of course, there is an unlimited number of flea markets, house and country auctions, church bazaars, and garage sales. However, if you are a specialized collector, you may spend days looking for something to add to your collection. If you add in your time to the cost of the object, its real cost will be much higher than the purchase price.

All of which brings us to the final source, the specialized dealer. The collectibles field is so broad that dealers do specialize. Find the dealers who handle your material and work with them to build your collection.

## BOARD OF ADVISORS

Our Board of Advisors are dealers, authors, collectors and leaders of collectors clubs from throughout the United States. All are dedicated to accuracy in description and pricing. If you wish to buy or sell an object in their field of expertise, drop them a note. Please include a stamped, self addressed envelope with all correspondence. If time or interest permits, they will respond.

We now list the name of our advisors at the end of their respective categories. Their full mailing address and often their phone numbers are in the front of this book.

## COMMENTS INVITED

*Warman's Americana & Collectibles* is a major effort to deal with a complex field. Our readers are encouraged to send their comments and suggestions to Rinker Enterprises, 5093 Vera Cruz Road, Emmaus, PA 18049.

## ACKNOWLEDGMENTS

The final creation and publication of the Warman Encyclopedia of Antiques and Collectibles, in which this book is one volume, occurred between the fifth edition and sixth editions of *Warman's Americana & Collectibles*. I consider the Warman Encyclopedia series, along with my development of the Warman format, as among the most important contributions that I have made to the trade.

*Warman's Americana & Collectibles* no longer stands alone. As I look up at the shelf that houses the volumes in the Warman Encyclopedia, I see six published titles. By the time the seventh edition of this book appears that number will double. I am pleased, proud, and excited. The future appears bright.

It is a fortunate editor who has a competent and supportive staff. I am blessed many times over. The Rinkettes, the staff at Rinker Enterprises, Inc., provides a level of professional support that is among the best available. Since they are multi–skilled staff, it is impossible to identify the specific work of any one individual anywhere in this book. Every Rinkette is capable of doing any part of this volume.

The Rinkettes' names appear as the Editorial Staff in the front of this book. You will note a new name this time around—Harry L. Rinker, Jr. Harry Junior serves as Art Director for Rinker Enterprises, Inc. His principal responsibility is to create fresh new pictures for the manuscripts prepared at Rinker Enterprises, Inc. His handiwork is evident in this edition. Eighty percent of the pictures are being published for the first time.

A special thanks to Chilton Books, parent company of Wallace–Homestead and Warman, for the professional and financial support that allows Rinker Enterprises, Inc., to keep its focus on manuscript production instead of operational concerns. Edna Jones, Managing Editor, and Troy Vozzella, Developmental Editor, did their usual fine job in the production of this title. We welcome Michael Campbell aboard as Director of Sales and Marketing and trust we have given him a product that makes "sell through" a relatively simple task.

The key to assembling the research base at Rinker Enterprises, Inc., is cooperation from thousands of individuals and organizations within the field. The most common response to our requests is "what can we do to help?" To all who made this your response, our deepest thanks and appreciation. You are our foundation.

I would like to tell you that the Rinkettes and I are going to take a well deserved rest now that this book is finally completed. Alas, we have no time. Our remaining 1993 commitments include *Warman's Paper*; *Warman's Coun-*

*try*, second edition; and *Warman's Antiques and Their Prices,* 28th edition. I guess we would consider taking a vacation if what we do is work. We consider it fun; and, one of the principal reasons is your support.

We hope we never fail to remember to thank *you*, the users of this and other Warman titles. There would be no *Warman's Americana & Collectibles* without your support. We especially thank those who have written to us with their praise and/or criticism. While we bask in the first, we learn from the second. Each edition of *Warman's Americana & Collectibles* builds upon its precedessor and, hopefully, grows as a result. You will never find the Rinkettes and I content simply to repeat what we did in the past.

Finally, best wishes in your collecting and/or selling in the years ahead.

5093 Vera Cruz Road
Emmaus, PA 18049

Harry L. Rinker
Editor
October 1993

# Auction Houses

The following auction houses cooperate with Rinker Enterprises, Inc., by providing catalogs of their auctions and price lists. This information is used to prepare *Warman's Antiques and Their Prices,* volumes in the Warman's Encyclopedia of Antiques and Collectibles, and Wallace–Homestead Book Company publications. This support is most appreciated.

Sanford Alderfer Auction Company
501 Fairgrounds Rd.
Hatfield, PA 19440
(215) 368-5477

Al Anderson
P. O. Box 644
Troy, OH 45373
(513) 339-0850

W. Graham Arader III
1000 Boxwood Ct.
King of Prussia, PA 19406
(215) 825-6570

Ark Antiques
Box 3133
New Haven, CT 06515
(203) 387-3754

Arthur Auctioneering
R. D. 2
Hughesville, PA 17737
(717) 584-3697

Noel Barrett Antiques and Auctions Ltd.
P. O. Box 1001
Carversville, PA 18913
(215) 297-5109

Robert F. Batchelder
1 West Butler Ave.
Ambler, PA 19002
(215) 643-1430

Biders Antiques, Inc.
241 South Union St.
Lawrence, MA 01843
(508) 688-4347

Richard A. Bourne Co., Inc.
Corporation St.
P. O. Box 141
Hyannis Port, MA 02647
(508) 775-0797

Butterfield's
220 San Bruno Ave.
San Francisco, CA 94103
(415) 861-7500

Christie's
502 Park Ave.
New York, NY 10022
(212) 546-1000

Christie's East
219 E. 67th St.
New York, NY 10021
(212) 606-0400

Christmas Morning
1850 Crown Rd., Suite 1111
Dallas, TX 75234
(817) 236-1155

Marvin Cohen Auctions
Box 425, Routes 20 & 22
New Lebanon, NY 12125
(518) 794-9333

Collector's Auction Services
P. O. Box 13732
Seneca, PA 16346
(814) 677-6070

Marlin G. Denlinger
RR 3, Box 3775
Morrisville, VT 05661
(802) 888-2774

William Doyle Galleries, Inc.
175 E. 87th St.
New York, NY 10128
(212) 427-2730

Early Auction Co.
123 Main St.
Milford, OH 45150
(513) 831-4833

Fine Arts Co. of Philadelphia, Inc.
1808 Chestnut St.
Philadelphia, PA 19103
(215) 563-9275

William A. Fox Auctions, Inc.
676 Morris Ave.
Springfield, NJ 07081
(201) 467-2366

Ron Fox
F. T. S. Inc.
416 Throop St.
N. Babylon, NY 11704
(516) 669-7232

Garth's Auction, Inc.
2690 Stratford Rd.
P. O. Box 369
Delaware, OH 43015
(614) 362-4771 or 369-5085

Glass-Works Auctions
P. O. Box 187-102 Jefferson St.
East Greenville, PA 18041
(215) 679-5849

Grandma's Trunk
The Millards
P. O. Box 404
Northport, NI 49670
(616) 386-5351

Guerney's
136 East 73rd St.
New York, NY 10021
(212) 794-2280

Ken Farmer Realty & Auction Co.
1122 Norwood St.
Radford, VA 24141
(703) 639-0939

Hake's Americana and Collectibles
P. O. Box 1444
York, PA 17405
(717) 848-1333

Harmer Rooke Numismatists, Inc.
3 East 57th St.
New York, NY 10022
(212) 751-4122

Hart Galleries
2311 Westheimer
Houston, TX 77098
(713) 524-2979 or 523-7389

Norman C. Heckler & Company
Bradford Corner RD.
Woodstock Valley, CT 06282
(203) 974-1634

Leslie Hindman, Inc.
215 West Ohio St.
Chicago, IL 60610
(312) 670-0010

Michael Ivankovich Antiques
P. O. Box 2458
Doylestown, PA 18901
(215) 345-6094

James D. Julia, Inc.
P. O. Box 830
Fairfield, ME 04937
(207) 453-7904

Charles E. Kirtley
P. O. Box 2273
Elizabeth City, NC 27906
(919) 335-1262

Howard Lowery
3818 W. Magnolia Blvd.
Burbank, CA 91505
(818) 972-9080

Les Paul's
2615 Magnolia St., Suite A
Oakland, CA 94607
(415) 832-2615

Alex G. Malloy, Inc.
P. O. Box 38
South Salem, NY 10590
(203) 438-0396

Martin Auctioneers, Inc.
Larry L. Martin
P. O. Box 477
Intercourse, PA 17534
(717) 768-8108

Robert Merry Auction Company
5501 Milburn Rd.
St. Louis, MO 63129
(314) 487-3992

Mid-Hudson Auction Galleries
One Idlewild Ave.
Cornwall-On-Hudson, NY 12520
(214) 534-7828

Milwaukee Auction Galleries
318 N. Water
Milwaukee, WI 53202
(414) 271-1105

Neal Alford Company
4139 Magazine St.
New Orleans, LA 70115
(504) 899-5329

New England Auction Gallery
Box 2273
W. Peabody, MA 01960
(508) 535-3140

New Hampshire Book Auctions
Woodbury Rd.
Weare, NH 03281
(603) 529-1700

Nostalgia Publications, Inc.
21 South Lake Dr.
Hackensack, NJ 07601
(201) 488-4536

Pettigrew Auction Company
1645 South Tejon St.
Colorado Springs, CO 80906
(719) 633-7963

Postcards International
P. O. Box 2930
New Haven, CT 06515-0030
(203) 865-0814

David Rago Arts & Crafts
P. O. Box 3592 Station E
Trenton, NJ 08629
(609) 585-2546

Lloyd Ralston Toys
173 Post Rd.
Fairfield, CT 06432
(203) 255-1233 or 366-3399

Renzel's Auction Service
P. O. Box 222
Emigsville, PA 17318
(717) 764-6412

R. Niel & Elaine Reynolds
Box 133
Waterford, VA 22190
(703) 882-3574

Roan Bros. Auction Gallery
R.D. 3, Box 118
Cogan Station, PA 17728
(717) 494-0170

Stanton's Auctioneers & Realtors
144 South Main St.
Vermontville, MI 49096
(517) 726-0181

Robert W. Skinner Inc.
Bolton Gallery
357 Main St.
Bolton, MA 01740
(508) 779-6241

Smith House Toy Sales
26 Adlington Rd.
Eliot, ME 03903
(207) 439-4614

Sotheby's
1334 York Ave.
New York, NY 10021
(212) 606-7000

Swann Galleries, Inc.
104 E. 25th St.
New York, NY 10010
(212) 254-4710

Theriault's
P. O. Box 151
Annapolis, MD 21401
(301) 224-3655

Western Glass Auctions
1288 W. 11th St., Suite #230
Tracy, CA 95376
(209) 832-4527

Winter Associates
21 Cooke St. Box 823
Plainville, CT 06062
(203) 793-0288

Wolf's Auction Gallery
13015 Larchmere Blvd.
Shaker Heights, OH 44120
(216) 231-3888

Woody Auction
Douglass, KS 67039
(316) 746-2694

# Abbreviations

The following are standard abbreviations which we have used throughout this edition of Warman's:

| | |
|---|---|
| 3D | = three dimensional |
| 4to | = 8 x 10" |
| 8vo | = 5 x 7" |
| 12mo | = 3 x 5" |
| ADS | = Autograph Document Signed |
| adv | = advertising |
| ah | = applied handle |
| ALS | = Autograph Letter Signed |
| AQS | = Autograph Quotation Signed |
| C | = century |
| c | = circa |
| CS | = Card Signed |
| circ | = circular |
| cov | = cover |
| d | = diameter or depth |
| dec | = decorated |
| dj | = dust jacket |
| DQ | = Diamond Quilted |
| DS | = Document Signed |
| emb | = embossed |
| ext. | = exterior |
| FE | = first edition |
| Folio | = 12 x 16" |
| ftd | = footed |
| gal | = gallon |
| ground | = background |
| h | = height |
| hp | = hand painted |
| hs | = high standard |
| illus | = illustrated, illustration |
| imp | = impressed |
| int. | = interior |
| irid | = iridescent |
| IVT | = inverted thumbprint |
| j | = jewels |
| K | = karat |
| l | = length |
| lb | = pound |
| litho | = lithograph |
| LS | = letter signed |
| ls | = low standard |
| mfg | = manufacturered |
| MIB | = mint in box |
| MIP | = mint in package |
| MOC | = mint on card |
| mkd | = marked |
| MOP | = mother of pearl |
| n.d. | = no date |
| NE | = New England |
| No. | = number |
| opal | = opalescent |
| orig | = original |
| os | = orig stopper |
| oz | = ounce |
| pat | = patent |
| pc | = piece |
| pcs | = pieces |
| pgs | = pages |
| pkg | = package |
| pr | = pair |
| PS | = Photograph Signed |
| pt | = pint |
| qt | = quart |
| rect | = rectangular |
| sgd | = signed |
| sngl | = single |
| SP | = silver plated |
| SS | = Sterling silver |
| sq | = square |
| teg | = top edges gilt |
| TLS | = Typed Letter Signed |
| unp | = unpaged |
| vol | = volume |
| w | = width |
| wraps | = paper covers |
| yg | = yellow gold |
| yr | = year |
| # | = numbered |

# ABINGDON POTTERY

**Collecting Hints:** Like many contemporary potteries, Abingdon pottery is readily available in the market. The company produced over 1,000 shapes and used over 150 colors to decorate their wares. Because of this tremendous variety, collectors are advised to specialize in a select number of forms and/or colors from the beginning.

Abingdon art pottery, with its vitreous body and semigloss and high gloss glazes, is found at all levels of the market from garage sales to antiques shows. For this reason, price fluctuation on identical pieces is quite common. Study the market carefully before buying. Learn to shop around.

While there is no price guide devoted exclusively to Abingdon pottery, price listings can now be found in all the general antiques and collectible price guides along with several of the specialized ceramic and pottery guides. Pieces regularly appear for sale in classified advertisements in most trade papers, thus allowing one to obtain a strong sense of the Abingdon market.

Collectors and dealers are still in the process of defining the market relative to the most desirable shapes and colors. At the moment black (gunmetal black), a semigloss dark blue, a metallic copper brown, and several shades of red are the favored colors. Decorated pieces command a premium of 15% to 20%.

**History:** The Abingdon Sanitary Manufacturing Company, Abingdon, Illinois, was founded in 1908 for the purpose of manufacturing plumbing fixtures. Sometime during 1933–34 Abingdon introduced a line of art pottery ranging from decorative pieces to vases. In 1945 the company changed its name to Abingdon Potteries, Inc. Production of the art pottery line continued until 1950 when fire destroyed the art pottery kiln.

After the fire, the company placed its emphasis once again on plumbing fixtures. Eventually, Abingdon Potteries became Briggs Manufacturing Company, a firm noted for its sanitary fixtures.

**Collectors' Club:** Abingdon Pottery Club, 212 South Fourth, Monmouth, IL 61462.

Ashtray, Sol Ellis adv, green .......... **20.00**
Bookends, pr
  Dolphins, #444 .......... **65.00**
  Horse Head, black, #441 .......... **50.00**
  Quill, black and white .......... **125.00**
Candleholders, pr, #716 .......... **25.00**
Cookie Jar
  Granny
    Green .......... **135.00**
    White .......... **225.00**
  Hobby Horse .......... **250.00**
  Humpty Dumpty, #163 .......... **185.00**
  Jack In Box, 11" h, #611 .......... **295.00**
  Jack–o'–lantern .......... **265.00**
  Little Bo Peep .......... **375.00**
  Little Miss Muffet .......... **295.00**
  Money Sack, #588 .......... **80.00**
  Pineapple, #664 .......... **75.00**
  Three Bears .......... **65.00**
  Windmill .......... **225.00**
Cornucopia, 4½" h, #449 .......... **25.00**
Dish, oblong, pink, two geese dec .......... **35.00**
Figure
  Fish, #444 .......... **30.00**
  Peacock, pink, #416 .......... **55.00**
  Pelican, green, #572 .......... **40.00**
  Shepherdess and Fawn, #3906 .......... **275.00**
Flower Pot
  Cattails, #150 .......... **30.00**
  Florals, hand dec .......... **45.00**
Geranium Bowl, #543 .......... **45.00**
Grease Jar, daisy dec, #679 .......... **40.00**
Mint Compote, plain, #568 .......... **30.00**
Pitcher, ice lip, two quart, #200 .......... **35.00**
Planter
  Cactus, Mexican man taking siesta, #600 .......... **75.00**
  Daffodil, #668D .......... **30.00**
  Donkey, blue, #669 .......... **35.00**
Vase
  Classic, blue, #115 .......... **45.00**
  Hourglass, blue, #594 .......... **20.00**
  Tulip, dec, #604D .......... **40.00**

**Vase, Classic, blue, emb leaf band, orig paper label, ink stamped "Abingdon, U.S.A." in rect on bottom, 9⅞" h, $25.00.**

Wall Pocket
  Butterfly, #601 .......... **65.00**
  Calla Lily, #586D .......... **45.00**
  Cookbook, #676D .......... **45.00**
  Leaf, #724 .......... **40.00**

# ACTION FIGURES

**Collecting Hints:** This is one of the hot, trendy collecting categories of the 1990s. While there is no question that action figure material is selling and selling well, much of the pricing is highly speculative. Trends change from month to month as one figure or group of figures becomes hot and another cools off.

The safest approach is to buy only objects in fine or better condition and, if possible, with or in their original packaging. Any figure that has been played with to any extent will never have long–term value. This is a category of off–the–rack expectations.

Be extremely cautious about paying premium prices for figures less than ten years old. For the past ten years dealers have made a regular practice of buying action figures in quantity, warehousing them, and releasing their stash slowly into the market once production ceases.

Also examine packaging very closely. A premium is placed on having a figure in the packaging in which he, she, or it was introduced into the market. Later packaging means a lower price.

**History:** An action figure is a die–cast metal or plastic posable model with flexible joints that portrays a real or fictional character. In addition to the figures themselves, great emphasis is placed on the collecting of clothing, personal equipment, vehicles, and other types of accessories.

Collectors need to be aware of the following practices: (1) limited production—a deliberate act on the part of manufacturers to hold back on production of one or more figures in a series; (2) variations—minor changes in figures made by manufacturers to increase sales (previously believed to be mistakes, but now viewed as a deliberate sales gimmick); and (3) prototypes—artist models used during the planning process. Any prototype should be investigated thoroughly since there are many examples in the market made by individuals solely for the purpose of deceiving collectors.

The earliest action figures were the hard plastic Hartland figures of popular television Western heroes of the 1950s. Louis Marx also utilized action figures in a number of its playsets in the late 1950s. Although Barbie, who made her appearance in 1959, is posable, she is not considered an action figure by collectors.

G.I. Joe, introduced by Hassenfield Bros. in 1964, triggered the modern action figure craze. In 1965 Gilbert introduced action figures for James Bond 007, The Man from U.N.C.L.E., and Honey West. Bonanza figures arrived in 1966.

Ideal Toy Corporation's Captain Action also arrived in 1966. By changing heads and costumes, the figure's personality and role were altered. Captain Action and his accessories were the hot collectible of the late 1980s.

In 1972 Mego introduced the first six superheroes in what would become a series of thirty–four different characters. Mego also established the link between action figures and the movies with its issue of Planet of the Apes and Star Trek: The Motion Picture series. Mego's television series figures included CHiPs, Dukes of Hazzard, and Star Trek. When Mego filed for Chapter 11 bankruptcy protection in 1982, the days of eight- and twelve-inch cloth–clothed action figures ceased.

The introductions in 1977 of Kenner's Star Wars figures set opened a floodgate. Action figures enjoyed enormous popularity. Manufacturers rushed into the action figure market. Mattel followed quickly on Kenner's heels. Before long, the market was flooded, not only by a large selection but by production runs in the hundreds of thousands.

Not all series were successful, just ask companies such as Colorform, Matchbox, and TYCO. Some sets were never produced when initial sales did not justify the costs of manufacture. These sets have limited collector value. Scarcity does not necessarily equate to high value in the action figure market.

**References:** Paris and Sue Manos, *Collectible Male Action Figures: Including G.I. Joe Figures, Captain Action Figures, and Ken Dolls,* Collector Books, 1990, 1992 value update; Carol Markowski and Bill Sikora, *Tomart's Price Guide To Action Figure Collectibles, Revised Edition* Tomart Publications, 1992.

**Periodicals:** *Action Figure News & Review,* 556 Monroe Turnpike, Monroe, CT 06468; *Action Figure Digest,* Tomart Publications, 3300 Encrete Lane, Dayton, OH 45439.

Aquaman
- 3″ h, Ideal, 1966–67, Justice League **60.00**
- 3¾″ h, Mego, 1975–1978, Comic Action Heroes .................... **75.00**

Archie, The Archies, Marx, 1975 ..... **40.00**

A–Team, Galoob, 1984
- Amy A Allen, 6½″ h .............. **35.00**
- Four Figure Set, 3¾″ h ............ **30.00**
- Hannibal, 6½″ h .................. **15.00**
- Rattler, 6½″ h .................... **15.00**

Batman
- Batgirl, 8″ h, Mego, 1974, carded .. **250.00**
- Batman
  - 3″ h, Ideal, 1966–67, Justice League ...................... **50.00**
  - 5″ h, Toy Biz, 1989, Keaton face, bat rope, #4401 ............. **12.00**
  - 12″ h, Remco, 1978, energized .. **120.00**
  - 12½″ h, Mego, 1976 ........... **140.00**
- Bruce Wayne, 4¾″ h, Kenner, 1990, Dark Knight Collection, quick

- change Batman costume, #63180 **15.00**
- Catwoman, Mego, 1972–74, Superhero, bendable **175.00**
- Joker
  - 3″ h, Ideal, 1966–67, Justice League **75.00**
  - 5″ h, Toy Biz, 1989, squirting orchid, no curl, #4406 **5.00**
- Penguin, 7″ h, Mego, 1974, carded **90.00**
- Riddler, 8″ h, Mego, 1974, boxed **200.00**
- Robin, 7″ h, Mego, 1975, fist fighting **300.00**

Battlestar: Galactica, Mattel, 1978
- Colonial Warrior, 12″ h **40.00**
- Starbuck **20.00**

Beetlejuice, Kenner, 1989, spin head, Creepy Cockroach, #30080 **4.00**

Best of the West, Marx, 1965
- Davy Crockett **175.00**
- Brave Eagle **70.00**
- Johnny West **60.00**

Big Jim's P.A.C.K., Mattel, 1976
- Big Jim **60.00**
- Dr Steel **50.00**

The Black Hole, Mego, 1979
- Dr Durant, 12″ h **40.00**
- Harry Booth, 3¾″ h **10.00**

Bonanza, Ben Cartwright, American Character, 1966 **110.00**

Bucky O'Hare, Hasbro, 1990, #7281 **5.00**

Captain Action, Ideal, 1966–68, first issue **500.00**

Captain America
- Just Toys, bendie **6.00**
- Mego, 12½″ h, 1979, fly away action **125.00**

Captain Marvel, 8″ h, Mego, Shazam, boxed **200.00**

Clash of the Titans, Mattel, 1980
- Charon **15.00**
- Pegasus **30.00**

Commando, 1985
- Blaster, 3¾″ h **8.00**
- Lead Head, 8″ h **10.00**
- Matrix, 18″ h **60.00**

Defenders of the Earth, Flash Gordon, 5½″ h, Galoob, 1986, battle action knob **12.00**

Dick Tracy, Playmates, 1990, #5701 **5.00**

Dracula, Remco, glow–in–the–dark **35.00**

Fantastic Four, Human Torch, 8″ h, Mego, blister pack **40.00**

Flash, 3″ h, Ideal, Justice League **80.00**

Frankenstein, 8″ h, Mego, 1974, Mad Monster Series **95.00**

Green Arrow, 5″ h, Kenner, 1985, DC Super Powers **30.00**

Green Goblin, 12″ h, Remco, energized **90.00**

Green Hornet, Lakeside, 1966, bendie **90.00**

Green Lantern, 5″ h, Toy Biz, 1989–90, DC Comics Super Heroes, water jet ring, #4413 **8.00**

Incredible Hulk, 8″ h, Mego, 1979, carded **40.00**

Indiana Jones
- Kenner, 1982, with whip **50.00**
- LJN, 1984, Temple of Doom **60.00**

Iron Man, 6″ h, Marx, 1976 **15.00**

James Bond, 12″ h, Mego, 1979 **100.00**

Johnny Apollo, Marx, 1968, Space Center box **125.00**

Major Matt Mason, Mattel, 1966
- Doug Davis, with lunar trac **200.00**
- Mason, with space sled **150.00**

Man From U.N.C.L.E., Gilbert, Napolean Solo **225.00**

M.A.S.H., Tri–Star
- Hawkeye, large **35.00**
- Klinger, small **15.00**

Masters of the Universe, Mattel, 5¾″ h
- He–Man, 1981, #5040 **10.00**
- Kobra Khan, 1980s, #7098 **6.00**

Mummy, 8″ h, Remco, 1980, Official Universal Studios Monsters **160.00**

Noble Knights, The Black Knight, Marx, 1968 **175.00**

Real Ghostbusters, Peter Venkman, 5¼″ h, Kenner, 1987, with Grabber Ghost **5.00**

Space: 1999, Professor Victor Bergman, Mattel **60.00**

Spider–Man
- 4¼″ h, Mattel, 1984, black outfit, #9153 **35.00**
- 5″ h, Toy Biz, 1990–91, Marvel Superheroes, web suction hands, #4802 **8.00**
- 6″ h, Marx, 1966 **20.00**

Star Trek, 8″ h, Mego, 1974
- Kirk **35.00**
- Romulan **450.00**

Star Trek: The Motion Picture, Mego, 1979
- McCoy, 3¾″ h **20.00**
- Spock, 12″ h **45.00**

Star Trek: The Next Generation, Captain Jean–Luc Picard, 3¾″ h, Galoob, 1988 **10.00**

Supergirl, 8″ h, Mego, carded **350.00**

Superman
- Lex Luthor, 3¾″ h, Mego, 1979, Pocket Super Heroes **15.00**
- Superman, 6″ h, Fun Things, rubber **25.00**

Swamp Thing, Kenner, 1990, with vine winch arm and monster trap, #41480 **6.00**

Tarzan, 5″ h, Mego, bendie **60.00**

Teenage Mutant Ninja Turtles, 4½″ h, Playmates
- Michaelangelo, 1988, with Turtle Force fan club flyer **20.00**
- Shredder, 1988, #5007 **8.00**

Tron, Warrior, 4″ h, Tomy, 1981 **10.00**

Wolfman, 3¾″ h, Remco, 1983, mini **75.00**

Wonder Girl, 7″ h, Mego, 1977, Teen Titans, carded **300.00**

Wonder Woman
- 5″ h, Toy Biz, 1989–90, DC Comics

Super Heroes, power arm, #4404 **5.00**
12" h, Mego, 1976, Diana Prince outfit, Linda Carter photo box ...... **100.00**

# ADVERTISING

**Collecting Hints:** Many factors affect the price of an advertising collectible to the product and its manufacturer, the objects or persons used in the advertisement, the period and aesthetics of design, the designer and illustrator of the piece, and the form the advertisement takes. Add to this the continued use of advertising material as decorative elements in bars, restaurants, and other public places. The interior decorator purchases at a very different price level than the collector.

In truth, almost every advertising item is sought by a specialized collector in one or more collectible areas. The result is a divergence in pricing, with the price quoted to an advertising collector usually lower than that quoted to a specialized collector.

Most collectors seem to concentrate on the period prior to 1940, with special emphasis on the decades from 1880 to 1910. New collectors should examine the advertising material from the post–1940 period. Much of this material still is very inexpensive and likely to rise in value as the decorator trends associated with the 1950s through the 1970s gain in importance.

**History:** The earliest advertising in America is found in colonial newspapers and printed broadsides. By the mid–19th century manufacturers began to examine how a product was packaged. The box could convey a message and help identify and sell more of the product. The advent of the high-speed lithograph printing press led to regional and national magazines, resulting in new advertising markets. The lithograph press also brought vivid colors into the advertising spectrum.

Simultaneously, the general store branched out into specialized departments or individual stores. By 1880 advertising premiums, such as mirrors, paperweights, trade cards, etc., arrived on the scene. Premiums remained popular through the early 1960s, especially with children.

Advertising continues to respond to changing opportunities and times. The advertising character developed in the early 1900s. By the 1950s the star endorser was established firmly as an advertising vehicle. Advertising became a big business as specialized firms, many headquartered in New York City, developed to meet manufacturers' needs.

**References:** Bob Alexander and Mike Bruner, *A Collectors Guide To Telephone, Telegraph, & Express Co. Advertising,* Guard Frog Books, 1992; Kit Barry, *The Advertising Trade Card: Information And Prices, Book I,* privately printed, 1981; Al Bergevin, *Drugstore Tins And Their Prices,* Wallace–Homestead, 1990; Al Bergevin, *Food Drink Containers And Their Prices,* Wallace–Homestead, 1988; Al Bergevin, *Tobacco Tins and Their Prices,* Wallace–Homestead, 1987; Leslie and Marcie Cabarga, *Trademark Designs of the Twenties,* Dover Publications, Inc., 1991; Douglas Congdon–Martin, *America For Sale: A Collector's Guide to Antique Advertising,* Schiffer Publishing Ltd., 1991; Douglas Congdon–Martin, *Tobacco Tins: A Collector's Guide,* Schiffer Publishing, 1992; Douglas Congdon–Martin and Robert Biondi, *Country Store Antiques: From Cradles to Caskets,* Schiffer Publishing Ltd., 1991; Douglas Congdon–Martin and Robert Biondi, *Country Store Collectibles,* Schiffer Publishing Ltd., 1990; Jim Cope, *Old Advertising,* Great American Publishing Co., 1980; M. J. Franklin, *British Biscuit Tins 1868–1939: An Aspect of Decorative Packaging,* Schiffer Publishing, 1979; Ted Hake, *Hake's Guide to Advertising Collectibles,* Wallace–Homestead, 1992; Ted Hake and Russ King, *Collectible Pin–Back Buttons, 1896–1986, An Illustrated Price Guide,* Wallace–Homestead, 1986; Sharon and Bob Huxford, *Huxford's Collectible Advertising: An Illustrated Value Guide,* Collector Books, 1993; Jerry Jankowski, *Shelf Life: Modern Package Design 1920–1945,* Chronicle Books, 1992; Robert Jay, *The Trade Card In Nineteenth–Century America,* University of Missouri Press, 1987; Franklyn Kircher, *Tobacco Pocket Tin Guide,* published by author, 1984; Ray Klug, *Antique Advertising Encyclopedia,* Vol. 1, (1978, 1992 value update) and Vol. 2 (1985), L–W Promotions; Ralph and Terry Kovel, *Kovels' Advertising Collectibles Price List,* Crown Publishers, Inc., 1986; L–W Promotions (ed.), *Antique Advertising Handbook and Price Guide,* L–W Book Sales, 1988; John Margolies and Emily Gwathmey, *Signs Of Our Time,* Abbeville Press, 1993; Norman E. Martinus and Harry L. Rinker, *Warman's Paper,* Wallace–Homestead, 1993; Tom Morrison, *Root Beer: Advertising and Collectibles,* Schiffer Publishing, Ltd., 1992; Dana Gehman Morykan and Harry L. Rinker, *Warman's Country Antiques & Collectibles,* Wallace–Homestead, 1992; Alice L. Muncaster and Ellen Sawyer, *The Black Cat Made Me Buy It!,* Crown Publishers, 1988; Alice L. Muncaster and Ellen Sawyer, *The Dog Made Me Buy It!,* Crown Publishers, 1990; Alice L. Muncaster, Ellen Sawyer, and Ken Kapson, *The Baby Made Me Buy It!,* Crown Publishers, Inc., 1991; Murray Cards (International) Ltd., *Cigarette Card Values: 1992 Catalog of Cigarette & Other Trade Cards* Murray Cards (International) Ltd., 1992; Robert Opie, *Packaging Source Book,* Chartwell Books, Inc., 1989; Robert Opie, *The Art of the Label: Designs of the Times,* Chartwell Books, Inc., 1987; Dawn E. Reno, *Advertising: Identification and Price Guide,* Avon Books; Joleen Robison and Kay Sellers, *Advertis-*

*ing Dolls: Identification and Value Guide*, Collector Books, 1980, 1992 value update; Robert W. and Harriett Swedberg, *Tins 'N' Bins*, Wallace–Homestead, 1985.

**Collectors' Clubs:** The Ephemera Society of America, P. O. Box 37, Schoharie, NY 12157; Tin Container Collectors Association, P. O. Box 440101, Aurora, CO 80014.

**Periodicals:** National Association of Paper and Advertising Collectibles, *P.A.C.*, P. O. Box 500, Mt Joy, PA 17552; *Paper Collectors' Marketplace* (PCM), P.O. Box 128, Scandinavia, WI 54917.

**REPRODUCTION ALERT**

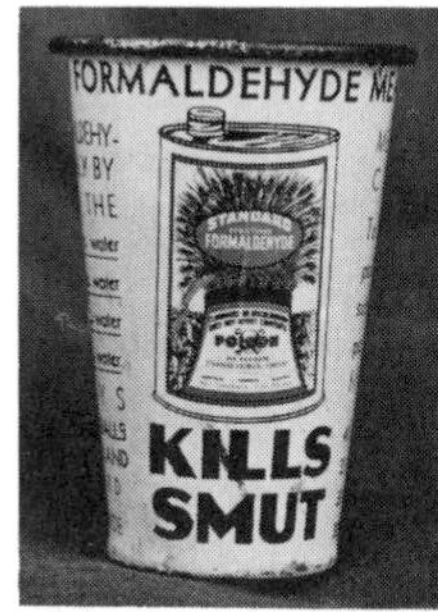


**Measure, Standard Formaldehyde, tapered cylinder, black lettering, red highlights, white ground, 2" d top, 2⅝" h, $38.00.**

## ASHTRAY

Chicago Motor Club, metal, round, figural logo upright in center, gold wings, red star, white border, 1940s **20.00**
Cities Service, china, green and white logo, c1940, 5¼" d **12.00**
Glenmore Whiskey, painted plaster, figural trademark figure behind tray, gold colored, 1930s, 5" d, 4" h **45.00**
Goodyear Super–Torque Tires, black rubber tire, c1940, 6½" d **25.00**
Heywood Wakefield, rubber **20.00**
Iron Fireman, furnace manufacturer, silvered metal, trademark figure standing on tray, c1930s, 4" h, 6½" l **50.00**
Kessler's Blended Whiskey, plaster, cube shaped tray in center, pair of top hatted men standing back to back either side, c1940, 8½" l, 6" h **100.00**
Michelin Tire, hard plastic, black, 4½" h seated figure on back, late 1930s **75.00**
Playboy Club, glass, orange, black lettering and key, c1970, 4 x 4" **32.00**
Pyrene Fire Extinguisher, brown steel, replica fire extinguisher in center, "Kills Fire, Saves Life," c1930, 5¼" d, 5" h **60.00**
Reddy Kilowatt, glass, red and white image, 1950s, 4" d **20..00**
Space Satellite Hotel, white china, rim inscription and satellite images, Royal China Inc, late 1950s, 5½" d **20.00**
Toyota Motor, gold colored metal, replica 1959 Toyota, orig box, 9" l **200.00**
William Marvy Co Sign Makers, glass, red, white, and blue rim "Porcelain Enameled Signs and Barber Poles," 1950s, 5" d **18.00**

## BOXES

Aunt Jemima Pancake Flour, cardboard, 13" w, 9" d, 14" h **55.00**
Bakers Chocolatiere, Art Deco design **25.00**
Bulldog Tobacco, wood, hinged lid, dog on front and back **70.00**
Castile Soap, Oletyme Products, Indianapolis, IN, pictures castle, "Made in Accordance with the Fair Labor Standards Act of 1933," three bars, 7¼ x 3½ x 1" **7.00**
Dr Hobson's Ox Marrow Pomade, includes jar dated 1921, picture of lady on label and box, 3½ x 2 x 2" **15.00**
El Vampiro Bellow, bug killer, Allaire Woodard & Co, Peoria, IL, dated June 15, 1918, 3¾ x 2¾ x ¾" **12.00**
La Florita Face Powder, blue with basket of flowers dec, logo, unopened, 1920s **15.00**
Lydia E Pinkham's Pills for Constipation, signature on side, includes bottle and pills, 2½ x 1¼ x 1¼" **10.00**
Old Nick Candy Bars **7.00**
Peters Cartridge Co, wood, red "P" on end panels, c1910, 9 x 9 x 15" **50.00**
Quaker Oats, wood, 26 x 18 x 11" **65.00**

## BROCHURE

Alpha–New England Salad Cream, recipes, premiums, 24 pgs, black and white, 1902, 6½ x 4½" **10.00**
Bell Telephone, Behind the Scenes, 16 pgs, black and white photos, 1915, 4½ x 9" **18.00**
Buick Motor Cars, 20 pgs, 1911 models, 3½ x 8½" **35.00**
Campbell Fanning Mill Co, How to Make Dollars Out of Wind, 1902 grain machines, red and white, 5½ x 7½" **6.00**
Chase & Sanborn Tea & Coffee, 48 pgs, black and white illus, 1889, color **15.00**
Clark's ONT Spool Cotton, The Hunters Three and ONT, 8 pgs, color **10.00**
Colleen Moore's Dollhouse, 1935 **35.00**
Colgate/Fab Laundering, 1921 **20.00**

Corticelli Silk, parody on House That Jack Built, 1893, 16 pgs, color ..... **20.00**
Drey Doppel Soap, daguerreotype, 1893, color ..................... **25.00**
Gold Standard Coffee, nursery rhymes, figural pkg, 4 pgs, color ........... **12.00**
Hires Un–Natural History, diecut strip pages, c1914 .................... **25.00**
H–O Cereal Sunny Jim Denslow, 1910, 32 pgs ......................... **55.00**
Ivory Soap, 24 pgs ................. **22.00**
Jell–O Girl Gives a Party, The, Rose O'Neill illus, 16 pgs, color, 5¼ x 7" **25.00**
Jewel Stoves, Cooking with Gas Jewel Stoves and Ranges, 32 pgs, illus, two tone, 5 x 7" ..................... **10.00**
Kellogg's Rice Krispies, six flaps create different pictures, art sgd Vernon Grant, color ..................... **20.00**
Lautz Brothers Pictorial, soap, 8 pgs, four full color illus, printed blue and green, 1887, 5½ x 7¼" ........... **18.00**
Magic Yeast, recipes, 12 pgs, color ... **8.00**
Maxwell House Coffee Co, Secrets of Coffee Flavor, 20 pgs, color, 1927 .. **10.00**
McCormick Farm Machine, Rand McNally & Co, black and white, 1892, 7 x 9½" .................. **20.00**
Metropolitan Life Insurance Co, First Aid in the Home, 30 pgs, color, 5½ x 8" **8.00**
New England Tours, 1915 ........... **25.00**
Old Grist Mill Flour, recipes, 16 pgs, Gies Litho, color ................ **8.00**
Pike's Peak, brochure and map, 1915 . **45.00**
Quick Meal Steel Ranges, Ringen Stove Co, c1904, 3 x 5" ............... **35.00**
Ralston Recipes, Nursery Rhymes, 23 pages, color ..................... **15.00**
Reliable Flour Co, Reliable Primer, recipes, 14 pgs, color, 3½ x 3¾" ..... **6.00**
Rules of the Winchester Junior Rifle Corps, c1915, 3¼ x 5¼" .......... **30.00**
Sinclair's Fidelity Meats, 6 pgs, color, 1902 .......................... **12.00**
Teddy Bear's Baking School, 1906 .... **50.00**
Thomas W Stevens Bazaar Shirt, four part foldout, calendar, black and white, 1875 ..................... **18.00**
Waltham Watches, 1904, 32 pages ... **25.00**
WD Sager Stoves, Chicago, 1915 .... **6.00**
Wrigley's, Mother Goose, 1930s, 4 x 6" **25.00**

## MIRRORS

Amulet Toilet Specialties, oval, multicolored portrait illus, gold lettering, rim inscription, 1906 copyright Whitehead & Hoag, 2¾" l ......... **200.00**
Angelus Marshmallows, oval, multicolored illus, blonde cherub, green background, rim inscription "Mirror Free With Package Angelus Marshmallows Or Mailed For 3–2 ct. Stamps. Ask Your Dealer, Rueckheim Bros & Eckstein, Chicago," 2¾" l ... **75.00**
Bastian Bros Gold and Silversmiths, celluloid, birthstone for each month on rim, c1930, 2⅛" d ............... **50.00**
Beeman Gum, pocket ............... **150.00**
Big Jo Flour, red, white, and blue flour bag, early 1900s, 2¼" d .......... **50.00**
Cascarets, All Going Out–Nothing Coming In, celluloid, full color illus, seated winged cherub, 1910, 2⅛" d **50.00**
CD Kenny Co, Teas, Coffees, Sugars, paper over metal, red and white, c1900 ......................... **30.00**
Ceresota Flour, Prize Bread Flour of the World, celluloid, c1920, 2⅛" d .... **50.00**
Checkers Popcorn, "Eat Eat Eat," celluloid, red, white, and blue, c1920, 2⅛" d ......................... **100.00**
Ceresota Flour, celluloid, multicolored illus, dark brown rim, early 1900s, 2⅛" d ......................... **50.00**
Garland Stoves and Ranges, tin, emb logo, inscription "Sold Everywhere/ The Worlds' Best," early 1900s, 1¾" d .............................. **25.00**
Horlick's Malted Milk, The Nutritious Food–Drink For All Ages, celluloid, c1900 ......................... **75.00**
JI Case Threshing Machine Co, oval, multicolored trademark image, rim inscription, early 1900s, 2¾" l ..... **100.00**
Lava Chemical Resolvant Soap, celluloid, c1910, 2½" d .............. **35.00**
Mennen's Powder, Violet Talcum Toilet Powder, oval, celluloid, c1910, 3" l **40.00**
Monitor Stoves and Ranges, celluloid, black and white, logo design, 1¾" d **20.00**
Morton's Salt, celluloid, 1940s ....... **35.00**
Muehlebach Pilsner, oval, multicolored illus, black lettering, early 1900s, 2¾" l ............................. **200.00**
Nature's Remedy Tablets, red rim, white lettering, inscription "Better Than Pills For Liver Ills/Get A 25¢ Box," early 1900s, 2⅛" d .............. **55.00**
Osgood C Cobb, jewelry dealer, oval, mulitcolored illus, early 1900s, 2¾" l **125.00**
Perfection Pull Cap, red, white, and blue design, 2⅛" d .............. **50.00**
Piedmont Cigarettes, opened cigarette pack, blue background, yellow lettering, early 1900s, 2⅛" d .......... **100.00**
Pilgrim Specialty Company, Pilgrim illus **30.00**
Regal Shoes, pretty girl illus ......... **75.00**
Reuter's Soap, mother and child, green background, 1912 copyright, 2⅛" d **45.00**
Robin Hood Flour, aluminum, emb Robin Hood image, inscription "None

So Good As Robin Hood," 1930s, 1½" d . . . . 20.00
Stacey Chocolates, sunset over water . 35.00
Thea–Nectar Pure Chinese Tea, emb brass shell back, Chinese symbols with entwined honeybee and "T," 1870s, 1½" d . . . . 50.00
The Derby Oil Co, celluloid, red, white, and blue, c1920, 2¼" d . . . . 50.00
Union Made Cigars, cigar label, buff background, black lettering, early 1900s, 2⅛" d . . . . 50.00
Warren Tanner Dry Goods, building illus . . . . 32.50
White House Coffee, The Flavor is Roasted In, red, white, and blue, 1920s, 2¼" d . . . . 25.00
White Rock Spring Water, "The World's Best Table Water," tin rim, multicolored illus of kneeling woman, 2" d . 150.00
White Rose Safety Club, red, white, and blue, 1930s, 2⅛" d . . . . 55.00
Woodford Club Whiskey, oval, multicolored illus, black lettering, early 1900s, 2¾" l . . . . 225.00

**Bank, Crown Savings, metal, Strong Heart pat., Chicago, IL, complete with key, $35.00.**

## MISCELLANEOUS

Bag, Black Draught Family Laxative, brown paper, people looking up at tall black and yellow box, 4¼ x 8¼" . . . 4.00
Bank
  Century Savings and Loan, figural, house, spring action behind chimney . . . . 20.00
  Sunoco, gas pump, tin, top lifts off to get change, blue, yellow, and red, 1940–60, 4" h . . . . 35.00
  Tootsie Roll, cylinder, cardboard and tin, 1960s, 12" l . . . . 12.00
Banner, Real Tobacco, cloth, man smoking cigarette surrounded by product images, 22½" sq . . . . 220.00

**Blotter, Little Boy Blue Crepe Toilet Paper, Father Goose Series, Regal Paper Co., 9½ x 4⅜", $8.00.**

Beach Bag, Maxwell House Coffee, figural, coffee can . . . . 25.00
Belt Buckle, Stroh's Beer . . . . 5.00
Bill Holder, Walker's Austex Products, wall mount . . . . 30.00
Blotter, Sunoco, Mickey and Minnie bride and groom in convertible . . . . 25.00
Bookmark
  Hood's Sarsaparilla, full color, c1900 10.00
  Peters Weatherbird Shoes, paper, 1930s, 3¾" l . . . . 10.00
  Red Goose Shoes, diecut cardboard, 1920s, 3" h . . . . 15.00
  Stollwerck Chocolate, Cocoa, celluloid . . . . 20.00
Bottle Opener, Dr Brown's Celery Tonic 20.00
Building Blocks, Uneeda Biscuit, cardboard boxes, set of six . . . . 175.00
Buttonhook, Johnson & Conde Clothiers, Ballston Spa, NY . . . . 12.00
Calendar Card
  Edison Mazda, celluloid, Maxfield Parrish illus "Prometheus," 1920, 2¼ x 3¾" . . . . 50.00
  Swift Premium, celluloid, yellow and red railroad boxcar, 1930, 1¾ x 3¾" . . . . 25.00
Camera, Kraft Velveeta Shells & Cheese Dinner, hard plastic, yellow, illus instruction leaflet, 1950–60 . . . . 12.00
Change Pad, Learn to Say Mi Lola, felt, 8" d . . . . 12.00
Cigar Cutter
  City Billiard Parlor, brass case, swingout blade, Gitsnife, 2½" l . . . . 25.00
  Waterman's Ideal Fountain Pen, celluloid, silvered metal swingout blade, 1920s, 2⅛" l . . . . 30.00
Clock, Ever–Ready, man shaving, 18" w, 22" h . . . . 45.00
Clothespin, Minneapolis–Moline Machinery Co, wood, ink stamped logo and slogan "Pin Down Costs, Bring Up Profits," painted silver top, late 1940s, 3¾" h . . . . 10.00
Counter Card, Dr Carman's Dentalaid, M A & G W Carman, Dentists, New York, full color illus, late 19th C . . . 15.00

Cup, Patton's Sun–Proof Paints, aluminum, collapsible . . . . . . . . . . . . . . . . . **20.00**
Display
- Whitman's Chocolates, painted wood, movable hand, blue dress, c1930 . . . . . . . . . . . . . . . . . . . . . . . . **120.00**
- Winchester, cardboard, standing, Model 55 & 77 guns, orig shipping box . . . . . . . . . . . . . . . . . . . . . . . . . **100.00**

Display Box, Shoe Lace Service Station, tin, three sided, man driving shoe shaped car, shelved int., 11¼″ w, 11″ h . . . . . . . . . . . . . . . . . . . . . . . . . . . . . **1,000.00**
Display Cabinet, Coleman's Mustard, tin, red and black lettering, yellow ground, three int. shelves, 10″ w, 7¼″ d, 16″ h . . . . . . . . . . . . . . . . . . . . . . . . . **70.00**
Doll
- C & H Sugar, cloth, price for pair . . **12.00**
- Gallo Salami . . . . . . . . . . . . . . . . . . . . **4.00**
- Jolly Green Giant Elf, 6″ h . . . . . . . . . **12.50**
- Magic Chef, 7½″ h . . . . . . . . . . . . . . . **12.50**
- Western Union, orig booklet . . . . . . . **12.00**

Door Push, Kuke's Mixture, porcelain . **115.00**
Fan
- Bissell's "Cyco" Bearing Carpet Sweeper, folding . . . . . . . . . . . . . . . **20.00**
- Nippon, Selz, Chicago . . . . . . . . . . . . **22.00**

**Fan, Haines the Shoe Wizard, adv text on back, $12.00.**

Game, Tootsie Roll Train Game, Hasbro, orig box, 1962–63 . . . . . . . . . . . **18.00**
Greeting Card, Bell System, diecut, candlestick telephone and holly wreath front, folding, 1917, closed size 3 x 5½″ . . . . . . . . . . . . . . . . . . . . **30.00**
Ink Blotter
- Arm & Hammer Baking Soda, cardboard, 1920s, 4 x 9¼″ . . . . . . . . . . **10.00**
- Bell Lines Reach Everywhere, cardboard, red, white, and blue, c1916, 4 x 8″ . . . . . . . . . . . . . . . . . . **20.00**
- Morton's Salt, black and white photo, c1930s, 3¼ x 6¼″ . . . . . . . . . . . . . **5.00**

Jar, Kiss Me Gum . . . . . . . . . . . . . . . . . . **95.00**
Key Chain
- General Motors Motorama of 1956, brass, souvenir, 2¼″ l . . . . . . . . . . . **5.00**
- Southern States Fertilizer, diecut plastic, bag shape, c1930, 1 x 1½″ . . **4.00**

Letter Folder, tin, Kellogg & Bulkeley, 3 x 12½″
- Aetna Insurance, horizontal, Mt Vesuvius . . . . . . . . . . . . . . . . . . . . . . . . **100.00**
- National Insurance, Liberty and flag **55.00**
- Western Assurance, Royal Canadian seal . . . . . . . . . . . . . . . . . . . . . . . . . **275.00**

Letter Opener
- Armour, celluloid, rooster head . . . . **55.00**
- Buck Printing Co . . . . . . . . . . . . . . . . . **15.00**
- National Office Registers, black and white, celluloid, c1900, 6″ l . . . . . **20.00**
- Uneeda Biscuits, metal, c1920, 8¼″ l **50.00**

Light, General Electric Radio & Radio–Phonographs, blue, 1940s, 21″ w, 11″ h . . . . . . . . . . . . . . . . . . . . . . . . . . . . . **325.00**
Magnifying Glass, Charles Johnson & Co Printing Inks, celluloid case, swingout lens, early 1900s, 1½ x 1¾″ . . . . . . . **30.00**
Match Holder
- Bowser Filtered Gasolene, brass, raised gas pump on red enameled oval, early 1900s, 2¼″ l . . . . . . . . **65.00**
- Ceresota/Prize Bread Flour of the World, diecut, full color litho tin, early 1900s . . . . . . . . . . . . . . . . . . . **175.00**
- De Laval . . . . . . . . . . . . . . . . . . . . . . . **145.00**

Match Safe
- Damon and Gould Co Hardware, silvered brass, early 1900s . . . . . . . . **45.00**
- Hercules Powder, celluloid covered silvered brass, c1900, 1½ x 2½″ . **75.00**
- Libby & Williams Paper Co, silvered brass, early 1900s . . . . . . . . . . . . . . **50.00**
- Sharples Tubular Cream Separator, tin, cows in pasture scene above image of mother and child using separator, 2″ w, 7″ h . . . . . . . . . . . **110.00**

**Needle Book, Hartford Federal Savings and Loan Association, litho paper, $4.00.**

Tadcaster Ale, silvered brass, celluloid wrapper, early 1900s ....... **25.00**
Menu, RH Macy's, 1937 ............ **25.00**
Palm Puzzle, Spinks Billiard Tables, early 1900s, 2⅛" d ............... **35.00**
Paper Clip, Edison Portland Cement Co, celluloid, 1920s, 1¾" l ........... **24.00**
Pencil Clip, celluloid
Christopher Milk, "Builds Champions," white lettering, blue ground, 1930s, ⅞" d ................... **15.00**
Diamond Crystal Salt, salt box, 1930s, ⅞" d ................... **18.00**
EIS Automotive Corp, red lettering, white ground, 1930s, ⅝" d ...... **12.00**
General Electric, GE logo, red and white, 1930s, ¾" d ............ **10.00**
Laurel Fertilizers, "Cut Crop Costs," red and blue lettering, white ground, 1930s, ¾" d ........... **15.00**
Ziegler's Clean Milk, milk bottle and flowers, early 1900s, ⅞" d ...... **25.00**
Pin Cushion, Bunny Bread, felt ....... **12.00**
Pitcher, Kellogg's Cereal, glass ....... **15.00**
Pocket Comb, leather case, Ramons, illus of little boy playing doctor ..... **20.00**
Pocket Knife, HJ Heinz Co, complimentary, silvered metal, two steel blades, text one side, "57" symbol other side, Meriden Knife Co, early 1900s, 3" l **25.00**
Pot Scraper, Babitts Cleanser ......... **225.00**
Puzzle
Calumet Baking Powder, cardboard, 9 pcs, early 1900s .............. **20.00**
Frito–Lay Inc, character symbol, 84 pcs, 1970s .................... **15.00**
Scorer, North American Life & Surety Co, celluloid, mechanical, early 1900s, 1¼ x 2¾" ............... **20.00**
Sherbet Glass, Jell–O Brand Dessert, fluted edge, red lettering, c1930, 3½" d, 4" h .......................... **28.00**
Shoe Horn, Normal Shoe Co ........ **11.00**
Slide, glass, Winchester Baseball Goods, player, mitt, and ball, hand colored, 3 x 4" .................. **110.00**
Stamp Case, Aetna Life Insurance Co, celluloid, red and blue text, white ground, 1905, 1¼ x 2¼" .......... **15.00**
Stickpin
Gold Dust Washing Powder, full color celluloid, brass rim, c1896 ...... **75.00**
John Deere 40 Line, brass logo and shank, inscription on reverse, early 1900s, 1½" w ................ **15.00**
Oliver Farm Equipment, diecut celluloid, corporate flag, 1920s, 1¼" w .......................... **18.00**
String Holder, Post Toasties, round, tin front ........................... **50.00**
Tape Measure
American Rolling Mills Co, celluloid, collie dog, "Lyle Products Like A Good Collie/Dependable," logo symbol reverse, cloth tape, 1920s, 1½" d ....................... **40.00**
Colt's Armory Press, celluloid, sepia factory machinery, cloth tape, early 1900s, 1½" d .................. **35.00**
Columbine Peas, celluloid, cloth tape, early 1900s, 1¾" d ........ **25.00**
Cone Pulley Transformers, celluloid, transformer image, cloth tape, early 1900s, 1¾" d .................. **30.00**
Edison Mazda Lamps, His Only Rival, celluloid, full color, 1920s, 1½" d **60.00**
Toothpick, Owbridge's Lung Tonic, celluloid holder and two foldout toothpicks, "For Coughs/For Colds," c1900, 1¾" l ................... **25.00**
Toy Top, Haller's Oliver Twist Bread, "A Dickens of a Good Loaf," litho tin, fortune teller, red, white, and blue, 1930s, 1½" d .................... **25.00**
Watch Fob
Bay State Casualty Co, brass, emb bandaged owl, 1905, 1⅜" d ..... **20.00**
Lackawanna Leather Co, bronzed metal, Mission building, early 1900s, 1½" d .................. **25.00**
Manhattan Rug, brass, enameled red, white, and blue bar logo surrounded by emb wreath rim, 1920s, 1¼" d .................. **50.00**
Northwestern Mutual Life Insurance Co, silvered brass, diamond shaped, emb office building, 1913, 1½" w ....................... **18.00**
Pointer Stoves & Ranges, brass, oval, emb hunting dog, text on reverse, early 1900s, 1¾" l ............. **30.00**
Whetstone, Cudahy's Blue Ribbon Meat Meal, pig, pocket size ............ **35.00**
Whisk Broom, Whiskbroom Cigars, cigar shaped ...................... **30.00**
Yardstick, Wm A Gehman & Sons Chevrolet, wood ...................... **12.00**

## PAPERWEIGHTS

ABCO Electronics, NJ, aircraft supplies, celluloid over glass and metal, maroon lettering and airplane image, buff ground, late 1930s, 3½" d ..... **25.00**
AMR Insurance Group, Neard, NJ, 100th Anniversary, brass, 1946 ..... **8.00**
Bell Telephone System, dark blue glass, replica bell, gold lettering, 1920s, 3½" d, 3" h ..................... **45.00**
Dutch Boy Paint, metal, white, figural, c1930, 2¼ x 3 x 4½" ............. **75.00**
Fairbanks Scale .................... **85.00**
Kool Cigarettes, painted plaster, figural

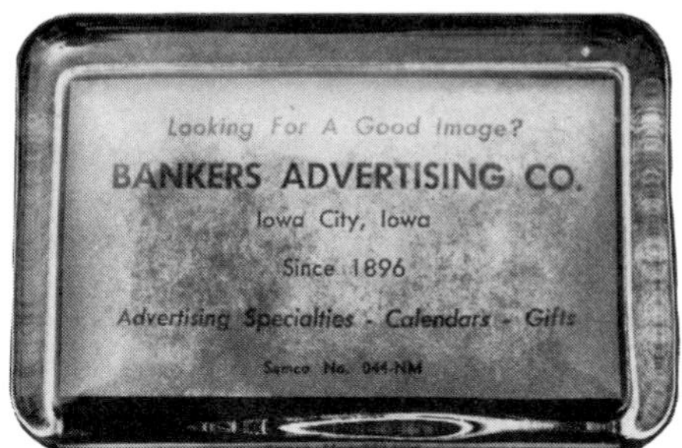


**Paperweight, Bankers Advertising Co., clear glass, blue lettering, red ground, slightly tapered sides, $4\frac{5}{16}$ x $2\frac{13}{16}$", $35.00.**

penguin carrying doctor's satchel, "Dr Kool," 1940s ................ **75.00**
National Molasses Co, figural railroad car, bronzed white metal, c1950, 5" l **25.00**
Raleigh Cigarettes, painted white metal, Sir Walter Raleigh bust, c1950, $4\frac{1}{2}$" h .............................. **80.00**
Stetson Hats, clear glass dome, black and white John B Stetson portrait, early 1900s, $3\frac{1}{2}$" d .............. **45.00**
Twenty One, nightclub, figural jockey, metal figure, china base, gold inscription, 1950s ..................... **75.00**
Westinghouse, Tuff Guy, composition, 1952, $4\frac{1}{2}$" h .................... **75.00**
Ziegenheim Brothers Ambulance Service, Texas, photo of 1900s ambulance ........................... **45.00**

**Pencil Sharpener, Symington's Soups, dark blue lettering, light blue ground, $20.00.**

## PINBACK BUTTONS

Bastian Bros Co, black and white, factory scene, c1910, $1\frac{1}{4}$" d ......... **20.00**
Borden's Fern Butter, red, white, and blue design, 1901–12, $\frac{7}{8}$" d ....... **15.00**
Bowman Milk, Bud Bowman character, 1940s, 1" d ...................... **12.00**
Columbian Stoves and Ranges, red, white, and blue, c1913, $2\frac{1}{8}$" d .... **35.00**
Davis OK Baking Powder, red, yellow, black, and white, c1896, $\frac{7}{8}$" d ..... **25.00**
Drink Satisfaction Coffee, blue and white, diecut flag, 1900–01, $\frac{5}{8}$" d .. **18.00**
DuPont Smokeless Powder, full color, 1900–12, $1\frac{1}{4}$" d ................ **50.00**
Dutch Kid School Shoes, multicolored, white rim, red lettering, 1907–20, $\frac{7}{8}$" d .......................... **25.00**
Fisher's Blend Flour, red, white, and blue flour sack, early 1900s, $1\frac{1}{2}$" d . **30.00**

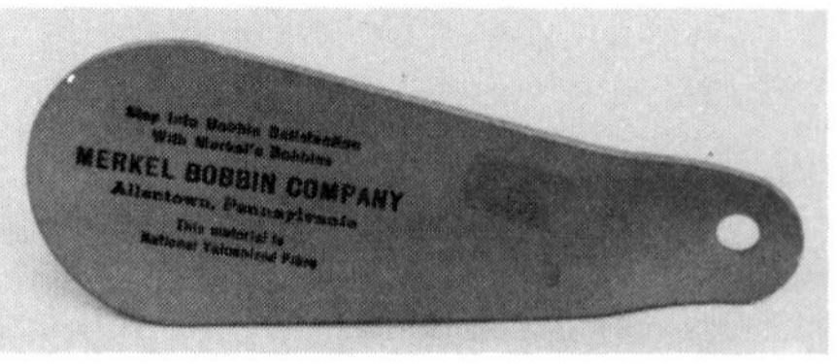


**Shoe Horn, Merkel Bobbin Company, Allentown, PA, vulcanized fibre, $4\frac{5}{8}$" l, $8.00.**

Fleischmann's Yeast, "John Dough Raised on Fleischmann's Yeast," oval, full color, baker with bread loaf body parts, c1915, $1\frac{1}{2}$" l ............... **40.00**
Frisbee's Alfalfa Clover Honey, multicolored design with three honey bees, 1901–12, $1\frac{1}{4}$" d ................ **50.00**
Garland Stoves and Ranges, red and white, list of company products, early 1900s, $1\frac{3}{4}$" d .................. **25.00**
Green Wheeler Shoe Co, celluloid, green spoked wheel, red inscription, early 1900s, $\frac{5}{8}$" d ................ **15.00**
Hamilton/The World's Best Watch, black and white, early 1900s, $1\frac{3}{4}$" d **75.00**
Heinz Tomato Soup, full color, c1896, $\frac{7}{8}$" d .......................... **35.00**
King Arthur Flour, multicolored design, c1896, $\frac{7}{8}$" d .................... **40.00**
Kodak, blue and white, 1940s, $1\frac{1}{4}$" d . **15.00**
Krug's Bread, red and white, 1930s, 1" d .......................... **12.00**
Lane's Pills Are Best For The Liver, blonde youngster, light blue background, 1907–20, $\frac{7}{8}$" d ........... **40.00**
Limetta/The Drink of Drinks, youngster riding St Bernard, $1\frac{1}{4}$" d .......... **75.00**
Lion Coffee, inscribed "Millions Drink It," coffee cup illus, early 1900s, $\frac{7}{8}$" d ............................... **25.00**
Mazda Lamps, blue and white, 1930s . **10.00**
Mennen's For Mine/Baby Week, full color, c1910, $\frac{7}{8}$" d .................. **35.00**

Nabisco Shredded Wheat, Top O' The Morning, red on white, c1940, 1¼" d ..... 20.00
Oscar Mayer Yellow Band Weiners, full color litho, 1930s, 1⅜" d ..... 10.00
Packard–Bell Radios and Televisions, dark red and white, late 1940s, 2¼" d ..... 40.00
Pillsbury's Flour, The Flour That Sells Around The World, c1910, 1¼" d ..... 50.00
Quaker Rolled White Oats, full color, red rim, c1920, 2" d ..... 75.00
RCA Victor Television Is Million–Proof, yellow and red, 1950s, 1¼" d ..... 15.00
Red Cross Macaroni, red, white, and blue, 1930s, 1¼" d ..... 25.00
Red Goose Club Member, brown, yellow background, 1930s, 1⅜" d ..... 20.00
Sears, Roebuck & Co, Sears Corral/Roy Rogers Riders, 1950s, 1¾" d ..... 35.00
Square Deal Bread/Safety Club, silvered brass, black incised inscription, 1930s, 1¼" d ..... 20.00
Star Brand Shoes, multicolored, hand holding red star, white background, blue lettering, 1920s, ⅞" d ..... 25.00
Time To Drink White House Coffee, full color, 1910, 1¼" d ..... 50.00
Towle's Log Cabin Maple Sugar, full color, c1896, ⅞" d ..... 20.00
Use Peters Referee Shells, full color, 1910, ⅞" d ..... 60.00
Whitehead & Hoag Company, c1897, 1¼" d ..... 50.00
White Ribbon Shoe Co, black, white, and red, bicycle wheel tied with white ribbon, inscribed "The New Shoe For Women," late 1890s, ⅞" d 22.00
Winchester Firearms, oval, full color, 1910, 1" l ..... 150.00

## POSTERS

Brook Thread, paper, Victorian exposition display from Paris Exhibition, 1878, 19¼ x 13¾" ..... 165.00
Coleman's Mustard, paper, trademark image in medallion insert, 16 x 22" . 150.00
Del Monte Foods, garden show, dog knocking over flower vase, vegetable can in corner, c1970, 24½ x 35" ... 15.00
DeVoe Varnish, cardboard, cloud raining on touring car, "Prevent Destruction," c1925, 23½ x 34½" ..... 325.00
Herbert Tareyton London Cigarettes, litho paper, trademark character, green, black, and white, 1930s, 9½ x 11" ..... 25.00
Lion Coffee, c1910, 11 x 14" ..... 100.00
Maytag, 1950, children illus ..... 15.00
Remington UMC, paper, animals, bullets, and guns, 20 x 24" ..... 125.00
Rice's Seeds, paper, jolly man holding very large turnip, printed by Cosack & Co, 20 x 27" ..... 950.00
St Jacob's Oil, paper, monk holding bottle, 9½ x 18" ..... 55.00
Swift's Animal Fertilizers, cloth, blue and white, c1900, 18 x 29¾" ..... 50.00
The World Newspaper, paper, goddess carrying torch over world, "Cheapest Newspaper in the United States," 11 x 14½" ..... 110.00
Wheaties, model planes, multicolored, "Wheaties, Breakfast of Champions" at bottom, c1944, 16 x 36" ..... 85.00

**Sign, Ingersoll Watches, tin, 25" d, $575.00.**

## SIGNS

Alligator Rainwear, counter type, alligator illus, 1950s, 5 x 10" ..... 22.00
Bell Canada, porcelain ..... 175.00
Blue Star Coal, emb tin, 1930s ..... 75.00
Briar Pipe, store card, black child holding two packages of pipe tobacco, 8 x 11¼" ..... 250.00
British–America Insurance, diecut tin, 1930s, orig cardboard box ..... 225.00
Clapperson's Sewing & Crochet Cottons, cardboard, hanging type, 1890s ..... 165.00
De Laval Cream Separators, tin, round, woman using cream separator, child carrying cream pail, emb rolled border, 26" d ..... 2,000.00
Golden Girl Sunspot, emb tin, green menu board, 1930s ..... 115.00
Heinz Mince Meat, paper, full color, 1930s, 12 x 22" ..... 75.00
Household Sewing Machine, paper, girl with flowers, metal strips top and bottom, 14¾ x 29" ..... 70.00
J & P Coats' Spool Cotton, treated paper on plaster backing, fisherman and lady friend, 22 x 17½" ..... 200.00

Jersey Creme, flange ................ **400.00**
Kellogg Telephone, fiddleback wall phones, paper, girl holding telephone earpiece to puppy's ear, c1902, 12 x 19" ................ **325.00**
Kool Cigarettes, emb tin, penguin, 1930s ................ **50.00**
Lautz Soap, paper, laughing man holding soap bar, 21 x 17½" ................ **225.00**
Lava Soap, full color, cardboard, c1910, 8 x 8" ................ **20.00**
Lion Hats, cardboard, stand–up, 1930s, 13 x 22" ................ **35.00**
Morton Salt, tin ................ **80.00**
New Bachelor Cigars, tin, monochromatic, cigar smoking man playing solitaire, woman's image in smoke, 8" x 11" ................ **72.00**
Our Fresh Up 7–Up, cardboard, diecut, easel back, elderly man and woman holding product, 1943, 12 x 18" ... **35.00**
Palmolive Soap, green, black, and white, 1930s, 14 x 22" ................ **20.00**
Peters—The Old Timer's Standby, cardboard, easel back, 1930s, 14 x 18" . **75.00**
Poll Parrot Shoes, cardboard, 1930s, 15" h ................ **100.00**
Remington UMC Steel Lined Shot Shells, cardboard, full color, 1910, 7 x 10" ................ **50.00**
Sensation Cut Plug, cardboard, man restraining dogs, product package in foreground, 25" x 17", framed ..... **85.00**
Sozodont Tooth Powder, paper, smiling woman, 8½ x 13" ................ **100.00**
Winchester New Rival Shells, cardboard, full color illus, c1910, 10 x 17" ................ **150.00**

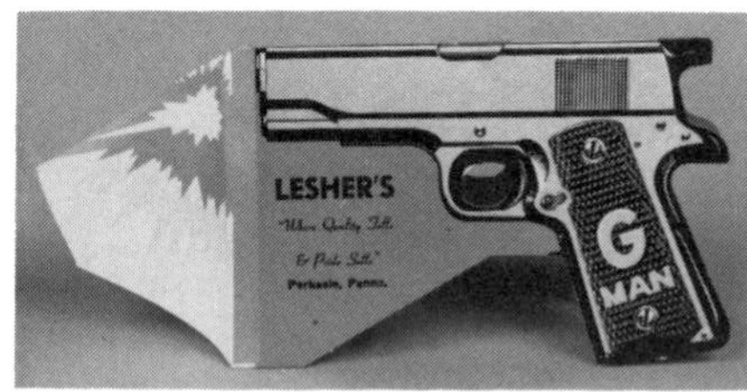


**Snap Gun, Lesher's, Perkasie, PA, cardboard, G Man, red, black, and gray, 7" l, $5.00.**

## THERMOMETERS

Doan's Pills, wood ................ **175.00**
Drink Dr Pepper, full color litho tin, c1930, 17" h ................ **150.00**
Ex–Lax, porcelain, 1915 ................ **185.00**
Gaines Dog Meal, tin ................ **75.00**
Lincoln Laundry, wood, early 1900s, 12 x 3" ................ **25.00**
Moxie, tin, bottle and man pointing, "Good At Any Temperature," 25½" h **550.00**
Pepsi–Cola, emb metal, red, white, and blue, c1932, 27" h ................ **100.00**
Prestone Anti–Freeze, porcelain, blue on gray, 1950s, 8¾" w, 36" h ...... **55.00**
Puritan Ice Cream, cardboard, c1923, 12½" h ................ **35.00**
Standard Home Heating Oils, tin, torch logo ................ **35.00**
Tracto Weather Station, tin, orig box .. **75.00**

**Tin, Elk Brand Allspice, paper label, 2¼ x 1½ x 2⅞", $9.50.**

## TIN

Bobwhite ................ **150.00**
Coleman Mustard, round ................ **105.00**
Colgate's La France Rose Talc Powder, brass, multicolored design, 2¼" h .. **30.00**
Colgate's Monad Violet Talc, brass finish, multicolored design, 2" d ...... **40.00**
Dearso Respicol Ointment ................ **15.00**
DuPont Gun Powder ................ **85.00**
Eden Beauty Face Powder, multicolored lid design, 1920s, 1½" d ................ **25.00**
Edgeworth, flat, 2 x 3" ................ **8.00**
Girard Putty, litho ................ **14.75**
Great American Tea, 2 lb, New York store image, black over red, 6" d, 7½" h ................ **55.00**
Gustav A Mayer Champagne Wafers, bottle of champagne, glasses, and wafers, orange and black lettering, black highlights, orange ground, c1935, 5" w, 2¾" h ................ **10.00**
Harry Horn Animal ................ **175.00**
Hartz Mountain Turtle Food ................ **15.00**
Heinrich's Poudre Adorable, litho, Art Nouveau lid, 1920s, 1⅝" d ................ **20.00**
Horlick's Malted Milk, 10 lb can ..... **45.00**
Hotel Research Lamps, litho, poison, wood alcohol fuel tablet ................ **15.75**
Hygenol Violet Talcum, litho image,

chartreuse, green, and red, 1920s, 2½″ l, 4¾″ h .......... **25.00**
Jackie Coogan, pail, black highlights, red ground, policeman chasing boy on back, emb lid, bail handle, sgd "Henry Clive," 1930s, 3¼″ d, 3½″ h **230.00**
Johnson's Wax, powdered wax .......... **30.00**
Laflin & Rand Gun Powder, duck illus **125.00**
Lauxes Tablets .......... **15.00**
Mellomint, 3¾″ d .......... **10.00**
Mentholatum, litho, portrait illus of young nurse, 1920–30, 1½″ d .......... **25.00**
Moses Cough Drops, Summers Brothers, orange and black, 6″ l, 4″ w, 1½″ h **300.00**
Nashes Liberty Bell Mustard .......... **30.00**
Peter Pan, 25 lbs .......... **195.00**
School Boy, peanut butter, 5 lb size .. **150.00**
Senator .......... **85.00**
Smith's Rosebud Salve .......... **20.00**
Snake Charmer .......... **275.00**
Sunray, litho, "As Sunshine Heals The Body–Sunray Heals The Skin," Basen Industries, 1920–30, 1½″ d .......... **18.00**
Sunset Train .......... **145.00**
Tak–A–Lax, chocolate laxative .......... **18.00**
Three Flowers Powder, Art Deco .......... **5.00**
Up To Date Pure Candy, 5 lb, tropic scene, orange lettering, 1920–1950, 5″ d, 8¾″ h .......... **15.00**
Zingo Sweets, gold race car, black ground, 1910–20, 10¼″ d, 8¼″ h .. **45.00**
Zulu .......... **65.00**

## TRADE CARDS

Adams' Pepsin Tutti Frutti, c1890, 4½ x 6½″ .......... **25.00**
Aromatic Pino–Palmiro Mattress, Wm Hort Lith .......... **15.00**
Boston & Waterbury Clothing Co, Bufford, 1885 .......... **6.00**
Brooklyn Bridge Electric Lighting, 1883, 3½ x 5½″ .......... **15.00**
Chase & Sanborn Coffee, full color illus, 1886, 3 x 5″ .......... **15.00**
Conqueror Wringer, Baking Day, Donaldson Bros .......... **10.00**
Crosse and Blackwells' Pickles, Sauces & Condiments, girl showing man pickle jar, color .......... **15.00**
Decker Pianos, color, 4½ x 7″ .......... **20.00**
Dr Strong's Tricara Corset, color .......... **12.00**
Eureka Knitting Silk, color .......... **10.00**
Glendale Coffee, child with googly eyes, color .......... **8.00**
Gold Dust Washing Powder, diecut, full color, c1890, 3 x 3½″ .......... **35.00**
Granite Iron Ware, color .......... **12.00**
Heinz, full color, diecut, pickle shape, girl holding can of baked beans, c1890, 2 x 5″ .......... **15.00**
Higgins Soap, afternoon in Central Park, horse and carriage, color .......... **6.00**

**Trade Card, Sapolio, Enoch Morgan's Sons, soaps and cleaners, black child's face in watermelon, multicolored, Donaldson Brothers, c1882, $12.00.**

Hires Root Beer, full color, c1900, 3 x 5″ .......... **20.00**
Hood's Sarsaparilla, full color, titled "First Lesson," dog capturing rat, c1890, 3¼ x 4¾″ .......... **10.00**
Hudson's Tower Clothing Co, Grand Rapids, MI, child, 4½ x 8¼″ .......... **12.00**
Lake Superior Mills Wonder Flour, Forbes Litho .......... **12.00**
Lenox Soap, The Village Belle, GH Bulk & Co, litho, 1887, color .......... **6.00**
Lightning Blizzard Ice Cream Freezers, two sided, window cutout .......... **20.00**
Lion Coffee, full color portrait, free pocket knife premium offer, 3½ x 5½″ **10.00**
Lydia Pinkham, black and white, 1890s, 2½ x 4″ .......... **10.00**
Mennens Borated Talcum, tin illus, color .......... **8.00**
Peninsular Ready Mixed Paints, Calvert Lith, color .......... **25.00**
Purina Chick Feed, mechanical, The Diver, 1901, 4¼ x 6¾″ .......... **25.00**
Quaker White Oats, full color, c1900, 2¾ x 5½″ .......... **20.00**
Red Cross Stoves & Ranges, The Crusaders Return, color .......... **6.00**
Smith & Sanford Carpet & Drapery House, Grand Rapids, MI, dog and nest, color .......... **8.00**
White Sewing Machine, color, WJ Morgan Litho .......... **18.00**
Wrigley's Great Opera Glass Offer, c1890, 4 x 8″ .......... **20.00**

## TRAY

Baker Cocoa, tip .......... **125.00**
Best on Record Flour .......... **25.00**
Clysmic Water, woman beside water holding bottle, silver design, green ground, c1945, 13¾″ d .......... **175.00**

Columbus Brewing Co, tip, early 1900s, 4¼" d . . . . 75.00
Domestic Sewing Machine, tip, early 1900s, 4¼" d . . . . 75.00
Fairy Soap, girl sitting on soap bar, holding flowers, orange center, brown rim, tip, c1936, 4¼" d . . . . 75.00
Firestone, Carriage Convention souvenir, brass, 1914, 6½" l . . . . 20.00
Franklin Life Insurance, tip . . . . 30.00
Goebel's Malt Extract, girl and chalkboard, tip . . . . 90.00
Incandescent Light & Stove Co, tip . . . . 75.00
King's Pure Malt, tip . . . . 35.00
Murray Co Sodawater Flavors, "Fresh Sodas Sundaes," two colonial men seated on benches, tapping sodas, 1930–50, 12" d . . . . 130.00
Rockford Watches, tip . . . . 55.00
Stollwerck Chocolate, tip . . . . 25.00
Teaberry & Beech Nut Gum, tip, glass, green, decals . . . . 38.00

## WHISTLES

Buster Brown Shoes, litho tin, 1930s . . . . 35.00
Cap'n Crunch . . . . 5.00
Checkers Popcorn, litho tin, red, white, and blue, c1920 . . . . 40.00
Cracker Jack/Angellus Marshmallows, cardboard, red, white, and blue, Jack one side, marshmallow box other side, 1930s, 2½" l . . . . 28.00
Keds . . . . 5.00
Oscar Mayer Weiner, plastic, red, 1950s 8.00
Peters Weatherbird Shoes, litho tin, green, blue, and red, 1930s, 1½" l . . . . 40.00
Poll Parrot Shoes, litho tin, 1930s . . . . 20.00
Red Goose Shoes, tin, red logo, yellow background, 1930s, 2¾" h . . . . 15.00
Sundial Shoes Wear Longer, litho tin, yellow, red, and black slogan, 1930s, 1½" l . . . . 35.00
Thirsty, Just Whistle, tin . . . . 15.00
Twinkie Shoes, "For Girls & Boys," litho tin, Twinkie character image, yellow, 1930s, 2¼" l . . . . 30.00
Weatherbird Shoes, litho tin, rooster shaped, Japan, 1930s, 1½" l . . . . 25.00
Zig Zag the Food Confection, litho tin cylinder, siren, red, white, and blue, Germany, 1920s, ½" d, 1⅜" l . . . . 50.00

# ADVERTISING CHARACTERS

**Collecting Hints:** Concentrate on one advertising character. Three-dimensional objects are more eagerly sought than two-dimensional objects. Some local dairies, restaurants and other businesses developed advertising characters. This area has received little focus from collectors.

**History:** Advertising characters represent a sampling of those characters used in advertising from the early 20th century to the present.

Americans learned to recognize specific products by their particular advertising characters. During the first half of the 1900s, many immigrants could not read but could identify with the colorful characters. The advertising character helped to sell the product.

Some manufacturers developed similar names for products of lesser quality, like Fariee Soap versus the popular Fairy Soap. Later, when trade laws were enacted, this practice was stopped. Use of trademarks had become popular by this time. The advertising character often was part of the trademark.

Trademarks and advertising characters are found on product labels, in magazines, as premiums, and on other types of advertising. Popular cartoon characters also were used to advertise products.

Some advertising characters were designed especially to promote a specific product like Mr. Peanut and the Campbell Kids. The first time the popular Campbell Kids appeared, it was on streetcar advertising in 1906. The illustrations of Grace G. Drayton were aimed at housewives. The Campbell Kids were gradually dropped from Campbell's advertising until the television industry expanded the advertising market. In 1951, Campbell redesigned the kids and successfully reissued them. The kids were redesigned again in 1966. Other advertising characters also have enjoyed a long life, e.g., Aunt Jemima. Others, like Kayo and the Yellow Kid, have disappeared from modern advertising.

**References:** Warren Dotz, *Advertising Character Collectibles: An Identification and Value Guide,* Collector Books, 1993; David Longest, *Character Toys and Collectibles,* Collector Books, 1984, 1992 value update; David Longest, *Character Toys and Collectibles, Second Series,* Collector Books, 1987; Norman E. Martinus and Harry L. Rinker, *Warman's Paper,* Wallace–Homestead, 1993; Richard D. and Barbara Reddock, *Planter's Peanuts, Advertising & Collectibles,* Wallace–Homestead, 1978; Joleen Robison and Kay Sellers, *Advertising Dolls, Identification and Value Guide,* Collector Books, 1980, 1992 value update; Dave Stivers, *The Nabisco Brands Collection of Cream of Wheat Advertising Art,* Collectors' Showcase, 1986.

**Periodical:** *Kids Illustrated Drayton Supplement* (K.I.D.S), 649 Bayview Drive, Akron, OH 44319.

**REPRODUCTION ALERT**

**See:** All advertising categories; Black Memorabilia; Cartoon Characters; Fast Food; Planter's Peanuts.

Aunt Jemima
- Cookie Jar, 11½" h, figural, F & F, 1950s .......... **300.00**
- Pinback Button, 4" d, full color litho, red background, black lettering .. **20.00**
- Poster, 16½ x 22", Aunt Jemima Spice Set, expiration date Nov 15, 1950 **125.00**

**Aunt Jemima, memo holder, plastic, No. 123, red, yellow turban, scarf, and broom, 10" h, $65.00.**

- Recipe Box, yellow .......... **110.00**
- Syrup Pitcher, 5" h, plastic, F & F, 1950s .......... **75.00**
- Tab, diecut, full color litho, c1960 . **10.00**

A & W Root Beer, Great Root Bear
- Figure, 13" h, plush, 1975 .......... **45.00**
- Hand Puppet, 10" h, 1976 .......... **30.00**

Bumble Bee Tuna, figure, 24" h, inflatable, 1974 .......... **30.00**

Buster Brown
- Bank, 5½" h, vinyl, red, globe base with Buster and Tige illus, 1960s . **25.00**
- Fan, Brown's 5–Star Shoes, cardboard, c1910 .......... **35.00**
- Ink Blotter, Buster Brown Shoes/For Boys/For Girls, 3½ x 6¼, 1930s .. **12.00**

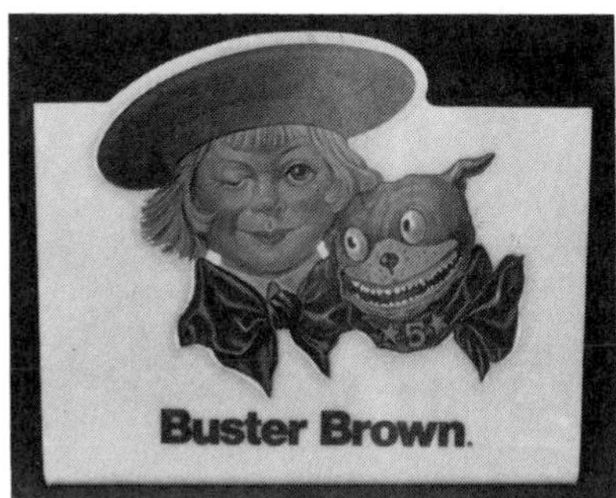


**Buster Brown and Tige, sign, plastic, decal, 7¼ x 6½", $25.00.**

- Mask, half mask, paper, diecut, Buster Brown Shoes on hat, c1905 **75.00**
- Pinback Button, Buster Brown's Guaranteed Hosiery, Buster Brown holding hosiery and Tige pulling on them, early 1900s .......... **75.00**
- Pitcher, 4" h, china, full color Buster and Tige illus, early 1900s ...... **75.00**

California Raisin
- Bank, 6½" h, vinyl, figural raisin and Sun–Maid Raisin box, orange sunglasses, 1987 copyright .......... **25.00**
- Figure, set of 4, 2" h, hard rubber, painted, CALRAB, 1987 .......... **20.00**
- Game, playing board .......... **25.00**
- Radio, 7½" h, figural, raisin, hard plastic, CALRAB copyright, 1988 . **35.00**

Campbell Kids
- Doll, vinyl, kilts, unused mint condition, price for pair .......... **50.00**
- Door Stop, 8½" h, cast iron, kids with dog, worn polychrome paint ..... **160.00**
- Pennant, 17½" l, felt, Campbell Kid and white inscription, 1930s ..... **40.00**
- Salt and Pepper Shakers, pr, 4½" h, plastic, girl and boy, 1950s ...... **35.00**
- Spoon .......... **10.00**
- Toy, squeeze, boy and girl, Oak Rubber, 1954 .......... **75.00**
- Wall Plaque, pr, 7" h, plaster, hook in base, 1940s .......... **75.00**

Cap'n Crunch
- Bank
  - 5" h, treasure chest, plastic, tan, gold stripes, rasied figure, metal handles, 1970s .......... **25.00**
  - 7½" h, plastic, figural, 1975 ..... **45.00**
- Doll, 15½" h, cloth, Animal Fair Inc, 1978 .......... **25.00**
- Hand Puppet, 1960s .......... **15.00**
- Nodder, blue, 1960s .......... **35.00**

Charlie Tuna
- Lamp, 9" h, figural, plaster, 1970 ... **50.00**
- Pinback Button, "Charlie For President," red, white, and blue, 1960s **30.00**
- Toy, squeeze, 7" h, vinyl, 1973 .... **25.00**
- Wristwatch, "Sorry Charlie," 1971 . **75.00**

Chester Cheetah, Cheetos, doll, 20" h, stuffed .......... **45.00**

Chicken Delight Chef, bank, 6" h, vinyl, figural, 1960s .......... **25.00**

Chiquita Banana
- Doll, 10" h, 1944 .......... **70.00**
- Toy, squeeze, 1950s .......... **30.00**

Choo Choo Charlie, doll, 10" h, Hasbro, 1972 .......... **30.00**

Dino the Dinosaur, Sinclair Oil
- Ashtray, 4½ x 7¼", silvered metal, dinosaur figure in center, c1950 .. **50.00**
- Clipboard, aluminum, 1960s ...... **35.00**
- Toy, 14" l, inflatable, green, 1970s . **35.00**

Dutch Boy
Doll, stuffed, 1953 .............. **35.00**
Puppet, 12" h, 1956 ............. **30.00**
Elsie the Cow
Calendar, 1943, full color Elsie cartoon, full pad ................. **50.00**
Cookie Jar, 1940s ............... **200.00**
Doll, 15" h, plush, vinyl head, 1950s **60.00**
Fan, cardboard, diecut, full color, wood handle, c1910 ........... **35.00**
Game, Elsie and Her Family, orig box, Selchow & Righter Co, c1941 .... **60.00**
Mug, 3" h, china, full color dancing Elsie, c1940 .................. **65.00**
Pin, figural, flower with head center ......................... **25.00**
Tumbler, 5½" h, clear, brown and yellow raised illus, 1950s .......... **35.00**
Esso Tiger
Bank, 8½" h, vinyl, Humble copyright, 1960s .................. **40.00**
Pillow, 10 x 12", cloth, stuffed, 1970s **15.00**
Pitcher, 9½" h, glass, clear, tiger illus and slogan in eight languages, late 1960s ....................... **25.00**
Waste Can, 10" h, metal, full color emb portrait, 1970s ............ **20.00**
Water Pitcher, "Tiger In Your Tank" **20.00**
Green Giant
Doll
Jolly Green Giant, 16" h, cloth, stuffed, 1966 ............... **50.00**
Little Sprout, 6½" h, vinyl, early 1970s ..................... **25.00**
Figure, 24" h, inflatable, 1976 ..... **10.00**
Johnny Bellhop, Philip Morris Cigarette, pinback button, 1¼" d, black, white, and red, 1940s ................. **20.00**
Keebler Elf
Doll, 6½" h, vinyl, movable head, Keebler Bakery, copyright 1974 .. **25.00**
Figure, 18" h, vinyl .............. **60.00**
Mug, plastic, F & F, 1972 ......... **10.00**
Kleek–O Eskimo, Cliquot Club
Bank, 7" h, plaster, holding Ginger Ale bottle, silvered base, 1930s .. **200.00**
Figure, 4½" h, metal, brass finish, 1930s ....................... **75.00**
Pinback Button, 1½" l, oval, 1930s . **25.00**
Sign, 6½ x 9", cardboard, full color illus, 1930s .................... **85.00**
Kool Aid Man, bank, 7" h, plastic, mechanical, 1970s ................. **25.00**
Magic Chef
Bank, 7½" h, vinyl, 1950–60 ...... **30.00**
Doll, 7½" h ...................... **12.50**
Salt and Pepper Shakers, pr, 5" h, plastic, painted, red raised script, 1950–60 ..................... **50.00**
Miss Sunbeam
Doll, 14" h, vinyl, Horsman, 1970 . **100.00**
Mr Peanut
Bookmark, 8" l, cardboard, diecut, black, white, and orange, 1930s . **20.00**
Doll, 8½" h, wood, 1930s ........ **50.00**
Mug, 4" h, plastic, green, 1960s ... **50.00**
Nodder, 6½" h ................... **50.00**
Nestle Quick Rabbit, mug, 4" h, plastic, 1970s ......................... **20.00**
Nipper
Figure, 4" h, plaster, 1930s ........ **70.00**
Pinback Button, 1" d, "I'm Voting For RCA Victor," black and white, yellow background, c1940 ......... **50.00**
Pillsbury Doughboy
Bank, 7" h, cylinder, cardboard, metal caps, blue and white, 1980s **10.00**
Doll, 16" h, cloth, 1971 .......... **10.00**
Figure, 5½" h, vinyl, 1968 ........ **25.00**
Radio, 6¼" h, plastic, earphones, 1985 ........................ **40.00**
Raid Bug
Radio, figural bug on top leaning on dial ......................... **200.00**
Telephone, figural ................ **100.00**
Toy, windup ..................... **175.00**
Red Goose
Bank, 5" h, plastic, red, c1930 ..... **15.00**
Clock, Red Goose Shoes/Friedman Shelby All Leather Shoes, New Haven Clock Co, patent date 1923 .. **125.00**
Pencil Clip, metal, red and white logo, 1930s .................. **15.00**
Shoe Horn, metal, yellow, silver logo, 1930s ....................... **10.00**
Tab, 2" h, tin, red, yellow, and black, 1950s ....................... **5.00**
Wristwatch, silvered brass case, 1930s ....................... **200.00**
Reddy Kilowatt
Ashtray, 4½" sq, glass, clear, c1950 **15.00**
Coaster, 3½" d, paper, c1950 ...... **15.00**
Figure, 5¼" h, plastic ............ **80.00**
Hot Pad, 5½" sq, red, white, and yellow, c1950 .................... **30.00**
Manual, *Basic Principles of First Aid Training,* Reddy illus on cov, 1950s **12.00**
Match Book .................... **5.00**
Pen and Pencil, mechanical ....... **20.00**
Pinback Button, ⅞" d, red, white, and blue, 1930s .................. **40.00**
Pocket Protector ................ **6.00**
Pot Holder ..................... **12.00**
Tie Bar, 5" l, brass, mounted figure, 1950s ....................... **25.00**
Tie Tac ........................ **22.00**
Sailor Jack, Cracker Jack, doll, 15" h, cloth, Mattel, 1974 ............... **30.00**
Smokey Bear
Bandanna, 1950s ................ **45.00**
Coloring Book, Whitman, 8 x 10½", 1960s ....................... **12.00**
Fan, cardboard, 1950s ............ **15.00**

Nodder, 5¾" h, composition, 1960s **75.00**
Snap, Crackle, Pop, Kellogg's Rice Krispies
Puppet, set of 3, 8" h, rubber head, fabric body, 1950s . . . . . . . . . . . . . **35.00**
Ring, brass, mounted flexible rubber head, 1950s . . . . . . . . . . . . . . . . . . . **200.00**
Toy, squeeze, 8" h, vinyl, 1975 premium . . . . . . . . . . . . . . . . . . . . . . . . **25.00**
Speedy Alka Seltzer
Bank, 5½" h, soft rubber, yellow hair **200.00**
Doll, 7½" h, vinyl . . . . . . . . . . . . . . . . **500.00**
Figure, 5½" h, soft rubber, red hair . **400.00**
Pinback Button, 1¼" d, full color illus, c1960 . . . . . . . . . . . . . . . . . . . . **40.00**
Tray, 12" d, litho tin, Spanish text, c1960 . . . . . . . . . . . . . . . . . . . . . . . **150.00**
Tony the Tiger
Bank, 8½" h, plastic, figural, 1970s **40.00**
Bowl, 5" d, cereal, plastic, large orange paw base, 1981 . . . . . . . . . . . **15.00**
Cookie Jar, 8" h, figural head, 1968 **60.00**
Lunch Box, metal, thermos, Aladdin Industries, c1969 . . . . . . . . . . . . . . . **125.00**
Toucan Sam
Bathtub Toy . . . . . . . . . . . . . . . . . . . . **25.00**
Doll, Talbot, 1984 . . . . . . . . . . . . . . . **30.00**
Trix Rabbit
Doll, vinyl, 1977 . . . . . . . . . . . . . . . . **30.00**
Hand Puppet, 12" h, cloth and vinyl, 1960s . . . . . . . . . . . . . . . . . . . . . . . **40.00**
Toy, squeaker, 9" h, vinyl, 1970s . . . **25.00**
Willie and Millie Penguin
Cigarette Lighter, figural, metal, adv **195.00**
Fan, cardboard, diecut, wood handle, 1930s . . . . . . . . . . . . . . . . . . . . . . . **30.00**
Figure, 4½" h, Willie, plastic, 1940s **75.00**
Salt and Pepper Shakers, pr, 3½" h, 1940s . . . . . . . . . . . . . . . . . . . . . . . **65.00**

# AKRO AGATE GLASS

**Collecting Hints:** Akro Agate is marked "Made in USA" and often includes a mold number. Some pieces also include a small crow in the mark. It is a thick type of glass; therefore, collectors should buy only mint pieces. The marbleized types of Akro Agate were made in many color combinations. The serious collector should be looking for unusual combinations.

**History:** The Akro Agate Co. was formed in 1911. Their major product was marbles. In 1914 the owners moved from near Akron, Ohio, to Clarksburg, West Virginia, where they opened a large factory. They continued to produce marbles profitably until after the Depression. In 1930, the competition in the marble business became too great, and Akro Agate Co. decided to diversify into other products.

Two of their most successful products were the floral ware lines and children's dishes, first made in 1935. The children's dishes were very popular until after World War II, when metal dishes captured the market.

The Akro Agate Co. also made special containers for cosmetics firms—including the Mexicali cigarette jar, which was originally filled with Pick Wick bath salts, and a special line made for the Jean Vivaudou Co., Inc. Operations continued successfully until 1948. The factory, a victim of imports, metals, and increased use of plastics, was sold to the Clarksburg Glass Co. in 1951.

**References:** Gene Florence, *The Collector's Encyclopedia of Akro Agate Glassware*, Revised Edition, Collector Books, 1975, 1992 value update; Roger and Claudia Hardy, *The Complete Line of Akro Agate*, published by the authors, 1992; Ellen Tischbein Schroy, *Warman's Glass*, Wallace–Homestead, 1992.

**Collectors' Clubs:** Akro Agate Art Association, P.O. Box, 758, Salem, NH 03079; Akro Agate Club, 10 Bailey St., Clarksburg, WV 26301.

**REPRODUCTION ALERT:** Pieces currently reproduced are not marked "Made In USA" and are missing the mold number and crow.

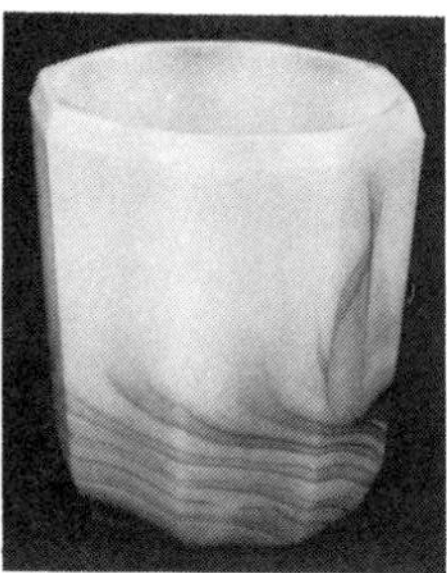

**Cigarette Holder, blue and white, eight sided, 2⅝" h, $10.00.**

Apothecary Jar, white, Jean Vivdoux . . **22.00**
Ashtray, 4" d, Goodrich Tire, blue and black marbleized . . . . . . . . . . . . . . . . . **40.00**
Basket, two handles, orange and white **30.00**
Bell, light blue . . . . . . . . . . . . . . . . . . . . **65.00**
Bowl
4¾" d, Fiesta style, blue, crow and USA mark . . . . . . . . . . . . . . . . . . . . . **650.00**
7½" d, tab handle, cream and red . . **28.00**
8" d, ftd, pumpkin . . . . . . . . . . . . . . . . **150.00**
Children's Dishes
Bowl, Concentric Ring, large, opaque blue . . . . . . . . . . . . . . . . . . . . . . . . . **20.00**
Cereal Bowl, Interior Panel, large, transparent green . . . . . . . . . . . . . . . **15.00**
Creamer
Chiquita, fired on cobalt blue . . . . **8.00**
Octagonal, green . . . . . . . . . . . . . . . **6.00**
Raised Daisy, yellow . . . . . . . . . . . . **45.00**

Stacked Disk & Panel, large, opaque cobalt blue ........... **24.50**
Stippled Band, large, blue ....... **35.00**
Cup and Saucer
Chiquita, transparent cobalt blue . **14.50**
Concentric Ring, large, transparent cobalt blue ................. **50.00**
Interior Panel, large, transparent green ...................... **19.50**
Raised Daisy, yellow ............ **50.00**
Pitcher, Stacked Disk, small, opaque green ........................ **9.75**
Plate, dinner
Chiquita, fired on green ......... **4.00**
Concentric Ring, small, opaque lime green ................. **6.00**
Octagonal, green .............. **3.00**
Raised Daisy, blue .............. **14.75**
Stippled Band, small, light amber **2.50**
Set
16 pieces
Concentric Ring, small, purple plates, yellow saucers, pumpkin cups, blue teapot, creamer, and sugar, orig box ......... **250.00**
Interior Panel, small, opaque pink, decals .............. **195.00**
17 pieces, Stippled Band, transparent green, orig box ........... **275.00**
21 pieces
Concentric Ring, water set, green, white sauce, lid, and tumbler .................. **145.00**
Interior Panel, tea set, large, opaque yellow, white teapot lid ...................... **400.00**
Sugar
Chiquita, transparent cobalt blue . **9.00**
Octagonal, closed handles, green, white lid .................... **12.00**
Raised Daisy, yellow ............ **45.00**
Stacked Disk & Panel, medium opaque blue ................ **9.00**
Teapot
Raised Daisy, blue .............. **65.00**
Stacked Disk & Panel, small, blue, white lid ................... **18.75**
Stippled Band, small, dark amber **15.00**
Tumbler
Octagonal, yellow .............. **10.00**
Raised Daisy, yellow ............ **25.00**
Stacked Disk, small, opaque pink **5.00**
Cornucopia, orange and white ....... **5.50**
Demitasse Cup and Saucer, orange and white .......................... **15.00**
Desk Accessory, pen holder, 3¼″ d, Goodrich Tire, black, orange and white center .................... **40.00**
Flower Pot
2″ h, Graduated Dart, orange and white ........................ **15.00**
2¼″ h, Ribbed Top
Green and white ............... **2.25**
Orange and white .............. **2.75**
2½″ h, Stacked Disk
Blue and white ................ **9.50**
Green and white ............... **9.50**
Orange and white .............. **9.50**
2⅝″ h, Ribbed Top, medium green . **3.50**
2¾″ h, Ribbed Top
Orange ....................... **14.00**
Yellow ........................ **12.00**
3″ h
Ribs and Flutes, scalloped, yellow **3.75**
Stacked Disk, blue and white .... **10.00**
4″ h
Ribbed Top, orange and cream .. **22.00**
Stacked Disk, blue and white .... **20.00**
Westite, green marble ........... **6.00**
5″ h, green and white, Westite ..... **18.00**
Game, Tiddley Winks, boxed set, J Pressman ....................... **25.00**
Hat, Mexicali, orange and white ..... **25.00**
Ivy Bowl
Brown and white, Westite ......... **25.00**
Green and white ................. **15.00**
Orange and white ................ **18.00**
Jar, 4¼″ h, 5″ d, green and brown, Vidrio ......................... **6.00**
Jardiniere, Graduated Dart, bell shape, tab handle, green and white ....... **28.00**
Lamp, 9″ h, orange and white ....... **65.00**
Match Holder, 3″ h, red and white ... **7.00**
Planter
6″ l
Oval, ribbed, green and white ... **12.00**
Rect, ribbed, orange and white, metal cart .................. **28.00**
8″ l, rect, No. 653, blue and white . **35.00**
8½″ l, oval, No. 651, Graduated Dart, scalloped top, green and white ........................ **45.00**
Powder Box, cov
Colonial Lady
Blue and white ................ **67.00**
Light green .................... **175.00**
Pink and white ................. **60.00**
Ivy, orange and white ............. **55.00**
Ribbed, yellow .................. **25.00**
Scotty Dog
Amber ....................... **250.00**
Light blue .................... **75.00**
Light pink .................... **50.00**
Transparent blue, small ear chip . **250.00**
White ........................ **50.00**
Treasure Trunk, marbleized, minor chip on lid ................... **90.00**
Shaving Mug, cov, black ........... **15.00**
Smoker Set, red and white, orig box .. **90.00**
Urn, ftd, sq, brown and white ....... **6.50**
Vase
6″ h, No. 312, Graduated Dart, ftd, tab, green and white, Westite .... **28.00**
6¼″ h, No. 316, Graduated Dart,

dark green, scalloped top ....... **55.00**
8¾" h, No. 312, Graduated Dart, white, green, cobalt blue, and pumpkin ..................... **55.00**
Wall Planter, 4" d, green smooth top container, metal hanging holder .... **22.00**

# ALUMINUM, HAND WROUGHT

**Collecting Hints:** Some manufacturers' marks are synonymous with quality, e.g., Continental Hand Wrought Silverlook. However, some quality pieces are not marked and should not be overlooked. Check carefully for pitting, deep scratches, and missing pieces of glassware.

**History:** During the late 1920s the use of aluminum for purely utilitarian purposes resulted in a variety of decorative household accessories. Although manufactured by a variety of methods, the hammered aluminum with repousse patterns appears to have been the most popular and certainly was more demanding of the skill of the craftsman producing the articles.

At one time many companies were competing for the aluminum giftware market, with numerous silver companies adding aluminum articles as promotional items or as a more competitive and affordable product during the depression years. Many well-known and highly esteemed metal–smiths contributed their skills to the production of hammered aluminum. With the advent of mass production methods and the accompanying wider distribution of aluminum giftware, the demand began to decline, leaving only a few producers who have continued to turn out quality work by the age-old and time–tested methods of metal crafting.

**References:** Dannie Woodard and Billie Wood, *Hammered Aluminum: Hand Wrought Collectibles*, published by authors, 1983; Dannie Woodard, *Revised 1990 Price List for Hammered Aluminum: Hand Wrought Collectibles*, Aluminum Collectors' Books, 1990.

**Periodical:** *The Aluminist*, P.O. Box 1346, Weatherford, TX 76086.

Ashtray, 6" d, berry dec, straight sides, Hand Forged/Everlast Metal ........ **8.00**
Basket
7¾", Chrysanthemum pattern, Continental Hand Wrought Silverlook, marked "No. 1088" ........... **18.00**
12", Harvest pattern, flared sides, scalloped handle, Hand Forged/Everlast Metal .................... **12.00**
Bowl
8" d, pine and mountains, anodized gold trim, Arthur Armour ........ **18.00**
10" d, tulip, flower ribbon handles, Hand Wrought Rodney Kent, marked "No. 450" ............ **20.00**
11¼" d, Chrysanthemum pattern, applied leaves, Continental Hand Wrought Silverlook, marked "No. 715" ......................... **15.00**
Bowl and Tray, Hand Wrought Rodney Kent ........................... **28.00**

**Silent Butler, Chrysanthemum pattern, Continental Silverlook, #505, 12" l, $25.00.**

Butter Dish, cov, round, domed cov, double loop finial, glass insert, Buenilum Hand Wrought ............. **20.00**
Candleholders, pr
2½" sq base, arrow shape, corners form feet, handle, Everlast Hand Forged Aluminum, marked "No. 1020" ........................ **10.00**
6" h, beaded edge base, aluminum stem with wooden ball, Buenilum castle mark .................... **12.00**
Coaster, 3¼" d, Edison Institute Museum Entrance, Wendell August Forge .... **4.00**
Cocktail Shaker, straight sides, grooved Art Deco style top, clear plastic knob lid, Buenilum castle mark ......... **20.00**
Compote, 5" h, Wild Rose pattern, Continental Hand Wrought Silverlook, marked "No. 1083" ............. **15.00**
Creamer and Sugar, cup shape, matching tray, World Hand Forge, price for three piece set .................. **12.00**
Crumber and Brush, Hand Wrought Rodney Kent, marked "No. 444" ... **30.00**
Desk Set, Bali Bamboo pattern, Hand Forged/Everlast Metal, marked "B 24," price for three piece set ....... **30.00**
Dish, cov, 5 x 12 x 8", Bakelite handle,

marked "Cellini Hand Wrought Aluminum, Chicago" ... **135.00**
Fruit Bowl, 11" d, floral and fruit relief, handles ... **20.00**
Gravy Boat, 7" l, curled handle, matching underplate and ladle, Hand Forged/Everlast Metal, price for three piece set ... **12.00**
Ice Bucket, ceramic lining ... **20.00**
Ladle, 14½" l, Argental Cellini Craft .. **18.00**
Lazy Susan, 16" d, cov glass dish, ribbon and flower trim, Hand Wrought Rodney Kent ... **15.00**
Napkin Holder, trefoil shape, ftd, fruit dec ... **8.50**
Pitcher, ovoid, slender neck, twisted handle, Buenilum Hand Wrought .. **35.00**
Salad Set, 13" d bowl, tulip dec, matching serving utensils, Buenilum Hand Wrought ... **20.00**
Teapot, 10 x 7", octagonal, wooden handle, Wagner Ware ... **35.00**
Tid Bit Server, two tiers, Continental Hand Wrought Silverlook, marked "No. 525" ... **30.00**
Tray
14" l, tulip motif, handles ... **35.00**
15½" l, fruit design, handles ... **22.00**
17 x 23", marlin fish scene, double fish hook handles, Wendell August Forge ... **120.00**
Wastebasket, 11 x 11", florals, exposed rivets, Hand Forged/Everlast Metal .. **35.00**

# ANIMATION ART

**Collecting Hints:** The vocabulary involving animation cels is very specific. The difference between a Courvoisier, Disneyland, master, key production, printed or publication, production, and studio background can mean thousands of dollars in value. Sotheby's and Christie's East, the two major auction houses selling animation art, do not agree on terminology. Read the glossary section of any catalog carefully.

A second of film requires more than twenty animation cels. If you multiply the length of a cartoon in minutes times sixty times twenty–four, you will derive the approximate number of cels used to make that cartoon. The question that no one seems to be asking as prices reach the ten- and hundred-thousand dollar level for some cels is what happened to all the other animation cels. Cels exist in storage in vast quantities.

There is no doubt that Walt Disney animation cels are king. Buying is being driven more by nostalgia, legend, and hype than historical importance or workmanship. The real bargains in the field lie outside the Disney material.

Although animation art has a clearly established track record, it also is an area that has proven itself subject to manipulation, representational abuse, and shifting nostalgia trends. It is not the place for the casual collector.

Avoid limited edition serigraphs. A serigraph is a color print made by the silk screen process. Although they appear to be animation cels, they are not.

**History:** Film historians credit Winsor McCay's 1909 "Gertie the Dinosaur" as the first animated cartoon. Early animated films were largely the work of comic strip artists. The invention of the celluloid process (a "cel" is an animation drawing on celluloid) is attributed to Earl Hurd. Although the technique reached perfection under animation giants such as Walt Disney and Max Fleischer, individuals such as Ub Iwerks, Walter Lantz, and Paul Terry along with studios such as Columbia: Charles Mints and Screen Gems, MGM, Paramount/Famous Studios, UPA, and Warner Brothers did pioneering work.

Leonard Maltin's *Of Mice and Magic: A History of American Animated Cartoons* (A Plume Book/New American Library, revised and updated edition 1987) is excellent for historical background.

**Reference:** Jerry Weist, *Original Comic Art: Identification and Price Guide,* Avon Books, 1992.

**Periodicals:** *Animation Film Art,* PO Box 25547, Los Angeles, CA 90025; *Storyboard/The Art of Laughter,* 80 Main St., Nashua, NH 03060.

**Museums:** International Museum of Cartoon Art, Boca Raton, FL; Museum of Cartoon Art, Rye Brook, NY.

Fleischer Studio, Mr Bug Goes to Town, 1941, 8 x 10" gouached on celluloid, watercolor and pastel, Hoppity, master background, studio notes in background margins, two W Robert Little signatures, background untrimmed, cel trimmed to outline of figure, framed ... **1,100.00**
King Features, Heinz Edelman, Yellow Submarine, 1968, 7½ x 9" gouache on celluloid, John Lennon and Ringo Starr ... **2,200.00**
MGM Studio, Chuck Jones
Chip and Dale, 1960s, 4 x 8½" gouache on celluloid, chipmunks carrying hobo packs, Disney TV show, untrimmed, framed ... **1,045.00**
Horton Hears a Who, 1970, 9 x 12" gouache on celluloid, tempera on background sheet, Horton portrait, studio notes on background ... **1,650.00**
Walt Disney Studio
Donald Duck, 1950s, 7 x 9½" gouache on celluloid, portrait, cel trimmed to 10½ x 12", framed ... **990.00**

**Bill Melendez, A Charlie Brown Christmas, 1965, gouache on celluloid, applied to a gouache key, production, pan background, multi-cel setup, 11¾ x 38½", $16,500.00. Photograph courtesy of Sotheby's.**

Make Mine Music, 1946, 5½ x 5" gouache on celluloid, animated hats named Alice Bluebonnet and Johnny Fedora sit atop horses' heads, cel trimmed to 8 x 9½", framed ...................... **1,100.00**

Melody Time, 1948, 6 x 6½" gouache on celluloid, couple in horse–drawn sleigh, Once Upon A Wintertime, cel trimmed to outline of figure, framed ................ **715.00**

Mickey's Christmas Carol, 1983, 9 x 14" gouache on celluloid, Willie the Giant as the Ghost of Christmas Present, laminated, Disney seal, untrimmed, framed ............ **475.00**

Mother Goose Goes Hollywood, 1938, 7½ x 7½" gouache on celluloid, Oliver Hardy as the Pieman, Silly Symphony, untrimmed, framed ...................... **1,650.00**

Peter Pan, 1953, 7 x 3" gouache on celluloid, full figure portrait of Michael as Indian, carrying teddy bear **800.00**

Sleeping Beauty, 1959, 10 x 9" gouache on celluloid, full figure Aurora in field, two birds fluttering overhead, color print background, Disneyland label on back, cel trimmed to 12 x 10", framed .... **2,310.00**

Test Pilot Donald, 1951, 5½ x 4" gouache on celluloid, full figure Donald Duck wearing mechanic's cap and aviator jacket, untrimmed, framed ....................... **935.00**

The Jungle Book, 1967, 6½ x 4" gouache on celluloid, full figure Baloo, cel trimmed to 10 x 12", unframed ..................... **880.00**

The Rescuers, 1977, 7½ x 10½" gouache on celluloid, Madame Medusa staring into Devil's Eye diamond, laminated, Disney seal, untrimmed, framed .............. **825.00**

Who Framed Roger Rabbit, 1988, 8½ x 11½" gouache on celluloid, Roger cel mounted on color frame enlargement of live action film, cel trimmed to outline of figure, unframed ...................... **1,760.00**

Walter Lantz Studio, Woody Woodpecker, late 1940s–early 1950s, 8½ x 11½" gouache on celluloid, colored pencil on animation sheet, Woody carving name from cartoon title opening, matching animation drawing of Woody, mat insets with recent Woody drawing and Lantz autograph, untrimmed, slit in cel paint ......... **1,650.00**

Warner Brothers Studio

Porky's Last Stand, 1940, 7½ x 7½" gouache on celluloid, full figure black and white Daffy Duck as short order cook, colored backing with printed Leon Schlesinger inscription and signature, laminated, cel trimmed to 9 x 12", framed .. **6,160.00**

Rabbit Rampage, 7¼ x 7" gouache on celluloid, full figure Bugs Bunny, untrimmed, framed, paint professionally restored ............... **1,870.00**

Tweety's Circus, 1955, 5½ x 12" gouache on celluloid, full figure Sylvester on high wire, Friz Freleng cartoon, untrimmed, framed, paint professionally restored ......... **1,760.00**

# AUTOGRAPHS

**Collecting Hints:** The condition and content of letters and documents bears significantly on value. Signatures should be crisp, clear, and located so that they do not detract from the rest of the item. Whenever possible, obtain a notarized statement of authenticity, especially for pieces over $100.

Forgeries abound. Copying machines compound the problem. Further, many signatures of political figures, especially presidents, movie stars, and sports heroes are machine- or secretary-signed rather than by the individual. Photographic reproduction can produce a signature resembling an original. Check all signatures using a good magnifying glass or microscope.

Presentation material, something marked "To ______," is of less value than a non–presentation item. The presentation personalizes the piece and often restricts interest, except to someone with the same name.

There are autograph mills throughout the country run by people who write to noteworthy individuals requesting their signatures on large groups of material. They in turn sell this material on the autograph market. Buy an autograph of a living person only after the most careful consideration and examination.

Autograph items are sold using standard abbreviations denoting type and size. They are:

| | |
|---|---|
| ADS | Autograph Document Signed |
| ALS | Autograph Letter Signed |
| AQS | Autograph Quotation Signed |
| CS | Card Signed |
| DS | Document (printed) Signed |
| LS | Letter Signed |
| PS | Photograph Signed |
| TLS | Typed Letter Signed |
| Folio | 12 x 16" |
| 4to | 8 x 10" |
| 8vo | 5 x 7" |
| 12mo | 3 x 5" |

**History:** Autograph collecting is an old established tradition, perhaps dating back to the first signed documents and letters. Early letters were few, and hence are treasured by individuals in private archives. Municipalities, churches, and other institutions maintained extensive archives to document past actions.

Autograph collecting became fashionable during the 19th century. However, early collectors focused on the signatures alone, clipping off the signed portion of a letter or document. Eventually collectors realized that the entire document was valuable.

The advent of movie stars, followed by sports, rock 'n roll, and television personalities, brought autograph collecting to the popular level. Fans pursued these individuals with autograph books, programs and photographs. Everything imaginable was offered for signatures. Realizing the value of their signatures and the speculation that occurs, modern stars and heroes are less willing to sign material than in the past.

**References:** Mary A. Benjamin, *Autographs: A Key To Collecting,* Dover Publications, 1986; Charles Hamilton, *American Autographs,* University of Oklahoma Press, 1983; Norman E. Martinus and Harry L. Rinker, *Warman's Paper,* Wallace–Homestead, 1993; Robert W. Pelton, *Collecting Autographs For Fun And Profit,* Betterway Publications, 1987; George Sanders, Helen Sanders, Ralph Roberts, *Collector's Guide To Autographs,* Wallace–Homestead, 1990; George Sanders, Helen Sanders, and Ralph Roberts, *The Price Guide to Autographs, Second Edition,* Wallace–Homestead, 1991.

**Collectors' Clubs:** Manuscript Society, 350 N. Niagara Street, Burbank, CA 91505; Universal Autograph Collectors Club, P. O. Box 6181, Washington, DC 20044.

Autographed Letters Signed (ALS)
- Brewer, David J, Supreme Court Assoc Justice, 1909, Supreme Court lined stationery ................ **150.00**
- De Havilland, Olivia ............. **12.00**
- Fall, John P, civil war soldier, Alexandria, VA, 5 x 8", 3¼" pages ... **75.00**
- Hale, Edward E, clergy and author, 2 pages, 1892, philosophical advice **135.00**
- McKaskey, Wm S, Calvary Major General, 6 pages, July 1906, HQ Dept of Texas, San Antonio, 5 x 8" plain stationery, holograph envelope ......................... **75.00**
- Rodgers, Jimmie, 8 x 10" personalized Honeycome Family Theatre, Branson, MO, stationery ........... **50.00**
- Young, Stella, WWI Salvation Army Doughnut Girl, 6 x 9" plain stationery, 1976, re hometown honors, newspaper article included ...... **45.00**

Autographed Quotations Signed (AQS), Wm Ordway Patridge, American sculptor of the Pieta, 5 x 3" notepaper, "...1915–Character is Destiny, An old greek motto which is true today...Wm. Ordway Patridge" ...... **95.00**

Book
- Adamski, George, *Inside Space Ships* **10.00**
- Allen, Maurice, *Mixed Cargo* ...... **5.00**
- Durant, Will, *Caesar and Christ,* Simon & Shuster, published 1944, 1st ed .......................... **60.00**
- Hollandersky, Abe, *Abe The Newsboy* ......................... **5.00**
- King, Stephen, *Skeleton Crew,* Putnam, 1985, 1st ed, dj, full signature and date beneath large title, 1990 **165.00**
- Palmer, Arnold, golfer ........... **40.00**
- Schulz, Charles M, *The Charlie Brown Dictionary,* Random House **125.00**
- Siegel, Jerry, black ink signature on cover of comic book, *The Death of Superman* .................... **60.00**
- Sinclair, Upton, *Presidential Agent,* self published, 1944, 1st ed ..... **85.00**
- Stefanson, Vihjalmur, *Hunters of the Great North* ................... **8.00**
- Walter, Ellery, *World On One Leg* .. **10.00**
- Welk, Lawrence, *You're Never Too Young* ....................... **10.00**

Cards Signed (CS)
- Ameche, Alan, Heisman Trophy winner, 3 x 5" card, inscribed ....... **35.00**

Armour, Tom, III, golfer, 3 x 5″ card **15.00**
Benchley, Peter, and John Williams, profile sketch of shark head, clearly signed beneath sketch, 6 x 4″ blue card **60.00**
Clinton, Roger C, penned blue felt tip, "Best thru Life, Clinton For President, Roger Clinton" **50.00**
Davis, Glenn, Heisman Trophy winner, 3 x 5″ card **7.00**
Diller, Phyllis, 3 x 5″ card **25.00**
Divine, 3 x 5″ card **35.00**
Gish, Lillian, 3 x 5″ card **40.00**
Madonna, 3 x 5″ card **125.00**
Olivier, Laurence, 5 x 7″ card **15.00**
Player, Gary, golfer, 3 x 5″ card **15.00**
Perkins, Carl, "Blue suede shoes Carl Perkins," 3 x 5″ blue card **95.00**
Quayle, Marilyn, 6 x 4″ card with Blair House engraving **35.00**
Remington, Frederic, 3 x 5″ card, matted **475.00**
Saroyan, William, 3 x 5″ card, matted **65.00**
Simon, Carly, matted **60.00**
Stanwyck, Barbara, 5 x 7″ **10.00**
Staubach, Roger, Heisman Trophy winner, 3 x 5″ card **9.00**
Tarkington, Booth, 3 x 5″ card, matted **45.00**
Truman, Harry S, 3 x 5″ card **40.00**
Walker, Doak, Heisman Trophy winner, 3 x 5″ card **8.00**
Watson, Tom, golfer, 3 x 5″ card **15.00**
Wood, Joe, baseball player, 3 x 5″ card, matted **75.00**

Document Signed (DS)

Barrow, Ed, 1957 bank check **165.00**
Cooper, Alice, album cov **60.00**
Jackson, Michael, album cov **150.00**
Kennedy, Ted, unused banquet ticket **65.00**
Longfellow, Henry, 1877, matted **175.00**
McQueen, Butterfly, bank check **20.00**
Nast, Thomas, bank check, 1895 **135.00**
Nixon, Richard, 37th President, menu, West Central Ohio Republican Victory Dinner, April 30, 1964, 6 x 8″, large signature on cov **195.00**
Rogers, Kenny, album cov **75.00**
Stewart, James, note **18.00**

First Day Covers (FDC)

Allen, Woody, FDC honoring America, cancelled Washington, DC, 1971 **25.00**
Alter, Hobie, FDC honoring America's Cup **25.00**
Anderson, K B, FDC honoring wood carving, bust sketch of Pinocchio **125.00**
Blanc, Mel, FDC honoring trees, cancelled Hot Springs, AK, 1978, black marker signed "Bugs Bunny & Mel Blanc" **100.00**
Channing, Carol, FDC honoring American Music, cancelled New York City, 1964 **20.00**
Colbert, Claudette, FDC honoring 50th Anniv of Motion Pictures, cancelled Los Angeles, 1944 **75.00**
Douglas, Wm O, 1962 FDC honoring Charles E Hughes **75.00**
Goodman, Benny, FDC honoring Martin Luther King **25.00**
Graf, Steffi, Virginia Wade, and Pete Sampras, FDC honoring tennis, cancelled Forest Hills **45.00**
Hayes, Helen, FDC honoring DW Griffith, cancelled Beverly Hills, 1975 **30.00**
Hoskins, Bob and Barry Temple, FDC honoring cable cars, cancelled in San Francisco, 1988, Temple sketch of Roger Rabbit with signature in the cancellation **75.00**
Hunter, Kim, Roddy McDowell, and Charlton Heston, FDC honoring Statue of Liberty, cancelled Liberty Island, 1986, bold signatures **55.00**
Kane, Bob, FDC picture Capitol Building, Washington, DC, orig sketch of Batman's face, sgd "Bob Kane '92" **300.00**
Keeshan, Bob, American Circus FDC, cancelled Delavan, WI **35.00**
LeMond, Greg, FDC honoring bicycling **35.00**
Marshall, Thurgood, Wm Brennan, and John Paul Stevens, FDC honoring Bill of Rights, cancelled Miami, FL, 1966 **150.00**
Mumy, Bill and Jonathan Harris, large FDC honoring earth, Washington, DC, 1988 **30.00**

**Eisenhower, Dwight D., framed and matted picture, autograph on separate card, $100.00.**

Owens, Jesse, FDC honoring physical fitness, large signature .......... **175.00**
Rogers, Roy and Dale Evans, FDC honoring Sitting Bull, cancelled Rapid City, SC, 1989 ........... **25.00**
Smith, Bob, cancelled Cody, WY, 1988, penned "Buffalo Bill" ..... **35.00**

Photograph Signed (PS)

Ali, Muhammad, 8 x 10″ color ..... **75.00**
Anderson, Loni, bathing suit, 8 x 10″ color ........................ **20.00**
Archer, Anne, movie scene, close up, 8 x 10″ color ................. **25.00**
Bach, Catherine, movie scene, close up, 8 x 10″ color .............. **20.00**
Berra, Yogi, uniform, 8 x 10″ color . **20.00**
Bolger, Ray, Scarecrow, 8 x 10″, matted ......................... **55.00**
Busey, Gary, movie scene, close up, 8 x 10″ color ................. **20.00**
Carter, Rosalyn, color snapshot, boarding plane with President .... **25.00**
Danson, Ted, close up, tux, bow tie, 8 x 10″ color ................. **25.00**
Domino, Fats, 8 x 10″ color ....... **25.00**
Erving, Julius, uniform, 8 x 10″ color **25.00**
Gabor, Eva, Pat Buttram, and Eddie Albert, *Green Acres*, 8 x 10″ ..... **40.00**
Grange, Red, uniform, 8 x 10″ black and white .................... **25.00**
Gretzky, Wayne, uniform, 8 x 10″ color .......................... **50.00**
Hahn, Jessica, close up portrait, 8 x 10″ color ..................... **25.00**
Hammer, M C, dancing, 8 x 10″ color **25.00**
Henley, Don, close up, 8 x 10″ color **25.00**
Jackson, Reggie, uniform, 8 x 10″ color .......................... **25.00**
Jackson, Victoria, close up, 8 x 10″ color ........................ **25.00**
Jones, Grace, full nude, 8 x 10″ color **35.00**
Keaton, Michael, as Batman, 8 x 10″ color ........................ **55.00**
Kensit, Patsy, in negligee, 8 x 10″ color .......................... **25.00**
Kerr, Deborah, movie scene, 8 x 10″ color ........................ **20.00**
Jordan, Michael, uniform, 8 x 10″ color .......................... **55.00**
Jorgensen, Spider, uniform, 8 x 10″ color ........................ **18.00**
Lewis, Huey, close up, 8 x 10″ color **25.00**
Maples, Marla, 8 x 10″ color ...... **25.00**
McQueen, Butterfly, GWTW photo as Prissy ........................ **30.00**
Murphy, Audie, 8 x 10″ ........... **100.00**
Parton, Dolly, bust pose, 8 x 10″ color **30.00**
Remick, Lee, 8 x 10″ ............. **12.00**
Richard, Maurice, 8 x 10″ color, uniform ......................... **25.00**
Ronstadt, Linda, close up, 8 x 10″ color ........................ **35.00**
Rypien, Mark, uniform, 8 x 10″ color **20.00**
Schmidt, Mike, uniform, 8 x 10″ color **25.00**
Schroeder, Jay, uniform, 8 x 10″ color **15.00**
Scroggins, Tracy, swimsuit, 8 x 10″ color ........................ **25.00**
Sinatra, Frank, 8 x 10″ ............ **85.00**
Springsteen, Bruce ............... **75.00**
Turner, Kathleen, close up, 8 x 10″ color ........................ **35.00**
Turner, Tina, full signature, 8 x 10″ color ........................ **25.00**
Wendt, George, *Cheers*, 8 x 10″ color **25.00**
White, Jo Jo, 8 x 10″ close up, action **25.00**
Wilbur, Crane, silent screen actor, inscribed, 8 x 10″ ............... **20.00**

Typed Letters Signed (TLS)

Andriola, Alfred, 8 x 7″ personal stationery, imprinted Charlie Chan profiles, fine ink signature ....... **45.00**
Burgess, T W, 8 x 5″ personal stationery, 1926, response to inquiry re display of work ............... **125.00**
Clark, Tom C, Supreme Court Assoc Justice, 8 x 10″ official stationery as Attorney General (Truman), 1946, to Salvation Army Captain, Washington, DC ................... **65.00**
Davis, Dwight, as Secretary of War, turning down invitation ......... **75.00**
Edison, Charles, Secretary of Navy, 1940, 6 x 8″ official stationery ... **45.00**
Eddy, Nelson, 7 x 9″ personal stationery, 1936, orig envelope, two aged 9 x 11″ fan club programs included **125.00**
Fox, Fontaine, 8 x 10″ The Toonerville Electric Railroad Company stationery, 1941, Pappy in center vignette ....................... **100.00**
Griffith, Corinne, 7 x 10″ personal stationery, 1960, itinerary .......... **95.00**
Moss, Sterling, 8 x 10″ personal business stationery, Sept 1992, full signature ....................... **65.00**
Roosevelt, Eleanor, personal stationery ......................... **60.00**
Shearer, Norma, 7 x 10″ personal stationery, 1937, includes unsigned 8 x 10″ glossy photo ............. **95.00**
Trudeau, Gary, 6 x 7″ personal stationery, 1991, declining to send orig sketch, full signature ........ **45.00**

# AVIATION COLLECTIBLES

**Collecting Hints:** This field developed in the 1980s and is now firmly established. The majority of collectors focus on personalities, especially

Charles Lindbergh and Amelia Earhart. New collectors are urged to look to the products of airlines, especially those items related to the pre–jet era.

**History:** The first airlines in the United States depended on subsidies from the government for carrying mail for most of their income. The first non–Post Office Department flight for mail carrying was in 1926 between Detroit and Chicago. By 1930 there were thirty-eight domestic and five international airlines operating in the United States. A typical passenger load was ten. After World War II, four-engine planes with a capacity of 100 or more passengers were introduced.

The jet age was launched in the 1950s. In 1955 Capital Airlines used British made turboprop airliners in domestic service. In 1958 National Airlines began domestic jet passenger service. The giant Boeing 747 went into operation in 1970 as part of the Pan American fleet. The Civil Aeronautics Board, which regulates the airline industry, ended control of routes in 1982 and fares in 1983.

Major American airlines include American Airlines, Delta Air Lines, Northwest Airlines, Trans World Airlines, and United Airlines. There are many regional lines as well; new airlines are forming as a result of deregulation.

**References:** Aeronautica & Air Label Collectors Club of Aerophilatelic Federation of America, *Air Transport Label Catalog,* published by club; Stan Baumwald, *Junior Crew Member Wings,* published by author; Trev Davis and Fred Chan, *Airline Playing Cards: Illustrated Reference Guide, 2nd Edition,* published by authors, 1987; Lynn Johnson and Michael O'Leary, *En Route: Label Art from the Golden Age of Air Travel,* Chronicle Books, 1993; Norman E. Martinus and Harry L. Rinker, *Warman's Paper,* Wallace–Homestead, 1993; Richard R. Wallin, *Commercial Aviation Collectibles: An Illustrated Price Guide*, Wallace–Homestead, 1990.

**Periodical:** *Airliners*, P.O. Box 52–1238, Miami, FL 33152.

**Collectors' Clubs:** Aeronautica & Air Label Collectors Club, P.O. Box 1239, Elgin, IL 60121; The World Airline Historical Society, 3381 Apple Tree Lane, Erlanger, KY 41018.

## AIRLINES

Ashtray
- Capital Airlines, 4" d, clear, red and white dec ........ **10.00**
- Mexicana, stainless steel ........ **5.00**
- TWA, Rosenthal ........ **20.00**

Baggage Tag, Shawnee International Airlines, plastic ........ **2.00**
Blanket, North Central Airlines, name and logo ........ **25.00**

**Ashtray, Air France, ceramic, white, gold logo and cigarette rests, 3¼" d, $12.00.**

Book, *Pan Am Jet Flight Story Book,* nursery rhyme characters ........ **4.00**
Booklet, Delta, *From Travel Air To Tristar* ........ **5.00**
Casserole Dish, National Airline, brown Sun King logo, Sterling China Co ... **25.00**
Cigarette Lighter, Pan Am ........ **25.00**

Coaster
- Delta, metal ........ **1.00**
- Western, paper ........ **.25**

Cup and Saucer
- Pan Am, PAA logo, Homer Laughlin **125.00**
- TWA, red stripe with TWA in gold crest ........ **10.00**
- United Air Lines, china, white, logo, silver rim ........ **35.00**

Dish, Avianca, burgundy and gold, Noritake China ........ **25.00**
Fan, British Overseas Airways Corp Airlines, full color illus, inscribed "All Over The World BOAC Takes Good Care Of You," airline logo on reverse, 1950s ........ **20.00**

Flatware
- Butter Knife, National Airlines ..... **22.00**
- Fork, TWA, silver plate, early 1930s **35.00**
- Knife, Garuda Indonesian Airways, stainless steel ........ **2.00**

Hat, pilot's, National Airlines, flag logo **75.00**
Headrest Cover, American Airlines, vinyl, 1970s ........ **4.00**
Manual, *Ozark Airlines DC–9 Weight and Balance* ........ **3.00**

Napkin
- Air Atlanta, 1985 ........ **5.00**
- Delta, 1958 ........ **10.00**

Pin, American Airlines, sterling silver . **20.00**
Pinback Button, Ozark Airline ....... **1.00**

Playing Cards
- Eastern Airlines, orig box ........ **15.00**
- Northwest Airlines, logo with directional points ........ **30.00**
- Pan Am, landscape scene ........ **5.00**

Sake Cup, Continental, name and logo in circle, Noritake China ........ **20.00**

Salt and Pepper Shakers, pr, Virgin Atlantic, Wedgwood ........ **30.00**
Shot Glass, Eastern Airlines ........ **2.00**
Soap Bar, TWA ........ **.50**
Swizzle Stick
- Ethiopian Pan Jets ........ **3.00**
- TWA ........ **1.00**

Timetable
- Chicago and Southern Air Lines ........ **35.00**
- Eastern Air Lines ........ **20.00**
- Pan Am, 1930s ........ **25.00**
- TWA, 1945 ........ **15.00**

Tray, TWA, Bakelite, late 1940s ........ **20.00**
Vase, Delta Air Lines, glass, clear, gold logo ........ **20.00**

## GENERAL

Baggage Sticker, $4\frac{1}{4}$ x 6", Graf Zeppelin, German inscription for Hamburg–America line, slogan "In Zeppelin Over The South Atlantic," c1929 ........ **75.00**
Bank, airplane, figural, aluminum, "Spirit of Saving" ........ **550.00**
Book
- *Airplanes of the USA,* Whitman, 1942, 64 pgs ........ **15.00**
- *Aviation Pocket–Book Reference,* Darien Press, Edinburgh, 1918, 362 pgs ........ **45.00**
- *Fundamentals of Elementary Flight Maneuvers,* Civil Aeronautics Administration, 1943, 82 pgs ........ **5.00**
- *The Story of the Airship,* Goodyear Tire & Rubber Co, Hugh Allen, 1931, 72 pgs ........ **50.00**

Booklet, *Scale Model Aircraft Construction Procedure,* Robert W Hambrook, Federal Security Agency, 1942, 20 pgs ........ **8.00**
Bulletin, Fundamentals of Elementary Flight Maneuvers, 82 pgs, 1943 ........ **4.00**
Committee Badge, $2\frac{1}{4}$ x $2\frac{3}{4}$", celluloid, diecut, red, white, and blue, Indianapolis Municipal Airport, Sept, 1931 ........ **25.00**
Decanter, Spirit of St Louis, Famous Firsts series, ceramic, hp, 1972 ........ **25.00**
Game, New York to Paris Aero Race, gold colored tin frame holds clear glass, paper playing surface, Lindbergh, Chamberlin, and Byrd flights, late 1920s ........ **50.00**
Harmonica, 4" l, silvered brass, mounted Graf Zeppelin, engraved name on sides, two blade propeller, marked on base "C A Seydel Sohne, Germany," 1920–30 ........ **100.00**
Hat Pin, stewardess ........ **25.00**
Ink Blotter, $3\frac{3}{4}$ x $8\frac{1}{2}$", cardboard, "World's First Flying Automobile," Dec. 1937 Blue Sunoco Motor Fuel issue ........ **18.00**
Lunch Pail, "History of Aviation," 1930s **120.00**
Magazine, *Air Facts,* 1941, 66 pgs ........ **15.00**
Medal Award, $1\frac{1}{2}$" d, National Air Races 1932, silver, inscribed "Meritorious Participation Award" on one side, other with "Happy Landings/ Presented by Miss Fidelity/Home Port/ Wheeling, West Virginia" ........ **30.00**
Model
- Boeing Jet Stratotanker, $10\frac{1}{2}$" l, chromed metal, United States Air Force decals on wings and fuselage, matching display stand, mid 1960s ........ **100.00**
- Republic F–84 Thunderjet USAF, metal, metal display arm base, raised lettering on base, 1950s ........ **200.00**
- USAF Convair Interceptor F–102A, plastic, gray, decals ........ **125.00**

Pin, $1\frac{1}{2}$" d, National Air Races 1929 Cleveland, silvered metal wings ........ **25.00**
Pinback Button
- $\frac{5}{8}$" d, blue and white, blimp style airship illus, 1920–30 ........ **15.00**
- 1" d, Wayne Aero Club, tan and black, biplane, 1930s ........ **18.00**
- $1\frac{1}{4}$" d
  - Aeronautical Mechanics Union of A F of L, silver and blue, c1940 **12.00**
  - Bremen East to West, black and white portraits, 1928 Trans–Atlantic aviators border ........ **50.00**
  - Welcome Boardman, black, white, and yellow, 1931 homecoming celebration of New York to Istanbul aviator ........ **25.00**
- $1\frac{3}{8}$" d, 1929 Chicago Endurance Flight, red, white, and blue ........ **25.00**
- $1\frac{3}{4}$" d
  - Dayton The Air City, blue and white, matte finish, 1930s ........ **30.00**
  - The Aircraft, chairman of safety committee, green and white, 1930s ........ **15.00**

Poker Chip, airplane design, Bakelite, boxed set, c1930 ........ **25.00**
Post Card, $7\frac{3}{4}$ x $20\frac{3}{4}$", International Aviation Meet, black and white, panoramic view of airplanes over Chicago lakefront, 1911 ........ **200.00**
Poster, 14 x 22", National Air Show, Feb 7, Del Webb's Sun City Airport ........ **18.00**
Stamp Book, $8\frac{1}{2}$ x 11", *Golden Play Book of Airplane Stamps,* Golden Press, 1954, 48 pgs, sixty stamps ........ **15.00**
Tie Bar, Spirit of St Louis, figural, gold plated ........ **36.00**
Watch Fob, $1\frac{1}{4}$ x $1\frac{1}{2}$", brass, diecut and emb, aircraft above landscape, early 1900s ........ **30.00**

## PERSONALITIES

Airplane, 7" w, steel, Doug Corrigan's Jalopy . . . . . . . . . . . . . . . . . . . . . . . . . **275.00**

Book

*Paramount Newsreel Men with Admiral Byrd in Little America*, Whitman, 1934, 92 pgs . . . . . . . . . . . . . **50.00**

*The Lone Eagle*, 8 x 9", Blakely Printing Co, Chicago, 1929, 20 pgs, full color illus and text of Lindbergh's life . . . . . . . . . . . . . . . . . . . . . . . . . **20.00**

Mirror, Captain Charles "Plucky" Lindbergh, red, white, blue, and black, cities, time, and dates, Lindbergh photo and airplane illus . . . . . . . . . . . **100.00**

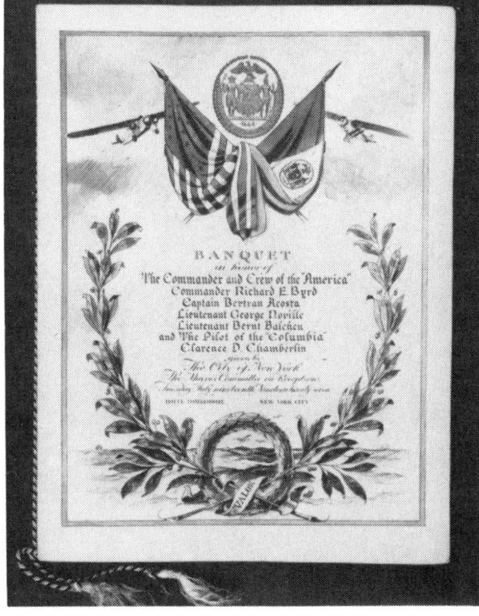


**Richard E. Byrd, program, banquet honoring Commander Byrd and crew of *America*, Hotel Commodore, NY, July 19, 1927, color litho cov, 4 pgs, 8½ x 11", $18.00.**

Newspaper

Chicago Daily News, May 21, 1927, Lindbergh In France . . . . . . . . . . . . **95.00**

Harper's Weekly

July 3, 1909, Wright Brothers celebrated in home town, full page photos . . . . . . . . . . . . . . . . . . . . . **20.00**

Sept 19, 1908, Wright's Flying Record Leads the World . . . . . . . . . **15.00**

Note Pad, 2¼ x 3¾", celluloid cov with black and white Lindbergh photo, inscribed "Visit to Sioux City, Aug 28, 1927" . . . . . . . . . . . . . . . . . . . . . . . . . . **100.00**

Photo, 8 x 10", Bobby Trout, Amelia Earhart, Ruth Elder, Florence Barnes, and other aviators, sgd "To Robbie/ Those Were The Good Old Days/ Bobby Trout" . . . . . . . . . . . . . . . . . . . . **15.00**

Pinback Button

⅞" d, Wright Brothers Home Celebration, June 17–18, 1909 . . . . . . . . . **100.00**

1¼" d

Captain Charles A Lindbergh, photo above red, white, and blue patriotic wings . . . . . . . . . . . . . . . **25.00**

Charles Levine, black and white, red, white, and blue rim, passenger in Chamberlin flight . . . . . . . **15.00**

Clarence Chamberlin, black and white photo, red, white, and blue rim . . . . . . . . . . . . . . . . . . . . **18.00**

Colonel James E Fitzmaurice, black and white portrait, "Our Irish Hero," green inscriptions, Irish flags . . . . . . . . . . . . . . . . . . . . . . . . **30.00**

Howard Hughes, black and white, red, white, and blue rim . . . . . . **25.00**

Welcome Lindy, black and white photo over gray aircraft silhouette . . . . . . . . . . . . . . . . . . . . . . . . . **28.00**

1¾" d, Welcome Corrigan, Douglas G Corrigan portrait on green background, red, white, and blue patriotic design . . . . . . . . . . . . . . . . . . **30.00**

Tapestry, 18 x 52", four leaf clover with Lindbergh, Chamberlin, Richard Byrd, and Ruth Elder photos, Nungesser photos on corners, late 1927 . . . **225.00**

# AVON

**Collecting Hints:** Avon collectibles cover a wide range of objects, including California Perfume Company bottles, decanters, soaps, children's items, jewelry, plates, catalogs, etc. Another phase of collecting focuses on Avon representatives and managers' awards.

Avon products are well marked. Four main marks exist. The name of the California Perfume Company appears from 1930 to 1936. The words "Avon Products, Inc." have been used since 1937 on the trademark.

Due to the vast number of Avon collectibles, a collector should buy only items of interest. Do not ignore foreign Avon material, although it is hard to find. New items take longer to increase in value than older items. Do not change the object in any way. This destroys the value.

**History:** David H. McConnell founded the California Perfume Co. in 1886. He hired saleswomen, a radical concept for that time. They used a door–to–door technique to sell their first product, "Little Dot," a set of five perfumes; thus was born the "Avon Lady." By 1979 there were more than one million.

In 1929, California Perfume Co. became the Avon Company. The tiny perfume company grew into a giant corporation. Avon bottles attracted collector interest in the 1960s.

**References:** Bud Hastin, *Bud Hastin's Avon Bottles Collectors Encyclopedia, 12th Edition,* 1991; Bud Hastin, *Bud Hastin's Avon Collectible Price Guide,* published by author, 1991; Joe Weiss, *Avon 8–Western World Handbook & Price Guide to Avon Bottles,* Western World Publishers, 1987.

**Periodical:** *Avon Times,* P.O. Box 9868, Kansas City, MO 64134.

**Collectors' Club:** Western World Avon Collectors Club, P.O. Box 23785, Pleasant Hills, CA 93535.

**Museum:** Nicholas Avon Museum, MTD Rt. Box 71, Clifton, VA 24422.

**REPRODUCTION ALERT**

**Note:** Prices quoted are for empty, mint and boxed condition.

**Rosepoint Bell, Charisma cologne, 4 oz, cranberry colored glass bell, gold colored plastic handle, 1978, 7¾" h, $8.00.**

Awards and Representatives Gifts
- Apron, white fabric, "I Love Summer With Avon," red and black lettering and trim, 1986 ........ **7.00**
- Figure, Albee Award, porcelain, green dress, 1987 ........ **40.00**
- Lemonade Set, Avon 100, white plastic, pitcher and four tumblers, 1986 **20.00**
- Pin, Queen's Award, 1¼" w, metal, crown shape, gold colored, 1964 **20.00**
- Scarf, silk, beige and brown, 4 A design, 1970 ........ **20.00**
- Tie Clip, 4 A service award, gold tone, 1970s ........ **25.00**

Bank, Ben Franklin, 4½" h, metal cylinder, white handkerchief inside, 1988 ........ **9.00**

Bowl, American Heirloom, 7" d, 4" h, porcelain, white, "Independence Day 1981" on bottom, black plastic base, 1981 ........ **20.00**

Box, Butterfly Fantasy, porcelain, fan shaped, dated 1980 on bottom ..... **13.00**

Candle
- Crystal Glow, perfumed, clear glass, 1972–73 ........ **12.00**
- Snug 'N Cozy Cat, clear glass cat, 1980–82 ........ **10.00**
- Turtle, white glass turtle, green glass shell top, 1972 ........ **12.00**

Candy Dish, cov, Hummingbird, 5" w, lead crystal, 1989 ........ **30.00**

Children's Items
- Clarence the Sea Serpent, sponge and soap, orange and yellow sponge, serpent soap in blue and yellow wrapper, 1968–69 ........ **12.00**
- Ella Elephant, scented stuffed animal, pink fabric, turquoise ears, pink ribbon, Avon tag, 1979–80 ........ **6.00**
- Giraffabath Bath Brush, orange and beige plastic, blue eyes, 1977–79 **3.50**
- Magic Rabbit Pin, plastic, white and pink rabbit, gray hat, 1975–76 ... **3.00**
- Sheriff's Badge, soap on a rope, yellow, emb sheriff's badge, 1962–63 **35.00**
- Superman, 8 oz, bubble bath, red and gray plastic, two red and yellow capes, 1978–79 ........ **5.00**
- Watering Can, 8 oz, bubble bath, yellow plastic, 1962–64 ........ **17.00**

Cookie Jar, bear, ceramic, brown, 1985 **25.00**

Creamer and Sugar, Santa creamer, Mrs Claus cov sugar bowl, ceramic, red, white, and green, 1983–84 ........ **25.00**

Doll, Cinderella, 9¼" h, porcelain head, hands, and feet, blond hair, blue dress, stand, 1984 ........ **25.00**

Figurine
- American Widgeon Duck, 3½" l, porcelain, 1989 ........ **13.00**
- Fred Astaire, 6¾" h, porcelain, 1984 **25.00**
- Wishful Thoughts, 5½" h, porcelain, blue and white, 1982–83 ....... **15.00**

Men's Items
- Atlantic 4–4–2, 5 oz, cologne, locomotive, silver over clear glass, silver plastic parts, 1973–75 ....... **14.00**
- Eight Ball, 3 oz, protein lotion, black glass, black cap, white "8", 1973 **7.00**
- Jeep Renegade, 3 oz, bracing lotion, black glass, decals, tan plastic top, black cap, 1981–82 ........ **7.00**
- Musk for Men, soap on a rope, 1983–84 ........ **3.00**
- Smooth Going Oil Can, 1.5 oz, after

shave, silver plated over clear glass, 1978 .......... 6.00
Thunderbird '55, 2 oz, after shave, blue glass, blue plastic closure, 1974–75 .......... 8.00
Mirror, NAAC Nashville Convention, red and white back, 1986 .......... 10.00
Music Box, Memories, 4¼" l, white porcelain box, music box in lid, 1983–84 .......... 28.00
Plate
Cardinal North American Song Bird, 10" d, ceramic, 1974–76 .......... 20.00
Singin' in the Rain, 8" d, porcelain, 1986 .......... 18.00
Playing Cards, NAAC, 1978 .......... 4.00
Stein, Ducks of American Wilderness, 8¾" h, ceramic, duck finial on lid, 1988 .......... 40.00
Women's Items
Blue Tranquility, 5 oz, soap on a rope, blue emb bar, white rope, 1978–80 .......... 4.00
Country Talc Shaker, 3 oz, perfumed talc, metal, gray and blue speckled and floral design, 1977–79 .......... 3.00
Heavenly Angel, .5 oz, perfume, blue glass, silver cap, 1981 .......... 2.00
Key Note, ¼ oz, perfume, glass key, gold plastic cap, 1967 .......... 20.00
La Belle Telephone, 1 oz, perfume concentrate, clear glass, gold top, 1974–76 .......... 9.00
Sea Treasure, 5 oz, irid glass, gold cap, 1971–72 .......... 10.00
Snail, ¼ oz, perfume, clear glass, cold cap, 1968–69 .......... 13.50
Victorian Sewing Basket, 5 oz, Skin–So–Soft, white milk glass basket, lavender plastic top, gold cord holds pink plastic flower, 1974–76 6.00

# BANKS, STILL

**Collecting Hints:** The rarity of a still bank has much to do with determining its value. Common banks, such as tin advertising banks, have limited value. The Statue of Liberty cast iron bank by A. C. Williams sells for hundreds of dollars. See Long and Pitman's book for a rarity scale for banks.

Banks are collected by maker, material, or subject. Subject is the most prominent, focusing on categories such as animals, food, mailboxes, safes, transportation, world's fair, etc. There is a heavy crossover in buyers from other collectible fields.

Banks are graded by condition. They should be in very good to mint condition and retain all original paint or decorative motif. Few banks are truly rare; hence, the collector should wait until he finds a bank in the condition he seeks.

**History:** Banks with no mechanical action are known as still banks. The first banks were made of wood, pottery, or from gourds. Redware and stoneware banks, made by America's early potters, are prized possessions of today's collector.

Still banks reached a "golden age" with the arrival of the cast iron bank. Leading manufacturing companies include Arcade Mfg. Co., J. Chein & Co., Hubley, J. & E. Stevens, and A. C. Williams. The banks often were ornately painted to enhance their appeal. During the cast iron era, some banks and other businesses used the still bank as a form of advertising.

The tin lithograph advertising bank reached its zenith between 1930 and 1955. The tin bank was an important premium, whether it be a Pabst Blue Ribbon beer can bank or a Gerber's Orange Juice bank. Most tin advertising banks resembled the packaging shape of the product.

Almost every substance has been used to make a still bank—die cast white metal, aluminum, brass, plastic, glass, etc. Many of the early glass candy containers also converted to banks once the candy was eaten. Thousands of varieties of still banks were made and hundreds of new varieties appear on the market each year.

**References:** Dick Heuser, *Heuser's Quarterly Price Guide To Official Collectible Banks,* Heuser Enterprises, 1992; Earnest and Ida Long and Jane Pitman, *Dictionary of Still Banks*, Long's Americana, 1980; Andy and Susan Moore, *Penny Bank Book: Collecting Still Banks,* Schiffer Publishing, Ltd., 1984; Hubert B. Whiting, *Old Iron Still Banks,* Forward's Color Productions, Inc., 1968, out of print.

**Periodical:** *Heuser's Quarterly Collectible Bank Newsletter,* 508 Clapson Road, P.O. Box 300, West Winfield, NY 13491.

**Collectors' Club:** Still Bank Collectors Club of America, 301-B Park Ave. N, Winter Park, FL 32789.

**REPRODUCTION ALERT**

Advertising
Chevrolet, figural, 1954 Chevy sedan, metal, marked "Banthrico Inc, Chicago, USA" .......... 50.00
Esso, 6¾" h, plastic, red, oil drop character, 1972 .......... 45.00
Eveready, 5½" h, "Save with the Cat," vinyl, figural, 1981 copyright, Union Carbide Corp .......... 20.00
Hush Puppies, 7½" h, figural dog, vinyl, 1960s .......... 25.00

**Advertising, Quakertown National Bank, book shape, emb vinyl over metal, key lock, $25.00.**

Lennie Lennox, 7½" h, figural, composition, painted, Lennox Aire–Flo Heating, Lennox Furnace Co and 1949 copyright on back . . . . . . . . . **200.00**
Log Cabin Syrup, figural, glass . . . . . **35.00**
Magic Chef . . . . . . . . . . . . . . . . . . . . . **4.00**
Sherwin–Williams, tin, old farm wagon, orig paper label . . . . . . . . . . . **25.00**
US Coffee & Tea, glass . . . . . . . . . . . . **20.00**
Wolf's Head Motor Oil, can shape . **15.00**

Cardboard, television, 4" h, black tin litho top and bottom, screen marked "Hallicrafters Easy Angle Tuning," 1950s . . . . . . . . . . . . . . . . . . . . . . . . **25.00**

Cast Iron
Bank Building, 4¾" h, domed top, silver . . . . . . . . . . . . . . . . . . . . . . . . **40.00**
Bear, 4" l, old paint traces . . . . . . . . . **50.00**
Black Boy, 3" h, figural, bust, flared collar, floppy hat, painted, early 1900s . . . . . . . . . . . . . . . . . . . . . . . **150.00**
Cat, 4¼" h, seated, polychrome paint **60.00**
House, 3¼" h, gold paint traces . . . . **60.00**
Lion, 5½" l, blue over gold . . . . . . . . **35.00**
Porky Pig, 6" h, painted outfit, raised black lettering, Hubley Co, c1950 **150.00**
Shed, figural, peaked roof, two brown bears sitting around gold beehive, orig paint . . . . . . . . . . . . . . . . . . . . **125.00**
Skyscraper, 5½" h, silver, gold accents, early 1900s . . . . . . . . . . . . . . **75.00**
Stag, 6¼" h, gold . . . . . . . . . . . . . . . . **25.00**

Ceramic
Alice In Wonderland, 7" h, Walt Disney Productions copyright, 1950s **125.00**
Casper, figural, holding large bag of money, 1940s . . . . . . . . . . . . . . . . **90.00**
Commercial Travelers, 5½" h, soft glossy beige finish, figure standing with currency and coin, stack of coins and Commercial Travelers building, 1950s . . . . . . . . . . . . . . . . **50.00**
Donald Duck, 7" h, blue hat, yellow accents, red bow tie, 1950s . . . . . **75.00**
Elephant, bobbing head . . . . . . . . . . . **50.00**
Pencil Shape, ABC's, W Germany . . **12.00**
Popeye, 8" h, glossy finish, rubber trap, 1980 copyright . . . . . . . . . . . . **25.00**
Tom and Jerry, 5½" h, Tom holding sleeping Jerry in arms, 1981 copyright, "Gorham/Made In Japan" sticker . . . . . . . . . . . . . . . . . . . . . . . **20.00**
Woody Woodpecker, 7" h, tree stump with bust figure on top, Applause Inc, 1957 Walter Lantz copyright, 1980s . . . . . . . . . . . . . . . . . . . . . . . **18.00**

China
Howdy Doody, 7" h, riding smiling pig, inscribed "Howdy Doody Bank," Bob Smith copyright 1948–51 . . . . . . . . . . . . . . . . . . . . . . . . . . **210.00**
Mr Peabody, 6" h, glazed, early 1960s **300.00**
Rocky, 5" h, glazed, late 1950s . . . . **250.00**
Smokey Bear, 6" h, figural . . . . . . . . . **30.00**

Composition
Adolf the Pig Bank, pig shape, Adolf Hitler features, yellow, black accents, inscription "Save For Victory–Make Him Squeal," orig box **250.00**
Andy Panda, 6" h, figural, orig cardboard trap, 1940s . . . . . . . . . . . . . . **125.00**
Mickey Mouse, 6" h, yellow pants, blue shirt, brown bow tie, c1960 . **40.00**
Raggedy Ann, 7½" h, nodder, gold inscription "A Penny Saved!," early 1960s . . . . . . . . . . . . . . . . . . . . . . . **30.00**
Snoopy, doghouse . . . . . . . . . . . . . . . . **25.00**
Uncle Scrooge, 8" h, holding bag with dollar sign decal, painted and glazed, Walt Disney Productions copyright, 1960s . . . . . . . . . . . . . . . **75.00**

Glass
Baseball . . . . . . . . . . . . . . . . . . . . . . . . **35.00**
Charlie Chaplin . . . . . . . . . . . . . . . . . . **110.00**
Liberty Bell . . . . . . . . . . . . . . . . . . . . . . **20.00**
Piggy . . . . . . . . . . . . . . . . . . . . . . . . . . . **20.00**

Metal
Book, 3 x 4", raised Mickey image, beige fabric covering . . . . . . . . . . . **75.00**
Cape Canaveral, 11½", rocket shape, decal "Launching Site of the Satellite/Cape Canaveral/Cocoa, Florida," early 1960s . . . . . . . . . . . . . . . **55.00**
Iowa State, 3 x 4½", 7" h, oval, dark brass colored finish, incised "Iowa State" on front, bird mascot . . . . . **18.00**
Popeye, 6½" h, holding life preserver, 1929 King Features copyright . . . . **200.00**
Porky Pig, 4½" h, barrel shape, 1950s **145.00**
Rocket Ship, 11" h, white, silver finish, Astro Mfg, 1950s . . . . . . . . . . . **50.00**
Texas Ranger Savings Bank, 6 x 8", full color portrait illus, raised gold plastic horseshoe, Ohio Art Co, 1957–59 . . . . . . . . . . . . . . . . . . . . . **55.00**
Wild West Strong Box, 4¼" h, book shape, dark red emb cov, unmarked

Lone Ranger on horse image, inscribed "A Cache For Coins," Zell Co, New York, late 1930s ....... **75.00**

Plastic

Baseball, 3" d, Phillies, sq black base inscribed "Union Bank & Trust Co," mid 1960s ................ **25.00**

Bugs Bunny, 12½" h, yellow basket base filled with carrots, movable head, Dakin & Co, 1960s ....... **35.00**

Little Black Box, 3½" h, battery operated, green rubber hand, orig box and instruction sheet, Poynter Products Inc, marked "Made in Japan," 1960s ........................ **25.00**

National Sports Council, 3 x 4¾ x 2½", oval, maroon, sporting symbols with "Mickey Mantle" and "Joe Louis" script, 1950s ........ **125.00**

Pinocchio, 10" h, molded vinyl head, Play Pal Plastics, 1970s ......... **25.00**

Robot, Dalek, 4" h, orig box, marked "Empire made/Copyright Cowan de Groot Ltd, c1965 ............... **100.00**

Underdog, 10" h, figural, 1977 .... **75.00**

**Plastic, Fred Flintstone, molded, Homecraft Products, Vinyl Prod. Corp., 1971, 12¼" h, $45.00.**

Silver Plated, bear, patent 1982 ...... **25.00**

Tin

Abraham Lincoln Brigade, 5" h, canister shape, gold paper label "Disabled Veterans Fund/Bring New Life To 180 Seriously Wounded Americans Who Fought In Spain" **50.00**

Church, multicolored litho, 3 x 4", Chein ........................ **60.00**

Hippopotamus, figural ........... **95.00**

Remember Pearl Harbor, 3" d, 2¼" h, drum shape, Ohio Art Co ....... **50.00**

Vinyl

Bullwinkle, 11½" h, leaning on tree stump, Play Pal Plastics Inc, 1973 PAT Ward copyright ........... **55.00**

Magic Chef ...................... **15.00**

Mr Magoo, 17" h, 1960 copyright .. **25.00**

Porky Pig, 6½" h, movable head and arm, marked "R Dakin & Co," Warner Bros 1976 copyright ......... **35.00**

Princess Kneesa, 6" h, Adam Joseph Industries Inc, copyright 1983 Lucasfilm Ltd .................... **15.00**

Sesame Street, Bert, 13" h, red, white, and blue outfit, copyright 1971 New York Vinyl Productions Crop **25.00**

Uncle Sam, Bicentennial, 10" h, figural, holding banner inscribed "200 Years," All States Management Corp copyright, Made in Hong Kong .................... **12.00**

Wood, Pinocchio, figural, nodder .... **30.00**

# BARBER SHOP COLLECTIBLES

**Collecting Hints:** Many barber shop collectibles have a porcelain finish. If chipped or cracked, the porcelain is difficult, if not impossible, to repair. Buy barber poles and chairs in very good or better condition. A good display appearance is a key consideration.

Many old barber shops are still in business. Their back rooms often contain excellent display pieces.

**History:** The neighborhood barber shop was an important social and cultural institution in the 19th and first half of the 20th centuries. Men and boys gathered to gossip, exchange business news, and check current fashions. "Girlie" magazines and comic books, usually forbidden at home, were among the reading literature, as were adventure and police gazettes and magazines.

In the 1960s the number of barber shops dropped by half in the United States. "Unisex" shops broke the traditional men–only barriers. In the 1980s several chains ran barber and hair dressing shops on a regional and national basis.

**References:** Ronald S. Barlow, *The Vanishing American Barber Shop,* Windmill Publishing, 1993; Richard Holiner, *Collecting Barber Bottles,* Collector Books, 1986; Phillip L. Krumholz, *A History of Shaving and Razors,* Ad Libs Publishing Co., 1987; Phillip L. Krumholz, *Value Guide For Barberiana & Shaving Collectibles,* Ad Libs Publishing Co, 1988; Norman E. Martinus and Harry L. Rinker, *Warman's Paper,* Wallace–Homestead, 1993.

**Collectors' Clubs:** National Shaving Mug Collectors' Association, 818 South Knight Avenue, Park

Ridge, IL 60068; Safety Razor Collectors' Guild, P. O. Box 885, Crescent City, CA 95531.

Blade Bank, figural
- Barber Pole, china ............... **15.00**
- Treasure Chest, white metal, bronzed, 3" h .................. **12.00**
- Blade Tin, Yankee, c1900 ......... **55.00**

Bleeder, brass, trigger ............... **135.00**
Booklet, Burma Shave, Vol I, roadside jingles, 1942 .................... **7.50**
Bottle
- Advertising, T Noonan Barber Supply, cobalt blue .................... **50.00**
- Amethyst, enameled floral dec, c1900, 8" h .................... **150.00**
- Milk Glass, floral dec, 8¼" h ...... **65.00**

Catalog
- Koken Barbers' Supply Co, color and black and white illus, c1890 ..... **75.00**
- Simms & Co, T S, shaving brushes, 31 pgs, c1920 ................ **15.00**

Chair
- Brass, upholstered headrest, back, and child's seat, porcelainized red armrests and seat, brass frame, footrest, and overhead fan brace, lighted fan, restored, 1920–30, 72" h ............................ **1,050.00**
- Lion's Head Type, restored ........ **950.00**
- Styling, hydraulic ................ **65.00**

Display Case
- Gillette, wood and glass, c1940, 4" h **45.00**
- Robeson Shur Edge Razors, wall mount, holds 18 straight edge razors, 32½" l, 10½" h .......... **1,400.00**

Hair Wax, Butch Hair Wax, crew cut boy illus on box, orig display sign and case, 12 bottles, 1940s ........... **70.00**
Mug Rack, wood, revolving, holds shaving mugs and barber tools, 41" h ... **150.00**
Perm Machine, Duart ............... **50.00**
Pole
- Leaded Glass, Koken, 48" h ....... **975.00**
- Wood
  - Acorn finial, 74" h, 5½" d ....... **200.00**
  - Stars dec ...................... **250.00**

Poster, Bickmore Shave Cream, man lathering shaving brush, 1930, 30" w, 21" h ........................... **25.00**
Razor Dispenser, elephant, Listerine adv **10.00**
Razor Hone, Keen Kutter, E C Simmons, cardboard box .................. **25.00**
Safety Razor, Star .................. **15.00**
Shaving Brush, turned wood handle, 1920s ......................... **8.00**
Shaving Mirror, silver plated, beveled mirror plate, 1920s, 10" w, 15" h ... **20.00**
Shaving Mug
- Fraternal, shield with letters "KGEFVH" and cross and crown, shield surmounted by spread winged eagle, crossed sword behind, gilt "C.W. Cox" flanked by floral sprigs, gilt trim ............ **25.00**
- Occupational
  - Baseball catcher with mask, pads, and mitt, gold leaf trim and lettering, 3½" d, 3½" h .......... **375.00**
  - Butcher chopping meat on wooden block, "Jos. Hiltz," gold leaf trim, 3½" d, 3½" h ........... **450.00**
  - Farmer with double horse–drawn harrow, "Prosper Fourmie," gold leaf trim, 3¾" d, 4" h ......... **325.00**
  - Horned cow in oval surround flanked by banners "John Keller," gold leaf trim on image, rim, and foot, 3¾" d, 4" h ............. **175.00**
  - Horse–drawn grocer's wagon, "G.D. Pottle," gold leaf trim, 3¾" d, 3¾" h ................ **300.00**
  - Shoe salesman and client trying on leather boots, "O. Stoner," gold leaf trim on rim and foot, 3½" d, 3¾" h ...................... **375.00**
  - Steam locomotive with tender marked "F.R.R." pulling three box cars, "T.D. Shotts," gold trim, 3¾" d, 3½" h ........... **475.00**
  - Telegraph in laurel surround, "C.G. Albright," gold leaf trim, 3½" d, 3¾" h ................ **250.00**
- Personalized, pink ground, white rim, foot, and handle, black letters, floral dec, gold trim, marked "Decorated by Koken & Boppert, St Louis, Telephone Razors, Oriental, Shaving Soap & Cosmetic," 3½" d, 3¾" h, 1920s .................. **70.00**
- Scenic, church .................. **275.00**

**Advertising, sign, Gillette Safety Razor, diecut tin, two sided, 13½ x 15", $3,025.00. Photograph courtesy of James D. Julia Inc.**

Shoe Shine Stand, Chattanooga Shoe Shine Co, two seater, wood, red upholstered seats, mirrored back, drawers under seats with polishing cloths and polish, ashtrays both sides, 54½" w, 36" d, 94" h, 1900–20 ........ **1,875.00**
Sign, adv
  Ayer's Hair Vigor, paper, naked nymph emerging from lily, "For the Toilet," 10¾" w, 13¾" h ....... **1,825.00**
  Chevalier's Hair Restorer, paper, Lady Godiva, 13" w, 10" h ........... **385.00**
  Dr Linus Hair Grower, 9 x 13", cardboard ........................ **30.00**
  Gold Tone Razor Blades, 5 x 13", cardboard ..................... **25.00**
  Japps Hair Rejuvenator, 9 x 13", tin . **60.00**
  Stephans, 16 x 18", tin ............ **30.00**
  Wild Root, 13 x 39", tin .......... **75.00**
Sterilizer, clambroth glass tumbler, metal base, "Antiseptic," mark with red star ......................... **45.00**
Straight Razor
  Keen Kutter, box ................. **15.00**
  Nude handle .................... **50.00**
  Terry, black handle, lady's head and vines dec, box ................. **10.00**
Strop, Criss Cross, box .............. **15.00**
Thermometer, Keen Kutter ........... **25.00**
Tin, Tuskeegee Belle Hair Cream, black girl wearing cap and gown ........ **40.00**
Trimmer, Quick Trimmer Inc, plastic .. **4.00**

# BARBIE

**Collecting Hints:** Never forget the quantities in which Barbie and related material was manufactured. Because of this, the real value rests only in material in excellent to mint condition and which has its original packaging in very good or better condition. If items show signs of heavy use, their value is probably minimal.

Collectors prefer items from the first decade of production. Learn how to distinguish a Barbie #1 doll from its successors. The Barbie market is one of subtleties. You must learn them.

Recently collectors have shifted their focus from the dolls themselves to the accessories. There have been rapid price increases in early clothing and accessories, with some of the prices bordering on speculation.

**History:** In 1945 Harold Matson (MATT) and Ruth and Elliott (EL) Handler founded Mattel. Initially the company made picture frames. The company became involved in the toy market when Elliott Handler began to make doll furniture from scrap material. When Harold Matson left the firm, Elliott Handler became chief designer and Ruth Handler principal marketer. In 1955 Mattel advertised its products on "The Mickey Mouse Club." The company prospered.

In 1958 Mattel patented a fashion doll. The doll was named "Barbie" and reached the toy shelves in 1959. By 1960 Barbie's popularity was assured.

Development of a boyfriend for Barbie, named Ken after the Handler's son, began in 1960. Over the years many other dolls were added to the line. Clothing, vehicles, room settings, and other accessories became an integral part of the line.

From September 1961 through July 1972 Mattel published a Barbie magazine. At its peak the Barbie Fan Club was the second largest girls' organization, next to the Girl Scouts, in the United States.

Barbie sales are approaching the 100 million mark. Annual sales exceed five million units. Barbie is one of the most successful dolls in history.

**References:** Billyboy, *Barbie: Her Life and Times*, Crown Publishers, Inc., 1987; Sibyl DeWein and Joan Ashabraner, *The Collectors Encyclopedia Of Barbie Dolls and Collectibles*, Collector Books, 1977, 1992 value update; Sarah Sink Eames, *Barbie Fashion, Volume 1, 1959–1967*, Collector Books, 1990; Paris and Susan Manos, *The Wonder Of Barbie: Dolls And Accessories 1976–1986*, Collector Books, 1987, 1993 value update; Paris and Susan Manos, *The World Of Barbie Dolls: An Illustrated Value Guide*, Collector Books, 1983, 1992 value update.

Accessories
  Barbie & Ken Campin' Out Set, 1983 **65.00**
  Barbie Fashion Stage, orig box ..... **30.00**
  Beach Bus, #7805, c1974 ........ **30.00**
  Cookin' Fun Kitchen .............. **35.00**
  Go Together Furniture, orig box, Mattel
    Barbie and Skipper Living Room Group ...................... **75.00**
    Chaise Lounge ................. **50.00**
    Lawn Swing and Planter ......... **100.00**
  Horse, Dallas, tan, blond mane and tail, 1981 .................... **15.00**
  Mountain Ski Cabin, Sear's Exclusive, #4283 ....................... **25.00**
  Skipper Jeweled Bed, Susy Goose Toys ......................... **35.00**
  Sports Car, pink convertible, Irwin Corporation, 1963 .............. **100.00**
  Teen Dream Bedroom ............ **35.00**
  Vanity, Bench, and Rug, Susy Goose Toys, 1964 .................... **75.00**
Beauty Kit, 1961 .................. **20.00**
Book
  *Barbie Solves A Mystery*, Lawrence, Random House ................ **8.00**
  *The World of Barbie*, Random House **15.00**

Carrying Case
- Barbie and Midge Travel Pals, black vinyl, zipper, 1963 .......... **40.00**
- Fashion Queen Barbie, Standard Plastic Productions .......... **30.00**
- Ken Campus Hero, light green vinyl, Ken wearing cheerleader uniform, 1963 .......... **40.00**
- Skipper & Skooter, 10½ x 15½", yellow vinyl, metal snap fastener, Standard Plastic Products, 1965 .. **60.00**

Clothing
- Barbie
  - After Five, #934, double breasted sleeveless dress, 1962–64 ..... **40.00**
  - Cruise Stripes, #918, 1959–62 ... **55.00**
  - Evening Splendor, #961, 1959 ... **60.00**
  - Friday Night Date, #979, 1960–64 **55.00**
  - Party Lines, Miss America series, #3490, 1972 .......... **60.00**
  - Winter Holiday, #975, 1959–63 . **45.00**
- Francie
  - Dance Party, #1257, 1965 ...... **45.00**
  - Shoppin' Spree, #1216, 1965 ... **40.00**

**Ken, #750, 12" h, painted hair, wearing American Airlines Captain outfit #0779, 1964, doll: $75.00; outfit: $80.00.**

- Ken
  - Army and Air Force, #797, 1963–65 .......... **70.00**
  - Campus Hero, #770, 1961–64 .. **50.00**
  - Graduation, #795, black robe, 1963–64 .......... **50.00**
  - Rovin' Reporter, #1417, 1964 ... **40.00**
  - Skin Diver, #1406, 1964–65 .... **55.00**
  - Special Date, #1401, 1964–65 .. **50.00**
  - Victory Dance, #1411, 1964 .... **55.00**
- Skipper
  - Ballet Class, #1905, 1964–65 ... **45.00**
  - Jeepers Creepers, #1966, 1968 .. **40.00**
  - Outdoor Casual, #1915, 1965–66 **50.00**
  - Rain or Shine, #1916, yellow slicker, 1965–66 .......... **50.00**
  - Red Sensation, #1901, 1964–65 . **30.00**

Diary, 1963 .......... **25.00**

Dictionary, 4 x 5½", black vinyl cov, color illus, Standard Products, 1963 **50.00**

Display Catalog, counter top, features dolls and fashions .......... **125.00**

Doll
- Allan #1, blue trunks, striped cover–up, 1963 .......... **80.00**
- Barbie
  - Ballerina Barbie, gold and white outfit, crown, toe shoes, stand, and roses, 1976 .......... **40.00**
  - Barbie #3, brunette, ponytail, 1960 .......... **600.00**
  - Bubble–Cut Barbie, red swimsuit, 1963 .......... **110.00**
  - Great Shape Barbie, aqua lycra bodysuit, headband, leg warmers, and pink belt, 1984 ....... **15.00**
  - Malibu Barbie, blonde waist length hair, blue swimsuit, tan line body, 1971 .......... **30.00**
  - My First Barbie, off the shoulder pink top, pink and white gingham skirt, 1983 .......... **15.00**
  - Quick Curl Barbie, pink gingham dress, hairstyling accessories, 1973 .......... **45.00**
  - Super Star Barbie, pink glitter gown, 1976 .......... **95.00**
  - Twist 'N Turn Barbie, 1968 ...... **100.00**
- Ken
  - Bendable Leg, blue swim trunks, red cover–up, 1964 .......... **200.00**
  - Dream Date, black tuxedo, black molded hair, 1983 .......... **18.00**
  - Live Action, gold pants and fringed vest, print shirt, painted brown hair, 1971 .......... **70.00**
  - Malibu, 1973 .......... **30.00**
  - Roller Skating, black shorts, red shirt, purple jacket, 1980 ...... **18.00**
  - Super Star, blue velour jumpsuit, painted blonde hair, 1976 ..... **45.00**
- Midge, half shirt tank top, bikini bottom, 1963 .......... **125.00**
- Skipper
  - Hot Stuff Skipper, pink tank top, red skirt, 1985 .......... **15.00**
  - Malibu Skipper, two piece orange swimsuit, 1971 .......... **15.00**
  - Skipper #1, red and white striped bodysuit, 1964 .......... **125.00**

Game
- Barbie Queen of the Prom, 1961–62 **35.00**
- Skipper, 16" sq playing board, orig box, 1964 .......... **20.00**

Knitting Kit, 1962 .................. **15.00**
Lunch Box
- Barbie, vinyl ..................... **85.00**
- Skipper, pink vinyl, 1966–67 ...... **50.00**

Manicure Set, Good Grooming Manicure Set, polish, nail brush, and emery boards, orig box ........... **35.00**
Paper Doll
- Book, Barbie and Her Friends, All Sports Tournament theme, Whitman, 1975 .................... **20.00**
- Kit, two 11½" figures, Whitman, 1967 ......................... **40.00**

Photo Album, Barbie on cov, 1963 ... **25.00**
Puzzle, Barbie and Ken, King Arthur court type setting, 100 pcs, 1964 ... **35.00**
Record, 45 rpm,"Barbie Sings!," six songs, 1961 ..................... **35.00**
Ring, The Official Barbie Fan Club Play Ring ............................ **50.00**
Telephone, Barbie Mattel–A–Phone ... **25.00**
Trading Card, Barbie and Ken Jumbo Trading Cards, orig box, Mattel, Inc, 1962 ........................... **45.00**
Wristwatch, orig box, Bradley ....... **50.00**

# BASEBALL CARDS

**Collecting Hints:** Condition is a key factor. The list below is priced for cards in excellent condition, and collectors should strive only for cards in excellent to mint condition.

Concentrate on the superstars; these cards are most likely to increase in value. Buy full sets of modern cards. In this way you have the superstars of tomorrow on hand. When a player becomes a member of the Baseball Hall of Fame, his cards and other memorabilia will increase significantly.

The price of cards fluctuates rapidly; it changes on a weekly basis. Spend time studying the market before investing heavily. Finally, reproduced cards and sets have become a fact of life in this category. Novice collectors should not buy cards until they can tell the difference between the originals and reproductions.

The latest trend is the collection of rookie cards, i.e., the first year of issue for a player. This is a highly speculative category at the moment.

**History:** Baseball cards date from the late 19th century. By 1900 the most common cards, known as "T" cards, were those produced by tobacco companies such as American Tobacco Co., with the majority of the tobacco–related cards being produced between 1909 and 1915. By far the most popular set was "T206" issued between 1909 and 1911. During the 1920s American Caramel, National Caramel, and York Caramel candy companies issued cards identified in lists as "E" cards.

From 1933 to 1941 Goudey Gum Co. of Boston and, in 1939, Gum, Inc., were the big producers of baseball cards. Following World War II, Bowman Gum of Philadelphia (B.G.H.L.I.), the successor to Gum, Inc., led the way. Topps, Inc. (T.C.G.) of Brooklyn, New York, followed. Topps bought Bowman in 1956 and enjoyed almost a monopoly in card production until 1981.

In 1981 Topps was challenged by Fleer of Philadelphia and Donruss of Memphis. All three companies annually produce sets of cards numbering 600 cards or more.

**References:** James Beckett, *The Official 1993 Price Guide to Baseball Cards, Twelfth Edition,* House of Collectibles, 1992; James Beckett, *Sports Americana Baseball Card Price Guide, No. 15,* Edgewater Book Co., Inc., 1992; Jeff Kurowski (ed.), *Baseball Card Price Guide, Seventh Edition,* Krause Publications, 1993; Jeff Kurowski (ed.), *Standard Catalog of Baseball Cards, Third Edition,* Krause Publications, 1992; Gene Florence, *The Standard Baseball Card Price Guide, Revised 5th Edition,* Collector Books, 1993; Allan Kaye and Michael McKeever,*Baseball Card Price Guide, 1994,* Avon Books, 1993; Troy Kirk, *Collector's Guide To Baseball Cards,* Wallace–Homestead, 1990; Mark Larson (ed.), *Baseball Cards Questions & Answers,* Krause Publications, 1992; Mark Larson, *Sports Collectors Digest Minor & Collegiate Card Price Guide,* Krause Publications, 1993; Bob Lemke (ed.), *Sportscard Counterfeit Detector,* Krause Publications, Inc., 1992.

**Periodicals:** The following appear on a monthly or semi– monthly basis: *Card News,* 700 E. State Street, Iola, WI 54990; *Beckett Baseball Card Monthly,* P.O. Box 1915, Marion, OH 13305-1915; *Sports Collectors Digest,* 700 E. State Street, Iola, WI 54990.

**Collectors' Clubs:** There are many local card collecting clubs throughout the United States. However, there is no national organization at the present time.

**REPRODUCTION ALERT:** The 1952 Topps set, except for 5 cards, was reproduced in 1983 and clearly marked by Topps. In addition, a number of cards have been illegally reprinted, including the following Topps cards:

1963 Peter Rose, rookie card, #537
1971 Pete Rose, #100
1971 Steve Garvey, #341
1972 Pete Rose, #559
1972 Steve Garvey, #686
1972 Rod Carew, #695
1973 Willie Mays, #100
1973 Hank Aaron, #305
1973 Mike Schmidt, rookie card, #615

**Note:** The listing for the cards beginning in 1948 shows the price for a complete set, common player, and superstars. The number of cards in each set is indicated in parentheses.

**Topps, 1972 Rookie Stars, #213, Angels, Billy Parker, Art Kusnyer, Tom Silverio, $.70.**

## BOWMAN ERA

1948 Bowman (black and white)
- Complete set (48) ... **1,500.00**
- Common player (1–36) ... **9.00**
- Common player (37–48) ... **12.50**
- 2 Ewell Blackwell ... **18.00**
- 21 Ferris Fain ... **10.50**
- 38 Red Schoendienst ... **67.50**
- 47 Bobby Thomson ... **34.00**

1949 Bowman
- Complete set (240) ... **7,000.00**
- Common player (1–144) ... **7.25**
- Common player (145–240) ... **36.00**
- 14 Curt Simmons ... **12.00**
- 36 Pee Wee Reese ... **80.00**
- 214 Richie Ashburn ... **225.00**

1950 Bowman
- Complete set (252) ... **4,500.00**
- Common player (1–72) ... **25.00**
- Common player (72–216) ... **7.50**
- Common player (217–252) ... **8.50**
- 35 Enos Slaughter ... **57.50**
- 112 Gil Hodges ... **45.00**
- 232 Al Rosen ... **27.00**

1952 Bowman
- Complete set (252) ... **4,200.00**
- Common player (1–36) ... **8.50**
- Common player (37–72) ... **7.50**
- Common player (73–144) ... **6.50**
- Common player (145–180) ... **6.25**
- Common player (181–216) ... **5.75**
- Common player (217–252) ... **13.50**
- 44 Roy Campanella ... **85.00**
- 101 Mickey Mantle ... **800.00**
- 196 Stan Musial ... **225.00**

1953 Bowman (black and white)
- Complete set (64) ... **1,000.00**
- Common player (1–64) ... **15.75**
- 15 Johnny Mize ... **60.00**
- 28 Hoyt Wilhelm ... **60.00**
- 51 Lou Burdette ... **22.00**

1954 Bowman
- Complete set (224) ... **1,800.00**
- Common player (1–128) ... **4.50**
- Common player (129–224) ... **6.25**
- 62 Enos Slaughter ... **18.00**
- 90 Roy Campanella ... **60.00**
- 138 Gil Hodges ... **29.00**
- 181 Les Moss ... **6.25**
- 224 Bill Bruton ... **9.00**

1955 Bowman
- Complete set (320) ... **2,350.00**
- Common player (1–96) ... **3.50**
- Common player (97–224) ... **3.00**
- Common player (225–320) ... **7.00**
- Common umpires (225–320) ... **13.50**
- 103 Eddie Mathews ... **22.50**
- 179 Hank Aaron ... **100.00**
- 202 Mickey Mantle ... **200.00**

## DONRUSS

1981 Donruss
- Complete set (605) ... **27.00**
- Common player (1–605) ... **.02**
- 33 Steve Carlton ... **.50**
- 62 Johnny Bench ... **.60**
- 119 Rickey Henderson ... **7.50**
- 468 Reggie Jackson UER ... **1.00**
- 538 Tim Raines ... **2.50**

1983 Donruss
- Complete set (660) ... **55.00**
- Common player (1–660) ... **.02**
- 118 Nolan Ryan ... **2.25**
- 190 Willie McGee ... **1.50**
- 270 Cal Ripken ... **5.50**
- 598 Tony Gwynn ... **10.00**

1986 Donruss
- Complete set (660) ... **80.00**
- Common player (1–660) ... **.03**
- 39 Jose Canseco RR ... **36.00**
- 72 Kirby Puckett ... **3.00**
- 172 Roger Clemens ... **3.50**
- 371 Wade Boggs ... **1.00**
- 512 Cecil Fielder ... **10.50**

1988 Donruss
- Complete set (660) ... **7.50**
- Common player (1–647) ... **.01**
- Common player (648–660) ... **.02**
- 34 Roberto Alomar RR ... **1.25**
- 654 Ron Gant SP ... **1.50**

1990 Donruss
- Complete set (716) ... **7.50**
- Common player (1–716) ... **.01**

## FLEER

1959 Fleer
- Complete set (80) ... **500.00**
- Common player (1–80) ... **2.50**

1960 Fleer
- Complete set (79) ... **180.00**

Common player (1–79) .......... **1.25**
Common player DP .......... **.90**
3 George H Ruth .......... **34.00**
28 Lou Gehrig .......... **18.00**
42 Ty Cobb .......... **18.00**

1963 Fleer
Complete set (67) .......... **500.00**
Common player (1–67) .......... **3.00**
8 Carl Yastrzemski .......... **40.00**
43 Maury Wills .......... **27.00**
56 Roberto Clemente .......... **40.00**
61 Bob Gibson .......... **14.25**

1981 Fleer
Complete set (660) .......... **27.00**
Common player (1–660) .......... **.02**
5 Mike Schmidt .......... **1.00**
140 Fernand Valenzuela .......... **1.10**
351 Ricky Henderson .......... **4.50**

1983 Fleer
Complete set (660) .......... **55.00**
Common player (1–660) .......... **.02**
22 Ozzie Smith .......... **.50**
179 Wade Boggs .......... **10.50**

1985 Fleer
Complete set (660) .......... **80.00**
Common player (1–660) .......... **.03**
82 Dwight Gooden .......... **5.50**
93 Darryl Strawberry .......... **5.50**
236 Terry Pendleton .......... **2.00**
286 Kirby Puckett .......... **13.50**

1988 Fleer
Complete set (660) .......... **16.00**
Common player (1–660) .......... **.02**
101 Matt Williams .......... **2.00**
276 Jose Canseco .......... **1.00**
583 Ron Gant .......... **2.50**

1990 Fleer Update
Complete set (132) .......... **4.50**
Common player (1–132) .......... **.02**
U87 Frank Thomas .......... **2.50**
U96 Travis Fryman .......... **.50**

## SCORE

1988 Score
Complete set (660) .......... **8.50**
Common player (1–660) .......... **.01**
93A Greg Walker ERR .......... **1.75**
638 Tom Glavine .......... **.40**
647 Ron Gant .......... **1.00**

1989 Score Traded
Complete set (110) .......... **5.25**
Common player (1–110) .......... **.02**
2T Nolan Ryan .......... **.60**
88T Jim Abbott .......... **.50**
100T Ken Griffey Jr .......... **2.50**

1990 Score Dream Team Rookies
Complete set (10) .......... **4.50**
Common player (1–10) .......... **.10**
B6 Robin Ventura .......... **2.25**
B8 Greg Vaughn .......... **1.50**

## TOPPS ERA

1951 Topps, blue backs
Complete set (52) .......... **900.00**
Common player (1–52) .......... **15.75**
3 Richie Ashburn .......... **75.00**
30 Enos Slaughter .......... **60.00**
50 Johnny Mize .......... **63.00**

1951 Topps, red backs
Complete set (52) .......... **325.00**
Common player (1–52) .......... **3.00**
1 Yogi Berra .......... **40.00**
38 Duke Snider .......... **36.00**

1953 Topps
Complete set (280) .......... **5,000.00**
Common player (1–165) .......... **11.00**
Common player (166–200) .......... **7.50**
Common player (221–280) .......... **42.00**
37 Eddie Mathews DP .......... **50.00**
77 Johnny Mize DP .......... **27.00**
82 Mickey Mantle .......... **750.00**
147 Warren Spahn .......... **60.00**
220 Satchell Paige .......... **200.00**
276 Ken Raffensberger .......... **42.00**

1955 Topps
Complete set (210) .......... **3,500.00**
Common player (1–150) .......... **4.00**
Common player (151–160) .......... **7.50**
Common player (161–210) .......... **12.00**
28 Ernie Banks .......... **90.00**
92 Don Zimmer .......... **16.25**
123 Sandy Koufax .......... **400.00**
194 Willie Mays .......... **215.00**
200 Jackie Jensen .......... **22.50**

1957 Topps
Complete set (407) .......... **3,500.00**
Common player (1–88) .......... **3.25**
Common player (89–176) .......... **2.75**
Common player (177–264) .......... **2.50**
Common player (265–352) .......... **8.50**
Common DP (265–352) .......... **5.25**
Common player (353–407) .......... **2.50**
1 Ted Williams .......... **125.00**
35 Frank Robinson .......... **120.00**
302 Sandy Koufax .......... **150.00**
400 Dodger's Sluggers .......... **80.00**

1959 Topps
Complete set (572) .......... **2,250.00**
Common player (1–110) .......... **2.50**
Common player (111–198) .......... **1.60**
Common player (199–506) .......... **1.35**
Common player (507–550) .......... **6.75**
Common player (551–572) .......... **7.50**
50 Willie Mays .......... **67.50**
380 Hank Aaron .......... **50.00**
514 Bob Gibson .......... **180.00**

1961 Topps
Complete set (589) .......... **2,400.00**
Common player (1–110) .......... **1.00**
Common player (111–370) .......... **1.25**
Common player (371–446) .......... **1.50**
Common player (447–522) .......... **2.00**

| | |
|---|---|
| Common player (523–565) | **13.50** |
| Common player (566–589) | **15.00** |
| 10 Brooks Robinson | **14.50** |
| 120 Eddie Mathews | **11.00** |
| 150 Willie Mays | **50.00** |
| 200 Warren Spahn | **13.50** |
| 287 Carl Yastrzemski | **63.00** |
| 429 Al Kaline | **20.00** |
| 517 Willie McCovey | **25.00** |
| 1963 Topps | |
| Complete set (576) | **2,250.00** |
| Common player (1–109) | **80.00** |
| Common player (110–283) | **1.10** |
| Common player (284–446) | **1.60** |
| Common player (447–522) | **5.75** |
| Common player (523–576) | **4.00** |
| 54A Rookie Stars | **6.50** |
| 115 Carl Yastrzemski | **34.50** |
| 210 Sandy Koufax | **63.00** |
| 242 Power Plus | **12.50** |
| 300 Willie Mays | **63.00** |
| 412 Dodger Big Three | **14.25** |
| 446 Whitey Ford | **17.00** |
| 500 Harmon Killebrew SP | **50.00** |
| 1965 Topps | |
| Complete set (598) | **1,750.00** |
| Common player (1–196) | **.50** |
| Common player (197–283) | **.80** |
| Common player (284–370) | **1.10** |
| Common player (371–446) | **1.75** |
| Common player (447–522) | **2.25** |
| Common player (523–598) | **2.50** |
| Common SP (523–598) | **5.00** |
| 16 Houston Rookies | **80.00** |
| 170 Hank Aaron | **40.00** |
| 207 Pete Rose | **72.00** |
| 350 Mickey Mantle | **180.00** |
| 510 Ernie Banks | **32.00** |
| 540 Lou Brock | **22.00** |
| 1967 Topps | |
| Complete set (609) | **2,300.00** |
| Common player (1–109) | **.55** |
| Common player (110–196) | **.70** |
| Common player (197–283) | **.80** |
| Common player (284–370) | **1.00** |
| Common player (371–457) | **1.25** |
| Common player (458–533) | **2.50** |
| Common player (534–609) | **7.50** |
| Common DP (534–609) | **4.00** |
| 45 Roger Maris | **18.00** |
| 146 Steve Carlton | **50.00** |
| 250 Hank Aaron | **38.00** |
| 400 Roberto Clemente | **29.00** |
| 430 Pete Rose | **34.00** |
| 598 White Sox Rookies | **10.50** |
| 600 Brooks Robinson | **110.00** |
| 1969 Topps | |
| Complete set (664) | **1,100.00** |
| Common player (1–218) | **.55** |
| Common player (219–327) | **.90** |
| Common player (328–512) | **.55** |
| Common player (513–588) | **.70** |
| Common player (589–664) | **.90** |
| 35 Joe Morgan | **5.25** |
| 95 Johnny Bench | **90.00** |
| 120 Pete Rose | **16.25** |
| 190 Willie Mays | **27.00** |
| 250 Frank Robinson | **11.00** |
| 480 Tom Seaver | **57.50** |
| 400 Don Drysdale | **4.50** |
| 533 Nolan Ryan | **190.00** |
| 1970 Topps | |
| Complete set (720) | **900.00** |
| Common player (1–132) | **.30** |
| Common player (133–263) | **.35** |
| Common player (264–372) | **.40** |
| Common player (373–459) | **.45** |
| Common player (460–546) | **.65** |
| Common player (547–633) | **1.10** |
| Common player (634–720) | **2.25** |
| 17 Hoyt Wilhelm | **1.75** |
| 140 Reggie Jackson | **67.50** |
| 189 Yankees Rookies | **45.00** |
| 220 Steve Carlton | **13.50** |
| 290 Rod Carew | **22.50** |
| 464 Johnny Bench AS | **6.25** |
| 470 Willie Stargell | **4.00** |
| 580 Pete Rose | **34.00** |
| 1971 Topps | |
| Complete set (752) | **900.00** |
| Common player (1–132) | **.35** |
| Common player (133–263) | **.40** |
| Common player (264–393) | **.40** |
| Common player (394–523) | **.65** |
| Common player (524–643) | **1.50** |
| Common player (644–752) | **2.25** |
| Common SP (644–752) | **3.25** |
| 14 Dave Concepcion | **6.50** |
| 30 Phil Niekro | **1.75** |
| 117 Ted Simmons | **6.50** |
| 341 Steve Garvey | **32.00** |
| 570 Jim Palmer | **15.00** |
| 1972 Topps | |
| Complete set (787) | **800.00** |
| Common player (1–132) | **.20** |
| Common player (133–263) | **.30** |
| Common player (264–394) | **.35** |
| Common player (395–525) | **.50** |
| Common player (526–656) | **1.10** |
| Common player (657–787) | **2.25** |
| 49 Willie Mays | **11.00** |
| 100 Frank Robinson | **2.50** |
| 147 Dave Kingman | **2.75** |
| 270 Jim Palmer | **6.00** |
| 285 Gaylord Perry | **2.75** |
| 309 Roberto Clemente | **15.00** |
| 595 Nolan Ryan | **75.00** |
| 761 Rookie Outfielders | **7.50** |
| 1974 Topps | |
| Complete set (660) | **275.00** |
| Common player | **.16** |
| 20 Nolan Ryan | **22.50** |
| 40 Jim Palmer | **4.00** |
| 130 Reggie Jackson | **9.00** |

**Topps, 1974, #215, Al Kaline, no copyright on back, 2$6\frac{1}{2}$ x $3\frac{1}{2}$", $2.70.**

283 Mike Schmidt ................ **45.00**
456 Dave Winfield ............... **36.00**

1976 Topps
Complete set (660) ............... **190.00**
Common player .................. **.12**
19 George Brett .................. **22.00**
98 Dennis Eckersley .............. **16.25**
355 Steve Carlton ................ **2.75**
441 Gary Carter ................... **4.50**
480 Mike Schmidt ................ **15.00**
542 Keith Hernandez ............ **2.50**

1978 Topps
Complete set (726) ............... **140.00**
Common player (1–726) .......... **.07**
Common DP .................... **.08**
36 Eddie Murray ................. **32.00**
72 Andre Dawson ................ **6.50**
360 Mike Schmidt ................ **6.50**
450 Tom Seaver .................. **2.25**
700 Johnny Bench ................ **2.00**

1980 Topps
Complete set (726) ............... **110.00**
Common player (1–726) .......... **.04**
Common DP .................... **.02**
40 Carlton Fisk .................. **1.75**
160 Eddie Murray ................ **4.00**
235 Andre Dawson ............... **2.75**
274 Dale Murphy ................ **2.25**
482 Rickey Henderson ............ **67.50**
580 Nolan Ryan ................. **6.57**
600 Reggie Jackson ............... **2.25**

1982 Topps
Complete set (792) ............... **63.00**
Common player .................. **.03**
21 Orioles Rookies ............... **29.00**
80 Jim Palmer .................... **.60**
90 Nolan Ryan ................... **3.25**
100 Mike Schmidt ................ **.85**
254 Jorge Bell ................... **5.00**
610 Ricky Henderson ............. **4.00**

1984 Topps
Complete set (792) ............... **45.00**
Common player .................. **.02**
30 Wade Boggs .................. **2.25**
182 Darryl Strawberry ............ **9.00**
470 Nolan Ryan ................. **2.50**
596 Ryne Sandberg ............... **4.00**

1988 Topps
Complete set (792) ............... **7.50**
Common player (1–792) .......... **.01**
250 Nolan Ryan ................. **.18**
635 Terry Pendleton .............. **.05**
650 Cal Ripken .................. **.15**
710 Darryl Strawberry ............ **.15**
750 Bo Jackson .................. **.25**
778A Keith Comstock ERR ......... **1.00**

1990 Topps
Complete set (792) ............... **8.50**
Common player (1–792) .......... **.01**
336 Ken Griffey Jr ................ **.60**
414A Frank Thomas FDP .......... **1.75**

## UPPER DECK

1989 Upper Deck
Complete set (700) ............... **67.50**
Common player (1–700) .......... **.03**
1 Ken Griffey Jr .................. **15.00**
145 Nolan Ryan ................. **1.50**
357A Dale Murphy ERR ........... **27.00**
652A Pat Sheridan ERR ........... **8.50**

1991 Upper Deck
Complete set (700) ............... **12.50**
Common player (1–700) .......... **.02**
40 Chuck Knoblauch ............. **.80**
522 Scott Erickson ................ **1.25**
555 Ken Griffey Jr UER ........... **.50**

# BASEBALL COLLECTIBLES

**Collecting Hints:** Baseball memorabilia spans a wide range of items that have been produced since baseball became the national pastime over 100 years ago. This variety has made it more difficult to establish reliable values, leaving it to the collector himself to identify and determine what price to pay for any particular item he uncovers. This "value in the eye of the beholder" approach works well with the veteran collector. The novice collector should solicit the advice of a reliable dealer or advanced collector about values before investing heavily. This is compounded by the emerging interest in unique pieces, especially items associated with superstars such as Cobb, Ruth, and Mantle that now command inordinately high prices.

Because of the unlimited variety of items available, it is virtually impossible to collect everything. Develop a collecting strategy, concentrating on particular player(s), team(s), or types of collectibles, such as Hartland Statues or Perez–Steele autographed postcards. This special emphasis allows the collector to become more familiar with the key elements affecting pricing within their area of interest, such as condition and availability, and permits him to build his collection within a prescribed budget.

**History:** Baseball has its beginnings in the mid–19th century and by 1900 had become the national pastime. Whether sandlot or big league, baseball was part of almost every male's life until the 1950s, when leisure activities expanded in a myriad of directions.

The superstar has always been the key element in the game. Baseball greats were popular visitors at banquets, parades, and more recently at baseball autograph shows. They were subjects of extensive newspaper coverage and, with heightened radio and TV exposure, achieved true celebrity status. The impact of baseball on American life has been enormous.

**References:** Mark Allen Baker, *Sports Collectors Digest Baseball Autograph Handbook,* Second Edition, Krause Publications, 1991; Mark Baker, *Team Baseballs: The Complete Guide to Autographed Team Baseballs,* Krause Publications, 1992; James Beckett, *The Sport Americana Baseball Collectibles Price Guide, No. 2,* Edgewater Book Company, Inc., 1988; Peter Capano, *Baseball Collectibles with Price Guide,* Schiffer Publishing, 1989; Bruce Chadwick and David Spindel, *The Boston Red Sox,* Abbeville Press, 1992; Bruce Chadwick and David Spindel, *The Bronx Bombers,* Abbeville Press, 1992; Bruce Chadwick and David Spindel, *The Dodgers: Memories and Memorabilia From Brooklyn To L.A.,* Abbeville Press, 1993; Bruce Chadwick and David Spindel, *The Giants: Memories and Memorabilia From A Century of Baseball,* Abbeville Press, 1993; Douglas Congdon–Martin and John Kashmanian, *Baseball Treasures: Memorabilia from the National Pastime,* Schiffer Publishing, 1993; Bruce Kronnick, *The Baseball Fan's Complete Guide to Collecting Autographs,* Betterway Publications, 1990; Mark Larson, *The Complete Guide to Baseball Memorabilia,* Krause Publications, 1992; Roderick A. Malloy, *Malloy's Sports Collectibles Value Guide,* Wallace–Homestead, 1993; Norman E. Martinus and Harry L. Rinker, *Warman's Paper,* Wallace–Homestead, 1993; Ron Menchine, *A Picture Postcard History of Baseball,* Almar Press Book Publishers, 1992; Don Raycraft, *Collecting Baseball Player Autographs,* Collector Books, 1991; M. Donald and R. Craig Raycraft, *Value Guide To Baseball Collectibles,* Collector Books, 1992.

**Collectors' Club:** Society for American Baseball Research, P. O. Box 93183, Cleveland, OH 44101–5183. Members receive *Baseball Research Journal, The SABR Bulletin* and *The National Pastime.*

**Museum:** National Baseball Hall of Fame and Museum, Cooperstown, NY.

**REPRODUCTION ALERT:** Autographs and equipment.

Advertising, glass slide, 3 x 4", Winchester, hand colored illus of player, mitt, and ball .................... **110.00**
Bank, 7" h, Cleveland Indians, china, figural, Indian holding baseball bat . **100.00**
Baseball, inscribed "Lou Brock/Hall of Famer Inducted July 28, 1985" and "The Only Player To Get 3000 Hits and Steal 900 Bases In A Career," orig box and plastic shopping bag marked "Lou Brock Sports Shop" .......... **20.00**
Belt, child's, 27" l, brown leather, tooled baseball symbols, gold finished metal buckle, c1940 ........ **30.00**
Book
*Budweiser Baseball Guide,* 3 x 7", 40 pgs .......................... **12.00**
*Lou Gehrig, Pride of the Yankees,* Paul Gallico, 1942, 125 pgs ......... **22.50**
*Major League Baseball,* 1951, Dell Publishing Co, 128 pgs ......... **15.00**
*Official Baseball Rules,* 1974 ...... **4.00**
*Pitchin' Man,* Satchel Paige biography, 1948, 96 pgs .............. **25.00**
*Who's Who in Baseball,* 1976, soft cov .......................... **5.00**
Booklet, *Famous Sluggers,* 3¼ x 5¼", Hillerich & Bradsby Co, 1933, 72 pgs **75.00**
Box, Babe Ruth Underwear, color portrait illus on lid, 1920–30 ......... **100.00**
Commemorative Card, 8 x 10", glossy, Ryan on pitching mound in process of striking out his 5000th batter, Aug 22, 1989, sgd blue marker, 1990 photo copyright TV Sports Mailbag . **25.00**
Doll, 13" h, Jackie Robinson, composition, jointed, Allied–Grand Mfg Co, c1950 .......................... **200.00**
Game
All–Pro Baseball, Ideal Toy Corp, 1969 copyright, orig box ........ **18.00**
NBC Sports In Action, Game of the Week, Hasbro, 1969 ........... **40.00**
Pocket Baseball, diamond game board, wood dice and pegs, orig box, Toy Creations, 1940s ....... **15.00**
Sports Illustrated Baseball Game, orig box, Time Inc, 1972 ............ **25.00**
Strat–O–Matic, 1962 copyright, orig box .......................... **20.00**

- Tudor Tru–Action Electric Baseball Game, Tudor Metal Products Corp, orig box, late 1940s ........ **75.00**

Glass, 5½" h, 1970 All–Star Game, clear, weighted bottom, Riverfront Stadium illus ........ **15.00**

Hartland Statue
- Babe Ruth, holding bat, Yankees uniform, cream and navy blue, 1960s **175.00**
- Stan Musial, 7½" h, plastic, 1950–60 **125.00**
- Willie Mays, 7½" h, plastic, 1958 .. **150.00**

Keychain Tag, 1½ x 1½", leather, brown, portrait illus of John Mize, 1950s series ........ **15.00**

License Plate, 6 x 11", tin litho, red, white, and blue batter, red "Phillies" slogan, early 1950s ........ **30.00**

Magazine
- *Life,* Sept 8, 1967, color photo of Carl Yastrzemski on cov, eight page article and photos, 10½ x 13½" ... **22.00**
- *Look,* Oct 10, 1939, Joe DiMaggio, three page article and photos, color photo on cov, 10½ x 13½" ...... **25.00**

Mitt
- Lew Burdette ........ **15.00**
- Gus Mancuso model, catcher's ..... **90.00**
- Brooks Robinson ........ **15.00**

Nodder
- Baltimore Orioles, figural, oriole ... **200.00**
- 6½" h, Cleveland Indians, composition, white square base, "Cleveland" decal, Japan, 1961 copyright **125.00**
- Hank Aaron ........ **60.00**
- New York Yankee, 7" h, composition, 1961–62 ........ **75.00**
- Roger Maris, 7" h, composition, white sq base with decal, base stamped "Patent Pending/Japan," c1962 ... **200.00**

Paperweight, 4¼" h, Chicago Cubs, metal, baseball on sq base, silver luster, blue lettering, inscribed "Glassenhart & Mayerhofer," c1920 ........ **225.00**

Pencil, 6½" l, mechanical, Joe DiMaggio, plastic, baseball bat shape, red, American League insignia and New York Yankees, name in white script, 1940s ........ **20.00**

Pennant
- Baltimore Orioles 1969 American League Championship, 29½" l, black, white inscriptions, orange, yellow, and gray accents, orange trim ........ **25.00**
- Baseball Hall of Fame, 11" l, green, white inscription, yellow trim, 1950s ........ **20.00**
- Boston Red Sox, 29" l, maroon, white inscription, pink and light blue accents, yellow gold trim and streamers, 1960s ........ **15.00**
- Cincinnati Reds, 29½" l, red, white inscription and design, soft gray and pink accents, late 1960s ..... **18.00**
- Cubs/Frank Demaree, 4½" l, maroon, yellow inked inscriptions ........ **15.00**
- Detroit Tigers, 29½" l, felt, red, white lettering, gray accents, c1950 .... **18.00**
- Milwaukee Braves, 29" l, dark blue, white team name and illus, 1953–65 ........ **25.00**
- New York Mets, 29½" l, blue, white, and orange inscriptions and design, late 1960s ........ **15.00**
- Philadelphia Phillies, 11" l, green, "Fightin' Phillies" in white, gray and soft pink accents, yellow trim, early 1950s ........ **20.00**

Photograph
- 6 x 8½", black and white, 1940 Phillies team, imposed "Philadelphia National League Baseball Club" symbol on upper corner ........ **15.00**
- 8 x 10", black and white glossy, Carl Hubbell, black marker signature .. **25.00**

Pin, 1 x 2", St Louis Cardinals, metallic plastic, diecut, gold, red accent, 1950s ........ **25.00**

**Pinback Button, Los Angeles Dodgers, celluloid, blue lettering, white ground, blue and white ribbons, 1¾" d, $2.50.**

Pinback Button
- Braves, "Go Braves," Miller Beer adv **10.00**
- 1957 World Series, Braves vs Yankees **12.00**
- Official American League Ball, ⅞" d, celluloid, baseball shape, blue lettering, A J Reach Co, 1900–12 ... **15.00**
- Thurman Munson MVP 1976, 2¼" d, celluloid, blue tone photo, Badge–A–Minit issue ........ **15.00**
- Willie Stargell, Pittsburgh Pirates, 3½" d, celluloid, 1969–72 ........ **15.00**

Plate, Baseball's Hall of Fame, Staffordshire . . . . . **15.00**

Program

- All Star, 1960 . . . . . **35.00**
- Cleveland Indians and Boston Red Sox, 1955, 6 x 9" . . . . . **15.00**
- Philadelphia Athletics, 7 x 11", Aug 8, 1943, Philadelphia and New York Yankees . . . . . **25.00**
- Salute to Hank Aaron, Sept 17, 1976, Milwaukee County Stadium, 5½ x 8½" . . . . . **12.00**
- St Louis Cardinals, 1949 . . . . . **45.00**
- Washington vs Boston, "Buy War Bonds" on back, scorecard, unused **30.00**
- World Series, Cardinals and Yankees, 1942 . . . . . **75.00**

Roster, 3¾ x 7" folder, 1947 St Louis Browns, game schedule, team managers, and minor league clubs listed on back . . . . . **25.00**

Record, 33⅓ rpm, "Take Me Out To The Ball Game," "The Umpire," and "Casey At The Bat," Golden Record Extra Play, orig paper envelope . . . . . **45.00**

Salt and Pepper Shakers, pr, 4½" h, china, figural, baseball player, painted, inscribed on base "Cooperstown, NY" . . . . . **30.00**

Schedule, National and American League Home Games, 1941 . . . . . **15.00**

Scorebook, Cincinnati Reds, 1942, adv, illus of players . . . . . **25.00**

Score Counter, 2 x 3½", cardboard, paper dials, restaurant adv, 1920s . . . . **22.00**

Soap Bottle, 10½" h, "Let's Go Mets," plastic, figural, baseball player, late 1960s . . . . . **50.00**

Tumbler, 5" h, clear, dark red and white Major League teams pennants, weighted bottom, 1960s . . . . . **25.00**

Wristwatch, All–Star, chrome, baseball on dial with signatures, 1950s . . . . . **110.00**

Yearbook

- Brooklyn Dodgers, 1952, 8½ x 11", Big League Books . . . . . **75.00**
- *Famous Slugger Yearbook,* 4½ x 6½", 1940, Hillerich & Bradsby Co, Louisville, KY . . . . . **25.00**

Yo Yo, Philadelphia Phillies, figural, baseball . . . . . **20.00**

# BATTERY OPERATED AUTOMATA

**Collecting Hints:** Prices fluctuate greatly. Many of the collectors are in Japan and dealers must allow enough margin for shipment of pieces overseas. Operating condition is a key factor. Many pieces had accessory parts; these must be present to have full value. The original box, especially if it has a label, adds 10% to 20% to the price. Also, the more elaborate the action, the higher the value.

**History:** Battery operated automata began as "cheap" Japanese import goods in the 1950s. They were meant for amusement only, many finding themselves located on the shelves of bars in the recreation rooms of private homes. They were marketed through 5 and 10 cent stores and outlets.

The subjects were animals—bears being favored—and humans. Quality of pieces varies greatly, with Linemar being among the best made.

**References:** Don Hultzman, "Battery Operated Toys," in Richard O'Brien, *Collecting Toys, No. 6: A Collector's Identification & Value Guide,* Books Americana, 1993; Brian Moran, *Battery Toys,* Schiffer Publishing Ltd, 1984.

**Cymbal Plain' Turn-Over Monkey, TN, Japan, remote control, brown plush monkey, plastic face and ears, fabric costume, metal cymbals, 7¼" h, orig box, $135.00.**

Apollo–X Moon Challenger, orig box . **200.00**

Ball Playing Bear, 9" h, tin, celluloid head, balls, duck, and parasol, litho base, orig box, Japan . . . . . **750.00**

Barber Bear, 8" h, cutting baby bear's hair, orig box, TN, Japan . . . . . **1,525.00**

Bear, mama feeding baby . . . . . **100.00**

Beauty Parlor Bear, beautician combs baby bear's hair, litho base, orig base, S & E, Japan . . . . . **1,425.00**

Bimbo Drumming Clown, 10" h, remote control, cloth over tin, plays drum, orig box, Alps, Japan . . . . . **500.00**

Blacksmith Bear, 8″ h, plush bear, lighted anvil, litho tin base, orig box, Al, Japan . . . . . . . . **260.00**
Blinky the Clown, 10″ h, remote control, cloth over tin, plays xylophone, walks, orig box, Amico, Japan . . . . . **500.00**
Broadway Trolley, 1950s . . . . . . . . **110.00**
Busy Housekeeper Bear, 9″ h, plush over tin, lighted vacuum cleaner, orig box, Alps, Japan . . . . . . . . **300.00**
Buttons The Puppy with a Brain, 12″ h, plush, orig box, Marx, Japan . . . . . . . **425.00**
Captain Blushwell, orig box . . . . . . . . **175.00**
Charlie the Drumming Clown, 9″ h, celluloid head, plays drum set, orig box, Alps, Japan . . . . . . . . **220.00**
Charlie Weaver Bartender, orig box . . . **100.00**
Chef Cook, 10″ h, tin, orig box, Y, Japan **215.00**
Circus Elephant, 10″ h, plush over tin, litho base with clowns, orig box, TN, Japan . . . . . . . . **275.00**
Clancy, roller skating monkey, Ideal . . **100.00**
Coffeetime Bear, 10″ h, plush over tin bear, tin tree trunk and bread loaf, holding coffeepot and cup, orig box, TN, Japan . . . . . . . . **200.00**
Crying Baby Bess, Alps . . . . . . . . **40.00**
Dozo the Steaming Clown, 14″ h, sweeping broom, orig box, TN, Japan **300.00**
Drinking Captain, orig box . . . . . . . . **175.00**
Father Bear, 10″ h, plush bear, tin rocking chair, holding cup and book, orig box, MT, Japan . . . . . . . . **315.00**
Frankenstein, orig box . . . . . . . . **285.00**
Fred Flintstone's Bedrock Band, 9″ h, Hanna–Barbera, 1962, orig box, Alps, Japan . . . . . . . . **1,500.00**

**Gino Neapolitan Balloon Blower, Rosko Toy #110, Tomiyama, Japan, litho tin, plastic head and hands, orig box, 10″ h, $275.00.**

Friendly Jocko, 12″ h, , orig box, Alps, Japan . . . . . . . . **300.00**
Funland Locomotive, orig box . . . . . . . **110.00**
Go–Go Girl, orig box . . . . . . . . **65.00**
Grandpa Bear, orig box . . . . . . . . **225.00**
Happy Santa
10″ h, sitting on tin chimney, rings bell, stands up–sits down, orig box, Japan . . . . . . . . **400.00**
12″ h, remote control, cloth over tin, celluloid face, orig box, Alps, Japan **230.00**
Jaguar, stunt car, orig box, Japanese . . **275.00**
Jocko the Drinking Monkey, 12″ h, holding bottle and glass, orig box, Linemar, Japan . . . . . . . . **150.00**
Jolly Bear, 7″ h, remote control, tin, plays drum, orig box, K, Japan . . . . . **200.00**
Jolly Chimp, musical, orig box . . . . . . . **90.00**
Jolly Santa on Snow, 12″ h, remote control, tin skis, orig box, Alps, Japan . . **275.00**
Jumbo the Bubble Blowing Elephant, 8″ h, plush over tin, pink elephant, cup, instructions, and bubble solution, orig box, Y, Japan . . . . . . . . **130.00**
Jumping Spaniel, frisky, orig box . . . . . **65.00**
Knitting Bear, orig box . . . . . . . . **295.00**
Mac the Turtle, 9″ h, pushes tin whiskey barrel, orig box, Y, Japan . . . . . . . . **240.00**
Magic Man, 11″ h, remote control, clown, tin face, cloth costume, orig box, MM, Japan . . . . . . . . **315.00**
McGregor, orig box . . . . . . . . **100.00**
Mickey the Magician, 10″ h, tin, black cloth cape, holding wand and top hat, orig box, Linemar, Japan . . . . . . . . **2,475.00**
Mighty Mike, 11″ h, plush bear, lifts barbells, orig box, K, Japan . . . . . . . . **350.00**
Mr Fox the Magician, 10″ h, tin, orig box, Y, Japan . . . . . . . . **650.00**
Monkey on a Picnic, 10″ h, plush and cloth, holding banana and orange juice, orig box, Alps, Japan . . . . . . . . **435.00**
Musical Clown, 9″ l, cloth over tin, vinyl head, litho tin base, plays xylophone, TN, Japan . . . . . . . . **750.00**
Picnic Bear, orig box . . . . . . . . **170.00**
Picnic Bunny, 10″ h, plush, pours carrot juice into egg cup, orig box, Alps, Japan . . . . . . . . **100.00**
Pierrot Monkey Cycle, 10″ h, tin, clown with vinyl head, monkey on back, tin car, orig box, MT, Japan . . . . . . . . **530.00**
Piggy Cook, 11″ h, vinyl and cloth, tin stove, orig box, Y, Japan . . . . . . . . **240.00**
Pirate Ship, 13″ l, tin, heavy paper sails, orig box, MT, Japan . . . . . . . . **425.00**
Police Car, 8″ l, 56 Chevrolet, tin, Marline, Japanese . . . . . . . . **175.00**
Pretty Peggy Parrot, 11″ h, plush, hanging tin perch, orig box, Japan . . . . . . **250.00**
Professor Owl, 8″ h, tin, orig box, Y, Japan . . . . . . . . **450.00**

Sammy Wong the Tea Totaler, 10" h, litho tin table, holding teapot and cup, orig box, TN, Japan .......... **340.00**
Santa Claus, 7" h, cloth, vinyl face, rings bell, waves candy cane, orig box, Alps, Japan ...................... **65.00**
Shoeshine Bear, 9" h, plush, smokes pipe, orig box, TN, Japan ......... **200.00**
Skipping Monkey, orig box .......... **80.00**
Sleeping Baby Bear, 9" l, tin, bed with clock, orig box, Linemar, Japan .... **350.00**
Smoking and Shoe Shining Panda Bear, 10" h, orig box, Alps, Japan ....... **250.00**
Smoking Grandpa, orig box ......... **275.00**
Smoking Papa Bear, 9" h, remote control, plush over tin, orig box, Amico, Japan .......................... **125.00**
Sneezing Bear, 10" h, plush, Linemar, Japan .......................... **180.00**
Snoopy, orig box .................. **85.00**
Talking Parrot, 14" h, plush, tin perch, Marx, Japan .................... **365.00**
Teddy the Artist, 9" h, draws pictures, templates, instructions, crayon, animal pictures, and paper tablet, orig box, Y, Japan ................... **600.00**
Traveler Bear, 9" h, remote control, plush over tin, holding suitcase and cane, orig box, K, Japan .......... **440.00**
Turn–Over Monkey, orig box ........ **75.00**
Yo–Yo Clown, 10" h, cloth over tin, vinyl face, orig box, S & E, Japan .... **360.00**

# BAUER POTTERY

**Collecting Hints:** The key is to focus on highly stylistic, designer forms. Bauer pieces range from Art Deco to Streamlined Modern. Interest in utilitarian redware and stoneware pieces is minimal.

Remember that jiggered and cast production was done in quantity. Hand–thrown pieces by Matt Carlton and Fred Johnson were done in limited quantity. Unfortunately, these pieces are not marked. Learn to identify them by studying photographs of known examples. Among the more desirable shapes are oil jars, with prices increasing as the jar becomes taller.

In the dinnerware patterns some colors are more highly prized than others. Burgundy, orange red, and white are premium colors in all patterns.

**History:** In 1885 John Bauer founded the Paducah Pottery, Paducah, Kentucky, to manufacture stoneware and earthenware utilitarian pieces such as crocks and jugs. Bauer died in 1898. John Andrew Bauer continued the business in Paducah until 1909, at which time the plant was moved to Los Angeles, California.

Bauer's initial California production consisted of redware flowerpots. Stoneware production did not resume immediately because of the difficulty of locating suitable stoneware clay. Utilitarian ware such as bean pots and mixing bowls remained a company staple.

In 1913 Matt Carlton, an Arkansas potter, and Louis Ipsen, a Danish designer, developed an artware line of glazed bowls, jardinieres, and vases. The company won a bronze medal at the Panama–California Exposition of 1915–16. Within a short period, the firm's artware line was replaced by a line of molded stoneware vases.

In 1922 John Andrew Bauer died. Just prior to his death, he established a partnership with Watson E. Brockmon, his son–in–law. The firm prospered under Brockmon's leadership.

In the early 1930s Bauer introduced a line of popular dinnerware designed by Ipsen and covered with glazes developed by Victor Houser, a ceramic engineer. In 1931 "ring" ware was introduced to contrast with the plain ware of a year earlier. Over a hundred different shapes and sizes were manufactured in table and kitchen lines. Among the more successful tableware lines are Brusche Contempo (1948–61), La Linda (1939–59), Monterey (1936–45), and Monterey Moderne (1948–1961). Ipsen's Aladdin teapot design was part of the Glass Pastel Kitchenware series.

The company continued operations during World War II, reformulating the glazes to correspond to wartime restrictions on some materials. Wheel-thrown artware featuring the work of Carlton and Fred Johnson was made. Cast forms were kept in production during the 1930s and 1940s. Tracy Irwin, a designer, developed a modern line of floral containers.

Following the war, the company faced stiff competition both in the national and California markets. A bitter strike in 1961 signaled the end. In 1962 W. E. Brockmon's widow closed the plant.

**References:** Jack Chipman, *Collector's Encyclopedia of California Pottery,* Collector Books, 1992; Lois Lehner, *Lehner's Encyclopedia of U. S. Marks on Pottery, Porcelain & Clay,* Collector Books, 1988.

**GLOSS PASTEL KITCHENWARE.** Introduced in 1942. Wide ribbed pattern available in both a matte and a glossy finish. Matte colors include Blue, Dusty Pink, Green, and Ivory. Glossy colors are Burgundy, Chartreuse, Dark Brown, Light Brown, Gray, Green, Ivory, Olive Green, Pink, Turquoise, and Yellow.

Batter Bowl, 2 quart, Ivory .......... **40.00**
Mixing Bowl, #18, Chartreuse ....... **24.00**
Pitcher, 1 quart, Green .............. **32.00**
Teapot, Aladdin, cov
 4 cup, Ivory ..................... **45.00**
 8 cup, Burgundy ................. **65.00**

**LA LINDA.** Dinnerware line produced from 1939 until 1959. Blue, Burgundy, Chartreuse, Dark and Light Brown, Gray, Green, Ivory, Olive Green, Pink, Turquoise, and Yellow are featured colors.

Ball Jug, Gray ..................... **45.00**
Cup and Saucer, Green ............. **20.00**
Custard, Turquoise ................. **8.00**
Plate
  6″ d, bread and butter, Ivory ....... **6.00**
  7½″ d, salad, Green .............. **10.00**
  9″ d, dinner, Chartreuse ........... **15.00**
Platter, oval, 12″ l, Yellow ........... **20.00**
Vegetable Dish, oval, 10″ l, Ivory .... **28.00**

**MONTEREY.** Line of dinnerware produced from 1936 until 1945. Burgundy, Green, Ivory, Monterey Blue, Orange–red, Red–brown, Turquoise Blue, White, and Yellow are featured colors.

Cake Plate, pedestal base, Orange–red **100.00**
Chop Plate, 13″ d, Monterey Blue .... **35.00**
Creamer and Sugar, individual, Ivory . **38.00**
Pitcher, 2 quart, Yellow ............. **40.00**
Plate
  6″ d, bread and butter, Turquoise Blue **10.00**
  10½″ d, dinner, Orange–red ....... **30.00**
Platter, oval, 12″ l, Ivory ............ **32.00**
Vegetable Bowl, oval, divided, Green . **45.00**

**RING.** Introduced in 1931. Original colors consisted of Black, Burgundy, Light and Dark Blue, Green, Ivory, Orange–red, White, and Yellow. Due to government restrictions during World War II, some glazes were either reformulated or replaced with pastel colors.

Ball Jug, Orange–red ............... **75.00**
Batter Jug, cov, Dark Blue ........... **95.00**
Berry Bowl, Yellow ................. **12.00**
Bowl, 14″ d, Green ................. **165.00**
Casserole, cov
  4¾″ d, individual, Green .......... **35.00**
  7½″ d, Ivory .................... **50.00**
Cereal Bowl, Dark Blue ............. **15.00**
Cookie Jar, cov, Orange–red ......... **125.00**
Creamer and Sugar, cov, Light Blue ... **35.00**
Cup and Saucer, Burgundy .......... **20.00**
Custard Cup, Black ................. **20.00**
Mustard Jar, cov, Ivory .............. **75.00**
Plate
  6″ d, bread and butter, Yellow ..... **10.00**
  7½″ d, salad, Light Blue .......... **15.00**
  10″ d, dinner, Orange–red ......... **25.00**
Soup Bowl, 7½″ d, Burgundy ........ **25.00**
Stack Set, cov, set of three, Orange–red, Green, and Yellow ............... **100.00**
Teapot, 6 cup, wood handle, Orange–red ............................ **60.00**
Vase, 6″ h, Green .................. **35.00**

# BEATLES

**Collecting Hints:** Beatles' collectibles date from 1964 to the present. The majority of memorabilia items were produced from 1964–68. The most valuable items are marked "NEMS." Most collectors are interested in mint or near mint items only. Some items in very good condition, especially if scarce, have considerable value as well.

Each year Sotheby's holds one or two auctions which include Beatles' memorabilia, primarily one of a kind items such as guitars and stage costumes. These items command high prices. The "average" collector generally does not participate.

**History:** The fascination with the Beatles began in 1964. Soon the whole country was caught up in Beatlemania. The members of the group included John Lennon, Paul McCartney, George Harrison and Ringo Starr. The group broke up in 1970. After this date, the members pursued their individual musical careers. Beatlemania took on new life after the death of John Lennon.

**References:** Jeff Augsburger, Marty Eck, and Rick Rann, *The Beatles Memorabilia Price Guide, Second Edition,* Wallace–Homestead, 1993; Barbara Fenick, *Collecting The Beatles, An Introduction and Price Guide to Fab Four Collectibles, Records and Memorabilia, Volume 1* (1984) and *Volume 2* (1988), Pierian Press; Norman E. Martinus and Harry L. Rinker, *Warman's Paper,* Wallace–Homestead, 1993; Jerry Osborne, Perry Cox, and Joe Lindsay, *The Official Price Guide To Memorabilia of Elvis Presley And The Beatles,* House of Collectibles, 1988; Michael Stern, Barbara Crawford, and Hollis Lamon, *The Beatles,* Collector Books, 1993.

**Periodicals:** *Beatlefan,* P. O. Box 33515, Decatur, GA 30033; *Good Day Sunshine,* 397 Edgewood Avenue, New Haven, CT 06511.

**Collectors' Clubs:** Beatles Fan Club of Great Britain, Superstore Productions, 123 Marina, St Leonards on Sea, East Sussex, England TN 38 OBN; Working Hero Club, 3311 Niagara St., Pittsburgh, PA 15213.

**REPRODUCTION ALERT:** Records, picture sleeves, and album jackets have been counterfeited. Sound quality may be inferior. Printing on labels and picture jackets usually is inferior to the original. Many pieces of memorabilia also have been reproduced, often with some change in size, color, design, etc.

Bag, 9½ x 14½″, translucent plastic, color illus, orig blue drawstring and instruction sheet, marked "Made in Japan," c1964 ................... **200.00**
Book
  *A Hard Day's Night,* Chelsea House, 1977, 300 pgs, dj ............. **20.00**

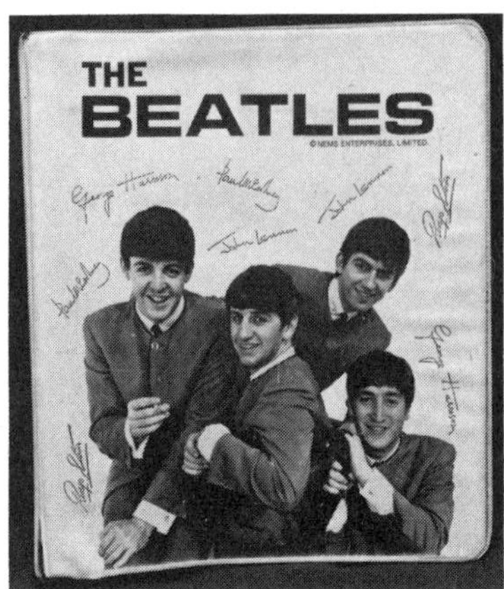


**Notebook, white ground, black lettering, sepia figures, NEMS Enterprises, $35.00.**

*The Beatles Yellow Submarine,* Signet Books, copyright 1968 King Features Syndicate, 128 pgs ........ **25.00**

Christmas Ornament, set of 4, 6″ h, glass, hollow, orig box marked "Made In Italy", c1964 ........... **700.00**

Comb, pink ...................... **48.00**

Cosmetic Bag, 4 x 7″, vinyl, zipper top, white, black illus, c1964 .......... **225.00**

Doll, 4½″ h, vinyl, Paul McCartney, Remco, 1964 Nems Enterprises Ltd copyright ...................... **75.00**

Figure, set of 4, 4″ h, plastic, gold painted molded base, movable head, marked "Made in Hong Kong," c1960 ...................... **50.00**

Flag, 8 x 10″, rayon, blue and white, LTE, 1960s ...................... **75.00**

Game, The Beatles Flip Your Wig Game, playing board with color photo, diecut playing pieces, orig box, Milton Bradley, copyright 1964 Nems Enterprises Ltd ............. **100.00**

Glass, 5½″ h, clear, black and white lettering and illus, c1964 .......... **75.00**

Guitar, 23″ h, hard plastic, orange and cream, black and orange illus and signatures, marked "Beatles New Sound Guitar/Selcol Products Ltd/Made In England Under License," c1964 .... **250.00**

Handbag, 10″ sq, vinyl, dark blue, cloth lined, built–in brass handles and name, white illus and signatures, zipper compartment, 1964 ........... **150.00**

Headband, 6″ l, stretch nylon, white, red and black lettering, hearts, and musical notes, orig plastic bag, copyright Sealtaeb Inc, c1964 .......... **55.00**

Lunch Box, Yellow Submarine, metal, color illus, King–Seeley Thermos Co, copyright 1968 King Features Syndicate ...................... **200.00**

Magazine

*All About The Beatles,* 8½ x 11″, YOPU Press Inc, copyright 1964 . **18.00**

*Aquarian Weekly,* Dec 2, 1970 ..... **10.00**

*Look,* January, 1968, Beatles pull out, John Lennon on cov ............ **75.00**

*16 Magazine,* Beatles Whole True Story, 8½ x 11″, published by Sixteen Magazine Inc, copyright 1966 **15.00**

*The Beatles USA,* Jamie Publications, 11 x 14″, 16 pgs, 1964 copyright . **25.00**

Magnet Set, set of 4, figural head, marked "Hong Kong" ............ **75.00**

Mask, 10″ h, George Harrison, plastic, molded, flocked black hair and eyebrows, c1960 .................... **50.00**

Mirror, pocket ..................... **65.00**

Model Kit, Yellow Submarine, orig box, 1968 ........................... **235.00**

Mug, 4″ h, ceramic, white, black, white, and blue photo, "England" imprint on bottom, c1964 ........... **75.00**

Patch, 2″ l, oval, cloth, embroidered, black, yellow lettering and border, c1970 ........................ **15.00**

Pin, 4″ l, plastic, guitar shape, gold accents, brown tone photo, 1964 .... **45.00**

Pinback Button

3½″ d, "The Beatles," black and white photo, c1965 ............ **50.00**

4″ d, "I'm A Beatles Fan," black and white photo, red and white background, marked "Green Duck Co," 1964 Nems Enterprises Ltd copyright ........................ **30.00**

Plate, 7″ d, ceramic, black, white, and blue photo, c1964 ............... **50.00**

Poster

19 x 28″, "Paul McCartney Wings Over America," June 13–14, 1976 concert, Cow Palace, San Francisco ........................ **50.00**

22 x 31″, John Lennon, glossy, psychedelic image, marked "John Lennon Photographed by Richard Avedon For Look Magazine," 1967 Nems Enterprises Ltd copyright ... **18.00**

22½ x 28½″, black, Beatles seated on motorcycles, Stanley Mouse ..... **10.00**

Program, souvenir, 1966 ............ **45.00**

Punch–Out Book, *The Beatles Yellow Submarine,* 8 pop–out pgs, unused, copyright 1968 King Features ...... **25.00**

Purse, 6 x 9½″, vinyl, blue, zipper top, orig strap handle, front illus and signatures, 1964 .................... **200.00**

Puzzle, The Beatles Yellow Submarine, Jaymar, 1968 King Features Syndicate **18.00**

Radio, 4 x 5″, plastic Lennon figure on black base with raised gold lettering

"John Lennon 1940–1980," orig box, marked "Hong Kong" ........... **40.00**
Record
*Hey Jude*, Capitol, 1978, purple label **8.00**
*Let It Be*, Apple, 1970 ........... **12.00**
*Magical Mystery Tour*, Apple, 1971 . **15.00**
*Please, Please Me*, Vee Jay, 1964, white label .................... **50.00**
*She Loves You*, Swan, 1963 ........ **125.00**
Record Case, 7½" d, 6¾" h, plastic, brown, holds 45 rpm records, black illus on front, white carrying handle, Charter Industries Inc, copyright 1966 Nems Enterprises Ltd ............ **150.00**
Record Player, 17½ x 10 x 6", wood, blue vinyl covering, black plastic carrying handle, color photo label on lid int., Nems Enterprises Ltd, London copyright, c1964 ................**1,500.00**
Scarf, 26" sq, synthetic fabric, large Beatle images, guitar and drum border, c1964 ......................... **200.00**
Sheet Music, Yesterday, 8½ x 11", 3 pgs, Paul photo on front cov, copyright 1965 Northern Songs Ltd .......... **12.00**
Soaky Bottle, 9½" h, Paul McCartney, plastic, copyright 1965 Nems Enterprises Ltd ...................... **75.00**
Switchplate Cover, 6 x 11½", Yellow Submarine, cardboard, day–glo illus, orig cellophane package, Dal Mfg Corp, copyright 1968 King Features Syndicate Subafilms Ltd ........... **55.00**
Tin, 7" h, talcum powder, black and white photos front and back, orig contents, marked "With The Beatles Talc Margo Or Mayfair" and "Manufactured in Great Britain by SM Ltd," 1960s ......................... **125.00**
T–Shirt, white cotton, three buttons, blue trim, portrait illus, size large, orig tag, copyright Nems Enterprises Ltd, c1964 ..................... **200.00**
Vest, vinyl, size medium ............ **200.00**
Wall Paper, 21 x 21", color photos, black signatures, unused, c1964 ... **40.00**
Wall Plaque, 9 x 20", cardboard, Yellow Submarine, blue glove illus, diecut hanging hole, copyright King Features Syndicate Subafilms Ltd, c1968 .... **75.00**

# BEER BOTTLES

**Collecting Hints:** Beer bottles often are found by digging in old dumps or wells. When found, these bottles may have discolored and flaked. However, the key is whether the bottle remains unbroken or not. Damage to the bottle is of greater concern in pricing than the discoloration.

Concentrate on the bottles from one brewery or area. When an example is brought back to an area of its origin, it is likely to command more money than when sold outside the local region. A brewery is likely to change its bottle style several times in the course of its history. This also is true for the paper label designs found on later bottles.

The early bottles had special closures. The bottle is worth more if the closure is intact. The metal caps are not critical to the value of later bottles. However, an active collecting interest in metal caps is growing, as witnessed by dealer displays at several recent beer collector shows.

**History:** Breweries began in America shortly after the arrival of the first settlers. By the mid–19th century most farmsteads had a small brewery on them. Local breweries dominated the market until the arrival of Prohibition. A few larger breweries were able to adjust, but the majority closed.

When Prohibition ended, a much smaller number of local breweries renewed production. The advertising, distribution, and production costs of the 1950s and 1960s led to the closing of most local breweries and the merger of many other breweries into a few nationally oriented companies.

In the 1960s imported beers from Europe entered the American market. Some companies signed licensing agreements to produce these foreign labels in the United States. The 1980s have witnessed the growing popularity of beers brewed in Canada and Mexico.

**References:** Ralph and Terry Kovel, *The Kovels' Bottle List, 9th Edition,* Crown Publishers, 1992; Jim Megura, *The Official Price Guide to Bottles, Eleventh Edition,* House of Collectibles, 1991; Carlo and Dorothy Sellari, *The Standard Old Bottle Price Guide,* Collector Books, 1989.

**Collectors' Club:** American Breweriana Association, Inc., P. O. Box 11157, Pueblo, CO 81001.

Embossed
Buffalo Brewing Co, Sacramento, CA, emb buffalo jumping through horseshoe, amber, blob top, 12" h ........................ **18.00**
Callie & Co Limited, emb dog's head, St Helens below center, dark green, ring type blob top, 8¼" h ....... **15.00**
Chattachoochee Brewing Co, Brownsville, AL, aqua, 9½" h .... **8.00**
Cumberland Brew Co, Cumberland, MD, amber ................... **8.00**
Excelsior, aqua, 9¼" h ........... **15.00**
Frank Steil Brewing Co, green, 12 oz **4.00**
Germania Brewing Co, aqua, 7½" h **12.00**
Hand Brew Co, Pawtucket, RI, aqua **12.00**
Hinckel Brew Co, Albany, Boston, Manchester, fancy, amber, blob top **15.00**
Iroquois, Buffalo, Indian head, amber **10.00**

McCormick Brewery, 1897, Boston, clear .......... **10.00**
National Brewing Co, Baltimore, eagle, amber, blob top .......... **17.50**
Piel Bros, East New York Brewery, fancy logo, aqua .......... **15.00**
Royal Ruby, ABM, 9½″ h .......... **18.00**
Trommer's Evergreen Brewery, aqua, 9¼″ h .......... **7.50**

Painted Label
Augusta Brewing Co, Augusta, GA, aqua, 7″ h .......... **12.00**
Camden City Brewery, amber, 9″ h . **9.00**
Cock n' Bull Ginger Beer, crown top, 7″ h .......... **4.00**
Gutsch Brew, red, 8½″ h .......... **15.00**
Rolling Rock Extra Pale, blue and white label, green bottle, unopened **15.00**
Schlitz Brewing Co, amber, 9½″ h .. **8.00**

**Painted Label, Old Reading Brewery, Inc., 8 oz, $6.00.**

Paper Label
Bushkill, cap, brown, 12 oz .......... **5.00**
Central Brand Extra Lager Beer, aqua, 9¼″ h .......... **5.00**
Cooks 500 Ale, aqua, 9½″ h .......... **3.50**
Diamond Jim's Beer, aqua, 9¼″ h .. **5.00**
Grand Prize Beer, Gulf Brewing Co, Houston, clear, crown top, 9″ h .. **7.50**
Mineral Spring Beer, aqua, 9″ h .... **5.00**
Old Reading, metal cap, brown, 12 oz .......... **3.00**
Pabst Extract, amber, two labels .... **8.00**
Pilsner, cap, brown, 12 oz .......... **4.00**
Schells Beer, Schells Brewing Co, amber, 9½″ h .......... **3.50**
Southern Brewing Co, machine made, green, 9½″ h .......... **2.50**
Utica Club, metal cap, brown, 12 oz **3.00**

Stoneware
Biscombe's, brown and tan, 8½″ h . **9.00**
Ginger Beer, c1915 .......... **35.00**
Pink's Ltd, Chichester, Ginger Beer, c1920, 7″ h .......... **5.00**

# BEER CANS

**Collecting Hints:** Rusted and dented cans have little value unless they are rare. Most collectors remove the beer from the cans. Cans should be opened from the bottom to preserve the top unopened.

As beer can collecting became popular, companies issued special collectors' cans which never contained beer. Many were bought on speculation; value has been shaky.

**History:** Before Prohibition, beer was stored and shipped in kegs and dispensed in returnable bottles. When the Prohibition Act was repealed in 1933, only 700 of 1700 breweries resumed operation. Expanding distribution created the need for an inexpensive container that would permit beer to be stored longer and shipped safely. Cans were the answer.

The first patent for a lined can was issued to the American Can Co. on Sept. 25, 1934, for their "Keglined" process. Gotfried Kruger Brewing Co., Newark, New Jersey, was the first brewery to use the can. Pabst was the first major company to join the canned beer movement.

Continental Can Co. introduced the conetop beer can in 1935. Schlitz was the first brewery to use this type of can. The next major change in beer can design was the aluminum pop–top in 1962.

**References:** House of Collectibles, *The Official Price Guide To Beer Cans & Collectibles, Fourth Edition,* House of Collectibles, 1986; Thomas Toepfer, *American Beer Can Encyclopedia,* Collector Books, 1983–84 edition, out-of-print.

**Collectors' Club:** Beer Can Collectors of America, 747 Merus Court, Fenton, MO 63026.

**Note:** The listings are the name, type of beer, brewery location, top identification, price. The following abbreviations are used in the listings:
CR—Crowntainer type cone top
CT—cone type
FT—flat top
PT—pull top
ML—malt liquor

Ace Hi ML, Ace, Chicago, IL, FT, 7 oz **100.00**
Aero Club Pale Select, East Idaho, Pocatello, ID, CT, 12 oz .......... **90.00**
Altes, National, Detroit, MI, PT, 15 oz **5.00**
American Dry, Eastern, Hammonton, NJ, FT, 12 oz .......... **60.00**
Ballantine Ale, Ballantine, Newark, NJ, PT, 12 oz .......... **4.00**
Bantam, Goebel, Detroit, MI, FT, 8 oz **25.00**

Berghoff 1887, Berghoff, Ft Wayne, IN, PT, red, gold, and white, 16 oz .... **18.00**
Blackhawk Topping, Cumberland, Cumberland, MD, CT, 12 oz ...... **95.00**
Breunig's Lager, Rice Lake, Rice Lake, WI, CT, 12 oz .................. **50.00**
Brown Derby, Maier, Los Angeles, CA, PT, 12 oz ...................... **3.50**
Busch Lager, Anheuser–Busch, St Louis, MO, FT, 12 oz .................. **65.00**
Champagne Velvet, Associated, three cities, PT, 15 oz ................. **10.00**
Chief Oshkosh, Oshkosh, Oshkosh, WI, FT, 10 oz ...................... **10.00**
Clyde Cream Ale, Enterprise, Fall River, MA, CT, orig cap, 1920s .......... **150.00**
Colorado Imperial, Walter, Pueblo, CO, PT, 12 oz ...................... **15.00**
Colt 45 ML, National, Baltimore, MD, PT, 10 oz ...................... **8.00**
Country Club, Pearl, two cities, PT, 8 oz ............................ **3.00**
Crown Darby, Westminister, Chicago, IL, FT, 10 oz .................... **200.00**
Dawson Lager, Dawson, Hammonton, NJ, PT, 10 oz ................... **2.00**
Duquesne Pilsner, Duquesne, Pittsburgh, PA, CT, 12 oz ............ **40.00**
Eastside Old Tap, Pabst, Los Angeles, CA, FT, 10 oz .................. **10.00**
Falls City, Falls City, Louisville, KY, FT, 10 oz .......................... **9.00**
Fisher's Ale, Queen City, Cumberland, MD, FT, red, blue, and white, 12 oz **30.00**
Fitger's, Fitger, Duluth, MN, PT, 12 oz **10.00**
Gablinger's, Forrest, New Bedford, MA, PT, 10 oz ...................... **4.50**
Grace Brothers, Bavarian, Maier, Los Angeles, CA, PT, 16 oz .......... **35.00**
Grain Belt, Grain Belt, Minneapolis, MN, FT, brown, gold, and white, 12 oz ............................ **6.00**
Grand Prize, Gulf, Houston, TX, FT, blue and silver, 12 oz ............ **35.00**
Great Falls Select, Great Falls, Great Falls, MT, FT, 10 oz ............. **15.00**
Haas Pilsner, Haas, Houghton, MI, CT, 12 oz .......................... **70.00**
Hamm's Draft, Hamm, three cities, PT, 15 oz .......................... **3.00**
Hapsburg Brand, Best, Chicago, IL, FT, 12 oz .......................... **35.00**
Heritage House, Pittsburgh, Pittsburgh, PA, PT, 12 oz .................... **3.50**
Holiday Bock, Holiday, Potosi, WI, PT, 12 oz .......................... **9.00**
Horlacher Pilsner, Horlacher, Allentown, PA, FT, 10 oz ............. **9.00**
Iroquois Draft, Iroquois, Buffalo, NY, PT, 12 oz .......................... **5.00**
Kentucky ML, Fehr, Louisville, KY, FT, 10 oz .......................... **35.00**

**World's Fair Beer, Great Lakes Brewery Co., Ft. Wayne, IN, 12 oz, $10.00.**

Krueger Pilsner, Krueger, Cranston, RI, PT, 12 oz ...................... **12.00**
Land of Lakes, Pilsen, Chicago, FT, 12 oz ............................ **20.00**
Lucky Lager, Lucky Lager, San Francisco, CA, FT, 7 oz .............. **10.00**
Manheim, Reading, Reading, PA, FT, 10 oz ............................ **8.00**
Menominee Champion, Menominee–Marinette, Menominee, MI, CT, 12 oz **50.00**
Mustang Malt Lager, Pittsburgh, Pittsburgh, PA, PT, 15 oz ............ **25.00**
National Bohemian, National, Detroit, MI, FT, 10 oz ................... **10.00**
Neuweiler, Neuweiler, Allentown, PA, FT, 8 oz ......................... **15.00**
Old Export, Cumberland, Cumberland, MD, CT, white and gold, 12 oz .... **85.00**
Olympia Light, Olympia, Olympia, WA, PT, 7 oz ...................... **3.50**
Pearl Light, Pearl, San Antonio, TX, PT, brown, red, and white, 12 oz ...... **4.00**
Piels Draft Ale, Piel, Willimansett, MA, PT, 10 oz ...................... **48.00**
Pike's Peak ML, Walter, Pueblo, CO, FT, 8 oz .......................... **40.00**
Primo, Schlitz, Honolulu, HI, PT, 12 oz **4.00**
Regal, American, New Orleans, LA, PT, blue, gold, and white, 16 oz ...... **4.00**
Rolling Rock, Latrobe, PA, PT, 12 oz .. **1.00**
Royal Amber, Heileman, four cities, PT, 10 oz .......................... **1.00**
Schlitz Light, Schlitz, six cities, PT, 10 oz ............................ **1.00**
Shell's City, S C Brewery, Miami, FL, PT, 12 oz .......................... **30.00**
Stag Premium Dry, Griesedieck–Western, two cities, CT, 12 oz ......... **20.00**
Sterling Draft, Sterling, Evansville, IN, PT, 15 oz ...................... **15.00**

Storz, Storz, Omaha, NB, FT, red, gold, and white, 12 oz . . . . . . . . . . . . . . . . . **12.00**
Tavern Pale, Atlantic, Chicago, IL, FT, 10 oz . . . . . . . . . . . . . . . . . . . . . . . . . . **20.00**
Tech Premium, Pittsburgh, Pittsburgh, PA, FT, 8 oz . . . . . . . . . . . . . . . . . . . . . **50.00**
Topper, Eastern, Hammonton, NJ, PT, 10 oz . . . . . . . . . . . . . . . . . . . . . . . . . . **1.50**
Tudor Ale, Metropolis, New York, NY, FT, green and white, 12 oz . . . . . . . . **15.00**
Valley Forge, Valley Forge, Norristown, PA, FT, 10 oz . . . . . . . . . . . . . . . . . . . . **15.00**
West Virginia Pilsner, Little Switzerland, Huntington, WV, PT, 10 oz . . . . . . . . **3.50**
Whale's White Ale, National, four cities, PT, 15 oz . . . . . . . . . . . . . . . . . . . . **25.00**
Ye Tavern, Lafayette, Lafayette, IN, CT, 12 oz . . . . . . . . . . . . . . . . . . . . . . . . . . **90.00**
Yuengling, Yuengling, Pottsville, PA, PT, 10 oz . . . . . . . . . . . . . . . . . . . . . . . . . . **4.00**

# BICYCLES

**Collecting Hints:** Collectors divide bicycles into two groups–antique and classic. The antique category covers early high wheelers through safety bikes made into the 1920s and 1930s. Highly stylized bicycles from the 1930s and 1940s represent the transitional step to the classic period, beginning in the late 1940s and running through the end of the balloon tire era.

Unfortunately there are no reliable guide books for the beginning collector. A good rule is that any older bike in good condition is worth collecting.

Never pay much for a bicycle that is rusted, incomplete, or repaired with non–original parts. Replacement of leather seats or rubber handlebars does not affect value since these have a short lifetime.

Restoration is an accepted practice. Make certain to store an old bicycle high (hung by its frame to protect the tires) and dry (no more than 50% humidity).

Do not forget all the secondary material, e.g., advertising premiums, brochures, catalogs, posters, etc. that featured the bicycle. This material provides important historical data for research, especially for restoration.

Bicycle collectors and dealers gather each year on the last weekend in April at the Saline/Ann Arbor Swap Meet and Show.

**History:** In 1818 Baron Karl von Drais, a German, invented the Draisienne, a push scooter, that is viewed as the "first" bicycle. In 1839 Patrick MacMillan, a Scot, added a treadle system; a few years later Pierre Michaux, a Frenchman, revolutionized the design by adding a pedal system. The bicycle was introduced in America at the 1876 Centennial.

Early bicycles were high wheelers with a heavy iron frame and two disportionately sized wheels with wooden rims and tires. The exaggerated front wheel was for speed, the small rear wheel for balance.

James Starley, an Englishman, is responsible for developing a bicycle with two wheels of equal size. Pedals drove the rear wheels by means of a chain and sprocket. By 1892 the wooden rim wheel was replaced by pneumatic air–filled tires to be followed by the standard rubber tire with inner tube.

1898 witnessed the development of the coaster brake. This important milestone made cycling a true family sport. Bicycling became a favorite activity among the urban middle class. As the new century dawned, over four million Americans owned bicycles.

The automobile challenged the popularity of bicycling beginning in the 1920s. Since that time, interest in bicycling has been cyclical. Technical advances continued. The 1970s was the decade of the ten speed.

The success of American Olympiads in cycling and cycle racing, especially the Tour de France, have kept the public's attention focused on the bicycle. However, the tremendous resurgence enjoyed by bicycling in the 1970s appears to have ended. The next craze is probably some distance in the future.

**References:** Frederick Alderson, *Bicycling: A History*, Praeger, 1972; A. Ritchie, *King Of The Road*, Ten Speed Press; Jim Hurd, *Introductory Guide to Collecting The Classics*, Antique/Classic Bicycle News, 1987; Jim Hurd, *1991 Bicycle Blue Book*, Antique/Classic Bicycle News, 1991.

**Periodicals:** *Antique/Classic Bicycle News*, P.O. Box 1049, Ann Arbor, MI 48106; *Bicycle Trader*, P. O. Box 5600, Pittsburgh, PA 15207.

**Collectors' Clubs:** Classic Bicycle and Whizzer Club, 35769 Simon, Fraser, MI 48026; The Wheelmen, 216 E. Sedgewick, Philadelphia, PA 19117.

**Museum:** Schwinn History Center, Chicago.

Advertising Trade Card, Clark Bicycle Co, Christmas, Santa on high wheeler, 1880s . . . . . . . . . . . . . . . . . . **24.00**
Badge
  1 x 1¼", bright brass, raised lion laying down against circular red enamel inset ground, inscribed "Phillips Cycles, Renowned The World Over," c1930, English . . . . . **25.00**
  1¼ x 1½", New Hampshire, brass, dark silver finish, two knights in armor riding single bicycle, 1895, back pin missing . . . . . . . . . . . . . . . **40.00**

1½ x 2", Century Run, sterling links, hanger bar with depiction of wooden fence, inscribed "New York to Islip & Return," profile portrait on pendant of bearded man, bicycle wheel with streamers, inscribed "September 30th, 1894" .. **85.00**

**Metal frame, wood spokes, c1870, $2,100.00. Photograph courtesy of Morton M. Goldberg Auction Galleries.**

Bicycle
- Columbia, boy's, "63," all orig .... **400.00**
- Comet, men's worn orig paint, coaster brake, aluminum fenders . **100.00**
- High Wheel, painted steel, rubber tires, 58" h .................. **1,300.00**
- Phantom, black, boy's ........... **1,475.00**
- Roadmaster, girl's, cream and blue, red pinstripe, horn tank, headlight, luggage carrier, chrome rims, orig condition .................... **175.00**
- Schwinn Jaguar Mark V, springer front, orig .................... **550.00**
- Victoria, #30, painted steel, wood rims and fenders, 38" h ......... **175.00**
- Ward Hawthorne, lady's, 1950s .... **750.00**

Bicycle Plate, 1¾ x 2¾", celluloid, curved, black and white portrait of McKinley, made by Baldwin & Gleason, 1896 ...................... **75.00**

Button Hook, ⅞" d celluloid, black and white, inscribed "Hunter Arms Co, Fulton, NY, Hunter Bicycles," hunting dog illus, brass button hook, early 1900s ......................... **45.00**

Catalog, Gardner Wire Co, Chicago, IL, "Mfgrs & Jobbers for Hardware, Cycle, & Furniture," black and white illus, 1930, 132 pgs, 6 x 9" ........ **30.00**

Charm, 1" h, brass, cross shape, center medallion, Phoenix-like bird rising from crown, "The Self–Oiling Racycle," and "Miami Cycle & Mfg Co" on front, name and Middletown, OH, location on back, late 1890s ....... **30.00**

Lapel Stud, advertising, c1896
- Brass, Gendron Bicycle, ⅞" d, diecut **18.00**
- Celluloid covered metal
  - American Traveler, ¾" d, red, white, and blue .............. **15.00**
  - Ariston Cycles, ⅞" d, blue and white, logo of Westboro, MA, bike maker .................. **20.00**
  - Buffalo Cycle Co, ¾" d, blue, white, and orange, buffalo logo, Envoy and Fleetwing lines ..... **18.00**
  - Chief Cycle, ⅞" d, purple and white, Indian chief symbol on bike wheel .................. **18.00**
  - Empire Cycles, ⅞" d, green, white lettering ..................... **12.00**
  - Fleetfoot, ¾" d, red, gold, and white, winged foot symbol, Imperial Cycle Co, Buffalo ....... **15.00**
  - Frontenac Bicycles, ⅞" d, black rim lettered in red, gold center inscribed "Syracuse Specialty Mfg Co" ....................... **12.00**
  - Hendees Silver King Bicycles, ⅞" d, silver blue, king figure on pedestal ....................... **15.00**
  - Henley Bicycles, ¾" d, yellow and orange ground, black lettering . **15.00**
  - Lenox, ⅞" d, blue and white, crisp red centered name, slogan "Second to None" .............. **15.00**
  - Majestic, ⅞" d, black lettering reads "Majestic, $85, Equal to $100 Value," soft pink background ...................... **15.00**
  - National Cycle, ¾" d, red, white, blue, and black, logo of Bay City, MI, maker .................. **15.00**
  - Phoenix, ¾" d, brown and red, mythological bird rising from ashes holding pair of bike wheels, slogan "Phoenix It Stands The Rackett" .......... **20.00**
  - Stearns Bicycle, ¾" d, red, white, and blue, US flag under slogan "Ride To The Front On A Stearns Bicycle" .................... **20.00**
  - Tanner Special, ⅞" d, purple and white, illus of bicycle, $85.00 under illus .................. **35.00**
  - The Majestic Bicycles, ⅞" d, purple and white .................. **15.00**
  - The Referee, ¾" d, blue and white, America's Cycle Journal ....... **18.00**
  - Zimmy Cycles, ¾" d, black, white, and orange .................. **15.00**

Light, Rowell & Hanmer, brass, carbide **100.00**

Matchsafe, metal, allover embossing,

high wheel bicycle with rider, Bryant & Mays Wax Vestas ............... **35.00**
Padlock, Slaymaker ................. **22.00**
Pencil Clip, ⅝" l, celluloid, silvered brass clip, Atherton Coaster Brake, black on white inscription, red border, early 1900s .................. **20.00**
Pin, figural
1¼ x 1½", advertising, brass, emb, figural, lantern with radiating light beam, inscribed "Search Light," 1890s ........................ **60.00**
2 x 2½" h, bright shell brass, mechanical, front and rear wheels move, high wheeler, rider, rhinestone accents missing, c1950 .... **20.00**
Pinback Button, advertising
American Traveler, ⅞" d, red, white, and blue, logo including handlebars, c1896 .................. **18.00**
Columbia Bicycles, ⅞" d, black and white, bicycle title plate which reads "You See Them Everywhere," c1896 ........................ **15.00**
Fowler Bicycle, ⅞" d, green, white lettering of anti–trust slogan ..... **10.00**
High Admiral Cigarettes, ⅞" d, black and white, League of American Wheelman symbol, c1896, solid filled back, embedded pin ....... **12.00**
6 to 1 Eclipse Bicycles, 1¼" d, red, white, and blue, adult riding bicycle, five youngsters balanced on it, slogan reads: "They Stand The Test, Made of the Best, Eclipse Riders Are Happy," c1898 ................ **45.00**
Poster, Cycle Trades of America
Do's & Don'ts For Bicycling Safety, c1940, 18½ x 24" ............. **12.00**
Rules of a Good Bicycle Rider, photo by Frank L Kramer, 17 x 22", black and white ..................... **15.00**
Seat, DeLuxe Messenger, leather, balloon tire type bicycle style ......... **25.00**
Sheet Music, Cyclists National Grand March, 10¼ x 14", four pages, 1897, blue photo cov of bicyclists and officials at starting line, illus ads for various bicycles and accessories ...... **20.00**
Stickpin
7/16", metal, rider hunched over bicycle, soft pink enamel cap and racing outfit, fleshtone enamel face, dark blue enamel spoke accents, 1890s ........................ **30.00**
13/16" h, rolled brass, monogram letter "S" in image of bicycle nameplate, inscribed "Acme Manufacturing Co, Stormer 1897," Reading, PA .......................... **30.00**
Tire, Schwinn, wide, wide sidewalls, knobby ......................... **15.00**
Tray, advertising, 3½ x 5", aluminum, portrait photos of C M Darling and C G Murphey, sign reads: "Around The United States By Wheel On A Cleveland," emb border pattern with inscription: "Members L.A.W./ Y.M.C.A./K.O.T.M.," underside printed with US tour schedule, 1904 **40.00**

# BIG LITTLE BOOKS

**Collecting Hints:** As more research is done and published on Big Little Books, the factors determining value shift. Condition always has been a key. Few examples are in pristine mint condition since the books were used heavily by the children who owned them. Each collector strives to obtain copies free from as many defects (bent edges on cover, missing spine, torn pages, mutilation with crayon or pencil, missing pages, etc.) as possible.

The main character in a book will determine price since it is a collector from another field who will vie with the Big Little Book collector for the same work. Dick Tracy, Disney characters, Buck Rogers, Flash Gordon, Charlie Chan, The Green Hornet and Tom Mix are examples. Other cowboy heroes are experiencing renewed popularity.

Until recently little attention has been directed to the artists who produced the books. Now examples by Alex Raymond and Henry Vallely command top dollar. Other desirable artists are Al Capp, Allen Dean, Alfred Andriola, and Will Gould. Personal taste still is a critical factor at this time.

Little is known as to how many copies of each book were printed. Scarcity charts have been prepared, but constantly are being revised. Books tend to hit the market in hoards, with prices fluctuating accordingly. However, the last decade has witnessed a stabilization of prices.

Larry Lowery, in the introduction to his book, has prepared an excellent section on the care and storage of Big Little Books. He also deserves credit for the detailed research which he has brought to each listing.

**History:** Big Little Books, although a trademark of the Whitman Publishing Co., is a term used to describe a wealth of children's books published during the 1930s and continuing to the present day. The origin of Big Little Books dates to a number of 1920s series by Whitman among which were Fairy Tales, Forest Friends and Boy Adventure.

The first Big Little Book appeared in 1933. Ten different page lengths and eight different sizes were tried by Whitman prior to the 1940s. Whitman and Saalfied Publishing Company dominated the field. However, other publishers did enter the market. Among them were Engel–Van Wiseman, Lynn Publishing Co., Goldsmith Publishing Co. and Dell Publishing Co.

Whitman also deserves attention for the various remarketing efforts it undertook with many of its titles. It contracted to provide Big Little Book premiums for Cocomalt, Kool Aid, Pan–Am Gas, Macy's, Lily–Tulip's Tarzan Ice Cream and others. Among its series names are Wee Little Books, Big Big Books, Nickel Books, Penny Books and Famous Comics.

In the 1950s television characters were introduced into Big Little Book format. Whitman Publishing became part of Western Publishing, owned by Mattel. Waldman and Son Publishing Co. under its subsidiary, Moby Books, issued their first Big Little Book– style book in 1977.

**References:** Larry Lowery, *Lowery's The Collector's Guide To Big Little Books and Similar Books,* privately printed, 1981; Norman E. Martinus and Harry L. Rinker, *Warman's Paper,* Wallace–Homestead, 1993; Robert M. Overstreet, *The Overstreet Comic Book Price Guide Companion, Sixth Edition,* Avon Books, 1993; James Stuart Thomas, *The Big Little Book Price Guide,* Wallace–Homestead, 1983, out–of–print.

**Collectors' Club:** Big Little Book Collector Club of America, P.O. Box 1242, Danville, CA 94526.

**Note:** Books are priced in very fine condition. Cover and spine are intact with only slight bending at the corners. All pages are present; only slightest discoloration of pages. Book has a crispness from cover color to inside.

No effort has been made to list the variations and premiums published by Whitman.

**See:** Cartoon Characters, Cowboy Heroes, Disneyana and Space Adventurers.

## SAALFIELD LITTLE BIG BOOKS

Abbie An' Slats, #1175, 1940 ....... **25.00**
Adventures of Pete the Tramp, The, #1082, 1935 .................... **30.00**
Broadway Bill, #1100, 1935 ........ **45.00**
Camels Are Coming, The, #1107, 1935 **25.00**
Cowboy Millionaire, The, #1106, 1935 **18.00**
Go Into Your Dance, #1097, 1935 ... **60.00**
It Happened One Night, #1098, 1935 **75.00**
Jackie Cooper in Peck's Bad Boy, #1084, 1934 .................... **80.00**
Katzenjammer Kids in the Mountains, #1055, 1934 .................... **35.00**
Laurel and Hardy, #1086, 1934 ...... **85.00**
Law of the Wild, The, #1092, 1935 .. **40.00**
Lost Jungle, The, #1103, 1936 ....... **20.00**
One Night of Love, #1099, 1935 .... **50.00**
Our Gang, #1085, 1934 ............ **80.00**
Peril Afloat, #1143, 1938 ........... **12.00**
Polly and Her Pals on the Farm, #1060, 1934 .......................... **32.00**
Popeye in Puddleburg, #1088, 1934 . **35.00**
Stan Kent, Freshman Fullback, #1120, 1936 .......................... **15.00**
Story of Freddie Bartholomew, The, #1110, 1935 .................... **70.00**
Story of Shirley Temple, The, #1089, 1934 .......................... **20.00**
Tom Mason on Top, #1102, 1935 ... **25.00**
We Three, Barrymore biography, #1109, 1935 .................... **40.00**
Winged Four, The, #1131, 1937 ..... **15.00**

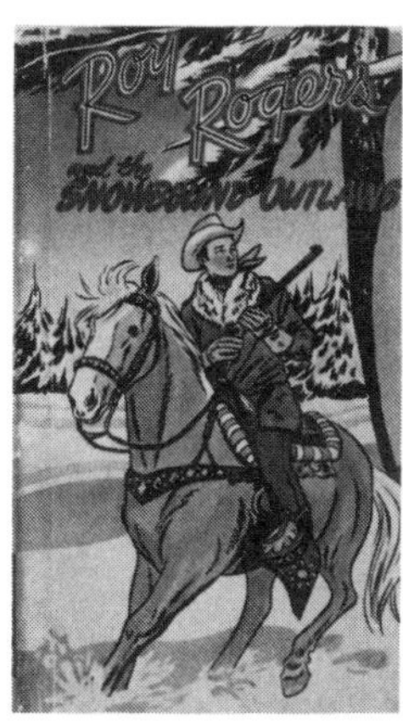


**Whitman Better Little Book, *Roy Rogers and the Snowbound Outlaws,* #701-10, 1948/49, $20.00.**

## WHITMAN BETTER LITTLE BOOKS

Adventures of Huckleberry Finn, The, #1422, 1939 .................... **15.00**
Andy Panda and the Mad Dog Mystery, #1431, 1947 .................... **25.00**
Bambi's Children, #1497, 1943 ...... **35.00**
Big Chief Wahoo, #1443, 1938 ...... **25.00**
Blondie, Cookie and Daisy's Pups, #1491, 1943 .................... **25.00**
Bugs Bunny, #1435, 1944 .......... **30.00**
Buzz Sawyer and Bomber 13, #1415, 1946 .......................... **35.00**
Captain Midnight and the Moon Woman, #1452, 1943 ............ **35.00**
Charlie Chan Solves a New Mystery, #1459, 1940 .................... **60.00**
Donald Duck and Ghost Morgan's Treasure, #1411, 1946 ............... **50.00**
Don Winslow of the Navy and the Great War Plot, #1489, 1940 ........... **20.00**
Flash Gordon in the Forest Kingdom of Mongo, #1492, 1938 ............ **50.00**
Flint Roper and the Six–Gun Showdown, #1467, 1941 .............. **30.00**

Foreign Spies, Doctor Doom and the Ghost Submarine, #1460, 1939 .... **30.00**
Gene Autry, Cowboy Detective, #1494, 1940 .... **40.00**
George O'Brien and the Hooded Riders, #1457, 1940 .... **20.00**
Ghost Avenger, #1462, 1943 .... **35.00**
Green Hornet Strikes, The, #1453, 1940 .... **90.00**
Inspector Charlie Chan, Villainy on the High Seas, #1424, 1942 .... **20.00**
Invisible Scarlet O'Neil Versus the King of the Slums, #1406, 1946 .... **35.00**
Jane Arden, The Vanished Princess, #1498, 1938 .... **25.00**
Junior Nebb Joins the Circus, #1470, 1939 .... **25.00**
Little Orphan Annie and the Secret of the Well, #1417, 1947 .... **50.00**
Lone Star Martin of the Texas Rangers, #1405, 1939 .... **32.00**
Marge's Little Lulu, Alvin and Tubby, #1429, 1947 .... **65.00**
Mickey Rooney and Judy Garland, And How They Got Into The Movies, #1493, 1941 .... **20.00**
Our Gang Adventures, #1456, 1948 . **18.00**
Peggy Brown and the Secret Treasure, #1423, 1947 .... **30.00**
Phantom and the Sign of the Skull, The, #1474, 1939 .... **25.00**
Popeye and Castor Oyl the Detective, #1497, 1941 .... **30.00**
Radio Adventures of Ellery Queen, The, #1406, 1940 .... **25.00**
Red Ryder in War on the Range, #1473, 1945 .... **35.00**
Skeezix Goes to War, #1414, 1944 .... **30.00**
Skyroads with Clipper Williams of the Flying Legion, #1439, 1938 .... **20.00**
Smilin' Jack and the Jungle Pipe Line, #1419, 1947 .... **50.00**
Tarzan Lord of the Jungle, #1407, 1946 **30.00**
Terry and War in the Jungle, #1420, 1946 .... **18.00**
Tom Beatty Ace of the Service and the Big Brain Gang, #1420, 1939 .... **15.00**
Uncle Wiggily's Adventures, #1405, 1946 .... **25.00**
Wings of the USA, #1407, 1940 .... **20.00**

## WHITMAN BIG LITTLE BOOKS

Apple Mary and Dennie Foil the Swindlers, #1130, 1936 .... **35.00**
Believe It Or Not!, #760, 1931 .... **75.00**
Betty Boop in Miss Gulliver's Travels, #1158, 1935 .... **45.00**
Blondie and Baby Dumpling, #1415, 1937 .... **50.00**
Brick Bradford with Brocco the Modern Buccaneer, #1468, 1938 .... **20.00**

**Whitman Big Little Book, *Hal Hardy in the Lost Land of Giants,* #1413, 1938, $15.00.**

Buck Jones and the Rock Creek Cattle War, #1461, 1938 .... **25.00**
Buck Rogers and the Doom Comet, #1178, 1935 .... **65.00**
Chester Gump Finds the Hidden Treasure, #766, 1934 .... **75.00**
Dan Dunn Secret Operative 48, #1118, 1934 .... **50.00**
David Copperfield, #1148, 1934 .... **85.00**
Dick Tracy from Colorado to Nova Scotia, #749, 1933 .... **40.00**
Dick Tracy and the Stolen Bonds, #1105, 1934 .... **60.00**
Dick Tracy Returns, #1495, 1939 .... **40.00**
Eddie Cantor In An Hour With You, #774, 1934 .... **75.00**
Gun Justice, Ken Maynard, #776, 1934 **75.00**
Hal Hardy in the Lost Land of Giants, The World 1,000,000 Years Ago, #1413, 1938 .... **15.00**
Houdini's Big Little Book of Magic, American Oil Co premium, #715, 1927 .... **30.00**
Jack Swift and His Rocket Ship, #1102, 1934 .... **25.00**
John Carter of Mars, #1402, 1940 .... **50.00**
Jungle Jim, #1138, 1936 .... **45.00**
Just Kids, #1401, 1937 .... **45.00**
King of the Royal Mounted Gets His Man, #1452, 1938 .... **15.00**
Li'l Abner in New York, #1198, 1936 **30.00**
Little Men, #1150, 1934 .... **75.00**
Little Women, #757, 1934 .... **75.00**
Lone Ranger and His Horse Silver, The, #1181, 1935 .... **40.00**
Major Matt Mason Moon Mission, #2022, 1968 .... **12.00**
Man From U.N.C.L.E., The, #2011, 1967 .... **15.00**

Mickey Mouse and the Sacred Jewel, #1187, 1936 .................... **35.00**
Mickey Mouse Sails for Treasure Island, #750, 1933 .................... **75.00**
Moon Mullins and the Plushbottom Twins, #1134, 1935 ............. **50.00**
Once Upon A Time, #718, 1933 .... **50.00**
Oswald the Lucky Rabbit, #1109, 1934 **60.00**
Prairie Bill and the Covered Wagon, #758, 1934 .................... **65.00**
Reg'lar Fellers, #754, 1933 ......... **75.00**
Rex Beach's Jaragu of the Jungle, #1424, 1937 .................... **12.00**
Silver Streak, The, #1155, 1935 ..... **75.00**
Story of Skippy, The, premium, #761, 1934 .......................... **60.00**
Sybil Jason in Little Big Shot, #1149, 1936 .......................... **60.00**
Tailspin Tommy, #747, 1933 ........ **85.00**
Tex Thorne Comes Out of the West, #1440, 1937 .................... **18.00**
Tom Mix and the Hoard of Montezuma, #1462, 1937 .................... **30.00**
Treasure Island, #720, 1933 ......... **45.00**
Treasure Island, #1141, 1934 ....... **85.00**
Uncle Ray's Story of the United States, #722, 1934 .................... **60.00**
Wash Tubbs in Pandemonia, #751, 1934 .......................... **50.00**
Wells Fargo, #1471, 1938 .......... **35.00**
West Point of the Air, #1164, 1935 .. **15.00**
World War in Photographs, The, #779, 1934 .......................... **75.00**

# BLACK MEMORABILIA

**Collecting Hints:** Black memorabilia was produced in vast quantities and variations. As a result, collectors have a large field from which to choose and should concentrate on one or a combination of limited categories.

Outstanding examples or extremely derogatory designs in any given area of the field command higher prices. Certain categories, e.g., cookie jars, draw a higher concentration of collector interest resulting in higher prices. Regional pricing also is a factor.

New collectors frequently overpay for common items of little worth because they mistakenly assume all Black collectibles are rare or of great value. As in any other collecting field, misinformation and a lack of knowledge leads to these exaggerated values. The Black memorabilia collector is particularly vulnerable to this practice since so little documentation exists on the subject.

New collectors should familiarize themselves with the field by first studying the market, price trends, and existing reference material. Again, because of the limited reference material and the relative newness of the field, seeking out other collectors is especially valuable for the novice.

Black memorabilia has developed into an established collecting field primarily within the past few years and continues to grow with increased public attention and interest.

**History:** The term "Black memorabilia" refers to a broad range of collectibles that often overlap other collecting fields, e.g., toys, postcards, etc. It also encompasses African artifacts, items created by slaves or related to the slavery era, modern Black cultural contributions to literature, art, etc., and material associated with the Civil Rights Movement and the Black experience throughout history.

The earliest known examples of Black memorabilia include primitive African designs and tribal artifacts. Black memorabilia dates back to the arrival of African natives upon American shores.

The advent of the 1900s launched an incredible amount and variety of material depicting Blacks, most often in a derogatory and dehumanizing manner that clearly reflected the stereotypical attitude held toward the Black race during this period. The popularity of Black portrayals in this unflattering fashion flourished as the century wore on.

As the growth of the Civil Rights Movement escalated and aroused public awareness to the Black plight, attitudes changed. Public outrage and pressure eventually put a halt to the offensive practice during the early 1950s.

Black representations still are being produced today in many forms, but no longer in the demoralizing designs of the past. These modern objects, while not as historically significant as earlier examples, will become the Black memorabilia of tomorrow.

**References:** Patiki Gibbs, *Black Collectibles Sold In America,* Collector Books, 1987, 1993 value update; Patiki Gibbs and Tyson Gibbs, *The Collector's Encyclopedia of Black Dolls,* Collector Books, 1987, 1989 value update; Douglas Congdon–Martin, *Images In Black: 150 Years of Black Collectibles,* Schiffer Publishing, 1990; Jan Lindenberger, *Black Memorabilia For the Kitchen: A Handbook and Price Guide,* Schiffer Publishing Ltd., 1992; Norman E. Martinus and Harry L. Rinker, *Warman's Paper,* Wallace–Homestead, 1993; Myla Perkins, *Black Dolls: An Identification And Value Guide,* Collector Books, 1993; Dawn Reno, *Collecting Black Americana,* Crown Publishing Co, 1986; Darrell A Smith, *Black Americana: A Personal Collection,* Black Relics, Inc., 1988; Jackie Young, *Black Collectibles: Mammy and Her Friends,* Schiffer Publishing, 1988.

**Periodical:** *Black Ethnic Collectibles,* 1401 Asbury Court, Hyattsville, MD 20782.

**Collectors' Club:** Black Memorabilia Collectors Association, 822 4th ST NE, Apt. 2, Washington DC 20002.

**Museums:** Black American West Museum, Denver, CO; Black Archives Research Center and Museum, Florida A&M University, Tallahassee, FL; National Baseball Hall of Fame, Cooperstown, NY; Studio Museum, Harlem, NY; Center for African Art, New York, NY; The Jazz Hall of Fame, New York, NY; Schomburg Center for Research in Black Culture, New York, NY; John Brown Wax Museum, Harper's Ferry, WV; The Museum of African Art, Smithsonian Institution, Washington, D.C.; Robeson Archives, Howard University, Washington, D.C.

**REPRODUCTION ALERT:** Black memorabilia reproductions have grown during the 1980s. Many are made of easily reproducible materials which generally show signs of "newness." Collectors should beware of any given item offered in large or unlimited quantities.

**Note:** The following price listing is based on items in excellent to mint condition. Major paint loss, chips, cracks, fading, tears, or other extreme signs of age warrant a considerable reduction in value, except in very rare or limited production items. Collectors should expect a certain amount of wear on susceptible surfaces.

**Advertising, poster, Gold Dust Washing Powder, paper, Uncle Sam and Teddy Roosevelt welcoming Gold Dust Twins, 20" w, 10½" h, framed, $1,375.00. Photograph courtesy of James D. Julia Inc.**

Advertising
- Booklet, Gold Dust Twins at work and play, Kemble illus, 1902 ........ **100.00**
- Thermometer, 5¼ x 12", wood, "Cocoa Flavored Sambo Dairy Drink," 1937 patent date ............... **50.00**

Animation Cel, 10½ x 12½", Fat Albert, 1981 copyright, William H Cosby, Jr–Filmation Associates .............. **75.00**

Ashtray
- 2 x 3½ x 2½", metal, painted white, caricature boy and girl seated on bench on top edge, raised mammy, banjo player, rooster, and clothes line, Copyright Kinsley Family, 1930s ...................... **75.00**
- 3 x 4½", 3¼" h, china, New Orleans souvenir, seated black man playing saxophone, Made in Japan, 1930s **50.00**

Autograph, photo, black and white, Satchel Paige, blue ink signature, gray mat border, 1948–49 ............. **150.00**

Bank
- 4½" h, Lucky Joe, clear glass, litho tin threaded lid, c1939 ............ **35.00**
- 5½" h, sharecropper, cast iron, polychrome paint .................. **135.00**
- 6" h, Mammy, cast iron, polychrome paint ........................ **100.00**

Bell, Mammy, ceramic, plaid dress ... **50.00**

Book
- *Adam Clayton Powell, Jr, Marching Blacks, An Interpretive History of the Rise of the Black Common Man,* Dial Press, 1945, 218 pgs, dj .... **25.00**
- *History of Slavery,* 1859 ........... **90.00**
- *Little Black Sambo Operetta* ....... **65.00**
- *Sex and Civil Rights, The True Selma Story,* Albert C Persons, Esco Publishers, Birmingham Alabama, 1965, 32 pgs .................. **30.00**
- *Uncle Tom's Cabin,* Donohue & Co, c1900, 64 pgs ................ **25.00**
- *When Malindy Sings,* Paul Laurence Dunbar, 1903, Dodd Mead & Co, several photographs ............ **125.00**

Booklet, 4½ x 6", Gold Dust Twins, 12 pgs, copyright 1907 ............. **50.00**

Bottle Opener, Minstrel, holding banjo **18.00**

Box
- Dixie Boy, firecrackers, black boy with watermelon on label ....... **20.00**
- Fun–To–Wash, 3¼" h, full color illus of mammy wearing red bandanna, early 1900s .................... **25.00**

Bust
- Lady, 7" h, wood base ............ **45.00**
- Mammy, Tiawane ................ **37.00**

Clock
- Caricature, 4½" h, metal, windup, full color illustration street organ grinder, dog, and children, Lux Clock Co, 1930s .............. **200.00**
- Mammy, blue and white, Red Wing, 1940s ....................... **245.00**

Condiment Set, catsup and mustard, ceramic, Pickaninny ................ **65.00**

Cookie Jar
- Aunt Jemima, vinyl .............. **270.00**
- Mammy
  - Brayton Laguna, blue ........... **700.00**
  - McCoy, white .................. **125.00**
  - National Silver ................ **325.00**
  - Pearl China, Cooky and Mammy, price for pair ............... **1,300.00**

Rockingham .................... **500.00**
Unknown maker, painted, 1930s, crude ........................ **160.00**
Creamer and Sugar, F & F ........... **110.00**
Doll
Bisque, diaper .................... **45.00**
Plastic, early, orig dress ........... **65.00**
Stuffed, 15″ h, Flip Wilson/Geraldine, orig box, Shindana Toys copyright 1981 Universal City Studios Inc .. **45.00**

**Doll, Golligwog, black felt body, purple fabric, pink bow tie, 13½″ h, $65.00.**

Egg Timer, Chef .................... **110.00**
Figure
2¾″ h, lead, black man eating watermelon, Happy Farm series, 1940s **75.00**
6″ h, china, young man smoking cigar, molded round base, stamped "Japan," 1930s ................ **75.00**
Game
Amos 'n Andy Card Party, three score pads, twelve tallies, orig box, copyright 1938 M Davis Co .......... **150.00**
Black Sambo, 16″ sq game board, spinner, and four wood markers, orig box, Stoll & Einson Inc, 1934 **200.00**
Greeting Card, 3¾ x 5¾″, black, white, and red photo of black man, "Yo–Birthday? Huh! Wimmen Don't Have Them Things!," Dick Calkins ...... **25.00**
Handbill, 7 x 9½″, black and maroon lettering, black and white photo of James Brown .................... **50.00**
Hose Caddy, 33½″ h, figural, black man, wood and metal, orig polychrome paint, "Sprinkling Sambo, The Firestone Tire & Rubber Co" ... **165.00**
Kitchen Towels, Mammy, "Days of the Week," cross stitched, unused, set of 7 .............................. **150.00**
Lunch Box, 7 x 9″, metal, Pele, inset bust with action soccer illus, green plastic thermos, copyright 1975 Warner Communications, Thermos Co .. **40.00**
Magazine
*Saturday Evening Post,* Nov 28, 1936, black Mammy cooking turkey and young boy watching on cov ..... **15.00**
*Sport,* Jan, 1957, full color cov photo of Wilt Chamberlain ............ **25.00**
Match Holder
Bellhop, wood .................. **45.00**
Coon Chicken Inn ................ **150.00**
Notepad Holder, 5 x 9″, plaster, figural, Mammy, red bandanna, yellow blouse, 1954 copyright, Miller Studio Inc ............................ **50.00**
Palm Puzzle
1¾″ d, silvered tin frame, Turkish style man smoking pipe, 1930s .. **50.00**
2″ d, tin, "Buy Star Soap," caricature of black man, 1930s ............ **75.00**
Pajama Bag, Mammy, 1930s ......... **42.00**
Pencil Clip, ¾″ l, Satchel Paige, brown and white, c1949 ................ **25.00**
Phonograph Record, Black Sambo, 78 rpm, story sleeve ................. **115.00**
Pinback Button
⅞″ d, Gold Dust Washing Powder, multicolored, black youngsters seated in tub, white background, black lettering, 1890–1900 ...... **55.00**
1¼″ d
Down in Dixie, two black youngsters eating watermelon, gold rim, inscribed "South Carolina Inter–State and West Indian Exposition/Charleston, 1901–1902" **125.00**
Parsons Feeder, black youngster eating from nest of ostrich eggs, "You Are The Sucker We've Been Laying For/Why Don't You Get A Parsons Feeder," 1900–12 ..... **150.00**
1¾″ d, Bob Montgomery, championship boxer, black and white portrait, mid 1940s ................ **15.00**
3½″ d, Martin Luther King, black and white photo, "SCLC/Jobs–Income/ Poor People's Campaign 1968/ Washington, DC/I Have A Dream," 1968 ......................... **50.00**
Portrait Plate, 9″ d, china, boy and girl illus, marked "Southern Pines, NC," scalloped edge with gold trim, Foley China, England, 1930s ............ **50.00**
Poster
9¾″ x 20″, Alaga Syrup adv, black and white Willie Mays photo, red lettering with black accents, c1958 . **50.00**
21 x 22″, cardboard, full color, Farrakhan standing before group of black people, "Power At

Last...Forever!" and "Farrakhan Calls The Entire Black Nation To Economic Rebirth/Saviour's Day '86 Sunday February 24 Richard L Jones Armory" ................ **15.00**
Potholder Plaque, pr, 4 x 4", plaster, boy and girl holding watermelon slice, brass hook, painted .............. **75.00**
Print, Penny Short, Harry Roseland ... **195.00**
Program, 9 x 12", The Singing Fool, Al Jolson, 16 pgs, 1928 ............. **150.00**
Puzzle, 8 x 10", Amos 'n Andy, color illus, copyright 1932 Pepsodent Co . **35.00**
Record
  Oh Susanna, black boy and girl illus, 1948, plastic .................. **23.00**
  The Lord's Prayer and Little Bitty Baby, Amos 'n Andy, 78 rpm, Columbia, 1950s ................ **40.00**
Salt and Pepper Shakers, pr
  Aunt Jemima and Uncle Mose, 5" h, plastic, figural, F & F, c1950 ..... **55.00**
  Babies in basket .................. **110.00**
  Boy and Dog, Van Telligen ........ **50.00**
  Chef, crying black holding chicken, white holding cat ............. **95.00**
  Liza and Mose, 2¾" h, plaster, figural, orig box, c1940 ............... **75.00**
  Mammy and Chef, ceramic, yellow, Brayton Laguna ............... **95.00**
Sheet Music
  Back, Back, Back to Baltimore ..... **15.00**
  Choo Choo Boogie, 9 x 12", 1944 copyright, Belwin Inc, Long Island, NY ......................... **15.00**
  I'd Leave Ma Happy Home For You, 1899 ........................ **15.00**
  Mammy's Little Coal Black Rose, Al Jolson, 1914–16 ............... **5.00**
  Tweedle Dee, 9 x 12", Laverne Baker, copyright 1954 Progressive Music Co Inc ....................... **15.00**
Spice Canister, Mammy, Treasure Craft **45.00**
Spice Set, 5 pcs, ceramic, emb Mammy and Chef ....................... **125.00**
Spoon Rest, 4 x 6", aluminum, figural head, relief black chef with wide open mouth, 1930s .............. **75.00**
Stickpin
  Metal, figural, woman, brass pin, early 1900s ................... **50.00**
  Plastic, diecut, flag, red, white, and blue design, blue photo, "Hero of Pearl Harbor/Dorie Miller," brass pin, 1942 copyright ........... **110.00**
String Holder, 7" h, china, mammy, stamped "Japan," 1930s .......... **75.00**
Swizzle Stick, 6" l, set of 6, Zulu–Lulu, plastic, transparent brown, orig display card, 1940s ................ **25.00**
Syrup Pitcher, 5½" h, Aunt Jemima, plastic, hinged head, 1950s ....... **75.00**
Table Set, 3 pcs, syrup, salt, and pepper, Mammy and Mose, F & F ......... **85.00**
Target, 14 x 23", Sambo Target, tin litho, orig box, unused, 1940s ..... **150.00**
Teapot, Gone with the Wind type Mammy ......................... **29.00**
Tea Set, 3 pcs, teapot, creamer, and sugar, black clowns .............. **45.00**
Toaster Cover, 16" h fabric Mammy doll, orig box, Bucilla Products, c1940 .......................... **225.00**
Toy
  Aunt Jemima Pastry Mix Set, tin baking pans and baking sheet, plastic cookie cutter, wood rolling pin, plastic spoon, and seven boxes of pastry mix, orig box, Junior Chef, 1950s ........................ **50.00**
  Squeeze, 6½" h, litho tin, black minstrel holding saxophone, arms and legs move apart and metal cymbals strike together, diecut eyes and mouth, marked "Germany," 1930s **200.00**
  Stepin Tom, 13½" h, wood, marked "Stepin Tom Made By Sturdy Mfg Co," 1930s .................... **50.00**
  Wood, dancing figure, jointed legs and arms ...................... **40.00**
Valentine, post card, 3½ x 5½", "Pore Little Mose," Raphael Tuck & Sons, Feb 13, 1911 postmark ........... **25.00**

# BLUE RIDGE POTTERY

**Collecting Hints:** Blue Ridge patterns are among the best established of the collectible American dinnerwares. Collectors pay a premium for artist-signed pieces. The Talisman Wallpaper dinnerware pattern, because of its failure to attract buyers, is the most difficult dinnerware pattern to find. Among the harder to find shapes are the China demi pot and the character jugs.

Among the most popular patterns and forms are those made in the 1940s. As in most dinnerware patterns, hollow ware pieces command higher prices than flat pieces. Demi sets that still have their tray are considered a real find. Blue Ridge collectors must compete with children's dish collectors for miniature pieces.

Because they are hand decorated, identical pieces often contain minor variations. Develop a practiced eye in respect to identifying those hands whose work is more aesthetically pleasing than others. Minor color changes also can change a highly pleasing pattern into one that is ordinary.

**History:** In 1917 the Carolina Clinchfield and Ohio Railroad, in an effort to promote industry along its line, purchased land along its right–of–way and established a pottery in Erwin, Tennessee. Erwin was an ideal location because of the local availability of white kaolin clay and feldspar, two of the chief ingredients in pottery. Workers for the new plant were recruited from East Liverpool and Sebring, Ohio, and Chester, Virginia.

In 1920 J. E. Owens purchased the pottery and received a charter for Southern Potteries, Incorporated. Within a few years the pottery was sold to Charles W. Foreman. Foreman introduced hand painting under glaze and trained girls and women from the nearby hills to do the painting. By 1938 Southern Potteries, Incorporated was producing Blue Ridge "Hand Painted Under The Glaze" dinnerware. The principal sales thrust was to contrast the Blue Ridge hand-painted ware with decal ware produced by most other manufacturers.

Blue Ridge maintained a large national sales organization, with eleven showrooms scattered nationwide. Few catalogs were issued and trade advertising was limited. As a result, researching Blue Ridge is difficult.

Most of the patterns used on Blue Ridge originated at the plant. Lena Watts, an Erwin native, was chief designer. Eventually Watts left Blue Ridge and went to Stetson China Company. Blue Ridge also produced limited production patterns for a number of leading department stores.

As the 1930s came to a close, Southern Potteries was experiencing strong competition from cheap imports from the Far East. World War II intervened and changed the company's fortune. Southern Potteries' work force increased tenfold. The company experienced a golden age between the mid–1940s and early 1950s. Production averaged over 300,000 pieces per week.

By the mid–1950s imports and the arrival of plastic dinnerware once again threatened Southern Potteries' market position. The company tried half–time production. The end came on January 31, 1957, when the stockholders voted to close the plant.

**References:** Jo Cunningham, *The Collector's Encyclopedia of American Dinnerware,* Collector Books, 1982, 1992 value update; Lois Lehner, *Lehner's Encyclopedia of U. S. marks on Pottery, Porcelain & Clay,* Collector Books, 1988; Betty and Bill Newbound, *Southern Potteries, Inc.: Blue Ridge Dinnerware, Revised Third Edition,* Collector Books, 1989, 1993 value update; Betty Newbound, *Price Update Southern Potteries, Blue Ridge Dinnerware,* published by author, 1992.

**Periodicals:** *National Blue Ridge Newsletter,* 144 Highland Drive, Blountville, TN 37617; *The Daze,* 10271 State Rd., PO Box 57, Otisville, MI 48463.

**Collectors' Club:** Blue Ridge Collectors Club, Rte. 3, Box 161, Erwin, TN 37650.

**Museum:** Unicoi Heritage Museum, Erwin, TN.

**Dogwood, vegetable bowl, oval, 9¼″ l, $15.00.**

## CHINAWARE ACCESSORY PIECES

Bonbon, flat shell shape, Nove Rose .. **65.00**
Cake Tray, Maple Leaf shape, Verna .. **55.00**
Candy Box, Nove Rose ............ **175.00**
Celery
  French Peasant, leafy ............ **45.00**
  Nove Rose, leafy ................ **35.00**
  Serenade ...................... **35.00**
  Summertime, leafy .............. **30.00**
Character Jug, Pioneer Lady ........ **400.00**
Chocolate Pot, Rose Marie .......... **150.00**
Creamer, French Peasant, pedestal base **70.00**
Creamer and Sugar, pedestal, Rose Marie ........................ **90.00**
Dish, deep shell shape, Tussie Mussie **50.00**
Pitcher
  Clara Shape, yellow cherries ....... **75.00**
  Grace Shape
    Pale Yellow .................. **55.00**
    Teal ........................ **55.00**
  Jane Shape, Scatter .............. **90.00**
  Sculptured Fruit, 7½″ h .......... **60.00**
  Spiral Shape, Tralee Rose ......... **65.00**
Relish
  Heart Shape, Buttons and Forget–Me–Nots ........................ **30.00**
  Top Handle Shape, four sections, Serenade ...................... **60.00**
Salt Shaker, French Peasant .......... **50.00**

## DINNERWARE

Blossom Top, Skyline shape, salt and pepper shakers, pr ............... **28.00**
Carnival, Candlewick shape
  Soup .......................... **10.00**
  Vegetable Bowl ................. **12.00**
Christmas Tree, Colonial shape, plate . **55.00**

Chrysanthemum
- Cup and Saucer .................. **9.00**
- Plate
  - 7″ d, salad .................... **4.00**
  - 9¾″ d, dinner ................. **10.00**
- Platter, oval, 12″ l ................ **10.00**
- Soup, flat, 8″ d .................. **10.00**
- Vegetable Bowl, 9½″ d ............ **12.00**

Corsage, Astor shape, soup bowl ..... **16.00**
County Fair, Colonial shape, salad plate **15.00**
Crab Apple, Colonial shape, creamer individual ......................... **20.00**
Garden Lane, Colonial shape, platter, 11¾″ l ......................... **10.00**
Green Briar, Piecrust shape, plate, 9″ d **4.50**
June Bouquet, Colonial shape, vegetable bowl, 9½″ d ................. **16.00**
Kismet, Skyline shape, teapot ........ **55.00**
Mountain Ivy, Candlewick shape, vegetable bowl ..................... **20.00**
Muriel, demitasse cup and saucer .... **32.00**
Normandie, Skyline shape, cereal bowl **18.00**

Pembrooke, Colonial shape
- Bowl, 5½″ d ..................... **3.25**
- Plate, 9″ d ....................... **4.75**

Red Rooster, Skyline shape
- Cup ........................... **20.00**
- Plate
  - 6″ d .......................... **8.00**
  - 9″ d .......................... **25.00**
- Platter, 11″ l ..................... **22.00**
- Saucer .......................... **6.00**

Rock Rose, Colonial shape, eggcup ... **18.00**

Rustic Plaid, Skyline shape
- Creamer and Sugar, cov ........... **7.00**
- Cup ........................... **2.00**

Saratoga, Skyline shape, salt and pepper shakers, pr ...................... **15.00**
Sunflower, Colonial shape, plate, 10″ d **8.50**

Sungold #1, Candlewick shape
- Bowl, 9½″ d ..................... **20.00**
- Creamer ........................ **12.00**
- Cup and Saucer .................. **12.00**
- Fruit Bowl ....................... **4.00**
- Plate, 10″ d, dinner ............... **10.00**
- Platter, 14″ l ..................... **22.00**
- Soup, flat, 8″ d .................. **10.00**
- Sugar, cov ....................... **15.00**

Sunny Spray, Skyline shape
- Cup and Saucer .................. **3.00**
- Tumbler
  - Juice ......................... **7.00**
  - Water ......................... **12.00**
- Wall Sconce ..................... **65.00**

Waltz Time
- Bowl, 6″ d ...................... **8.00**
- Cup and Saucer .................. **10.00**
- Plate
  - 7½″ sq ........................ **15.00**
  - 10½″ d, dinner ................ **15.00**
- Platter, 14½″ l ................... **25.00**
- Sugar, cov ...................... **15.00**

Wrinkled Rose, Colonial shape, salad bowl, 10″ d ..................... **40.00**

Yellow Nocturne, Colonial shape
- Bowl, 5½″ d ..................... **8.00**
- Cup and Saucer .................. **6.00**
- Plate
  - 6″ d, bread and butter .......... **3.50**
  - 9¼″ d, luncheon ............... **8.00**
  - 10″ d, dinner .................. **9.00**
- Salad Bowl, 9¼″ d ............... **17.00**
- Soup, flat ........................ **10.00**

# BOOKMARKS

**Collecting Hints:** The best place to search for bookmarks is specialized paper shows. Be sure to check all related categories. Most dealers do not have a separate category for bookmarks. Instead they file them under subject headings, e.g., Insurance, Ocean Liners, World's Fairs, etc.

**History:** Bookmark collecting dates back to the early nineteenth century. A bookmark is any object used to mark a reader's place in a book. Bookmarks have been made in a wide variety of material, including celluloid, cloth, cross–stitched needlepoint in punched paper, paper, Sterling silver, wood, and woven silk. Heavily embossed leather markers were popular between 1800 and 1860. Advertising markers appeared after 1860.

Woven silk markers are a favorite among collectors. T. Stevens of Coventry, England, manufacturer of Stevensgraphs, is among the most famous makers. Paterson, New Jersey, was the silk weaving center in the United States. John Best & Co., Phoenix Silk Manufacturing Company, and Warner Manufacturing Co. produced bookmarks. Other important United States companies that made woven silk bookmarks were J. J. Mannion of Chicago and Tilt & Son of Providence, Rhode Island.

Recently collectors have discovered the colorful folk art quality of cross–stitched bookmarks created between the 1840s and 1910s. These were a popular handcraft of young women who followed the pre–punched paper strips imprinted with a design. Plain strips were available for those wishing to design their own bookmark. Most have a religious theme, but examples have been found for birthdays, Christmas, temperance (anti–drink), and other themes. Most were attached to colorful silk ribbons.

**References:** A. W. Coysh, *Collecting Bookmarks*, Drake Publishers, 1974, out–of–print; Norman E. Martinus and Harry L. Rinker, *Warman's Paper*, Wallace–Homestead, 1993.

**Periodical:** *Bookmark Collector*, 1002 West 25th Street, Erie, PA 16502.

**Advisor:** John S. Waldsmith.

Advertising
- Aluminum, Eberhart & Miller, Shoes & Rubbers, Warren, PA, emb floral design, attached silk cord ....... **6.00**
- Brass, United Sates Fidelity & Guarantee Co, etched logo and "Home Office Baltimore USF & G" ...... **3.00**
- Paper, many are diecuts
  - Antikammia Tablets, The Antikammia Chemical Co, St Louis, two colors ..................... **6.00**
  - Climax Catarrah Cure, woman with fur coat, multicolored ......... **10.00**
  - Daggets Chocolates, Clapsaddle girl, emb butterfly, multicolored **10.00**
  - Hoyt's German Cologne, multicolored ......................... **6.00**
  - James Fitzgerald, Bookseller & Stationer, MA, rural scene ....... **6.00**

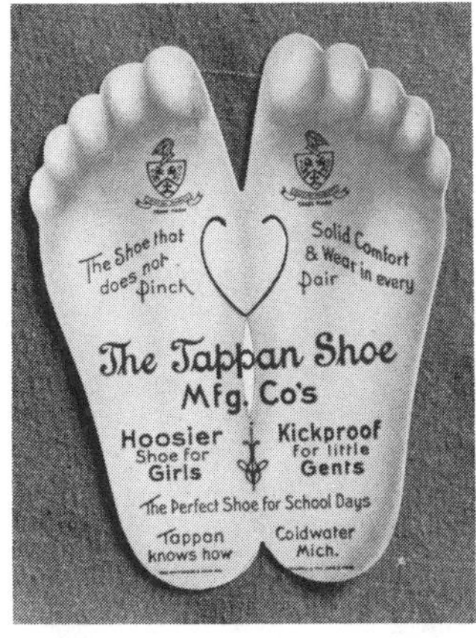


**Advertising, The Tappan Shoe Mfg. Co., feet shape, flesh tone, black letters, $18.00.**

Celluloid, Mickey Mouse, Goofy, and Daisy Duck, fish shape, copyright Walt Disney Productions, c1950 ... **12.00**

Cloisonne, Arizona, Grand Canyon State, deep blue, gold, and white design ........................... **3.00**

Cross–stitched, on punched paper, usually attached to silk ribbon
- Florals, c1890 ................... **4.00**
- God is Love, green, lilac, and purple design, royal blue silk ribbon, 4" l **8.00**
- Love, beige, salmon and green dec, 6¼" l ......................... **6.00**
- Merry Christmas, red and green holly dec ........................... **20.00**
- My Best Wishes, beige, multicolored flowers, light blue gray lettering, woven silk ribbon, 5⅜" ! ........ **8.00**
- So–Far, 8" l, red and silver, silk ribbon **10.00**

Metal
- Shield type, R K Company
  - Balance Rock, Pittsfield, MA, burnished copper type finish ...... **8.00**
  - Statue of Liberty, New York City, emb fireworks design ......... **6.00**
  - The Flume of Franconia Notch, White Mts, NH .............. **3.00**
  - Washington's Mansion, Mt Vernon, VA, mansion scene ........... **10.00**
- World's Fair
  - Chicago, Century of Progress, 1933–34, copper type finish, etched logo, deep red design .. **10.00**
  - New York World's Fair, 1939, airplane on top, logo medallion .. **12.00**

Sterling Silver
- Etched lace design, multicolored silk string and tassel, marked "Sterling, R & G Co" .................... **10.00**
- Provincetown, MA, souvenir, emb tower scene, silk cord, marked "Sterling" ..................... **10.00**
- Sword with flower design, curved blade, engraved "J L R,", marked "Sterling 925 Fine," c1900 ...... **14.00**

Wood, souvenir, Ireland, hand carved, clover leaves and "Erin," swivel design, imp "Blarney," painted black . **10.00**

# BOOKS—DETECTIVE AND MYSTERY FIRST EDITIONS

**Collecting Hints:** Collecting first editions of any subject can be financially and aesthetically rewarding. However, understand that some pricing is highly speculative. Buy selectively and plan to hold for an extended period of time.

There are a number of factors that increase the value of a first edition: (1) binding, (2) a numbered presentation copy, (3) author signature, (4) author inscription, and (5) first work of the author. Add extra value for an inscription only if the content is rich, otherwise value it as you would an author-signed work. Also have any author signature authenticated.

When purchasing a first edition, attempt to research the size of the first edition run. Many modern titles have initial runs that exceed one hundred thousand copies.

Many of these books had dust jackets. The book should not be considered complete if the jacket has been lost. Also check to make certain that all illustrations are present if the book had illustrations.

There are a wealth of dealers who specialize in out–of–print books. Your local librarian can help you find them. Do not hesitate to ask. It may take from a few months to several years to find a particular book, but eventually your patience will be rewarded.

**History:** Collecting first editions has been one of the mainstays of the antiquarian book market. Major collections were assembled as early as the eighteenth century.

Because of the tremendous number of books printed today, first edition collectors often specialize by genre. One of the most popular are first editions of detective and mystery fiction and non–fiction.

There is no easy method to identify a first edition. Collectors are urged to consult Jacob Blanck's *Bibliography of American Literature* (Yale University Press, 1955–1983) or Jack Tannen's *How to Identify & Collect American First Editions* (Arco Publishing, 1985).

**References:** Allen Ahearn, *Book Collecting: A Comprehensive Guide*, G. P. Putnam's Sons, 1989; Allen and Patricia Ahearn, *Collected Books, The Guide To Values*, G. P. Putnam's Sons, 1991; *American Book Prices Current, Volume 98, 1992*, Bancroft/Parkman, Inc., 1993; John Carter (revised by Nicolas Barker), *ABC For Book Collectors, Sixth Edition*, Granada Publishing, 1980; Editors of Collector Books, *Huxford's Old Book Value Guide, Fifth Edition*, Collector Books, 1993; Jean Peters, ed., *Book Collecting: A Modern Guide*, R. R. Bowker Company, 1977; Jean Peters, ed., *Collectible Books: Some New Paths*, R. R. Bowker Company, 1979.

**Advisor:** Ron Lieberman.

Adams, Samuel Hopkins, *Average Jones*, illus by M Leone Bracker, Queen's Quorum, Indianapolis, 1911, 8vo, cloth ... **55.00**

Anderson, Frederick Irving, *Book of Murder*, Haycraft–Queen Cornerstone, New York, 1930, 8vo, cloth, dj, worn at edges, tape reinforced along edges and folds on verso, rubbed ... **330.00**

Anthology, edited by Graham Greene and Hugh Greene, *The Spy's Bedside Book*, London, 1957, 8vo, cloth, dj, some wear, fraying at edges ... **80.00**

Asimov, Isaac, *Asimov's Sherlockian Limericks*, illus by Gahan Wilson, New York, 1978, sq 8vo, cloth, dj, one of 250 numbered copies sgd by Asimov and Wilson ... **200.00**

Bangs, John Kendrick, *A House–Boat on the Styx*, illus, New York, 1896, small 8vo, orig pictorial cloth, inscribed and sgd by Bangs ... **90.00**

Bayly, A Eric, *The House of Strange Secrets*, Glover & Greene, New York, 1899, 8vo, orig cloth, front hinge cracked ... **70.00**

Bentley, E C, *Trent's Last Case*, Haycraft–Queen Cornerstone, London, 1913, frontispiece, 8vo, orig cloth, covers dec in blind, gilt lettered on spine ... **165.00**

Biggers, Earl Derr

*Behind That Curtain*, Indianapolis, 1928, 8vo, cloth, backstrip slightly faded, dj ... **220.00**

*Charlie Chan Carries On*, Indianapolis, 1930, 8vo, cloth, dj, few short closed tears ... **165.00**

*Keeper of the Keys: a Charlie Chan Story*, Indianapolis, 1932, 8vo, wrappers ... **385.00**

Boyle, Jack, *Boston Blackie*, New York, 1919, illus, 8vo, pictorial cloth, slight rubbing, cloth with a few creases; hinges tender ... **100.00**

Braddon, M E, *Rough Justice*, London, 1898, Glover & Greene, illus, 8vo, orig red cloth ... **80.00**

Brand, Max, *Destry Rides Again*, New York, 1930, 8vo, orig cloth, dj ... **220.00**

Buchan, John, *The Thirty–Nine Steps*, Haycraft–Queen Cornerstone, Edinburgh, 1915, 8vo, orig cloth, backstrip slightly faded, minor soiling ... **165.00**

Burnett, W R, *Little Caesar*, Haycraft–Queen Cornerstone, New York, 1929, 8vo, orig cloth, spine ends and corners slightly worn and rubbed ... **80.00**

Butler, Ellis Parker, *Philo Gubb: Correspondence School Detective*, Queen's Quorum, Boston, 1918, illus, 8vo, pictorial cloth, front hinge tender ... **70.00**

Chandler, Raymond, *The Big Sleep*, New York, 1939, 8vo, cloth, dj, slight wear with some minor browning, trimmed ¼" along bottom edge ... **990.00**

Charteris, Leslie, *Thieves' Picnic*, London, 1937, 8vo, cloth, dj, some wear at edges, rubbed ... **250.00**

Chesterton, G K, *The Innocence of Father Brown*, Haycraft–Queen Cornerstone, London, 1911, illus, 8vo, orig gilt lettered cloth ... **195.00**

Christie, Agatha, *The Mysterious Mr. Quin*, London, 1930, 8vo, orig cloth, scattered light foxing ... **250.00**

Cobb, Irvin S, *Faith, Hope and Charity*,

Queen's Quorum, Indianapolis, 1934, 8vo, cloth, dj, few short closed tears and small chips at edges ...... **100.00**

Crofts, Freeman Wills, *The Cask,* Haycraft–Queen Cornerstone, London, 1920, 8vo, cloth, quite worn, endpapers slightly darkened, cloth folding case ........................ **525.00**

Derleth, August, *Murder Stalks the Wakely Family,* New York, 1934, 8vo, orig cloth, backstrip slightly faded .. **110.00**

Donovan, Dick, *From Clue to Capture,* Glover & Greene, London, 1893, illus, 8vo, orig cloth, front hinge cracked, endpapers slightly browned, bookplate ...................... **90.00**

Doyle, A Conan

*His Last Bow,* London, 1917, 8vo, orig gilt stamped cloth, backstrip slightly darkened, protective cloth sleeve ....................... **250.00**

*The Exploits of Brigadier Gerard,* London, 1896, illus, 8vo, gilt lettered cloth, minor scattered foxing ..... **80.00**

*The Return of Sherlock Holmes,* New York, 1905, 8vo, pictorial black cloth, some color worn away from covers, hinges cracked .......... **470.00**

Eustis, Helen, *The Horizontal Man,* Haycraft–Queen Cornerstone, New York, 1946, 8vo, cloth, dj, minor wear at edges .................. **165.00**

Flagg, James Montgomery, *The Mystery of the Hated Man,* New York, 1916, illus by Flagg, 8vo, cloth, minor wear at extremities, pictorial front cov label, dj, some chipping at edges, piece missing from head of spine panel ... **90.00**

Ford, Paul Leicester, *The Great K. & A. (Train) Robbery,* Glover & Greene, New York, 1897, frontispiece, 8vo, orig pictorial cloth ............... **55.00**

Gardner, Erle Stanley, *The Case of the Stuttering Bishop,* New York, 1936, 8vo, cloth, dj some wear with chipping along edges, splitting along front joint fold ...................... **165.00**

Graeme, Bruce, *Blackshirt,* London, 1925, 8vo, orig cloth ............ **55.00**

Grant, Maxwell, *The Living Shadow,* New York, 1931, 8vo, pictorial boards, text browned ............ **330.00**

Greene, Graham, *The Third Man and the Fallen Idol,* London, 1950, 8vo, cloth, dj, few small chips, spine panel slightly darkened ................ **100.00**

Hammett, Dashiell, *The Adventures of Sam Spade and Other Stories,* New York, 1944, Introduction by Ellery Queen, 8vo, orig wrappers, light wear at edges, short tear on rear cover **385.00**

Hornung, E W, *Mr Justice Raffles,* London, 1909, 8vo, orig pictorial cloth, gilt lettered on spine ............. **135.00**

Hume, Fergus, *The White Prior,* Glover & Greene, London, 1895, 8vo, pictorial boards, minor wear along edges, some rubbing ............. **165.00**

Leroux, Gaston, *The Mystery of the Yellow Room,* Haycraft, New York, 1908, 8vo, orig pictorial yellow cloth, slight rubbing ................... **90.00**

Maugham, W Somerset, *Ashenden, or the British Agent,* Queen's Quorum, London, 1928, 8vo, orig blue cloth, backstrip slightly dulled, minor wear at edges ........................ **250.00**

Orczy, Baroness, *The Elusive Pimpernel,* London, 1908, 8vo, orig cloth, spine ends and extremities rubbed, endpapers browned, faded owner's inscription on half title ................. **220.00**

Pinkerton, Allan, *The Expressman and the Detective,* Haycraft–Queen Cornerstone, Chicago, 1874, illus, 8vo, orig blue cloth, stamped in gilt and black, some wear to spine ends and corners ........................ **165.00**

Queen, Ellery

*The Adventures of Ellery Queen,* Queen's Quorum, New York, 1934, 8vo, cloth, front hinge cracked, few preliminaries loose, dj worn with some chips and tears, few ink calculations on front flap . **135.00**

*The Misadventures of Sherlock Holmes,* Boston, 1944, 8vo, cloth, dj ........................... **550.00**

*Twentieth Century Detective Stories,* Cleveland, 1948, 8vo, cloth, dj .. **100.00**

Rinehart, Mary Roberts, *The Circular Staircase,* Haycraft–Queen Cornerstone, Indianapolis, 1908, illus, 8vo, pictorial cloth, slight wear to spine ends, owner's signature on front free endpaper ...................... **70.00**

Rohmer, Sax, *The Mystery of Dr Fu–Manchu,* London, 1913, 8vo, orig gilt dec cloth, minor light foxing to preliminaries, ¼ morocco folding case . **715.00**

Spillane, Mickey, *I, The Jury,* New York, 1947, 8vo, pictorial wrappers, several fore margins chipped from rough opening of the pages ............ **415.00**

Starrett, Vincent, *The Case–Book of Jimmy Lavender,* New York, 1944, 8vo, cloth, dj, some wear at edges, spine panel faded, foxed on verso .. **80.00**

Stevenson, Robert Louis and Lloyd Osbourne, *The Wrong Box,* Glover & Greene, London, 1889, 8vo, cloth . **110.00**

Stout, Rex, *Black Orchids,* New York, 1942, 8vo, cloth, dj, chipped along edges ........................ **605.00**

Taine, John, *The Purple Sapphire,* New York, 1924, 8vo, orig purple cloth, slight fading, dj, chipped and torn, few larger pieces on rear panel missing . . . . . . . . . . . . . . . . . . . . . . . . . . . . **90.00**
Twain, Mark, *The Tragedy of Pudd'n head Wilson,* Haycraft–Queen Cornerstone, Hartford, 1894, illus, large 8vo, orig cloth, spine ends slightly frayed . . . . . . . . . . . . . . . . . . . . . . . . . **220.00**
Wallace, Edgar, *The Four Just Men,* London, 1905; frontispiece, 8vo, orig yellow cloth, minor rubbing and soiling, front hinge starting, scattered light foxing, owner's signature on front free endpaper . . . . . . . . . . . . . . . . . . . . . . . **165.00**

# BOTTLE OPENERS, FIGURAL

**Collecting Hints:** Condition is most important. Worn or missing paint and repainted surfaces lower value. Damaged or rusty pieces have greatly diminished value.

**History:** Figural bottle openers were produced expressly for removing a bottle cap from a bottle. They were made in a variety of metals, including cast iron, brass, bronze, and white metal. Cast iron, brass, and bronze openers are generally solid castings; white metal openers are usually cast in hollow blown molds.

The vast majority of figural bottle openers date from the 1950s and 1960s. Paint variation on a figure is very common.

**References:** Donald Bull, *A Price Guide to Beer Advertising, Openers and Corkscrews,* Donald Bull, 1981; Figural Bottle Openers Collectors, *Figural Bottle Openers: Identification Guide,* Figural Bottle Openers Collectors, 1992; Michael Jordan, *Figural Bottle Openers,* published by author, 1981.

**Collectors' Clubs:** Figural Bottle Opener Collectors, 117 Basin Hill Rd., Duncannon, PA 17020; Just For Openers, 63 October Lane, Trumbull, CT 06611.

**Advisor:** Craig Dinner.

**REPRODUCTION ALERT**

All American Football Player, 4¾" h, L & L Favors, cast iron, navy blue helmet and jersey, brown pants and football, football tucked in left hand, right hand on hip, "ZBT" on jersey . . . . . **395.00**
Amish Boy, 4" h, cast iron, black pants, hat, and suspenders, red shirt, barefoot, Wilton Products . . . . . . . . . . . . . **235.00**

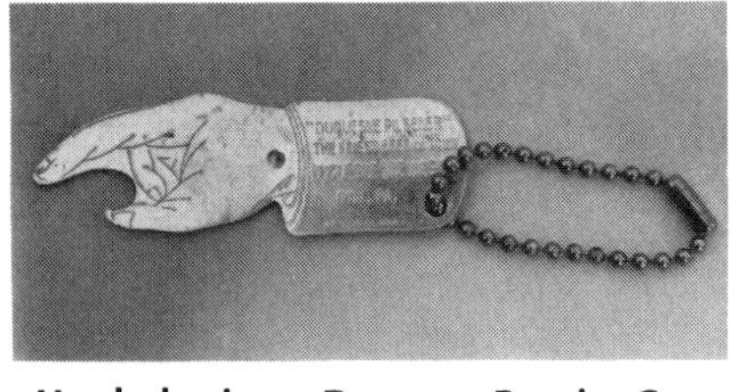

**Hand, aluminum, Duquesne Brewing Co., Pittsburgh, PA, 3¾" l, $3.00.**

Bear, 3⅞ x 3¹⁄₁₆", brass, wall mount, head, black highlights, John Wright Co . . . . . . . . . . . . . . . . . . . . . . . . . . . **100.00**
Black Boy with alligator
- 2⅝" h, hands down, green alligator, Wilton Products . . . . . . . . . . . . . . . . **155.00**
- 3" h, hand in air, green alligator and base, John Wright Co . . . . . . . . . . . **175.00**

Black Man, 4⅜ x 3¾", wall mount, smiling, red bow tie, Wilton Products **135.00**
Caddy, 5¾" h, cast iron, black man, yellow #19 hole marker, Patent 86608 on back, bottle in back pocket, carrying tan golf bag, red shirt, green pants . . . . . . . . . . . . . . . . . . . . . . . . . . **295.00**
Cathy Coed, 4⅛" h, cast iron, preppy girl holding stack of books, green base with white front, sgd "L & L Favors" **525.00**
Clown, 4⅛ x 4", brass, wall mount, white bow tie with red polka dots, bald head, sgd "495" on back, John Wright Co . . . . . . . . . . . . . . . . . . . . . . . **85.00**
Cockatoo, 3¼" h, cast iron, orange and yellow chest, red and orange comb, green base with black background, John Wright Co . . . . . . . . . . . . . . . . . . **125.00**
Cowboy with Guitar, 4⅞" h, cast iron, yellow, brown, and gray guitar, green cactus, black shoes, red bandanna, John Wright Co . . . . . . . . . . . . . . . . . . **100.00**
Dinky Dan, 3¹³⁄₁₆" h, cast iron, preppy boy with hands in pockets, green base, sgd "GADZIK PHILA" on back **345.00**
Do Do Bird, 2¾" h, cast iron, cream, black highlights, red beak . . . . . . . . . **185.00**
Elephant, 3¹⁄₁₆" h
- John Wright Co, sitting on four legs, white highlights on mouth and trunk, trunk in circle, red mouth and nostrils . . . . . . . . . . . . . . . . . . . . **30.00**
- Wilton Products, sitting, trunk in circle, gray, pink nostrils, white toe nails . . . . . . . . . . . . . . . . . . . . . . . . . **30.00**

Drunk
- Cowboy, 4⅜" h, cast iron, signpost, blue pants, yellow hat and jacket, red bandanna, John Wright Co . . . **95.00**

Lamp Post, 4 5/16", green lamp post, black tux, hat, shoes, and base, John Wright Co ................ **10.00**
Sign Post, 3 7/8" h, man holding post, white sign, black post, tux, and hat **15.00**
Fish, cast iron
4 3/4" l, yellow and green body, tail raised, John Wright Co .......... **135.00**
5" l, trout, red, orange, and green body, Wilton Products .......... **75.00**
Foundry Man, 3 1/8" h, cast iron, pouring melted iron, white pants, black belt, no shirt, black hair, John Wright Co **145.00**
Four Eyes, two sets of eyes
Bald Man, 3 3/4 x 3 3/8", blue eyes, large black mustache, Wilton Products . **30.00**
Man, 4 x 3 7/8", black hair and mustache, John Wright Co .......... **30.00**
Women, blue eyes, marked "Wilton Products" on back ............. **30.00**
Freddie Frosh, 4" h, cast iron, preppy boy standing with hands in pockets, legs crossed, green base with white front, sgd "L & L Favors" on back .. **325.00**
Grass Skirt Greek, 5" h, cast iron, black native girl, white sign and post, green base, sgd "GADZIK Phila" on back . **365.00**
Mademoiselle, 4 1/2" h, cast iron, streetwalker by lamp post, black, flesh face, hands, and legs, yellow light, John Wright Co .................. **20.00**
Monkey, 2 1/2" h, cast iron, dark brown body and face, tan mask, orange–brown tree, John Wright Co ....... **135.00**
Paddy the Pledgemaster, 4" h, cast iron, preppy boy, green base with white front, sgd "GADZIK PHILA" ....... **285.00**
Patty Pep, 4" h, L & L Favors, cast iron, girl with hand to her head, yellow hat and skirt, blue blouse, black shoes . **525.00**
Pelican, cast iron
3 1/4" h, white, black and red highlights, yellow beak, orange feet, ruffled black comb, green base ... **155.00**
3 3/8", red and black, yellow beak, orange feet, green base, Wilton Products ......................... **55.00**
3 3/4" h, cream, orange beak and feet, head up, green base, John Wright Co .......................... **165.00**
Rooster
3 3/16" h, cast iron, yellow, orange, black, and white body, orange–yellow feet, green base, tail opener, Wilton Products ................ **35.00**
3 7/8" h, metal, black body, red comb, orange–yellow beak and feet, green base, opener under tail, John Wright Co .................... **45.00**
Sailor, 3 3/4" h, hitchhiking, white uniform, black tie and shoes, white sign with black trim, John Wright Co .... **45.00**
Sea Gull, 3 3/16" h, cast iron, cream, black and gray highlights, red beak, orange feet, gray and black stump, John Wright Co .................. **40.00**
Seahorse, 4 1/4" h, brass, green, white highlights, green base with blue and black highlights .................. **90.00**

# BOYD CRYSTAL ART GLASS

**Collecting Hints:** The Boyds have gone to great length to see that their production of pieces utilizing the Degenhart molds is not confused with pieces made during the Degenhart period. Look for the "B" in a diamond mark to identify a Boyd product.

Boyd can be collected in two distinct ways: color and shape. Most collectors find concentrating on just a few colors too confining. Shape is the collecting preference.

Because of its contemporary nature, a firm secondary resale market has not yet been established for Boyd. Prices remain modest, with dealers charging a premium for their particular favorites. Pieces do appear for sale on a regular basis in trade papers.

A visit to the Boyd plant in Cambridge, Ohio, is strongly recommended. In addition to a buying opportunity, it also provides an excellent way to learn about new issues. When visiting Cambridge, take time to visit the Degenhart Museum, which houses the extensive glass collection of Elizabeth Degenhart.

**History:** The Boyd family has a long tradition associated with glass making. Zackary Thomas Boyd (1888–1964) worked for over twenty–one different glass companies, including Cambridge, Imperial, and New Martinsville. Bernard C. Boyd (1907–1988) began working at Cambridge Glass as an apprentice in his early teens. By sixteen he was employed in the glass business full time.

While working at Lornetta Glass, near Point Marion, Pennsylvania, Bernard began working with a chemist on glass formulas. Most formulas were developed through trial and error. Bernard focused on identifying the glass characteristic produced by specific chemicals. Using this information, he was able to create a number of new formulas.

Zack Boyd developed a reputation as a maker of paperweights while working for Degenhart Glass. In addition, he gained experience in pressing novelty items. After a brief period of retirement, Elizabeth Degenhart asked Zack Boyd to assist her in the management of Degenhart Glass in 1964. When Zack Boyd died in 1968, Bernard

Boyd, who was working full–time at the Cambridge State Hospital, was asked by Elizabeth Degenhart to take over his father's responsibilities. Between 1968 and 1972 Bernard was assisted by Gus Therat. In 1976 Bernard gave up his job at the Cambridge State Hospital to become a full–time glassmaker.

Bernard F. Boyd, son of Bernard C., was discouraged from entering the glass business. Although working as a barber and beauty school instructor, Bernard F. could not hide his love of glass. When Elizabeth Degenhart died in 1978, Bernard C. and Bernard F. purchased the Degenhart factory.

Fifty Degenhart molds were included in the acquisition. The Degenhart "D" was replaced with the Boyd "B" in a diamond. The Boyds began production on October 10, 1978. Today the firm has available over two hundred different molds. A new color is produced about every six weeks. The firm's color list is rapidly approaching three hundred different colors.

John, son of Bernard F., joined the firm after graduating from the University of Wisconsin–Milwaukee. Among his special interests are the pressing process.

The Boyds carefully document all production molds and colors. This information is made available to collectors through *Boyd's Crystal Art Glass* published by the company.

**References:** Boyd's Crystal Art Glass, *Boyd's Crystal Art Glass: The Tradition Continues,* Boyd's Crystal Art Glass, n.d.; Todd Holmes, *Boyd Glass Workbook,* published by author, 1992.

**Periodicals:** *Boyd's Crystal Art Glass,* PO Box 127, 1203 Morton Ave., Cambridge, OH 43725; *Jody & Darrell's Glass Collectibles,* PO Box 180833, Arlington, TX 76096.

**Collectors' Club:** Boyd Art Glass Collectors Guild, PO Box 52, Hatboro, PA 19040.

**Advisor:** Todd Holmes.

Baby Shoe, toothpick holder, early color **6.00**
Balloon Bear, figurine, Patrick, limited to 30 colors, 2" h, solid glass
  Alexandrite **6.00**
  Country Red **6.50**
Bernie, The Eagle, figurine, 2½" h, limited to thirty colors, first color: cardinal red carnival **9.00**
Bingo Deer, figurine, retired 1987
  Azure Blue **8.00**
  Candyland **8.00**
  Carmel **8.00**
  Custard **8.00**
  Heliotrope **8.00**
  Indian Orange **8.00**
  Milk White **8.00**
  Misty Vale **8.00**
  Skytop Blue **9.00**
Boyd Airplane, figurine, 4" l, 3¼" w, 2" h, introduced in Nov, 1991, first color: Classic Black **15.00**
Bull Dog Head
  Heather **10.00**
  Ice Green **10.00**
Candy Dish, Dawn **12.00**
Chick Salt, orig Degenhart mold, Degenhart logo replaced by Boyd diamond B trademark in 1978, produced in over 125 colors.
  Alexandrite, #104, 1989 **7.00**
  Butterscotch, #5, 1979 **25.00**
  Candyland, #86, 1987 **7.00**
  Cardinal Red, #126, 1992 **8.00**
  Colonial Blue, #84, 1987 **10.00**
  Copper Glo, #20, 1979 **10.00**
  Crown Tuscan Carnival, #115, 1990 **7.00**
  Daffodil, #54, 1984 **8.00**
  English Yew, #43, 1983 **6.00**
  Flame, #32, 1981 **20.00**
  Grape Parfait Carnival, #109, 1989 **8.00**
  Ivorene, 1992, hp Christmas dec **10.00**
  Jadite, #100, 1988 **8.00**
  Kumquat, #81, 1986 **9.50**
  Mulberry Mist, #65, 1985 **11.00**
  Peanut Butter, #30, 1980 **12.00**
  Pippin Green, #39, 1982 **8.00**
  Robin Egg Blue, #12, 1979 **20.00**
  Royalty, #2, 1978 **10.00**
  Thanksgiving, #72, 1985 **7.00**
  Vaseline Carnival, #93, 1988 **8.00**
Chuckles The Clown, figurine
  Baby Blue **7.00**
  Confetti **7.00**
  Lullaby **7.00**
  Pistachio **7.50**
  Ritz Blue **7.00**
  Sea Green **7.00**
  Vaseline **8.00**
  White Opal **8.00**
Colonial Doll, doll, introduced October 1984, limited to 26 different names and colors **14.00**
Debbie Duck, figurine, introduced July 21, 1981, trademark on all items "B" in a diamond
  Mardi Gras **6.00**
  Snow **5.00**
Ducklings, figurine, introduced Sept 15, 1981, trademark on all items "B" in a diamond
  Furr Green **3.00**
  Golden Delight **2.50**
  Light Rose **2.50**
Duck, salt
  Buckeye **6.00**
  Cardinal Red **6.00**
  Classic Black **6.00**
  Cobalt Carnival **6.00**

- Crown Tuscan **6.00**
- Dove Blue **6.00**
- Lime Carnival **6.00**
- Nile Green **6.00**
- Orange Spice **6.00**
- Patriot White **6.00**
- Spinnaker Blue **6.00**
- Vaseline **6.00**

Fuzzy Bear, figurine, retired 1989
- Alexandrite **10.00**
- Autumn Beige **12.00**
- Carmel Slag **10.00**
- Country Red **10.00**
- Orange Calico **12.00**
- Oxford Gray **10.00**
- Pistachio **10.00**
- Rosewood **10.00**
- Sea Green **10.00**
- Sunflower Yellow **10.00**
- Thistlebloom **10.00**

Grape, card holder
- Buckeye **6.00**
- Cardinal Red **7.00**
- Classic Black Slag **6.00**
- Columbus Blue **6.00**
- Primrose **6.00**

Hobo Clown, figurine, Freddie, limited to 30 colors, 3″ h, solid glass
- Alexandrite **8.00**
- Cobalt **8.50**

Jeremy, introduced October, 1992, 2¼″ l, 1¼″ h, vaseline **6.00**

Joey, figurine, leaping pony, introduced March, 1980, trademark on all items "B" in a diamond
- Candyland **40.00**
- Lavender **12.00**
- Lime Carnival **18.00**
- Misty Vale **20.00**
- Persimmon **12.00**
- Ruby **25.00**
- Zack Boyd Slag **12.00**

Kitten on Pillow, figurine **15.00**

Louise, doll, introduced Sept 1979, trademark on all items "B" in a diamond
- Apricot **20.00**
- Cornsilk **15.00**
- Firefly **15.00**
- Flame **15.00**
- Golden Delight **10.00**
- Lemon Ice **100.00**
- Persimmon **12.00**
- Pink Champagne **25.00**
- Sunburst **12.00**
- Violet Slate **15.00**

Lucky Unicorn, figurine **12.00**

Owl, figurine
- Aggravation **15.00**
- Apricot Slag **50.00**
- Candy Swirl **9.00**
- Crown Tuscan **9.00**
- Dawn **9.00**
- Delphinium **9.00**
- Heather **9.00**
- Lavender N' Lace **9.00**
- Light Rose **9.00**
- Mardi Gras **9.00**
- Old Ivory **9.00**
- Olympic White Carnival **15.00**
- Peanut Butter **20.00**
- Redwood **50.00**
- Shasta White **15.00**
- Teal Swirl **15.00**

Pooch, figurine
- Confetti **20.00**
- Honey Pink **15.00**
- Marigold **9.00**
- Tropical Green Slag **9.00**
- Walnut Green Slag **9.00**
- Winter Green Slag **9.00**

**Toothpick Holder, gypsy pot, chocolate, $6.00.**

Sammy The Squirrel, figurine
- Alexandrite **5.00**
- Autumn Beige **5.00**
- Cashmere Pink **6.00**
- Classic Black Carnival **6.00**
- Dijon **5.00**
- Enchantment **5.00**
- Grape Parfait **5.00**
- Mulberry Carnival **6.00**
- Peach **5.00**
- Shasta White **5.00**
- Windsor Blue **5.00**

Santa, bell
- Cardinal Red Carnival **17.00**
- Cobalt **15.00**
- Olde Lyme **15.00**
- Rubina **16.00**
- Spinnaker Blue **15.00**

Scottie Dog, JB, figurine, mold retired in 1988, marked with "R," vaseline carnival **10.00**

Skippy, figurine, sitting dog, trademark on all items "B" in a diamond
- Bermuda **8.00**
- Cornsilk **8.00**
- Crown Tuscan **8.00**
- Golden Delight **8.00**

Light Rose . . . . . . . . 8.00
Mint Green . . . . . . . . 8.00
Pippin Green Slag . . . . . . . . 8.00
Pocono . . . . . . . . 8.00
Violet Slate Carnival . . . . . . . . 8.00

Swan, 4½" h, master salt
Lemonade . . . . . . . . 12.00
Lilac . . . . . . . . 13.00
Milk White . . . . . . . . 12.00
Olde Lyme . . . . . . . . 12.00
Orange Spice . . . . . . . . 13.00
Seafoam . . . . . . . . 12.00
Spinnaker Blue . . . . . . . . 12.00

Willie The Mouse, figurine, 2" h, introduced April, 1990
Christmas Willie, 1991 . . . . . . . . 12.00
Lime Carnival, 1990 . . . . . . . . 8.00

Woodchuck, (Ground Hog), figurine, Bermuda Slag . . . . . . . . 10.00

Zack Elephant, figurine
Crystal . . . . . . . . 12.00
Lilac . . . . . . . . 11.00

# BREWERIANA

**Collecting Hints:** Many collectors concentrate on items from one specific brewery or region. An item will bring slightly more when it is sold in its locality. Regional collector clubs and shows abound.

**History:** Collecting material associated with the brewing industry developed in the 1960s, when many local breweries ceased production. Three areas occupy the collectors' interest: pre–Prohibition material, advertising items for use in taverns and premiums designed for individual use.

**References:** George J. Baley, *Back Bar Breweriana: A Guide To Advertising Beer Statues and Beer Shelf Signs,* L–W Book Sales, 1992; Donald Bull, *A Price Guide To Beer Advertising Openers And Corkscrews,* privately printed, 1981; Donald Bull, Manfred Friedrich, and Robert Gottschalk, *American Breweries,* Bullworks, 1984; Norman E. Martinus and Harry L. Rinker, *Warman's Paper,* Wallace–Homestead, 1993; Keith Osborne and Brian Pipe, *The International Book of Beer Labels, Mats, & Coasters,* Chartwell Books, 1979.

**Collectors' Clubs:** American Breweriana Association Inc., P. O. Box 11157, Pueblo, CO 81001; East Coast Breweriana Association, 2010 N. Broad St., Lansdale, PA 19446; National Association of Breweriana, Advertising, 2343 Mattu–Wee Lane, Wauwatosa, WI 53226.

**REPRODUCTION ALERT:** Advertising trays have been heavily reproduced.

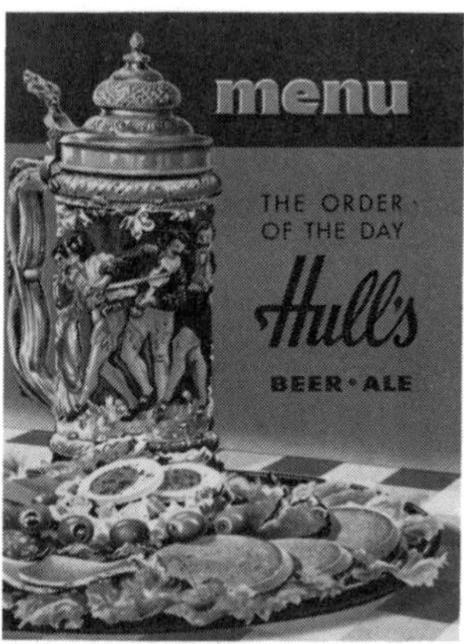


**Menu, Hull's Beer-Ale, Hull's Brewing Co., New Haven, CT, 8¼ x 11", $1.00.**

Banner, Cold Spring Brewing Co, Lawrence, MA, cloth, embroidered, period gentleman raising mug, 1898 calendar attached, 18½" w, 24" h . . . . . 135.00

Barrel Printing Blocks, Old Reading Beer, Reading, PA, brass, side and end printing plates, set of six . . . . . . 55.00

Beer Cooler, oak, brass hardware, three spigots, tin lined ice chest below, copper inserts and sink assembly, Cleveland faucet pressure gauge, 42" w, 24" d, 37" h . . . . . . . . 375.00

Bottle Opener, Munchen–Sapporo, chrome, tap shaped handle . . . . . . . . 25.00

Calendar
Ballantine's Breweries, Newark, NJ, cardboard, factory illus at top, 1908 calendar pad, 12½" w, 20" h 350.00
John C Stocker Brewer, Reading, PA, paper, pretty girl lounging on ornate chair, 1903 calendar pad, printed by Kaufmann & Strauss, 14½" w, 19" d . . . . . . . . 600.00
Weisbrod & Hess Brewery, Philadelphia, PA, paper, seashore, sailing, and boardwalk vignettes, 1903 calendar pad, 20" w, 28" h . . . . . . . . 1,100.00

Charger, tin
Early Times Distillery Co, backwoods Kentucky scene, Blacks tending still, 24" d . . . . . . . . 550.00
McCormick Brewery, Boston, MA, table setting illus, lobster, beer bottles, and flowers, 24" d . . . . . . . . 100.00

Clock
Budweiser, watch shape . . . . . . . . 75.00
Sunshine Beer, Sunshine Brewing Co, Reading, PA, round, electric, "Drink Premium," 15" d . . . . . . . . 115.00

Display, Stroh's, 1910 delivery truck illus . . . . . . . . 55.00

Foam Scraper, celluloid, white, black inscription "Berghoff–Old Munich Process" both sides, c1920 ........ **15.00**

Lamp Shade, glass globe, hanging, two sided, adv inserts both sides, orig fitter rings and screw caps, 15″ d

- Arrow Beer, Globe Brewing Co, "77" superimposed over globe showing American continents, milk glass .. **725.00**
- Gunther's Beer, reverse glass inserts with company logo, red, yellow, and black, clear crinkled glass body ........................ **2,000.00**

Match Safe, Olde Stock Lager, Bergner & Ensel Brewing Co, celluloid wrapped tin, Phoenix logo one side, girl portrait other side, 1½″ w, 2¾″ h **65.00**

Mirror, pocket

- Lyken's Cream Topped Lager, oval, woman wearing red shawl, 1¾″ w, 2¾″ h ........................ **50.00**
- Ryan's Pure Beers, Syracuse, NY, celluloid, Indian wearing headdress, 2″ d .......................... **200.00**

Pocket Knife, Anheuser–Busch, emb case, factory scene one side, logo and banner other side, three blades, 3¼″ l, ¾″ w ........................ **150.00**

Pocket Watch, Fox Valley Brewing Co, Ingersoll Jr, adv on enameled back, 1¾″ w, 2½″ h .................. **275.00**

Poster, Rising Sun Brewing Co, Philadelphia, PA, paper, brewmeister holding raised beer glass, 15″ w, 23″ h .. **650.00**

Pressure Testing Gauge, nickel plated, 7″ w, 19″ h ..................... **35.00**

Salt and Pepper Shakers, pr, Ballantine Beer, aluminum and cardboard, can design, c1940 .................. **25.00**

Sign

- Bartels Beer, painted canvas, man holding raised beer glass, "Bartels The Professor Says Is A Pure Beer," 26″ w, 56″ h .................. **375.00**
- Eckart Bro's Lager Beer, Eagle Brewery, Bridgeport, CT, emb tin, eagle on globe, 18″ w, 24″ h .......... **825.00**
- Falstaff Beer, 24″ d, tin, round, concave, old man and family in castle **125.00**
- Miller High Life, neon, logo script within shield, orig packing crate, 29½″ w, 13″ d, 23″ h ........... **250.00**
- Progress Beer, cardboard, three black men playing poker and drinking beer ......................... **175.00**
- Yuengling's Beer, Pottsville, PA, corner sign, glass, reverse painted, oval, center eagle and beer barrel logo, wooden backframe, 16″ w, 20″ h ........................ **3,850.00**

Stationery, Stroh's Brewery, five sheets **10.00**

Stein, Budweiser, 1983 ............. **20.00**

Tap, Scheidt's Rams Head Ale, chromeplated, enameled front, 1¾″ w, 2″ h ............................... **15.00**

Thermometer, Lone Star Beer, round, 1958 .......................... **125.00**

**Tray, Lang's Beer and Ale, Gerhard Lang Brewery, Buffalo, NY, cream, black, and red, 13½″ d, $28.00.**

Tray

- Serving
  - Augustiner Beer, Reading, PA, seated man and woman, man holding bottle, 13″ d .......... **450.00**
  - Baltimore Brewing Co, rect, center oval portrait of woman holding glass, 10½″ w, 13¼″ h ........ **185.00**
  - Buffalo Brewing, Sacramento, CA, girl's portrait, 13″ d ........... **100.00**
  - Cleveland and Sandusky Brewing Co, factory illus, hops border, 14″ d ....................... **165.00**
  - Conrad Seipp Brewing Co, girl with braids drinking beer, "Pure Food Beer," 13½″ d ............... **100.00**
  - Consumers' Brewing Co, Erie, PA, "Beer, Ale & Porter," flying eagle, flag and hops in talons, vacuum tank in background, 12″ d **675.00**
  - Heim Brewery, East St Louis, Art Nouveau, woman and elf ..... **85.00**
  - Jos Doelger's Sons, portly brewmeister holding foaming glass of beer, Kaufmann & Strauss, 12″ d ......................... **1,265.00**
  - Liberty Beer, Liberty Brewing Co, Tamaqua, PA, three white horses, 12¼″ d ............. **350.00**
  - National Beer, National Brewing Co, San Francisco, CA, judge pouring glass of beer, "A Good Judge," 13¼″ d ............. **80.00**
  - Pabst, Milwaukee, emb, center sunburst logo surrounded by hops, 12″ d .................. **30.00**
  - Stroh's, Detroit, oval, hooded child

carrying case of beer, 10½" w, 13" h ........................ **225.00**
Wayne Brewing, frontier fort, "Mad Anthony Wayne Blockhouse, Erie, PA," 12" d .............. **100.00**

Tip, round
Stegmaier Brewing Co, PA, factory scene, 4¼" d ................ **100.00**
Terre Haute Brewing Co, diners raising glasses in toast to cherubs above table, "That Ever–Welcome Beer," 4½" d ........... **85.00**

# BRITISH ROYALTY COMMEMORATIVES

**Collecting Hints:** Some collectors choose one monarch around whom to build their collections. Others choose only pieces for special occasions, such as coronations, jubilees, marriages, investitures, births, or memorials. Another approach is to specialize in only one form, e.g., thimbles, mugs, beakers, teapots, spoons, etc.

Since most early pieces were used in the home for eating and drinking, it is especially difficult to find older commemoratives in good condition. Wear from use and age often shows through fading and loss of colors and transfers. Porous pottery pieces lend themselves to crazing inside and out from age and shrinkage.

Serious collectors seek the older and rarer pieces, while keeping up–to–date with examples from the modern events. Crown shaped teapots, etched and cut crystal, hand and machine woven tapestries, and jewelry are just a few of the things that link old and new collecting.

**History:** British commemorative china was first produced rather crudely in design and form. These were basically cheaper and more available pieces of Delft, stoneware, and slipware. With John Brook's invention of transfer printing in the mid–18th century, British commemorative wares bore a closer likeness to the reigning monarch.

King George IV's coronation was the first royal occasion for which children received municipal gifts. Some towns presented medals, while others gave plates with commemorative inscriptions. China commemorative pieces were produced by the thousands for Queen Victoria's 1887 and 1897 jubilees. It was not until 1902 that the presentation of municipal gifts became widespread; the practice is continued today. Thousands of children received mugs with the official coronation design of Queen Elizabeth II in celebration of her 1953 coronation.

Through the years, improved production techniques combined with finer artistic design have enhanced the overall appearance of British Royalty commemoratives. Aynsley, Minton, Paragon, Royal Doulton, Shelley, Wedgwood, and other leading manufacturers have produced outstanding limited and unlimited edition items. Artists such as Clarice Cliff, Dame Laura Knight, and Professor Richard Guyatt have designed special pieces.

Some British Royalty commemoratives are easily recognized by the portraits of the monarchs they honor. Often these portraits are surrounded by decorations such as flags, the national flowers (roses, thistles, daffodils, and shamrocks), ribbons with commemorative messages or lions and unicorns. Cyphers and crowns also are popular decorations. Royal residences such as Windsor Castle, Balmoral and Highgrove House may also appear. Town mottos or crests were added to individualize municipal gifts for earlier coronations. Advertisers often linked their products to royal events.

Other British Royalty commemoratives are not easy to recognize. Many do not have portraits of monarchs on them, although there might be a silhouette profile. Other characteristics include crowns, dragons, royal coats of arms, national flowers, swords, scepters, dates, messages and cyphers of the monarch. Earlier pieces sometimes bear crude likenesses of early monarchs. Timely verses or couplets may be inscribed, e.g., "God Save The King," "Long Live The Queen."

A listing of outstanding achievements or inventions during a monarch's reign may appear on jubilee or memorial pieces. Some newer items list the order of succession to the throne, previous holders of a title, and family trees.

**References:** Susan and Al Bagdade, *Warman's English & Continental Pottery & Porcelain,* 2nd Edition, Wallace–Homestead, 1991; M. H. Davey and D. J. Mannion, *Fifty Years Of Royal Commemorative China 1887–1937,* Dayman Publications, 1988; Lincoln Hallinan, *British Commemoratives: Royalty, Politics, War and Sport,* Antique Collectors' Club, 1993; Josephine Jackson, *Fired For Royalty,* Heaton Moor, 1977; David Rogers, *Coronation Souvenirs and Commemoratives,* Latimer New Dimensions, Ltd., 1975; Peter Johnson, *Royal Memorabilia: A Phillips Collectors Guide,* Dunestyle Publishing, Ltd., 1988; John May, *Victoria Remembered, A Royal History 1817–1861,* Heinemann, London, 1983; John and Jennifer May, *Commemorative Pottery 1780–1900, A Guide for Collectors,* Charles Scribner's Sons, 1972; Sussex Commemorative Ware Centre, *200 Commemoratives,* Metra Print Enterprises, 1979; Geoffrey Warren, *Royal Souvenirs,* Orbis, 1977; Audrey B. Zeder, *British Royal Commemoratives,* Wallace–Homestead, 1986.

**Advisors:** Doug Flynn and Al Bolton.

Queen Elizabeth II, February 6, 1952, to present

**Queen Elizabeth II, candy tin, George W. Horner & Co, Ltd., commemorates opening of the St. Lawrence Seaway, 5″ w, 4¼″ d, 3″ h, $15.00.**

Coronation, June 2, 1953
- Bowl, 8″ d, 4½″ h, pressed glass, crowns and commemoration around side panels ........... **45.00**
- Box, cov
  - 5¼″ h, orb shape, emb gold, white ground, limited edition of 600, Minton, bone china . **375.00**
  - 5¼″ h, 3½″ d, raised profile portrait, brass clad wood ....... **55.00**
- Bust, 2¾″ h, molded glass, 1¼″ sterling silver base ............ **45.00**
- Cup and Saucer, bone china
  - Paragon, color floral dec, cypher and crown in cup well, gold trim ...................... **50.00**
  - Royal Standard, sepia portrait, color dec, gold trim ........ **45.00**
- Dish, 4½″ d, commemorative coin center, hallmarked sterling silver **165.00**
- Jug, musical, 6″ h, raised profile portrait, cypher and crown, arms on reverse, Royal Winton ..... **145.00**
- Mug, bone china
  - 3″ h, sepia portrait, color dec, crown and scepter on reverse, Shelley .................. **45.00**
  - 3¼″ h, brown tone portrait, pale green ground, large color crown on reverse, Aynsley .. **100.00**
  - 3½″ h, color and gold lion and unicorn, cypher, and crown outlined in black on reverse, Crown Staffordshire ......... **45.00**
  - 4″ h, royal cypher and crown, partially hand painted, commemoration on reverse, Stanley ...................... **90.00**
- Plate, bone china
  - 10¼ x 9″, brown tone portrait with crown above, color dec, Aynsley .................. **95.00**
  - 10¾″ d, large lion, unicorn, and royal standard, commemoration around border, Paragon . **225.00**
- Pocket Knife, 3¼″ l, color portrait, mother–of–pearl background .. **60.00**
- Puzzle, jigsaw
  - 12 x 9¼″, color portraits, Queen in white gown, Prince Philip in formal attire, 160 plywood backed pieces, Langley Kolorbax ...................... **50.00**
  - 14 x 12″, color portrait of Queen, color scenes around border, 250 plywood backed pieces . **70.00**
- Textile, luncheon cloth, 34″ sq, linen, hand embroidered color dec, hem stitched border ...... **75.00**
- Tin
  - 6¼ x 4¾″, color portrait, gold dec, dark blue ground, Cadbury Brothers .............. **20.00**
  - 6¾ x 6″, color portrait, red dec, gold tone ground, McVitie & Price Ltd .................. **30.00**
  - 7 x 3½″ h, color portraits, color and silver dec, medium blue ground, Wright's ........... **25.00**
  - 9 x 6″, color portraits in Garter robes, W & R Jacob & Co ... **30.00**
  - 11¼ x 7¼″, color portraits, royal residences on sides, Carr & Co Biscuits ................... **25.00**

40th Anniversary of Accession, 1992
- Box, cov, 2⅛″ l, color national flowers and commemoration on lid, black profile inside lid, vignette tree tops inside base, Halcyon Days, enamel ........... **125.00**
- Toby Jug, 8½″ h, Queen in pink gown, seated with corgi at her side, waving right hand, limited edition of 400, Kevin Francis .. **220.00**

Silver Jubilee, 1977
- Bowl, 9¼″ d, gold profile portrait, white and ruby ground, small gold dec, limited edition of 500, Wedgwood, bone china ....... **395.00**
- Cigarette Lighter, 3¾″ h, white applied profile portrait and decorative band on royal blue jasperware, Ronson lighter, Wedgwood ................. **125.00**
- Jug, 8½″ h, raised coronation scene on front, Westminster Abbey on reverse, orig produced in color for 1953 coronation, white and pale blue, silver trim, Burleigh . **175.00**
- Plate
  - 8″ d, white profile portrait and rim band, pale blue jasperware ground, Wedgwood ........ **60.00**
  - 10½″ d, royal arms and gold

commemoration in center, wide blue on blue lattice border, limited edition of 2,000, Royal Worcester, bone china **150.00**

Teapot, 5½" h, black and white portrait, gold cypher and commemorative band, Price ....... **85.00**

Prince Charles

Investiture as Prince of Wales, July 1, 1969

Chalice, 4½" h, gold Caernarvon Castle, Welsh dragon, royal emblems, and commemoration, white ground, Coalport, bone china ...................... **150.00**

Mug, 4" h, feathers, dragon and crown in black and gold, commemoration in gold inside rim, R Guyatt design, Wedgwood .... **125.00**

Vase, 8½" h, color and gold coat of arms, gold commemoration inside top rim, previous Princes of Wales in gold on reverse with Prince of Wales feathers above, limited edition of 250, made by Spode for Thomas Goode & Co, Ltd, London, bone china ...... **525.00**

Prince Charles and Lady Diana Spencer

Royal Wedding, July 29, 1981

Bust, 6" h, Prince Charles, hp, limited edition of 1,000, Coalport, bone china ................. **85.00**

Chalice, 5" h, engraved commemoration around gilt Prince of Wales feathers, gold wash int., presentation case, hallmarked sterling silver ............... **275.00**

Figure, Charles and Diana, full length, standing

7" h, bone china, wedding attire, modeled by John Bromley, limited edition of 500, Coalport . **850.00**

9½" h, cast bronze, sgd "P Parsons," limited edition of 1,000, Heridities Ltd ........ **395.00**

Ginger Jar, 5" h, sepia portraits, color dec, Mason's ............. **60.00**

Loving Cup, bone china

3½" h, betrothal, color engagement portrait, Lady Diana's hand wearing engagement ring on reverse, Caverswall ...... **100.00**

6¼" h, color portraits, three dragon shaped handles, Prince of Wales feathers, national flowers, Highgrove House on sides, limited edition of 500, Caverswall ................ **450.00**

Mug, bone china

3¼" h, color portraits and dec, family arms on reverse, Coalport ..................... **75.00**

4¼" h, brown tone portraits, color dec, commemoration on reverse, Hammersley ......... **45.00**

4½" h, color portraits, family arms with crown above on reverse, commemorative band inside rim, Crown Staffordshire **55.00**

Paperweight

2¾" d, sulphide portraits, cobalt blue ground, CR Albert ..... **265.00**

3" d, etched portraits and commemoration, purple ground, limited edition of 750, Caithness ..................... **175.00**

Pin Tray, 6 x 3¾", white applied portraits and dec, pale blue jasperware, Wedgwood ......... **65.00**

Plaque, 9½ x 7¼", black and white portraits, color dec, emb border, Britannia Pottery Ltd .......... **45.00**

Plate

6½" d, white profile portraits, Prince of Wales feathers, pale blue jasperware, Wedgwood . **75.00**

10" d, engraved commemoration and arms, names below, copper, limited edition of 1,250, C Morgan ................ **65.00**

10½" d, gold profiles and dec, cobalt blue ground, limited edition of 2,500, Bing and Grondahl ................ **135.00**

Tin

4½" h, post box shape, color portrait and dec, red ground, commemoration on reverse .. **20.00**

5¾" h, color portraits on all sides, red, white, and blue dec **30.00**

6" h, octagonal, color portraits on four sides, Prince of Wales feathers on other four, dark blue ground ............... **25.00**

Prince William of Wales

Born June 21, 1982

Box, cov, 1½" d, color dec includes angels and years, name inside, blue base, enamel, Crummles .. **100.00**

Loving Cup

3" h, color and gold dec, cherubs, flowers, ribbons, and name, limited edition of 500, Royal Crown Derby ........ **250.00**

3½" h, bone china, color portrait of Charles, Diana, and William by Lord Snowdon, commemoration in English and Welsh on reverse, limited edition of 250, Coronet ........ **70.00**

Mug

3½" h, bone china, cherubs above name and date, blue, gold, and white ground, Spode **50.00**

4" h, blue dec, crown on pillow, name and date below, R Guyatt design, limited edition of 1,000, Wedgwood ......... **65.00**
Plate, bone china
8¼" d, crown in center, name and date below, color dec, limited edition of 3,000, Royal Doulton .................. **125.00**
10½" d, crown, Union Jack, Welsh dragon in center, members of Royal Family around border, limited edition of 2,000, Caverwall ........... **80.00**

Prince Henry of Wales
Born Sept 15, 1984
Loving Cup, 3¼" h, bone china, name surrounded by ribbons and flowers, gold lion handles, Paragon ....................... **95.00**
Money Box, 4¼" h, book shape, colorful Bunnykins design, commemoration, Royal Doulton ... **45.00**

Prince Andrew and Miss Sarah Ferguson
Royal Wedding, July 23, 1986
Cup and Saucer, bone china
Coalport, color portraits and dec, commemoration on reverse of cup ..................... **45.00**
Colclough, color portraits, commemoration on reverse of cup, "A" with crown above on saucer ...................... **25.00**
Loving Cup, 3¼" h, bone china
Paragon, initials above crown, arms on reverse, gold lion handles ..................... **95.00**
Sutherland for Peter Jones Collection, color portraits, initials, flowers, and doves ......... **120.00**
Mug
2⅞" h, bone china, gold silhouette portraits, conferment of Dukedom of York commemoration on reverse, Wedgwood **70.00**
3" h, colorful Bunnykins dec, commemorative band inside rim, Royal Doulton ......... **35.00**
3½" h, musical, light activated, color portraits inside green wreath frame with crown above ................... **25.00**
3¾" h, bone china, color dec with lion and unicorn, family trees on reverse, commemorative band inside rim, Aynsley **45.00**
Plate, bone china
8" d, color portrait in wedding attire, conferment of Dukedom of York commemoration, lists previous Dukes of York and their dates, Coronet ........ **50.00**
8½" d, brown silhouette portraits, Westminster Abbey, bells and flags, limited edition of 1,500, Caverswall ....... **55.00**

Princess Beatrice
Born August 8, 1988
Mug, 3" h, bone china, gold profile portraits of Andrew and Sarah, gold dec, white ground, limited edition of 2,500, Coalport ..... **75.00**

Princess Eugenie
Born March 23, 1990
Plate, 8½" d, bone china, color portrait of Andrew, Sarah, Beatrice, and Eugenie, coat of arms, limited edition of 1,000, Caverswall ....................... **55.00**

**King George VI and Queen Elizabeth, 1939 United States visit commemorative plate, blue and white, beaded rim, Royal Ivory, John Maddock & Sons, Ltd., England, 8¾" w, $40.00.**

King George VI and Queen Elizabeth, Dec 10, 1936 to Feb 6, 1952
Coronation May 12, 1937
Beaker, 4" h, beige tone portraits, color dec, Crown Ducal ...... **45.00**
Butter Dish, 6 x 5 x 3½" h, beige tone portraits, color dec, Lancaster and Sons ................. **80.00**
Cup and Saucer
Beige tone portraits, color dec, blue trim, no mark ......... **40.00**
Sepia Marcus Adams portrait, Princesses Elizabeth and Margaret, bone china, Royal Albert ..................... **115.00**
Flag, 33 x 22", cotton, black and white portraits above world maps, coat of arms, 1937 below, Union Jack background ....... **45.00**
Loving Cup, 5½" h, crystal, etched "G VI R" with crown above,

"Coronation," date, and national flowers etched on reverse, Cambridge ...................... 125.00
Mug, 3½" h, sepia portraits, small portrait of Princess Elizabeth on reverse ...................... 50.00
Plate
5½" d, bone china, color arms, cypher and date, commemorative band around border, Paragon .................. 55.00
6" d, pottery, sepia portraits, small portrait of Princess Elizabeth .................... 45.00
9" d, bone china, large cypher and color shields of empire countries, Hammersley ...... 200.00
Playing Cards, double deck, color Vandyk portraits, King on one deck, Queen on other ........ 65.00
Puzzle, jigsaw, 16 x 12", color portraits, (one on each puzzle), wooden back, price for pair ... 100.00
Tin
4½" sq, raised gold portraits, deep blue ground .......... 55.00
5¼" d, large color portraits and dec, Mackintosh's .......... 45.00
Queen Elizabeth, The Queen Mother
80th Birthday, August 4, 1980
Box, cov, 4" d, bone china, color portrait and dec, commemoration on base, Crown Staffordshire 65.00
Goblet, 8" h, crystal, etched portrait, commemoration on reverse 125.00
Mug, 3½" h, color floral dec surrounds gold commemoration, designed by Dorn Williams for National Trust ............... 45.00
Plate, 8¼" d, bone china, large maroon tone portrait with crown and flower, commemorative band around border, Coronet .. 65.00
90th Birthday, August 4, 1990, miniature cup and saucer, 1" h, bone china, color portrait, national flowers and commemoration on reverse, Caverswall .............. 30.00

**Edward VIII, coronation, tumbler, Royal seal on reverse, Ayusley Bone China, England, 4⅛" h, $35.00.**

King Edward VIII, Jan 20, 1936, abdicated Dec 10, 1936, coronation scheduled for May 12, 1937. Coronation items are not rare since most were in stores before the abdication.
Cup and Saucer, color portrait and dec, cypher and crown on reverse, Creampetal by Grindley ......... 60.00
Flag, 8½ x 12½", cotton, black and white portrait above two globe, Union Jack background ......... 25.00
Jug, 7½" h, pottery, large cypher with "1937" below, blue and white squares with red dots, designed by Charlotte Rhead, Crown Ducal ... 200.00
Loving Cup, 3" h, bone china, sepia portrait front and reverse, color dec, floral band around inside, ext. rims, and handle, Anchor ....... 120.00
Medal, 1" d, 2¾" ribbon, raised profile portrait and date, orig card, orig box .......................... 50.00
Mug
3½" h, bone china, sepia portrait, crown above, commemoration below, Delphine ............. 60.00
4¼" h, large sepia portrait, dressed in leisure suit, name below, sepia flags on reverse, no mark ...... 115.00
Plaque, 12½ x 12", brass, large profile portrait in center, Cameograph Co Ltd ........................ 225.00
Plate, 9" d, Accession, color portrait and dec, Ruwaha Belgium ....... 175.00
Tin
3" h, large color portrait by Bertram Park ......................... 60.00
6" d, sepia portrait, castle in background, Walter's Palm Toffee .. 45.00
King George V and Queen Mary, May 6, 1910 to Jan 20, 1936
Coronation, June 26, 1911
Bank, 6¾" h, cast iron, raised profiles in center, arms above, date below ...................... 220.00
Beaker, 4" h, black and white portraits, birth, marriage, and coronation dates, S Fielding & Co .. 65.00
Handkerchief, 20" sq, linen, blue, full length portraits in coronation robes with Prince of Wales below 70.00
Mug
3" h, raised portraits, green and blue slip dec, terra cotta ground, no mark ........... 100.00
4" h, black and white portrait, purple slip dec, at top and handle, leadless glaze .......... 125.00

Plate, 9″ d, color portraits and dec, Royal Winton ................ **65.00**
Pocket Knife, 2¾″ l, raised portraits with crowns above and arms below, silvertone metal ......... **55.00**
Tin, 4 x 3″, color portraits and dec, Rountree .................... **40.00**
Royal Wedding, 1893, tin, 6½″ sq, 7¼″ h, color portraits of bride and groom, their parents, and bridesmaids, Queen Victoria on lid .... **245.00**
Silver Jubilee, 1935
Egg Cup, color portraits and crown, silver trim .................. **40.00**
Mug
4″ h, sepia portraits, crown, and commemoration on reverse, Alfred Meakin ............. **45.00**
4¼″ h, bone china, brown portraits in coronation robes, Tuscan ...................... **95.00**
Plate, 6¼″ d, bone china, sepia portraits, commemoration band around rim, silver trim, Paragon **65.00**

King Edward VII and Queen Alexandra, Jan 22, 1901 to May 6, 1910.Coronation originally scheduled for June 26, 1902, but postponed to Aug 9, 1902, because of King's appendicitis attack. Most coronation items carry the earlier date, and those with the correct date are difficult to find.
Beaker, 3¾″ h, green profile portraits and dec, Royal Doulton ......... **65.00**
Box, cov, 1½″ d, silverplate, King's name and royal arms in color enamel ...................... **45.00**
Cup and Saucer, metal, color portraits and dec on cup, color crown and coronet on saucer .............. **100.00**
Figure, 8¼″ h, King and Queen in coronation robes, hp color and gold dec, flat back ............ **325.00**
Jar, cov, 6″ h, terra cotta, hp cypher, royal arms and Prince of Wales feathers around sides ........... **200.00**
Mug, 3″ h, bone china, coronation chair and House of Lords throne on sides, royal coat of arms, Aynsley **125.00**
Plate, 7″ d, bone china, sepia portraits, color dec, partially hp, William Whitely Ltd .............. **70.00**
Teapot, 3½″ h, bone china, hp crown, flags, and flowers, commemoration ribbon below, Hammersley ...................... **145.00**
Tin, 4¾ x 2¼″, color portraits and dec, yellow ground, Rountree & Co **40.00**

Queen Victoria and Prince Albert, June 20, 1837 to Jan 22, 1901
Coronation, June 28, 1838
Mug, 3¼″ h, Queen Victoria on front, Duchess of Kent (her mother) on reverse, deep red transfer, proclamation and coronation dates ................ **1,800.00**
Diamond Jubilee, 1897
Cup and Saucer, bone china, black and white portraits of four generations, color flowers on sides, emb, made in Germany ....... **125.00**
Plaque, 8½ x 7½″, blue on white portraits and dec, gold on green border ...................... **250.00**
Plate, 8¾″ d, brown tone portrait, color dec, birth and accession dates, Hines Bros ............ **220.00**
Tin, 8½ x 5¼″ h, color portrait in coronation robes on lid, events of her reign including coronation scene on sides, Coleman Mustard ........................ **125.00**
Golden Jubilee, 1887
Bowl, 6″ d, pressed glass, ftd, "Jubilee of Queen Victoria 1837–1887" in beading, amber ...... **90.00**
Cup and Saucer, bone china, color crown with ribbons and date, William Whiteley Ltd ......... **75.00**
Jug, 4¼″ h, stoneware, raised scene of Queen seated on coronation chair, beige and brown dec, Doulton Lambeth ............ **225.00**
Tile, 6″ sq, raised crown, cypher, and dates, yellow on dark ground ground, JC Edwards (Wales) ... **120.00**
Royal Wedding, Feb 10, 1840
Plate, 7″ d, crown in center surrounded by commemoration, color emb flowers ............ **400.00**

King William IV and Queen Adelaide, June 26, 1830 to June 20, 1837
Coronation, Sept 8, 1831
Jug, purple transfer
5½″ h, King William on front, coronation scene on reverse . **650.00**
6″ h, King William on front, Queen Adelaide on reverse .. **575.00**

King George IV and Queen Caroline, Jan 29, 1820 to Jan 26, 1830
Coronation
Bust, 5¾″ h, wax, George IV, on plinth, D Morison Fecit ...... **1,400.00**
Plate, 5¾″ d, large profile portrait of Queen Caroline, blue dec, emb ........................ **525.00**
Vase, 6″ h, color portrait of King, coronation robes, gilded floral and foliage border ........... **1,200.00**
Queen Caroline In Memoriam
Plate
4″ d, central motif of mausoleum, "To The Memory of Queen

Caroline of England," Pratt .. **700.00**
7½" d, portrait of Queen above her tomb, Britannia weeping, dark brown transfer, emb red and yellow floral border, In Memoriam commemoration on tomb .................. **1,000.00**
Princess Charlotte In Memoriam
Jug, 5½" h, large portrait of Charlotte on front, Leopold on reverse, In Memoriam commemoration on reverse ............. **500.00**
King George III and Queen Charlotte, Oct 25, 1760 to Jan 29, 1820
King George III In Memoriam
Bowl, 10" d, "Sacred to the Memory of George III who died 29 Jan, 1820" surrounds the King's portrait, blue transfer ......... **1,100.00**

# BUBBLE GUM CARDS, NON–SPORT

**Collecting Hints:** Don't buy individual cards; buy full sets. The price of a set is below the sum of individual cards. By collecting sets you do lose some of the fun of trading cards; nevertheless, cards from this vintage are sold by sets. Any set should contain a sample of the wrapper plus any stickers that belong to the set.

Because of the availability of these cards, make certain the sets you buy are in mint condition. You can buy boxes of gum packages. With Topps you are 100% certain you will get at least one full set from a box. Donruss and Fleer average 85%.

Collectors should store cards in plastic sleeves. Place the wrapper first and then the cards in numerical order.

**History:** The birthplace of the modern bubble gum (trading) card is the tobacco insert cards of the late 19th century. From 1885 to 1894 there were over 500 sets issued, with only about 25 devoted to sports. Trading cards lost their popularity in the decade following World War I. However, in 1933 "Indian Gum" issued a product containing a stick of bubble gum and a card in a waxed paper package. A revolution had begun.

Goudey Gum and National Chicle controlled the market until the arrival of Gum, Inc., in 1936. Gum, Inc., issued The Lone Ranger and Superman sets in 1940. From 1943 to 1947 the market in cards was again quiet. In 1948 Bowman entered the picture. A year later Topps Chewing Gum produced some non–sports cards. A war between Bowman and Topps ensued until 1956 when Topps bought Bowman.

Although Topps enjoyed a dominant position in the baseball card market, it had continual rivals in the non–sports field. Frank Fleer Company, Leaf Brands, and Philadelphia Chewing Gum provided competition in the 1960s. Fleer and Donruss Chewing Gum provide the modern day assault.

**References:** Christopher Benjamin, *The Sport Americana Price Guide To Non–Sports Cards, 1930–1960, No. 2,* Edgewater Book Co., 1993; Christopher Benjamin, *The Sport Americana Price Guide To Non–Sports Cards, No. 4,* Edgewater Book Co., 1993; Norman E. Martinus and Harry L. Rinker, *Warman's Paper,* Wallace–Homestead, 1993; John Neuner, *Checklist & Prices of U. S. Non–Sport Wrappers,* Wrapper King Inc., 1992; Robert Reed, *Collector's Guide To Trading Cards: Identification & Values,* Collector Books, 1993.

**Periodicals:** *The Non–Sport Report* (Catalog from The Card Coach, but loaded with articles), P.O. Box 128, Plover, WI 54467; *The Non–Sport Update,* c/o Christopher Benjamin, 9 Davis Street, St. Augustine, FL 32095; *The Wrapper,* 1903 Ronzheimer Ave., St. Charles, IL 60174.

## BOWMAN

1948, Movie Stars, 36 cards ......... **275.00**
1949
America Salutes The FBI, 36 cards .. **225.00**
Wild West, 180 cards ............. **950.00**
1950, Bring 'Em Back Alive, 100 cards **375.00**
1951
Jets, Rockets, Spacemen, 108 cards **1,250.00**
Red Menace, 48 cards, gray backs . **500.00**
1952
Television & Radio Stars of NBC, 36 cards ......................... **275.00**
US Presidents, 36 cards ........... **85.00**

**Bowman, U.S. Presidents, No. 34, Franklin D. Roosevelt, 2½ x 3 ¾", 1952, $2.00.**

1953
Antique Autos, 48 cards ........... **175.00**
Frontier Days, 128 cards .......... **375.00**

## DONRUSS

1964
Addams Family, 66 cards .......... **80.00**
Combat, Series 1, 66 cards ........ **75.00**
1965
Disneyland, 66 cards, blue back ... **120.00**
Freddie & the Dreamers, 66 cards .. **55.00**
1966, Marvel Super Heroes, 66 cards . **60.00**
1968, Flying Nun, 66 cards ......... **75.00**
1972, Vote, 33 stickers ............. **8.00**
1973, Osmonds, 66 cards ........... **40.00**
1978
Elvis Presley, 66 cards ........... **5.00**
Sgt Pepper's Lonely Hearts Club Band, 66 cards ................ **5.00**
1980, Dukes of Hazard, 66 cards .... **5.50**
1981, Dallas, 56 cards .............. **5.00**
1982, Dark Crystal, 78 cards ........ **6.00**
1983
Knight Rider, 55 cards ............ **4.50**
Magnum PI, 66 cards ............. **5.00**

## GOUDEY GUM

1933, Sea Raiders, 48 cards ........ **1,325.00**
1936, History of Aviation, 10 cards ... **250.00**
1940, First Column Defenders, 24 cards **500.00**
1941, Sky Birds, 24 cards ........... **300.00**

## FLEER

1959, The 3 Stooges, 96 cards ....... **850.00**
1960
Casper, 66 cards ................. **250.00**
Spins and Needles, 80 cards ....... **300.00**
1963, Goofy Gags, 55 cards ......... **22.50**
1965, Gomer Pyle, 66 cards ......... **15.00**
1970, Believe It Or Not, 84 cards .... **50.00**
1981, Here's Bo, 72 cards, 12 paper posters .......................... **8.00**
1984, Dragon's Lair, 63 stickers, 30 rub off games ...................... **18.00**
1987, Grossville High, 66 cards ...... **7.00**

## LEAF

1960, Foney Ads, 72 cards .......... **120.00**
1966, Good Guys & Bad Guys, 72 cards **65.00**
1967
Garrisons' Gorillas, 72 cards ....... **65.00**
Star Trek, 72 cards ............... **700.00**

## PHILADELPHIA CHEWING GUM CO

1953, Blackstone's Magic Tricks, 24 cards .......................... **90.00**
1965, James Bond, 66 cards ......... **75.00**
1966
Daktari, 66 cards ................. **30.00**
Green Berets, 66 cards ............ **50.00**
1968
Dark Shadows, 66 cards, pink ..... **125.00**
Robert F Kennedy, 55 cards ........ **60.00**
1972, Happy Horoscopes, 72 cards .. **30.00**

## TOPPS

1950, Hopalong Cassidy, 238 cards .. **1,200.00**
1953, Fighting Marines, 96 cards ..... **550.00**
1955, Rails and Sails, 200 cards ..... **700.00**
1956
Davy Crockett, 80 cards, orange backs ......................... **290.00**
Jets, 240 cards ................... **415.00**
1957
Hit Stars, 88 cards ................ **575.00**
Robin Hood, 60 cards ............ **180.00**
1958
TV Westerns, 71 cards ............ **260.00**
Zorro, 88 cards .................. **250.00**
1959, Fabian, 55 cards ............. **100.00**
1962, Casey & Kildare, 110 cards .... **125.00**
1963
Astronauts, 55 cards ............. **70.00**
Beverly Hillbillies, 66 cards ....... **100.00**
1964, Beatles, Series 1, 60 cards ..... **75.00**
1965, Battle, 66 cards .............. **250.00**
1966, Batman–A Series, 44 cards .... **50.00**
1971, Bobby Sherman, Getting Together, 55 cards .................. **600.00**
1973, Kung Fu, 60 cards ............ **30.00**
1974
Evel Knievel, 60 cards ............ **50.00**
Six Million Dollar Man, 55 cards ... **500.00**
1979, Buck Rogers, 88 cards, 22 stickers ........................... **10.00**
1983, A–Team, 66 cards, 12 stickers . **5.00**
1985, Cyndi Lauper, 66 cards ........ **7.00**
1987, Alf, 69 cards, 18 stickers ...... **12.00**

# BUSINESS AND OFFICE EQUIPMENT

**Collecting Hints:** The most important considerations are condition and function. Mechanical novelty and clearly identifiable period styles heighten desirability.

Calculators and adding machines are the most commonly collected items. However, other types of machines are becoming more collectible because of their inherent scarcity. Other types of office equipment include: accounting machines, account registers, check writers and punches, dictating machines (wax cylinder machines), pencil sharpeners, staplers, mimeograph duplicators, autographic and key–driven cash registers, time recorders, slide rules, stenographic machines, telephones, etc.

Collectibility of office and business equipment has less to do with age than with its novelty and/or function. Many individuals buy them to keep at their offices or places of business as conversation pieces. Collectors are few and not very well organized. Calculator and adding machine collectors, often linked to the typewriter collecting community, are the exception.

Generally speaking, the smaller an item is, the more collectible it is. An example of the reverse are accounting machines. They are very scarce and difficult to find, yet they usually cost very little. The major cost involved is in the shipping hassle and expense to get them home. Many of these mechanical monsters weigh over 200 pounds.

**History:** The enormous growth in large business enterprises in the latter half of the 19th century demanded increased efficiency in office operations. The old methods of record generation and organization were not sufficient to keep up with the explosion of industrial and commercial activity of the late 1800s and early 1900s. Combined with the tremendous mechanical inventiveness of many individuals, this resulted in a large number of, and sometimes unique, mechanical devices which offered increased efficiency and profitability.

Most office machines fall within two categories: financial record keeping and communication.

The duplicator was one of the earliest types of office equipment. It took on a number of forms, the first recognizable one being the simple letter press. A recently penned letter, its ink still wet, would be sandwiched with a number of thin absorbent sheets of paper and pressed. Copies were poor, but more easily produced than the labor intensive hand copying. Thomas Edison's invention of the Mimeograph in the 1870s coupled with skilled marketing by A. B. Dick made the Mimeograph a common sight in nearly every turn–of–the–century office.

Calculating machines have been a part of some offices since the 1830s through the use of the Thomas Arithmometer or its variations. They were not particularly suitable for high volume and high speed addition. Truly practical and useful adding machines and calculators were not perfected until late in the 19th century. Early successful machines included Dorr E. Felt's Comptometer, Burrough's adding machines, and the numerous variations of the Baldwin–Ohdner type rotary calculators.

Checkpunches were the earliest mechanical attempts to limit the losses inflicted upon businesses through altered checks. The early machines actually punched figures in the paper check to show the true amount. They were quite slow and tedious to operate. Checkwriters in which the amount on the check was printed and the ink permanently imbedded into the paper fibers by the use of a perforating wheel or gear was the next natural evolutionary step. These machines became very popular after 1920. Next to the typewriter, the smaller checkwriters have more variations based on style than most other office equipment. Perhaps this had to do with the fact that these were generally kept on (or in) the boss's desk.

**References:** William Aspray, *Computing Before Computers*, Iowa State University Press, 1989; *The Business Machines and Equipment Digest 1927*, Chicago, 1927; Norman E. Martinus and Harry L. Rinker, *Warman's Paper,* Wallace–Homestead, 1993; NCR, *Celebrating the Future, 1884–1984*, published by company, 1984; Michael R. Williams, *A History of Computing Technology*, Prentice Hall, 1985.

**Collectors' Clubs:** Early Typewriter Collectors Association, 2591 Military Ave., Los Angeles, CA 90064; Internationales Forum Historische Burowelt e.w. (IFHB), P. O. Box 50 11 68, D–5000 Koln 50, Germany.

**Museums:** The Computer Museum, Boston, MA; Henry Ford Museum, Dearborn, MI; Smithsonian Institution, National Museum of American History, Division of Engineering & Industry, Washington, DC.

**Advisor:** Todd Holmes.

**See:** Typewriters.

## Accounting and Related Machines

Dalton bookkeeping machine ........ **100.00**
McCaskey account register .......... **40.00**
Moon Hopkins/Burroughs accounting machine ........................ **350.00**
Remington Model 23 bookkeeping machine .......................... **350.00**
Sundstrand bookkeeping machine .... **20.00**
Underwood bookkeeping machine ... **400.00**

## Adding Machines and Calculators

American Adding Machine .......... **25.00**
Burroughs adding machine .......... **15.00**
Dalton, calculator, 1912 patent ...... **85.00**
Fell & Tarrant Adding Machine, fine orig condition ....................... **65.00**
Golden Gem adding machine ........ **80.00**
Star adding machine ................ **15.00**

## Checkpunches and Checkwriters

F & E
International Detective Agency, check writer ......................... **25.00**
Lightning Checkwriter Model 500 .. **20.00**

Instant Checkwriter .......... **20.00**
Paymaster, check protector .......... **25.00**
S & P Checkwriter .......... **100.00**
SafeGuard Checkwriter .......... **20.00**

## Dictating Machines, Wax Cylinder Machines

Dictaphone
- Type A, Model 10 dictating machine **50.00**
- Type B, Model 10, transcribing machine .......... **50.00**
- Type S, Saving machine .......... **50.00**

Ediphone
- Dictating machine .......... **40.00**
- Shaving machine .......... **40.00**
- Transcribing machine .......... **40.00**
- Typease typewriter attachment .......... **15.00**

## Duplicators and Mimeographs

A. B. Dick
- Edison Mimeoscope .......... **300.00**
- Edison Model 1 .......... **175.00**
- Edison Model 75 .......... **20.00**

Gem notecard duplicator .......... **10.00**
Rotary Neostyle 8–F duplicator .......... **45.00**

## Office Related

Catalog
- A C McClurg & Co, Chicago, IL, Office Supplies & New Year Specials, 1925, 64 pages, 10¼ x 14¼" .......... **24.00**
- Irwin Paper Co, Quincy, IL, Empire bond papers, 1931, 28 pages, 5¼ x 8" .......... **22.00**
- Latsch Brothers, Lincoln, NE, Commercial Stationers' Complete Line of Office Supplies, 1931, 304 pages, 8¼ x 10¾" .......... **30.00**
- L C Smith & Corona Typewriter Co, Syracuse, NY, "How To Use Corona Silent, The Portable Typewriter," 1935, 30 pages, 5½ x 8¾" **10.00**

Stapler, Pilot, chrome .......... **16.00**
Stock Ticker, Western Union, glass dome, matching walnut base, c1910 .......... **3,750.00**

# CALENDARS

**Collecting Hints:** Value increases if all monthly pages are attached. Most calendars are bought by collectors interested in the subject on the calendar as opposed to the calendar itself.

**History:** Calendars were a popular advertising giveaway in the late 19th century and first five decades of the 20th. Recently, a calendar craze has swept bookstores throughout America. These topic–oriented calendars contain little or no advertising.

**Reference:** Norman E. Martinus and Harry L. Rinker, *Warman's Paper,* Wallace–Homestead, 1993.

**Additional Listing:** Pin–up Art.

**REPRODUCTION ALERT**

1900, Montgomery Ward, building illus, 23 x 16" .......... **325.00**
1902, Ballard Hardware & Farm Tools, movable arm points to dates .......... **35.00**
1903, A & P Tea Co, 19 x 15" .......... **180.00**
1906, Fleischmann's, July pad, 14 x 10" **110.00**
1907, Tuck, Venice, four calendar pages .......... **45.00**
1909, Chattanooga Medicine Co, 4 x 20", twelve sheets .......... **30.00**
1913, Dr Daniels, girl feeding dogs, 20 x 14" .......... **200.00**
1915, Magic Yeast, barefoot boy, 18 x 10" .......... **225.00**
1916, Weed Tire Chains, four women wearing hats, framed, 30 x 10" .......... **250.00**
1917, US Ammunition, May pad, framed, 28 x 18" .......... **260.00**
1922
- Sharples Tubular Cream Separators, January pad .......... **110.00**
- Ulmer Installment Co, emb, Indian calling moose, full pad, 21 x 11" . **160.00**

1925, Herrington's Drugs, 14 x 8½" .. **35.00**
1928, Harrisburg Pilot, gypsy girl, framed, 45 x 22" .......... **90.00**
1929, Star Brand Shoes, woman by stained glass window, framed, 26 x 11" .......... **140.00**
1930, A C Stram Groceries–URMA Brand–Green Bay, Dawn of Day print, full pad .......... **20.00**
1931
- August Wichman Work Clothes & Hosiery, Wear–U–Well Shoes, full pad **10.00**
- Charlotte Becker baby print .......... **25.00**
- Great Northern Railroad, July, Indian portrait, 28 x 15" .......... **120.00**

1932, American Stores, 31 x 18", full pad, framed .......... **120.00**
1933, Coca–Cola, The Village Blacksmith, full pad .......... **325.00**
1935, Thinking of You, full color portrait, full pad, 7 x 14" .......... **50.00**
1937
- Centennial Beer, 31 x 19", full pad, framed .......... **300.00**
- De Laval Cream Separator .......... **60.00**

**Calendar, 1953, Howard L. Ayers Builder and Contractor, pin-up poster, full pad, 15 x 23", $10.00.**

1938, De Laval, full pad, pretty woman **35.00**
Texaco Sky Chief, paper litho ........ **50.00**
1941
A Kraft Shoe Store, full pad ........ **10.00**
Rosseau Shoes, Rubbers, Repairing Men's & Women's Hosiery, full pad **8.00**
1942
Sheer Beauty, seated blonde in lavender satin gown ............... **12.00**
Sweet As You Are, Frush, 6 x 10", full pad ......................... **10.00**
1944
Pepsi–Cola, lady on rocker and two men ......................... **60.00**
Will Rogers ..................... **18.00**
1946, It's A Date, Rolf Armstrong, Seattle Jeweler's date book, unused ... **25.00**
1948
Mac Pherson Sketches, spiral bound, 9½ x 12½" .................... **50.00**
The Varga Girl, spiral bound, 8½ x 12" ......................... **75.00**
1949
Deluxe Esquire Girl, spiral bound, 11 x 16" ........................ **75.00**
Elvgren, men working, desk top type, twelve sheets ................. **15.00**
Lehigh Moving Train .............. **18.00**
Movie Star, black and white photo for each month, 8¼ x 11¼" ........ **25.00**
1950, Esquire Girl, Al Moore, March to December ...................... **12.00**
1952, Studio Sketches, T N Thompson, spiral bound, 8¾ x 13¼" .......... **50.00**
1954, US Royal Tires, pin–up girl, rolled ......................... **20.00**
1955
Coca–Cola, orig wrapper, home type **25.00**
John Deere, full pad, wildlife book . **35.00**
1957, Studio Sketches, T N Thompson **10.00**
1958, National Life Insurance Co, bear illus ........................... **10.00**
1959, Playboy Playmate, spiral bound, orig envelope, 8½ x 12½" ......... **50.00**
1969
Playboy, orig folder ............... **25.00**
The All–American Calendar, President portraits, Dec sheet ........ **10.00**
1971, Playboy Playmate, spiral bound, 8 x 12½" ....................... **25.00**
1972, Playboy, orig folder ........... **20.00**

# CALIFORNIA POTTERY

**Collecting Hints:** The 1980s was a period of discovery for collectors of the various wares from West Coast potteries. Part of the excitement comes from the fact that many of the pieces speak to the stylish trends of the 1940s through the 1960s. What California collectors have kept secret for over a decade is now drawing nationwide attention. Collecting California potteries is "in."

California pottery is collected either by firm, pattern, or period. Bauer and Vernon Kiln are two firms whose full line attracts collectors. Gladding–McBean's Franciscan patterns are now achieving the same popularity among collectors as did those of Russel Wright a decade ago. Sascha Brastoff material is among the most trendy of Fab 50s collectibles.

California pottery is currently experiencing a price run. Speculation is rampant. No one is quite certain how much is available. Prices vary regionally. Pieces are more scarce on the East Coast than on the West Coast. It is truly a roller coaster market.

**History:** Two important pottery trends developed in California in the 1930s. The first involved large commercial potteries who manufactured vividly colored earthenware dinnerware. J. A. Bauer Pottery Company of Los Angeles and Catalina Clay Products Company are two examples. The second centered around small potteries operating throughout southern California that manufactured decorative housewares and giftwares. In 1948 there were over eight hundred of these firms.

Bright, solid–colored California dinnerware and accessories kept pace with changes in American living standards. They worked well with the arrival of patio and sun room dining. They also served as a stark contrast to the more formal dinnerware of the 1920s and 1930s. The irony to this story is that it was Homer Laughlin's Fiesta, the product of a West Virginia company, that popularized the California look across the nation. It was dominant as America went to war in 1941.

Ready accessibility to material meant that the California potteries were able to sustain production during the war. The Big 5 (Bauer, Gladding–McBean, Metlox, Pacific, and Vernon) used talc from nearby deserts as the principal ingredient in their ceramic bodies. With production from Europe and the Far East unavailable, American department stores turned to the California potteries for common household dinnerware. It was a boom time.

Household figurines and pottery giftwares also were needed. Led by firms such as Brayton Laguna, the California potteries responded. When larger companies could not keep up with demand, hundreds of small, family–owned potteries were organized. Names such as Will and George Climes, Kay Finch, Brad Keeler, Hedi Schoop, and Florence Ward are well known among collectors.

Boom turned to bust by the mid–1950s. Some firms such as Sascha Brastoff survived. Most failed. Today only a handful remain.

**References:** Jack Chipman, *Collector's Encyclopedia of California Pottery,* Collector Books, 1992; Jo Cunningham, *The Collector's Encyclopedia of American Dinnerware,* Collector Books, 1982, 1992 value update; Lois Lehner, *Lehner's Encyclopedia of U. S. Marks on Pottery, Porcelain & Clay,* Collector Books, 1988.

Batchelder
  Bowl, oval, pink, 12" l ............ **125.00**
  Tile
    Castle, 6" sq .................. **85.00**
    Flower, #443, 6" sq ........... **75.00**
California Faience
  Bowl, turquoise and yellow, 9" d, 1½" h ........................... **115.00**
  Tile, ship, 6" sq ................. **285.00**
  Vase, black matte glaze, crazed, 5" h **175.00**
California Originals, cookie jar
  Ark ........................... **48.00**
  Big Bird ...................... **45.00**
  Cookie Monster ................ **50.00**
  Cookie Time ................... **35.00**
  Ernie ......................... **50.00**
  Juggler ....................... **75.00**
  Leisure Frog .................. **35.00**
  Owl ........................... **25.00**
  Pelican ....................... **50.00**
  Rooster ....................... **35.00**
  Santa ......................... **55.00**
  Sheriff, hole in hat .......... **45.00**
  Squirrel on Stump ............. **30.00**
  Tortoise and Hare ............. **35.00**
  Train ......................... **35.00**
  Turtle, sitting ............... **20.00**
  Winnie the Pooh ............... **90.00**
Catalina Pottery
  Ashtray, cowboy hat, green ........ **100.00**
  Flower Frog, pelican .............. **225.00**
  Planter, square, green ............ **14.00**
  Vase, handled, green, 8" h ........ **250.00**
Clay Sketches, figurine, cockatoo ..... **20.00**
Cleminson
  Hair Receiver, girl, 2 pcs ......... **28.00**
  Pie Bird, rooster .................. **25.00**
  Pitcher, Distelfink, 9½" h ......... **25.00**
  Plate, hillbilly girl .............. **20.00**
  Spoon Rest, leaf shaped ............ **12.00**
  Wall Pocket, clock ................. **13.00**
De Lee Art, figurine
  Dutch Girl, marked on base ....... **35.00**
  Katrina Dutch Girl, two paper labels, crazed ......................... **30.00**
Hedi Schoop
  Figurine
    Debutante, 12½" h ............. **40.00**
    Margie, 12" h ................. **45.00**
  Planter, hobby horse .............. **30.00**
Howard Pierce
  Figurine
    Cat, seated ................... **45.00**
    Raccoon, brown and white, pr ... **30.00**
  Flower Frog, mother quail and two young ........................ **38.00**
Josef Originals, figurine, girl, October Opal, sgd, 4" h ................. **20.00**

**Josef Originals, figure, Mary Ann, yellow dress, gold trim, paper labels and ink stamped signature, 3½" h, $18.00.**

Kay Finch
  Bank, pig, floral dec, 10" h ........ **75.00**
  Console Set, Oriental, Celadon green, two ladies and vase, sgd, 3 pcs .. **145.00**
  Figure
    Angel ......................... **30.00**
    Lady .......................... **35.00**
    Turkey ........................ **45.00**
  Plaque, cocker spaniel ............ **15.00**

Maddux
  Figure
    Horse, #982 .................. **15.00**
    Siamese cat, sgd ............... **32.00**
  Planter, flamingo, sgd ............. **38.00**
  Television Lamp, horse, prancing, #810, 12″ l .................. **25.00**
Pacific Clay Products
  Figurine, nude, holding feather, 15½″ h ............................ **50.00**
  Vase
    Fan, #3401 ................... **25.00**
    Turquoise, #3060 .............. **20.00**
Roselane
  Figurine
    Boy with dog, white and brown, 5½″ h ...................... **8.00**
    Giraffe, stylized, glossy gray, 5½″ h **20.00**
    Owl, small .................... **15.00**
  Vase, Chinese Modern, white ext., terra cotta int., 8″ h ........... **18.00**
Sascha Brastoff
  Ashtray
    Domed, round, 5¼″ d .......... **20.00**
    Leaf, enamelware, brown tones, sgd, 5½″ l .................. **20.00**
  Figure, poodle, crackle glaze, sgd, 9″ l ............................ **100.00**
Sorcha Boru, figurine
  Blue Bird ........................ **100.00**
  Blue Jay, 6½″ h .................. **165.00**
Brayton Laguna
  Figurine
    Boy with dog .................. **45.00**
    Girl, knitting sock ............. **30.00**
    Sally .......................... **25.00**
  Planter, baby with pillow .......... **35.00**
Weil Ware, vase
  Girl, paper label ................. **30.00**
  Sailor Boy, 10¾″ h, stamped mark .. **25.00**
Will–George, figure
  Dachshund, stamped mark, 9″ l .... **50.00**
  Flamingos, male and female, sgd, pr **195.00**

# CAMERAS

**Collecting Hints:** The camera market seems to fluctuate weekly. However, the long range average price for any camera is steady. The Leica market no longer is in an upward movement, but interest in unusual cameras, e. g., subminiatures and stereo cameras, is growing.

Leather covered cameras should have all the leather. Some wear does not detract from the value.

Folding cameras should have the bellows in good condition. Black bellows should be light tight. Colored bellows matching colored cameras need not be light tight. Having a matching bellow adds to the value of a colored camera.

**History:** A German monk, Johann Zahn, is credited with creating in the early 1800s the first fully portable wood box camera with a movable lens, an adjustable aperture, and a mirror to project the image. Zahn could view his image, but had no film on which to record it. In 1826 Joseph Nicephore Niepce produced the first photographic plate. Louise Jacques Mande Daguerre joined Niepce in his efforts. Peter Von Voigtlander of Vienna developed the quality lens needed. The photography industry was born.

The Germans were the initial leaders in camera manufacture. By the late 19th century the English and French had a strong market position. American strength would begin around 1900. America's strongest contributions have come in the development of films and the Polaroid camera, invented by Dr. Land and marketed in late 1948.

George Eastman revolutionized the photography industry in 1888 when his simple box camera was introduced. It was small, 3¼ x 3¾ x 6½″, and was modeled after earlier European examples. The camera had a magazine and could take 100 pictures without being reloaded. The pictures were 2½″ in diameter. Many later models built upon the success of Kodak No. 1. Kodak's first folding camera was Model No. 4; the Brownie arrived in 1900.

Prior to World War II Japan made the Konica and Minolta. After the war Japan made a strong commitment to the camera market. The Japanese have introduced many technical changes into the camera, including solar power.

**References:** Norman E. Martinus and Harry L. Rinker, *Warman's Paper,* Wallace–Homestead, 1993; Michael McBroom, *McBroom's Camera Blue Book 1993–1994,* Amherst Media, 1993; Jim and Joan McKeown (eds.), *Price Guide To Antique And Classic Cameras, 1992–1993, 8th Edition,* Centennial Photo Service, 1992; Jason Schneider, *Jason Schneider On Camera Collecting,* Wallace–Homestead, 1985, out–of–print; Douglas St. Denny, *The Hove International Blue Book Guide Prices for Classic and Collectable Cameras: 1922–1993,* Hove Foto Books, 1992.

**Periodical:** *Camera Shopper Magazine,* One Magnolia Hill, West Hartford, CT 06117.

**Collectors' Clubs:** American Society of Camera Collectors, 4918 Alcove Ave., North Hollywood, CA 91607; National Stereoscopic Association, P.O. Box 14801, Columbus, OH 43214; Leica Historical Society of America, 7611 Dornoch Lane, Dallas, TX 94116; Nikon Historical Society, P.O. Box 3213, Munster, IN 46321; Photographic Historical Society, P. O. Box 39563, Rochester, NY 14604.

**Museum:** International Museum of Photography at George Eastman House, 900 East Avenue, Rochester, NY 14607.

## CAMERAS

Agfa Kamerawerke (Munich, Germany) merged with Ansco 1928
- Agfaflex, SLR, Prontor 1–300, c1959 **50.00**
- Karat 36, 35mm, c1952 **45.00**
- Isolette III, c1952 **30.00**

Ansco (Binghamton, NY), merged with Agfa in 1928
- Ansco–Risdon Model A, movie, hand wound **24.00**
- Buster Brown, MIB **40.00**
- Dollar Box Camera, 127 film, green, c1910 **15.00**

Bell Howell, 1,9,8mm, movie, leather case **30.00**

Blair Camera Co (Boston, MA), became part of Eastman Kodak in 1908
- Baby Hawk Eye, 7 oz, box, c1896 **125.00**
- Tourist Hawk Eye, folding rollfilm, wooden standard conceals lens and shutter, c1900 **120.00**

Brownie Jr, 6–20 **38.00**

Camera Corp of America (New York, NY,) B2, 35mm, 1949–56 **25.00**

Cinex Candid Camera, 50mm, bakelite **23.00**

Craig Movie Supply Splicer, chrome and mahogany, 1930s **30.00**

Eastman Kodak Co (Rochester, NY)
- Bantam RF, 828 film **30.00**

**Kodak Jr. No. 2C Autographic, folding, 1916–27, $15.00.**

- Brownie
  - #2A **25.00**
  - #F120 #2, red **45.00**
- Boy Scout, 127, green, orig case, 1920s **115.00**
- Bullet, orig box, 1936 **18.00**
- Buster Brownie #2 **50.00**
- Duaflex, twin lens reflex **8.00**
- Hawkeye Special #2 **35.00**
- Junior, 1A Autographic, leather case **45.00**
- Kodak Stereo, 35mm **85.00**
- Signet 35, 35mm **25.00**
- Vest Pocket Hawkeye **35.00**

Franke & Heidecke (Braunschweig, Germany), Rolleicord V, twin lens reflex **80.00**

Minolta (Chiyoda Kogaku Seiko Co, Ltd, Osaka, Japan)
- Minolta 24 Rapid 24 x 24mm, 35mm rangefinder, built–in meter **80.00**
- Minolta SR–1S, 1964 **75.00**

Norton Laboratories, Norton, black plastic, stamped metal viewfinder, c1934 **25.00**

Olympic Camera Works (Japan)
- Olympic, bakelite half frame, Olympic shutter, c1934 **75.00**
- Super Olympic, bakelite body, first Japanese 35mm, c1935 **85.00**

Pentacon (Dresden, Germany)
- Contz F, 35mm, SLR, semi automatic cocking diaphragm, c1957 **85.00**
- Taxona, 24 x 24mm exposures on 35mm film, Novonar lens, Tempor 1–300 shutter, 1950 **32.00**

Stewart Warner Hollywood Model, movie **23.00**

## CAMERA RELATED

Advertising
- Booklet
  - Kodak & Kodak Supplies, 1916, 64 pages **15.00**
  - Leitz Close–Up and Photomicrography with the Leica Camera, E Leitz, NY, 48 pages **12.00**
- Brochure, Kodak Medalist II, 24 pages, c1949 **24.00**
- Newsletter, Kodak News, Sept 1949 **4.00**
- Trade Card, Heywood's Mammouth Photograph, Ambrotype Gallery, Boston, MA **18.00**

Book, Aaram Naadell, *Richardson's Bluebook of Projection,* paper cov, 644 pages **25.00**

Case, Kodak Retina Automatic **8.00**

Catalog
- Eastman Kodak Co, Rochester, NY
  - 1915, 96 pages, 3¾ x 5¼", Autographic Kodak Jr, Meniscus lens **15.00**
  - 1924, 28 pages, 5½ x 8½" **15.00**
- Lafayette Camera Co, Cat No. 81R, Cameras and Supplies, 1940, 48 pages, 7 x 10" **10.00**
- M & H Sporting Goods Co, Philadelphia, PA, Cameras and Supplies Catalogue, 1929, 16 pages, 6 x 9" **12.00**

Taylor, Taylor & Hobson, New York, NY, Catalogue of Cooke Anastigmats For Fine Photography With Helps To Photographers, 1908, 24 pages, 4¼ x 8" ................ **20.00**
Chemical Box, Eastman Kodak Developing Powders For Use In Brownie Tank Developer, c1900 ........... **10.00**
Cut Film Plate Holder, Kodak Recomar, 9 x 12 cm ...................... **4.00**
Drying Rack, 12" h, wood ........... **15.00**
Film Box
Ansco Dollar Camera, black, 127 size **20.00**
Kodak, Verichrome Film Pack, c1933 **15.00**
Instruction Manual
Kodak, 1A Kodak Jr, 1916, 64 pages **15.00**
Sears Roebuck 1907, "Complete Instructions In Photography" ...... **15.00**
Manual, Graflex Service and Parts Manual, 60 pages, punched for binder, c1948 ........................ **15.00**
Tote Bag, Canon, Montreal 1976 Olympic insignia ...................... **25.00**
Tripod, wood ...................... **35.00**

# CANAL COLLECTIBLES

**Collecting Hints:** Concentrate on one state or one specific canal. Look not only for canal material, but for the canal motif on non–canal items.

Beware of people trying to pass off tools and lanterns as having a canal origin. Ship boatyards used exactly the same tools as the canal boatyards. Insist on a good provenance for any canal item and check out the family name in the canal records.

Canal buffs are extremely well organized. Try to make contact early in your collecting interest with individuals working on the same topics as you. Many collectors own more than one example of an item and will gladly sell the duplicate to a new collector.

**History:** The American canal era has its origins in the 18th century with projects in New England, along the Potomac, and Louisiana. George Washington was intensely interested in canals and was a shareholder in several canal companies.

The building of the Erie and Champlain canals in New York launched canal mania. From 1825 to 1840 hundreds of canal projects were begun. States such as Pennsylvania and Ohio actually had more miles of canals than New York.

While the railroads contributed in the demise of the canals, it was the high maintenance costs, repair due to floods, and economic depressions which finally closed many of the canals.

A number of canals continued into the twentieth century. Modern canals include the Chesapeake and Delaware Canal and the Erie Barge Canal.

**References:** James Lee, *Tales The Boatmen Told,* Canal Press, 1977; William J. McKelvey, *Champlain To Chesapeake: A Canal Era Pictorial Cruise,* Canal Press, 1978; Harry L. Rinker, *"The Old Raging Erie . . . There Have Been Several Changes": A Postcard History Of The Erie And Other New York State Canals (1895 to 1915),* Canal Captain's Press, 1984; Harry L. Rinker, *The Schuylkill Canal: A Photographic History,* Canal Captain's Press, 1991.

**Collectors' Clubs:** American Canal Society, 117 Main St., Freemansburg, PA 18017; Canal Society of Ohio, 550 Copley Road, Akron, OH 44320; Pennsylvania Canal Society, c/o Canal Museum, P. O. Box 877, Easton, PA 18042.

**Museums:** Canal Museum, Hugh Moore Park, Easton, PA; Chesapeake and Delaware Canal Museum, Chesapeake City, DE; Erie Canal Museum, Syracuse, NY.

**Advisor:** Harry L. Rinker.

Advertising Trade Card, Burdett Organ Co, Erie, PA, dated 1883, features the Lehigh River and Lehigh Canal at the bend of Bear Mountain in Mauch Chunk, PA ...................... **6.00**
Ashtray, 5" d, Pennsbury Pottery, shows Lehigh Canal boat at dock, camelback bridge in background, advertising premium from "The Solebury National Bank of New Hope Pa.", green, gray, and brown, light brown ground **20.00**
Autograph, letter signed
Abner Lacock, Office of Western Division of Penna. Canal, February 11, 1828, to Alexander Mahon, Treasurer of the Board of Canal Commissioners, letter informing Mahon that Lacock has issued a check for $35,000 .............. **40.00**
R & G D Coleman, Lebanon Furnaces, May 31, 1849, to Eckert & Stone, concerning passage of boats on Susquehanna and Tidewater Canal near Safe Harbor, PA ...... **25.00**
Bank Note, broken
Chemung Canal Bank, $10 note, No. 1896, September 1, 1846, Elmira, NY, vignette of Greek god reclining in front of flight of canal locks, engraved by Rawdon, Wright, Hatch & Co ........................ **30.00**
Sanford Bank, GA, $10 note, No. 10 A, January 17, 1861, issued in Sanford, center vignette of Rockville

bridge in Harrisburg, PA, showing train in foreground with eastern division of Pennsylvania Main Line Canal between railroad and river, engraved by Toppan, Carpenter, Caslier & Co . . . . . . . . . . . . . . . . . . **15.00**

Tide Water Canal, $1 note, No. 10782C, May 1, 1840, issued in Baltimore, MD, two vignettes, first with oval showing mule pulling canalboat, second of New York scene, engraved by Draper, Toppan & Co . . . . . . . . . . . . . . . . . . . . . . . . . **50.00**

Book

Doran, Edith M, *High–Water Cargo*, New Brunswick, NJ: Rutgers University Press: 1950 and 1965, 224 pgs, hardcover, orig dj, illus by Forrest Orr, novel about life along the Delaware and Raritan Canal in the 1850s . . . . . . . . . . . . . . . . . . . . . . . **20.00**

Gard, R Max and William H Vodrey, Jr, *The Sandy And Beaver Canal*, East Liverpool, OH: East Liverpool Historical Society: 1952, 210 pgs, softcover, map insert . . . . . . . . . . . . **40.00**

Robert J McClellan, *The Delaware Canal: A Picture Story*, New Brunswick, NJ: Rutgers University Press: 1967, 112 pgs, hardcover, orig dj **15.00**

Whitford, Noble E, *History Of The Canal System Of New York Together With Brief Histories Of The Canals Of The United States and Canada, Volume 1 and Volume 2*, issued as a *Supplement To The Annual Report Of The State Engineer And Surveyor Of The State Of New York*, Albany: Brandow Printing Company: 1906, hardcover, and foldout charts, price for set of two volumes . . . . . . . . . . . . . . . . . . . . . . **100.00**

Check

Albany City Bank, No. 82871, March 27, 1857, $10,116 deposited by H H Martin to the credit of The Treasurer of the State of New York an a/c of the Canal Fund . . . . . . . . . . . . **15.00**

The First National Bank of Liverpool, Pennsylvania, yellow ground, sq photograph in upper left corner marked "Old Canal Boat Days, Liverpool, Pennsylvania, 1906," photograph actually of boats on Chesapeake and Ohio Canal near Williamsport, MD, unissued . . . . . **5.00**

Document

Pay Order, Ohio Canal, No. 2007, April 5, 1828, $100 for work done under the contract of Wilcox & Dill for Section 115 of the Ohio Canal south of Portage Summit . . . . . . . . **10.00**

**Towing Receipt, N. M. Tyerell, NJ, 1886, 7 x 3", $25.00.**

Towing receipt, "B." and "S." Towing Line, Bernard & Samsel, Steam Tug *William Cramp*, towing from Bristol to Bridesburg for Lehigh Coal and Navigation Co canalboat, Philadelphia, June 5, 1916 . . . . . . . . . . . . . **5.00**

Medal, commemorative, 100th Anniversary of Hamburg Savings And Trust Company, 1872–1972, bronze, obverse shows bank bldg, reverse shows mules pulling canalboat, bronze, 1½" d, orig packaging . . . . . . . . . . . . . . . . **10.00**

Patent Model

#154,978, William Baxter and William Baxter, Jr, September 15, 1874, wooden boat model, introduction of steam propulsion, the Baxters won a special prize awarded by New York for the best method of introducing steam propulsion to canals . . . . . . . . . . . . . . . **300.00**

#218,363, Bernard Bird, Buffalo, New York, August 12, 1879, coupling devices for lines, white metal working model, spring powered whiffletree that snaps open when a lever is thrown . . . . . . . . . . . . . . . . . **150.00**

Photograph, Minetto Shade Cloth Co, Minetto, NY, black and white, 8⅞" x 6⅛", shows canal and lock in lower left quadrant, river through center, and town in background . . . . . . . . . . **20.00**

Pinback Button

1¾", Power House And Locks, Sault St Marie, MI, black and white photograph, attached red ribbon . . . . . **10.00**

3⅛" x 2⅛", Canal Days Badge, Manayunk, PA, May 17, 1980, blue ground, photo of canal passing under railroad bridge . . . . . . . . . . . . . **4.00**

Post Card

Canada, On the Canal, Lachine, multicolored, Valentine Series, shows pleasure boats and work scows tied up along bank . . . . . . . **2.50**

Delaware Canal, photo post card of aqueduct at Point Pleasant, PA, sepia tone . . . . . . . . . . . . . . . . . . . . . . . **7.50**

Erie Canal, American Locomotive Works, Schenectady, NY, full view, multicolored, shows plant bldgs, railroad lines, and canal (to left) .. **5.00**

James River and Kanawha Canal, Old Libby Prison, Richmond, VA, multicolored, made by Hugh C Leighton Co, Portland, ME, #25682, printed in Germany, c1910, shows canal horizontally across center, Libby Prison bldg in background, sailing vessels to right **4.00**

Soo Locks, Birds' Eye View Of Locks, Soo, MI, multicolored, published by Young, Lord & Rhoades, Sault Ste Marie, MI, shows boat ready to enter lock on left and boat exiting lock on right .................. **3.00**

Puzzle, wooden, jigsaw, Joseph K. Straus, No. P–201, "Great Falls Tavern" (Chesapeake and Ohio Canal), 9" x 12", 200 pieces, orig box ..... **25.00**

Staffordshire, American Historical

Jackson, Job and John, View of Canal, Little Falls, Mohawk River, soup plate, 10½" d, light pink transfer, long stem roses border .......... **80.00**

William Ridgway, Harper's Ferry From The Potomac Side, plate, 9" d, black transfer, shows Chesapeake and Ohio Canal at base of mountain in background ........ **50.00**

Unknown Maker, Canal View Series, pitcher, 7" h, featuring three transfers (View of Lake George, View of Aqueduct Bridge at Rochester, and Lafayette), yellowish cream ground, carmine line at top, "v" floral motif on handle, cracked .. **1,500.00**

Wedgwood, plate, 9¼" d, Poe Lock, Sault Ste Marie, MI, shows boats exiting lock, dark blue, first quarter of 20th C, made for Rudell Drug Co in Sault Ste Marie .............. **50.00**

Enoch Wood & Sons, Erie Canal, View Of The Aqueduct Bridge At Little Falls, chamber pot lid, 8⅜" d, dark blue, oval handle held in place with support piece screwed into top ...................... **275.00**

Stereograph

Chesapeake and Ohio Canal, No. 327 Harper's Ferry, photographed and published by Kilburn Brothers, Littleton, NH, shows railroad bridge across Potomac, C & O canal in foreground ............. **7.50**

Lehigh Canal, View in the Gap–Early Morning, Klechner's Stereoscopic Views of the Lehigh and Wyoming Valleys On The Line of the Central Railroad of New Jersey (L. & S. Div), shows canal aqueduct at Lehigh Gap, yellow ground ........ **10.00**

Pennsylvania Main Line Canal, #217. Jack's Narrows, part of The Scenery Of The Pennsylvania Railroad series, Purviance, Philadelphia, yellow card, shows canal with bridge across river in background ....... **5.00**

Stock Certificate or Mortgage Bond

Black River Canal, New York, No. 109, issued November 9, 1837, center vignette of goddesses flanking oval shield featuring sunrise scene with spread–winged eagle on top, three vignettes on left of which two are oval New York State Stock cuts, a small railroad and a small steamship vignette on right, signed by Robert White, canceled with large oval cuts, engraved by Rawdon, Wright & Hatch ........... **75.00**

Chesapeake & Delaware Canal, No. 2427, 15 shares, issued June 15, 1913, vignette of wooden summit bridge built in 1826, light yellow tone, canceled ................. **15.00**

New York State 5 per cent Stock on behalf of the Delaware and Hudson Canal, No. 70, March 16, 1827, side identification vignettes only, hand canceled, engraved by J H Hill ......................... **45.00**

Pennsylvania Canal Company, Six Percent Mortgage Bond, Principal Payable July 1st, 1910, No. 4, center vignette of canalboat about to cross under stone arch railroad bridge, stamp canceled, coupons clipped, folded ................ **50.00**

Ticket, C M Reed's Passage Ticket, 10⅜" x 4¼", unissued, c1840, features a small vignette of a steamship and a small vignette of a canalboat at top ........................ **20.00**

# CANDLEWICK

**Collecting Hints:** Select pieces without chips, cracks, or scratches. Learn the characteristics, shapes, and types of Imperial pieces made. Many items have been made that are similar to Candlewick and are often mixed with or labeled Candlewick at shops and shows. Learn to identify "look alikes." Be wary and beware!

**History:** Candlewick, Imperial Glass Corp.'s No. 400 pattern, introduced in 1936, was made continuously until October 1982 when Imperial declared bankruptcy. In 1984 Imperial was sold to Lancaster–Colony Corp and Consolidated Stores International, Inc. Imperial's assets including inventory, molds, buildings, and equipment were liquidated in 1985.

The buildings and site were purchased by Anna Maroon of Maroon Enterprises, Bridgeport, Ohio. At present, the site is being developed as a tourist attraction with sales shops, a glass–making shop, and plans for a museum.

Imperial's Candlewick molds were bought by various groups, companies, and individuals. Approximately 200 molds were purchased by Mirror Images, Lansing, Michigan. Eighteen small molds were bought by Boyd Crystal Art Glass, Cambridge, Ohio. At present, the location of some Candlewick molds is unknown.

Anna Maroon Enterprises, Bridgeport, Ohio, purchased the building and lands belonging to the Imperial Glass Corporation in 1985. The planned tourist attraction never developed.

Candlewick is characterized by the crystal–drop beading used around the edge of many pieces; around the foot of tumblers, shakers, and other items; in the stems of glasses, compotes, cake and cheese stands; on the handles of cups, pitchers, bowls, and serving pieces; on stoppers and finials; and on the handles of ladles, forks, and spoons. The beading is small on some pieces, while on others it is larger and heavier.

A large variety of pieces were produced in the Candlewick pattern. Over 650 items and sets are known. Shapes include round, oval, oblong, heart, and square. Imperial added or discontinued items according to popularity and demand. The largest assortment of pieces and sets were made during the late 1940s and early 1950s.

Candlewick was produced mostly in crystal. Viennese Blue (pale blue, 1937–38), Ritz Blue (cobalt, 1938–41), and Ruby Red (red, 1937–41) were made. Other colors that have been found include amber, black, emerald green, lavender, pink, and light yellow. From 1977 to 1980, four items of 3400 Candlewick stemware were made in solid color Ultra Blue, Nut Brown, Verde Green, and Sunshine Yellow. Solid black stemware was made on an experimental basis at the same time.

Other decorations on Candlewick include silver overlay, gold encrustations, cuttings, etchings, and hand–painted designs. Pieces have been found with fired–on gold, red, blue, and green beading. Other companies encased Candlewick pieces in silver, chrome, brass, and wood.

**References:** Virginia R. Scott, *The Collector's Guide to Imperial Candlewick, 2nd Edition,* privately printed, (available from the author), 1987; Ellen Tischbein Schroy, *Warman's Glass,* Wallace-Homestead, 1992; Mary M. Wetzel, *Candlewick: The Jewel of Imperial,* Ferguson Communications, 1981, 1990 value update.

**Periodical:** The National Candlewick Collector Newsletter, 275 Milledge Terrace, Athens, GA 30606.

**Museum:** Bellaire Museum, Bellaire, OH 43906.

**Advisor:** Virginia R. Scott.

**REPRODUCTION ALERT:** Six-inch baskets in pink and Alexandrite and a pink four-piece child's set (consisting of a demitasse cup and saucer, 6" plate, and 5" nappy) have been made by Viking Glass Co., New Martinsville, Ohio, for Mirror Images, Lansing, Michigan. In 1987 Viking made clear plates, bowls, cups, saucers, large and small flat–base sugars and creamers (400/30 and 400/122), and 6½" trays (400/29) for Mirror Images. These pieces have ground bottoms and are somewhat heavier than original Candlewick pieces. They are not marked.

Light green Candlewick items have recently appeared. The origin of these items is not presently known.

Boyd Crystal Art Glass, Cambridge, Ohio, has used Candlewick molds to make items in various slag and clear colors. All Boyd molds have been marked with a B in a diamond trademark.

In late 1990 Dalzell–Viking Corporation, New Martinsville, WV, began making a five piece place setting (6" plate, 8½" plate, 10" dinner plate, cup and saucer) in Crystal, Black, Cobalt, Evergreen, and Ruby Red. Retail price is $75 to $95 a place setting. The 1991 Dalzell–Viking Price List also includes a 5" and 6" two-handled bowl, 7" and 8" two-handled tray, and 10" five part relish dish in Crystal. These new pieces are quite heavy when compared to period Candlewick, have ground bottoms, and etched "Dalzell" on the center base rim.

Ashtray
- 4½" l, oblong, large beads, 400/134/1 ........ **6.00**
- 5" d, round, 400/133 ........ **8.00**

Ashtray Set, nested, 4", 5", 6", three piece
- Blue, yellow, and pink, 400/550 ........ **28.50**
- Crystal, 400/550 ........ **20.00**
- Red, white, and blue, patriotic, 400/550 ........ **125.00**

Banana Stand, 11" d plate, 2 sides turned up, 4–bead stem, 400/103E . **500.00**

Basket, applied handle, 6½" h, turned up sides, 400/40/0 ........ **35.00**

Bonbon, 6" d, beaded edge, heart shaped, curved over center handle, 400/51T
- Crystal ........ **22.50**
- Light blue ........ **35.00**
- Ruby red with crystal handle ........ **95.00**

Bowl, beaded edge
- 8½" d, two handles, 400/72B ........ **24.00**
- 10½" d, 400/75 ........ **40.00**
- 11" d, float, cupped edge, 400/75F . **45.00**
- 14" d, belled, large beads on sides, 400/104B ........ **85.00**

Buffet Set
400/92D, 14″ d plate, 2 pcs ....... **50.00**
400/166B, 5½″ d cheese compote, plain stem .................... **50.00**
400/9266B ..................... **50.00**
Butter Dish, cov
California, 6¾″ x 4″, 400/276 ...... **110.00**
Rect,¼ lb, graduated beads on cov, 400/161 ..................... **30.00**
Round, 5½″ d, 2–bead finial, 400/144 ......................... **30.00**
Cake Stand/Plate
10″ d, domed foot, wedge marked plate, 400/67D ............... **55.00**
11″ d, hand painted roses, 3–bead stem, 400/103D ............... **95.00**
14″ d, birthday cake plate, 72 candle holes, 400/160 ................ **250.00**
Candleholder
3½″ h
Domed foot, small beads, round handle, 400/81 .............. **40.00**
Rolled saucer, small beads, 400/79R ...................... **10.50**
5″ h, round bowl with beaded or fluted insert vase, 400/40CV ..... **85.00**
5½″ h, ftd, three sections arched beads on stem, 400/224 ......... **80.00**
6½″ h, 3–bead stem, 400/175 ..... **50.00**
Candy Box, cov, 5½″ w, 2–bead finial, 400/59 ......................... **45.00**
Candy Dish, cov
6½″ d, round bowl, sq cov, 2–bead finial, 400/245 ................ **125.00**
7″ h, 2–bead finial, three partitions, 400/110 ..................... **60.00**
Celery Tray, 8½″ l, 400/58 .......... **20.00**
Cheese and Cracker Set, 400/151 cheese compote, 400/145D 11½″ d handled plate, 2 pc set 400/145 .... **50.00**
Cheese, Toast or Butter Plate, 7¾″ d, cupped edge, domed cov, bubble knob, 400/123 .................. **95.00**
Cigarette Set, frosted crystal, 6½″ d 1776/eagle ashtray, 3″ h cigarette jar, small beads, 2 pc set ............ **65.00**
Clock, 4″ h, beaded edge ........... **250.00**
Coaster, 3½″ d, round, spoon rest, 400/226 ........................... **12.00**
Cocktail Set, 6″ d plate, 2½″ off–center indent, 400/39; 1–bead cocktail glass; set, 400/97 ............... **35.00**
Compote, beaded edge, ftd
5″ h, 3 sections, arched beads in stem, 400/220 ................ **45.00**
8″ h, 4 bead stem, 400/48F ........ **70.00**
9″ h
Domed foot, large bead stem, ribbed, 400/67B ............ **75.00**
Flat foot, plain or crimped beaded edge, 400/67B ............... **65.00**

Condiment Set
Jam Set, two cov marmalade jars, 3–bead ladles, 400/159 oval tray; 5 pc set 400/1589 ............... **95.00**
Oil and Vinegar Set, two 400/164 and 400/166 cruets, beaded foot, 400/29 7″ kidney shaped tray; 3 pc set 400/2946 .................... **85.00**
Console Set, bowl and pr candleholders
12″ d float bowl, 92F, cupped edge, 2–light candleholders, 400/100; set 400/920F .................... **95.00**
13″ d mushroom bowl, 400/92L on 400/127B 7½″ base, 6″ h ftd urn candleholders, 400/129R; set 400/136 ......................... **120.00**
Creamer and Sugar Set, ftd, beaded foot, plain handles, c1937, 400/31
Crystal ......................... **35.00**
Light blue ...................... **55.00**
Cruet, 4 oz, bead base, 400/164 ..... **22.75**
Cup and Saucer
After Dinner, small, slender, 4½″ d beaded saucer, set 400/77 ....... **24.50**
Coffee, slender, beaded handle, 400/37, saucer, 400/35, set 400/37 ... **17.00**
Tea, round, beaded handle, 400/35, beaded saucer, 400/35, set 400/35 **19.50**
Deviled Egg Tray, 11½″ d, twelve indentations, heart shaped center handle, 400/154 ................... **80.00**
Dresser Set, 4 pcs, round mirrored tray, 400/151, powder jar, beaded base, 3–bead cov; two round perfume bottles, beaded base, 4–bead stoppers, made for I Rice Co, 1940s ......... **165.00**
Epergne Set, 9″ d ftd crimped bowl, 1–bead stem, 400/196, 7¾″ h 2–bead peg vase, set 400/196 ............ **165.00**
Iced Tea Tumbler, floral cut, 12 oz, 400/18 ........................... **16.00**
Juice Tumbler, floral cut, 400/19 ..... **13.00**
Lemon Tray, 5½″ d plate, center handle of 3 sections of arched beads, large bead on top, 400/221 ............ **30.00**
Marmalade Jar, round, beaded edge cover, 2–bead finial, 400/89 ....... **25.00**
Marmalade Ladle, 4¾″ l, small bowl, 3–bead handle, 400/130 .......... **6.00**
Marmalade Set, 400/19 old fashion tumbler, beaded notched cov, 2–bead finial, 400/130 ladle, set, 400/1989 .. **35.00**
Mayonnaise Set, handled bowl, ladle, and handled tray, floral cut, gold trim, 400/52/3 ....................... **75.00**
Mint Tray, 9″ d, heart shaped center handle, 400/149 ................ **25.00**
Mirror, 4½″ d, domed beaded glass base, brass holder and frame, two–sided mirror flips on hinges, maker unknown ........................ **85.00**
Muddler, mallard cut ............... **12.00**

Mustard Jar, beaded foot, notched beaded cover, 2–bead finial, 3½" l glass spoon, shell bowl, fleur–de–lis handle, 3 pc set, 400/156 ......... **30.00**
Nappy, 6" d, beaded edge, 400/3F ... **9.50**

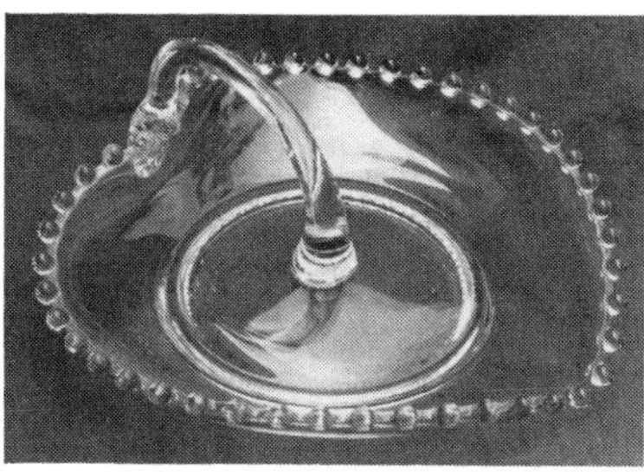

**Nappy, sweetheart shape, $17.50.**

Parfait, 6 oz, 3400 ................. **40.00**
Pastry Tray, 11½" l, beaded plate, heart shaped center handle, 400/68D .... **30.00**
Perfume Bottle, beaded base
- Amethyst ........................ **95.00**
- Green .......................... **75.00**

Pitcher
- Manhattan, beaded foot, plain handle, 400/18, 40 oz ............. **190.00**
- Water, 80 oz, 400/24 ............. **125.00**

Plate, beaded edge
- 6" d, bread and butter, 400/1D ..... **6.00**
- 8½" d, salad–dessert, 400/5D ...... **8.00**
- 9" d, luncheon, 400/7D ........... **12.00**
- 10" d, 2 handles, crimped, 400/72C **25.00**
- 10½" d, dinner, 400/10D .......... **22.50**
- 12" d, 2 open handles, 400/145D .. **30.00**

Punch Set
- 11 pcs, cov family punch jar, domed beaded foot, notched 2–bead cov, 400/139, small 400/139 ladle, eight 400/77 demi–cups, 400/139/77 set ....................... **225.00**
- 15 pcs, 6 quart, 400/20 bowl, 400/128B base, 400/91 ladle, twelve 400/37 cups, question–mark handle .......................... **250.00**

Relish and Dressing Set, 10½" d, round 4 part relish, 400/112, 400/89 cov jar fits center well, long ladle 3–beads, c1941 .......................... **75.00**
Relish Dish, beaded edge
- 6½" d, 2 part, 2 tab handles, 400/54 **10.00**
- 10½" d
  - 2 part, 2 tab handles, 400/256 ... **22.00**
  - 3 part, 2 tab handles, also called "Butter 'n Jam", (center holds stick of butter), 400/262 ....... **45.00**
- 12" d, rect, 3 sections one side, long section on other, tab handle each end, 400/215 ................. **50.00**

Salad Set, 10½" d beaded bowl, 400/75B, 13" d cupped edge plate, 400/75V, fork and spoon set, 400/75, 400/75 set .......................... **85.00**
Salt and Pepper Shakers, pr, beaded foot
- Bulbous, 9 beads, plastic tops, c1941, 400/96 ................. **15.00**
- Individual, chrome tops, 400/109 .. **10.00**
- Round
  - 400/96, 8 beads, chrome tops ... **15.00**
  - 400/116, 1–bead stem, plastic or metal tops, c1941 ............ **45.00**
  - 400/190, trumpet foot, chrome tops **32.50**

Sauce Boat Set, oval handled gravy boat, 9" oval plate with indent, 400/169 ........................... **90.00**
Sherbet, floral cut, 400/19 ........... **13.00**
Stemware
- 400/190 Line, bell shaped bowl, hollow trumpet shaped stems, beaded around foot, crystal
  - Cocktail, 4 oz ................. **16.50**
  - Goblet, 10 oz ................. **16.50**
  - Seafood Icer .................. **35.00**
  - Wine, 5 oz ................... **17.50**
- 3400 Line, flared bell top, four graduated beads in stem, crystal
  - Cordial, 1 oz ................. **25.00**
  - Goblet, 9 oz .................. **15.00**
  - Wine, 4 oz ................... **20.00**

Sugar, floral cutting, domed foot, 400/18 ............................ **115.00**
Tid–Bit Server, two tier, 7½" d and 10½" d plates joined with metal rod, round handle at top, 400/2701
- Crystal .......................... **50.00**
- Emerald green .................. **450.00**

Torte Plate, 17" d, beaded edge, flat or cupped edge, 400/20V ........... **40.00**
Tray, 9" l, 400/148 ................ **22.00**
Tumbler, 400/18, domed beaded foot, rounded top
- Dessert, 6 oz .................... **25.00**
- Water, 9 oz ..................... **20.00**

Vase
- 3¾" h, bud, beaded foot, ball, crimped top, 400/25 ........... **20.00**
- 5¾" h, bud, beaded foot, tapered large beads, crimped top, 400/107 **25.00**
- 7" h, rolled beaded top, solid glass arched handles with small bead edging, flat foot, 400/87R ....... **35.00**
- 8" h
  - Crimped beaded top, graduated beads down sides, 400/87C ... **22.50**
  - Fan shape, beaded top, solid glass arched handles with small bead edging, flat foot, 400/87F ..... **25.00**
- 8½" h, bud, beaded foot, ball
  - Narrowed top slants, applied handle, 400/227 ................ **85.00**
  - Trumpet shape top, crimped, 400/28C ....................... **35.00**

# CANDY CONTAINERS

**Collecting Hints:** Candy containers with original paint, candy and closures command a high premium, but be aware of reproduced parts and repainting. The closure is a critical part of each container; its loss detracts significantly from the value.

Small figural perfumes and other miniatures often are sold as candy containers. Study all reference books available and talk with other collectors before entering the market. Be aware of reproductions.

**History:** One of the first candy containers was manufactured in 1876 by Croft, Wilbur and Co., confectioneries. They filled a small glass Liberty Bell with candy and sold it at the 1876 Centennial Exposition in Philadelphia.

Jeannette, Pennsylvania, was a center for the packaging of candy in containers. Principal firms included Victory Glass, J. H. Millstein, T. H. Stough, and J. C. Crosetti. Earlier manufacturers were West Bros. of Grapeville, Pennsylvania, L. E. Smith of Mt. Pleasant, Pennsylvania, and Cambridge Glass of Cambridge, Ohio.

Containers were produced in shapes that would appeal to children and usually sold for ten cents. Candy containers remained popular until the 1960s when they became too expensive to mass produce.

**References:** Eikelberner and Agadjanian, *American Glass Candy Containers* (out–of–print); Jennie Long, *An Album of Candy Containers,* published by author, 1978; Robert Matthews, *Antiquers of Glass Candy Containers,* published by author, 1970; Mary Louise Stanley, *A Century of Glass Toys,* published by author, n.d.

**Collectors' Club:** Candy Container Collectors of America, 864 Paterson Ave., Maywood, NJ 07607.

**REPRODUCTION ALERT**

Airplane, 4⅛″ l, glass, red plastic wing, T H Stough Co, 1957 ............ **45.00**
Apothecary Jar, 5¼″ h, glass, two parts, hobnail, T H Stough Co .......... **60.00**
Automobile, 4″ l, limousine, glass, tin wheels, West Specialty Co, 1912–14 **70.00**
Baby Chick, 3⅜″ h, standing, glass, oblong base, tin slide closure, painted, Victory Glass Company .......... **60.00**
Battleship, 5¼″ l, glass, wave base, tin slide closure .................... **110.00**
Bird Cage, 2½″ d, 4½″ h, glass, brass screw cap, Westmoreland Specialty Co ........................... **90.00**
Boat, *USN Dreadnaught,* 5¾″ l, glass, metal screw cap ................ **100.00**
Bug, 8½″ h, composition, sitting up, wearing black top hat and glasses, holding red umbrella, Germany .... **125.00**
Bus, 4⅞″ l, Victory Lines Special, glass, blue painted windows, silver wheels and headlights, Victory Glass Inc, c1942 ......................... **35.00**
Candlestick, 3¾″ h, Colonial style, glass, candle socket, tin slide closure **300.00**
Cane, 4⅝″ l, glass, knob handle, push-in cork stopper .................. **40.00**
Carpet Sweeper, Dolly Sweeper, 3 x 2¼″, glass, clear, tin snap on closure, 6″ l wire handle, movable wheels, West Bros Co, c1914 ............ **280.00**
Cat, papier mache ................. **60.00**

**Chenille, Santa on basket, celluloid face, Japan, c1930, 4″ h, $75.00.**

Chest of Drawers, 3⅞″ h, attached mirror, orig paint, tin closure, c1913 .. **150.00**
Chicken on the Nest, 4⅝″ h, glass, clear, cardboard closure, J H Millstein Co, c1946 ......................... **25.00**
Church, litho tin, glass insert ........ **25.00**
Clarinet, 2$\frac{15}{16}$″ h, glass, red and white swirl stripped cardboard tube top with yellow enameled tin whistle, white enameled tin screw cap, T H Stough Co ........................... **15.00**
Clock, 2⅞″ w, 3¾″ h, mantel, painted dec, paper dial, tin closure, c1913 . **120.00**
Dirigible, Los Angeles, 5¾″ l, glass, painted silver, aluminum screw on cap, Victory Glass Co, c1925 ...... **160.00**
Dog, 4¼″ h, bulldog, gilt collar, painted, round base, metal screw closure, marked "USA," c1930 ....... **80.00**
Doll Carriage, Fanny Farmer ......... **75.00**
Donkey, 5″ h, papier mache, glass eyes, Germany ...................... **215.00**

Duck
Composition, 7" h, wearing pink bonnet, purple int., Germany ....... **85.00**
Glass, 2¾" h, sitting on basket, painted orange, metal slide closure **85.00**
Elephant, GOP, 2¾" h, 2⅞" w, glass, painted gray, red tin slide, Victory Glass Co ........................ **150.00**
Fire Engine, No 11, 4¾" l, 2⅛" h, glass, paper push–in closure, T H Stough Co **25.00**
Football, tin ...................... **15.00**
Gas Pump, 4¼" h, glass, red painted pump, silver top disc and pump reserve, tin screw on cap, 1927–28 .. **200.00**
Girl and Geese, 5¾" h, glass, oval base, L E Smith Glass Co, 1950s ........ **30.00**
Gun
Colt, glass, silver metal screw cap, T H Stough Co, c1942 ............ **15.00**
Flintlock, 9⅜" l, glass, frosted grip, cork stopper closure ............ **25.00**
Hat
Top, 2" h, glass, tin brim, cardboard disc closure .................. **60.00**
Uncle Sam, 2½" h, glass, white opaque, incised stars and alternating vertical stripes, painted red, white, and blue, tin push in slot .. **100.00**
Happifats on Drum, orig paint, orig closure .......................... **350.00**
Iron, 4½" l, 2⅜" h, glass, string electric cord with paper plug, cardboard push in closure, Play–Toy Company, c1946 .......................... **50.00**
Jack–o'–lantern, 3¾" h, 4" d, glass, melon ribbed, raised eyes and nose, depressed mouth with raised teeth, painted pumpkin yellow, white, black, and red accents, tin screw closure, attached wire bail handle ..... **100.00**
Kerosene Lamp, 4⅝" h, glass, painted red, black painted oil font, metal screw on cap ................... **50.00**
Kettle, 1⅞" d, 2" h, ruby stained, round bail handle, canted legs ........... **40.00**
Lamp, hurricane, 1¾" h, glass, oblong base with cut corners, brass cup holds swirled chimney, red tin screw on cap, T H STough Co, c1950 ....... **150.00**
Lantern, 4⅛" h, glass, raised beveled panel square panels on sides, gilded corners, tin slide closure, wire bail handle ......................... **50.00**
Liberty Bell, 3⅜" h, green, hanger .... **75.00**
Locomotive, 2⅝" l, glass, stippled sides and top, cork closure, T H Stough's Tiny One, 1945–47 ............. **25.00**
Mail Box, 3¼" h, glass, painted aluminum, gilt "Souvenir–Dubua la," tin slide closure .................... **125.00**
Milk Carrier, 3¼" h, wire frame, six glass jugs, paper disc closure, marked "Kiddies Fancies" ................ **110.00**
Mug, 4¹⁄₁₆" h, glass, vertical ribs, solid glass handle, pierced aluminum screw on top .................... **12.00**
Nursing Bottle, Baby Nurser No 1, glass, red rubber nipple closure .......... **15.00**
Owl, 4⅜" h, glass, stylized feathers, gold tin screw cap ................ **80.00**
Powder Horn, 6" l, glass, bubble end, tin screw on cap, wire ring handle . **35.00**
Rabbit
4¼" l, running on log, tin closure .. **150.00**
5½" h, sitting on hind legs, glass, blue tint, ribbon with bow on neck, gold tin screw on cap .............. **75.00**
Rocking Horse, glass, impressed star and dots on saddle, flowing tail and mane, tin slide closure ............ **180.00**
Santa, 9" l, four wooden wheels, pulled by reindeer, 1940s ............... **45.00**
School House, litho tin, glass insert ... **20.00**
Snowman, 9½" h, clear glass body, removable plastic head, Sears Roebuck & Co, 1967 .................... **10.00**
Suitcase, 3⅝" l, 2½" h, orig closure, c1910 ......................... **60.00**
Telephone, 9" h, wood receiver and mouthpiece, metal bell and closure, marked "Redlich's Cork Top," c1907 **400.00**
Top, 3¾" h, winding disc, c1929 .... **85.00**
Trumpet, 5½" l, milk glass, gilt dec, gold metal screw on cap .......... **140.00**
Trunk, 3½" l, 2⅛" h, glass, dome top, opaque white, gilt accents, tin slide on closure ...................... **75.00**
Turkey, 8" h, papier mache .......... **25.00**
Wheelbarrow, 6" l, tin closure ....... **65.00**
Windmill, Dutch, 4⅞" h, glass, six sided, four tin blades, cardboard disc closure, Play–Toy Co, c1946 ...... **100.00**

# CANDY MOLDS

**Collecting Hints:** Insist on molds in very good or mint condition. The candy shop had to carefully clean molds to insure good impressions each time. Molds with rust or signs of wear rapidly lose value.

**History:** The chocolate or candy shops of Europe and America used molds to make elaborate chocolate candy items for holiday and other festive occasions. The heyday for these items was 1880 to 1940. Mass production, competition, and the high cost of labor and supplies brought an end to local candy shops.

The makers of chocolate molds are often difficult to determine. Unlike pewter ice cream molds, maker's marks were not always on the mold or were covered by frames. Eppelsheimer & Co. of New York marked many of their molds, either with their name or a design resembling a child's toy shop with "Trade Mark" and "NY."

Many chocolate molds were imported from Germany and Holland and are marked with the country of origin and, in some cases, the mold maker's name.

**References:** Ray Broekel, *The Chocolate Chronicles,* Wallace-Homestead, 1985, out-of-print; Eleanore Bunn, *Metal Molds,* Collector Books, 1981, out of print; Judene Divone, *Anton Reiche Chocolate Mould Reprint Catalog,* Oakton Hills Publications, 1983.

**Museum:** Wilbur's Americana Candy Museum, Lititz, PA.

**REPRODUCTION ALERT**

**Hard Candy, clamp type, bust of Dewey, 6¼ x 2¾", marked "254, T. Mills & Bro. Philadelphia," $60.00.**

Birds, flying, cast aluminum, 7" h, c1950 .......... **25.00**
Bugs Bunny, standing, two 9½" h rabbits, marked "Warner Bros. Productions, Inc.," clamp type, c1960 .... **100.00**
Candy Bars, Wilbur Candy Co, fourteen bars, cast metal tray .......... **20.00**
Champagne Bucket and Bottle, stamped metal, bucket marked "Eppelsheimer #4580," 2¾" h bucket, 4¾" h bottle, c1920 .......... **75.00**
Chicken, tin, marked #2031, 4" h, c1900 .......... **30.00**
Cigars, five tubes, 4½" w, 5" h .......... **35.00**
Dirigible, tin, flat, c1910 .......... **70.00**
Egg, Man in the Moon smoking pipe image, Eppelsheimer & Co, NY, 3" w, 4¼" h .......... **60.00**
Hands, flat, nickel alloy .......... **35.00**
Jack and the Beanstalk, tinned copper, 8¼ x 5¼" .......... **125.00**
Jiggs, tinned nickel silver .......... **35.00**
Lamb, Kanter Mfg Co, Cleveland, OH, 12" w, 8" h .......... **40.00**
Necktie, striped design, looped knot, stamped tin, flat rect frame, marked #12680, 11½" w .......... **35.00**
Rabbit, sitting up, basket on back, tinned metal, top hinge, Eppelsheimer & Co, NY, 4" w, 9" h, c1935 .......... **50.00**
Rocket, two parts, flat, 6" w, 9½" h, c1966 .......... **45.00**
Santa Claus, with sack, stamped metal, clips on edges .......... **35.00**
Stars, row of six, bronzed metal, tray type, A F Tool Co, NY, 6" w, 1½" h **75.00**
Swan, two parts, stamped tin, Thomas Mills & Bros, Philadelphia, PA, 10½" w, 8½" h, c1900 .......... **125.00**
Top Hats, ten, flat tray, metal, 14½" w, 1¼" h .......... **25.00**
Train, steam locomotive, high smokestack, pewter, clamp type .......... **200.00**
Turkeys, pair standing back to back, 9½" w, 6" h .......... **50.00**

# CAP GUNS

**Collecting Hints:** Condition is a critical pricing element. A broken spring that can be replaced is far less critical than a crack that cannot be repaired. Many older cast iron cap pistols rusted and suffered other ravages of time. While restoration is acceptable, an unrestored gun in fine condition is valued more highly than a restored example.

Beware of restrikes, reproductions, and new issues. Several of the molds for cast iron cap pistols have survived. Owners have authorized restrikes as a means of raising money. Often these restrikes are passed as period examples to the unknowing. Reproductions based on recasts often have a sandy or pebbled finish and lack the details found on period examples. New issues are frequently done with the intention of deceiving. Examples include the Liberty Bell cap bomb and the Deadshot powder keg cap bomb.

It is important to know the full history of any post-World War II cap pistol, especially if it is part of a pair. Toy guns associated with a character or personality sell better than their generic counterparts. Some of the price difference can be overcome when a leading manufacturer, e.g., Hubley, is a factor. The presence of the original box, holster, and/or other accessories can add as much as 100% to the value of the gun.

**History:** Although the first toy gun patents date from the 1850s, toy guns did not play an important part in the American toy market until after the Civil War. In the 1870s the toy cap gun was introduced.

The golden age of cast iron cap pistols is 1870 to 1900, with J. & E. Stevens and Ives among the leading manufacturers. Realism took second place to artistic imagination. Designs ranged from leaf and scroll to animal and human heads. The use of cast iron persisted until the advent of World War II, although guns made of glass, lead, paper, rubber, steel, tin, wood, and zinc are known from the 1920 to 1940 period.

In the 1950s diecast metal and plastic became the principal material from which cap guns were manufactured. Leading manufacturers of diecast guns were Hubley, Kilgore, Mattel, and Nichols. Many of the guns were associated with television cowboys and detective heroes. Often the guns were part of larger sets that consisted of a holster and numerous other accessories.

Collecting cap and other toy guns began in the 1930s with the principal emphasis on early cast iron examples from the 1875 to 1915 period. In the mid–1980s the collecting emphasis shifted to the cap pistols of the post–World War II period.

**Reference:** Samuel H. Logan and Charles W. Best, Cast Iron Toy Guns and Capshooters, published by authors, 1990.

**Stevens Ecko, 1930, $30.00.**

E J Cossman Co, Hollywood, CA, Speed Gun, No. 504, metal, 6½ x 3⅛" l .. **40.00**
Flyrite Products, Atom Water Gun, diecast, orig box, tear in flap, 1940s .. **75.00**
Hubley
 Cowboy, gold plated, black grips, 12 x 5¼", near mint ............... **200.00**
 Midget, flintlock, all metal, engraved all over, 5¾ x 2¼", mint ........ **35.00**
 Mountie, automatic, engraving all over gun, mint ................. **125.00**
 Rodeo Pistol, cowboy on bucking horse, red, white, and blue, 8¼ x 3½ x 1⅜" orig box, near mint ... **125.00**
 Texan, revolving cylinder, lever on side, 10¼ x 4¾", near mint ..... **150.00**
 Texan Jr, gold plated, black grips, 9 x 4½", near mint ................ **175.00**
 Texan 38, engraved all over, turquoise grips, 10½ x 5¼", near mint **250.00**
 The Rifleman, Flip Special, rifle, 33¼ x 7¾ x 1⅞" orig box, MIB ....... **600.00**
 Western Cap Pistol, white grips, black steer, 9½ x 4½" ............... **45.00**
Ideal, Yo Gun, red and yellow, plastic, 6½ x 7", 1950s, near mint ........ **30.00**
Kelmar Corp, Milwaukee, WI, Pow'r Pop, automatic, bakelite, maroon, 6½ x 4¼", near mint ............. **35.00**
Kilgore
 Buck, No. 407, red, navy, and white, black grips, 7¼ x 3⅝ x 1¼" orig box with illus of buck deer, near mint ........................ **100.00**
 Deputy, single holster, 2¼" wide fancy belt ..................... **195.00**
 Hawkeye, automatic, Indian head and eagle on barrel, 4¼ x 3⅛" ... **40.00**
 Pal, 5½ x 3", mint ............... **10.00**
 Ranger, cast iron, mint ............ **75.00**
Leslie Henry
 Gene Autry Flying A Ranch, double leather holster set, two 44s, complete with bullets, tan and black, near mint ..................... **600.00**
 Wagon Train, #48, pistol, antique bronze, 16 x 9½ x 1⅞" shadow box with six bullets ................ **400.00**
 Wild Bill Hickok, double leather holster set, two Marshall guns, bronze grips, tan leather, felt lining, near mint ........................ **500.00**
Mason, National Automatic, 45 cap, brown grips, 4½ x 6½", 1940s, near mint .......................... **60.00**
Mattel
 Bandolier, Winchester, leather, thirty two all metal play bullets, belt, 1958, end flaps missing on box .. **125.00**
 Shootin Shell Fanner, 9¾ x 4¾", near mint ........................ **75.00**
 Shootin Shell Remington Derringer, buckle gun, Matty's Funday Funnies, ABC TV, 1958–59, mint on card ......................... **100.00**
 Winchester Saddle Gun, Official, stock no. 544, 33¾ x 6⅜ x 1½" orig box ..................... **500.00**
Nichols
 Civil War Period Model 1861, revolver, shell firing, Model 61, orig 10½ x 16 x 2⅛" shadow box, six shells, eighteen bullets, mint gun, near mint box ................ **600.00**
 Dyna–Mite Derringer, #2782, presentation box, 3½ x 4⅞ x ¾" orig box, jewel on top, "It's a Jewel," mint ........................ **40.00**
 Spit Fire Rifle, 8⅞" l, near mint .... **70.00**
 Stallion 38, two oak leaves on side, white grips, 10½ x 4½", six brass colored shells on lever on side ... **125.00**

Parris Mfg Co, Savannah, TN, Kadet Officer, target pistol, holster, shoots corks, 28 page Kadet handbook and ammo included, orig 5½ x 11" package . . . . . . **50.00**

Remco

Okinawa Pistol, Monkey Division, 1964, 13" l, near mint . . . . . . **35.00**

Screaming Mee–Mee–E Rifle, 38¼ x 15¼ x 3½" box, never opened . . . **300.00**

Unknown Maker

Automatic, 45, chrome steel, 4½ x 6½" . . . . . . **45.00**

Big Scout, cast iron, white grips, 7½ x 3½", near mint . . . . . . **100.00**

Cowboy Pistol, tin, red, black, gold, and white, cowboy riding horse on grips, 11 x 4⅛", 1940s, near mint **30.00**

G–Men Automatic, windup, black, G–Men illus, red, yellow, and green, steel, 1940s, near mint . . . **75.00**

Hero, cast iron, 5¾ x 3", cowboy on cast iron grips, mint . . . . . . **40.00**

Pistol, metal, cork stopper, red, black, and silver, 9¾" l . . . . . . **30.00**

Police, automatic, steel, picture of policeman on both sides, 8" l, 1940s . . . . . . **40.00**

Scout, cast iron, metal grips with cowboy, 3 x 6½", near mint . . . . . **90.00**

Smoky, gold plated, 2½ x 5½", mint **10.00**

Wells Fargo, pistol, brown and white grips, horse head, designs on barrel, 11½ x 4½", near mint . . . . . . . **125.00**

# CARNIVAL CHALKWARE

**Collecting Hints:** Most chalkware pieces appear worn, either because of age or inexpensive production techniques. These factors do not affect the value, provided the piece is whole and has no repairs. Some pieces are decorated with brightly silver. This adds nothing to the authenticity of the piece or its value. Carnival chalkware in bank form is considered part of this category.

**History:** Carnival chalkware, cheerfully painted plaster of paris figures, was manufactured as a cheap, decorative art form. Doll and novelty companies mass produced and sold chalkware for as little as a dollar a dozen. Many independents, mostly immigrants, molded chalkware figures in their garages. They sold directly to carnival booth owners.

Some pieces are marked and dated; most are not. The soft nature of chalkware means it is easily chipped or broken.

Carnival chalkware was marketed for a nominal price at dime stores. However, its prime popularity was as a prize at games of chance located along carnival midways. Concessionaires, e.g., breaking a balloon with a dart, awarded small prizes, called a "build up." As you won, you accumulated the smaller prizes and finally traded them for a larger prize, often a piece of chalkware.

Chalkware ranges in size from three to twenty-four inches. Most pieces were three dimensional. However, some had flat backs, ranging from a plaque format to a half thick figure. Colors depended upon the taste of each individual decorator.

A wide variety of animal, character, and personality figures were made in chalkware. You can find Betty Boop, Sally Rand, Mae West, Shirley Temple, Charlie McCarthy, W. C. Fields, Mickey Mouse, etc. However, you will not find these names on the figures or in the advertising literature of the company who made them. Shirley Temple was the "Smile Doll"; Mae West was the "Mae Doll." Most character dolls were bootlegged, made without permission.

Although some carnival chalkware was made before the 1920s, its peak popularity was in the 1930s and 40s. The use of chalkware prizes declined in the late 1950s and met its demise in the 1960s.

**References:** Thomas G. Morris, *The Carnival Chalk Prize,* Prize Publishers, 1985; Ted Sroufer, *Midway Mania,* L-W, Inc., 1985.

**Horse, black and white, gold mica dec, red, green, and yellow dec base, 9¼" l, 11" h, $35.00.**

Alice The Goon, 10", King Features Syndicate, c1945 . . . . . . **60.00**

Buddy Lee, 13½", hand painted, cotton cap, c1930 . . . . . . **65.00**

Bugs Bunny . . . . . . **60.00**

Captain Marvel, 14½", c1940 ........ **50.00**
Cardinal, 1940s .................... **12.00**
Cat, 10", bank, c1940 .............. **10.00**
Circus Horse, 10", c1930 ........... **18.00**
Dog
Bull Dog, 6", Bonzo, English, cap, bottle in mouth, c1930 ......... **75.00**
Collie, 18", c1940 ................ **15.00**
Terrier, 8", black and white, rhinestone eyes, c1940 .............. **10.00**
Donald Duck, long bill ............. **60.00**
Dopey, 6", c1937 ................... **42.00**
Elephant, bank, c1930 .............. **12.00**
Fan Dancer, 16", marked "Portland Statuary Co," c1935 ................. **50.00**
Felix The Cat, 12½" ................ **65.00**
Ferdinand The Bull, 8½", c1940 ..... **20.00**
Fields, W C, 6", plaque, top hat and cigar, c1937 ..................... **20.00**
Flapper, 10", reclining girl, painted bobbed air, red pants and top, 1920 **100.00**
Gigolo, string holder ................ **28.00**
Hula Girl, 17", grass skirt, c1940 ..... **20.00**
Irish Setters, bookends, pr ........... **35.00**
Johnny, 12", Phillip Morris, marked "Jenkins, 1934" .................. **60.00**
Lady and Dog, 11¼", full ruffled skirt, floral trim, c1935 ................ **12.00**
Lamb, 7", flat back, marked "Rosemead Novelty Co," c1940 .............. **5.00**
Lamp Doll, 15", movable arms, long marcelled hair, c1920 ............ **125.00**
Lone Ranger ....................... **70.00**
Majorette, 12", marked "El Segundo Novelty Co," 1949 ............... **24.00**
McCarthy, Charlie .................. **40.00**
Mickey Mouse ...................... **65.00**
Miss America, 15", bathing suit, c1940 **20.00**
Monk, playing violin ............... **24.00**
Nude Lady, bookends, pr ............ **40.00**
Pig, 10", standing, carrying tray, wearing jacket and hat, marked "J. Y. Jenkins, 1937" ..................... **20.00**
Pirate, Captain Kiddo, 1929 ......... **60.00**
Popeye, 18", King Features Syndicate, c1930 ......................... **90.00**
Ship, 10", flat back, c1940 .......... **5.00**
Snow White ....................... **45.00**
Squirrel, 12", eating corn, c1940 ..... **7.50**
Stripper, 13½", heart shaped medallion, c1935 ......................... **35.00**
Sweater Girl, 11½", c1930 .......... **24.00**
Teepee and Indian, lamp ............ **85.00**
Temple, Shirley, 12", 1935 .......... **60.00**
Valentino, Rudolph, 15", dressed as sheik, c1925 .................... **100.00**
Washington, George, 12", marked "A Incrocci, Pittsburgh, PA," c1940 .... **60.00**
West, Mae, 14", white dress, c1937 .. **65.00**
Wimpy, 18", c1940 ................. **32.00**
World War II GI, 6", face in center of victory sign, c1945 ............... **15.00**

# CARTOON CHARACTERS

**Collecting Hints:** A vast majority of collectible categories yield an object related to a cartoon character. Cartoon characters appeared in advertising, books, comics, movies, television, and as a theme in thousands of products designed for children.

Concentrate on one character or the characters from a single strip. Most collectors tend to focus on a cartoon character that was part of their childhood. Another method is to focus on the work of a single artist. Several artists produced more than one cartoon character.

The most popular cartoon characters of the early period are Barney Google, Betty Boop, Dick Tracy, Gasoline Alley, Li'l Abner, Little Orphan Annie, and Popeye. The movie cartoons produced Bugs Bunny, Felix the Cat, Mighty Mouse, Porky Pig, and a wealth of Disney characters. The popular modern cartoon characters include Garfield, Peanuts and Snoopy.

**History:** The first daily comic strip was Bud Fisher's Mutt and Jeff, which appeared in 1907. By the 1920s the Sunday comics became an American institution. One of the leading syndicators was Captain Joseph Patterson of the News–Tribune. Patterson, who partially conceived and named "Moon Mullins" and "Little Orphan Annie," worked with Chester Gould to develop "Dick Tracy" in the early 1930s.

Walt Disney and others pioneered the movie cartoon, both in short and full length form. Disney and Warner Brothers characters dominated the 1940 to 1960 period. With the advent of television the cartoon characters of Hanna–Barbera, e.g., the Flintstones, added a third major force. Independent studios produced cartoon characters for the television and characters multiplied rapidly. By the 1970s the trend was to produce strips with human characters, rather than the animated animals of the earlier period.

A successful cartoon character created many spin–offs. Comic books and paperback books, earlier Big Little Books, followed quickly. Games, dolls, room furnishings, and other materials which appealed to children are marketed. The secondary market products may produce more income for the cartoonist than the drawings themselves.

**References:** Bill Bruegman, *Cartoon Friends of the Baby-Boom Era: A Pictorial Price Guide,* Cap'n Penny Productions, 1993, Ted Hake, *Hake's Guide to Comic Character Collectibles,* Wallace–Homestead, 1993; Maurice Horn and Richard Marshall (eds.), *World Encyclopedia of Comics,* Chelsea House Publications, 1976; David Longest, *Character Toys and Collectibles, First Series,* (1984, 1992 value update) and *Sec-*

*ond Series,* (1987, 1990 value update), Collector Books; Freddi Margolin and Andrea Podley, *The Official Price Guide To Peanuts Collectibles,* House of Collectibles, 1990; Norman E. Martinus and Harry L. Rinker, *Warman's Paper,* Wallace–Homestead, 1993.

**Museum:** The Museum of Cartoon Art, Port Chester, NY.

**See:** Disneyana and index for specific character.

Andy Panda
- Bank, 6" h, composition, wearing red bib overalls, inscribed "Andy Panda Bank," 1940s ............ **100.00**
- Planter, 3 x 5", china, white, high relief figure on front, stamped 1958 Walter Lantz copyright on base .. **75.00**

Atom Ant and Secret Squirrel
- Lunch Box, steel, 6½" h thermos with red plastic cup, King–Seeley Thermos Co, 1966 Hanna–Barbera copyright ...................... **100.00**
- Push Puppet, 2¼" h, plastic, blue circular base with plunger, Kohner Bros, c1966 .................. **25.00**

Baby Huey, puppet, 10" h, fabric body, soft vinyl head, Gund Mfg, 1960s .. **40.00**

Barney Google, figurine, 4" h, composition and wood, 1944 ............ **75.00**

Beany & Cecil
- Bath Set, washcloth and bubble bath, unopened clear plastic bag with header card, 1961 .............. **50.00**
- Coloring Book, Artgraft, 1969 ...... **25.00**
- Disguise Kit, Mattel, 1962 ......... **45.00**
- Flashlight, 3" l, blue, keychain, 1960s **45.00**
- Game
  - Ring Toss, Pressman, 1961 ...... **35.00**
  - Talk to Cecil Adventure Game, includes Cecil pull string hand puppet, Mattel, 1961 ......... **40.00**
- Little Golden Book, *Beany Goes to Sea,* 24 pgs, 1963 .............. **30.00**
- Purse, 5" l, vinyl, red, Bob Clampett, 1961 ......................... **25.00**
- Soap Container, 8" h, vinyl, Roclar Distributors, 1960s ............. **80.00**
- Thermos, 8½" h, steel, red plastic cup, King–Seeley Thermos Co, 1961 ......................... **50.00**
- Toy, stuffed, 12½" h, Mattel, 1950 . **80.00**

Beetle Bailey
- Costume, Spook Town Halloween Costume, orig box, 1960s ....... **50.00**
- Game, The Old Army Game, orig box, Milton Bradley, 1963 ....... **35.00**

Betty Boop
- Big Little Book, *Betty Boop in Snow White Assisted By Bimbo and Ko–Ko,* Whitman, 1934 ............ **100.00**
- Figure, 3¾" h, bisque, Japan, 1930s **100.00**
- Napkin Ring, Erphila ............. **40.00**
- Pencil Holder, 2½" h, Happy House, celluloid, decal on roof marked "Bloomsburg Fair, PA," base marked "Made In Occupied Japan" **300.00**
- Perfume Bottle, 3½" h, glass, clear, 1930s ........................ **80.00**
- Playing Cards, complete deck, orange, black, and white design, 1930s ........................ **75.00**

Blondie
- Coloring Book, #338, Treasure Book, 1959 ......................... **15.00**
- Game, Blondie Goes To Leisureland, Westinghouse premium, 1940 copyright ...................... **50.00**
- Lunch Box, 7 x 8½", steel, King–Seeley, 1969 ...................... **75.00**
- Paint Book, #1151, Whitman, 1947 **22.00**

Bozo the Clown
- Glass, 5½" h, blue inscriptions, 1965 Larry Harmon and Capitol Records copyright ...................... **50.00**
- Mask, 10½ x 12½", paper, diecut, full color portrait image, fourteen children's Capitol records illus on back, 1950s ................... **25.00**

Bugs Bunny
- Alarm Clock, 4 x 4½", full color, animated arm holding carrot, Ingraham Co, c1951 ................ **165.00**
- Christmas Card, 4½ x 6½", full color, Dell Comics .................. **35.00**
- Cookie Jar, 8" h, ceramic, marked on bottom "McCoy USA," 1971–72 . **100.00**
- Costume, Collegeville, 1965 ....... **60.00**
- Doll, 20" h, plush, vinyl face, 1¾" litho button on chest, Mattel, 1960s **75.00**
- Egg Cup, 2½" h, china, white, raised figure on side ................. **45.00**
- Figure, 7" h, china, Warner Bros copyright, 1940s ............... **80.00**
- Neck Tie, 10½" l, child's, clip–on, plum color, yellow and white Bugs, c1940 ....................... **50.00**
- Nodder, 7" h, composition, gold circular base with decal, stamped "Warner Bros Pictures Inc, Japan," 1960s ....................... **100.00**
- Planter, 3 x 6 x 7½", china, wheelbarrow, glossy white Bugs, late 1940s ....................... **140.00**
- Radio, 6 x 8½", figural, head, 1960s **60.00**
- Toy, Talking Target, mechanical, Transogram, 1976 ............. **140.00**
- Vase, 7½" h, bud, china, figural, Bugs resting against tree, Warner Bros copyright, c1940 ............... **90.00**
- Wristwatch, United Import/Rexall Drug Co, orig box ............. **145.00**

Casper the Friendly Ghost
- Costume, Ben Cooper, 1961 ....... **50.00**

Game, Casper the Friendly Ghost Game, 15¼" sq playing board, Milton Bradley, 1959 ... **30.00**
Hand Puppet, 8" h, cloth, plastic head **40.00**
Lamp, 17" h, figural, Archlamp Mfg, 1950 ... **50.00**
Night Light, 6½" h, Duncan, 1975 . **45.00**
Party Set, 6 pcs, tablecloth, cups, napkins, and plates, Reed, 1965 . **32.00**
Pencil Clip, ⅝" h, brass, white enamel figure, 1950–60 ... **15.00**
Playing Cards, Casper and His TV Pals, Ed–U–Cards Corp, 1960s ... **18.00**
Toy, pull, 20" l, Casper's Ghost Train, wood, late 1950s ... **60.00**

Chilly Willy
Figure, 8" h, ceramic, 1975 ... **50.00**
Puzzle, set of 4, Saalfield, 1963 ... **80.00**
Toy, squeeze, rubber, orig box, Oak Rubber, 1950s ... **50.00**

Chipmunks
Doll, 15" h, Alvin, talking, Mattel, 1962 ... **50.00**
Game, The Three Chipmunks Big Record New Surprise Game, Hassenfeld, 1960 ... **60.00**
Glass, 4¾" h, Alvin, blue and yellow illus, M H Buell copyright, c1960 **50.00**
Paint Set, Alvin, Hasbro, 1959 ... **75.00**
Wallet, vinyl, 1959 ... **10.00**

Crusader Rabbit
Activity Book, *Crusader Rabbit Trace and Color Book,* Whitman, 1959 . **35.00**
Book, *Crusader Rabbit in Bubble Trouble,* Whitman, 1960 ... **20.00**
Game, Crusader Rabbit TV Game, A Jay Ward Cartoon ... **150.00**
Paint Set, orig 13 x 19" box ... **45.00**

**Dick Tracy, card game, 1934, $50.00.**

Curious George, game, The Curious George Game, Parker Brothers, 1977 **20.00**
Dudley Doright, puzzle, 100 pcs, Fairchild series, 1971 copyright ... **30.00**

Deputy Dawg
Coloring Book, Treasure, 1961 ... **25.00**
Costume, Ben Cooper, 1961 ... **65.00**
Doll, 14" h, vinyl head, 1961 ... **80.00**
Game, Deputy Dawg Hoss Toss Horseshoe Pitch Game, orig box, 1973 ... **65.00**
Pencil Box, 1960 ... **50.00**
Soaky Bottle, 10" h, plastic, 1966 copyright ... **15.00**

Dick Tracy
Badge, Secret Service Patrol, 1930s . **45.00**
Greeting Card, 1960s ... **22.00**

Elmer Fudd
Figure, 4" h, hollow ceramic, wearing hunting outfit, glazed, American Pottery Co, 1940s ... **80.00**
Figure, 5" h, china, crawling, rifle under one hand, American Pottery, 1940s ... **50.00**
Hand Puppet, 9" h, fabric, soft vinyl head, c1950 ... **60.00**
Toy, pull, 9" l, Elmer Fudd–Fire Chief, musical bell, Brice Toy Novelty Inc, 1940s ... **100.00**

Felix the Cat
Book, *A Surprise For Felix,* Wonder Book, 20 pgs, 1959 ... **15.00**
Cup, 5" h, Sip A Drink ... **30.00**
Flashlight, whistle ... **15.00**
Game, Milton Bradley, 1968 ... **25.00**
Pencil Case, 9" l, cardboard, 1933 . **60.00**
Puzzle, frame tray, Built–Rite, 1960 **20.00**
Toy
Figure, 4" h, wood, jointed, black leather ears, decal on chest, Schoenhut Toys, 1920–30 ... **150.00**
Squeaker, 6" h, soft rubber ... **30.00**

Flintstones
Ashtray, Barney, ceramic, Arrow Houseware Products of Chicago, 1961 copyright ... **35.00**
Bank, 6" h, 4½" w, book form, plastic, color character images, 1964 copyright ... **75.00**
Christmas Ornament
4" h, Dino, vinyl, purple, black spots, tan muzzle, 1976 copyright ... **25.00**
4¼" h, Barney Rubble, plastic, Bradford Novelty Co, copyright 1976 ... **15.00**
Game
Dino the Dinosaur ... **55.00**
Flintstones Stoneage Game, Transogram, 1961 ... **30.00**
Lunch Box, Pebbles and Bamm–

Bamm, emb steel, plastic thermos, Aladdin Industries copyright 1971 **50.00**

Gumby and Pokey

Drawing Set, Adventures of Gumby, electric, Lakeside, 1966 ......... **30.00**

Figure, 5″ h, Gumby, rubber, posable, Lakeside, 1965 ............... **35.00**

Game, Gumby and Pokey Playful Trails Game, CO–5 Company, 1968 ........................ **80.00**

Hand Puppet, 9″ h, Gumby, vinyl head, Lakeside Toys, 1965 ...... **20.00**

Toy, windup, 4″ h, vinyl, orange, Lakeside, 1966 ............... **70.00**

Happy Hooligan

Figure, 8¼″ h, bisque, worried expression, "3534" on back, early 1900s ....................... **75.00**

Post Card, 3½ x 5½″, full color photo, "I'll Help You's," inscription, Nov 14, 1905 postmark ............ **15.00**

Heckle and Jeckle, coloring book, Treasure, 1957 ..................... **15.00**

Huckleberry Hound

Colorforms, Huckleberry Hound Cartoon Kit, orig box, Colorforms Toys, 1960 ................... **75.00**

Coloring Book, 8½ x 11″, #1117, Whitman, 1959 ............... **25.00**

Doll, 27″ h, red plush body, vinyl head, Knickerbocker Toy Co, 1959 Hanna–Barbera copyright ....... **75.00**

Game

Huckleberry Hound Card Game, Ed–U–Cards, 1961 .......... **20.00**

Huckleberry Hound Western Game, Milton Bradley, 1959 ... **50.00**

Lunch Box, Huckleberry Hound and His Friends, emb steel, thermos with red plastic cup, Aladdin Industries copyright 1961 ......... **75.00**

Pencil Case, 4½ x 8½″, cardboard, snap fastener, color character sticker, 1960 copyright .......... **22.00**

Jetsons

Chalkboard Set, wood frame chalkboard, boxed chalk sticks, boxed crayons, and character stencil sheets, orig unopened shrink wrap, Standard Toykraft, 1960s ........ **100.00**

Game, Jetsons Out of This World Game, Transogram, 1962 ....... **75.00**

Puppet, 10″ h, Jane, fabric body, painted soft vinyl head, Knickerbocker Toy Co, early 1960s ..... **200.00**

Toy, Space Copter, hard vinyl, yellow plastic blades, orig display card, Transogram, 1962 ............. **75.00**

Li'l Abner

Coloring Book, #2370, Saalfield, 1941 ........................ **20.00**

Greeting Card, set of 4, 5 x 6¾″, black and white Abner and Daisy Mae on back, unused, Superior Greeting Co, 1940–50 .......... **25.00**

Little Lulu

Bank, 8″ h, vinyl, figural, Play Pal Plastics, 1970s ................ **25.00**

Book, *Little Lulu Plays Pirate,* McLoughlin Bros, 1946, 42 pgs, hardcover ......................... **35.00**

Coloring Book, 8 x 11″, Tubby, Whitman, 1963 ................... **35.00**

Clothes Line and Pin Set, Arandell, 1940s ....................... **50.00**

Doll, 14″ h, vinyl, inflatable, Made in Taiwan for Sani Toy copyright 1973 by Western Publishing Co ....... **25.00**

Valentine, stand–up, Little Lulu and Tubby ....................... **15.00**

Magilla Gorilla, 11″ h, puppet, fabric body, soft vinyl head, Ideal Toy, Hanna–Barbera copyright, early 1960s ......................... **50.00**

Maggie & Jiggs, paperweight ......... **55.00**

**Jiggs, figure, composition face, wood hands and feet, orig costume, Schoenhut, 7½″ h, $300.00**

Mighty Mouse

Book, *Mighty Mouse to the Rescue,* Wonder Book, 1958, 20 pgs ..... **20.00**

Figure, 12″ h, vinyl, 1950s ........ **75.00**

Game, Mighty Mouse Game, orig box, copyright 1957 Milton Bradley Co and 1958 Terrytoons ........ **40.00**

Magic Slate, 1958 ................ **40.00**

Paint Set, Mighty Mouse Presto Paint Set, Kenner, 1963 .............. **55.00**

Puzzle, Whitman, 1967 ........... **20.00**

Moon Mullins

Figure, 7″ h, bisque .............. **95.00**

Salt and Pepper Shakers, pr, Moon Mullins and Kayo .............. **45.00**

Mr Magoo
- Ashtray, 7 x 9", adv, Magoo holding General Electric light bulb, 1960s . . . **70.00**
- Bank, 17" h, vinyl, A J Renz, 1960 . . . **50.00**
- Doll, 12" h, Ideal, 1970 . . . **50.00**
- Game, Mr Magoo Visits The Zoo, orig box, Lowell, 1961 . . . **40.00**
- Glass, 5½" h, 1962 . . . **30.00**
- Toy, 9" l, The Official Mr Magoo Car, battery operated, yellow litho tin, cloth top, vinyl Magoo figure, Hubley, 1961 . . . **300.00**

Peanuts
- Bank, 7" h, plaster, doghouse with Snoopy on roof, Made in Japan, 1960s . . . **25.00**
- Bicycle Bell, Snoopy . . . **10.00**
- Candleholder, pr, 8" h Charlie Brown, 7½" h Lucy, plaster, brass candle cup, Hallmark Candles sticker . . . **25.00**
- Doll, 7½" h, Snoopy, astronaut uniform, plastic and vinyl, Determined Productions Inc, 1969 . . . **50.00**
- Figure, 9" h, vinyl, early 1960s . . . **25.00**
- Lunch Kit, 8½" h, yellow vinyl zippered bag with carrying strap, 7½" h plastic thermos, c1965 . . . **50.00**

Pink Panther
- Coloring Book, *Pink Panther Roasting Hot Dog,* Whitman, 1976 . . . **15.00**
- Figure, 11" h, plastic, poseable, Bendy Toys . . . **10.00**
- Game, Pink Panther Game, Warren, 1977 . . . **35.00**
- Little Golden Book, *Pink Panther & the Fancy Party* . . . **10.00**
- Lunch Box, Pink Panther & Sons, steel, plastic thermos, King Seeley, 1984 . . . **45.00**
- Socks, pr, 1971 . . . **25.00**

Popeye
- Bank, 1929 . . . **42.00**
- Game, Pipe Toss . . . **50.00**
- Gum Wrapper Tattoo . . . **10.00**
- Pencil, metal, 1929 . . . **30.00**
- Toy
  - Friction, moving van . . . **275.00**
  - Windup, Popeye the Pilot, Marx . . . **850.00**

Porky Pig
- Doll, 14" h, Gund, 1950 . . . **100.00**
- Figure, 5½" h, hollow china, wearing blue jacket and pink bow tie, American Pottery Co . . . **80.00**
- Planter, figural, Warner Brothers, 1940s . . . **65.00**
- Sponge, 4 x 7½", Bath Tub Buddies, foam, printed image, unused, orig cellophane bag, 1960s . . . **15.00**
- Wristwatch, metal case, dial with Porky wearing blue jacket, Ingraham Co, c1949 . . . **175.00**

Quick Draw McGraw
- Figure, 7½" h, china, 2" d base marked "Quick Draw McGraw" . . . **100.00**
- Game, Quick Draw McGraw Private Eye Game, Milton Bradley, 1960 . . . **32.00**

Roadrunner
- Figure, 5" h, rubber, Hong Kong, 1976 copyright . . . **15.00**
- Game, Roadrunner Pop–Up Game, Whitman, 1982 . . . **20.00**

Rocky & Bullwinkle
- Bank, 6" h, china, Rocky & His Friends, early 1960s . . . **200.00**
- Book, *Rocky & Bullwinkle Go To Hollywood,* Whitman, 1961 . . . **25.00**
- Bumper Sticker, "Bullwinkle for President, He's A lot Of Bull," 1972 . . . **20.00**
- Coloring Book
  - Dudley Do–Right, Whitman, 1972 . . . **20.00**
  - Rocky the Flying Squirrel, 8 x 12", Whitman, 1960 . . . **40.00**
- Doll, 13" h, Bullwinkle, stuffed, Gund, 1970 . . . **50.00**
- Game
  - Bullwinkle Card Game, Ed–U–Cards, 1962 . . . **25.00**
  - Rocky and Bullwinkle Role Playing Game, TSR, 1988 . . . **15.00**
- Hat, white cotton canvas, transparent dark green plastic visor, color illus of Bullwinkle, Boris, Natasha, and Rocky, 1960s . . . **25.00**
- Little Golden Book, *Rocky and His Friends,* 1960 . . . **15.00**
- Magic Slate, Bullwinkle, 1963 . . . **45.00**
- Mug, 4" h, Rocky & His Friends, 1960 . . . **65.00**
- Paint Book, #1421, Whitman, 1960 . . . **35.00**
- Pencil Case, 4 x 8½", vinyl, 1962 . . . **40.00**
- Puzzle, Whitman, 1962 . . . **40.00**
- Sewing Cards, Rocky and His Friends, six cards, Whitman, 1961 . . . **75.00**
- Waste Can, 11" h, metal, 1961 . . . **75.00**

Skeezix
- Coloring Book, 9½ x 10¼", McLoughlin Bros, 24 pgs, 1929 . . . **22.00**
- Planter, 3 x 3 x 5", bisque, Uncle Walt and Skeezix images, inscribed names and "Featured Artists Syndicate" copyright on back, Made in Japan, 1930s . . . **50.00**

Smokey Bear
- Bank, 8" h, Smokey holding shovel, "Save With Smokey/Prevent Forest Fires" on base, 1970s . . . **30.00**
- Canteen, 2 x 6 x 7", vinyl, 1950s . . . **20.00**
- Display Sign, 11½ x 14", "Prevent Woods Fires," cardboard, Craig Pineo, US Dept of Agriculture, Forest Service, 1955 . . . **60.00**
- Lunch Box, steel, plastic thermos, Okay Industry, 1975–78 . . . **55.00**
- Nodder, 6¼" h, late 1960s . . . **35.00**

Salt and Pepper Shakers, pr, 3½" h, china, late 1960s ............... **20.00**
Speedy Gonzalez, figure, 5½" h, china, 1980s .......................... **25.00**
Tom & Jerry
Bookends, pr, 8" h, Gorham, 1980 . **40.00**
Costume, Tom, Halco, 1952 ....... **40.00**
Figure, 4" h, Jerry, orig box, Marx, 1973 ........................ **30.00**
Game, The Tom & Jerry Game, Selchow & Righter, 1962 .......... **50.00**
Mug, china, white, Staffordshire, 1970 ........................ **20.00**
Music Box, 3 x 5½ x 6½", Tom and Jerry on skateboard, plays "King of the Road," Gorham, 1981 ....... **25.00**
Puppet, Tom, cloth body, plastic head, talking, orig box, Mattel, 1965 ........................ **70.00**
Top Cat, game, Whitman, 1962 ...... **150.00**
Tweety Bird, egg cup, 2½" h, china, raised image, marked "Peele St Pottery Co Ltd of England, 1953 Warner Bros" .......................... **25.00**

**Sylvester and Tweety Bird, hot water bottle, Warner Bros. Inc., Duarry, Spain, mid 20th c, 12¾" h, $65.00.**

Underdog
Coloring Book, Whitman, 1965 .... **15.00**
Costume, Ben Cooper, 1973 ....... **70.00**
Game, Underdog Alphabet Tray Game, 1969 .................. **22.00**
Glass, 6½" h, clear, weighted bottom, Pepsi series, Leonardo–TV copyright ........................ **20.00**
Puzzle, 100 pcs, orig box, Whitman, 1975 ........................ **20.00**
Woody Woodpecker
Alarm Clock, 4¼" d, animated, Columbia Time Products, 1959 .... **100.00**
Big Little Book, *Woody Woodpecker & The Meteor Menace,* Whitman, #2010, 1967 .................. **20.00**
Breakfast Set, bowl and mug, plastic, full color raised portrait on mug, hollowed log form bowl marked "F & F Mold & Dye Works," 1950s . **50.00**
Costume, Collegeville, 1950 ....... **50.00**
Game, Woody Woodpecker Game, Fairchild, 1968 ................ **30.00**
Lamp, 20" h, figural, plastic, 1974 . **25.00**
Salt and Pepper Shakers, pr, 4" h, Woody Woodpecker and friends, ceramic, Napco, Japan, 1958 .... **50.00**
Slippers, 1957 .................. **20.00**
Yellow Kid
Figure, 7¼" h, papier mache, dark red paint, Old King Cole Papier Mache Co, Canton, OH sticker ......... **200.00**
Yogi Bear
Game, Yogi Bear Card Game, Ed–U–Cards, 1961 .................. **25.00**
Lunch Box, steel, emb, plastic thermos, Aladdin Industries, copyright 1974 ........................ **75.00**
Paste Jar, 3½" h, plastic, figural, head, marked "Yogi Bear White Paste By Le Pages" on back, 1965 copyright **40.00**
Puppet, 12" h, Boo Boo, fabric body, painted soft vinyl head, 1970s ... **40.00**
Yosemite Sam, salt and pepper shakers, pr, 4" h, china, foil sticker "Lego of Japan," Warner Bros copyright stamped on bottom, early 1970s ... **75.00**

# CATALOGS

**Collecting Hints:** The price of an old catalog is affected by the condition, data, type of material advertised, and location of advertiser.

**History:** Catalogs are used as excellent research sources. The complete manufacturing line of a given item is often described, along with prices, styles, colors, etc. Old catalogs provide a good way to date objects.

Many old catalogs are reprinted for use by collectors as an aid to identification of their specialities, such as Imperial and The Cambridge Glass Co.

**References:** Don Fredgant, *American Trade Catalogs,* Collector Books, 1984, out–of–print; Norman E. Martinus and Harry L. Rinker, *Warman's Paper,* Wallace–Homestead, 1993; Lawrence B. Romaine, *A Guide to American Trade Catalogs,* Dover Publications, 1960, 1990 reprint.

A C Becon Co, 1930, 1046 pgs ...... **75.00**
American Chair Co Tropique Rattan & Simulated Rattan, 1940, 16 pgs .... **14.00**

Angelica Uniforms, 1932, illus ....... **42.00**
Army and Navy General Merchandise, 1923 .......................... **18.00**
Arnold Fisher Wholesale Florists, March 1, 1940 ........................ **22.00**
Bastian Bros Co, Badges, 1908, 36 pgs **50.00**
Betty and Bob's Adventures in Toyland, 1956, comic books, 16 pgs ........ **25.00**

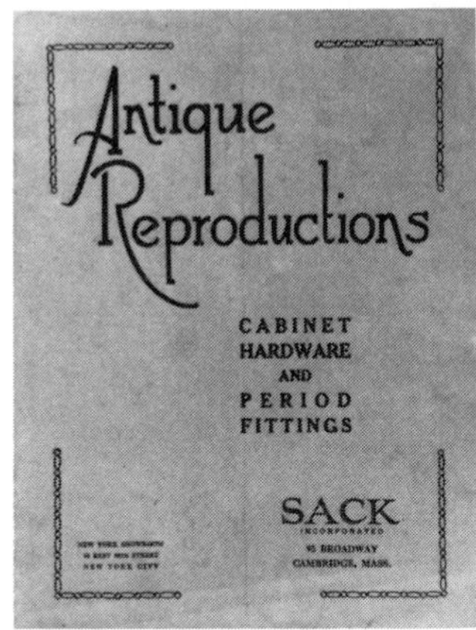


**Sack Inc., Antique Reproductions Cabinet Hardware and Period Fittings, 16 pgs., 1946, 8½ x 11", $35.00.**

Betty Wales Dress, c1920, 5 x 7" ..... **24.00**
Billy and Ruth Christmas Catalog, 1952, 44 pgs, toys ..................... **75.00**
Boy Scouts Official Scouting Equipment, 1921, 36 pgs ................... **75.00**
Butler Bros, Santa Claus Edition, 1922, 240 pgs ........................ **110.00**
Cadillac, 1973, 24 pgs ............. **10.00**
Chase, Parker & Co, Boston/Bangor, 1930, 600 pgs .................. **40.00**
Chrysler Imperial, 1968, 24 pgs ...... **15.00**
Collum & Doren, 1961, athletic supplies and guns .................. **20.00**
Columbia Disc Graphophone and Grafonala, 1911, 31 pgs ............ **55.00**
Colt Fire Arms, March, 1934, 40 pgs, orig mailing envelope ............ **25.00**
Corgi Toys, 1966, 48 pgs, full color illus **25.00**
Crandall–Bennette Porter Co, 1907, 35 pgs, oak dining room tables ....... **48.00**
Daisy Gun & Toy, 1963 ............ **28.00**
Dent Hardware Co, Fullerton, A, 1911, Catalogue of Refrigerator Hardware & Hardware Specialties, Volume B, red and black leather binder .......... **125.00**
Dent Toys Catalog No 10, c1930, 48 pgs ............................ **125.00**
Dinky Toys, Feb, 1968, 4 pgs ........ **20.00**
Estes Model Rocketry, 1975 .......... **25.00**
F C Taylor Fur Co, 1924, 48 pgs ..... **50.00**
Firestone, Spring and Summer, 1954, 42 pgs ............................ **25.00**
Fisher–Price, 1959, 12 pgs .......... **30.00**
Ford Motor Co Passenger Car, 1967, 16 pgs, full color photos ............ **18.00**
Fouke Fur Co, 1925, 24 pgs ......... **30.00**
F W Aldens, Fall and Winter, 1956–57 **35.00**
General Electric Refrigerator, 1939, 8½ x 11", black and white photos ..... **15.00**
Gilbert Toys, Superman at the Gilbert Hall of Science, 1948, 28 pgs ..... **100.00**
Gordon & Ferguson Outdoor Clothing, St Paul, MN, 1938–39, 28 pgs ..... **6.00**
H J Cummins Fishing Tackle, 1909, 90 pgs ........................... **125.00**
Hollander's Auto Stores, Spring and Summer, 1941, 66 pgs ........... **18.00**
Hollywood Television Service, 1940–50, 100 pgs, films available for television distribution ................ **25.00**
Hopkins & Allen Gun, 1908, 48 pgs .. **150.00**
Indian Motorcycles, 1927, 18 pgs .... **100.00**
J C Penney 1972 Christmas, 472 pgs .. **15.00**
Lincoln Continental, 1966, 16 pgs .... **15.00**
Lionel, 1957, 52 pgs, train sets and accessories ....................... **15.00**
L L Bean, Spring, 1942, 80 pgs ...... **15.00**
McCormick Machinery, 1900 ........ **75.00**
Meccano Prize Models, 1914 ........ **28.00**
Milton Bradley, 1953 .............. **50.00**
Montgomery Ward
Christmas, 1947 ................ **35.00**
Fall/Winter, 1953 ............... **37.50**
Motion Picture Music, 1917 ......... **25.00**
Nash Howe, Fall, 1961, sporting goods **18.00**
Old Town Canoe, 1930, 37 pgs ...... **60.00**
Parkers Distributors, 1958, 128 pgs, hunting and fishing equipment ..... **15.00**
Pep Boys Auto Accessories, May, 1930 **15.00**
Peters Arms & Sporting Goods Co, 1910, 136 pgs, 6 x 8" ........... **75.00**
Poly–Choke, 1940, 16 pgs, Aero–Dyne Super Poly–Choke rifle attachment, orig mailing envelope ............ **15.00**
Pontiac, 1968, 22 pgs, full color photos of car models ................... **12.00**
Portland Cement, steps, curbs, and garden accessories ................. **22.00**
Rears & Robust, outhouse .......... **65.00**
Remco Industries Inc, 1961, 16 pgs ... **25.00**
REO Automobile, 1907, 24 pgs ...... **25.00**
Sears, Roebuck & Co, Christmas, 1933, 88 pgs ......................... **200.00**
S & H Green Stamp Premiums, 1928 . **25.00**
Singer, 1905, color lithos ........... **30.00**
South Bend Bait Co, 1935, 108 pgs, 5½ x 6¼" ......................... **50.00**
Southern Supply, 1957, farm implements ......................... **12.50**
Spiegel, Fall/Winter, 1952 .......... **37.50**
Spring Time At Woolworth's, 1953, 36 pgs ........................... **25.00**

Stevens Rifles and Shotguns, 1940, 30 pgs, orig mailing envelope ........ **18.00**
Stoeger Co, New York, Shooting Bible, 1952, 416 pgs .................. **8.00**
The Toy Yearbook 1955–56, 64 pgs, full color .......................... **75.00**
Thunderbird, 1967, 8 pgs ........... **15.00**
Tonka, 1964, 12 pgs .............. **25.00**
Tri–ang Minic, vehicles and windup illus, unfolds to 26" l, 1950s ........ **25.00**
Vetter Mfg Co Standard Design, 1919, 368 pgs ........................ **18.00**
Victor Hawaiian Records, 1916, 8 x 11", full color .................... **20.00**
Victorian Bead Craft, 32 pgs ......... **15.00**
Vogue Coiffures, 1924, 46 pgs, wigs and hair pieces ...................... **60.00**
Winchester Guns and Ammunition, 1936, 56 pgs, orig mailing envelope **40.00**
Woolworth's New Christmas Book–Santa Comes to the Big Top, 1954, 32 pgs ......................... **15.00**
Wright, Kay & Co, Jewelers, 1941, 24 pgs ............................ **8.00**

# CAT COLLECTIBLES

**Collecting Hints:** Cat related material can be found in almost all collecting categories—advertising items, dolls, figurines, folk art, jewelry, needlework, plates, postcards, and stamps to name a few. Because of the popularity of cats, modern objets d'feline constantly are appearing on the market. However, as cat collectors become more experienced, their interests are more with antique rather than newer items.

The cat collector competes with collectors from other areas. Chessie, the C & O Railroad cat, is collected by railroad and advertising buffs. Felix is a favorite of toy and cartoon character enthusiasts.

Because cat collectors are attracted to all cat items, all breeds, and realistic or abstract depictions, they tend to buy too many items. It is best to specialize. Money and display space extend only so far; time for research is limited. Three of the most popular new areas of cat collecting are cat cards, calendars, and stickers.

Throughout the 1980s cats have grown in popularity as the pets of choice and along with this has grown the love of collecting cat items. The new and newer (secondary) market, tomorrow's collectibles, has grown by leaps and bounds. Some cat pieces bought ten years ago are showing considerable price increases. As true antique cats become rare and costly, buy what you can, but also concentrate on quality, limited editions, and original pieces in the current market.

**History:** Cats always have been on a roller coaster ride between peaks of favoritism and valleys of superstition. In ancient Egypt cats were deified. Cats were feared by Europeans in the Middle Ages. Customs and rituals bore down brutally on felines. Cats became associated with witchcraft, resulting in tales and superstitions which linger to the present. This lack of popularity is why antique cat items are scarce.

Cats appear in TV programs, movies, cartoons, and many advertising ads in addition to those for cat food. Garfield remains popular; Felix has made a comeback; and a new feline, Motley, is emerging. Objects associated with these modern cartoon cats are tomorrow's collectibles.

**References:** Pauline Flick, *Cat Collectibles,* Wallace–Homestead, 1992; Marbena Jean Fyke, *Collectible Cats: An Identification & Value Guide,* Collector Books, 1993; Bruce Johnson, *American Catalogue: The Cat in American Folk Art,* Avon Books, 1976; J. L. Lynnlee, *Purrrfection: The Cat,* Schiffer Publishing, 1990; Norman E. Martinus and Harry L. Rinker, *Warman's Paper,* Wallace–Homestead, 1993; Alice L. Muncaster and Ellen Sawyer, *The Black Cat Made Me Buy It!,* Crown Publishers, 1988; Alice Muncaster and Ellen Yanow; *The Cat Made Me Buy It,* Crown Publishers, 1984; Alice L. Muncaster and Ellen Yanow Sawyer, *The Cat Sold It!,* Crown Publishers, 1986; Silvester and Mobbs, *The Cat Fancier: A Guide To Catland Postcards,* Longman Group, 1982.

**Collectors' Club:** Cat Collectors, 33161 Wendy Dr., Sterling Hts., MI 48315.

**Museums:** The Metropolitan Museum of Art, New York, NY; British Museum, London, England; The Cat Museum, Basel, Switzerland.

**Advisor:** Marilyn Dipboye.

### REPRODUCTION ALERT

Avon Bottle
Ming Cat Cologne, white, blue details, 1971, MIB ................ **15.00**
Sitting Pretty Cologne, kitten on pillow, 1976, MIB ................ **10.00**
Bank
5" l, 5¼" h, ceramic, white, orange stripes, gray mouse atop cat, incised, orig paper label reads "QQ Japan" ........................ **25.00**
5½" h, ceramic, white kitten on rose colored ball of yarn ............ **22.00**
Bell, 4¾" h, porcelain, white, dark gray tabby, gold trim, marked "Enesco 1980" .......................... **12.00**
Biscuit Jar, 6" h, ceramic, black cat head, painted features ............ **55.00**
Bookends, pr, 4½" w, 6¼" h, composition, antique gold wash, kitten with

ball of yarn, marked "Universal Statuary Corp, Orig Sculpture B/W Marotta" . . . . 75.00

Candy Dish, 4" l, 3¾" h, bisque, white, kitten, red bows, marked "Lefton" . . 10.00

Character Jug, Royal Doulton
- 6¾" h, The Wizard . . . . 110.00
- 7" h, Cook and Cheshire Cat, discontinued . . . . 135.00

Christmas Ornament, 4" h, blown glass, painted face, applied fuzzy tail, felt ears . . . . 20.00

Cookie Jar, 12" h, white cat, blue fisherman's hat, blue fish, yellow details 35.00

**Pin, cat faces, sterling silver, Beau, 1½" d, $35.00.**

Creamer
- 4" h, ceramic, black cat handle, cream ground, green neck, orange lip, stamped "Goldcastle, Made in Japan" . . . . 35.00
- 13" d, 4" h, ceramic, white, green contemporary cat, marked "Arabia Made In Finland" . . . . 38.00

Figure
- 1½" h, pewter, kitten, sitting, tongue sticking out, marked "English Pewter Model #M476" . . . . 12.00
- 2¾" h, pewter, cat wearing heart necklace, marked "Ampersand Pewter USA" . . . . 26.00
- 2⅞" h, lead crystal, black eyes, silver tail, Swarovski . . . . 45.00
- 3½" h
  - Bisque, white, sitting, orig paper label reads "Lefton #1513" . . . . 8.00
  - Pottery, ming turquoise, smiling kittens, Van Briggle, Colorado Springs . . . . 65.00
- 4½" h, pottery, ming turquoise, smiling kittens, Van Briggle, Colorado Springs . . . . 65.00
- 4½" l, porcelain
  - Cream and brown tabby, marked "Eisenberg, Germany" . . . . 65.00
  - Gray, yellow eyes, Goebel, Germany, #31020–06 . . . . 24.00
- 5½" l, bisque, white, laying down, orig paper label reads "Lefton #1513" . . . . 16.00
- 6" l, porcelain, high glaze, white, mother with baby resting on back, orig paper label reads "Takahaski Japan" . . . . 35.00
- 6¼" h, Forty Winks, napping woman in rocker, black cat at feet, Royal Doulton HN1974, 1945–73 . . . . 225.00
- 6½" h, bisque, white, orig paper label reads "Lefton #1517" . . . . 16.00
- 6½" l, Solitude, woman on couch, reading, white cat, Royal Doulton HN2810, 1976–83 . . . . 325.00
- 6¾" h, ceramic, high glaze, black cat, rhinestone collar, gold rhinestone eyes, paper label reads "Norcrest Japan" . . . . 9.50
- 7¼" h, carnival chalkware, white and brown spots, red ears and mouth, blue bow and ball . . . . 20.00
- 7½" h, Save Some For Me, Childhood Days Series, red headed girl, aqua dress, holding bowl, orange kitten at feet, Royal Doulton HN2959, 1982–85 . . . . 125.00
- 7¾" h, Dorothy, seated woman, black cat climbing up her dress, Royal Doulton HN3098, 1987–90 . . . . 225.00
- 8" h, The Favorite, woman in aqua dress, pouring milk for golden tabby, Royal Doulton HN2249, design by Mary Nicholl . . . . 150.00

Folk Art, 11" h, wood, gray striped cat, red vest, serving bowl of goldfish . . . 35.00

Lamp, 15" h, Cat N' Fiddle, ceramic, cream colored cat, blue jacket, brown fiddle, pleated fabric shade . . . . 75.00

Letter Holder, 6½" l, ceramic, black cat, painted face, pen as tail, marked "Japan" . . . . 30.00

Marmalade Jar, 5" h, figural, ceramic, blue, rose colored bowl, orig matching spoon, orig paper label reads "Norcrest Japan" . . . . 22.00

Medallion, one troy ounce silver
- Garfield, Christmas Stocking, inscribed "Garfield, Merry Christmas, 1987," Silver Towne, orig box . . . . 25.00
- Pink Panther, holding heart, inscribed "With Love, Pink Panther" . . . . 25.00

Music Box
- 2½" h, porcelain, grand piano shape, white, calico cat face transfer, gold details, plays "Music Box Dancer" 30.00
- 8½" h, wood box, porcelain head, fabric ruffled color, Lesley Anne Ivory, plays "Serenade" . . . . 150.00

Night Light, 5½" l, 7" h, stoneware, shelf sitter, flame shaped bulb . . . . . . **25.00**
Nut Dish, 5" sq, cat face transfer, marked "Crown Staffordshire England" . . . . . . **10.00**
Paperweight, 8" l, 4" d, brass cat, wood base . . . . . . **40.00**
Pillow, 13" l, 9" h, yellow satin, red rose floral design, hp and sgd "Jan Feenstra, 1976" . . . . . . **48.00**
Planter, 4" l, 4¼" h, ceramic, smiling gray kitten climbing side of white rectangular planter, green leaf spray, marked "USA" . . . . . . **25.00**
Playing Cards, gray kitten, daisies, blue ground, unopened deck, orig box . . **6.50**

**Post Card, Christmas, $1.00.**

Print, framed
- Boyd, Bertha, gray and white cat family taking drive, green car, 12 x 15" **45.00**
- Bracker, Charles E, Chessie, Peake returned home with war injury, 13¼" sq . . . . . . **85.00**
- Gray Litho Co, Yard of Cats, eleven playful kittens, 1908, 36" l . . . . . . **95.00**

Quilt, 52 x 35", baby, cross stitch, Three Little Kittens, gray kittens, rose, pink, and blue details . . . . . . **110.00**
Roly Poly, 4½" h, gray cat, blue ball . . **20.00**
Salt and Pepper Shakers, pr
- 2¾" and 3" h, ceramic, calico, orig paper label reads "Enesco" . . . . . . **8.00**
- 3¼" h, ceramic, Siamese cats, red bows, marked "Japan" . . . . . . **8.50**
- 3½" h, plastic, white, red ears and bows, black facial features, squeaker . . . . . . **7.50**
- 4½" h, ceramic, one gray, other brown and white, large yellow eyes **7.50**

Spoon Rest, 3" h, ceramic, cat face, white, pink ears, blue bow, marked "Japan" . . . . . . **10.00**
String Holder, 6½" h, chalkware, black and cream cat, red ball of string . . . . **30.00**
Teapot, 9¾" h, figural, ceramic, golden striped cat, green bow, marked "Pussyfoot HJ Wood England" . . . . . . **55.00**
Toaster Cover, cloth, cream, black Kliban cat, "Love a cat" . . . . . . **5.00**
Toy, 4¾" h, wood, jointed press type, red and white cat, yellow base, marked "Made in Czechoslovakia" . **16.50**
Wall Plaque
- 2½" h, chalkware, white kittens, pink ears and bows, yellow and black eyes, price for pair . . . . . . **18.00**
- 3½" h, 4¼" w, chalkware, face, incised "1954 Miller Studio Inc" . . . **30.00**

# CEREAL BOXES

**Collecting Hints:** There are two keys to collecting cereal boxes. The first is graphics, i.e., the box features the picture of a major character or personality or a design that is extremely characteristic of its period. The second hinges on the premium advertised on the box.

Cereal boxes are divided into vintage boxes (those dating before 1970s) and modern boxes. Hoarding of modern cereal boxes began in the mid–1980s. Hence, beware of paying premium prices for any boxes after this date.

There is no question that a small group of dealers and collectors are attempting to manipulate the cereal box market, much as was done to the lunch kit market in the early 1980s. While there is some collector resistance, prices keep rising. Before paying hundreds of dollars for a particular box, remember the lunch kit market collapse currently in process. What goes up, etc., etc.

More desirable than cereal boxes themselves are large countertop and other cereal box display pieces. Cereal box collectors compete actively against advertising collectors for these items, thus driving up prices.

Many cereal box themes also cross over into other collecting categories. In many cases, these secondary collectors are responsible for maintaining a "high" price for some boxes. Once the outside demand is met, prices drop. Carefully study which market component is the principal price determinant.

**History:** Oatmeal and wheat cereals achieved popularity in the nineteenth century. They were available in quantity purchase from any general store. The first packaged, ready–to–eat breakfast cereals appeared around 1900. Initially, the packaging pitch contained an appeal directed to mothers.

Everything changed in the late 1930s and early 1940s. Companies such as General Mills, Quaker, Post, and Ralston redirected the packaging appeal to children, using as a hook the lure of premiums for the submittal of one or more box lids or coupons. Many of these promotions were geared to the popular radio shows of the period. However, it was the arrival of television and its advertising that established a firm link between cereal manufacturers and children.

In the 1940s General Mills successfully used the premium approach to introduce Cheerios and Kix. In the 1950s sugar-coated cereals were the rage. By the 1960s and 1970s cereal manufacturers linked the sale of their brands to licensed characters. As the popularity of characters faded, the box was changed but not the cereal. Today an endless variety of cereal brands parade across supermarket shelves, some lasting less than a year.

**References:** Norman E. Martinus and Harry L. Rinker, *Warman's Paper*, Wallace–Homestead, 1993; Tom Tumbusch, *Tomart's Price Guide to Radio Premiums and Cereal Box Collectibles*, Wallace–Homestead, 1991.

**Periodicals:** *Flake*, PO Box 481, Cambridge, MA 02140; *Free Inside*, PO Box 178844, San Diego, CA 92117.

Addams Family, orig figural Fester flashlight, movie portrait cut–out on back, Ralston, 1991 .................... **15.00**
Aunt Sally Quick Cooking Oats, 10" h, cylindrical, yellow and red, 1940s .. **40.00**
Cheerios, Muppet Movie Trading Cards, 1980 .......................... **15.00**
Clover Farm Regular Cooking Rolled Oats, 10" h, cylindrical, bee and clover flower, 1930s ................ **40.00**
Corn Chex, Party Mix recipe on back, 1950s .......................... **65.00**
Corn Flakes, Kellogg's, Vanessa Williams, 1984 ..................... **45.00**
Cocoa Krispies, Choco–Cluster Recipe Box, 1965 ....................... **50.00**
Fairway Oat Flakes, 10" h, cylindrical, boy and girl, c1910 .............. **90.00**
Frosted Flakes, Kellogg's, Tony the Tiger spoon offer on back, 1975 ........ **40.00**
George Washington Corn Flakes, unopened ......................... **60.00**
Jersey Corn Flakes, 1920s, unopened, multicolored box, family eating cereal **40.00**
Kellogg's, baseball games and graphics int., 1910 ....................... **110.00**
Nabisco Shredded Wheat, 1942 ...... **65.00**
Post Super Sugar Crisp, 1974 ........ **35.00**
Quaker Puffed Wheat
  No 8 Space Flight To Moon, 1953 .. **100.00**
  Sgt Preston, Yukon Trial No 2, 1949 **100.00**
Red Owl Quick Cooking Oats, 10" h, cylindrical, c1940 ................ **35.00**
Rice Chex, red check dec, 1950s ..... **65.00**
Wheaties
  Minnesota Twins, 1987 ........... **7.00**
  Pete Rose color photo, unopened .. **15.00**
  World Series, 1985 ............... **5.50**

**Wheaties, 1987 World Champions Minnesota Twins, 18 oz, General Mills, $7.00.**

White Swan Oatmeal, 4 oz .......... **28.00**
White Villa Rolled Oats, 10" h, cylindrical, house and landscape scene, 1920s ......................... **55.00**

# CEREAL PREMIUMS

**Collecting Hints:** The rising collectibility of cereal premiums reflects the shift of emphasis in collectibles from the 1920–40 period to the post–1945 era. The radio premium generation is getting older. They have watched the price of their childhood treasures rise to the point of unaffordability for the scarcer pieces. Further, they are reaching an age when selling, rather than buying, dominates their mindset. It is time for a new generation to enter the picture. Herald the arrival of the cereal premium.

At the moment, collectors do not differentiate between premiums that were found in the box versus those that were obtained by sending in the requisite number of box tops. As collectors become more sophisticated, look for this distinction to occur.

The cereal premiums of most interest in the current market are those associated with a fictional advertising, cartoon, or television character. As a result, much of the pricing in this category is being driven by the non–cereal premium collector. This does not appear likely to change in the decade ahead.

Collectors of cereal premiums narrow their collecting by focusing on the premiums found in a single brand of cereal or cereals distributed by one manufacturer. These change depending on whether one concentrates on the 1945–1962 or post–1962 period. The lack of a comprehensive list of manufacturers, brands, and premiums often makes attribution a problem. When buying a cereal premium with which you are unfamiliar, insist that the seller indicate the manufacturer, brand name, and date on the sales receipt.

Unclear at the moment is the importance of original packaging, much of which was nondescript. Current collectors tend to leave unopened packages sealed when found. Most examples are found with their packaging missing.

At the moment there is little enthusiasm for generic pieces. However, anyone who compares the history of Cracker Jack premium collecting with that of cereal premiums will quickly see the long–term potential for generic material.

**History:** Cereal premiums first appeared in the 1930s when manufacturers such as General Mills, Post, Quaker, and Ralston offered premiums to individuals who sent in the requisite number of box tops or coupons. Many of these premiums had a radio show tie–in.

Although the use of in–the–box premiums and on–pack promotions date from the 1930s, this approach achieved its greatest popularity in the post–1945 period. Buildings, dolls, games, masks, and puzzles were just a few of the many items that a child could obtain by carefully following the cut-out directions on the back of a cereal box. Many of these in–box and on–pack promotional premiums related to a popular television program or movie.

When sugar-coated cereals were introduced in the mid–1950s, advertising characters were developed to assist in the merchandising effort. Characters such as Captain Crunch, Sugar Bear, Tony the Tiger, and Toucan Sam achieved widespread recognition. Often in–box and on–pack promotions tied in directly with these characters.

In the 1970s shorter run tie–ins were developed. Cereals responded almost immediately to the latest movie or television craze. Local and regional promotions became prominent. One result of this trend is that emphasis shifted from the premium to the box itself as the important collectible unit. Cereal box collecting is now a separate category. The value of most boxes now exceeds any value for the premium associated with it.

**Reference:** Tom Tumbusch, *Tomart's Price Guide to Radio Premiums and Cereal Box Collectibles,* Wallace–Homestead, 1991.

**Periodicals:** *Flake,* PO Box 481, Cambridge, MA 02140; *Free Inside,* PO Box 178844, San Diego, CA 92117.

Book, *Dick Tracy*, Quaker Oats, c1939 **25.00**
Cereal Bowl and Mug, Digger Frog illus on bowl, figural mug, Sugar Smacks, 1973 .......... **20.00**
Comic Book, *Baseball Facts & Fun*, 52 pgs, Post Sugar Crisp .......... **30.00**
Cut–out
Rocket Firing Star Fighter Jet and Exploding Light Tank, Cheerios, 1950s .......... **12.00**
Decoder, 3" l, Toucan Sam, figural, plastic, Fruit Loops, 1970s .......... **10.00**
Doll, Quaker, stuffed, 1960s .......... **28.00**
Eraser, Yogi Bear, 2" h, Kellogg's, 1960s **20.00**
Figure
Caveman, Ogg, blonde hair, Cocoa Krispies, 1970 .......... **28.00**
Cap'n Crunch, 8" h, vinyl, 1971 ... **35.00**
Crackle, jointed, Kellogg's Rice Krispies .......... **15.00**
Huckleberry Hound, plastic, removable head with secret storage space, Kellogg's, 1960s .......... **30.00**
Mr Jinx, plastic, 3 pc, Kellogg's, 1960 **100.00**
Game
Rin Tin Tin Bead In Hole Game, circular casing, Nabisco, 1956 ..... **12.00**
Space Match Card Game, color illus box, Quisp, 1968 .......... **25.00**
Mug, plastic, black and white, three different illus, Cheerios, 1950s ....... **30.00**
Party Kit, Singing Lady Party Kit, masks, uncut, Kellogg's, 1936 .......... **60.00**
Pin
Dennis the Menace .......... **15.00**
Roy Rogers, Grape Nut Flakes, 1953 **5.00**
Pinback Button, 3" d, Huck Hound For President, Kellogg's, 1960 .......... **15.00**
Plate, 8" d, plastic, white, Bullwinkle jumping off diving board with Cheerios kid watching, General Mills .... **25.00**
Post Card
Cheerios Kid and Donald Duck, Huey, Louie, and Disneyland, 3½ x 6", black and white, Cheerios, 1957 .......... **10.00**
Lone Ranger, 3 x 6", photo with signature, Cheerios, 1956 .......... **10.00**
Punch–Out Card, 4 x 7", Train–O–Gram, Santa Fe Twin Unit Diesel, set of 3, unused, Shredded Wheat, 1956 **30.00**
Puppet
Banana Splits, Bingo, plastic, Kelloggs, 1969 .......... **10.00**

**Wheaties, Philippines license plate, white and green, 1953, 3⅛ x 2¼", $1.00.**

Cap'n Crunch, plastic, 1960s ...... **24.00**
Trix Rabbit, 12", cloth and vinyl, 1960s ........................ **30.00**
Radio, Tony the Tiger, 8" h, figural, plastic, 1970s ...................... **20.00**
Record, 33⅓ rpm, Archies, Jingle–Jangle, Post Cereal, 1968–70 ......... **5.00**
Ring
Flasher, Yogi and Boo Boo, Kellogg's, 1960 ......................... **18.00**
Quisp Meteorite, Quaker, 1960s ... **55.00**
Spoon, Dennis The Menace, silver plate, Kellogg's .................. **20.00**
Telescope, 12" l extended, plastic, emb illus of Quake, marked "Quake is Better," 1960s ..................... **40.00**
Toy
Cap'n Crunch Sea Cycle, plastic, Cap'n Crunch and Seadog figure, rubber band powered, orig mailing box, unused, Quaker, 1960s ..... **60.00**
Car, Chitty Chitty Bang Bang, plastic, two–tone, cardboard wings, Post, 1968 ........................ **30.00**
Mighty Mouse Merry–Pack, punch–out sheets, Alpha Bits, Post Cereal, c1956 ....................... **60.00**
Rickshaw, plastic, So–Hi figure pulls cart, Rice Krinkles, Post, 1965 ... **85.00**
Satelite Launcher, 2" d, plastic, rubber band powered launcher with emb "Quake" on each side, unused, Quisp, Quaker, 1960s .......... **40.00**
Wacky Races Bi–Plane, Muttley, missing one wing support, Kellogg's, 1969 ........................ **50.00**
Wall Plaque, 8 x 10", Oath of Allegiance, paper, color illus, unused, Cap'n Crunch, 1960s ............ **24.00**

# CHARACTER AND PROMOTIONAL GLASSES

**Collecting Hints:** Contemporary character and promotional glasses are usually produced in series. It is important to collect the full series, including any color variations. This is not as easy as it sounds. Sports team glasses are frequently issued regionally, i.e., Philadelphia Eagles glasses can appear just in the Philadelphia market while San Diego Charger glasses are available only in the area around San Diego. Before paying a great deal of money for a recent glass, ask yourself if what may be rare in your area is common somewhere else. Any serious collector needs this sense of perspective.

Some early examples were decorated with lead-based paint. They should not be used for drinking purposes.

Collectors place a premium on glasses with out–of–the–box luster. The mere act of washing a glass in a dishwasher or sink can lessen its value. Avoid examples with any evidence of fading.

Because of their wide availability, character and promotional drinking glasses should be collected only if they are in excellent to mint condition. Pay premium prices only for glasses that pre–date 1980. After that date, glasses were hoarded in quantity by distributors, dealers, and collectors.

**History:** Character and promotional drinking glasses date to the movie premier of *Snow White and the Seven Dwarfs* in December of 1937. Libbey Glass and Walt Disney designed tumblers with a safety edge and sold the glasses through variety stores and local dairies. The glasses proved extremely popular. Today collector glasses can be found for almost every Disney character, cartoon, and movie theme.

In 1953 Welch's began to package their jelly in decorated tumblers that featured Howdy Doody and his friends. Once again, the public's response was overwhelming. Welch's soon introduced other cartoon characters, such as Mr. Magoo, in their tumbler series.

In the late 1960s, fast food restaurants and gasoline stations started to use drinking glasses as advertising premiums. Soft drink manufacturers like Coke and Pepsi saw the advertising potential and developed marketing plans focusing on licensed characters and movies. Sport team licensing also entered the picture. By the early 1980s hundreds of new glasses were being issued each year.

As the 1980s drew to a close, plastic drinking cups replaced glasses. The use of licensed images continued. While most collectors still prefer to collect glass, a few far–sighted individuals are stashing away pristine plastic examples.

**References:** Mark E. Chase and Michael Kelly, *Contemporary Fast Food and Drinking Glass Collectibles,* Wallace–Homestead, 1988, out–of–print; John Hervey, *Collector's Guide To Cartoon & Promotional Drinking Glasses,* L–W Book Sales, 1990, 1992 value update; Carol and Gene Markowski, *Tomart's Price Guide to Character &*

*Promotional Glasses, Second Edition*, Tomart Publications, 1993.

**Periodical:** *Collector Glass News*, PO Box 308, Slippery Rock, PA 16057.

Animal Crackers, 1978
  Dodo .......... **8.00**
  Lyle .......... **8.50**
Annie and Sandy, Swenson's, 1982 .... **5.00**
Arby's
  BC Ice Age, riding on wheel, 1981 . **8.00**
  Bicentennial, 1976
    Bullwinkle, Crossing the Delaware, 11 oz .......... **8.00**
    Rocky, In The Dawn's Early Light, 11 oz .......... **8.00**
    Underdog, Never Fear, 16 oz .... **9.00**
  Movie Star Series, Charlie Chaplin .. **6.00**
  Thought Factory Series, First Flake, 1982 .......... **7.00**
  Wizard of Id, 1983
    King .......... **12.00**
    Knight .......... **10.00**
    Wizard .......... **8.00**
Archies, 1971, 8 oz
  Archie Takes The Gang For A Ride . **4.00**
  Betty and Veronica Fashion Show .. **4.00**
  Hot Dog Goes To School .......... **3.50**
Battlestar Galactica, Universal Studios, 1979
  Apollo .......... **7.50**
  Commander Adama .......... **7.50**
  Cyclon Warriors .......... **9.00**
  Starbuck .......... **7.00**
Beatles, 6½" h, clear glass, black letters and illus, repeated illus of Beatles and Yea, Yea, Yea, 1960s .......... **45.00**
Big Top Peanut Butter, 1940–50
  Chicago .......... **8.00**
  Dixieland .......... **7.00**
  The Band Played On .......... **7.50**
Bugs Bunny, Happy Birthday Bugs .... **2.00**
Burger Chef
  Endangered Series, Bengal Tiger, 1978 .......... **6.00**
  Frankenburger Scores A TD, 1977 .. **8.00**
  Jefferson, Thomas, Presidents Series . **5.00**
  Washington, 1975 Bicentennial Series **6.00**
Burger King
  Burger King, 1979 .......... **9.00**
  Dallas Cowboys, Charlie Waters .... **5.00**
  Denver Broncos, Moses .......... **7.50**
  Empire Strikes Back .......... **2.50**
  I've Got The Magic That It Takes, 1978 .......... **10.00**
  Jabba, Star Wars, 1983 .......... **2.00**
  Luke Skywalker, 1977 .......... **3.00**
  Shake A Lot, 1979 .......... **8.00**
Coca Cola
  Betty, tray girl .......... **10.00**
  Coke, German .......... **5.00**
  Heritage Collector Series, Patrick Henry .......... **5.00**
  Holly Hobbie, Good Friends Are Like Sunshine .......... **5.00**
  Olympics, Sam the Eagle, boxing, 1980 .......... **1.00**
  Outdoor Scene, buttered corn ...... **5.00**
  Santa
    Elves .......... **5.00**
    Reindeer flying over house, McCroy Stores .......... **10.00**
Crockett, Davy, 6½" h .......... **10.00**
DC Comics
  Aquaman, 1978 .......... **5.00**
  Batman, 1966 .......... **4.00**
  Green Lantern .......... **8.00**
  Shazam .......... **3.00**
  Superman, 1975 .......... **5.00**
  Wonder Woman .......... **3.00**
Disney, Walt
  Donald Duck and Daisy, orange, 5" h **10.00**
  Fantasia, Canadian .......... **10.00**
  Ferdinand The Bull, 1930s .......... **12.00**
  Goofy, 1930s .......... **15.00**
  Mickey, 1930s .......... **18.00**
  Minnie, Mickey Mouse Club ....... **9.00**
  Snow White and the Seven Dwarfs, 4¾" h, 1939 .......... **12.00**
  Winnie The Pooh, Winnie and friends, Sears .......... **7.50**
Domino's Pizza, 1988
  Noid, beach chair .......... **2.00**
  Noid, tennis .......... **2.00**
Dr Pepper
  Hot Air Balloon .......... **7.00**
  Mr Spock, Star Trek, 1976 .......... **7.00**
  Tiffany type dec .......... **3.00**
Good To The Last Drop, 5¼" h, clear glass, two black illus of cartoon type gas station attendants, orange ring bands, c1950 .......... **10.00**
Harvey Cartoons
  Casper, blue .......... **5.00**
  Ritchie Rich .......... **3.00**
  Wendy .......... **4.00**
Kellogg's, Tony .......... **3.00**
Kentucky Derby
  1945, tall .......... **375.00**
  1952, gold cup .......... **125.00**
  1958, gold bar .......... **140.00**
  1962 .......... **50.00**
  1964 .......... **40.00**
  1965 .......... **50.00**
  1966 .......... **38.00**
  1967 .......... **38.00**
  1968 .......... **38.00**
  1970 .......... **38.00**
  1991 .......... **4.00**
Indy 500, 1954 .......... **25.00**
Lone Ranger, 1938 .......... **50.00**
McDonalds
  Big Mac, McVote, 1986 .......... **3.50**

Camp Snoopy, Civilization is Overrated . . . 1.00
Garfield, mug . . . 1.50
Hamburglar, 5⅝" h . . . 2.00
Kermit the Frog, 1981 . . . 3.00
Mac Tonight, microphone, 1988 . . . 4.00
Mayor McCheese Taking Pictures, 1977 . . . 2.00
Olympics, sailing, blue dec, mug . . . 1.50
Pittsburgh Steelers, Superbowl XIII, Bradshaw, Webster, and Greenwood . . . 2.00
Ronald McDonald Saves The Falling Star, 1977 . . . 3.50

**MacDonald's, Camp Snoopy Collection, "Civilization is Overrated!", 1983, 6" h, $1.00.**

Marvel Comics
- Amazing Spiderman, 1977 . . . 4.00
- Fantastic Four, 1977 . . . 2.00
- Howard The Duck, 1977 . . . 3.00
- Hulk, 1978 . . . 3.00

MGM, Wizard of Oz . . . 10.00
Mobil, football, ten different logos, price for set . . . 17.50
National Periodical Publications
- Batman . . . 8.00
- Joker . . . 8.00
- Superman, Fighting the Dragon, clear glass, blue and pink text and illus, 1965 copyright, 5¼" h . . . 10.00
- Wonder Woman . . . 7.00

Pan American Airlines, 5½" h, clear glass, weighted bottom, solid color illus of Holland, Portugal, France, or Italy, Pan Am logo, c1950, price for set of four . . . 25.00
Paramount Pictures, Inc, 1939
- Gulliver's Travels Sneak . . . 35.00
- Little King . . . 35.00

Pepsi
- Bambi . . . 4.00
- Caterpillar Tractor . . . 3.00
- Happy Birthday Goofy, 1978 . . . 6.00
- Jingle Bells, 1984 . . . 5.00
- Mickey, 1979 . . . 5.00
- Shere Kahn, 1977 . . . 8.00

Pizza Hut
- Bullwinkle, blue truck . . . 7.50
- Care Bears, Funshine Bear, 1983 . . . 8.00
- Dudley Do–Right, helicopter . . . 7.00
- ET, Universal Studios, 1982 . . . 5.00

Schmoo, Al Capp, 1949 . . . 35.00
Warner Bros
- Beaky Buzzard, Cool Cat, kite, Action Series, 1976 . . . 6.00
- Cool Cat, 1973 . . . 4.00
- Daffy Duck, Bugs Bunny, hunting, Action Series, 1976 . . . 6.00
- Elmer Fudd, Bugs Bunny, Shotgun Sam, carrots, Action Series, 1976 . . . 6.00
- Foghorn Leghorn, 1973 . . . 4.00
- Pepe Le Pew, Canadian, 1978 . . . 7.50
- Porky Pig, 1973 . . . 3.00
- Road Runner, catapult, tunnel, Action Series, 1976 . . . 6.00
- Sylvester, 1973 . . . 4.00
- Tasmanian Devil, 1973 . . . 6.00
- Yosemite Sam, Speedy Gonzales, panning for gold, Action Series, 1976 . . . 6.00

Welch's, 8 oz
- Archies . . . 3.50
- Flintstones . . . 6.00
- Howdy Doody, 1953 . . . 45.00

# CHILDREN'S BOOKS

**Collecting Hints:** Most collectors look for books by a certain author or illustrator. Others are interested in books from a certain time period such as the 19th century. Accumulating the complete run of a series such as Tom Swift, Nancy Drew, or the Hardy Boys is of interest to some collectors. Subject categories are popular too, and include ethnic books, mechanical books, first editions, award winning books, certain kinds of animals, rag books, Big Little Books, and those with photographic illustrations.

A good way to learn about children's books is to go to libraries and museums where special children's collections have been developed. Books on various aspects of children's literature are a necessity. You also should read a general book on book collecting to provide you with background information. Significant bits of information can be found on the title page and verso of the title page of a book. This information is especially important in determining the edition of a book. You eventually will want to own a few reference books most closely associated with your collection.

Although children's books can be found at all the usual places where antiques and collectibles are for sale, also seek out book and paper shows. Get to know dealers who specialize in children's books; ask to receive their lists or catalogs. Some dealers offer to locate certain books for you. Most used and out–of–print book stores have a section with children's books. If your author or illustrator is still actively writing or illustrating, a regular book store may carry his most recent book.

Things to be considered when purchasing books are the presence of a dust jacket or box, condition of the book, the edition, quality of illustrations and binding, and the prominence of the author or illustrator. Books should be examined very carefully to make sure that all pages and illustrations are present. Missing pages will reduce the value of the book. Try to buy books in the best condition you can afford. Even if your budget is limited, you can still find very nice inexpensive children's books if you keep looking.

**History:** William Caxton, a printer in England, is considered to have been the first publisher of children's books. Among his early publications was *Aesop's Fables* printed in 1484. Other very early books include John Cotton's *Spiritual Milk for Boston Babes* in 1646, *Orbis Pictis* translated from the Latin about 1657, and *The New England Primer* in 1691.

Children's classics had their beginning with *Robinson Crusoe* in 1719, *Gulliver's Travels* in 1726, and Perrault's *Tales of Mother Goose* translated into English in 1729. The well known *A Visit from St. Nicholas* by Clement C. Moore appeared in 1823. Some of the best known children's works were published between 1840 and 1900. A few are Lear's *Book of Nonsense, Andersen's and Grimm's Fairy Tales, Alice in Wonderland, Hans Brinker, Little Women, Tom Sawyer, Treasure Island, Heidi, A Child's Garden of Verses,* and *Little Black Sambo.*

Series books for boys and girls began around the turn of the century. The Stratemeyer Syndicate, established about 1906, became especially well known for their series, such as Tom Swift, The Bobbsey Twins, Nancy Drew, Hardy Boys, and many others.

Following the turn of the century, informational books such as Van Loon's *The Story of Mankind* were published. This book received the first Newbery Medal in 1922. This award, given for the year's most distinguished literature for children, was established to honor John Newbery, an English publisher of children's books. Biographies and poetry also became popular.

The most extensive development, however, has been with picture books. Photography and new technologies for reproducing illustrations have made picture book publishing a major part of the children's book field. The Caldecott Medal, given for the most distinguished picture book published in the United States, was established in 1938. The award, which honors Randolph Caldecott, an English illustrator from the 1800s, was first given in 1938 to Dorothy Lathrop for *Animals of the Bible.*

During the late 1800s, novelty children's books appeared. Lothar Meggendorfer, Ernest Nister, and Raphael Tuck were the most well known publishers of these fascinating pop–up and mechanical or movable books. The popularity of this type of book has continued to the present. Some of the early movable books are being reproduced especially by Intervisual Communication, Inc. of California.

Books that tie in with children's television programs, e.g., "Sesame Street," and toys, e.g., Cabbage Patch dolls, have become prominent. Modern merchandising methods include multimedia packaging of various combinations of books, toys, puzzles, cassette tapes, videos, etc. There are even books which unfold and become a costume to be worn by children.

**References:** Barbara Bader, *American Picture Books From Noah's Ark To The Beast Within,* Macmillan, 1976; E. Lee Baumgarten, *Price List for Children's and Illustrated Books for the Years 1880–1940, Sorted by Artist,* published by author, 1993; E. Lee Baumgarten, *Price List for Children's and Illustrated Books for the Years 1880–1940, Sorted by Author,* published by author, 1993; Margery Fisher, *Who's Who In Children's Books: A Treasury of the Familiar Characters of Childhood,* Holt, Rinehart and Winston, 1975; Virginia Haviland, *Children's Literature, A Guide To Reference Sources,* Library of Congress, 1966, first supplement 1972, second supplement 1977, third supplement 1982; Bettina Hurlimann, *Three Centuries Of Children's Books In Europe,* tr. and ed. by Brian W. Alderson, World, 1968; Norman E. Martinus and Harry L. Rinker, *Warman's Paper,* Wallace–Homestead, 1993; Cornelia L. Meigs, ed., *A Critical History of Children's Literature,* Macmillan, 1969, 2nd ed.

**Periodicals:** *Book Source Monthly,* P. O. Box 567, Cazenovia, NY 13035; *Martha's KidLit Newsletter,* P. O. Box 1488, Ames, IA 50010; *Yellowback Library,* P. O. Box 36172, Des Moines, IA 50315.

**Collectors' Clubs:** (Membership fees are not given because of the large number of listings and the frequency of change).

Louisa May Alcott Memorial Assoc., P. O. Box 343, Concord, MA 01742; Horatio Alger Society, 4907 Allison Drive, Lansing, MI 48910; International Wizard of Oz Club (L. Frank Baum), Box 95, Kinderhook, IL 62345; Thorton W. Burgess Society, Inc., P. O. Box 45, Dept. B, East

Sandwich, MA 02537; Burroughs Bibliophiles (Edgar Rice Burroughs), Burroughs Memorial Collection, University of Louisville Library, Louisville, KY 40292; Lewis Carroll Society of North America, 617 Rockford Road, Silver Spring, MD 20902; Dickens Society, 100 Institute Rd., Worcester Polytech, Dept. of Humanities, Worcester, MA 016009; Kate Greenaway Society, P. O. Box 8, Norwood, PA 19074; Happyhours Brotherhood, 87 School Street, Fall River, MA 02770; Uncle Remus Museum (Joel Chandler Harris), P. O. Box 184, Eatonton, GA 31024; Kipling Society (Rudyard Kipling), c/o Dr. Enamul Karim, Dept. of English, Rockford College, Rockford, IL 61107; Melville Society (Herman Melville), c/o Donald Yannella, Dept. of English, Glassboro State College, Glassboro, NJ 08028; Mystery and Detective Series Review, P. O. Box 3488, Tucson, AZ 85722; Mythopoeic Society, P. O. Box 6707, Altadena, CA 91003; National Fantasy Fan Federation, 1920 Division St., Murphysboro, IL 62966; New York C. S. Lewis Society, c/o Jerry L. Daniel, 419 Springfield Ave., Westfield NJ 07092; Series Book Collector Society, c/o Jack Brahce, 5270 Moceri Ln, Grand Blanc, MI 48439; Stowe–Day Foundation (Harriet Beecher Stowe), 77 Forest St., Hartford, CT 06105; American Hobbit Association (J. R. R. Tolkien), Rivendell–EA, 730 F Northland Rd., Forest Park, OH 45240; American Tolkien Society, P. O. Box 373, Highland, MI 48031; Tolkien Fellowships, c/o Bill Spicer, 329 N. Avenue 66, Los Angeles, CA 90042; Mark Twain Boyhood Home Association, 208 Hill Street, Hannibal, MO 63401; Mark Twain Memorial, 351 Farmington Ave., Hartford, CT 06105; Mark Twain Research Foundation, Perry, MO 63462.

**Libraries and Museums:** Many of the clubs maintain museums. *Subject Collections* by Lee Ash (ed.) contains a list of public and academic libraries which have children's book collections. Large collections can be found at: Florida State University, Tallahassee, FL; Free Library of Philadelphia, PA; Library of Congress, Washington, DC; Pierpont Morgan Library, New York, NY; Toronto Public Library, Toronto, Ontario, Canada; University of Minnesota, Walter Library, Minneapolis, MN; University of South Florida, Tampa, FL.

**Advisor:** Joyce Magee.

**Notes:** Prices are based on first editions with a dust jacket (dj) and in very good condition. The absence of a dust jacket, later printings and a condition less than "very good" are all factors that lessen the value of a book.

Autographed copies and those that come in a special box are additional factors that will increase the value. Books that have been award winners, e.g., Newbery, Caldecott, etc., generally are higher in value.

**Reprints:** A number of replicas of antique originals are now appearing on the market, with most being done by Evergreen Press and Merrimack. A new "Children's Classics" series offers reprints of books illustrated by Jessie Willcox Smith, Edmund Dulac, Frederick Richardson and possibly others.

***In The Forest,* published by C. Prang Co., Boston, 2¾ x 4¼", $45.00.**

Anglund, Joan Walsh, *A Friend Is Someone Who Likes You,* Joan Anglund, illus, Harcourt, Brace, 1958, 1st ed . **8.00**

*Animals On The Farm,* Clara Burd, illus, Saalfield, 1936, unp, wraps ....... **28.00**

Appleton, Victor, *Tom Swift And His Jetmarine,* Kaye, illus, Grosset & Dunlap, 1950s, dj .................. **8.00**

Austin, *Mother Goose Rhymes,* Platt & Munk, 1944 ..................... **12.00**

Bailey, Arthur Scott, *The Tale Of Cuffy Bear,* Harry L. Smith, illus, Grossett & Dunlap, 1915, 112 pgs, dj ........ **10.00**

Bakewell, *True Fairy Stories, illus, American, 1902* .................. **7.00**

Bannerman, Helen, *Little Black Sambo,* LaMont, illus, Whitman, 1959 ..... **60.00**

Barbour, Ralph Henry, *Behind The Line,* Appleton, 1906, 258 pgs .......... **7.00**

Baruch, Dorothy, *Dick And Jane, Good Times With Our Friends,* Eleanor Campbell, illus, Scott, Foresman & Co, 1941 ....................... **28.00**

Baum, L. Frank, *The Road To Oz,* Harry McNaught, illus, Simon & Schuster, 1951, unp, 1st ed, Golden Book ... **15.00**

Bemelmans, Ludwig, *Madeline,* Ludwig Bemelmans, illus, Simon & Schuster, 1939, dj, 1st ed .................. **60.00**

Brandeis, Madeline, *Mitz and Fritz Of Germany,* Grosset & Dunlap, 1933, 160 pgs ......................... **4.00**

*Brenda Starr,* Whitman, 1943, dj ..... **5.00**

Burgess, Thorton W., *Adventures Of Bobby Coon,* H. Cady, illus, Little, Brown, 1919 .................... **20.00**

Burtis, Thomson, *Rex Lee Trailing Air Bandits,* Grossett & Dunlap, 1931, 248 pgs, dj ...................... **4.00**

Campbell, Ruth

*Cat Whose Whiskers Slipped And Other Stories,* Cadie, illus, Volland, 1925, 5th ed ................. **25.00**

*Small Fry And The Winged Horse,* G. Tenggren, illus, Volland, 1927, 1st ed .......................... **22.00**

Chadwick, Lester, *Baseball Joe, Champion Of The League,* Cupples & Leon, 1925, 246 pgs, dj ................ **9.00**

*Chatterbox,* J. Erskine Clarde, editor, Esxes & Lauriat, 1896, 412 pgs .... **16.00**

*Cinderella,* Wehn, illus, Daye, 1945, action book .................... **30.00**

Clark, Betsey, *Hello, Sunshine,* 1912, dj **8.00**

Clifton, Oliver Lee, *The Camp Fire Boys At Silver Fox Farm* Barse & Hopkins, 1924, 246 pgs .................. **6.00**

Cooper, James F., *Last Of The Mohicans,* Wyeth, illus, Scribner, 1919 ....... **90.00**

Cunningham, *PomPom Fuzzy Wuzzy Book,* Barnes, illus, Whitman, 1947 **12.00**

Curtis, Alice Turner, *Little Maid Of Quebec,* Penn Pub Co., 1936, 224 pgs, dj ............................ **8.00**

D'Aulaire, Ingri and Parin, E., *Pocahontas,* D'Aulaire illus, Doubleday, 1946, 1st ed ......................... **35.00**

Dawson, Lucy, *Lucy Dawson's Dogs,* Whitman, 1938, unp, wraps ....... **25.00**

DeAngeli, Marguerite, *Thee, Hannah!,* M. DeAngeli, illus, Doubleday, 1940, dj ............................ **35.00**

*Dick And Jane, Fun With Our Friends,* Scott, Foresman & Co, 1962, workbook, unused .................... **12.00**

Disney, Walt, *Pinocchio And His Puppet Show Adventure,* Random House, 1973, unp, 1st ed, Disney's Wonderful World of Reading ............ **8.00**

Dixon, Franklin W., *Footprints Under The Window,* Crossett & Dunlap, 1933, 214 pgs, Hardy Boys ........ **4.00**

Fabre, J. H., Hasbrouck, *Insect Adventures,* Goldberg, illus, World Book Co., 1918 ....................... **7.00**

Farley, Walter, *The Black Stallion Races,* Random House, 1955, 256 pgs, dj, 1st ed ......................... **18.00**

Field, Eugene

*In Wink–A–Way Land,* 1930, library **15.00**

*Sugar–Plum Tree,* F. B. Peat, illus, Saalfield, 1930 ................. **40.00**

Finley, Martha, *Elsie Dinsmore,* Donohue, no date, c1920, 395 pgs ...... **10.00**

***The Cold-Blooded Penguin,* Walt Disney's Little Library, Simon Schuster, NY, 1944, $12.00.**

Flint, *Betty Fairy Book,* M. E. Price, illus, Stecher, 1919 .................... **30.00**

Fryer, Jane Eayre, *The Mary Frances Storybook,* Edwin John Prittie, illus, Winston, 1921, 328 pgs .............. **45.00**

Gag, Wanda, *Snow White And The Seven Dwarfs,* Coward–McCann, 1938, 43 pgs, dj ................ **20.00**

Garis, Howard R.

*Uncle Wiggily And The Troublesome Boys,* Stover, illus, American Crayon, 1943 ..................... **10.00**

*Uncle Wiggily's Story Book,* L. Cambell, illus, Platt & Munk, 1939 ... **40.00**

Gruelle, Johnny, Riley, *Orphan Annie Story Book,* Johnny Gruelle, illus, Bobbs Merrill, 1921 .............. **50.00**

Hayes, Clair W., *The Boy Troopers On Duty,* A. L. Burt, 1922, 221 pgs, Army series .......................... **3.00**

Hazlett, Edward E., *He's Jake, The Story Of A Submarine Dog,* Paul Brown, illus, Dodd Mead, 1947, 154 pgs, dj **6.00**

Henry, Marguerite, *Geraldine Belinda,* Blackwood, illus, Platt & Munk, 1942, dj ....................... **20.00**

Hogan, I., *Nicodemus Laughs,* I. Hogan, illus, Dutton, 1953, 6th ed .... **60.00**

Holling, Holling C., *Claws Of The Thunderbird,* H. C. Holling, illus, Volland, 1928, 1st ed ............. **50.00**

Hope, Laura Lee

*Bobbsey Twins*

Goldsmith, no date, dj .......... **8.00**

Grosset & Dunlap, 1950 ........ **4.00**

*Bunny Brown Camp Rest–A–While,* 1916 ........................ **3.00**

*Bunny Brown Giving A Show,* 1919 **4.00**

Hughes, Thomas, *Tom Brown's School Days,* Dodd Mead, 1900, 339 pgs .. **10.00**

Irwin, Inez Haynes, *Marda's Little Houseboat,* Grossett & Dunlap, 1943, 207 pgs .......... **13.00**
Jackson, Leroy F., *The Peter Patter Book,* Blanche Fisher Wright, illus, Rand McNally, 1915, 110 pgs .......... **30.00**
Johnston, A. F., *Two Little Knights Of Kentucky,* Barry, illus, L. C. Page, 1907 .......... **6.00**
Keene, Carolyn, *Mystery Of The Tolling Bell,* Grosset & Dunlap, Nancy Drew **6.00**
King, Frank, *Skeezix and Pal,* Reilly & Lee, 1925, unp .......... **16.00**
LaRue, *The F–U–N Book,* M. & M. Petersham, illus, Macmillan, 1933 .... **25.00**
LeFevre, F., *Cock, Mouse, Little Red Hen,* T. Sarg, illus, Macrae Smith, no date .......... **12.00**
Lenski, Lois, *The Little Farm,* Oxford Univ Press, 1942, unp, dj, 1st ed .. **18.00**
MacDonald, G., *Princess And The Goblin,* M. Kirk, illus, Lippincott, 1907, 13th ed .......... **35.00**
Mariana, *Miss Flora McFlimsey And The Baby New Year,* Lothrop, Lee & Shepard, 1951, unp, dj .......... **22.00**
Marge, *Little Lulu,* Marge, illus, Rand McNally, 1936 .......... **15.00**
Merrill, Marion, *The Animated Pinocchio,* Citadel Press, 1945, unp, 3 pop–ups .......... **25.00**
Miller, Olive Beaupre, *My Bookhouse,* 1920, 6 vol .......... **120.00**
Milne, A. A., *Gallery of Children,* LeMair Saida, illus, McKay, 1925 ... **160.00**
Minarik, E. H., *A Kiss For Little Bear,* Sendak, illus, Harper & Row, 1968 . **15.00**
Montgomery, Frances Trego, *Billy Wiskers' Kids,* W. H. Fry, illus, Saalfield, 1903, 134 pgs, dj .......... **25.00**
Moore, Clement C., *Night Before Christmas,* Hays, illus, Saalfield, #219, 1941, wraps .......... **6.00**
*Mother Goose,* Mary Lafetya Russell, illus, Sam Gabried, 1911, unp ...... **15.00**
Newberry, Clare Turlay, *Mittens,* Harper, 1936, unp, dj, 1st ed .......... **50.00**
Peat, Frank, *Christmas Carols,* Fern Peat, illus, Saalfield, 1937, dj, 1st ed **40.00**
Petersham, Maud & Miska, *The Story Book of Food,* Winston, 1947, unp . **7.00**
Piper, Watty, *Mother Goose Rhymes,* Eulalie, Lenski, illus, Platt & Munk, 1955 .......... **30.00**
Schulz, Charles, M., *He's Your Dog, Charlie Brown!,* World, 1968, unp, 1st ed .......... **8.00**
Segar, *Popeye Calls On Olive Oyl,* Segar, illus, Whitman, 1937 .......... **20.00**
Seuss, Dr.
*Boners,* Dr. Seuss, illus, Viking, 1931, 1st ed, 4th printing .......... **100.00**
Hop On Pop, Dr. Seuss, illus, Beginner/Random House, 1963, dj .... **18.00**
Sidney, Margaret, *Five Little Peppers Grown Up,* Mente, illus, D. Lathrop, 1892, 527 pgs, 1st ed .......... **75.00**
Spyri, Johanna, *Heidi's Children,* Doane, illus, Grosset & Dunlap, 1939 **6.00**
Stevenson, Robert L., *Child's Garden Of Verses*
Frissell, illus, U. S. Camera, 1944 .. **30.00**
O'Reilly, illus, Grosset & Dunlap, 1923 .......... **12.00**
Stockton, Frank R., *The Bee–man Of Orb,* Maurice Sendak, illus, Holt, Rinehart & Winston, 1964, 46 pgs, dj, 1st ed, sgd by illus .......... **100.00**
Striker, F., *Lone Ranger Traps The Smugglers,* Grosset & Dunlap, dj ........ **8.00**
Sutton, Margaret, *Who Will Play With Me?,* Corinne Dillon, illus, Wonder Books, 1951, unp .......... **12.00**
Thompson, Kay, *Eloise At Christmas Time,* Knight, illus, Random House, 1937, dj, 1st ed .......... **70.00**
Thompson, R. P., *Princess Of Cozytown,* J. L. Scott, illus, Volland, 1922, ex–library, 1st ed .......... **25.00**
Thorne–Thomsen, Gudrun, *East O' The Sun And West O' The Moon,* Frederick Richardson, illus, Row, Peterson, 1912, 218 pfg .......... **20.00**
Uttley, Alison, *Little Grey Rabbit's Pancake Day,* Maragret Tempest, illus, Collins, 1967, 63 pgs .......... **25.00**
Wells, Helen, *Cherry Ames, Army Nurse,* 1944 .......... **5.00**
White, Stewart Edward, *Daniel Boone: Wilderness Scout,* James Daugherty, illus, Garden City, 1922, 274 pgs .. **15.00**
Wiggin, Kate Douglas, *The New Chronicles of Rebecca,* F. C. Yohn, illus, Houghton Mifflin, 1907, 278 pgs, 1st ed .......... **22.00**

# CHILDREN'S DISHES

**Collecting Hints:** Children's dishes were played with, so a bit of wear is to be expected. Avoid rusty metal dishes. Also avoid broken glass dishes.

**History:** Dishes for children to play with have been popular from Victorian times to the present. Many glass companies made small child–size sets in the same patterns as large table sets. Many young girls delighted in using a set just like mother's.

During the period when Depression glass was popular, the manufacturers also made child–size pieces to complement the full-size lines. These child–size dishes were used for tea parties, doll parties, and many other happy occasions.

Child–size dishes are found in aluminum, tin, china, and glass.

**References:** Doris Anderson Lechler, *Children's Glass Dishes, China and Furniture,* Collector Books, 1983, 1991 value update; Doris Anderson Lechler, *Children's Glass Dishes, China, Furniture, Volume II* Collector Books, 1986, 1993 value update; Doris Lechler, *English Toy China,* Antique Publications, 1989; Doris Lechler, *Toy Glass,* Antique Publications, 1989; Lorraine May Punchard, *Child's Play,* published by author, 1982; Ellen Tischbein Schroy, *Warman's Glass,* Wallace–Homestead, 1992; Margaret and Kenn Whitmyer, *Collector's Encyclopedia of Children's Dishes: An Illustrated Value Guide,* Collector Books, 1993.

**Collectors' Club:** Toy Dish Collectors, P. O. Box 351, Camilius, NY 13031.

**See:** Akro Agate

Akro Agate Glass
- Tea Set, orig box
  - Concentric Ring, small, purple plates, yellow saucers, pumpkin cups, blue teapot, creamer, and sugar, price for sixteen piece set **250.00**
  - Stippled Band, amber, price for eight piece set ............... **225.00**
  - Transparent Stacked Disk and Panel, green, small size, price for sixteen piece set ............ **235.00**

Aluminum
- Cutlery, Little Bo Peep, 1940s, orig 6½ x 8½" card, price for nine piece set, MOC ..................... **20.00**
- Tea Set, Little Bo Peep, emb dec, 3¾ x 6 x 6½" orig box, price for nineteen piece set, MIB ............ **35.00**

Celluloid, dinner set, lacy edge, baby blue trim, matching play silverware, orig box, price for twenty–one piece set ............................ **30.00**

China
- Cake Plate, 5" d, Willow Ware, round, handles, marked "Japan" . **65.00**
- Casserole, cov, 5½ x 3¼", Willow Ware, marked "Japan" .......... **45.00**
- Creamer, Willow Ware
  - 1¾" h, marked "Occupied Japan" **15.00**
  - 2" h, marked "Japan" ........... **12.00**
- Cup and Saucer, Willow Ware, marked "Japan" ................ **14.75**
- Dinner Set, Willow Ware
  - 12 pieces, medium size, four cups and saucers, plates, creamer, gravy boat, platter, and cov sugar, marked "Japan," price for set ......................... **155.00**
  - 15 pieces, large size, four cups and saucers, plates, cov casserole, platter, and cov teapot, marked "Japan," price for set ......... **155.00**
- Gravy, attached platter, Willow Ware, marked "Japan" ................ **65.00**
- Plate, Willow Ware
  - 3¾" d, marked "Occupied Japan" **15.00**
  - 4⅜" d, marked "Japan" ......... **15.00**
- Platter, 6½ x 3¾", Willow Ware, oval, marked "Japan" ........... **38.00**
- Sugar, cov, Willow Ware
  - 2" h, marked "Occupied Japan" **30.00**
  - 2½" h, marked "Japan" ......... **25.00**
- Teapot, cov, Willow Ware, marked "Occupied Japan" ............. **75.00**

**Tea Set, litho tin, cup, 1½" h, Ohio Art, price for 8 pc set, $35.00.**

- Tea Set
  - Blond girl with three rabbits, woodland setting, service for six, casserole, platter, creamer, cov sugar, teapot, salt and pepper, marked "Japan," orig box, price for twenty–four piece set ...... **195.00**
  - Pink and red roses, creamer, sugar, teapot, six cups, saucers, and plates, price for twenty–two piece set .................... **85.00**

Depression Glass
- Creamer
  - Cherry Blossom
    - Delphite .................... **37.50**
    - Pink ........................ **40.00**
  - Doric & Pansy, pink ........... **27.75**
  - Moderntone, orange ............ **15.00**
- Cup
  - Doric & Pansy, pink ........... **28.00**
  - Laurel, McKee, green .......... **40.00**
  - Moderntone
    - Gray ....................... **6.75**
    - Orange ..................... **6.75**
    - Pastel Blue ................ **6.50**
    - Pastel Green ............... **6.50**
    - Pastel Pink ................ **6.50**
    - Pastel Yellow .............. **6.50**
    - Turquoise .................. **6.75**

- Cup and Saucer
  - Cherry Blossom, pink **40.00**
  - Diana
    - Crystal **8.75**
    - Crystal cup, ruby stained saucer **9.75**
- Plate
  - Doric & Pansy, pink **8.00**
  - Homespun, pink **9.00**
  - Houze, blue **15.00**
  - Moderntone
    - Gold **6.75**
    - Gray **6.75**
    - Orange **6.75**
    - Pastel Blue **6.50**
    - Pastel Chartreuse **12.00**
    - Pastel Green **6.50**
    - Pastel Pink **6.50**
    - Pastel Yellow **6.50**
    - Turquoise **6.75**
- Saucer
  - Doric & Pansy, pink **5.00**
  - Moderntone
    - Gold **3.50**
    - Gray **3.50**
    - Orange **3.50**
    - Pastel Blue **2.50**
    - Pastel Pink **2.50**
    - Pastel Yellow **2.50**
- Sugar
  - Cherry Blossom, pink **42.75**
  - Moderntone, orange **15.00**
- Tea Set
  - Cherry Blossom pink, orig box, price for fourteen piece set **325.00**
  - Moderntone, dark, turquoise teapot, price for 16 piece set **145.00**

Pattern Glass
- Berry Set, Lacy Daisy **65.00**
- Butter, cov
  - Oval Star **30.00**
  - Nursery Rhyme **85.00**
  - Tulip Honeycomb **60.00**
- Creamer
  - Amazon **40.00**
  - Drum **70.00**
  - Fancy Cut (Rex) **35.00**
  - Lamb **75.00**
  - Lion **70.00**
  - Michigan **35.00**
  - Nursery Rhyme **50.00**
  - Pennsylvania, green **40.00**
  - Sweetheart, Cambridge **15.00**
  - Tappan **25.00**
  - Twist, opalescent, blue **95.00**
- Ice Cream Plate, Tulip Honeycomb **30.00**
- Pitcher
  - Fancy Cut (Rex) **75.00**
  - Galloway, gold trim **35.00**
  - Michigan, gold trim **35.00**
  - Nursery Rhyme **90.00**
  - Wheat Sheaf **45.00**
- Sugar
  - Drum **65.00**
  - Lamb, milk glass **90.00**
  - Michigan **40.00**
- Table Set, cov butter, creamer, spooner, sugar
  - La Belle, two bands **135.00**
  - Oval Star, gold trim **125.00**
- Tumbler
  - Deep Star **8.00**
  - Fancy Cut (Rex) **14.00**
  - Oval Star **12.00**
- Water Set, pitcher and four tumblers, Oval Star **110.00**

Plastic
- Chocolate Set, pink, service for four, silverware, and napkin holder, Banner, orig box, price for thirty piece set **75.00**
- Dinner Set, Alice in Wonderland, beige, service for four, orig box, Plasco, price for seventeen piece set **40.00**

Tin
- Cake Set, German, orig box, price for six piece set **85.00**
- Flatware, German, six place settings, wire utensil rack **95.00**

# CHRISTMAS ITEMS

**Collecting Hints:** Beware of reproduction ornaments. New reproductions are usually brighter in color and have shiny paint. Older ornaments should show some signs of handling. It is common to find tops replaced on ornaments.

**History:** Early Christmas decorations and ornaments were handmade. In 1865 the Pennsylvania Dutch brought the first glass ornaments to America. By 1870, glass ornaments were being sold in major cities. By the turn of the century, the demand created a cottage industry in European countries. Several towns in Germany and Czechoslovakia produced lovely ornaments, which were imported by F. W. Woolworth, Sears, etc., who found a ready market.

**References:** Ann Bahar, *Santa Dolls: Historical to Contemporary,* Hobby House Press, 1992; Robert Brenner, *Christmas Past,* Shiffer Publishing, Inc., 1986; Polly and Pam Judd, *Santa Dolls & Figurines Price Guide: Antique to Contemporary,* Hobby House Press, 1992; Norman E. Martinus and Harry L. Rinker, *Warman's Paper,* Wallace–Homestead, 1993; Robert M. Merck, *Deck The Halls: Treasures of Christmases Past,* Abbeville Press, 1992; Maggie Rogers and Peter Hallinan, *The Santa Claus Picture Book,* E. P. Dutton, Inc., 1984; Maggie Rogers and Judith Hawkins, *The Glass Christmas Ornament, Old & New*, Timber Press, 1977; Nancy Schiffer, *Christmas Ornaments: A Festive Study*, Schiffer Publishing, Ltd, 1984.

**Periodicals:** *Golden Glow of Christmas Past*, P.O. Box 14808, Chicago, IL 60614; *Ornament Collector*, R.R. #1, Canton, IL 61520.

**Museums:** Many museums prepare special Christmas exhibits.

**Additional Listings:** Santa Claus.

**REPRODUCTION ALERT**

Book
- *A Christmas Sermon,* by Robert Louis Stevenson, Charles Scribner & Sons, NY, 1919 ........ **3.50**
- *A Gift From St Nicholas,* McLoughlin Brothers, 1899 ........ **25.00**

Candle Clip, 2" l, silvered tin, spring clip **1.50**
Candy Box, 3 x 5 x 1½", cardboard, Christmas scenes, 1930s ........ **5.00**
Candy Cane Holder, Santa standing beside chimney, 10" h, molded cardboard, 1940s ........ **50.00**
Candy Container
- Belsnickle, 6" h, papier mâché, gold robe, holding feather tree, Germany, c1900 ........ **275.00**
- Cone, cotton cloth, scrap and tinsel dec, tree ornament ........ **30.00**
- Santa, 7" h, celluloid head, hands, and boots, net body, Japan ........ **65.00**

Chocolate Mold, Father Christmas, 9" h, tin, clamp style, c1930 ........ **90.00**
Cookie Jar, Santa head, ceramic, American Bisque Co ........ **80.00**
Diecut, Father Christmas leading mule laden with gifts, 7½" w, 9½" h ........ **120.00**
Doll, Santa, 19" h, composition body, cotton suit, leather belt, carrying sack, 1930s ........ **250.00**
Figure
- Santa, 9" h, celluloid, late 1920s–early 1940s ........ **80.00**
- Santa on sleigh pulled by reindeer, 4¾" l, celluloid, red, white, and green, c1930 ........ **38.00**
- Snowman holding bubble light, plastic ........ **45.00**

Garland, 24" l, glass, alternating berries and balls ........ **30.00**
Greeting Card, "A Merry Christmas," three children in winter clothes, huddled beneath an umbrella, Wolf & Co, NY ........ **2.50**
Lamp
- Santa, 19" h, papier mâché, light bulb on head, marked "Unger's Fiber Product, Cell–U–Pon–Unger Doll and Toy Company, Milwaukee, Wisconsin," 1930s ........ **125.00**
- Wreath, 8¾" h, cast iron, painted, candle center ........ **50.00**

Light Bulb, figural, painted milk glass, Japan
- Bird ........ **15.00**
- Lantern, c1930 ........ **10.00**
- Santa ........ **20.00**

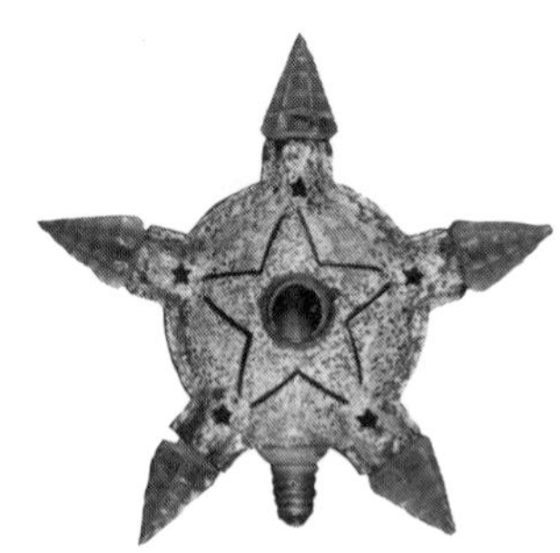

**Light Bulb, Kristal Star, five point star, painted and mica coated tin, plastic points, Mazda bulb, c1935, 4¼" h, $10.00.**

Lights, string or set
- Color Wheel ........ **25.00**
- Noma
  - Bubble ........ **30.00**
  - Luminous candles, 1940s ........ **40.00**
- Zelco, eight sockets, Mazda lamps, 1920s ........ **100.00**

Music Box, church, windup, plastic, white, stained windows, detachable spire, illuminated ........ **25.00**
Nativity Scene, 8 plaster figures, 5 plaster animals, wood stable ........ **90.00**
Ornament
- Celluloid, swan ........ **8.00**
- Chenille
  - Candy cane, 12" l ........ **8.00**
  - Santa, 4" h, scrap face ........ **6.00**
- Chromolithograph, woman, reading book, litho upper torso, crepe paper skirt ........ **14.00**
- Cotton, Santa, 7" h, plaster face, Japan ........ **40.00**
- Foil, cornucopia, bright colors ........ **2.00**
- Glass, figural
  - Bird, spun glass tail, spring clip .. **15.00**
  - Christ child head, 2½" h, silver and gold ........ **65.00**
  - Chubby Clown, 4" h, 1920s ........ **45.00**
  - Father Christmas, 2½" h ........ **40.00**
  - Fish, wire wrapped ........ **25.00**
  - Grape cluster, 7½" h, blue, early 1900s ........ **115.00**

Icicle, 14″ l, spiraled, 1950s ..... **20.00**
Mandolin, 5″ l, wire wrapped .... **50.00**
Mushroom, 3¼″ h, unsilvered, red and white, spring clip, 1920s .. **25.00**
Owl, c1930 .................. **35.00**
Pinecone ..................... **5.00**
Teapot, hp floral dec ........... **12.00**
Hard Plastic, 3″ h, boot, red and white ........................ **5.00**
Kugel, 2″ d, round, silver, brass hook **25.00**
Pressed Cotton, pear, 3½″ h ....... **18.00**
Scrap
Angel, 4½″ h, scrap head and wings, spun glass halo and gown **20.00**
Children, 4½″ h, tinsel dec ...... **15.00**
Father Christmas, 7½″ h, scrap upper body, spun glass lower body **60.00**
Wax, angel, 4″ l, spun glass wings .. **75.00**
Post Card, Father Christmas outside lighted house, wearing green robe, "A Merry Christmas," Germany, c1910 ......................... **5.00**
Putz Items
Church, 3½″ h, litho cardboard .... **6.00**
Dog, celluloid, brown, Japan ...... **5.00**
Fence, 36″ l, 6″ h, wood, painted green, three rail fence, three sections ......................... **30.00**
Horse, cotton batten, saddle ....... **120.00**
House, 2¾″ h, cardboard, mica coated ....................... **18.00**
Sheep, 5″ h, wood, cotton fleece, ribbon collar, Germany, early 1900s **60.00**
Reindeer, metal, lying down ......... **35.00**
Snow Baby, 3¼″ h, waving, Japan .... **20.00**
Stocking, 24″ l, cotton, outdoor scene one side, indoor scene other side, c1910 ......................... **185.00**
Toy, Santa
Battery Operated, 12″ h, Happy Santa, tin body, plastic face, red and white cotton flannel suit, orig box, Cragston Corp, 1950s ...... **80.00**
Windup, 5½″ h, litho tin, Chein, c1930 ........................ **90.00**
Trade Card, Santa and children, decorated tree in background, Woolson Spice Co adv, early 1900s ......... **15.00**
Tree
Aluminum, 18″ h, silver, 1960s .... **20.00**
Bottle Brush, 10″ h, snow covered bristles, wood base ............. **12.00**
Cellophane, 19″ h, bubble lights, plastic base, 1950s ............. **60.00**
Feather, Germany
24½″ h, red berries, wood block base marked "Made in USA" .. **100.00**
31″ h, white painted turned wood base ....................... **100.00**
68″ h, red berries, red painted wood stepped base ........... **300.00**
Fiber, 47″ h, green, red painted rect wood base ................... **25.00**
Tree Stand
Cast Iron, square, 1930s .......... **50.00**
Concrete, 11½″ h, Santa head, painted red and white .......... **200.00**
Tree Topper
Angel, 9″ h, hard plastic, yellow hair, white robe with gold stars, clear wings, electric, 1950s .......... **20.00**
Star, tin, 5 bulbs at points, Noma, c1930 ....................... **24.00**
Wreath, chenille, electric candle center, orig box ...................... **20.00**

**Toy, Santa riding reindeer, windup, litho tin Santa with molded vinyl head, plush over tin reindeer with rubber antlers and nose, key wind, paper label "Made in Japan," 5″ l, 5¾″ h, $75.00.**

# CIGAR COLLECTIBLES

**Collecting Hints:** Concentrate on one geographical region or company. Cigar box labels usually are found in large concentrations. Check on availability before paying high prices.

**History:** Tobacco was one of the first export products of the American colonies. By 1750 smoking began to become socially acceptable for males. The cigar reached its zenith from 1880 to 1930 when it was the boardroom and after dinner symbol for the withdrawal of males to privacy and conversation.

Cigar companies were quick to recognize national political, sports and popular heroes. They encouraged them to use cigars and placed their faces on promotional material.

The lithograph printing press brought color and popularity to labels, seals and bands. Many have memories of a cigar band ring given by a grandfather or family friend. The popularity of the cigarette in the 1940s reduced the cigar to second place in the tobacco field. Today, cigar related material is minimal due to the smaller number of companies making cigars.

**References:** Douglas Congdon–Martin, *Tobacco Tins: A Collector's Guide,* Schiffer Publishing, Ltd., 1992; Joe Davidson, *The Art of the Cigar Label,* Wellfleet, 1989; Glyn V. Farber, *Hickey Brothers Cigar Store Tokens,* The Token and Medal Society, Inc., 1992; Tony Hyman, *Handbook of American Cigar Boxes,* Arnet Art Museum, 1979; Franklyn Kircher, *Tobacco Pocket Tin Guide,* published by author, 1984; Norman E. Martinus and Harry L. Rinker, *Warman's Paper,* Wallace–Homestead, 1993.

**Collectors' Club:** International Seal, Label and Cigar Band Society, 8915 E. Bellevue St., Tucson, AZ 85715.

**Museum:** Arnet Collection, New York Public Library, New York, NY.

Ashtray
- Cigar Band, 4½" sq ............... **10.00**
- H Fendrick Cigar Co, brass ........ **18.00**
- Souvenir, 1936 Havana Convention, model Philco Radio, pottery, 2¾ x 4" ........................... **125.00**

Bottle, figural cigar, amber glass, sheared lip, 1870–1900, 7½" l, .... **28.00**
Box, Linita Cigars, 1920 ............ **45.00**
Cigar Cutter, Don Equestra Havana Cigars, ornate cast iron, oval mirror, countertop model, 8½" w, 8" h .... **250.00**
Cigar Cutter/Match Vendor, Yankee, ornate cast iron, countertop model, plated, 7" w, 8" d, 6" h ........... **450.00**

**Cigar Cutter, souvenir, 1933 Century of Progress, green enameled design, Byrd's Polar Ship on reverse, 4⅛" l, $35.00.**

Holder, celluloid ................... **5.00**
Humidor, Don Porto Cigar, tin ....... **18.00**
Matchbook Holder, Muriel Cigars, blued metal, multicolored celluloid insert, woman's portrait, dark red ground, 1⅛ x 1⅝" ................ **60.00**
Match Safe, Union Made Cigars, silvered brass, celluloid cover with light blue Union Cigar label, black lettering, issued by Cigar Makers Union #97, Boston, 21¼ x 2¾" .......... **80.00**
Mirror, pocket, Union Made Cigars adv, celluloid, light blue union label, black lettering, c1900, 2⅛" l ...... **50.00**
Pinback Button, "American's Favorite, The People's Choice Cigar," black and white portraits, Tom Moore and Henry George, red text, blue baseball stitch design, paper insert, c1898, 2⅛" d .......................... **65.00**
Poster, Tennyson, proof ............. **195.00**

Sign
- Black Prince and Humming Bird Cigars, paper, parlor scene, Victorian lady, cigar box on table, Clay & Richmond litho, c1880, 15½" w, 25" h, matted and framed ....... **225.00**
- Henrietta Cigar, emb tin, man seated at desk smoking cigar, 9¼" w, 13¼" h ............................ **275.00**
- Oliver & Robinson Cigars, paper, Victorian woman holding fan, cherubs, 10½" w, 13¼" h ........... **220.00**
- Robert Burns 10¢ Cigar, tin charger, portrait image and cigar box, Scottish plaid background, 24" d ..... **220.00**
- Sanchez & Haya Havana Cigars, reverse painted glass, etched seals, 36" w, 24" h .................. **220.00**
- Y–B Havana Cigars, emb tin, cigar box, "Give Universal Satisfaction," printed by Standard Adv Co, 13½" w, 19½" h ..................... **200.00**

Tin
- Chamberlain Cigars ............... **145.00**
- Los Ramos Cigars, 5" w, 3¾" h ..... **10.00**
- Old Abe Cigars, round, paper label . **60.00**
- Reichard's Cadet Cigars ........... **65.00**

Tray
- El Symphonie Havana Cigars, tin, oval, composer portrait, Shonk, 15" w, 18" h ...................... **275.00**
- Havana Superfina Cigars, Indian, tip, 3" d .......................... **125.00**
- Red Earl Cigars, tip, 3½" d ........ **50.00**

# CIGARETTE ITEMS

**Collecting Hints:** Don't overlook the advertising which appeared in the national magazines from the 1940s to 1960s. The number of star and public heroes endorsing cigarettes is large. Modern promotional material for brands such as Marlboro and Salem has been issued in large numbers, and much has been put aside by collectors. Most collectors tend to concentrate on the pre–1950 period.

**History:** Although the cigarette industry dates back to the late 19th century, it was the decades of the 1930s and 1940s that saw cigarettes become the dominant tobacco product. The cigarette industry launched massive advertising and promotional campaigns. Radio was one of the principal advertising vehicles. In the 1950s, television became the dominant advertising medium.

The Surgeon General's Report, which warned of the danger of cigarette smoking, led to restrictions on advertising and limited the places where cigarettes could be smoked. The industry reacted with a new advertising approach aimed at females and people in the 20 to 40 year age bracket. The need to continue the strong positive public image for cigarette smoking still leads to more and more cigarette related items entering the collectibles marketplace.

**References:** Philip Collins, *Smokerama: Classic Tobacco Accoutrements,* Chronicle Books, 1992; Douglas Congdon–Martin, *Tobacco Tins: A Collector's Guide,* Schiffer Publishing, Ltd., 1992; Norman E. Martinus and Harry L. Rinker, *Warman's Paper,* Wallace–Homestead, 1993; Urban K. Cummings Ronson, *World's Greatest Lighter,* Bird Dog Books, 1993; Franklyn Kircher, *Tobacco Pocket Tin Guide,* published by author, 1984; Murray Cards International, Ltd. (comp.), *Cigarette Card Values: 1992 Catalogue of Cigarette & Other Trade Cards,* Murray Cards International Ltd., 1992.

**Periodicals:** *On The Lighter Side,* Route 3, 136 Circle Dr., Quitman, TX 75783; *Flint & Flame,* 36 Four Seasons, Chesterfield, MO 63017.

**Collectors' Clubs:** Cigarette Pack Collectors Association, 61 Searle St., Georgetown, MA 01833; International Seal, Label & Cigar Band Society, 8915 East Bellevue St, Tuscon, AZ 85715; Pocket Lighter Preservation Guild & Historical Society, Inc., 36 Four Seasons, Chesterfield, MO 63017.

Ashtray, custard glass, free form, emb pipe and pouch, 7½" l ........ **15.00**
Box, polished aluminum, bakelite base, lift handle ........ **24.00**
Case, woman's, enameled peacock design, 3 x 4" ........ **45.00**
Chair, wood, folding, "Duke's Cameo Cigarettes" stenciled on back, paper label inserts with woman's portrait on front and back ........ **110.00**
Cigarette Card
  Indian Chiefs, set of 10 ........ **55.00**
  WWI, zeppelins, ships, planes, 1920s, complete set of 30 ........ **95.00**
Cigarette Card Album, Quadrupeds, Allen & Ginter, 1889 ........ **50.00**
Cigarette Pack, sample, Philip Morris, "Guest Package," Johnny on both sides, orig cellophane seal, unopened, 1930–40, 1½" w, 3" h ........ **25.00**
Coaster, Lucky Strike ........ **20.00**
Dispenser, mechanical, inlaid wood, geometric Art Deco design, drawer opens, bird serves cigarette ........ **65.00**
Lighter
  Advertising, Hastings Piston Ring, tin tube, removable black cap, red, yellow, and black trademark, yellow ground, c1940, 3" l ........ **15.00**
  Figural
    Dog, whippet ........ **20.00**
    Rearing Horse, brushed chrome ........ **35.00**
    Squirrel, Occupied Japan ........ **20.00**
    Stein, eagle emblem ........ **15.00**
    Sulky, jockey and horse ........ **20.00**
  Ronson, oval, SP, Art Nouveau design, ftd, patent 1002 ........ **18.00**
  Windsor, six shooter, 7" l, 4" h, metal, free standing ........ **75.00**

**Silk, Richmond Straight Cut Cigarettes, West Point theme, $12.00.**

Matchbox Holder, Fatima Turkish Cigarettes, ceramic, 6" w ........ **85.00**
Photo Card, Admiral Cigarettes, burlesque girls, 1890s, set of 38 ........ **35.00**
Pinback Button, Kool Cigarettes, Willie flanked by donkey and elephant, 1930s, 1" d ........ **20.00**
Playing Cards, Camel Cigarettes, Camel Joe ........ **8.00**
Rolling Papers, OCB, orig box holds 50 books ........ **55.00**
Sign
  Duke Cigarettes, paper, portrait of woman wearing feathered hat,

black ground, "The Best in the World," 25" w, 33" h, framed .... **450.00**
Egyptienne Straights Cigarettes, paper, girl head wearing bonnet, cigarette package, 17½" w, 19½" h . **175.00**
Melachrino Cigarettes, tin, cigarette packages, "The Cigarette Elect of all Nations," self framed, 19½" w, 15½" h ...................... **165.00**
Mogul Egyptian Cigarettes, tin, oval, Arabian smoking cigarette, self framed, 20" w, 24" h .......... **85.00**
Raleigh Cigarettes, Tyrone Power smoking illus, "Star of 'The Razor's Edge'," 1947 .................. **50.00**
Silk, Hamilton King Ladies
Nebo .......................... **22.00**
Zira, 4 x 6" ..................... **22.00**
Thermometer, Chesterfield Cigarettes, porcelain, 13" l ................. **40.00**
Tin
Black Cat Cigarettes .............. **10.00**
Velvet Pipe & Cigarette Tobacco ... **5.00**
Trade Card, Gypsy Queen Cigarettes, c1900 ......................... **2.00**

# CIRCUS ITEMS

**Collecting Hints:** Circus programs are one of the most popular items in this category. Individuals have collected them since the 1920s. Programs prior to the 1930s are hard to find; post-1930 material is readily available.

Model building plays an active part in collecting. Some kits are available. However, most collectors like to build their models from scratch. Great attention is placed on accuracy of detail.

There is a wealth of books published about the circus. These are sought by collectors both for intrinsic as well as research value.

**History:** The 18th century circus was a small traveling company of acrobats and jugglers, and the first record of an American troupe was at that time. Washington is known to have attended a circus performance.

By the mid–19th century the tent circus with accompanying side shows and menagerie became popular throughout America. P. T. Barnum was one of the early circus promoters. His American Museum in New York in 1841 featured live animal acts. Other successful Barnum promotions included Jenny Lind in 1850, Tom Thumb from 1843 to 1883, and the purchase of Jumbo from the London Zoo in 1883.

The Ringlings and Barnum and Bailey brought a magical quality to the circus. The golden age of the tent circus was the 1920s to the 1940s, when a large circus would consist of over 100 railroad cars.

As television challenged live entertainment, the tent circus fell on hard times. Expenses for travel, food, staff, etc., mounted. A number of mergers took place, and many smaller companies simply went out of business. There are a few tent circuses remaining. However, most modern circuses now perform inside large convention centers.

**Reference:** Norman E. Martinus and Harry L. Rinker, *Warman's Paper,* Wallace–Homestead, 1993.

**Periodical:** *Circus Report,* 525 Oak Street, El Cerrito, CA 94530.

**Collectors' Clubs:** Circus Fans of America, Four Center Drive, Camp Hill, PA 17011; The Circus Historical Society, 743 Beverly Park Place, Jackson, MI 49203; The Circus Model Builders International, 347 Lonsdale Avenue, Dayton, OH 45419.

**Museums:** P.T. Barnum Museum, Bridgeport, CT; Circus World Museum Library–Research Center, Baraboo, WI; Ringling Circus Museum, Sarasota, FL.

Bank, Ringling Bros ................ **15.00**
Big Little Book, *Lions and Tigers,* Clyde Beatty, Whitman, 1934 ........... **100.00**
Book
*Randy Starr Leading Air Circus,* Eugene Martin, Saalfield Publishing, 1932 ........................ **15.00**
*Toby Tyler or 10 Weeks With a Circus,* James Otis, Goldsmith Publishing, c1930 ....................... **5.00**
Cabinet Photo
Fat Lady, inscribed "Miss Gertie Plath, 510 lbs, 5 ft 11 in," late 1890s ....................... **25.00**
Midget, inscribed "Bertha Carnihan, age 28 years, 38 lbs," c1890 .... **28.00**
Game
Emmett Kelly's Circus, orig box, All–Fair, 1953 ..................... **45.00**
Magic Circus Roll, 12 x 10" tin plate, litho clowns and circus acts, magnetized balls, orig box, American Toys, 1950s .................. **35.00**
Glass, 5" h, Big Top Circus, clear, yellow and black cartoon tiger illus, red and blue performing stand, 1960s .. **15.00**
Newspaper, St Paul Dispatch, MN, June 30, 1876, The Great Circus, back page ad ........................ **12.00**
Pass, 2¼ x 3⅝", inscribed "P T Barnum/ Bridgeport Ct, Feb 8, 1882," black inked sgd "Two To See Bailey Elephant From 2 to 3½ P.M. P T Barnum" ....................... **150.00**
Pennant, 24" l, Ringling Bros and Barnum & Bailey Circus, felt, brown,

white lettering and circus scenes, yellow trim and streamers, 1940s ..... **25.00**
Photo, 5 x 7", dirt street scene with John Robinson & Franklin Bros Circus wagon, c1890 ...................... **28.00**
Pinback Button
  Clyde Beatty, 1¾" d, black and white Beatty photo, blue background, 1930s ........................ **15.00**
  Clyde Beatty Circus, man holding chair and lion illus ............. **30.00**
  Clyde Beatty/Cole Bros Circus, 1¾" d, black and gray, Beatty wearing leather gloves holding young tiger, 1930s ........................ **25.00**
  I Am A Lion Tamer in Mandel Brothers Circus, 1⅜" d, litho, black, white, red, and yellow, 1930–40 . **15.00**
  Ringling Bros Barnum & Bailey Circus, 1¼" d, clown face, black, white, and red, "Madison Square Garden," 1950s ................ **15.00**
Post Card, Ringling Bros, fold–out, 1943 **20.00**

**Poster, Cole Brothers, 20 x 28", $85.00.**

Poster
  Cole Bros, 28 x 41", Quarter Million Pounds of Elephants ............ **165.00**
  Downie Bros, 27 x 28", Teddy, Hippodrome elephant .............. **200.00**
  Hunt Bros Circus and Wild West, Show, 21 x 28", Wild West scene **200.00**
  King Bros, clown face, red and yellow, arrival adv, 1946 .......... **210.00**
  Miller Bros, 28 x 42", Miss Bonro–Shot from Cannon, temple ....... **200.00**
  Ringling Bros, 28 x 41", multicolored **275.00**
  Ringling Bros and Barnum & Bailey
    20 x 28", Combined Shows ...... **110.00**
    20 x 60", multicolored Antalek Troupe ...................... **125.00**
  Skippy & Bum, 28 x 41", elephant and clown, Erie .................... **125.00**
Program
  Cole Bros, 1943 ................. **12.00**
  Cole Bros Clyde Beatty, 24 pgs, forty photos, 1969 .................. **5.00**
  Hamid–Morgan, 1948 ............ **8.00**
  Ringling Bros and Barnum & Bailey Circus
    1953 ......................... **12.00**
    1977 ......................... **5.00**
Punchout Album, Clyde Beatty & His Wild Animal Act, 9 x 13", Fold–A–Way Toys copyright 1935 Will Pente **75.00**
Receipt, Wallace Bros Circus ........ **4.00**
Ticket, Von Brothers Circus .......... **4.00**
Ticket Booklet, pr, Von Bros 3 Ring Circus, orig 50 count tickets, 1940s ... **15.00**
Token, Ringling Brothers and Barnum & Bailey Circus, aluminum, sealed cellophane packet, 100th Anniversary issue ............................ **12.00**
Toy
  Circus Bus, 9" l, tin, orig box ...... **150.00**
  Circus Motor Cycle U–Turn, 6" l, windup, tin .................... **145.00**
  Mechanical Acrobatic Monkeys, 10" d tin base with litho circus acts, clown on motorcycle moves in circle and two monkeys attached to road spin, orig box, Wyandotte .. **285.00**

# CLICKERS

**Collecting Hints:** Clickers with pictures are more desirable than clickers with just printing. Value is reduced by scratches in the paint and rust. Some companies issued several variations of a single design—be alert for them in your collecting.

**History:** Clickers were a popular advertising medium for products and services ranging from plumbing supplies, political aspirants, soft drinks, hotels, to beer and whiskey. The most commonly found clickers are those which were given to children in shoe stores. Brands include Buster Brown, Poll Parrot, and Red Goose. Many shoe store clickers have advertising whistle mates.

Clickers were not confined to advertising. They were a popular holiday item, especially at Halloween. Impressed animal forms also provided a style for clickers.

The vast majority of clickers were made of tin. The older and rarer clickers were made of celluloid.

## ADVERTISING

Allen's Parlor Furnace, 2" l, heating stove, yellow background ......... **30.00**
Barton's Dyanshine Shoe Polish, 1¼" d, brown and white, c1920 .......... **50.00**
Benzo Gas, 2" l, red, black, white, and

**Advertising, Tastykake, white lettering, blue ground, $10.00.**

lime green, "Does What Gasoline Can't" . . . . . . . . . . 12.00
Billiken Shoes, 2" l, "The Billykid" illus, yellow, blue, and white, light blue background, 1930s . . . . . . . . 30.00
Buster Brown Shoes, 2" l, five star symbol with emb title and portrait, 1920s 35.00
Endicott–Johnson Shoes, 2" l, yellow and black . . . . . . . . 12.00
Gridley Milk Did It!, 2" l, milk bottle with baby face, red background . . . . 25.00
Hafner's 365 Brand Coffee, 2" l, orange, blue, and white, 1930s . . . . . . . 18.00
Jolly Time Popcorn, 1⅞" l, blue and white popcorn box, yellow accents, 1930s . . . . . . . . 50.00
Mule–Hide Roofing and Shingles, yellow and black . . . . . . . . 18.00
Penn Maid Sour Cream, 2½" l, blue and white, 1930s . . . . . . . . 25.00
Peters Weatherbird Shoes, 1½" l, 1930s 25.00
Red Goose Shoes, 1⅞" l, 1930s . . . . . . 20.00
Reid's Ice Cream, 1¼" d, red and white, 1930s . . . . . . . . 28.00
Sapolio, 1¼" d, red, white, and blue, yellow product name, 1930s . . . . . . . 30.00
Thom McAn, 1¼" d, green and white, 1930s . . . . . . . . 25.00
Twinkies Shoes For Boys and Girls, Twinkie character, blue background 30.00
Weatherbird Shoes, 2" l, red, yellow, and black . . . . . . . . 12.00

## NON–ADVERTISING

Beetle, metal, diecut, Zig Zag . . . . . . . . 15.00
Bonzo, black, white, and red, 1930s . 20.00
Cricket, 2" l, litho tin, yellow and black 8.00
Halloween, orange, black, and white, 1930s . . . . . . . . 15.00
Ladybug, red and black, 1946 . . . . . . . 8.00
Pig, black and white, marked "O.I.C." on back . . . . . . . . 10.00
Santa, 1½" l, green, red, black, and white, Grant's Toy Dept, 1930s . . . . 35.00

# CLOCKS

**Collecting Hints:** Many clocks of the twentieth century were reproductions of earlier styles. Therefore, dating should be checked by patent dates on the mechanism, maker's label, and construction techniques.

The principal buyers for advertising and figural clocks are not the clock collectors, but the specialist whose area of interest the clock overlaps. For example, the Pluto alarm clock is of far greater importance to a Disneyana collector than to most clock collectors.

Condition is critical. Rust and non–working condition detract heavily from the price.

**History:** The clock always has served dual functions: decorative and utilitarian. Beginning in the late 19th century, the clock became an important advertising vehicle, a tradition still continuing today. As character and personality became part of the American scene, the clock was a logical target, whether an alarm or wall model. The novelty clock, especially figural, was common in the 1930 to the 1960 period.

In the 1970s the popularity of digital wrist watches and clocks has led to less emphasis on the clock as a promotional item.

**References:** Robert W. D. Ball, *American Shelf and Wall Clocks: A Pictorial History,* Schiffer Publishing, Ltd., 1992; Howard S. Brenner, *Identification and Value Guide To Collecting Comic Character Clocks and Watches,* Books Americana, 1987; Hy Brown, *Comic Character Timepieces: Seven Decades of Memories,* Schiffer Publishing Ltd., 1992; Philip Collins, *Pastime: Telling Time from 1920 to 1960,* Chronicle Books, 1993; Alan and Rita Shenton, *The Price Guide To Collectible Clocks, 1840–1940,* Antique Collectors' Club.

**Collectors' Club:** National Association of Watch and Clock Collectors, Inc., 514 Poplar St., Columbia, PA 17512.

**Museum:** Museum of National Association of Watch and Clock Collectors, Columbia, PA.

**Additional Listings:** See *Warman's Antiques and Their Prices.*

Advertising
Big Smith Work Clothes, light–up, 1950s . . . . . . . . 110.00
Dig 'Em, Kellogg's Cereal, 4" d, 5½" h, metal, windup, alarm, full color character illus, red case, brass trim and alarm bells, 1979 Kellogg copyright . . . . . . . . 50.00
Old Southern Belle Dairy, 16" sq, girl in red dress . . . . . . . . 65.00
Peters Shoes, 4 x 4", metal, green and silver, black numerals, 1930s . . . . 100.00

Purina Poultry Cows, 5″ h, metal, ivory, red, white, and blue dial, windup, 1932 . . . . . . . . . . . . . . . . **25.00**
Purolator Oil Filters, light–up . . . . . . **125.00**
Teddy Snow Crop, Snow Crop Frozen Foods, wall, mechanical, wood, 1950s . . . . . . . . . . . . . . . . . . . . . . . **75.00**
Tip Top Tailors, 1950s, lights up . . . **150.00**
Trix Cereal, 4″ d, 6″ h, metal, windup, alarm, character illus, orig box, Lafayette Watch Co, 1970–80 . . . . . . **45.00**
Art Deco, 9″ w, 11¼″ h, Ballerina, walnut stained case, gold plated figure, Sessions, 1937 . . . . . . . . . . . . . . . . . . **65.00**

**Character, Mickey Mouse, windup, Ingersoll, 1934, 2¼″ h, $935.00. Photograph courtesy of James D. Julia Inc.**

Character
Bugs Bunny, 3″ d, travel, windup, alarm, hinged case, Seth Thomas, 1970 Warner Bros copyright . . . . . **25.00**
Cat In The Hat, 4″ d, 6″ h, windup, alarm, steel, red enamel, 1978 copyright . . . . . . . . . . . . . . . . . . . . . **75.00**
Davy Crockett, 11″ h, gold toned metal, Davy holding rifle on one side, Indian with tomahawk on other, lighted screen on front with revolving scene panel, United, 1950s . . . . . . . . . . . . . . . . . . . . . . . **450.00**
Hopalong Cassidy, 5½ x 6″, glossy black baked enamel, black and white Hoppy and Topper photo on dial, red numerals and hands, orig box, US Time Corp, 1950 . . . . . . . **350.00**
Howdy Doody Time Teacher, 10 x 18″ . . . . . . . . . . . . . . . . . . . . . . . . . . **25.00**
Joe Louis/World Champion, 12″ h, metal, copper finish, United Clock Corp . . . . . . . . . . . . . . . . . . . . . . . **300.00**
Peter Max, 9″ d, floral design, orange day–glo hands, General Electric, copyright Peter Max, late 1960s . . **100.00**
Roy Rogers, 2 x 4¼″, 4½″ h, windup, alarm, metal, E Ingraham Co, c1951 . . . . . . . . . . . . . . . . . . . . . . . **200.00**
Shmoo, 4 x 6″, figural, plastic, white, orig box . . . . . . . . . . . . . . . . . . . . . **225.00**
Underdog, 3″ d, octagonal, plastic and metal, windup, dial illus, Made in West Germany, Leonardo-T T V copyright, mid 1970s . . . . . . . . . . . **100.00**
Woody Woodpecker, alarm, animated, Woody on tree trunk, moves back and forth, illuminated hands, orig box, copyright Walter Lantz, Columbia, 1959 . . . . . . . . . **285.00**

Figural
Clown, 6½″ h, composition, Lux . . . **75.00**
Grandfather Clock, 11″ h, wood, E Ingraham . . . . . . . . . . . . . . . . . . . . . **65.00**
Owl, 5½″ h, composition, Lux . . . . . **100.00**
Ship, 20″ w, 19″ h, walnut veneered, electric, Sessions . . . . . . . . . . . . . . . **38.00**
Television, 3½ x 6 x 5″, plastic, red and black wood grain design, marked "Tele–Vision," stamped Dec 1961 on back . . . . . . . . . . . . . **100.00**

Kitchen
Banjo shape, 30″ h, New Haven Clock Co . . . . . . . . . . . . . . . . . . . . . **140.00**
Gingerbread, grape design, Gilbert . **125.00**

Mantel
Ansonia, 12″ w, 10½″ h, black enameled metal case, gilt dec . . . . . . . . **100.00**
E Ingraham, 18″ w, 11½″ h, black enameled wood case, marbleized trim, gilt dec . . . . . . . . . . . . . . . . . **125.00**
Sessions, 15″ w, 10½″ h, black enameled wood case, marbleized trim, gilt dec . . . . . . . . . . . . . . . . . . . . . . **75.00**

Neon, Canadian Neon Ray, two neon rings . . . . . . . . . . . . . . . . . . . . . . . . . . . **600.00**

Wall
Liberty Bell, pendulum, Lux . . . . . . . **200.00**
Mickey Mouse, wall, red plastic case, inset color paper photo, orig shipping box, Elgin, 1970s . . . . . . . . . . **50.00**
Sunflower, pendulum, Lux . . . . . . . . . **125.00**

# CLOTHING AND CLOTHING ACCESSORIES

**Collecting Hints:** Vintage clothing should be clean and in good repair. Designer labels and original boxes can add to the value.

Collecting vintage clothing appears to have reached a plateau. Although there are still dedicated collectors, the category is no longer attracting a rash of new collectors annually.

**History:** Clothing is collected and studied as a reference source in learning about fashion, construction and types of materials used.

**References:** C. Willett and Phillis Cunnington, *The History of Underclothes,* Dover Publications, Inc., 1992; Maryanne Dolan, *Vintage Clothing, 1880–1960, Second Edition,* Books Americana, 1988; Kate E. Dooner, *Plastic Handbags: Sculpture to Wear,* Schiffer Publishing Ltd., 1993; Dover Publications, Inc., *Women's Fashions of the Early 1900s: An Unabridged Republication of New York Fashions, National Cloak & Suit Co.,* Dover Publications, Inc., 1992; Joanne Dubbs Ball and Dorothy Hehl Torem, *The Art of Fashion Accessories,* Schiffer Publishing Ltd., 1993; Rod Dyer and Ron Spaark, *Fit To Be Tied: Vintage Ties of the Forties and Early Fifties,* Abbeville Press, 1987; Roseann Ettinger, *Handbags,* Schiffer Publishing, Ltd., 1991; Evelyn Haertig, *Antique Combs & Purses,* Gallery Press, 1983; Richard Holiner, *Antique Purses, Second Edition,* Collector Books, 1987, 1990 value update; Tina Irick–Nauer, *The First Price Guide to Antique and Vintage Clothes,* E. P. Dutton, 1983; Sheila Malouff, *Collectible Clothing With Prices,* Wallace Homestead, 1983, out–of–print; Terry McCormick, *The Consumer's Guide To Vintage Clothing,* Dembner Books, 1987; Diane McGee, *A Passion For Fashion,* Simmons–Boardman Books, Inc, 1987; JoAnne Olian (ed.), *Everyday Fashions of The Forties As Pictured in Sears Catalogs,* Dover Publications, Inc., 1992; Mary Trasko, *Heavenly Soles: Extraordinary Twentieth Century Shoes,* Abbeville Press, 1989; Merideth Wright, *Everday Dress of Rural America: 1783–1800,* Dover Publications, 1992.

**Periodicals:** *Vintage Clothing Newsletter,* P.O. Box 1422, Corvallis, OR 97339; *Vintage Fashions,* 900 Frederick St., Cumberland, MD 21502.

**Collectors' Club:** The Costume Society of America, 55 Edgewater Dr., P. O. Box 73, Earleville, MD 21919.

**Museums:** Metropolitan Museum of Art, New York, NY; The Costume and Textile Department of the Los Angeles County Museum of Art, Los Angeles, CA; Philadelphia Museum of Art, Philadelphia, PA.

19th Century
- Bathing suit, black and white, matching slippers and hat, 1890s ...... **50.00**
- Bloomers
  - Cotton, white, long, split type ... **20.00**
  - Wool, black, gym type .......... **30.00**
- Capelet, beaded, allover design, beaded fringe, 1850s ........... **90.00**
- Christening Gown, 30" l, silk ...... **125.00**
- Coat, paisley, hand embroidered, 1880s ........................ **375.00**
- Dress
  - Brocade, rust, two pieces, owl buttons, 1880s .................. **85.00**
  - Silk, beige, 1880s .............. **100.00**
  - Silk Faille, black, mourning, 1890 **90.00**
  - Wool, pink, lace trim, 1890 ..... **85.00**
- Hat, black, small ................. **40.00**
- Mittens, pr, child's, fur trim ........ **6.00**
- Petticoat, blue stripes ............. **32.00**
- Shoes, pr
  - Baby's, three button
    - Black and white .............. **38.00**
    - Brown, laced ................ **20.00**
  - Child's, high button ............ **52.00**
  - Woman's, high lace ............ **75.00**
- Smoking Jacket, chintz and calico, 1880s ........................ **100.00**
- Stockings, pr, baby's, hand knitted . **6.00**

1900s
- Blouse, silk, cream, embroidered ... **65.00**
- Dress
  - Batiste, white, lace, high neck, full skirt, long sleeves ............ **150.00**
  - Calico, blue, two piece style, matching bonnet ............. **175.00**
  - Cotton, gold, net trim ........... **20.00**
- Duster, linen, shawl collar ......... **100.00**
- Umbrella, red, white, and blue, parade type ...................... **65.00**

1910s
- Blouse, poplin, white, middy style .. **15.00**
- Coat, evening, silk, black, three quarter length ..................... **40.00**
- Dress
  - Girl's
    - Lawn, white, lace trim, drop waist ..................... **60.00**
    - Silk, red, black trim, drop waist, bowed sash ............... **75.00**
  - Lady's, silk, brown, black accents **50.00**

1920s
- Bloomers, crepe satin, peach, silk embroidery, lace trim ........... **20.00**
- Boa, feather ..................... **75.00**
- Cape, wool, dark blue, quilted lining, 18" l .......................... **65.00**
- Coat
  - Velvet, navy blue, black fox collar and cuffs, beaded dec, red satin lining ....................... **200.00**
  - Wool, blue, beaver collar and cuffs, blouson, drop waist style **95.00**
- Dress, chiffon, blue, edges trimmed with braided fabric ............. **40.00**
- Evening Dress, black, chemise style, Paris label ..................... **48.00**
- Gloves, men's, driving, leather, black **25.00**
- Purse, gold beads ................ **125.00**
- Shawl, cotton, mint green, full embroidered, fringed edges ........ **35.00**
- Shoes
  - Lady's, suede, gray ............. **25.00**

Men's, tennis, high top . . . . . . . . . **20.00**
Suit, lady's, wool, navy, pintucks, silk lining . . . . . . . . . . . . . . . . . . . . . . . . **50.00**

1930s

Bathing Suit, stretchy black fabric, back buttons, flared skirt . . . . . . . . **45.00**
Bed Jacket, satin, pink, lavish ecru lace, labeled "B Altman & Co, NY" **30.00**
Cape, mohair, black, ankle length . . **75.00**
Coat, fur, seal, 1935 . . . . . . . . . . . . . . **950.00**
Collar, beaded, white . . . . . . . . . . . . . **15.00**
Dress
Girl's, rayon, raspberry, accordion pleats . . . . . . . . . . . . . . . . . . . . . . **15.00**
Lady's, deep blue, peplum style, small size . . . . . . . . . . . . . . . . . . **55.00**
Dressing Gown, satin, ruby red, fagoted ruffled edges . . . . . . . . . . . . . **30.00**
Evening Gown
Chiffon and velvet, black, empire waist, shirred bodice . . . . . . . . . **40.00**
Crepe, brown, matching velvet capelet with feather trim . . . . . . **35.00**
Satin, green, gold sequins, matching jacket, NRA Dress Code Authority label . . . . . . . . . . . . . . . . **20.00**
Hat
Boater, straw . . . . . . . . . . . . . . . . . . **35.00**
Top, beaver . . . . . . . . . . . . . . . . . . . **75.00**
Purse
Bakelite, white, elegant . . . . . . . . . **28.00**
Lucite, rhinestones . . . . . . . . . . . . . **12.00**
Silk, clutch, black, cut steel beads, label marked "France" . . . . . . . . **40.00**

**Handbag, lucite, faux tortoise shell, marked "Lewisd Jewel/Llewellyn Inc," $36.00.**

Shawl
Silk, 60" sq, satin stitch embroidery **42.00**
Wool, ivory, exquisite border embroidery . . . . . . . . . . . . . . . . . . . **28.50**
Shoes, brown lace up, heels . . . . . . . **35.00**
Uniform, Girl Scout, green, matching cap . . . . . . . . . . . . . . . . . . . . . . . . . . **36.00**
Wedding Dress, slipper satin, train, size 7 . . . . . . . . . . . . . . . . . . . . . . . . **95.00**

1940s

Coat
Cashmere, red, silver fox collar, full length . . . . . . . . . . . . . . . . . . . . . . **45.00**
Fur
Alaskan Seal, black, mink trim, padded shoulders . . . . . . . . . . **60.00**
Muskrat, bell shaped sleeves . . . **45.00**
Dress
Girl's, velvet, red, white nylon trim, Shirley Temple style, Cinderella tag . . . . . . . . . . . . . . . . . . **15.00**
Lady's, satin, black, padded shoulders, waist swag . . . . . . . . . . . . . **75.00**
Evening Gown
Net and Taffeta, black, lace flowers **40.00**
Organza, white, shirred, rhinestones . . . . . . . . . . . . . . . . . . . . . . **35.00**
Evening Jacket, crepe, pink, floral patterned sequins, lined . . . . . . . . . . . **50.00**
Hat
Derby . . . . . . . . . . . . . . . . . . . . . . . . **75.00**
Straw, wide brim, multicolored chiffon flowers . . . . . . . . . . . . . . . **20.00**

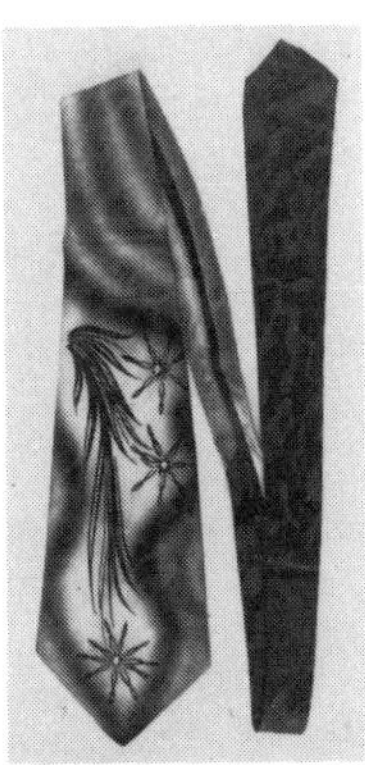

**Necktie, hand painted silk, Van Heusen, multicolored ground, dark red flowers with rhinestone centers, 4¼" w, $25.00.**

Muff, fur, black . . . . . . . . . . . . . . . . . . **20.00**
Night Gown
Rayon, lace trim . . . . . . . . . . . . . . . **8.00**
Satin, lace trim . . . . . . . . . . . . . . . . **5.00**
Purse
Alligator, baby alligator head, Cuba **40.00**
Satin, red, drawstring type, metal opening . . . . . . . . . . . . . . . . . . . . **50.00**
Scarf, white mesh, rectangular, lurex threads . . . . . . . . . . . . . . . . . . . . . . . **20.00**
Shoes, Lucite, high heels, rhinestones, ankle strap . . . . . . . . . . . . . . **22.00**
Travel Kit, gentleman's, alligator case, seven accessories . . . . . . . . . **20.00**
Uniform, dress, Girl Scout, Brownie **12.00**

Wedding Gown, satin, ivory, padded shoulders, sweetheart neckline, waist swag, self train, matching veiled hat ..................... **125.00**

1950s

Blouse, lace, ecru, evening style, gathered waist ................. **20.00**

Dungarees, lady's, flannel lined, unused .......................... **20.00**

Handbag, hard plastic

Pink, clear etched lid ........... **100.00**

White, hp flowers, opens from center ........................ **110.00**

Hat, Christian Dior, cloche style, brown ribbon loops, amber beading .......................... **16.50**

Playsuit, child's, Herman Iskin & Co, Telford, PA

Confederate Soldier, gray, yellow and red trim ................. **200.00**

Cowboy, red, black, and green, orig 10⅝ x 12¾ x 1½" box, MIB **175.00**

Jet Pilot Commander, light blue and yellow, orig 10⅝ x 12¾ x 1½" box ....................... **175.00**

Lone Wolf, Indian outfit, orig 10⅝ x 12¾ x 1½" box, MIB ....... **200.00**

Military Officer, tan, yellow dec, pants, jack, and cap .......... **150.00**

Nurse, navy blue cape, white dress **150.00**

Train Engineer, orig 10⅝ x 12¾ x 1½" box, MIB .............. **200.00**

Prom Gown, net and taffeta, pink, layered skirt, bow trim .......... **30.00**

Skirt, polished cotton, floral pink, full **20.00**

1960s

Dress, Indian squaw style, yellow and black, lots of colorful ric–rac and silver, lady's size 14 ............ **250.00**

Prom Gown, georgette, yellow, embroidered bodice ............... **25.00**

Shoes, plaid, lace up boots, chunk heel .......................... **35.00**

Skirt, satin, hot pink, black floral flocked designs, full ............ **10.00**

1970s, pant suit, black, silver studs, lady's size 14 ..................... **15.00**

1980s, sweat suit, LA Olympic worker, orange and blue, 2 pc ........... **65.00**

# COCA–COLA ITEMS

**Collecting Hints:** Most Coca–Cola items were produced in large quantity; the company was a leader in sales and promotional materials. Don't ignore the large amount of Coca–Cola material in languages other than English. Remember, "Coke" has a worldwide market.

**History:** The originator of Coca–Cola was John Pemberton, a pharmacist from Atlanta, Georgia. In 1886, Dr. Pemberton introduced a patent medicine to relieve headaches, stomach disorders, and other minor maladies. Unfortunately, his failing health and meager finances forced him to sell his interest.

In 1888, Asa G. Candler became the sole owner of Coca–Cola. Candler improved the formula, increased the advertising budget, and widened the distribution. Accidentally, a patient was given a dose of the syrup mixed with carbonated water instead of the usual still water. The result was a tastier, more refreshing drink.

As sales increased in the 1890s, Candler recognized that the product was more suitable for the soft drink market and began advertising it as such. From these beginnings a myriad of advertising items have been issued to invite all to "Drink Coca– Cola."

Dates of interest: "Coke" was first used in advertising in 1941. The distinctive shaped bottle was registered as a trademark on April 12, 1960.

**References:** Shelly Goldstein, *Goldstein's Coca–Cola Collectibles: An Illustrated Value Guide,* Collector Books, 1991, 1993 value update; Shelly and Helen Goldstein, *Coca–Cola Collectibles,* (four volumes, plus index), published by author, 1970s; Deborah Goldstein Hill, *Wallace–Homestead Price Guide To Coca–Cola Collectibles,* Wallace–Homestead, 1984, 1991 value update; Norman E. Martinus and Harry L. Rinker, *Warman's Paper,* Wallace–Homestead, 1993; Allan Petretti, *Petretti's Coca–Cola Collectibles Price Guide, 8th Edition,* Wallace–Homestead, 1992; Al Wilson, *Collectors Guide to Coca–Cola Items, Volume I, Revised* L–W Book Sales, 1985; Al Wilson, *Collectors Guide To Coca–Cola Items,* Volume I (1985, 1992 value update) and Volume II (1987, 1993 value update), L–W Book Sales.

**Collectors' Club:** The Coca–Cola Collectors Club International, P. O. Box 546, Holmdel, NJ 07733.

**Museum:** Coca–Cola Memorabilia Museum of Elizabeth, Inc., Elizabethtown, KY.

**REPRODUCTION ALERT,** especially in the area of Coca–Cola trays.

Awning, canvas, red and white striped, white and green lettering, "Drink Coca–Cola, Refreshment Center," metal frame rods ................. **775.00**

Booklet, "Romance of Coca–Cola," 16 pgs, 1916 ....................... **85.00**

Box, wooden, Omaha, NE .......... **24.00**

Carrier, 8" h, aluminum, silver colored, white lettering on red label both sides, "Delicious Coca–Cola Refreshing," slide handle, holds six green bottles, 1950s .......................... **60.00**

Coupon, free bottle, creased ......... **3.00**

Door Push, porcelain, red, yellow and white lettering, yellow border, "Merci Revenez Pour un Coca–Cola," c1941 **150.00**
Jack Knife, plastic case, "In Bottles 5 Cents" . . . . . . . . . . **22.00**
Light Pull, 10" w, 15" h, diecut cardboard, Coca–Cola boy's head, wearing bottle cap hat, holding bottle in outstretched hand . . . . . . . . **250.00**
Miniature, wooden case, nine glass bottles, some syrup left . . . . . . **52.00**
Needle Tin . . . . . . . . . . **18.00**
Score Pad, unused . . . . . . . . **12.00**
Seltzer Bottle, 11½" h, glass, metal top, "Coca–Cola Bottling Works, Alliance, Ohio, Contents 26 fl oz," 1950s **150.00**
Sign
- 20" w, 32" h, rect, metal, sidewalk sign, white ground, hand holding early waisted glass mug, stenciled lettering "For Headache and Exhaustion, Drink Coca–Cola, 5¢ a Glass, Delicious & Refreshing" . . **4,850.00**
- 24" w, 20¼" h, flange, enamel, red and white, "Drink Coca–Cola," bottle . . . . . . . . . . **325.00**
- 26" w, 15" h, rect, rounded bottom edge, porcelain, red ground, "Drink Coca–Cola," yellow and white lettering, bottom stamped "Made in U.S.A. 1942" . . . . . **135.00**
- 36" d, round, porcelain, red, white lettering, "Drink Coca–Cola in Bottles," c1960 . . . . . . . . **265.00**

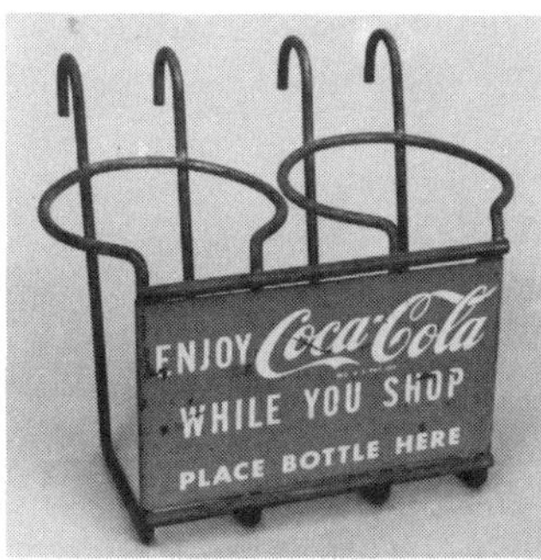


**Bottle Holder, wire frame, red tin label with white lettering, 1950s, 5⅝" w, 4⅞" h, $15.00.**

Table Tennis Paddle, used . . . . . . **8.00**
Thermometer, 12" d, round, red center with gold outline of bottle and white lettering "Drink Coca–Cola," green rim with black numbers and degrees, Pam Clock Corp, Mt Vernon, NY, 1948 . . . . . . . . . . **250.00**

**Serving Tray, screened background, first tray produced after WWII, 1950–52, 10½ x 13¼", $45.00.**

Tray, serving
- 1916, 8½" w, 19" h, rect, "Elaine," girl wearing cream colored dress and hat, sitting, holding glass, sitting by basket of roses, "Drink Coca–Cola" at top, gold graphic border . . . . . . . . . . **360.00**
- 1925, 10½" w, 13" h, rect, "Girl at Party," woman wearing white fur wrap, holding glass, "Coca–Cola" at top . . . . . . . . . . **110.00**
- 1927, 13" w, 10½" h, rect, "Curb Service," waiter serving couple in early car, "Drink Coca–Cola" both sides . . . . . . . . . . **400.00**
- 1930, 10½" w, 13" h, rect, "Bathing Beauty," woman wearing bathing suit, holding bottle, "Drink Coca–Cola" top and bottom . . . . . **235.00**
- 1938, 10½" w, 13" h, rect, "Girl in the Afternoon," woman wearing yellow dress and hat, holding bottle, "Drink Coca–Cola" top and bottom, sgd . . . . . . . . **50.00**
- 1939, 10½" w, 13¼" h, rect, "Spring Board Girl," woman in bathing suit sitting on diving board, holding bottle, "Drink Coca–Cola Delicious and Refreshing" at top . . . . . **35.00**
- 1941, 10½" w, 13" h, rect, girl with ice skates, sitting on log, holding bottle, "Drink Coca–Cola" top and bottom . . . . . . . . . . **120.00**

Vending Machine
- Model 44, 16" w, 20" d, 58" h, red and white, red lettering "Drink Coca–Cola, 10¢," The Vendo Company, Kansas City . . . . . . **1,750.00**
- Model CS72, 24¾" w, 47" h, red, hand holding bottle, white letter-

ing, "Drink Coca–Cola, Ice Cold 10¢," c1955 .................. **1,650.00**

Watch Fob, 1¾" h, brass, bottle in center, "Drink a Bottle of Carbonated Coca–Cola The Most Refreshing Drink in the World, 5¢," 1920s .... **100.00**

# COCKTAIL SHAKERS

**Collecting Hints:** Concentrate on cocktail shakers that are style statements for their era. Make aesthetics, line, form, and materials principal focus points. A collection numbering in the hundreds can be built around examples of the streamlined modern style.

When buying glass shakers run your fingers around the edge to look for chipping. A small chip reduces the price by a minimum of 30%. Shakers with brilliant sharp colors are more desirable than those comprised of clear glass.

Be on the constant alert for cracks and fractures. Most individuals want shakers that are fine or better in appearance and can be used if necessary.

Figural shakers are in a class of their own. Among the more common forms are bowling pins, dumbbells, golf bags, and penguins. Shakers based on the designs of Norman Bel Geddes often command in excess of $500.00.

**History:** The cocktail shaker traces its origins back to 7,000 B.C. and the South American jar gourd, a closed container used to mix liquids. The ancient Egyptians of 3,500 B.C. added spices to their grain fermentations before serving them, perhaps history's first cocktails. History records the use of alcoholic drinks through the modern era.

By the late 1800s, bartenders used a shaker as a standard tool of their craft. Passing the liquid back and forth between two containers created a much-appreciated show.

The modern cocktail shaker arrived on the scene in the 1920s, when martinis were in vogue. Shapes tended to be stylish. Materials ranged from glass to sterling silver. Perhaps nothing symbolizes the Jazz Age more than the flapper dress and cocktail shaker. When Prohibition ended in 1933, the cocktail shaker enjoyed another surge of popularity.

Movies helped popularize the cocktail shaker. William Powell instructed a bartender how to mix a proper martini in *The Thin Man*, a tradition continued by James Bond 007. Tom Cruise's portrayal of a bartender in *Cocktail* helped solidify the collecting interest that was shown in cocktail shakers during the 1980s.

Following World War II, the home bar became a common fixture in most homes. Every home bar featured one or more cocktail shakers and/or cocktail shaker sets. Chrome-plated stainless steel shakers replaced the sterling silver shakers of the 1920s and 1930s. Major glass companies such as Cambridge, Heisey, and Imperial offered cocktail shakers.

Life in the fabulous fifties was filled with novelties. Cocktail shakers were no exception. Figural and other forms of novelty shakers appeared.

The electric blender and ready mix cocktail packets ended the reign of the cocktail shaker. Showmanship was replaced by button pushing. An era passed.

Bartender Set, 2½" d, 6½" h, extreme caricature black bartender figure, die-cut aluminum, painted features, white towel, spring jiggle action, wooden bar holds removable silvered metal cocktail picks, c1930 ............. **300.00**

Beverage Set

Depression Glass, pitcher, decanter, orig stopper, seven 4" h tumblers, eight 3½" h tumblers, Scottie dog dec on each, price for set ....... **90.00**

Ruby Glass, 8" h pitcher, six matching tumblers, ruby, monogrammed "B" **125.00**

Cocktail Set, Art Deco style, glass shaker, six tall glasses, five shorter glasses, frosted stippled surface, gold and colored mid bands, 1950s ..... **60.00**

Cocktail Shaker

Aluminum, hand wrought, straight sides, grooved Modernistic top, clear plastic knob lid, Buenilum .. **20.00**

Glass, Cambridge

Diane pattern, crystal, glass top .. **125.00**

Wildflower pattern, crystal, chrome top ......................... **75.00**

**Cocktail Shaker, Art Deco, ruby red glass, chrome top, 12½" h, $55.00.**

Cordial Set, Central Glass Co, Balda Orchid pattern, decanter, six matching cordial glasses .................. **365.00**

- Decanter, orig stopper
  - Cambridge, Cleo pattern, pink ..... **225.00**
  - Imperial, Cape Cod pattern, crystal . **65.00**
  - Waterford, Irish, cut crystal, Balfray pattern ..... **150.00**
- Hor D'oeuvre Pick
  - Dog ..... **3.00**
  - Fruit, set of twelve ..... **20.00**
  - Man, top hat ..... **3.00**
- Ice Bucket
  - Aluminum, hand wrought
    - Buenilum, ridged band handles, ring finial ..... **15.00**
    - Lehman, double twisted handles, plastic knob ..... **15.00**
  - Glass
    - Cambridge
      - Decagon pattern, amethyst .... **35.00**
      - Mt Vernon pattern, red ..... **75.00**
    - Fenton, Plymouth pattern, red ... **50.00**
    - Fostoria, green, polar bear dec ... **30.00**
    - Paden City
      - Black Forest pattern, green .... **110.00**
      - Party Line pattern, pink ..... **25.00**
- Liquor Set, brass ring holds four gold banded glasses, c1950 ..... **18.00**
- Martini Pitcher, Cambridge, Diane pattern, crystal ..... **750.00**
- Martini Set, glass, pheasants on pitcher and glasses, brass stirrer ..... **18.00**
- Punch Bowl Set
  - Duncan Miller, Caribbean pattern, crystal, 10″ d bowl, dozen punch cups, matching ladle, price for fourteen piece set ..... **225.00**
  - Heisey, Lariat pattern, crystal, seven quart punch bowl, ten cups, price for eleven piece set ..... **175.00**
- Stemware, glass
  - Claret
    - Cambridge, Rose Point pattern, crystal, 4½ oz ..... **45.00**
    - Fostoria, Hermitage pattern, amber **15.00**
    - Tiffin, Flanders pattern, pink ..... **95.00**
  - Cocktail
    - Heisey, Plantation pattern, crystal, pressed ..... **50.00**
    - Tiffin, Cadena pattern, yellow, 5¼″ h ..... **25.00**
    - US Glass, Deerwood pattern, green, 5″ h ..... **30.00**
  - Cordial
    - Cambridge
      - Caprice pattern, blue, 1 oz .... **125.00**
      - Chantilly pattern, crystal, gold dec, 1 oz ..... **65.00**
    - Heisey, Plantation pattern, crystal, blown ..... **90.00**
  - Wine
    - Cambridge
      - Imperial Hunt Scene pattern, emerald green, 2½ oz ..... **55.00**
      - Valencia pattern, crystal, 2½ oz **30.00**
    - Fostoria, Fairfax pattern, rose, 3 oz **30.00**
- Swizzle Stick, glass
  - Advertising, colored ..... **3.00**
  - Amber ..... **1.25**
  - Black ..... **2.00**
  - Blue and Crystal, clear spoon ..... **2.00**
  - Blue–green, clear spoon ..... **2.25**
  - Christmas, set of six ..... **20.00**
  - Cobalt Blue ..... **1.25**
  - Colored Knob, clear stirrer ..... **1.75**
  - Man, top hat ..... **3.00**
  - Plain, crystal ..... **1.00**
  - Red and Crystal, clear spoon ..... **2.00**
  - Souvenir, Hotel Lexington, amethyst, 1939 World's Fair ..... **15.00**
  - Spatter knob, clear stirrer ..... **.75**

**Swizzle Sticks, adv, plastic, price each, $.25.**

- Tom & Jerry, Skokie Green, McKee
  - Bowl ..... **65.00**
  - Cup ..... **9.00**
  - Mug ..... **10.00**
- Tumbler
  - Bar
    - Cambridge, Portia pattern, crystal, 2½ oz ..... **30.00**
    - Heisey
      - Ridgeleigh pattern, crystal, 2½ oz ..... **30.00**
      - Victorian pattern, crystal, 2 oz . **35.00**
  - Old Fashioned
    - Duncan Miller, Tear Drop pattern, crystal, 7 oz ..... **10.00**
    - Fostoria, Baroque pattern, blue, 6½ oz ..... **75.00**
    - Heisey, Saturn pattern, 7 oz, crystal **10.00**
- Whiskey Glass
  - Duncan Miller, Tear Drop pattern, crystal, 2 oz ..... **15.00**
  - Fostoria
    - American pattern, crystal, 2½″ h . **10.00**
    - Kasmir pattern, yellow, ftd, 2 oz . **25.00**
  - Heisey, Plantation pattern, crystal, blown ..... **50.00**
  - McKee
    - Aztec pattern, crystal ..... **15.00**
    - Rock Crystal pattern, crystal ..... **20.00**

# COMIC BOOKS

**Collecting Hints:** Remember, age does *not* determine value! Prices fluctuate according to supply and demand in the marketplace. Collectors should always buy comic books in the best possible condition. While archival restoration is available, it's frequently costly and may involve a certain amount of risk.

Comic books should be stored in an upright position away from sunlight, dampness, and insect infestations. Avoid stacking comic books because the weight of the uppermost books may cause acid and oils to migrate. This results in stains on the covers of books near the bottom of the stack which are difficult or impossible to remove.

Golden Age (1939–1950s) Marvel and D.C. first issues and key appearances continue to gain in popularity as do more current favorites like Marvel's "X–Men" and D.C.'s "The New Teen Titans."

**History:** Who would ever believe that a cheap, disposable product sold in the 1890s would be responsible for the multi–million dollar industry composed of comic books and their spin–offs today? That 2¢ item was none other than the Sunday newspaper. Improved printing techniques helped 1890s newspaper publishers change from a weekly format to a daily one that included a full page of comics. The rotary printing press allowed the use of color in the "funnies." Comics were soon reprinted as advertising promotions by companies such as Procter & Gamble products and movie theaters.

It wasn't long until reprint books like these promotional giveaways were selling in candy and stationery stores for 10¢ each. They appeared in various formats and sizes, many with odd shapes and cardboard covers. Others were printed on newsprint and resembled comic books sold today.

Comics printed prior to 1938 have value today only as historical artifacts or intellectual curiosities.

From 1939 to 1950 comic book publishers regaled readers with humor, adventure, Western, and mystery tales. Super–heroes such as Batman, Superman, and Captain America first appeared in books during this era. This was the "Golden Age" of comics, a time for expansion and growth.

Unfortunately, the bubble burst in the spring of 1954 when Fredric Wertham published his book, *Seduction of the Innocent.* That book pointed a guilt–laden finger at the comic industry for corrupting youth, causing juvenile delinquency, and undermining American values. This book forced many publishers out of business, while others fought to establish a "comics code" to assure parents that their comics were compliant with morality and decency censures upheld by the code authority.

Thus, the Silver Age of comics is marked by a declining number of publishers due to the public uproar surrounding Wertham's book and the increased production costs of an inflationary economy.

The period starting with 1960 and continuing to the present has been marked by a revitalizing surge of interest in comic books. Starting with Marvel's introduction of "The Fantastic Four" and "The Amazing Spiderman," the market has increased to the extent that many new publishers are now rubbing elbows with the giants and the competition is keen!

Part of the reason for this upswing must be credited to that same inflationary economy that spelled disaster for publishers in the 1950s. This time, however, people are buying valuable comics as a hedge against inflation. Even young people are aware of the market potential. Today's piggy bank investors may well be tomorrow's Wall Street tycoons.

**References:** Stephen Becker, *Comic Art In America,* Simon And Schuster, Inc., 1959; Mike Benton, *Horror Comics: The Illustrated History,* Taylor Publishing, 1991; Mike Benton, *Science Fiction Comics: The Illustrated History,* Taylor Publishing, 1992; Mike Benton, *Superhero Comics of the Golden Age: The Illustrated History,* Taylor Publishing, 1992; Mike Benton, *Superhero Comics of the Silver Age: The Illustrated History,* Taylor Publishing, 1992; Mike Benton, *The Comic Book in America: An Illustrated History,* Taylor Publishing, 1989; Pierre Couperie and Maurice C. Horn, *A History of the Comic Strip,* Crown Publishers, Inc. 1968; Hubert H. Crawford, *Crawford's Encyclopedia of Comic Books,* Jonathan David Publisher's, Inc., 1978; Les Daniels, *COMIX, A History of Comic Books in America,* Bonanza Books, 1971; Ernst and Mary Gerber (compilers), *Photo–Journal Guide To Comics, Volume One (A–J)* and *Volume 2 (K–Z),* Gerber Publishing Co., 1990; John Hegenberger, *Collector's Guide To Comic Books,* Wallace–Homestead, 1990; Maurice Horn (ed.), *World Encyclopedia of Comics,* Chelsea House; D. W. Howard, *Investing In Comics,* The World of Yesterday, 1988; Alex Malloy, *Comic Values Annual 1993–94, The Comic Books Price Guide,* Wallace–Homestead, 1993; Robert M. Overstreet, *The Overstreet Comic Book Price Guide, 23rd Edition,* Avon Books, 1992; Robert M. Overstreet and Gary M. Carter, *The Overstreet Comic Book Grading Guide,* Avon Books, 1992; Jerry Robinson, *The Comics, An Illustrated History of Comic Strip Art,* G. P. Putnam's Sons, 1974; Jerry Weist, *Original Comic Art: Identification and Price Guide,* Avon Books, 1993.

**Periodicals:** *Comic Buyers Guide,* 700 State Street, Iola, WI 54990; *Comics Values Monthly,* Attic Books, 15 Danbury Road, Ridgefield, CT 06877; *Overstreet Comic Book Marketplace,* 801 20th St. NW, Suite 3, Cleveland, TN 37320.

**Museum:** Museum of Cartoon Art, Rye, NY.

**REPRODUCTION ALERT:** Publishers frequently reprint popular stories, even complete books, so the buyer must pay strict attention to the title, not just the portion printed in outsized letters on the front cover. If there's ever any doubt, look inside at the fine print on the bottom of the inside cover or first page. The correct title will be printed there in capital letters.

Buyers also should pay attention to the size of the comic they purchase. Many customers have been misled by unscrupulous dealers recently. The comics offered are exact replicas of expensive Golden Age D.C. titles, which would normally sell for thousands of dollars. The seller offers the large, 10 by 13½", copy of Superman #1 in mint condition for ten to a hundred dollars. The novice collector jumps at the chance since he knows this book sells for thousands on the open market. When the buyer gets his "find" home and checks the value, he discovers that he's paid way too much for the treasury sized "Famous First Edition" comic printed in the mid–seventies by D.C. These comics originally sold for one dollar each and are exact reprints except for the size. Several came with outer covers which announced the fact that they were reprints, but it didn't take long for dishonest dealers to remove these and sell the remaining portion for greatly inflated prices.

**Notes:** Just like advertising, comic books affect and reflect the culture which nurtures them. Large letters, bright colors, and "pulse–pounding" action seem to hype this product. Many would say comics are as American as mom's apple pie since good almost always triumphs over evil. Yet there's truly something for every taste in the vast array of comics available today. There are underground (adult situation) comics, foreign comics, educational comics, and comics intended to promote the sale of products or services.

The following listing concentrates on "mainstream" American comics published between 1938 and 1985. Prices may vary from region to region due to excessive demand in some areas. Prices given are for comic books in fine condition; that is, these comics are like new in most respects, but may show a little wear. Comics should be complete; no pages or chunks cut out.

AC Comics
- Americomics, #4, Dragonfly ...... **2.00**
- Spark Ark, #1 .................... **3.00**

Archie
- Adventures of the Fly, #6 ......... **45.00**
- Flyman, #35 ..................... **15.00**
- Zen Intergalactic Ninja, #2 ........ **1.25**

Classics Illustrated, first
- #8, Dr Jekyll and Mr Hyde ........ **3.75**
- #20, The Invisible Man ........... **4.00**
- #24, Rime of the Ancient Mariner .. **4.00**

Comico
- Grendel, #7 ...................... **2.50**
- Jonny Quest, #6 .................. **2.00**
- Star Blazers, #2 .................. **1.75**
- Troll Lords, #3 .................. **1.75**

Dark Horse
- Aliens, Earth War, #3 ............. **7.00**
- Give Me Liberty, #2 .............. **7.50**
- Indiana Jones, #3 ................ **3.00**
- Mask, #3 ........................ **3.00**
- Robocop, Prime Suspect .......... **2.50**
- Star Wars, Dark Empire, #4 ....... **6.00**

DC
- Action
  - #236, Lex Luthor .............. **110.00**
  - #354, Captain Incredible ....... **7.00**
  - #491, Hawkman ............... **2.50**
  - #531, Atom ................... **2.00**
- Advanced Dungeons & Dragons
  - #1, introduction of Onyx, Priam, Timoth, Cybriana, Vajr, and Luna **12.00**
  - #5, Spirit of Myrrth I ........... **7.00**
  - #17, Kyriani's Story I ........... **4.00**
  - #23, Siege Dragons I ........... **3.00**
  - #35, Waterdeep, Part 3 ......... **1.75**
- Adventure
  - #269, introducing Aqualad, ending of Green Arrow ........... **120.00**
  - #282, Legion, introducing Starboy **85.00**
  - #285, introducing Bizzaro World **65.00**
  - #398, Maid of Doom, Superman, Streaky, Krypto, and Comet .... **3.00**
  - #494, Challengers, reprint, cover by Keith Giffen .............. **1.50**
- Adventures of Superman
  - #430, Superman versus Fearsome Five ........................ **2.50**
  - #470, Soul Search #3, death of Jerry White .................. **1.50**
  - #495, Forever People, Darkseid . **1.50**
- All Star Squadron
  - #20, versus Brainwave ......... **1.00**
  - #37, versus The Real American .. **1.00**
  - #63, origin of Robotman ........ **1.00**
- Animal–Man
  - #15, Dolphin ................. **5.50**
  - #25, Grant Morrison ........... **3.00**
  - #43, Vixen .................... **2.25**
- Aquaman
  - #10, Quisp ................... **60.00**
  - #27, Battle of the Rival Aquamen **25.00**
  - #61, Batman .................. **6.50**
- Batman
  - #143, Bathound ............... **85.00**

#201, Joker .......... **16.00**
#319, Gentleman Ghost, ending of Catwoman .......... **5.00**
#418, Ten Nights .......... **11.00**

Blackhawk
#176, Stone Age Blackhawks .......... **8.50**
#204, Queen Killer Shark .......... **4.00**
#243, Mission Incredible .......... **3.50**

Camelot 3000
#1, origin of Arthur and Merlin .. **3.50**
#10, versus Morgan Le Fay .......... **3.00**

Caption Atom
#16, versus Red Tornado .......... **1.75**
#40, versus Kobra .......... **1.25**

DC Comics Presents
#15, Atom and Batman .......... **2.00**
#41, New Wonder Woman .......... **4.00**

DC Superstars
#1, Teen Titans .......... **2.50**
#8, Adam Strange .......... **4.00**

Detective
#237, Robin .......... **175.00**
#256, Outer Space .......... **140.00**
#324, Mad Hatter .......... **35.00**
#503, Batgirl, Robin versus Scarecrow .......... **5.00**
#597, versus Sladek .......... **3.00**
#622, Demon Within, Part 1 .......... **2.00**

Flash
#109, Mirror Master .......... **275.00**
#121, Trickster .......... **75.00**
#145, Weather Wizard .......... **40.00**
#176, giant size .......... **21.00**
#258, Black Hand .......... **2.75**

Green Lantern
#75, Qward .......... **13.00**
#93, War Against the World Builders .......... **3.50**
#115, versus Crumbler .......... **3.00**

Hawkman
#11 .......... **35.00**
#23 .......... **25.00**

House of Mystery
#121, Beam That Transformed Men .......... **15.00**
#156, Dial H for Hero .......... **35.00**
#195, Things Old, Things Forgotten .......... **12.00**
#266, Demon Blade .......... **3.00**
#321, last issue .......... **3.00**

House of Secrets
#17, Lady in the Moon .......... **42.00**
#32, Mark Merlin .......... **25.00**
#81, new mystery format .......... **8.00**
#106, This Will Kill You .......... **5.00**

Justice League of America
#138, Adam Strange .......... **2.50**
#201, Ultraa .......... **2.00**
#222, Beasts #2 .......... **1.75**

Legions of Super–Heroes
#263, Dagon the Avenger .......... **3.00**
#296, Cosmic Boys .......... **1.50**

**Fawcett Publications, *Dennis the Menace in Hawaii*, No. 174, 1978, $1.00.**

Metal Men
#1, Missile Men .......... **200.00**
#5 .......... **60.00**
#39 .......... **15.00**

New Teen Titans
#3, Fearsome Five .......... **7.00**
#21, Brother Blood .......... **3.00**
#33, Trident .......... **1.50**

Phantom Stranger, Silver Age series
#4 .......... **20.00**
#21 .......... **5.00**
#35 .......... **6.00**

Saga of the Swamp Thing
#14, Phantom Stranger .......... **2.00**
#40, The Curse .......... **5.50**

Shazam!
#3 .......... **2.00**
#11 .......... **1.50**

Showcase
#44, Tommy Tomorrow .......... **45.00**
#64, Spectre .......... **50.00**
#70, Binky .......... **14.00**
#93, Manhunter .......... **5.00**

Star Trek
#5, Mortal Gods .......... **5.00**
#43, Paradise Lost, Part 1 .......... **2.00**
#55, Finnegan's Wake .......... **2.00**

Superboy
#82, Bizarro Krypto .......... **32.00**
#106, Brainac .......... **11.00**
#127, Insect Queen .......... **5.00**

Superman
#124, Lois Lane .......... **120.00**
#139, Red Kryptonite .......... **85.00**
#165, Saturn Woman .......... **25.00**
#220, Flash .......... **9.00**
#345, Phantom Stranger .......... **1.75**

Vigilante
#2 .......... **4.00**
#7 .......... **4.00**
#26 .......... **2.00**

Warlord
#13, Stryker .................... **5.00**
#39, Feast of Agravar ........... **4.00**
#95, Dragon's Doom ........... **1.75**
Wonder Woman
#104, Duke of Deception ....... **35.00**
#130, Angle Man .............. **10.00**
#144 ......................... **8.00**
#230, Cheetah ................ **1.50**
World's Finest Comics
#132, Denny Kale & Shorty Biggs **22.00**
#160, Fatal Forecasts of Dr Zodiac **7.50**
#222, Evil in Paradise .......... **3.00**
#275, Mr Freeze ............... **2.25**

Gold Key, Little Lulu, Tubby the Spider Spins Again ..................... **8.00**

Harvey
Beetle Bailey, #2 ................ **1.25**
Beetlejuice, Holiday Special ....... **1.25**
Casper & Friends, #4 ............. **1.00**
Felix the Cat, #5 ................ **1.50**
Tom and Jerry, Holiday Special .... **1.25**

Marvel
Akira
#5, Cycle Wars ................ **9.00**
#34 .......................... **4.50**
Alpha Flight
#15, Master ................... **2.50**
#38, Pestilence ................ **2.50**
Amazing Spiderman
#16, Daredevil versus Ringmaster **225.00**
#45, Lizard ................... **65.00**
#74, Silvermane .............. **30.00**
#131, Hammerhead ............ **15.00**
#188, Jigsaw .................. **8.00**
#243, Peter Quits School ....... **6.00**
#340, Femme Fatales ........... **3.50**
Avengers
#9, Wonder Man ............. **215.00**
#88, Professor X .............. **9.00**
#226, Black Knight ............ **2.25**
#285, Zeus .................. **2.00**
Captain America
#182, Madam Hydra ........... **7.00**
#253, Baron Blood ............. **5.50**
#332, Rogers Resigns ........... **12.00**
#380, Serpent Society .......... **2.00**
Conan The Barbarian
#2, Lair of the Beast Men ....... **70.00**
#22, reprint of Conan #1 ....... **24.00**
#31, Shadow in the Tomb ...... **4.00**
#158, Night of the Wolf ........ **1.50**
#248, Zulo .................. **1.50**
Daredevil
#28, Aliens ................... **27.00**
#142, Cobra .................. **4.00**
#218, Jester .................. **2.00**
#294, The Hand .............. **1.75**
Dazzler
#9, Klaw ..................... **1.25**
#30, Moves to California ....... **1.25**
Defenders
#10, Thor versus Hulk .......... **25.00**
#32, Rhino ................... **5.00**
#79, Tunnel World ............. **2.50**
#145, Moondragon ............ **1.50**
Fantastic Four
#10, Doctor Doom ............ **475.00**
#89, Mole Man ................ **24.00**
#105, Crystal .................. **12.00**
#111, Hulk ................... **12.00**
#216, Blastaar ................. **4.00**
#329, Mole Man .............. **1.50**
GI Joe
#3, Trojan Robot .............. **3.00**
#34, Shakedown ............... **2.00**
Howard The Duck
#1, Spiderman ................ **7.00**
#20, Sudd .................... **1.00**
Hulk
#115, Leader .................. **25.00**
#216, Gen Ross ............... **3.50**
#281, Trapped in Space ........ **2.00**
#378, Christmas ............... **3.50**
Iron Man
#9, Mandarin ................. **42.00**
#21, Eddie .................... **20.00**
#58, Mandarin ................ **10.00**
#226, Armor Wars ............ **4.50**
Marvel Comics Presents
#5, Wolverine, Master of Kung Fu **4.00**
#24, Black Panther ............. **3.00**
#70, Black Widow, Darkstar .... **4.00**
Marvel Tales
#137, Amazing Fantasy #15 .... **7.00**
#257, Amazing Spiderman, #238 **1.25**
Master of Kung Fu
#22, Death .................. **5.00**
#53 ......................... **2.00**
Punisher
#16, Kingpin .................. **7.50**
#63, Thieves ................. **1.50**
Quasar
#16 ......................... **2.25**
#42 ......................... **1.25**
Spider–Man
#15, Beast .................... **3.00**
#27, Handgun ................. **2.00**
Spiderwoman
#22, Killer Clown ............. **1.50**
#47, Daddy Longlegs ........... **1.50**
Star Wars
#12, Doomworld ............. **2.00**
#48, Leia versus Darth Vader .... **2.00**
Strange Tales
#130, Beatles ................ **35.00**
#143, Hydra .................. **20.00**
#188, Dr Strange .............. **3.00**
Thor
#166, Warlock ................ **37.00**
#229, Hercules ................ **3.50**
#437, Quasar ................. **1.50**

Transformers
- #9, Circuit Breaker .......... **1.50**
- #27, Head Hunter .......... **1.25**

Wolverine
- #27, Lazarus Project .......... **4.00**
- #55, Sunfire .......... **2.50**

X–Men
- #3, Blob .......... **450.00**
- #121, Alpha Flight .......... **38.00**
- #211, Marauders .......... **20.00**
- #292, Morlocks .......... **1.50**

Now
- Racer–X, #1 .......... **2.50**
- Speed Racer, #34 .......... **1.75**
- Supercops, #2 .......... **1.75**

Walt Disney
- Chip 'N' Dale, #7 .......... **2.50**
- Disney Adventures, #17 .......... **2.00**

# COMPACTS

**Collecting Hints:** Only mirrors that are broken should be removed and replaced in a vintage compact. Do not replace a mirror that is discolored, flawed, or in need of resilvering. The original mirror enhances the value of the compact.

Never apply a sticker directly to the surface of a compact. The acids from the glue may discolor or irreparably damage the finish, especially an enamel finish.

If a compact comes in the original box or pouch, do not destroy or discard it. The value of the compact is increased if it has its original presentation box.

**History:** In the first quarter of the 20th century attitudes regarding cosmetics changed drastically. The use of make–up during the day was no longer looked upon with disdain. As women became "liberated" and as more and more of them entered the business world the use of cosmetics became a routine and necessary part of a woman's grooming. Portable containers for cosmetics became a necessity.

Compacts were made in a myriad of shapes, styles, combinations and motifs, all reflecting the mood of the times. Every conceivable natural or man–made medium was used in the manufacture of compacts. Commemorative, premium, souvenir, patriotic, figural, combination compacts, Art Deco, and enamel compacts are a few examples of the compacts that were made in the United States and abroad. Compacts combined with cigarette cases, music boxes, watches, hatpins, canes, lighters, etc. also were very popular.

Compacts were made and used until the late 1950s when women opted for the "au natural" look. Compacts manufactured prior to that time are considered vintage compacts.

Some vintage compacts were exquisitely crafted, often enameled or encrusted with precious or synthetic jewels. These compacts were considered a form of jewelry or fashion accessory. The intricate and exacting workmanship of some vintage compacts would be virtually impossible to duplicate today.

**References:** Roseann Ettinger, *Compacts and Smoking Accessories,* Schiffer Publishing Ltd., 1991; Roselyn Gerson, *Ladies' Compacts of the 19th and 20th Centuries,* Wallace–Homestead, 1989.

**Collectors' Club:** Compact Collectors Club, P. O. Box Letter S, Lynbrook, NY 11563.

**Periodical:** *The Powder Puff Newsletter,* P. O. Box Letter S, Lynbrook, NY 11563.

**Advisor:** Roselyn Gerson.

Amita, Damascene, black matte finish, inlaid with gold and silver view of Mt Fuji, capped in silver, Japan .......... **125.00**

Arden, Elizabeth, light blue enamel, harlequin mask dec .......... **80.00**

Avon, oval, lid dec with blue and green checkerboard pattern .......... **25.00**

Bojouis, Evening in Paris, chrome, navy enamel, pie shaped wedges .......... **30.00**

Djer–Kiss, silver overlay, Art Nouveau fairy motif, orig satin lined box .......... **85.00**

E A M, Art Deco, blue enameled tango–chain compact, red and yellow abstract design, powder sifter and attached lipstick, finger ring carrying chain .......... **175.00**

Elgin, American
- Brushed Silver Metal, floral engraving, faux amethyst catch .......... **75.00**
- Enamel, white, engraved goldtone floral dec, 1946 .......... **50.00**
- Goldtone
  - Rectangular, engraved floral design **40.00**
  - Shell shaped .......... **55.00**

Evans, goldtone and mother–of–pearl, compact and lipstick combination .. **35.00**

Henriette, enameled, square, British crown matte, paper label, British War Relief .......... **80.00**

Hudnut, Richard, Deauville
- Blue Cloisonne, tango–chain vanity, metal mirror, compartments for powder and rouge, lipstick attached to finger ring chain .......... **175.00**
- Chrome, round, deco .......... **40.00**
- Enamel, blue, Art Deco style, goldtone accents .......... **35.00**

Kamra–Pak Style, multicolored tooled leather cov with Persian design .... **65.00**

K & K, brass colored engine tooled dec basket compact, multicolored silk flowers enclosed in plastic domed lid, emb swinging handle .......... **90.00**

Margaret Rose, goldtone, round .......... **25.00**

Melissa, goldtone, round, shadow rose design .......... **45.00**
Rex of 5th Avenue
  Goldtone, round, geometric design . **40.00**
  Leather, round, hand tooled grapevine, 4½" d .......... **75.00**
  Mother–Of–Pearl, square .......... **60.00**
Rowenta, brown enamel, oval, petit point .......... **40.00**
  New York World's Fair, 1939, plastic Du Pont Chemistry Building on cov, brass trim, 2⅞" d .......... **40.00**
Souvenir
  Remember Pearl Harbor, brass, porcelain lid insert with harbor scene, 3" d .......... **100.00**
  Sesquicentennial International Exposition, Philadelphia, PA, 1926, silvered metal, rotating mirror, powder puff, George Washington profile portrait on cov, 2" d .......... **25.00**

**Souvenir, 1937 Great Lakes Exposition, Cleveland Centennial, metal, black and silver, raised sailboats, powder and rouge compartments, 2½" d, $80.00.**

Stratton
  Enameled, square, hp, sgd "Cecel Golding," some crazing .......... **40.00**
  Goldtone, round, stars .......... **40.00**
Unknown Maker
  Ebony Enamel
    Art Deco style goldtone design ... **30.00**
    Eight Ball style .......... **90.00**
  Enamel and goldtone, roll top style, Germany .......... **115.00**
  German Silver, fluted, vanity, chatelaine, orig compact, coin holder, memo book, locket, pin container, and stamp holder, complete .......... **450.00**
  Goldtone, heart shaped, brocade lid **40.00**
  Lucite, blue, sterling repousse medallion of two doves .......... **100.00**
  Plastic, red, white, and blue, Naval Officer's cap shape .......... **65.00**
  Silvered Metal, lilac enamel, geometric design, chain .......... **45.00**
  Silver Plated, antique, triangular, hand mirror shape, lipstick concealed in handle, int. and ext. mirrors, turquoise cabochon thumbpiece .......... **135.00**
  Sterling Silver
    Combination compact/coin holder/cigarette case .......... **110.00**
    Enamel painted lid scene, gilded int., Italy .......... **300.00**
Volupte
  Gold Metal, square, engraved rays, sq clusters of rhinestones .......... **38.00**
  Goldtone
    Hand shaped .......... **85.00**
    Square, geometric design .......... **35.00**
  Watchcase compact, picture locket on flower dec lid .......... **60.00**
Weltzunder, blue marbleized enamel, Kamra–Pak style, vanity case and matching cigarette lighter, silvered metal cut out map of US Zone on lid, front opens to reveal powder compartment, reverse side reveals cigarette compartment, slide out lipstick, orig presentation box, Germany .... **165.00**
Whiting & Davis Co, Piccadilly, gilded mesh, vanity bag, compact incorporated in front lid, carrying chain .... **200.00**
Woodworth, Karess, polished goldtone, corset shape, vanity case, powder and rouge compartments .......... **25.00**
Yardley, goldtone, vanity case
  Red, white, and blue emb design on lid, powder and rouge compartments .......... **50.00**
  White enamel feather dec on lid, powder and rouge compartments, tandem lipstick .......... **50.00**

# COOKBOOKS

**Collecting Hints:** Look for books in good, clean condition. Watch for special interesting notes in margins.

**History:** Among the earliest Americana cookbooks are *The Frugal Housewife* or *Complete Woman Cook* by Susanna Carter, published in Philadelphia in 1796, and *American Cookery* by Amelia Simmons, published in Hartford, Connecticut, in 1796. Cookbooks of this era are crudely written, for most cooks could not read well and measuring devices were not yet refined.

Other types of collectible cookbooks include those used as premiums or advertisements. This type is much less expensive than the rare 18th century books.

**References:** Bob Allen, *A Guide To Collecting Cookbooks and Advertising Cookbooks*, Collector Books, 1990; Mary Barile, *Cookbooks Worth Collecting,* Wallace–Homestead, 1993; Mary–Margaret Barile, *Just Cookbooks!,* published by author, 1990; Linda J. Dickinson, *A Price Guide to Cookbooks, and Recipe Leaflets,* Collector Books, 1990, 1993 value update; Norman E. Martinus and Harry L. Rinker, *Warman's Paper,* Wallace–Homestead, 1993; Dana Gehman Morykan and Harry L. Rinker, *Warman's Country Antiques & Collectibles,* Wallace–Homestead, 1992.

**Collectors' Club:** Cook Book Collectors Club of America, 231 E. James Blvd., P. O. Box 85, St. James, MO 65559.

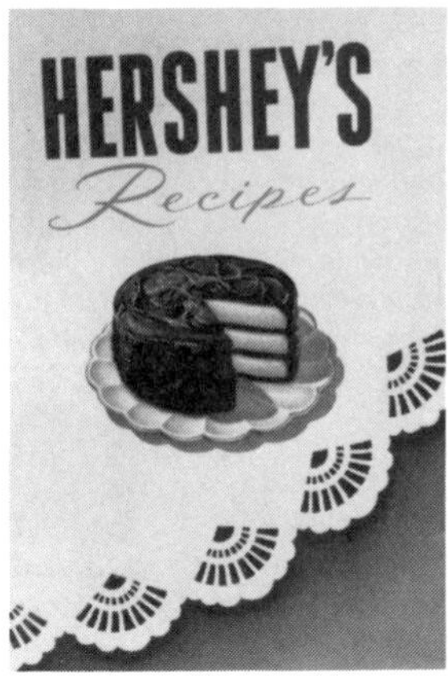


**Hershey's Recipes, 1949, Hershey Chocolate Corp., Hershey, PA, 32 pgs., 4⅝ x 6½", $5.00.**

A Calendar of Desserts, 48 pgs, 1940 . **5.00**
All About Home Baking, General Foods, 144 pgs, 1933 . . . . **6.00**
Arm & Hammer Baking Soda, *Good Things to Eat–Tested Recipes,* 32 pgs, 1936 . . . . **10.00**
Aunt Ellen, Griswold, 1928 . . . . **15.00**
Betty Crocker
Dinner In A Dish, 152 pgs, 1965 . . . **7.00**
Let's Eat Outdoors, 27 pgs, 1969 . . . **3.00**
Bewley's Best Bakes Better, 8 x 6" . . . . **10.00**
Calumet Baking Powder Baking Book, 1931 . . . . **4.00**
Ceresota Flour, 32 pgs, 9 x 5", 1930s . **18.00**
Certo Recipes For Making Jams & Jellies, 31 pgs, 1937 . . . . **4.00**
Chiquita Banana Presents 18 Recipes, 18 pgs, 1951 . . . . **6.00**
Cottolene Shortening Recipes, 1905 . . **15.00**
Cox's Delicious Recipes, 30 pgs, 1933 **4.00**
Crisco Better Baking, 16 pgs, 9 x 11", 1967 . . . . **5.00**
Dr King's New Discovery Electric Bitters Prize Cookbook, 1900 . . . . **15.00**
Eline's Old Style Cocoa, c1910 . . . . **5.00**
Gold Medal Flour Cook Book, 1917, 74 pgs . . . . **10.00**
Grand National, 1928 . . . . **10.00**
Heinz Book of Salads, 95 pgs, 1925 . . **10.00**
*Jell–O The Dainty Dessert,* 4½ x 4½", c1915 . . . . **25.00**
Karo Syrup, 1910, 47 pgs, Leyendecker cov . . . . **25.00**
Kellogg's, 1978 . . . . **6.00**
Knox Dainty Desserts For Dainty People, 41 pgs, 1915 . . . . **12.00**
Magic Baking Powder, 32 pages . . . . **15.75**
Mary Dunbar's New Cook Book, 1933, Jewel Tea Co . . . . **15.00**
Maxwell House Coffee, 22 pgs, 1927 . **7.00**
Occident's Baking Made Easy, 1931 . . **5.00**
Out of Alaska's Kitchens . . . . **15.00**
Pillsbury Silver Anniversary Bake–Off, 92 pgs, 1974 . . . . **7.00**
Pure Food Cookbook, Mary J Lincoln, 77 pages . . . . **45.00**
Pyrex Prize Recipes, 128 pgs, 1953 . . . **5.00**
Rival Crock–Pot Cooking, 208 pgs, 1975 . . . . **7.00**
Royal Cookbook, 65 pages . . . . **27.50**
Spry Shortening Cookbook, Aunt Jenny's Favorite Recipes, color illus, 50 pgs, 1930s . . . . **12.00**
Standard Brands Cookbook, 65 pages . **27.50**
Sunkist Recipes For Everyday, 35 pgs, 1933 . . . . **3.00**
The Gold Medal Sandwich Book Dedicated to the Earl of Sandwich . . . . **4.00**
Walter Baker Choice Recipes, 1923, 64 pgs . . . . **10.00**

# COOKIE CUTTERS

**Collecting Hints:** Cookie cutters exist in abundance throughout the United States. The early cutters were handmade, and the tradition and skill survives to the present time. By the late 19th century, cutters also were manufactured and sold for a few pennies through mail order houses and in general stores.

A collector should develop a collection theme—shape, broad general approach, or cutters for use. In buying old or used cutters, carefully examine the cutters which now are available new. Many cutters identical with "old" cutters still are made. Learn which old cutters were handcrafted and which were machine made. When uncertain about whether a cutter is old and valued for its age, ask "What would I pay for it new?" This method helps to eliminate wild purchases and disappointments when a cutter is misjudged.

There are many tinsmiths working today who will duplicate any cutter, often using old techniques to make it. Cutters can be aged. Sellers often misrepresent the age of cutters out of ignorance, rather than an obvious attempt to deceive.

**History:** Late in the 19th century, factories began producing cookie cutters resembling the handcrafted cutters of an earlier period. It was soon obvious that making uniform backs of relatively thin material speeded up the process and cut costs. Many unusual cutters were patented during this period; advertising cutters also were made.

The 1869 Dover Stamping Company catalog is the first documented record of a manufactured cookie cutter. The cutter pictured in the catalog is well developed, far beyond a "beginning" status. Manufactured cutters probably were made before the 1869 date.

Two innovations in the 1925–1950 period were the use of aluminum and plastic. Since 1965, two events occurred which influenced the cookie cutter collecting field. The first is an influx of younger people into the collecting field through the interest in crafts. The second is the Hallmark cutters in their varied plastic tones, which renewed interest in cutter use.

**Reference:** Phyllis S. Wetherill, *Art in the Kitchen: Cookie Cutters and Cookie Molds*, Schiffer Publishing, Ltd, 1985.

**Periodical:** *Cookies*, 5426 27th St. NW, Washington, DC 20015.

**Collectors' Club:** Cookie Cutter Collector Club, 1167 Teal Road, S. W., Dellroy, OH 44620.

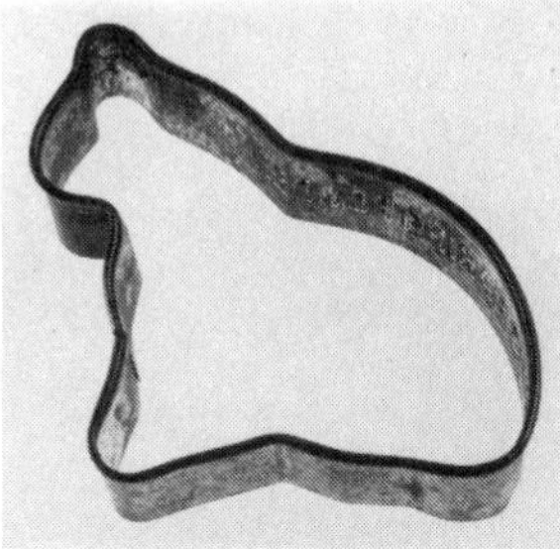

**Cat, Davis Baking Powder, tin, c1920, 3½" h, $8.00.**

## ADVERTISING AND PREMIUM CUTTERS

Betty Crocker, premium, gingerbread boy, plastic, blue, flatback, handle . **1.50**
Egg Baking Powder Co, adv, 1½" d, metal, egg handle, 1902 .......... **40.00**
Fanchon Flour, adv, round, fold down handle .......................... **10.00**
Garland Stoves and Ranges, fire shape, flames across top ................. **22.00**
Hills Brothers Co, Dromedary Coconut premium, metal, camel outline, rounded handle, 1916 ............ **25.00**
Quaker Oats, premium, standing bear, flatback, handle, plastic, yellow .... **3.00**
Swans Down Cake Flour, premium, aluminum, card party shapes, riveted handles ......................... **25.00**
Wrigley, premium, Troll, aluminum, self handle, Mirro .................... **15.00**

## HANDCRAFTED CUTTERS

Antique
- Bear, 2½ x 3", irregular back, handle missing, narrow cutting edge, one corner slightly bent ............. **10.00**
- Cow, four legged, flatback, handle . **15.00**
- Dog, four legged, flatback, handle .. **15.00**
- Man, 3 x 5½", high hat, frock coat, handle removed ................ **85.00**
- Pitcher, 4 x 6", irregular back, handle **70.00**
- Rabbit, 4 x 6", irregular back, short ears, missing handle ............ **100.00**
- Reindeer, 5 x 6", irregular back, strutting position, four legs and grouped antlers, handle ................. **115.00**
- Woman, 3 x 9", flat back, front view, large head, small body, fuzzy hair **120.00**

Modern

Tinsmiths stopped making handcrafted cutters eventually because of change of circumstances, retirement, or death. The following cutters are no longer available new.

Dautrich, 6 x 7", heart, inner tulip design, sgd "Dautrich, 1976" ........ **25.00**
- Hastings, 2½ x 5", rabbit, flatback, sgd "H" ..................... **10.00**
- John Holochwest, coal oil lamp, 1" w handle identifies cutter .......... **7.00**
- Wib Lauter, 5 x 7", US map, flatback, handle, humorous saying, sgd ... **12.00**
- W Roberts, anvil, flatback, handle, sgd "W Roberts" ............... **8.00**

## METAL

Identified
- A & J
  - Children's Set, gingerbread boy and rabbit, backs, wood handles, sgd "A & J" in diamond
    - Gingerbread Boy ............. **15.00**
    - Rabbit ...................... **15.00**
  - Outline cutters, A & J handles or handles with faces
    - Gingerbread Boy ............. **15.00**
    - Rabbit ...................... **15.00**

Dixon Specialities, Inc., Wonder Bridge Cutters, cardboard box showing woman making cookies, blue and orange colors, four large cutters, card party shapes, c1940 . **25.00**

Fox Run, 6½ x 10½", colonial man and woman, backs painted in mottled brown–gray design, inner designs, c1965, price for pair ...... **50.00**

J. W. Shull, round, slightly domed top, sgd ...................... **10.00**

Lenore Deskow, round, SS cube, cuts heart, triangle, 3 part design, sgd "1972 Sterling Lenore Deskow, Inc." ........................ **35.00**

Unidentified

Children's Set, outline with brace, woman's face drawn on yellow wood handles

Chicken ...................... **10.00**

Gingerbread Boy .............. **10.00**

German or Italian, 16 round outline cutters, plain, graduated sizes, rust, bending, or other wear, (Similar cutters available new, design interest and present availability do not override condition) ............ **10.00**

## PLASTIC

Some plastic cookie cutters have a value based partly on the fact that reproduction is difficult. (The many examples of plastic cutters reproduced without permission ordinarily occur within a few years after the original cutters are made.)

Education Products, marbleized, multicolored, sgd "Kleeware, England"

Burro ......................... **3.50**

Camel ......................... **3.50**

Elephant ...................... **3.50**

Horse ......................... **3.50**

Set, 4 pcs .................... **20.00**

Hallmark, large, orange, Snoopy and the Great Pumpkin ............... **25.00**

Life Like, cherry red, handles, cutters now made with Educational Products signature ...................... **1.00**

McB's, red, back, handle, cutters are not sgd but can be identified because they have no corners

Angle, profile view .............. **3.50**

Cowboy, hands at waist, knees bent **3.50**

Miller Cookie Cutter Co, gingerbread boy, back and handle, orig card

Green ......................... **10.00**

Red ........................... **6.00**

Nord Cutters, circular handles

Angel ......................... **2.50**

Cat ........................... **3.00**

Cherry Tree .................... **2.50**

Clock ......................... **2.50**

Man in the Moon ............... **3.00**

Northwestern Products Co, Little Deb cutters, pastel colors, yellow and aqua, 1" cutters with two parallel handles, currently available in red plastic from Arthur Douglas Company, England

Elephant ...................... **.75**

Horse ......................... **.50**

Santa ......................... **1.00**

Set of 6 ...................... **6.00**

Ohio Art Co Pastry and Canister Set, originally 23 items, c1953

Cowboy ........................ **2.00**

Indian ........................ **2.00**

Set, 23 items ................. **25.00**

Southwest Indian Foundation, outline, hanger, orig card

Star, red ..................... **5.00**

Tree, green ................... **5.00**

## SPECIAL TYPES

Cookie Mold, Lamb of God, clay, sgd "EE, Switzerland" ............... **10.00**

Cookie Pan

Ladyfinger, made in England ....... **4.00**

Twelve animals, cast iron ......... **12.00**

Cookie Press, Ateco, bag, design mechanism ......................... **25.00**

Doughnut Cutter, rolling, wood and brass, sgd "D. D. Hetherinton, Birmingham, Patent No 16798" ...... **12.00**

Rolling Cutter, 10" l, five attached cutters, handle, metal and plastic, made in Italy or Hong Kong, sold by many companies for decades and still available new ....................... **4.00**

Springerle

Board, 4 x 5", six sections, orig sticker "Nayco," c1940 ............... **6.00**

Rolling Pin, twelve machine carved squares ...................... **10.00**

## STORYBOOK CUTTERS

More and more different sets of cutters illustrating famous children's stories are being located. They are of great interest to collectors; many are scarce.

Blondie and Dagwood Set, six cutters, plastic, yellow, Dagwood, Blondie, Daisy, two children, and puppies, orig box ........................ **40.00**

Goldilocks and the Three Bears, four outline cutters, plastic, red, orig box **40.00**

Little Red Riding Hood Set, metal outline cutters, braces, Little Red Riding Hood, house, wolf, and grandmother, may be stamped "Made in Germany for S. J. Company" or S. Joseph Company," orig box ...... **45.00**

Tom and Jerry, six plastic cutters, backs and handles, set of 6, sgd "oews"
- Ivory ..... **20.00**
- Red ..... **10.00**

# COOKIE JARS

**Collecting Hints:** Cookie jars are subject to chips and paint flaking. Collectors should concentrate on jars which have their original lid and are in very good or better condition.

Learn to identify makers' marks and codes. Do not fail to include some of the contemporary manufacturers in your collection.

Above all, ignore the prices and hype associated with the cookie jars sold at the Andy Warhol sale in 1988. Neither is realistic.

**History:** Cookie jars, colorful and often whimsical, are one of the fastest growing categories in the collectibles field. Many cookie jars have been made by more than one company and as a result can be found with different marks. This resulted from mergers or splits by manufacturers, e.g., Brush–McCoy, which is now Nelson McCoy. Molds also were traded and sold among companies.

Cookie jars often were redesigned to reflect newer tastes. Hence, the same jar may be found in several different style variations.

**References:** John W. Humphries, *Humphries Price Guide To Cookie Jars,* published by author, 1992; Harold Nichols, *McCoy Cookie Jars: From The First To The Latest, Second Edition,* Nichols Publishing, 1991; Fred and Joyce Roerig, *Collector's Encyclopedia of Cookie Jars,* Collector Books, (1990, 1993 value update); Mike Schneider, *The Complete Cookie Jar Book,* Schiffer Publishing Ltd., 1991; Ermagene Westfall, *An Illustrated Value Guide To Cookie Jars,* Collector Books, (1983, 1993 value update), Book II (1993), Collector Books.

ABC
- Donkey, milk wagon ..... **75.00**
- Popeye ..... **950.00**
- Rubbles House ..... **1,200.00**
- Train ..... **40.00**

Abingdon Pottery
- Hobby Horse ..... **250.00**
- Humpty Dumpty ..... **185.00**
- Jack In Box ..... **295.00**
- Little Miss Muffet ..... **225.00**
- Three Bears ..... **65.00**

American Bisque
- After School ..... **65.00**
- Chef ..... **95.00**
- Chick ..... **57.00**
- Coffeepot, pinecones dec ..... **42.00**
- Cookie Truck ..... **65.00**
- Dog, with toothache ..... **425.00**
- Donkey, milk cart wagon ..... **125.00**
- Grandma ..... **70.00**
- Jack In Box ..... **65.00**
- Majorette ..... **255.00**
- Mrs Rabbit ..... **250.00**
- Pig, straw hat ..... **90.00**
- Rabbit in Hat ..... **75.00**
- Saddle ..... **225.00**
- Sandman, flasher ..... **335.00**
- Seal, igloo ..... **225.00**
- Train ..... **40.00**
- Umbrella Kids ..... **295.00**
- Yarn Doll ..... **60.00**
- Yogi Bear ..... **325.00**

**Brush-McCoy, Cow, cat finial, brown, green bell, marked "Brush, USA" in pallette, "W10," 12½" w, 8" h, $75.00.**

Brush
- Bunny, white ..... **150.00**
- Clown Bust ..... **275.00**
- Cow, brown, cat finial ..... **75.00**
- Davy Crockett, gold trim ..... **875.00**
- Elephant, ice cream cone ..... **325.00**
- Granny ..... **225.00**
- Hippo ..... **395.00**
- House, green ..... **75.00**
- Humpty Dumpty, cowboy hat ..... **175.00**
- Squirrel, sitting on green log ..... **90.00**
- Treasure Chest ..... **125.00**

California Originals
- Advertising, Avon, bear ..... **60.00**
- Bert & Ernie ..... **350.00**
- Big Bird Chef ..... **100.00**
- Bulldog on Safe ..... **110.00**
- Disney Bulldog Cafe ..... **55.00**
- Dog ..... **35.00**

Elf Schoolhouse .......... **45.00**
Frog, green .......... **65.00**
Koala, holding stump .......... **275.00**
Mickey Mouse Chef .......... **100.00**
Squirrel on Stump .......... **50.00**
Tortoise and Hair .......... **40.00**
Turtle
Sitting .......... **40.00**
Upside Down, brown .......... **47.00**
Doranne of CA
Advertising, Oreo .......... **45.00**
Frog, green, blue bow tie .......... **60.00**
Ice Cream Cone .......... **35.00**
Mother Goose, green .......... **140.00**
F & F, advertising, Keebler, Ernie Elf .. **95.00**
Holiday Designs, advertising, Nestle Toll House Cookie .......... **125.00**
Hull Pottery
Apple, yellow and pink, green leaf . **45.00**
Daisy .......... **32.00**
Gingerbread Boy, brown .......... **95.00**
Red Riding Hood, closed basket .... **300.00**
Maurice of California, monkey, puzzled expression .......... **95.00**
McCoy
Advertising
Keebler, Tree House .......... **75.00**
Nabisco .......... **125.00**
Apple, red .......... **37.00**
Barnum's Animals, clear glaze ..... **55.00**
Bean Pot, red .......... **47.00**
Beehive .......... **70.00**
Betsy Baker .......... **150.00**
Caboose .......... **135.00**
Chef, head .......... **80.00**
Chipmunk .......... **85.00**
Circus Horse .......... **170.00**
Coffee Cup .......... **40.00**
Coffee Grinder .......... **30.00**
Coffeepot, turquoise .......... **45.00**
Cookie Barrel, 8¾″ h .......... **27.00**
Cook Stove, white .......... **40.00**
Covered Wagon .......... **75.00**
Dalmatians .......... **295.00**
Engine
Black .......... **140.00**
Yellow .......... **175.00**
Fireplace .......... **90.00**
Fortune, black and red .......... **42.00**
Frontier Family .......... **70.00**
Grandfather Clock .......... **75.00**
Grandma .......... **85.00**
Honey Bear .......... **90.00**
Indian .......... **350.00**
Jug, brown and white .......... **30.00**
Kangaroo, tan .......... **350.00**
Koala Bear .......... **125.00**
Kookie Kettle
Black .......... **30.00**
Bronze .......... **25.00**
Lamb, basketweave .......... **55.00**
Lantern, black .......... **60.00**
Lollipop .......... **35.00**
MacDog .......... **70.00**
Mammy, yellow, cold paint .......... **650.00**
Milk Can, Early American, silver ... **70.00**
Monkey on Stump .......... **70.00**
Mr & Mrs Owl .......... **95.00**
Nibble Kettle, black .......... **45.00**
Oaken Bucket .......... **25.00**
Patriotic Owl, brown .......... **45.00**
Pear .......... **60.00**
Picnic Basket .......... **50.00**
Pineapple .......... **90.00**
Potbelly Stove, black .......... **57.00**
Raggedy Ann .......... **90.00**
Rooster
Black and white .......... **85.00**
Gray .......... **115.00**
Yellow .......... **70.00**
Snoopy .......... **160.00**
Spaceship .......... **145.00**
Strawberry, red .......... **42.00**
Thinking Puppy .......... **30.00**
Timmy Turtle .......... **40.00**
Touring Car, black .......... **110.00**
W C Fields .......... **125.00**
Wishing Well .......... **40.00**
Woodsy Owl .......... **255.00**
Wren House .......... **95.00**
Yosemite Sam .......... **150.00**
Metlox
Cabbage with rabbit .......... **65.00**
Pinocchio .......... **125.00**
Scottie, black .......... **185.00**
Sir Francis Drake .......... **40.00**
Teddy Bear, blue .......... **75.00**
Morton, turkey .......... **80.00**
Mosaic Tile, Mammy, blue .......... **550.00**
NAPCO, Bo Peep, 1950s .......... **225.00**
Pottery Guild, Red Riding Hood ...... **125.00**
Ransbottom, Old King Cole .......... **145.00**
Red Wing
Chef, speckled pink and black ..... **165.00**
Monk, yellow .......... **70.00**
Regal
Advertising, Quaker Oats .......... **170.00**
Diaper Pin Pig .......... **375.00**
Goldilocks .......... **270.00**
Hobby Horse .......... **275.00**
Hubert The Lion .......... **975.00**
Humpty Dumpty .......... **195.00**
Puss N' Boots, gold trim, flowers ... **385.00**
Robisson–Ransbottom
Chef, bowl of eggs .......... **175.00**
Frosty the Snowman .......... **695.00**
Jocko Ape .......... **325.00**
Sheriff Pig, yellow hat .......... **125.00**
Wise Owl, gold trim .......... **110.00**
Twin Winton
Bear .......... **35.00**
Elf, log .......... **35.00**
Monk, c1960 .......... **75.00**
Vandor, Betty Boop, standing .......... **700.00**

# COORS POTTERY

**Collecting Hints:** Cookie jars and the bright, solid–colored dinnerware lines, in the tradition of Bauer and Homer Laughlin's Fiesta, are the principal focuses of Coors Pottery collectors. Kitchen collectors focus on the company's utilitarian products.

Coors products were meant to be used, and they were. When collecting, concentrate on pieces whose decorative elements are still bright and complete. Add ten percent if a piece still has a period paper sales label attached.

**History:** J. J. Herold, a former designer and manager for companies such as J. B. Owens, Roseville Pottery, and Weller Pottery, moved to Golden, Colorado, late in the first decade of the twentieth century. His experiments in producing pottery from local clay attracted the attention of Adolph Coors, a local brewery owner. In 1910 Coors offered Herold the use of his abandoned Colorado Glass Works plant. Shortly thereafter Herold founded the Herold China and Pottery Company for the purpose of making ovenproof china cooking utensils.

Herold left in January 1912 to work for Western Pottery Company in Denver. Coors and other stockholders kept the plant open and expanded its product line to include spark plugs and scientific wares. Herold Pottery also was known as the Golden Pottery. By 1914 a line of chemical porcelain products was available. Herold returned for a one-year stint as manager in 1915. The company received an injunction against Herold's new employer, Guernsey Earthenware Company (Cambridge Art Pottery), to prevent it from using the formula knowledge Herold gained while in Golden.

In 1920 the company's name legally became Coors Porcelain Company. The company continued to concentrate on chemical, industrial, and scientific porcelain products. The household cooking line was trademarked "Thermo–Porcelain." A Thermo–Porcelain White Hotel Ware line was developed, one result of which was Coors involvement in the manufacture of dinnerware and other kitchen accessories.

In the 1930s Coors introduced six colored, decorated dinnerware lines: Coorado, Golden Ivory, Golden Rainbow, Mello–Tone, Rock–Mount, and Rosebud Cook–N–Serve. Dinnerware had a high gloss, colored glaze while vases tended to be matte glazed. When Prohibition ended in 1933, Coors also began making accessories for the tavern trade.

Dinnerware production ended when the company switched to wartime production in 1941. When the war was over, the company did manufacture some ovenware, teapots, coffee makers, beer mugs, ashtrays, and novelty items, but no dinnerware. Coffee makers, ovenware, teapots, and vases were discontinued in the 1950s, mugs in the early 1960s, and ashtrays by the late 1970s.

Herman Coors, third son of Adolph Coors, founded the H. F. Coors Company at Englewood, California, in 1925. It was an entirely separate company from Coors Porcelain Company. H. F. Coors Company made hotel and institutional commercial pottery, doll heads, plumbing fixtures, and wall tiles.

**References:** Lois Lehner, *Lehner's Encyclopedia of U. S. Marks on Pottery, Porcelain & Clay,* Collector Books, 1988; Robert H. Schneider, *Coors Rosebud Pottery*, published by author, 1984.

**Periodical:** *Coors Pottery Newsletter,* 3808 Carr Pl. N., Seattle, WA 98103.

**MELLO-TONE.** Produced in the late 1930s and early 1940s. Pastel colors of Azure Blue, Canary Yellow, Coral Pink, and Spring Green. Pieces are marked with the "Rising Sun" backstamp.

Cereal Bowl, 6¼" d, Spring Green .... **10.00**
Cup and Saucer, Azure Blue ......... **15.00**
Gravy, attached underplate, Spring Green ......................... **20.00**
Pitcher, 2 quart, Canary Yellow ...... **25.00**
Plate
  4" d, bread and butter, Canary Yellow **8.00**
  7" d, dinner, Coral Pink ........... **12.00**
Platter, 15" l, oval, Spring Green ..... **20.00**
Vegetable Bowl, 9" d, Azure Blue .... **20.00**

**ROSEBUD.** Introduced in 1934. Embossed and hand painted rosebud and leaves on solid colored dinnerware. Original four colors were Blue, Green, Rose, and Yellow. Ivory and Orange colors were added later.

Cake Plate, Blue ................... **30.00**
Casserole
  French
    Blue ......................... **50.00**
    Orange ....................... **50.00**
    Rose ......................... **50.00**
  Straight, Rose .................... **35.00**
  Triple Service
    Medium, Green ............... **40.00**
    Small, Rose ................... **35.00**
Cream Soup, Rose .................. **18.00**
Custard, Blue ...................... **15.00**
Fruit Bowl
  Orange ........................ **12.00**
  Rose ........................... **12.00**
Mixing Bowl, handled, Orange ...... **35.00**
Platter
  Ivory .......................... **35.00**
  Orange ........................ **25.00**
Pudding
  Large, Orange ................... **60.00**

Medium, Rose .................. **30.00**
Small, Rose .................... **10.00**
Teapot Lid, Blue .................. **20.00**
Utility Jar, Blue ................... **45.00**

# COWAN POTTERY

**Collecting Hints:** Cowan was primarily a modernistic designer. In addition to focusing on design, he also developed glaze formulas that complemented his work. Several pieces were made in limited numbers.

Focus on pieces that have delicate decorative elements. Aesthetics is a major pricing factor. A slight difference in glaze or assembly can affect price.

In 1931 Cowan brought together a group of distinguished potters including Alexander Blazys, Paul Bogatay, Thelma Frazier, Waylande Gregory, A. D. Jacobson, and Margaret Postgate. Pieces made by these artists while at Cowan often command premium prices.

Several individuals are currently attempting to find publishers for books about Cowan pottery. The sudden appearance of several new books certainly will trigger renewed market interest in Cowan material. Be alert to the possibility of market price manipulation on the part of one or more authors.

**History:** R. Guy Cowan operated a pottery on Nicholson Avenue in Lakewood, Ohio, a suburb of Cleveland, between 1912 and 1917. Lakewood pieces have a red clay body. After a period of service during World War I, Cowan returned to Lakewood and reopened the pottery. Within a short period, Cowan's gas well ran dry, necessitating a move to Rocky River.

Upon arriving in Rocky River, Cowan switched from his red clay body to one of high-fired porcelain. By 1921 he had developed over 1,000 outlets for his wares. A commercial line was launched in the early 1920s. By 1925 Cowan was involved in the manufacture of dinnerware place settings, console sets, and figures. One of his clients was Wahl Pen Company, for whom he made ceramic desk sets. The 1930 product line included planters and ivy jars.

In addition to utilitarian products, Cowan also made art pottery. He exhibited regularly at the Cleveland Museum of Art, the Pennsylvania Academy of Art, and the Metropolitan Museum of Art, winning numerous awards for his work. In 1930 Cowan Potters, Inc., was organized as an artists' colony. The project lasted only one year, a period when many of the most desirable Cowan pieces were produced. Cowan ceased operations in December 1931.

Initially, the name Cowan Pottery was incised on pieces. Later a black stamp with "Cowan" or "Cowan Potteries" or a mark with the initials "R.G." and "Cowan" in a circle were used.

**References:** Paul Evans, *Art Pottery of the United States, 2nd Edition,* Feingold & Lewis Publishing Corp., 1987; Ralph and Terry Kovel, *The Kovels' Collector's Guide to American Art Pottery,* Crown Publishers, Inc., 1974; Tim and Jamie Saloff, *The Collector's Encyclopedia of Cowan Pottery: Identification & Values,* Collector Books, 1993.

**Museums:** Cowan Pottery Museum, Rocky River Public Library, Rocky River, OH; Everson Museum of Art, Syracuse, NY.

**Orange Lustre, sea horse standard, stamped mark, 7⅞" h, $65.00.**

Candlesticks, pr
Gazelles, tan ..................... **150.00**
Sea horses, green ................ **48.00**
Cigarette Holder, sea horse, aqua .... **28.00**
Compote, 2" h, diamond shaped
Cream, green lining .............. **20.00**
Tan, green lining ................. **20.00**
Console Bowl, 17" d, 3" h, cream, pink lining, minor base chips ........... **35.00**
Cup and Saucer, melon dec, tan glaze **35.00**
Figure
Elephant, postgate ................ **190.00**
Radio Woman, 9" h, dec, black on cream ....................... **4,500.00**
Flower Frog, 11" h, flamingo, perforated base, white glaze, die stamped mark **325.00**
Soap Dish, 4" d, sea horse, blue ..... **50.00**
Trivet, 6½" d, scalloped rim, bust of young girl framed by flowers, sgd .. **275.00**
Vase
Egyptian Blue .................... **125.00**
5" h, fan, apple green, gold specks . **80.00**
5½" h, ftd, fluted, blue luster ...... **95.00**
6¼" h, 5½" d, bulbous, yellow .... **28.00**
7½" h, classic shape, blue luster, ink stamp mark .................... **50.00**

# COWBOY HEROES

**Collecting Hints:** Cowboy hero material was collected and saved in great numbers. Don't get fooled into thinking an object is rare until you have checked carefully. Tom Mix material remains the most desirable, followed closely by Hopalong Cassidy, Roy Rogers, and Gene Autry memorabilia. Material associated with the Western stars of the silent era and early talking films still has not achieved its full potential as a collectible.

**History:** The era when the cowboy and longhorn cattle dominated the Great Western Plains was short, lasting only from the end of the Civil War to the late 1880s. Dime store novelists romanticized this period and created a love affair in America's heart for the Golden West.

Motion pictures saw the cowboy as a prime entertainment feature. William S. Hart developed the character of the cowboy hero—often in love with his horse more than the girl. He was followed by Tom Mix, Ken Maynard, Tim McCoy, and Buck Jones. The "B" movie, the second feature of a double bill, was often of the cowboy genre.

In 1935 William Boyd starred in the first of the Hopalong Cassidy films. Gene Autry, a "singing cowboy," gained popularity over the airwaves of the West and Midwest. By the late 1930s, Autry's Melody Ranch was a national institution on the air as well as the screen. Roy Rogers replaced Autry as the featured cowboy at Republic Pictures in the mid–1940s. Although the Lone Ranger was first heard on the airwaves in 1933, he did not enter the movie medium until 1938.

The early years of television enhanced the careers of the big three—Autry, Boyd, and Rogers. The appearance of the Lone Ranger in shows made specifically for television strengthened the key role held by the cowboy hero. "Gunsmoke," "Wagon Train," "Rawhide," "The Rifleman," "Paladin," and "Bonanza" were just a few of the shows that followed.

By the early 1970s the cowboy hero had fallen from grace, relegated to reruns or specials. In early 1983 The Library of Congress in Washington conducted a major show on the "Cowboy Hero," perhaps a true indication that he is now a part of past history.

**References:** Joseph J. Caro, *Collector's Guide Hopalong Cassidy Memorabilia,* L–W Book Sales, 1992; Bernard A. Drew, *Hopalong Cassidy: The Clarence E. Mulford Story,* The Scarecrow Press, Inc., 1991; Theodore L. Hake and Robert D. Cauler, *Six Gun Heroes: A Price Guide To Movie Cowboy Collectibles,* Wallace Homestead, 1976; Robert Heide and John Gilman, *Box–Office Buckaroos,* Abbeville Press, 1989; Lee J. Felbinger, *The Lone Ranger Pictorial Scrapbook,* published by author, 1988; Norman E. Martinus and Harry L. Rinker, *Warman's Paper,* Wallace–Homestead, 1993; David Rothel, *The Gene Autry Book,* Empire Publishing Co, 1988; David Rothel, *The Roy Rogers Book,* Empire Publishing Company, 1987; Neil Summers, *The Official TV Western Book,* Vol. 1 (1987), Vol. 2 (1989), Vol. 3 (1991), and Vol. 4 (1992), The Old West Shop Publishing; Richard West, *Television Westerns: Major and Minor Series, 1946–1978,* McFarland & Company, 1987.

**Periodicals:** *Favorite Westerns & Serial World,* Route One, Box 103, Vernon Center, MN 56090; *The Westerner,* Box 5232–17, Vienna, WV 26105.

**Museums:** Gene Autry Western Heritage Museum, Los Angeles, CA; National Cowboy Hall of Fame and Western Heroes, Oklahoma City, OK; Roy Rogers Museum, Victorville, CA.

## GENE AUTRY

Arcade Card, c1950 . . . . . . . . . . . . . . . . **2.00**

Award, 10 x 12", Doublemint Melody Ranch, diecut cardboard with black and white photo, framed, mid 1940s **75.00**

Bandanna, 18 x 21", silk, purple, green, dark blue, and white illus and design, Autry with guitar in horseshoe in corner, western motifs, 1940s . . . . . . . . . **75.00**

Belt . . . . . . . . . . . . . . . . . . . . . . . . . . . **40.00**

Belt Buckle, brass, name and figure outlined in red, c1950 . . . . . . . . . . . . . . . **35.00**

Better Little Book, *Gene Autry in Special Ranger Rule,* #1456, Whitman, 1945 **50.00**

Book, *Gene Autry Adventure Comic and Fun Book,* Pillsbury, 1947 . . . . . . . . . **30.00**

Briefcase, school type . . . . . . . . . . . . . . . **175.00**

Cap Gun, 7½" l, metal, white, gold finish, white plastic grips with rearing horse, 1950s . . . . . . . . . . . . . . . . . . . . **75.00**

Cereal Box Panel, 6¼ x 8¼", Wheaties, *The Big Show* release, yellow and black photo of Autry on Champion, blue background, c1936 . . . . . . . . . . **25.00**

Comic Book, Gene Autry Comics, February 1948, Vol. 1, No. 12 . . . . . . . . **8.00**

Dixie Lid, 2¼" d, brown photo, rim inscription, 1937 . . . . . . . . . . . . . . . . . . **15.00**

Galoshes, MIB . . . . . . . . . . . . . . . . . . . . . **150.00**

Guitar, 36" l, wood, natural walnut, yellow and brownish–red western scene, metal strings, brown plastic tuning pegs . . . . . . . . . . . . . . . . . . . . . . . . . . . **125.00**

Holster Set, Gene Autry Flying A Ranch, black and tan double leather holster, two 44's, bullets, Leslie Henry, near mint . . . . . . . . . . . . . . . . . . . . . . . . . . . **600.00**

Iron–On Transfer, 5 x 7", Autry and Champ Junior, black, white, and red, c1950 . . . . . . . . . . . . . . . . . . . . . . . . . **8.00**

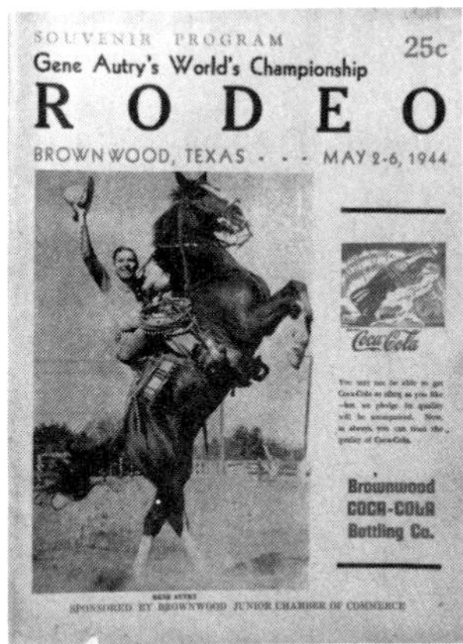


**Gene Autry, program, Gene Autry's World's Championship Rodeo, May 1944, Brownwood, TX, 36 pgs., 8½ x 11", $35.00.**

Lunch Box ........................ **70.00**
Magazine, Screen Stories, May 1948, "The Strawberry Roan" story and photos ........................ **5.00**
Magic Slate, Lowe ........................ **65.00**
Movie Serial, VHS, "Phantom Empire" **35.00**
Paper Doll Book, 10½ x 13", Whitman, four punch–out figures, six uncut clothing pgs, 1950 .............. **150.00**
Photograph, 8 x 10", black and white glossy, black marker signature ...... **25.00**
Pinback Button, 1¼" d, flesh tones, red, white, and blue ................ **15.00**
Plaque, 4½ x 5½", masonite, full color photo, beveled edges, metal hanging loop on back, c1950 ............ **40.00**
Plate, 9½" d, white china, Autry with Champion center, brands border ... **25.00**
Post Card, 3½ x 5", "Home of Gene Autry," full color, c1940 .......... **10.00**
Poster, 27 x 41", "Rim Of The Canyon," Columbia Pictures, Morgan Litho, 1949 ........................ **35.00**
Puzzle, frame tray, Autry and Champion, Whitman, #2981, c1950 .... **8.50**
Record Set, Western Classic, four record set, 1947 ........................ **75.00**
School Bag, 10 x 14", vinyl, dark tan pebble grained design, fabric int., carrying strap, Autry on Champion on front, 1940–50 .................. **100.00**
Sheet Music, 9 x 12", *Goodbye, Little Darlin', Goodbye,* 6 pgs, blue tone photo, 1940 copyright ........... **20.00**
Suspenders, 20" l, child's, elastic, blue, red, yellow, and white repeated illus, silvered metal adjustment buckle with emb horse head, 1940s ........... **25.00**
Tablet, 5½ x 9", full color cover photo, black signature, 1940–50 ......... **20.00**
Thermos ........................ **25.00**
Tie Bar, 2¾" l, brass, portrait, small western symbols, c1950 ........... **35.00**
View Master Reel, #950, "Gene Autry and His Wonder Horse Champion" and #951, "The Kidnapping," orig envelope, early 1950s ............ **15.00**
Waste Can, 6 x 7 x 12", oval, white ground, decal inscribed "Gene Autry, America's No. 1 Cowboy and Champion, His Wonder Horse" ......... **40.00**
Wrist Watch ........................ **125.00**

## HOPALONG CASSIDY

Badge, Sheriff ........................ **25.00**
Bank, bust, plastic .................. **65.00**
Banner, 28" l, black and white felt, Hoppy on horse, 1950 ............ **12.50**
Barrette, orig card, MOC ............ **45.00**
Bedspread
  Chenille ........................ **225.00**
  Cotton ........................ **275.00**
Belt, large card, extra buckle, MOC .. **215.00**
Binoculars, 5" l, black metal and plastic, blue, white, and yellow decal, orig box, 1940 William Boyd copyright . **100.00**
Book
  *Hopalong Cassidy Lends A Helping Hand,* Bonnie Book, Samuel Lowe Co, 1950, 24 pgs, 6½ x 8" ...... **25.00**
  *Hoppy and Danny,* mechanical .... **55.00**
  *Hoppy and Lucky,* pop–up ......... **95.00**
Box
  Dental Kit ........................ **65.00**
  T–Shirt ........................ **95.00**
Breakfast Set, 3 pcs, 7" d plate, 5" d bowl, 4" h glass, milk glass, black illus and name .................. **100.00**
Bubble Pipe ........................ **12.00**
Camera ........................ **95.00**
Cap Gun, 8½" l, silvered white metal, ivory plastic grips, Wyandotte Toys, early 1950s ..................... **75.00**
Cereal Bowl, WS George ............ **37.00**
Coaster, 4" d, black, white, and yellow, "Spun Honey Spreads like Butter," set of four ........................ **10.00**
Coloring Book ........................ **35.00**
Compass ........................ **65.00**
Crayon and Stencil Set, MIB ......... **95.00**
Decals, set of 3, watercolor Hoppy and Topper transfers, unused, c1950 ... **25.00**
Dental Kit, MIB .................... **325.00**
Display, Butternut Bread ............ **100.00**
Figure
  Carnival Chalk .................. **500.00**
  Ideal, set of Hoppy and Topper .... **120.00**
  Lead, set of Hoppy and Topper .... **120.00**

Game
Chinese Checkers, orig box ........ **125.00**
Hopalong Canasta, black plastic tray, 96 playing cards, orig box, Pacific Playing Card Co, 1950 copyright . **125.00**
Hoppy Lasso, orig box ........... **250.00**
Glass ........................... **20.00**
Greeting Card, 6½ x 7½" diecut card with slot, 3 x 7" diecut pistol, inscriptions "Shoot The Works! It's Your Birthday!," and "Put Your Belt Through The Slits and Wear The Gun And Holster Just Like Hoppy," Buzza Cardozo, Hollywood, early 1950s .. **40.00**
Holster Set, two guns, leather holster, Hoppy picture on black handles, gold barrels ......................... **550.00**
Ice Cream Wrapper, 5¼ x 12", silver foil, insulated, blue, silver background, blue photo, inscription "Enjoy Hoppy's Favorite Brand," unused, early 1950s ..................... **40.00**
Lamp, beige glass, color decal and shade .......................... **725.00**
Lobby Card, 11 x 14", full color scene, 1947 United Artists film *Unexpected Guest,* Hoppy holding fainted woman **20.00**
Lunch Box and Thermos, 1954 ....... **70.00**
Magazine, *Life,* 1950s ............. **45.00**
Matchbook ....................... **20.00**
Milk Bottle, quart ................. **90.00**
Mug, 3" h, white glass, red picture and signature ....................... **15.00**
Neckerchief, 12 x 12 x 17", dark blue, multicolored inked portrait, rope script, snap fastener ............. **25.00**
Necktie .......................... **45.00**
Night Light, holster shape, Aladdin ... **200.00**
Notebook ........................ **80.00**
Notebook Filler Paper, MIP .......... **25.00**
Paint Set, large, MIB, 1950 .......... **65.00**
Party Plate, paper, large, set of four, MIP **55.00**
Pen, ballpoint, three dimensional head, orig refill, MIB .................. **225.00**
Pencil Case, 3 x 8", stiff paper, faux wood grain finish, black and white photo, PA shoe store adv stamped on back ........................... **40.00**
Photo Album, leather, front cov with large emb figure of Hoppy on Topper **145.00**
Pillow Cover, 18" sq, glossy fabric, yellow thread fringe, Hoppy on Topper **50.00**
Playsuit, girl's, skirt, shirt, belt with small gun, orig box ............... **300.00**
Pocket Knife, Hammer Brand ........ **50.00**
Post Card, birthday ................ **15.00**
Poster, Hoppy and Topper, compliments of Sunny Spread ................. **25.00**
Potato Chip Can .................. **200.00**
Puppet, 10½" h, printed fabric body, molded vinyl head and black hat, inscribed name, 1951 copyright ..... **100.00**
Puzzle, frame tray .................. **85.00**
Ring
Face ............................ **110.00**
Hat, compass .................... **150.00**
Picture, plastic ................... **20.00**
Projector, seven films, orig gun and box **275.00**
Record Set, "Hopalong and Singing Bandit," two records .............. **37.50**
Rocking Horse, Topper ............. **225.00**
Roller Skates ...................... **135.00**
Savings Club Kit, orig envelope ...... **225.00**
School Bag, 10½ x 14", fabric, brown, Hoppy on Topper portrait, white cloth circle with silvered metal star badge inscribed "Hoppy" .............. **75.00**
Shoe Bag ......................... **125.00**
Shooting Gallery, Hoppy, Lucky, and California, moving cowboy on horses as target, orig box ............... **290.00**
Sign, 11 x 41½", cardboard, red and white Hoppy picture, painted litho, simulated wood grain background, "Hoppy's Favorite" and Melville Milk **100.00**
Sheet Music, *Lazy Rolls The Rio Grande,* blue and white, Hoppy riding Topper, cattle herd background, 1939 ...... **15.00**
Stationery, orig folder ............... **65.00**
Sweater, child's, brown tones, portrait and name on front, sleeves with mountains and cactus ............. **150.00**
Swim Trunks, boy's size 6, blue cotton, Hoppy and Topper on front corner . **30.00**
Thermos ......................... **50.00**
Tie .............................. **50.00**
Tie Bar, gun and holster ............ **40.00**
Token, metal, c1950 ............... **5.00**
View Master Reel, No. 955, Hopalong Cassidy and Topper, c1950 ........ **12.00**
Wallet, orig card, lucky coin ......... **95.00**
Wrist Watch, boxed ................ **150.00**

## DAVY CROCKETT

Badge, orig card ................... **15.00**
Bank, dime register, 2½ x 2½ x ⅝", litho metal, full color scenes, mid 1950s . **75.00**
Belt, size 24, leather, diecut brass buckle with red accents, "Davy Crockett," three repeated long rifles and tooled designs, mid 1950s ......... **40.00**
Bow tie .......................... **15.00**
Cookie Jar, 7 x 8 x 10", china, raised gold lettering, name on front, C Miller copyright and "55" on bottom, no lid **75.00**
Game
Davy Crockett's Alamo Game, sixteen playing cards, 94 paper marker playing pieces, 8 pgs instruction leaflet, 13¼ x 17 x 1½" box, Lowell Toy Corp, mid 1950s ........... **50.00**
Horseshoes, four rubber horseshoes with name and western symbols,

two rubber bases with wood pegs, Auburn Toys, mid 1950s ........ **40.00**
Glass, 3" h, Crockett on horseback, brown and yellow, mid 1950s ..... **15.00**
Lamp, 7½" h, china, glazed, green base, felt bottom, 1950s .......... **75.00**
Handkerchief, 14" sq, cotton, white and black action scenes, dark blue background, Walt Disney Productions copyright ........................ **25.00**
Lunch Box, steel, Holtemp of American Thermos Bottle Co, 1955 .......... **110.00**
Pen, 5" l, ballpoint, plastic, white, brass finished metal cap, blue portrait, red name .......................... **20.00**
Ruler, 6" l, paper, Atlas Soap adv ..... **5.00**
School Bag, 11 x 12", fabric, brown, tan vinyl fringe, vinyl cover with Crockett scene, brown shoulder strap, brass buckle, unused, 1950s ............ **75.00**
Teepee, full size ................... **65.00**
Toy Knife, 7" l, vinyl, red grain texture, portrait handle ................... **25.00**
Wallet, 3 x 3½", vinyl, brown, gold foil–like picture sticker, molded clear plastic cov, blue accents, red name .... **25.00**

## LONE RANGER

Badge, Silver Cup Bread ............ **22.50**
Binoculars, orig decals .............. **75.00**
Book
  *Heigh–Yo Silver!*, Dell, 1938, 72 pgs **55.00**
  *The Lone Ranger and the Texas Renegades,* Fran Striker, Grosset & Dunlap, 1938, 24 pgs .......... **50.00**
Briefcase, school, unused ........... **195.00**
Brooch, gardenia .................. **150.00**
Bullet, secret compartment .......... **20.00**
Calendar, 1939 .................... **75.00**
Cereal Box, Cheerios, Frontiertown ... **75.00**
Clicker Gun ....................... **85.00**
Coloring Book ..................... **7.50**
Comic Book
  #90 ........................... **7.00**
  #112 .......................... **27.00**
Costume, child's
  Lone Ranger, suit, holster, pistol, mask, and scarf, early 1950s, Herman Iskin & Co, Telford, PA, orig 10⅝ x 12¾ x 1½" box, MIB ..... **500.00**
  Tonto, trousers and jacket, red accent striping, Indian style symbols, 1940s ....................... **75.00**
Cowboy Outfit, five pcs, Yankiboy, orig box, 1947 ....................... **150.00**
Deputy Kit, orig mailer, 1980 ........ **12.00**
Figure, Hartland ................... **100.00**
Flashlight Gun, secret compartment ... **150.00**
Game
  Lone Ranger Double Target, 11 x 17" target, 8" l black enameled steel dart gun, orig box, 1939 copyright **125.00**
  Round–Up, c1950 ............... **40.00**
  The Lone Ranger & Tonto Board Game, unopened, Warren, 1978 . **15.00**
Hairbrush, late 1930s ............... **45.00**
Handcuffs ......................... **50.00**
Harmonica, orig package ............ **45.00**
Hat, 11½ x 13 x 3", felt, brown, molded and starched, red label attachment, adjustable drawstring, orig label stitched on brim, Arlington Co, 1966 copyright ....................... **50.00**
Holster Set, guns, orig box, 1947 ..... **375.00**
Identification Card .................. **15.00**
Lobby Card Set, 1956 ............... **400.00**
Lunch Box, "The Legend of the Lone Ranger," emb steel, plastic thermos, Aladdin Industries, 1980 copyright . **20.00**
Manual, *Cramer's Lone Ranger Safety Club,* 5¼ x 8¼", 32 pgs, issued by Cramer's Butter-Cream Sliced Bread, 1939 copyright .................. **150.00**
Model Kit, Tonto, plastic, 3–D action display, 8 page comic book and instructions, orig sealed box, Aurora Plastics, 1974 copyright ........... **25.00**
Noisemaker, horn, 5" l, litho metal, white plastic mouthpiece, Ichi, Japan, 1960s ......................... **15.00**
Paint Book, 1938, large size, heavy stock color cov, some pages colored **30.00**
Peace Patrol Card .................. **35.00**
Pedometer, 2¾" d, aluminum rim, fabric straps, Cheerios premium, orig mailing box, c1948 .................. **50.00**
Pen, Danger Signal ................. **45.00**
Pencil Case, Official School Kit, cardboard, red textured surface, emb portrait on lid, gold inscriptions ....... **75.00**
Pencil Sharpener, bullet shape ....... **27.50**
Photograph, Silver Cup premium, 1936 **25.00**
Playing Cards, dated 1938 ........... **25.00**
Play Set, The Carson City Bank Robbery, orig box, Hubley, 1972 ........... **22.00**
Pocket Knife ....................... **70.00**
Post Card, 1951 coloring contest ..... **6.00**
Poster, 17 x 22", Lone Ranger 6–Shooter Ring adv, c1947 ................ **150.00**
Record, He Saves Booneville Gold, 78 rpm, 10 x 10" jacket, Decca No. 6, 1952 .......................... **15.00**
Record Player, wood ............... **185.00**
Ring
  Atom Bomb ..................... **75.00**
  Flashlight, orig instructions ........ **110.00**
  Saddle, filmstrip .................. **150.00**
  Six Gun ........................ **75.00**
School Bag, 10" h, leather textured fabric, black, color portrait on flap, early 1940s ......................... **100.00**
Snowdome, Lone Ranger roping calf .. **65.00**

Spoon, 6″ l, silvered brass, "The Lone Ranger Hi-Yo Silver" on handle, 1938 copyright . . . . . . . . . . . . . . . . . . . . . . . . **35.00**

Suspenders, child's, Lone Ranger, Tonto, silver guns, and other illus, 1938 patent date . . . . . . . . . . . . . . . . . **450.00**

Toothbrush Holder, 4″ h, plaster, painted, 1938 . . . . . . . . . . . . . . . . . . . **75.00**

Wrist Watch, metal case, clear plexiglas crystal, Lone Ranger on galloping Silver, black numerals, orig tan leather straps, c1940 . . . . . . . . . . . . . . . . . . . . **150.00**

## TOM MIX

Arrowhead, Lucite . . . . . . . . . . . . . . . . . . **55.00**

Badge

- Dobie County Sheriff, siren . . . . . . . . **75.00**
- Sharp Shooters
  - Gold . . . . . . . . . . . . . . . . . . . . . . . . . **55.00**
  - Silver . . . . . . . . . . . . . . . . . . . . . . . . . **70.00**

Bandanna, multicolored, Mix on horseback, "Best Wishes—Tom Mix" . . . . **50.00**

Belt, 26″ l, glow in the dark, secret compartment, brass buckle, 1945 . . . . . . **90.00**

Belt Buckle . . . . . . . . . . . . . . . . . . . . . . . . **45.00**

Book

- *Tom Mix Died For Your Sins,* Darryl Ponicsan, Delacorte Press, NY, 1975 copyright, 300 pgs . . . . . . . . **15.00**
- *Trail of Terrible Six* . . . . . . . . . . . . . . . **35.00**

**Tom Mix, photo card, sepia tone, Ex. Sup. Co., Chicago, 3¼ x 5¼″, $20.00.**

Branding Iron . . . . . . . . . . . . . . . . . . . . . . **65.00**

Card Game, Wildcat . . . . . . . . . . . . . . . . **65.00**

Catalog, premiums, 1938 . . . . . . . . . . . **40.00**

Coloring Book, 11 x 14″, Whitman, 96 pgs, full color portrait on cov, 1935 **50.00**

Comic Book, #7, Ralston premium, early 1940s . . . . . . . . . . . . . . . . . . . . . . **50.00**

Compass, magnifier, brass . . . . . . . . . . . **55.00**

Decoder, six gun . . . . . . . . . . . . . . . . . . . . **70.00**

Flashlight, three color . . . . . . . . . . . . . . . **125.00**

Glass Slide . . . . . . . . . . . . . . . . . . . . . . . . . **10.00**

Good Luck Spinner . . . . . . . . . . . . . . . . . **45.00**

Gun, wooden, 1939 . . . . . . . . . . . . . . . . **160.00**

Hand Puppet, 9″ h, fabric body, molded vinyl head, 1950–60 . . . . . . . . . . . . . **60.00**

Instruction Sheet and Envelope, Tom Mix Siren Ring, 3 x 5″ sheet with red ink, 6″ l gray envelope, dated Dec, 1944 . . . . . . . . . . . . . . . . . . . . . . . . . . **50.00**

Jewelry

- Identification Bracelet . . . . . . . . . . . . . **45.00**
- Ring
  - Look In Picture . . . . . . . . . . . . . . . . **200.00**
  - Magnet . . . . . . . . . . . . . . . . . . . . . . . **50.00**
  - Signature . . . . . . . . . . . . . . . . . . . . . . **185.00**
  - Sliding Whistle . . . . . . . . . . . . . . . . . **85.00**
  - Straight Shooters . . . . . . . . . . . . . . . **60.00**
  - Tiger Eye . . . . . . . . . . . . . . . . . . . . . . **250.00**
- Wrist Band, orig leather strap . . . . . . **60.00**

Lariat, orig mailing envelope . . . . . . . . . **40.00**

Letterhead, 8 x 11″, black and white photo, red with blue outline "Tom Mix Circus" title, bamboo frame under glass, late 1930s . . . . . . . . . . . . . . **75.00**

Magazine, *Motion Picture Classic,* 1929, "Just Him and Tony" story . . . **20.00**

Make–Up Kit, black mustache and beard, two grease pencil stubs, five silvered grease paint tins individually titled, instruction sheet, Ralston premium, c1937 . . . . . . . . . . . . . . . . . . . **100.00**

Marbles . . . . . . . . . . . . . . . . . . . . . . . . . . . **40.00**

Paint Book, 8½ x 11½″, Whitman, 1940 copyright, unused . . . . . . . . . . . . . . . . **40.00**

Pamphlet, 2¼ x 3¼″, brown and white paper, front cov photo, Ry–Krisp Box on back, dated 1937 . . . . . . . . . . . . . **20.00**

Pennant, 22½″ l, felt, "Tom Mix Circus and Wild West," Mix on horseback, burnt orange background, streamers on end . . . . . . . . . . . . . . . . . . . . . . . . . **120.00**

Periscope, 9″ l, cardboard, blue, inscribed "Ralston Straight Shooters" . **65.00**

Photograph, silver frame . . . . . . . . . . . . **80.00**

Pocket Knife . . . . . . . . . . . . . . . . . . . . . . . **50.00**

Rocking Horse, Tony . . . . . . . . . . . . . . . **360.00**

Secret Manual

- 1941 . . . . . . . . . . . . . . . . . . . . . . . . . . **85.00**
- 1944 . . . . . . . . . . . . . . . . . . . . . . . . . . **65.00**

Sign, 6 x 24″, paper, "Round Up The Boys And Bring 'Em In," orange, yellow, black, and white print, Imperial Knife Co, Providence, RI, 1930s . . . **150.00**

Spurs, glow in the dark . . . . . . . . . . . . . **125.00**

Target, 12 x 15″, Indian Blow Gun Target, paper mounted on cardboard, red, white, and blue, Ralston Cereal premium, 1940 . . . . . . . . . . . . . . . . . . **60.00**

Telegraph Set, 5 x 7½″, metal telegraph

key, blue and white cardboard box with Mix and Ralston photo ....... **40.00**
Telescope, bird call ................ **85.00**
Watch Fob, gold colored metal, clear dome with granular ore samples, certificate dated March 11, 1940 ...... **75.00**

## ROY ROGERS

Bandanna, Roy and Trigger, red ...... **35.00**
Bank, 5″ h, boot shape, white metal, copper luster finish, Roy on rearing Trigger, Alma Metal Arts, Point Marion, PA, 1950s .................. **55.00**
Bedspread
Chenille ....................... **195.00**
Cotton, 68 x 92″, beige, continuous designs ...................... **150.00**
Better Little Book, *Roy Rogers/King of the Cowboys,* Whitman, 1943 ..... **50.00**
Binoculars, 5 x 6″, plastic, black, two color decals ..................... **30.00**
Bolo Tie, slide .................... **37.50**
Book
*Lost Gold Mine,* Dale Evans, 1954 .. **8.50**
*Roy Rogers and the Raiders of Sawtooth Ridge,* Whitman, 1946, dj .. **20.00**
*Roy Rogers' Trigger To The Rescue,* Whitman Cozy–Corner Book, 1950, 24 pgs ................. **25.00**
*Sure Enough Cowboy,* paperback, 1952 ........................ **8.50**
Camera, box type, MIB ............ **45.00**
Cap Gun, 10″ l .................... **65.00**
Card, fan club .................... **15.00**
Card Holder, fan club ............... **10.00**
Chaps, vinyl ...................... **30.00**
Clock
Alarm, color dial, c1970 .......... **25.00**
Motion, Roy and Trigger, marked "Ingraham" ..................... **225.00**
Coloring Book, 15 x 11″, Roy Rogers and Dale Evans, color cov, 1952 ... **20.00**
Comic Book, Dell, Vol. 1, #8, Aug 1948 ......................... **45.00**
Cowboy Outfit, vest and chaps, cowhide .......................... **60.00**
Cowgirl Outfit, Dale Evans, 2 pcs .... **80.00**
Cuff Links and Tie Clip, orig card .... **35.00**
Cup, plastic ...................... **40.00**
Display, 9 x 12½″, "Roy Rogers Cub Hunter Pocket Knives," adv, cardboard, c1950 .................... **90.00**
Figure, Bullet, Hartland ............ **45.00**
Film Slide, Colorado ................ **12.50**
Flashlight, signal, code, orig box ..... **95.00**
Game, Horseshoes, orig box ......... **165.00**
Glass, Roy and Trigger ............. **65.00**
Gloves, 9″ l, leather, yellow silhouette of Roy on Trigger, western motifs, fringe sides ..................... **40.00**
Guitar, no strings .................. **37.50**
Harmonica ........................ **35.00**
Holster Set, Roy Rogers Flash–Draw, cap gun and double holster, 1958 copyright ........................ **400.00**
Letter, fan club .................... **10.00**
Lobby Card, 11 x 14″, *Utah,* color scene of Roy, Dale, and Gabby Hayes, 1945 Republic Picture ................. **15.00**
Lucky Coin ........................ **10.00**
Lunch Box, Roy Rogers Saddlebag, vinyl, tan, emb portrait, American Thermos Products Co, 1960 copyright .. **100.00**
Magazine
*Movie Life Magazine,* Life Story in Pix of Roy's Bride–Dale Evans story, black and white photos, March, 1948 ........................ **25.00**
*Saturday Evening Post,* Roy and Dale on cov, full page photo inside, April, 1980 .................... **8.50**
*TV Guide,* three page article and color photos, color photo on cov, July 17, 1954 ........................ **40.00**
Mug, plastic ....................... **15.00**
Necklace, Dale Evans, orig card ..... **25.00**
Nodder, 6½″ h, square green base, Japan, 1962 copyright ............. **125.00**
Notebook, zipper compartment ...... **150.00**
Paint Book, 8½ x 11″, Whitman, 128 unused pages, 1944 ............. **55.00**
Paper Dolls, Roy and Dale, cut–out, orig folder, 1953 ................ **65.00**
Pen, 5″ l, retractable ballpoint, silvered metal top with "RR" initials, light blue plastic bottom with black Roy and Trigger and inscription, 1950s .. **30.00**
Pencil, Roy, Dale, and Bullet ........ **65.00**
Pinback Button, 1¼″ d, celluloid, black, yellow, and white, c1950 ......... **5.00**
Pocket Watch ..................... **260.00**
Program, 8½ x 11″, 20th Annual Rodeo, 48 glossy pages, photos and event listings ........................... **50.00**
Puzzle, frame tray, 9¼ x 11½″, Whitman, 1952 copyright ............ **25.00**
Record, 10″ d, Dale Evans, *When The White Roses Bloom and I'm The Rage Of The Sage,* Majestic Records Inc, 78 rpm, 1940s .................. **18.00**
Rifle, 26″ l, silver plastic, metal cocking and loading levers for caps, brown script, Marx, 1950s ............... **75.00**
Ring, microscope .................. **65.00**
Saddle Blanket, MIP ............... **250.00**
Shirt ............................. **35.00**
Sweater .......................... **100.00**
Tablet ........................... **10.00**
Tab, Post premium
Boots .......................... **20.00**
Dale Evans ..................... **22.50**
Roy Rogers ..................... **22.50**
Trigger ......................... **20.00**

Telephone, western, orig box ........ **400.00**
Tent, canvas ........................ **125.00**
Thermos, 8½" h, "Double R Bar Ranch," steel, red plastic cup, American Thermos Bottle Co, 1953 ..... **40.00**
Toy, Roy, Trigger, and Trigger Jr, tin horse trailer truck, orig figures ..... **250.00**
Wallet ............................ **35.00**
Wrist Watch
Dale Evans with Buttermilk, orig straps, 1950s .................. **50.00**
Roy and Trigger .................. **100.00**
Yo–Yo, promotion, Roy and Trigger, orig wrapper ......................... **40.00**

## CHARACTERS, OTHER

Cisco Kid
Gun, premium, red, white, and blue cardboard, Cisco's picture on handle, clicker mounted inside, TV show and Tip–Top Bread adv .... **40.00**
Label Sheet, 8 x 8¼" folded, holds 16 adventure pictures from Ward's Tip–Top Bread end labels, titled "Bolder & Bullets Story," black and white photo front panel, premium **75.00**
Tablet, 8 x 10", color picture on pink ground, inscribed "From Your Good Amigo, Duncan Renaldo—Cisco Kid" ................... **20.00**
Tie Clasp ........................ **15.00**
View Master Reel, Cisco Kid, Duncan Renaldo, 1950 ................ **10.00**
Earp, Wyatt
Badge, Marshall, metal, orig card .. **10.00**
Figure, Hartland, orig package ..... **95.00**
Holster Set, two guns ............ **75.00**
Puzzle, 11½ x 14½", frame tray, Whitman, full color photo portrait, 1958 copyright ............... **25.00**
Sunglasses, 12½ x 19" display card holding twelve pairs plastic sunglasses with green lenses, 1" flasher picture in center of each, Merit Mfg Co, 1950–60 ................. **75.00**
Hickok, Wild Bill
Game
Cavalry and Indians, 14" sq board, punched cardboard disks, 7½ x 14 x 1½" box with Hickok on horse talking to Indian Chief ... **40.00**
Wild Bill Hickok, Bilt–Rite, 1956 . **15.00**
Map, 24 x 36", paper, "Wild Bill Hickok Treasure Map," Hickok drawing and jingles in lower left corner, western motif, shows over 300 treasure sites, Rand McNally, 1950s ....................... **60.00**
Poster, 27 x 41", "The Ghost of Crossbone Canyon," full color, red sky background, red and blue lettering, yellow ground ................. **50.00**
View Master Reel, set of 3, T–2, T–18, and T–19, Tru–Vue ......... **25.00**
Masterson, Bat
Arcade Card, c1950 .............. **2.00**
Costume, orig box ................ **125.00**
Game, Bat Masterson Board Game, Lowell Toy Mfg Co, 1958 ....... **15.00**
Oakley, Annie
Book, *Annie Oakley,* Shannon Garst, Julian Messner, 1968, 186 pgs ... **10.00**
Cabinet Photo, 4 x 6½", holding rifle **95.00**
Costume, child's, red, white, and blue, illus of Annie on pockets, Herman Iskin & Co, Telford, PA .. **175.00**
Craft Set, two full color cloth pictures, diecut cardboard frames, unopened sequins and beads, Gabriel, 1955 copyright, 12 x 17 x 1½" box, unused ......................... **75.00**
Game, 16" sq adventure map board, Annie on horseback center, markers, disks, spinner, play money, 8½ x 16½ x 1½" box, Milton Bradley **20.00**
Lunch Box, Aladdin, 1955 ........ **25.00**
Pinback Button, ⅞" d, black and white portrait surrounded by gray horseshoe, green four leaf clover, red slogan "I Use U.M.C. Ammunition To Obtain The Best Results," back paper text "Compliments Of Annie Oakley," brass pin ........ **90.00**
Better Little Book, Whitman
*Desert Eagle And The Hidden Fortress,* #1431, James O Parson, author, J R White, artist, 1941, standard size, 432 pgs, hard cov **15.00**
*The Range Busters in Saddle Mountain Roundup,* #1441, Eleanor Packer, author, Henry E Vallely, artist, 1942, standard size, 432 pgs, hardcover, flip–it feature .. **15.00**
Big Little Book, Whitman
*Guns In The Roaring West,* #1426, Steve Saxton, author, 1937, standard size, 300 pgs, hard cov ... **12.00**
*Riders of Lone Trails,* #1425, Steve Saxton, author, 1937, standard size, 300 pgs, hard cov ....... **15.00**
*The Texas Kid,* #1429, Steve Saxton, author, Milt Youngren, artist, 1936, standard size, 432 pgs, hard cov ................... **18.00**
Paladin
Business Card, 2 x 3½", black and white ........................ **5.00**
Game, checkers, 12" sq board with pictures of Paladin on side, plastic playing pieces, plastic bag with label, 1960 ..................... **18.00**
Lunch Box, Aladdin, 1960 ........ **25.00**

Ranger Joe
- Gun, 6½" l, wood, painted black, white cardboard grips, yellow lettering, red insignia, fires rubber bands, c1950 .................. **75.00**
- Mug, 3" h, glass, white, blue portrait illus, c1950 .................. **15.00**

Red Ryder
- BB Gun ........................ **100.00**
- Better Little Book, Whitman
  - *Red Ryder And The Secret Canyon*, 1948, standard size, 288 pgs, hardcover .................. **18.00**
  - *Red Ryder In War On The Range*, #1473, 1945, standard size, 352 pgs, hard cov ................ **15.00**
  - *Red Ryder, The Fighting Westerner*, 1940 ...................... **20.00**
- Coin, metal, gold, JC Penney premium, 1942–45 ................ **5.00**
- Gloves, pr, leather, black, white suede fringe, silver Red Ryder image, tag with premium offer on reverse, Wells Lamont Corp, sized for 8–10 years .................. **50.00**
- Handkerchief, 11 x 13", white, red, green, and tan print design, c1940 **15.00**
- Pillowcase ...................... **25.00**
- Pocket Knife, 3½" l, steel, light yellow marbled plastic inserts, red portrait and name on one side, two blades, Camco USA, c1940 ........... **75.00**

Rifleman
- Costume, child's, Herman Iskin & Co, Telford, PA, 1959, orig 10⅝ x 12¾ x 1½" box, MIB ................ **350.00**
- Game, Rifleman, Milton Bradley, 1959 ........................ **20.00**
- Hat, 11 x 13 x 3", red felt, diecut fabric label on front with silvery black and white photo on yellow and red background, gold dec crown cord with adjustable chin strap, orig label "Official Western Hat As Seen On TV," Tex–Felt, 1958 copyright ................ **75.00**
- Lunch Box, Aladdin, 1961 ........ **25.00**
- Rifle, 32" l, metal and plastic, Hubley New Flip Special, orig box, 1958 **70.00**

Rin–Tin–Tin
- Book, *Rin–Tin–Tin Book of Dog Care*, 7 x 10", 182 pgs, Lee Duncan ... **40.00**
- Figure, Hartland, c1950 ........... **35.00**
- Game, Adventures of Rin–Tin–Tin, orig box, 1955 Transogram ...... **50.00**
- Little Golden Book, *Rin–Tin–Tin and Rusty*, 1955 .................... **8.00**
- Post Card, 3½ x 5½", premium, black and white glossy photo, Rip and Rusty signatures and paw print, 1950s ........................ **25.00**
- Puzzle, 14 x 18½" assembled, full color photo, 7½ x 10 x 2½" box, Jaymar, 1957 copyright ......... **40.00**
- Record, Rinty Breaks Through, 78 rpm, 10 x 10" cardboard cover, Columbia label, 1955 copyright .... **35.00**
- Wonda–Scope, magentic compass, mirror, magnifying lenses, plastic frames, Nabisco premium, 1954–56 ........................... **50.00**
- View Master Reel, set of 3, 930–A, 930–B, and 930–C, 1955 copyright **25.00**

**Straight Arrow, Injun-uity Manual, Nabisco Shredded Wheat cereal premium, book 3, cardboard, green lettering, 1949, 3⅞ x 7⅜", $30.00.**

Straight Arrow
- Bandanna, 16½ x 18", red, white, and blue portrait, Straight Arrow on racing horse, Indian motifs, red background, inscribed "Kaneewah Fury," 1949 copyright, Nabisco premium ...................... **60.00**
- Bracelet, Mystic Wrist Kit, gold plastic, Straight Arrow profile on lid, gold colored metal arrowhead inscribed "Straight Arrow," removable secret compartment, keychain, gold plastic charm, Nabisco premium, 1950 .................. **150.00**
- Game, Target Game, 10½ x 14" litho tin board, three magnetic feather tipped arrows, spring steel crossbow gun, orig box, National Biscuit Co, c1950 .................... **70.00**
- Ring, club ...................... **40.00**
- Tie Slide ....................... **25.00**

## PERSONALITIES

Benson, Bobby
- Big Little Book, *Bobby Benson On The H–Bar–O Ranch*, Whitman, 1934 ........................ **40.00**

**Bobby Benson, 3¼ x 4½" code book and 5⅛ x 2" code rule, orig mailing envelope, 1935, $75.00.**

Hobby Kit, diecut leather, gun belt and double holster, grained western motifs, plastic stitching, cords and rivets, orig packaging and box, 1954 copyright, Street & Smith Publications .................. **50.00**

Brown, Johnny Mack

Lobby Card, 11 x 14", *Rustlers of Red Dog,* blue and white, Universal .. **8.00**

Photograph, 8 x 10", *Border Renegades,* full color, yellow margin band on top, 1950s ........... **15.00**

Cody, Buffalo Bill

Cabinet Photo, 4¼ x 6½", black and white close–up portrait, c1890 ... **75.00**

Figurine, 2⅞" h, metal, Blenheim .. **20.00**

Elliott, Wild Bill, arcade card, 3¼ x 5¼", ¾ length portrait, pink ....... **3.00**

Hale, Monte, arcade card, 3¼ x 5¼", Monte and horse, black ........... **3.00**

Hart, William S

Exhibit Card, 3½ x 5½", yellowtone photo, 1931 .................. **15.00**

Tablet, 6 x 9", brown and white portrait, Picture Land Stars series, c1920 ....................... **40.00**

Hayes, Gabby

Coloring Book, 8 x 10½", Magic Dial Funny Coloring Book, diecut television screen opening in front with disk wheel, Samuel Lowe Co, c1950 ....................... **50.00**

Dixie Lid, 2¼" d, brown photo, rim inscription titled "Wyoming," 1947 **25.00**

Puzzle, frame tray, 10¼ x 14½", full color illus, Hayes and Kagran copyrights, early 1950s .............. **25.00**

Rocking Horse .................. **200.00**

Jones, Buck

BB Gun, 36" l, wood stock with printed sundial, metal side with name, metal compass insert, Daisy **90.00**

Better Little Book, *Buck Jones and The Two–Gun Kid,* Whitman, #1404, 1937 ........................ **30.00**

Big Little Book, *The Fighting Code,* #1104, Pat Patterson, author, Columbia Pictures, artists, 1934, 160 pgs, hard cov, soft spine ........ **35.00**

Book, *Songs of the Western Trails,* 60 pgs, words and music, 9 x 12", 1940 copyright ................ **40.00**

Five Star Library Series, *Rocky Rhodes,* #15, Engel–Van Wiseman, Universal Pictures, artist, adapted by Harry Ormiston, 1935, 160 pgs, hard cov .............. **35.00**

Magazine, *Remember When Magazine,* 8½ x 11", Jones on cov, story and black and white photos, 1974 **7.50**

Pinback Button, Buck Jones Club, enameled brass, horseshoe, picture in center, 1930s ................ **15.00**

Song Book ...................... **30.00**

Maynard, Ken

Autograph, 8 x 10", glossy black and white photo, black inked signature "Ken Maynard 1941" ........... **125.00**

Big Little Book, *Ken Maynard in Western Justice,* #1430, Whitman, Rex Loomis, author, Irwin Myers, artist, 1938, standard size, 432 pgs, hard cov .......................... **22.00**

Little Big Book, *Strawberry Roan,* Saalfield, Grace Mack, author, Universal Pictures, artist, 1934, 4¾ x 5¼", 160 pgs, hardcover ........ **22.00**

Photograph, 9 x 11", color, black and white scene from *In Old Santa Fe* on reverse, Dixie premium ...... **30.00**

McCoy, Tim

Autograph, 8 x 10" glossy black and white photo, purple inked signature "Best Wishes Tim McCoy," c1940 **75.00**

Better Little Book, *Tim McCoy And The Sandy Gulch Stampede,* #1490, Whitman, 1939 ......... **40.00**

Big Little Book, *The Prescott Kid,* #1152, Whitman, adapted by Eleanor Packer, Columbia Pictures, artist, 1935, 4⅝ x 5¼", 160 pgs, hardcover, soft spine ............ **25.00**

Lobby Poster, 11 x 14", set of 8, 1930s

*Fighting Renegade* .............. **100.00**

*Straight Shooter* ................ **125.00**

Photograph, 9 x 11", color, black and white movie scenes on back, Dixie premium ...................... **15.00**

Montgomery, George, arcade card, 3¼ x 5¼", bust, black ................ **2.50**

Morgan, Tex, comic book, Tex Morgan Comic, Aug 1948, Vol. 1 ......... **45.00**

Robertson, Dale, platter, 12½" l, oval, china, western scene includes "Star Hotel," "Dale Robertson" on top, Wellsville China Co signature on bottom ............................ **75.00**

Rogers, Will, figure, 5⅞" h, wood, wearing brown suit, name on front, 1940s copyright .................. **50.00**

Walker, Clint

Autograph, blue inked signature on 8 x 10" glossy photo .............. **100.00**

Tablet, 8 x 10", "Cheyenne" ...... **8.00**

Wayne, John

Arcade Card, c1950 .............. **2.00**

Coin, metal, gold, c1979 .......... **7.50**

Coloring Book, 11 x 15", Saalfield, #2354–14 32 pgs, ten colored pages, 1951 copyright .......... **50.00**

Holster Set, leather belt, two holsters with name on side, orig box, early 1950s ........................ **45.00**

Knife, memorial, metal and plastic, "The Duke—John Wayne (1907–1979)" ........................ **10.00**

Movie Still, 8 x 10", black and white **4.00**

Pinback Button, 2½" d, "In Memory of a Great American" ........... **5.00**

Ring, photo ..................... **20.00**

Sheet Music, *Put Your Arms Around Me, Honey,* 9 x 12", 4 pgs, black and white photo of Wayne, Martha Scott, and Dale Evans, 1937 copyright .......................... **15.00**

Stationery, black and white drawing, includes envelope .............. **2.50**

# COW COLLECTIBLES

**Collecting Hints:** Image is everything. It makes no difference if the object was made yesterday or one hundred years ago as long as it pictures the collector's favorite bovine. It goes without saying that the representation must be a favorable one.

Cow collectors collect in quantity. Advertising pieces and folk art are two groups of cow images where secondary collectors frequently outbid cow collectors.

Cow creamers, some dating as early as the eighteenth century, are a favorite specialized collecting category. Antiques devotees focus on examples from the early period, but most cow collectors are perfectly willing to settle for twentieth century examples.

In order for an object to be considered a true cow collectible, it must either be in the shape of a cow or have a picture of a cow on its surface. Milk- and dairy-related material without a cow image is not a cow collectible. T–shirts with cow sayings fall into a gray area.

**History:** The domesticated cow has been around for over 8,000 years. Cows are part of Greek mythology. The Egyptians worshiped Hathor the cow–goddess. The Hindus venerate the cow as a sacred being. From the beginning the cow has been a focal point for artists and sculptors.

Some of the more famous nursery rhymes feature a cow, e.g. Hey, Diddle, Diddle and The House That Jack Built. Poetry and literature are rich with cow references.

It is impossible to divorce the cow from the dairy industry. Cow motifs appear throughout a wide range of dairy product advertising. The three most popular images are the Guernsey, Holstein, and Jersey.

There are a number of famous twentieth century cows. Early Disney cartoons featured Clarabelle. The dairy industry created Brooksie, Bossie, *La Vache Qui Ri*, and, of course, Elsie.

When she was at her peak, only the president of the United States had more public recognition than Elsie the Borden Cow. In the late 1930s Elsie made her initial appearances in a series of medical journal advertisements for Borden's Eagle Brand condensed milk. Her popularity grew as a result of Borden's 1939–40 World's Fair exhibition. A 1940 Hollywood appearance further enhanced her national reputation. In 1957 a "name Elsie's calf" contest produced three million entries. Borden briefly retired Elsie in the late 1960s; the public demanded her return. Today she is once again found on labels, in animated commercials, and at live appearances across the country.

In this age of equality, alas, the fabled bull receives short shrift. With the exception of Walt Disney's Ferdinand, the male of the species is regulated to a conspicuous second place.

**Reference:** Emily Margolin Gwathmey, *Wholly Cow!,* Abbeville Press, 1988.

**Periodical:** *Moosletter,* 240 Wahl Ave., Evans City, PA 16033.

Advertising Trade Card, 3¼ x 5¼", Dwight's Saleratus, black, white, and gold, cow on front, text on back, 1890s .......................... **15.00**

Book, *Herd Book,* Holstein Breeder's Assoc, 1884, 684 pgs, engraved and litho cow and bull illus ........... **18.00**

Butter Print

4½" d, round, standing cow, one piece turned handle, dark finish .. **330.00**

5¼" d, round, cow with tree and flower, scrubbed white, one piece turned handle .................. **150.00**

Cookie Jar, 11½" h, ceramic, barrel shape, tan, cov with figural Elsie bust, Pottery Guild, late 1940s .......... **225.00**

Figure, 3 x 5½ x 4", Ferdinand, rubber, Seiberling, Walt Disney Enterprises copyright, c1930 ................. **75.00**

Glass, 3½" h, clear, Aunt Elsie, brown illus, 1930–40 .................. **25.00**

**Tin, lunch box, Cow Brand Baking Soda, 10 lb, orange, bail handle, Church & Dwight Co., 7¾" w, 5½" d, 7½" h, $160.00.**

Ink Blotter, 4 x 9¼", Cow Brand Baking Soda, product package with cow, c1920 .......... **10.00**
Keychain Charm, 1" d, Swift's Brookfield, brass, emb, cow on award base, inscribed "June Dairy Month Award," early 1900s .......... **15.00**
Mug, 2½" h, china, white, full color Elsie illus, blue accent stripe, Juvenile Ware and Borden copyright, c1940 . **75.00**
Pinback Button
- ⅞" d
  - "Dairy Class '01," black and white cow and initials, "KSAC" ..... **15.00**
  - Livestock Steer, blue and white, bull illus, 1901–12 .......... **12.00**
- 1¼" d
  - Ayrshires, standing cow, US outline background, maroon and white, 1940s .......... **15.00**
  - Guernsey's Rich Inheritance, cow illus, yellow, brown, and white, 1930–40 .......... **18.00**
  - Jerseys For Mine, tan, blue rim, white lettering, "Compliments of AJCC" on back paper, c1920 .. **20.00**
- 3½" d, "Save Your Bull...For Your Victory Garden," celluloid, red and white cartoon bull, white background, blue lettering .......... **100.00**

Poster, Evaporated Milk–Pure Cow's Milk, black and white illus of cows, green background, c1940 .......... **15.00**
- Swift's Animal Fertilizers, 18 x 29½", linen, dark blue steer illus and print, 1920s .......... **55.00**

Sugar, Elmer, figural, china, 1930–40 . **40.00**
Toy
- Mechanical, 5¼" h, Elsie, hard rubber, jointed wood legs, dark green base with white name decal, Mespo Products Co, late 1940s .. **75.00**
- Milky the Marvelous Milking Cow, Kenner, copyright 1977 General Mills Fun Group, plastic cow, bell, milk pail, water trough pasture play mat, storybook, and package of milk tablets, orig box, unused .... **45.00**
- Ramp Walker, 3½" l, plastic, brown and white, orig sealed cellophane bag, marked "Made In Hong Kong," 1950s .......... **25.00**
- Windup, Walking Cow, plush, built–in key, walks forward, head moves, and mooing sound, orig box, T N, Japan, 1960s .......... **75.00**

Windmill Weight, 24½" l, cast iron, bull, red, white, and orange repaint, Made by Fairbury, Nebraska ....... **770.00**

# CRACKER JACK

**Collecting Hints:** Most collectors concentrate on the pre-plastic era. Toys in the original packaging are very rare. One possibility for specializing is toys from a given decade, for example in World War II soldiers, tanks, artillery pieces and other war related items.

Many prizes are marked "Cracker Jack" or carry a picture of the Sailor Boy and Bingo, his dog. Unmarked prizes can be confused with gumball machine novelties or prizes from Checkers, a rival firm.

**History:** F. W. Rueckheim, a popcorn store owner in Chicago, introduced a mixture of popcorn, peanuts, and molasses at the World's Columbian Exposition in 1893. Three years later the name "Cracker Jack" was applied to it. It gained popularity quickly and by 1908 appeared in the lyrics of *Take Me Out To The Ball Game.*

In 1910 Rueckheim included coupons on the box which could be redeemed for prizes. In 1912 prizes appeared in the box itself. The early prizes were made of paper, tin, lead, wood and porcelain. Plastic was introduced in 1948.

The Borden Company's Cracker Jack prize collection numbers over 10,000 examples; but this is not all of them. Knowledge continues to expand as more examples are found in bottoms of drawers, old jewelry boxes and attics.

Today's items are largely paper, the plastic magnifying glass being one exception. The company buys toys in lots of 25 million and keeps hundreds of prizes in circulation at one time. Borden's annual production is about 400 million boxes.

**Reference:** Alex Jaramillo, *Cracker Jack Prizes,* Abbeville Press, 1989.

Bank, 1 x 1½ x 1¾", litho tin, book form, 1920s .......... **150.00**
Book, *Cracker Jack Painting & Drawing Book,* Saalfield, 1917, 24 pgs ...... **35.00**
Booklet
 Cracker Jack In Switzerland, prize, 4 pgs, 1926 copyright ........... **50.00**
 Cracker Jack Riddles, red, white, and blue cov, 42 pgs, 1920s ......... **50.00**
Box, 7" h, red, white and blue, cardboard, 1930s .................. **40.00**
Cereal Cup, Ralston ................ **4.00**
Charm, 1¼" d, plastic, diecut, initial M, dark rose, back marked "C J Co," 1950s ......................... **12.00**
Coin, 1" d, Mystery Club, emb aluminum, presidential profile, back with "Join Cracker Jack Mystery Club/Save This Coin," 1930s ................ **18.00**
Doll, 12" h, vinyl, orig unopened display card, Vogue Dolls, 1980 copyright .......................... **25.00**
Figure, 2" h, Uncle Walt, Skeezix, tin . **45.00**
Game
 Card, 1976, one card missing, wear to orig box ................... **15.00**
 Cracker Jack Toy Surprise Game, Milton Bradley, orig box, 1976 ...... **25.00**
Lapel Stud
 1" l, oval, metal, emb Sailor Boy Jack and dog, dark finish, early 1920s . **25.00**
 2" l, wing shape, metal, center inscription, 1930s ............... **50.00**
Lunch Box, metal, Aladdin Industries, c1979 ......................... **30.00**
Pencil, 3½" l, red name ............ **15.00**
Pinback Button, 1¼" d, multicolored portrait illus of young lady, back inscribed "Cracker Jack 5¢ Candied Popcorn & Roasted Peanuts," early 1900s ......................... **50.00**
Post Card, 3 x 5½", Cracker Jack Bears #7, bears greeting President Roosevelt, 1907 postmark ............. **25.00**
Prize
 Cracker Jack Magnetic Fortune Teller, diecut, transparent red and gold, orig brown paper envelope with printed directions, 1920s ........ **25.00**
 Drawing Book, 1¼ x 2½", blue and white cov design, 4 pgs, nursery rhyme characters on each side, tracing sheets between each page, unused, 1920s ................. **30.00**
 Figure, plastic, 1950s
  Bear, 1¾" h, standing, back marked "Cracker Jack" ............... **10.00**
  Billy Goat, 1¼" h, gray, marked "Cracker Jack" ............... **10.00**
  Buddha, 1¼" h, seated, inscribed on back "Hoki/God of Childish Mischief" .................. **12.00**
  Dutch Girl, 1½", tan, inscribed on base "Holland" .............. **15.00**
  Milkmaid, 1½" h, holding bucket, gray and pink, marked "C J Co" **12.00**
 Game No 7, Magic Words, 1½ x 2½", paper and cardboard, 1920–30 .. **50.00**
 Game No 8, The Farmer's Fence, 1920–30 ...................... **35.00**
 Horsedrawn Delivery Wagon, 2" l, litho tin, red, white, and blue, Cracker Jack box on one side, Angelus Marshmallows box on other, 1920s ........................ **50.00**
 Mirror, 2½" l, cardboard, back marked "Made In Germany," 1930s **15.00**
 Palm Puzzle, 1¼" sq, cardboard, plastic dome over face, diecut eyes with black ball, back is "Gee Cracker Jack Is Good," 1930s .... **50.00**
 Rocking Horse, 1⅛" l, metal, metallic purple finish, 1920s ............ **15.00**
 Watch, 1½" d, tin, 1930s ......... **25.00**
Toy
 Railroad Car, 3" l, metal, emb, orange, black rubber wheels, Tootsietoy, 1930s ..................... **50.00**
 Top, 1⅜" d, litho tin, diecut, red, white, and blue, 1930s ......... **55.00**
 Wheelbarrow, litho tin, yellow and green, green wheels, 4½" l wood rod, c1930 .................... **25.00**
Watch, litho, 1940s, near mint ....... **75.00**
Whistle, 2¼" l, tin, marked "Cracker Jack" on top, silver luster, 1920s ... **15.00**

**Prize, caboose, plastic, gray, $5.00.**

# CREDIT COINS AND TOKENS

**Collecting Hints:** Specialization is the key to successful collecting. Plan a collection that can be completed. Completeness tends to increase a collection's value.

When collecting charge coins, stay away from rusted or damaged pieces. Inferior pieces attract little interest unless rare.

Metal charge plates have little collector interest. They should remain affordable for years which means they'll probably not advance in value.

Most interest is in credit cards. Scarce and rare cards, when they can be located, are still affordable. National credit cards are eagerly sought. American Express is the most popular.

Paper and laminated paper credit cards are highly desirable. When it comes to collecting these, don't concern yourself with condition. Go ahead and acquire any you find. They're so difficult to locate that it could take years to find another specimen. Some are so rare that they might be unique!

Plastic credit cards issued before 1970 are scarce. Occasionally, you'll find a mint condition card. Generally, you'll have to settle for used. Plastic cards issued after 1980 should be collected in mint condition.

The best collecting hint is, collect what you like. You'll provide yourself with years of enjoyment and that's the best investment you'll ever make!

**History:** Charge coins, the first credit pieces, started being issued in the 1890s. Charge coins are approximately the size of a quarter or half dollar. Because of their size, they were often carried with change. This is why they were commonly referred to as coins.

Charge coins come in various shapes, sizes and materials. Most are square, round or oval. Some are in the shapes of shirts, socks or hats. They're made from various materials such as fiber, German silver, celluloid, steel and copper. The issuing store has its name, monogram or initials on the coin. Each coin has a customer identification number. Charge coins were still in use as late as 1959.

Metal charge plates were in use from the 1930s to the 1950s. These plates look like military dog tags. The front of the plate contains the customer's name, address and account number. The back has a piece of cardboard that carries the store's name and customer's signature space.

Paper credit cards were in use in the early 1930s. They were easily damaged, so some companies began laminating them with clear plastic in the 1940s. Laminated cards were issued until the 1950s. The plastic cards we know today replaced the laminated cards in the late 1950s.

**References:** Stephen P. Albert and Lawrence E. Elman, *Tokens and Medals: A Guide to the Identification and Values of United States Exonumia,* published by authors, 1991; Glyn V. Farber, *Hickey Brothers Cigar Store Tokens,* The Token and Medal Society, Inc., 1992; Russell Rulau, *Early American Tokens: 1700–1832, 3rd Edition,* Krause Publications, 1991; Russell Rulau, *Hard Times Tokens: 1832–1844,* Krause Publications, 4th Edition, 1992; Russell Rulau, *Tokens of the Gay Nineties,* Krause Publications, 1987; Russell Rulau, *U.S. Merchant Tokens: 1845–1860,* Krause Publications, 1990; Russell Rulau, *U.S. Trade Tokens: 1866–1889, Second Edition,* Krause Publications, 1988; Greg Tunks, *Credit Card Collecting Bonanza, Second Edition,* published by author, 1989.

**Periodical:** *Credit Card Collector,* 150 Hohldale, Houston, TX 77022.

**Collectors' Clubs:** American Numismatic Association, 818 N. Cascade Ave., Colorado Springs, CO 80903; Token & Medal Society, Inc., P. O. Box 951988, Lake Mary, FL 32795.

## CARDS

American Airlines, March 1986 ...... **6.00**
American Express
 1958, red printing, purplish blue ground, paper ................ **500.00**
 1968, violet, centurion on upper left **100.00**
 1970, green, "The Money Card" ... **25.00**
 1972, gold, "The Executive Money Card," card appears to change colors when rotated ............... **50.00**
ARCO, 1976, Atlantic Richfield Company ........................... **4.00**
AT&T, phone card, plastic ........... **3.00**
Bank Americard, account number in tan area
 Magnetic stripe .................. **15.00**
 Without magnetic stripe ........... **7.50**
Bell System Credit Card, 1964, high gloss paperboard, dime holder ..... **15.00**
Bloomingdale's, brown on white, tan border .......................... **10.00**
Carte Blanche
 1973, gold, blue on gold .......... **40.00**
 1977, blue on white, gold border .. **7.50**
Champlin, 1967, "A great name in the Great Plains," gas pump island drawing ............................ **12.00**
Chevron National Credit Card, 1967, attendants servicing car ............ **20.00**
Choice, 1984 ...................... **4.00**
Diners Club
 Booklet, April 30, 1956, 126 pgs, Hertz ad in back with drawing of '55 Ford, blank memo pgs bound inside to record charge transactions **175.00**
 Colored blocks, 1967, blue top .... **45.00**
 Gray ground, Citicorp ............ **12.50**
 Red top, expires Nov 30, 1962 .... **55.00**
 Silver and blue logo, white ground . **6.00**
Eastern, October 1984 ............. **7.50**
Esso, 1966, "Happy Motoring," waving attendant ....................... **15.00**
Fina, early 1970s, large blue Fina .... **5.00**
Frederick's of Hollywood, "Fabulous Hollywood Fashions" ............. **17.50**

General Tire, December 31, 1953, paperboard, lightly soiled, calendar on back . . . . . . . . . . . . . . . . . . . . . . . . . **25.00**
Gimbels, black on brown, New York and all branch stores . . . . . . . . . . . . **4.00**
Goodyear, blimp illus . . . . . . . . . . . . . . . **7.50**
Gulf Travel Card, land, sea, air, car, boat, and plane drawing . . . . . . . . . . **10.00**
Hilton Hotels
 1955, paperboard . . . . . . . . . . . . . . . **35.00**
 1958, paperboard, large size, high gloss finish . . . . . . . . . . . . . . . . . . . **45.00**
Hotel McLure, 1951–52, paperboard . **25.00**
Hotels Statler, 1952, paperboard . . . . . **45.00**
Illinois Bankcharge, red, white, and blue shield . . . . . . . . . . . . . . . . . . . . . **15.00**
International Credit Card, 1960, sailing ship logo . . . . . . . . . . . . . . . . . . . . . . **30.00**
Jordan Marsh Co, blue on white, store drawing, good in Boston, Framingham, Malden, and Peabody . . . **20.00**
Korvettes, personal charge plate . . . . . . **3.00**
Levy's, paperboard, c1950s or early 60s, tan with brown top, Tucson, Douglans, and Warren . . . . . . . . . . . . **22.50**
Lit Brothers, blue and white stripes . . . **10.00**

**Top: Zollinger Harned, Allentown, red on white; middle: Zollinger's, four store system, blue on white; bottom: Lit Brothers, Philadelphia, alternating blue and white stripes; price each $10.00.**

Lord & Taylor, flower on front . . . . . . . **6.00**
Macy's, red star, "It's smart to be thrifty" **5.00**
Marshall Field & Company, green and white . . . . . . . . . . . . . . . . . . . . . . . . . . **5.00**
Mastercard
 Pre–hologram . . . . . . . . . . . . . . . . . . . . **3.00**
 Pre–hologram, cardholder photograph on back . . . . . . . . . . . . . . . . . **6.00**
 Pre–hologram, gold card . . . . . . . . . . **6.00**
Mastercharge
 Cardholder photograph on back, early 1970s . . . . . . . . . . . . . . . . . . . . **60.00**
 Magnetic stripe . . . . . . . . . . . . . . . . . . **7.50**
Midwest Bank Card, Charge–It, Harris Bank, 05/67, blue top . . . . . . . . . . . . **22.50**
Mobil, Pegasus on Mobil sign on front upper left . . . . . . . . . . . . . . . . . . . . . . **10.00**
Montgomery Ward, yellow and white, national charge–all card . . . . . . . . . . . **7.50**
Neiman Marcus, commemorative credit card, 75th anniversary . . . . . . . . . . . **15.00**
Pan Am Take Off Card, 1970 . . . . . . . . **10.00**
Penneys, black on blue, "always first quality" . . . . . . . . . . . . . . . . . . . . . . . . **8.00**
Phillips 66, non–expiring, "passport to everywhere" . . . . . . . . . . . . . . . . . . . . . **12.00**
Playboy Club International
 Gold, Jan 1979 . . . . . . . . . . . . . . . . . . **6.00**
 Membership Card, Feb 1986 . . . . . . . **5.00**
Saks Fifth Avenue, paper, charge account identification card . . . . . . . . . . **30.00**
Sears, Sears in box . . . . . . . . . . . . . . . . . **8.00**
Shannon's Furniture, 1939, Tulsa, OK, black on blue, paper, store drawing **12.00**
Sinclair, 1971, motoring credit, waving green dinosaur . . . . . . . . . . . . . . . . . . . **6.00**
Skelly, ladies credit card, two gloved hands holding Skelly symbol . . . . . . . **20.00**
Spur, 10/70 . . . . . . . . . . . . . . . . . . . . . . . **12.00**
Standard Oil, 1972, red and blue map of United States . . . . . . . . . . . . . . . . . . **15.00**
Sunoco, custom blended gasoline pump drawing . . . . . . . . . . . . . . . . . . . . . . . . **7.50**
Texaco Travel Card, car, boat, and plane drawings . . . . . . . . . . . . . . . . . . **5.00**
The Texas Company (Texaco), 1957, tan and white, paper . . . . . . . . . . . . . . . . **60.00**
TWA, 1974, getaway card, couple wearing swim suits holding hands . . **10.00**
Uni–Card, 1970s . . . . . . . . . . . . . . . . . . . **10.00**
Vickers Refining Co, lifetime courtesy card, crown over V logo . . . . . . . . . . **17.50**
Visa
 Atlanta Falcons, 4/89 . . . . . . . . . . . . . **15.00**
 Pre–hologram . . . . . . . . . . . . . . . . . . . . **2.50**
Wallachs, undated, high gloss paperboard . . . . . . . . . . . . . . . . . . . . . . . . . . **25.00**
John Wanamaker, metal charge plate, carrying case . . . . . . . . . . . . . . . . . . . **17.50**
Woolco, orange on white . . . . . . . . . . . **10.00**

## TOKENS

Boggs and Buhl, Pittsburgh, PA, oval, white metal, knight's helmet between backward and regular B . . . . . . . . . . . **15.00**
Conrad's, Boston, MA, irregular round, golden plating, picture of store . . . . . **25.00**
Dives, Pomeroy & Stewart, Reading Pottsville, PA, rect, white metal, initials D F & S, thistles . . . . . . . . . . . . . **12.00**

George B Evans, Philadelphia, PA, diamond shape, white metal, drugs and gifts .......... **15.00**
Gilchrist, Boston, MA, golden shield, G Co .......... **17.50**
Gimble Brothers
- Philadelphia, PA, rect, white metal, lion holding shield, GB initials, finder mailing instructions on back **14.00**
- New York City, oval, white metal, GB in circle at top, New York at bottom **18.00**

Lit Brothers, Philadelphia, PA, irregular oval, white metal, LB, date of issue . **20.00**
C F Massey, Rochester, MN, octagonal, white metal, ornate interlocking C F M .......... **15.00**
Neill, Philadelphia, PA, sq, white metal, Neill script .......... **12.50**
Plotkin Brothers, Boston, MA, rect, white metal, lion head over shield containing PB .......... **17.50**
Pocohontas Pioneer Garage, Philadelphia, PA, oval, white metal, high relief Indian profile .......... **17.50**
R H Stearns, Boston, MA, oval, white metal, interlocking R H S Co ...... **15.00**
John Wanamaker, Philadelphia, PA, irregular oval, German silver, JW, fleur–de–lis, ornamental border, 1890s .......... **40.00**
R H White, Boston, MA, pear shape, white metal, interlocking R H W Co script .......... **20.00**

# CROOKSVILLE POTTERY

**Collecting Hints:** Concentrate your collecting efforts on a single shape and decal pattern. One of the more easily found patterns is Silhouette, featuring a black silhouette decal of two men sitting at a table with a begging dog in the foreground. While pieces appear regularly in the market, a commitment to the hunt is required from any Crooksville collector.

In the early 1940s Crooksville made "Raggedy Ann and Andy Ware." These pieces are highly priced. The back stamp contains a line reading "COPYRIGHT 1941 JOHNY GRUELLE CO."

Make certain when buying any decaled piece that the decal image is crisp and free of marks. Crooksville pieces were produced in quantity so it is critical to set high acquisition standards.

**History:** The Crooksville China Company, Crooksville, Ohio, was founded in 1902. The company manufactured an inexpensive line of semi–porcelain dinnerware priced and designed to fit the tastes of middle-class America. Decoration focused on country motifs.

Crooksville's ovenware line was "Pantry–Bak–In" ware that had a hard, smooth, attractively decaled body. The initial product was a waffle set. By 1932 five sizes of bowls, coffeepots, two covered jugs, two teapots, and numerous other kitchen accessory pieces were added to the line.

Crooksville made "Stinthal China," a fine, thin, semi–porcelain ware. There is no mention of Crooksville in the mark.

Crooksville usually did not include a pattern name as part of its marking. Hence, patterns are hard to identify. Two easily recognized shapes are the modernistic Dartmouth (introduced in 1939) and Euclid a.k.a Fruits (introduced in 1935) which has an embossed fruit and leaf design. Both are found with a variety of decal patterns. Sun Lure is a mark found on wares with a light cream–to–yellow color.

The company ceased operations in 1959. During its last three decades of operation, it averaged between 250 and 300 employees.

**References:** Jo Cunningham, *The Collector's Encyclopedia of American Dinnerware,* Collector Books, 1982, 1992 value update; Harvey Duke, *The Official Identification and Price Guide to Pottery and Porcelain, Seventh Edition* , House of Collectibles, 1989; Lois Lehner, *Lehner's Encyclopedia of U. S. Marks on Pottery, Porcelain & Clay,* Collector Books, 1988.

**PETIT POINT HOUSE.** Cottage decal on white ground. Trimmed with red band.

Berry Bowl .......... **4.00**
Cereal Bowl, 6″ d .......... **5.00**
Cup and Saucer .......... **7.00**
Plate
- 6″ d, bread and butter .......... **4.00**
- 7″ d, salad .......... **5.00**
- 10″ d, dinner .......... **8.00**

**RUST BOUQUET.** Rust colored floral decal on white ground.

Coffeepot .......... **25.00**
Cup and Saucer .......... **6.00**
Mixing Bowl, 8½″ d .......... **15.00**
Pie Baker, 10″ d .......... **14.00**
Plate
- 6″ d, bread and butter .......... **3.00**
- 9¾″ d, dinner .......... **6.00**

Platter, oblong, 11½″ l .......... **8.00**

**SILHOUETTE.** Black silhouette decal of two men sitting at a table, begging dog in foreground. White ground. Produced during the 1930s.

Creamer .......... **12.00**
Mixing Bowl, Pantry Bak–In .......... **10.00**

**Silhouette, pitcher, $18.00.**

Pie Baker, 10" d, Pantry Bak–In ...... **20.00**
Plate
8" d, salad ...................... **8.00**
10" d, dinner .................... **10.00**
Platter, oval, 11½" l ................ **15.00**
Serving Tray, 11¾" w, handled ....... **18.00**

# DAIRY ITEMS

**Collecting Hints:** Concentrate on the material associated with one specific dairy, region or national firm. Much of the material available relates to advertising such as blotters, brochures, postcards, and trade cards.

Collectors of dairy items compete with many other groups. Milk bottle collectors try to supplement their collection with these "go–withs." Farm item collectors concentrate on cream separator materials and other farm related items. Ice cream collectors seek cartons and other material. Finally, home decorators like the milk cans and other large, showy objects.

**History:** There were hundreds of small dairies and creameries scattered throughout the United States during the late 19th to mid-20th centuries. Many issued a variety of material to promote their products.

Eventually regional cooperatives expanded the marketing regions, and many smaller dairies closed. Companies such as Borden distributed products on a national level. Borden created the advertising character of "Elsie, the Borden Cow" to help sell its products. Additional consolidation of firms has occurred, encouraged in part by state milk marketing boards and federal subsidies.

**References:** Dana Gehman Morykan and Harry L. Rinker, *Warman's Country Antiques & Collectibles,* Wallace–Homestead, 1992; John Tutton, *Udder Delight,* published by author.

**Periodical:** *The Milk Route,* 4 Ox Bow Road, Westport, CT 06880.

**Museums:** The Farmers Museum, Cooperstown, NY; Southwest Dairy Museum, Arlington, TX; Billings Farm Museum, Woodstock, VT.

**Advisors:** Tom Gallagher and Tony Knipp.

**Notes:** A milk bottle cap refers to a plug type cap placed on a bottle by the dairy in a bottling room. A milk bottle cover was made of either metal or glass and often contained dairy advertising. It was used to cover the bottle after the paper cap was removed. A milk bottle cap pick was used to remove the plug type milk bottle caps. A milk bottle cap opener had the same function but was used to remove a different style cap found on more modern bottles, known as the DACRO type.

**See:** Milk Bottles.

Advertising Trade Card
Borden's, three children hugging each other and holding a can of Borden's Condensed Milk, directions for use, New York city address on back, copyright 1889 ................ **10.00**
T W Decker & Sons, little girl swinging on the moon, discussion of Decker's new plant at Pawling, NY, and listing of New York city depots on back ....................... **12.00**
Bank, Rutter Bros. Dairy Products, dairy truck, plastic, white, red decal, c1960 **40.00**
Blotter
Union Grove Dairy, display ........ **30.00**
Universal Super Strength Milk Bottles, picture of plant in Parkersburg, WV, address of NE representative in Hartford, CT, white and orange lettering, white ground ............ **9.00**
Booklet, We Pull for Windsor, picture of Windsor Farm Dairy, Denver, CO, on front, picture of horses on back, pictures of plant and workers inside, 18 pgs, early 1930s ................. **15.00**
Butter Box, Bossie's Best Brand Butter, four color picture of Jersey cow, Aberdeen Creamery Co, folded ....... **5.00**
Calendar, 1927, Broad View Farm, pure milk from our accredited herd, Rochester, NH, little girl climbs steps of house and reaches for giant bottle of Broad View Farm's milk, sheet for each month with saying about milk . **15.00**
Clock, Old Southern Belle Dairy, 16" sq, girl in red dress .................. **65.00**
Cream Siphon, Marvel, aluminum, fits in bottle and siphons cream into cream pitcher or other vessel ...... **6.00**
Cream Top Spoon, used with cream top bottle, Fritchett Bros Dairy, Pat Applied For ........................ **12.00**
Creamer
American Dairy Foods ............ **12.00**
Anthony's Cream ................. **13.00**
Casey's Dairy .................... **12.00**
Progressive ...................... **10.00**

Rosebud Dairy .................. **9.00**
Swaner's, orig cap .............. **16.00**
Velvet, Owensboro, KY .......... **17.50**
Crock, Model Dairy .............. **30.00**
Fan, girl in highchair, spilled milk from her cup on front, Compliments of Lebel's Dairy, 145 E Hollis Street, Nashua, NH, on back .............. **10.00**
Hanger, 9¾" h, Gridley Dairy, assorted colors, Little Miss Curleylocks pictured in various outfits, price for set of five .......................... **45.00**
Hot Pad Holder, 4¼ x 4¼", Kriebel's Dairies, Hereford, PA, muslin, hemp backing ........................ **1.50**
Ice Pick, Pevely Dairy, metal ........ **12.00**
Measuring Cup, Pyrex, 8 oz, Lenkerbrook Farms, Inc, red markings .... **5.00**
Measuring Tape, Cass Dairy Farm, Inc, Jersey & Ayshire Milk on front, You Can Whip Our Cream But You Can't Beat Our Milk, Try Our Cream on reverse, celluloid container ........ **30.00**
Milk Book, Fairfield Dairy, multicolored Hoen illus, c1900 ................ **15.00**
Milk Bottle
Grasslands Dairy, qt ............. **10.00**
Thatchers Dairy, 1884, emb man milking cow .................. **250.00**

**Bottle, miniature, Freemans Dairy, Best by Test, 2" h, $6.50.**

Milk Bottle Cap
Christmas Seal Cap of 1939, Christmas seal illus ................. **5.00**
Davol Anti Germ, rubber, fits over lip of milk bottle to keep out dirt, orig container .................... **8.00**
Grade A Raw Milk, red and white .. **.50**
Heber Springs Dairy, Heber Springs, AR .......................... **.25**
I.O.O.F. Independent Order of Odd Fellows, Home Pasteurized Milk, Greensburg, IN ............... **.25**
Kents Dairy Farms, Vitamin D, Olean, NY .......................... **.20**
Parker Goat Dairy, Raw Milk, picture of goat ....................... **1.25**
Set, US Presidents, 35 in set, price for 35 piece set .................. **12.00**
War Cap, "Milk wouldn't be here if (large swastika) were" .......... **5.00**
Milk Bottle Cap Opener, DACRO
Brock Hall Dairy Products on front, Purity Protected Dacro Sealed Milk on back ...................... **5.00**
Deerfoot Farms, Southborough, MA **5.00**
Milk Bottle Cap Pick
Borden Select Milk ............... **5.00**
Sheffield Farms Co, Inc ........... **5.00**
Milk Bottle Cap Pick and Bottle Opener, Forest Glen Creamery Co .......... **6.00**
Milk Bottle Carrier, metal, wire handle, holds six round quarts ............ **10.00**
Milk Bottle Cover
Dorsey, aluminum, clamps on milk bottle, movable cover with pouring spout underneath ............... **5.00**
Frigidaire, green glass, fits over bottle lip to keep out dirt ............. **8.00**
Milk Box, wood, dairy name, holds four to six quarts .................... **9.00**
Milk Can, ten gallon size
Brass nameplate showing name of shipper ...................... **18.00**
Plain or with dairy's name ......... **10.00**
Mug
Dairy Dell ...................... **16.00**
Isaly Buttermilk, barrel shape, ironstone ........................ **75.00**
Pencil, Rutter Dairy, York and Hanover, PA, wood, unused ............... **4.00**
Pickle Fork, 8" l, Dayton, OH, Finest Dairy Products Co ................ **6.00**
Playing Cards, Quality Dairy, Q motif on each, complete deck ........... **8.00**
Post Card
Borden's Condensed Milk Plant No. 1, Brewster, NY, side view of plant, signed on front by plant manager, addressed to Borden's office in NYC ......................... **10.00**
Ebert Ice Cream Company, factory pictured ...................... **5.00**
Elsie, Elmer, and Beauregard, traveling representatives of Borden's family of fine foods, shows characters in traveling bedroom, explanation of bedroom furnishings on back, color ........................ **7.50**
Poster
Evaporated Milk–Pure Cow's Milk, black and white cows, green ground, 1940 .................. **8.00**
Healthy & Happy, colorful portrait of boy and girl eating bananas, milk, Lawrence Wileur, full color, 17 x 21" ......................... **10.00**

Premium List, Mohawk Condensed Milk Co, can of Sweet Clover Brand Condensed Milk on front, can of Gold Cross Brand Condensed Milk on back, 40 pgs, 1927 . . . . . . . . . . . . . . . **5.00**
Printer's Dies, to print milk bottle caps, dairy name, town, and state . . . . . . . **5.00**
Ruler, 6″ l, Bryant & Champman Dairy, Hartford, CT, wood . . . . . . . . . . . . . . . **4.00**
Sewing Kit, Borden's Mitchell Dairy, Elsie pictured on cov, Milk's Good Anytime, Better still Make It Borden's slogan . . . . . . . . . . . . . . . . . . . . . . . . **8.00**
Stamp Case, Evans Dairy, 1⅜ x 2¼″, black and white horse–drawn dairy wagon photo, red inscription . . . . . . **20.00**
Stickpin
  Empire Cream Separator . . . . . . . . . . . **20.00**
  National Cream Separator, Quaker . **10.00**
  Sharples Separator . . . . . . . . . . . . . . . . **25.00**
Table Mat, Dengler Dairies, Telford, PA, When Baking Use This Mat, When Cooking Use our Milk, There's Health in Every Drop, Dengler Dairies, Telford, PA . . . . . . . . . . . . . . . . . . . . . . . . **5.00**
Tip Tray, DeLaval . . . . . . . . . . . . . . . . . . **85.00**
Token, Muskalonge View Dairy, Fremont, OH, plastic, good for one quart of homogenized milk . . . . . . . . . . . . . **5.00**
Toy, milk tanker, Lesney, England, plastic, blue and white, Milk's The One on side . . . . . . . . . . . . . . . . . . . . . . . . **6.00**

# DEGENHART GLASS

**Collecting Hints:** Degenhart pressed glass novelties are collected by mold (Forget–Me–Not toothpick holders or all Degenhart toothpick holders), by individual colors (Rubina or Bloody Mary), or by group colors (opaque, iridescent, crystal, or slag).

Correct color identification is the key to full enjoyment of collecting Degenhart glass. Because of the slight variations in the hundreds of colors produced at the Degenhart Crystal Art Glass factory from 1947 to 1978, it is important for beginning collectors to acquire the eye for distinguishing Degenhart colors, particularly the green and blue variations. A knowledgeable collector or dealer should be sought for guidance. Side by side color comparison is extremely helpful.

Later glass produced by the factory can be distinguished by the trademark of a "D" in a heart or only a "D" on certain molds where space prohibited the full mark. Use of this mark began around 1972 and by late 1977 most of the molds had been marked. Prior to this time, c1947–1972, no glass was marked with the exception of the owl, and occasionally other pieces that were identified by hand stamping a block letter "D" to the object as it came out of the mold. This hand stamping was started and continued during the period 1967 to 1972.

Collecting unmarked Degenhart glass made from 1947 to c1970 poses no problem once a collector becomes familiar with molds and colors being worked during that period. Some of the most sought after colors such as Amethyst & White Slag, Amethyst Carnival, and Custard Slag are unmarked, yet are the most desirable. Keep in mind that some colors such as Custard (opaque yellow), Heliotrope (opaque purple), and Tomato (opaque orange red) were repeated and can be found marked and unmarked depending on production date.

**History:** John (1884–1964) and Elizabeth (1889–1978) Degenhart operated the Crystal Art Glass factory of Cambridge, Ohio, from 1947 to 1978. The factory specialized in reproduction pressed glass novelties and paperweights. Over 50 molds were worked by this factory including ten toothpick holders, five salts, and six animal covered dishes of various sizes.

When the factory ceased operation, many of the molds were purchased by Boyd Crystal Art Glass, Cambridge, OH. Boyd has issued pieces in many new colors. All are marked with a "B" in a diamond.

**References:** Gene Florence, *Degenhart Glass and Paperweights: A Collector's Guide To Colors And Values,* Degenhart Paperweight and Glass Museum, 1982; Ellen Tischbein Schroy, *Warman's Glass,* Wallace–Homestead, 1992.

**Collectors' Club:** The Friends of Degenhart, Degenhart Paperweight and Glass Museum, Inc., 65323 Highland Hills Rd., P. O. Box 186, Cambridge, OH 43725.

**Museum:** The Degenhart Paperweight and Glass Museum, Inc., Cambridge, OH. The museum covers all types of Ohio Valley glass.

**REPRODUCTION ALERT:** Although most of the Degenhart molds were reproductions themselves, there are contemporary pieces that can be confusing such as Kanawha's bird salt and bow slipper; L. G. Wright's mini–slipper, daisy & button salt, and 5″ robin covered dish; and many other contemporary American pieces. The 3″ bird salt and mini–pitcher also are made by an unknown glassmaker in Taiwan.

Animal Covered Dish
  Hen, 3″, introduced 1968, marked 1973
    Champagne . . . . . . . . . . . . . . . . . . . **35.00**
    Dark Green . . . . . . . . . . . . . . . . . . . **25.00**
    Pigeon Blood . . . . . . . . . . . . . . . . . **48.00**
    Sapphire Blue . . . . . . . . . . . . . . . . . **20.00**

Robin, introduced 1960, marked 1972
- Bloody Mary .......... 90.00
- Taffeta .......... 50.00

Turkey, introduced 1971, marked 1972
- Amethyst .......... 50.00
- Crown Tuscan .......... 50.00
- Custard .......... 60.00
- Slag, gray .......... 80.00

Basket, cobalt blue .......... 18.00

Bicentennial Bell, introduced 1974, marked 1974
- Amethyst .......... 4.00
- Canary .......... 15.00
- Elizabeth's Lime Ice .......... 15.00
- Heatherbloom .......... 4.00
- Peach .......... 8.50
- Seafoam .......... 9.00

Candy Dish, cov, Wildflower pattern, introduced 1971, marked 1972
- Crystal .......... 15.00
- Pink .......... 25.00
- Twilight Blue .......... 25.00

Chick, 2"
- Crown Tuscan .......... 30.00
- Vaseline .......... 18.00

Creamer and Sugar, Texas, introduced 1962, marked 1972
- Emerald Green .......... 50.00
- Pink .......... 45.00

Cup Plate
- Heart and Lyre, introduced 1965, marked c1977
  - Cobalt Blue .......... 12.00
  - Gold .......... 9.00
  - Sapphire Blue .......... 12.50
- Seal of Ohio, introduced 1971, marked c1977
  - Amethyst .......... 15.00
  - Cobalt Blue .......... 17.50
  - Sunset .......... 10.00

Gypsy Pot, introduced 1962, marked 1972
- Blue Jay .......... 20.00
- Canary .......... 20.00
- Pigeon Blood .......... 25.00
- Tomato .......... 30.00

**Pitcher, miniature, marked 1973, $20.00.**

Hand, introduced 1949, marked c1975
- Amethyst .......... 8.50
- Blue and White .......... 20.00
- Crown Tuscan .......... 18.00
- Frosty Jade .......... 15.00
- Persimmon .......... 8.00

Hat, Daisy and Button, introduced 1974, marked 1972
- Amethyst .......... 8.00
- Custard .......... 20.00
- Opalescent .......... 12.00
- Vaseline .......... 15.00

Jewelry Box, Heart, introduced 1964, marked 1972
- Baby Green .......... 25.00
- Crown Tuscan .......... 48.00
- Fawn .......... 18.00
- Light Chocolate Creme .......... 35.00
- Old Lavender .......... 25.00

Owl, introduced 1967, marked 1967, over 200 colors made
- Amberina .......... 35.00
- Amethyst .......... 30.00
- Bluebell .......... 30.00
- Charcoal .......... 40.00
- Crown Tuscan .......... 40.00
- Frosty Jade .......... 45.00
- Ivorina .......... 30.00
- Lavender Blue .......... 50.00
- Midnight Sun .......... 30.00
- Seafoam .......... 36.00
- Sunset .......... 25.00
- Willow Blue .......... 48.00

Paperweight
- Crystal Art Glass Paperweight, Zack and Bernard Boyd, Rollin Braden, Gus Theret, and William Degenhart
  - Ceramic animal encased in air traps 135.00
  - Decal Weight .......... 50.00
  - Five Bubble .......... 50.00
  - Name Weight .......... 50.00
  - Peacock Feather .......... 50.00
- Paperweight by John or Charles Degenhart
  - Cartoon Characters .......... 175.00
  - Double Tree .......... 80.00
  - Flower Pot .......... 85.00
  - Gear Shift Knob, patented 1929 .. 125.00
  - Name Weight .......... 50.00
  - Rose, red and white .......... 300.00
  - Window Weight, overlay .......... 400.00

Pooch, introduced 1976, marked 1976, approximately 110 colors made
- April Green .......... 15.00
- Bernard Boyd's Ebony .......... 20.00
- Fawn .......... 20.00
- Royal Violet .......... 17.50
- Slag
  - Caramel Custard .......... 22.00
  - Ivory .......... 20.00
  - Marble, blue .......... 20.00

Priscilla, introduced 1976, marked 1976, 40 colors made
- Amethyst ........ **85.00**
- Blue and White ........ **88.00**
- Crown Tuscan ........ **75.00**
- Crystal ........ **40.00**
- Delft ........ **90.00**
- Ivory ........ **85.00**
- Jade Green ........ **100.00**
- Peach ........ **60.00**

Salt
- Daisy and Button, introduced 1970, marked 1972
  - Amethyst ........ **15.00**
  - Bittersweet ........ **15.00**
  - Lime Ice ........ **15.00**
- Star and Dewdrop, introduced 1952, marked 1972
  - Aqua ........ **15.00**
  - Henry's Blue ........ **16.50**
  - Opalescent ........ **15.00**
  - Sapphire Blue ........ **16.50**
  - Topaz ........ **18.00**

Salt and Pepper Shakers, pr, Birds, introduced 1958, marked 1973
- Amberina ........ **25.00**
- Antique Blue ........ **20.00**
- Gun Metal ........ **18.00**
- Taffeta ........ **22.00**

Shoe, figural
- Baby Shoe, milk glass ........ **15.00**
- High Button Boot, light blue ........ **25.00**
- Slipper, bow, caramel ........ **30.00**
- Skate, green, orig decal ........ **30.00**

Smoky Bear, jade green ........ **30.00**

Tiger, lavender blue ........ **30.00**

Tomahawk, introduced 1947, marked c1975
- Blue Green ........ **20.00**
- Persimmon ........ **30.00**

Toothpick Holder
- Baby or Tramp Shoe, introduced 1962, marked 1972
  - Bluebell ........ **15.00**
  - Chocolate Creme ........ **16.75**
  - Opaque Blue ........ **18.00**
  - Pearl Gray ........ **15.00**
- Beaded Oval, introduced 1967, marked 1972
  - Fog ........ **14.00**
  - Old Lavender ........ **20.00**
  - Sapphire Blue ........ **20.00**
  - Teal ........ **18.00**
- Colonial Drape and Heart, introduced 1961, marked 1974
  - Amber ........ **15.00**
  - Clear ........ **15.00**
  - Custard ........ **20.00**
- Daisy and Button, introduced 1970, marked 1972
  - Dichromatic ........ **24.00**
  - Light Blue Slag ........ **25.00**
  - Pink ........ **17.50**
- Forget–Me–Not, introduced 1965, marked 1972, made in over 150 colors
  - Caramel ........ **8.50**
  - Dogwood ........ **24.00**
  - Heatherbloom ........ **20.00**
  - Misty Green ........ **12.00**
  - Persimmon ........ **15.00**
  - Toffee ........ **20.00**
- Heart
  - Amethyst ........ **15.00**
  - Crystal ........ **7.50**
  - Opaque Glass, blue ........ **35.00**

# DEPRESSION GLASS

**Collecting Hint:** Many collectors specialize in one pattern; others collect by a particular color. Prices listed are for pieces in mint condition—no chips, scratches, etc.

**History:** Depression glass is glassware made during the period 1920–1940. It was an inexpensive machine–made glass, produced by several different glass companies.

The colors varied from company to company. The number of items made for each pattern also varied. Like pattern glass, depression glass pattern names are sometimes confusing; therefore, a collector should learn all names for their particular pattern.

**References:** Gene Florence, *Collectible Glassware from the 40's, 50's & 60's,* Collector Books, 1992; Gene Florence, *Elegant Glassware of the Depression Era, Fifth Edition,* Collector Books, 1993; Gene Florence, *The Collector's Encyclopedia of Depression Glass, Revised Tenth Edition,* Collector Books, 1992; Gene Florence, *Very Rare Glassware of the Depression Years, First Series* (1988, 1990 value update) and *Second Series* (1990), *Third Series* (1993), Collector Books; Carl F. Luckey and Mary Burris, *An Identification & Value Guide To Depression Era Glassware, Second Edition,* Books Americana, 1984; Mark Schliesmann, *Price Survey, Second Edition,* Park Avenue Publications, Ltd, 1984; Ellen Tischbein Schroy, *Warman's Glass,* Wallace–Homestead, 1992; Hazel Marie Weatherman, *1984 Supplement & Price Trends for Colored Glassware of the Depression Era, Book 1,* published by author, 1984.

**Periodical:** *The Daze,* 10271 State Rd., Box 57, Ottisville, MI 48463.

**Collectors' Club:** National Depression Glass Association, Inc., P. O. Box 69843, Odessa, TX 79769.

**REPRODUCTION ALERT:** Because of recent interest in collecting depression glass, many reproductions are surfacing. Most reproductions are made in colors not originally made. They are sometimes made in the original molds and often marked. However, several patterns have been reproduced in original colors but the molds are slightly different. Thorough knowledge of patterns, colors and markings is very important.

Send a self addressed stamped business envelope to *The Daze* and request a copy of their glass reproduction list. It is one of the best bargains in the collectibles field.

## ADAM

Jeannette Glass Co., 1932–1934. Made in crystal, Delphite (opaque blue), green, pink, and yellow.

| | Green | Pink |
|---|---|---|
| Ashtray, 3¾″ d | **20.00** | **25.00** |
| Bowl | | |
| 7¾″ d | **18.50** | **17.50** |
| 9″ d, cov | **35.00** | **20.00** |
| 10″ l, oval | **20.00** | **20.00** |
| Butter Dish, cov | **275.00** | **75.00** |
| Cake Plate, 10″ d, ftd | **20.00** | **20.00** |
| Candlesticks, 4″ h, pr | **80.00** | **75.00** |
| Candy Jar, cov | **80.00** | **65.00** |
| Cereal Bowl, 5¾″ d | **35.00** | **35.00** |
| Coaster | **16.00** | **15.00** |
| Creamer | **17.50** | **15.00** |
| Cup | **16.00** | **20.00** |
| Dessert Bowl, 4¾″ d | **12.00** | **12.00** |
| Iced Tea Tumbler, 5½″ h | **40.00** | **45.00** |
| Lamp | **250.00** | **240.00** |
| Pitcher, 8″ h, 32 oz | **37.50** | **35.00** |
| Plate, sq | | |
| 6″ w, sherbet | **5.00** | **5.00** |
| 7¾″ w, salad | **15.00** | **9.00** |
| 9″ w, dinner | **18.00** | **20.00** |
| 9″ w, grill | **15.00** | **15.00** |
| Platter, 11¾″ l | **17.50** | **16.50** |
| Relish Dish, 8″ l, divided | **17.50** | **15.00** |
| Salt and Pepper Shakers, pr | **85.00** | **55.00** |
| Saucer, 6″ sq | **7.00** | **6.00** |
| Sherbet, 3″ h | **30.00** | **25.00** |
| Sugar | **15.00** | **14.00** |
| Tumbler, 4½″ h | **22.00** | **25.00** |
| Vase, 7½″ h | **40.00** | **200.00** |

## AMERICAN SWEETHEART

MacBeth-Evans Glass Co., 1930–1936. Made in blue, Cremax (opaque cream), Monax (white), pink, red, and color trimmed Monax.

| | Blue | Cremax | Monax | Monax Color Rimmed | Pink | Red |
|---|---|---|---|---|---|---|
| Berry Bowl | | | | | | |
| Individual, 3¾″ d | — | — | — | — | **30.00** | — |
| Master, 9″ d | — | **30.00** | **62.00** | — | **30.00** | — |
| Cereal Bowl, 6″ d | — | **8.00** | **14.00** | **12.50** | **12.50** | — |
| Console Bowl, 18″ d | **850.00** | — | **315.00** | — | — | **700.00** |
| Creamer, ftd | **90.00** | — | **12.00** | **13.00** | **13.00** | **75.00** |
| Cream Soup, 4½″ d | — | — | **110.00** | — | **40.00** | — |
| Cup and Saucer | **120.00** | **12.50** | **12.50** | **18.50** | **18.50** | **72.00** |
| Lamp Shade | | **425.00** | **575.00** | — | — | — |
| Pitcher | | | | | | |
| 7½″ h, 60 oz | — | — | — | — | **475.00** | — |
| 8″ h, 80 oz | — | — | — | — | **425.00** | — |
| Plate | | | | | | |
| 6″ d, bread and butter | — | — | **5.50** | **5.00** | **5.00** | — |
| 8″ d, salad | **65.00** | — | **8.50** | — | **8.50** | **40.00** |
| 9″ d, luncheon | — | — | **11.00** | — | — | — |
| 9¾″ d, dinner | — | — | **22.00** | **32.00** | **32.00** | — |
| 11″ d, chop | — | — | **10.00** | — | — | — |
| Salt and Pepper Shakers, pr | — | — | **225.00** | — | **375.00** | — |
| Salver, 12″ d | **145.00** | — | **22.00** | **16.00** | **16.00** | **115.00** |
| Serving Plate, 15½″ d | **285.00** | — | **175.00** | — | — | **225.00** |
| Sherbet | | | | | | |
| 3¼″ h, ftd | — | — | — | — | **15.00** | — |
| 4¼″ h, ftd | — | — | **17.00** | — | **12.00** | — |

| | Blue | Cremax | Monax | Monax Color Rimmed | Pink | Red |
|---|---|---|---|---|---|---|
| Soup Bowl, 9½″ d, flat | — | — | 75.00 | — | 35.00 | |
| Sugar | | | | | | |
| Cov | | | 325.00 | | — | — |
| Open, ftd | 100.00 | — | 10.00 | — | 9.00 | 75.00 |
| Tidbit, two tiers, 8″ d and 12″ d | 225.00 | — | 95.00 | — | 50.00 | 175.00 |
| Tumbler | | | | | | |
| 3½″ h, 5 oz | — | — | — | 75.00 | 75.00 | — |
| 4¼″ h, 9 oz | — | — | — | 68.00 | 68.00 | |
| Vegetable Bowl, 11″ l, oval | — | — | 55.00 | — | 37.50 | — |

## ANNIVERSARY

| | Clear | Irid | Pink |
|---|---|---|---|
| Berry Bowl | | | |
| Individual, 4⅞″ d | 3.00 | 4.00 | — |
| Master, 9″ d | — | 10.00 | — |
| Butter Dish, cov | 25.00 | — | 55.00 |
| Cake Plate, 12½″ d, ftd | 8.00 | — | — |
| Candy, cov | — | — | 45.00 |
| Compote, three legs | — | 4.50 | 14.00 |
| Creamer and Sugar | 6.50 | — | — |
| Cup | 2.00 | 3.75 | — |
| Plate | | | |
| 6″ d | 1.00 | — | — |
| 9″ d | — | 5.25 | — |
| Dinner | 5.00 | — | 12.00 |
| Sandwich Plate | 5.50 | — | — |
| Saucer | 1.00 | — | — |
| Soup Bowl | 6.50 | — | — |
| Vase | 12.00 | — | 30.00 |

## BOWKNOT

Manufacturer unknown, probably late 1920s. Made in green.

| | Green | | Green |
|---|---|---|---|
| Berry Bowl, 4½″ d | 12.00 | Sherbet, ftd | 12.00 |
| Cereal Bowl, 5½″ d | 14.50 | Tumbler, 5″ h | 15.00 |
| Cup | 11.00 | 10 oz, flat | 16.50 |
| Plate, 7″ d, salad | 12.50 | 10 oz, ftd | 15.00 |

## CHERRYBERRY

U.S. Glass Co., early 1930s. Made in crystal, green, and pink. Limited iridized production.

| | Crystal | Green | Iridized | Pink |
|---|---|---|---|---|
| Berry Bowl | | | | |
| Individual, 4″ d | 6.00 | 15.00 | 6.00 | 15.00 |
| Master, 7½″ d | 32.00 | 45.00 | 32.00 | 45.00 |
| Bowl, 6½″ d | 15.00 | 17.50 | 15.00 | 17.50 |
| Butter Dish, cov | 145.00 | 150.00 | 145.00 | 150.00 |
| Coaster | 8.00 | 11.50 | 8.00 | 11.50 |
| Compote, 5¾″ d | 15.00 | 20.00 | 15.00 | 20.00 |

**Adam, vase, pink, 7½" h, $200.00.**

**American Sweetheart, soup, flat, pink, 9½" d, $35.00.**

| | Crystal | Green | Iridized | Pink |
|---|---|---|---|---|
| Creamer | | | | |
| Large | 15.00 | 30.00 | 15.00 | 30.00 |
| Small | 12.00 | 17.50 | 12.00 | 17.50 |
| Cup and Saucer | — | 24.50 | — | 24.50 |
| Fruit Bowl, 10½" d, three legs | — | 75.00 | — | 75.00 |
| Mug | — | 165.00 | — | 165.00 |
| Olive Dish, 5" l, handle | 7.50 | 12.00 | 7.50 | 12.00 |
| Pickle Dish, 8¾" oval | 8.00 | 12.50 | 8.00 | 12.50 |
| Pitcher, 7¾" h | 150.00 | 145.00 | 150.00 | 145.00 |
| Plate | | | | |
| 6" d, sherbet | 6.50 | 8.00 | 6.50 | 8.00 |
| 7½" d, salad | 7.00 | 12.00 | 7.00 | 12.00 |
| 9" d, dinner | — | 20.00 | — | 20.00 |
| 9" d, grill | — | 22.00 | — | 22.00 |
| Salad Bowl, 6½" d | 15.00 | 17.50 | 15.00 | 17.50 |
| Sherbet | 6.00 | 7.50 | 6.00 | 7.50 |
| Sugar, open | | | | |
| Large | 15.00 | 24.00 | 15.00 | 24.00 |
| Small | 12.00 | 18.00 | 12.00 | 18.00 |
| Tumbler | | | | |
| 3⅝" h, 9 oz, flat | 16.00 | 22.00 | 16.00 | 22.00 |
| 4¼" h, 9 oz, flat | — | 21.00 | — | 21.00 |
| 4½" h, 8 oz, ftd | — | 35.00 | — | 35.00 |
| 5" h, 12 oz, flat | — | 65.00 | — | 65.00 |

## CHERRY BLOSSOM

Jeannette Glass Co., 1930–1939. Made in crystal, Delphite (opaque blue), green, Jadite (opaque green), pink, and red.

| | Delphite | Green | Pink |
|---|---|---|---|
| Berry Bowl | | | |
| Ind, 4¾" d | 9.00 | 14.00 | 12.00 |
| Master, 8½" d | 42.00 | 37.50 | 37.50 |
| Bowl, 9" d, two handles | 20.00 | 30.00 | 36.00 |
| Butter Dish, cov | — | 88.00 | 70.00 |
| Cake Plate, 10¼" d, 3 legs | — | 30.00 | 27.50 |
| Coaster | — | 12.50 | 14.00 |
| Creamer | 18.50 | 18.50 | 18.00 |
| Cup and Saucer | 20.00 | 24.00 | 22.00 |
| Fruit Bowl, 10½" d, 3 legs | — | 77.00 | 80.00 |

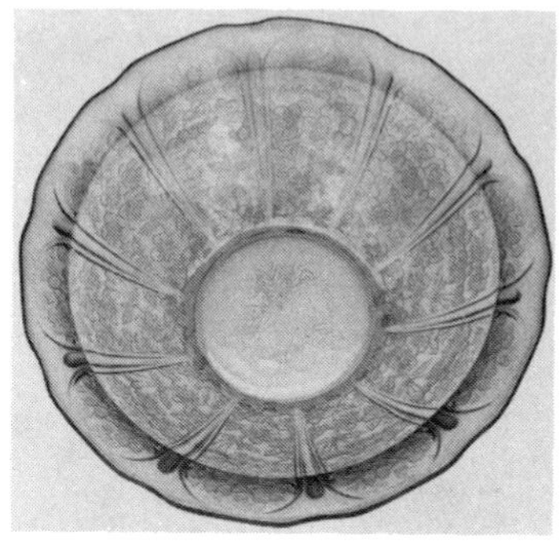

**Cherry Blossom, berry bowl, master, 8½" d, pink, $37.50.**

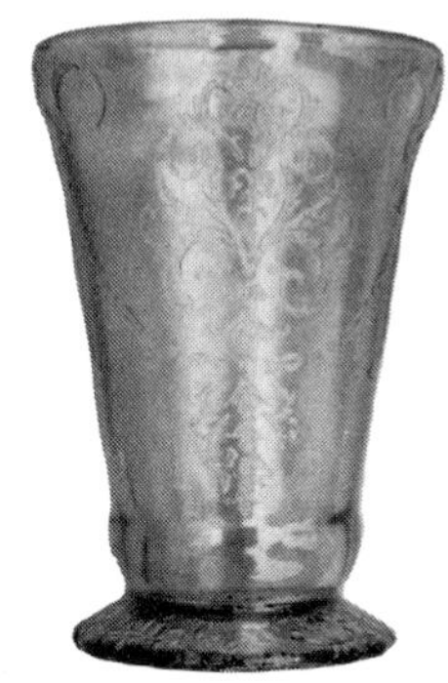

**Bowknot, tumbler, footed, green, $15.00.**

| | Delphite | Green | Pink |
|---|---|---|---|
| Pitcher, 8" h, PAT, 36 oz, ftd | 75.00 | 55.00 | 60.00 |
| Plate | | | |
| 6" d, sherbet | 7.50 | 5.00 | 5.00 |
| 7" d, salad | — | 19.50 | 18.50 |
| 9" d, dinner | 18.00 | 20.00 | 18.00 |
| 10" d, grill | — | 22.00 | — |
| Platter | | | |
| 13" l | — | 59.00 | 59.00 |
| 13" l, divided | — | 59.00 | 59.00 |
| Sandwich Tray, 10½" l | — | 20.00 | 19.50 |
| Sherbet | | | |
| Round base | 12.00 | 15.00 | 15.00 |
| Scalloped base | 12.00 | 17.00 | 15.00 |
| Sugar | | | |
| Cov | — | 34.00 | 30.00 |
| Open | 18.00 | 13.50 | 12.00 |
| Tumbler | | | |
| 3½" h, 4 oz, flat | — | 25.00 | 25.00 |
| 3¾" h, 4 oz, ftd | 17.50 | 18.50 | 18.50 |
| 4¼" h, 9 oz, flat | 18.50 | 22.00 | 22.00 |
| 4½" h, 8 oz, ftd | 20.00 | 28.00 | 28.00 |
| 4½" h, 9 oz, ftd | 20.00 | 32.00 | 32.00 |
| Vegetable Bowl | | | |
| 9" oval | 45.00 | 36.00 | 30.00 |

## CIRCLE

Hocking Glass Co., 1930s. Made in crystal, green, and pink.

| | Green | Pink |
|---|---|---|
| Berry Bowl | | |
| Individual, 4½" d | 5.00 | 5.00 |
| Master, 8" d | 12.00 | 12.00 |
| Creamer | 8.00 | 8.00 |
| Cup | 4.50 | 4.50 |
| Decanter | 35.00 | 35.00 |
| Goblet, 8 oz, water | 9.00 | 9.00 |
| Iced Tea Tumbler, 5" h, 10 oz | 14.00 | 14.00 |
| Juice Tumbler, 3½" h, 4 oz | 8.00 | 8.00 |
| Pitcher, 80 oz | 25.00 | 25.00 |
| Plate | | |
| 6" d, sherbet | 1.50 | 1.50 |
| 8" d, luncheon | 5.00 | 5.00 |
| 9½" d, dinner | 6.50 | 6.50 |
| Saucer | 1.50 | 1.50 |
| Sherbet | | |
| 3⅛" h | 4.00 | 4.00 |
| 4¾" h | 6.00 | 6.00 |
| Sugar | 7.50 | 7.50 |
| Tumbler, 4" h, 8 oz | 8.00 | 8.00 |
| Vase | 8.00 | 8.00 |
| Wine, 4½" h | 10.00 | 10.00 |

## COLONIAL BLOCK

Hazel Atlas Co., early 1930s. Made in black, crystal, green, and pink. White made in 1950s.

| | Green | Pink | White |
|---|---|---|---|
| Berry Bowl, 4″ d | **6.00** | **6.00** | — |
| Bowl, 7″ d | **15.00** | **15.00** | — |
| Butter Dish, cov | **40.00** | **35.00** | — |
| Candy Dish, cov | **32.00** | **30.00** | — |
| Creamer | **9.00** | **8.00** | **6.00** |
| Goblet | **9.00** | **8.00** | — |
| Pitcher | **35.00** | **35.00** | — |
| Sugar, cov | **20.00** | **20.00** | **10.00** |

## COLONIAL FLUTED

"Rope," Federal Glass Co., 1928–1933. Made in crystal and green.

| | Green |
|---|---|
| Berry Bowl | |
| Individual, 4″ d | **4.50** |
| Master, 7½″ d | **14.00** |
| Cereal Bowl, 6″ d | **7.50** |
| Creamer | **5.00** |
| Cup | **4.00** |
| Plate | |
| 6″ d, sherbet | **2.00** |
| 8″ d, luncheon | **4.00** |
| 9¼″ d, dinner | **5.00** |
| Salad Bowl, 6½″ d | **15.00** |
| Saucer | **1.50** |
| Sherbet | **4.00** |
| Sugar, cov | **15.00** |

## CUBE

"Cubist," Jeannette Glass Co., 1929–1933. Made in amber, blue, canary yellow, crystal, green, pink, ultramarine, and white.

| | Green | Pink |
|---|---|---|
| Butter Dish, cov | **40.00** | **40.00** |
| Candy Jar, cov, 6½″ h | **25.00** | **22.00** |
| Coaster, 3¼″ d | **6.00** | **5.00** |
| Creamer, 5″ h | **5.00** | **5.00** |
| Cup | **7.50** | **7.00** |
| Dessert Bowl, 4½″ d | **6.00** | **5.00** |
| Pitcher, 8¾″ h, 45 oz | **195.00** | **180.00** |
| Plate | | |
| 6″ d, sherbet | **6.00** | **5.00** |
| 8″ d, luncheon | **5.00** | **4.00** |
| Powder Jar, cov | **20.00** | **20.00** |
| Salad Bowl, 6½″ d | **12.00** | **8.00** |
| Salt and Pepper Shakers, pr | **25.00** | **30.00** |
| Saucer | **2.00** | **2.00** |
| Sherbet, ftd | **6.00** | **5.00** |
| Sugar, cov, 5″ h | **15.00** | **15.00** |
| Tray, 7½″ | **4.00** | **4.00** |
| Tumbler, 4″ h, 9 oz | **50.00** | **50.00** |

**Cube, creamer and sugar, pink, 5″ h, price for pair, $20.00.**

**Circle, cup and saucer, green, $6.00.**

## DIAMOND QUILTED

"Flat Diamond," Imperial Glass Co., late 1920s, early 1930s. Made in amber, black, blue, crystal, green, pink, and red.

| | Black | Blue | Green | Pink |
|---|---|---|---|---|
| Bowl, 7" d, crimped | **15.00** | **14.00** | **6.50** | **6.50** |
| Candlesticks, pr | **45.00** | **45.00** | **22.00** | **22.00** |
| Candy Dish, cov | — | — | **50.00** | **50.00** |
| Cereal Bowl, 5" d | **12.00** | **10.00** | **6.00** | **6.00** |
| Champagne, 6" h, 9 oz | — | — | **10.00** | **10.00** |
| Compote, cov, 11½" d | — | — | **65.00** | **65.00** |
| Cordial, 1 oz | — | — | **10.00** | **10.00** |
| Creamer | **15.00** | **15.00** | **7.50** | **7.50** |
| Cream Soup, 4¾" d | **17.50** | **17.50** | **8.00** | **8.00** |
| Cup | **15.00** | **14.00** | **9.00** | **9.00** |
| Ice Bucket | **85.00** | **80.00** | **40.00** | **45.00** |
| Iced Tea Tumbler, 12 oz | — | — | **8.50** | **8.50** |
| Mayonnaise, 3 pcs | **55.00** | **55.00** | **35.00** | **35.00** |
| Nappy, 5½", handle | **15.00** | **15.00** | **6.50** | **6.00** |
| Pitcher, 64 oz | — | — | **45.00** | **45.00** |
| Plate | | | | |
| 6" d, sherbet | **5.00** | **5.00** | **3.00** | **3.00** |
| 7" d, salad | **8.50** | **8.00** | **5.00** | **5.00** |
| 8" d, luncheon | **12.00** | **12.00** | **5.00** | **5.00** |
| Sandwich Server | **45.00** | **45.00** | **20.00** | **20.00** |
| Saucer | **4.00** | **4.00** | **3.00** | **3.00** |
| Sherbet | **15.00** | **14.00** | **4.50** | **4.50** |
| Sugar | **17.50** | **15.00** | **7.50** | **7.50** |
| Tumbler | | | | |
| 6 oz | — | — | **8.50** | **8.50** |
| 9 oz, water | — | — | **12.00** | **12.00** |
| Whiskey, 1½ oz | — | — | **7.50** | **7.50** |
| Wine | — | — | **10.00** | **10.00** |

## DIANA

Federal Glass Co., 1937–1941. Made in amber, crystal, and pink.

| | Amber | Crystal | Pink |
|---|---|---|---|
| Ashtray, 3½" d | — | **2.00** | **3.00** |
| Bowl, 12" d, scalloped edge | **15.00** | **7.00** | **20.00** |
| Candy Dish, cov | **30.00** | **12.00** | **25.00** |
| Cereal Bowl, 5" d | **10.00** | **3.50** | **18.00** |
| Coaster, 3½" d | — | **2.00** | **4.00** |
| Console Bowl, 11" d | **12.00** | **6.00** | **25.00** |
| Creamer | **8.50** | **3.00** | **14.00** |
| Cream Soup, 5½" d | **12.00** | **2.50** | **15.00** |
| Cup | **6.00** | **4.00** | **15.00** |
| Demitasse Set, 2 oz | — | **7.00** | **35.00** |
| Plate | | | |
| 6" d, bread and butter | **1.50** | **1.00** | **4.00** |
| 9½" d, dinner | **8.00** | **5.00** | **12.50** |
| Platter, 12" l, oval | **12.00** | **7.50** | **20.00** |
| Salad Bowl, 9" d | — | **5.00** | **19.00** |
| Salt and Pepper Shakers, pr | **90.00** | **25.00** | **60.00** |
| Sandwich Plate, 11¾" d | **9.00** | **4.50** | **18.00** |
| Saucer | **2.00** | **1.00** | **3.00** |
| Sherbet | **8.00** | **3.00** | **10.00** |
| Sugar | **9.00** | **4.00** | **12.50** |
| Tumbler, 4⅛" h, 9 oz | **24.00** | **20.00** | **30.00** |

**Floragold, salt and pepper shakers, pr, iridescent, white plastic top, $40.00.**

**Florentine No. 2, gravy, platter, yellow, $82.50.**

## FLORAGOLD

Made by Jeannette Glass Co., 1950s. Made in iridescent, limited production in crystal, ice blue, and shell pink.

| | Irid |
|---|---|
| Ashtray | **5.50** |
| Bowl | |
| 4½" w, sq | **5.00** |
| 9½" d, ruffled | **9.00** |
| Butter Dish, cov, ¼ lb | **72.50** |
| Candlesticks, double, pr | **45.00** |
| Candy Dish, cov, 6¾" | **48.00** |
| Celery Vase | **175.00** |
| Cereal Bowl, 5½" d | **24.00** |
| Coaster, 4" d | **5.50** |
| Creamer | **6.50** |
| Cup and Saucer | **15.00** |
| Fruit Bowl, ruffled | |
| 5½" d | **8.50** |
| 12" d | **8.00** |
| Pitcher, 64 oz | **25.00** |
| Plate | |
| 5¾" d, sherbet | **7.00** |
| 8½" d, dinner | |
| Platter, 11¼" l | **17.00** |
| Salad Bowl, 9½" d, deep | **34.00** |
| Salt and Pepper Shakers, pr | **40.00** |
| Sherbet | **12.00** |
| Snack Plate, 13½" d, indent | **50.00** |
| Sugar, open | **7.00** |
| Tid-Bit Server | **20.00** |
| Tray, 13½" d | **17.50** |
| Tumbler | |
| 10 oz, ftd | **18.50** |
| 11 oz | **17.50** |
| 15 oz, ftd | **99.00** |
| Vase | **175.00** |

## FLORENTINE NO. 2

"Poppy No. 2," Hazel Atlas Glass Co., 1932–1935. Made in amber, crystal, cobalt blue, green, ice blue, pink, and yellow.

| | Crystal | Green | Pink | Yellow |
|---|---|---|---|---|
| Ashtray, 5½" d | **15.00** | **17.00** | **15.00** | **32.00** |
| Berry Bowl | | | | |
| Individual, 4½" | **10.00** | **10.00** | **12.00** | **17.00** |
| Master, 8" d | **18.00** | **18.00** | **25.00** | **28.00** |
| Bowl, 9" d | **24.00** | **24.00** | — | — |
| Butter Dish, cov | **85.00** | **95.00** | — | **135.00** |
| Candlesticks, pr | **30.00** | **40.00** | — | **60.00** |
| Candy Dish, cov | **45.00** | **45.00** | **95.00** | **115.00** |
| Cereal Bowl, 6" d | **18.00** | **20.00** | — | **35.00** |

| | Crystal | Green | Pink | Yellow |
|---|---|---|---|---|
| Coaster | | | | |
| 3¼″ d | **12.00** | **12.00** | **15.00** | **20.00** |
| 3¾″ d | **12.00** | **12.00** | **15.00** | **20.00** |
| Compote, 3½″ d, ruffled | **18.00** | **20.00** | **10.00** | — |
| Creamer and Sugar | **15.00** | **15.00** | — | **18.00** |
| Cream Soup | **9.00** | **8.00** | **12.00** | **19.00** |
| Cup and Saucer | **7.00** | **9.00** | — | **12.00** |
| Custard Cup | **45.00** | **45.00** | — | **75.00** |
| Gravy, platter | — | — | — | **82.50** |
| Iced Tea Tumbler, 5″ h, 12 oz | **30.00** | **30.00** | — | **40.00** |
| Juice Tumbler, 3⅜″ h, 5 oz | **10.00** | **10.00** | **10.00** | **18.00** |
| Parfait, 6″ h | **30.00** | **30.00** | — | **55.00** |
| Pitcher | | | | |
| 6¼″ h, 24 oz cone | — | — | — | **29.00** |
| 7½″ h, 28 oz cone | **25.00** | **25.00** | — | — |
| 7½″ h, 48 oz flat | **50.00** | **50.00** | **100.00** | **150.00** |
| 8″ h, 76 oz | **80.00** | **80.00** | **200.00** | **300.00** |
| Plate | | | | |
| 6″ d, sherbet | **3.50** | **3.50** | — | **5.00** |
| 8½″ d, salad | **6.00** | **6.00** | **7.00** | **8.00** |
| 10″ d, dinner | **12.00** | **13.00** | **14.00** | **13.00** |
| 10¼″ d, grill | **10.00** | **12.00** | — | **12.00** |
| Platter, 11″ | **14.00** | **14.00** | **15.00** | **16.00** |
| Relish, 10″ d, 3 part | **17.50** | **17.50** | **22.00** | — |
| Salt and Pepper Shakers, pr | **34.00** | **40.00** | — | **46.00** |
| Sherbet, ftd | **9.00** | **9.00** | — | **10.00** |
| Sugar, cov | **20.00** | **20.00** | — | **30.00** |
| Tray, condiment | — | — | — | **60.00** |
| Tumbler | | | | |
| 3¼″ h, 5 oz, ftd | **12.00** | **12.00** | — | **14.00** |
| 4″ h, 5 oz, ftd | **12.00** | **12.00** | — | **15.00** |
| 4″ h, 9 oz | **13.00** | **13.00** | **10.00** | **18.00** |
| 4½″ h, 9 oz, ftd | **18.00** | **18.00** | — | **27.00** |
| Vase, 6″ h | **30.00** | **30.00** | — | **55.00** |

## FOREST GREEN

Made by Anchor Hocking Glass Co., 1950–1957.

| | Green |
|---|---|
| Ashtray, 3½″ d | **3.00** |
| Bowl, 5¼″ d, deep | **8.00** |
| Creamer and Sugar | **11.00** |
| Cup and Saucer | **5.00** |
| Dessert Bowl, 4¾″ d | **5.50** |
| Juice Tumbler | **3.00** |
| Mixing Bowl, 3 pc set | **25.00** |
| Pitcher | |
| 22 oz | **18.00** |
| 86 oz, upright | **25.00** |
| Plate | |
| 6½″ d, salad | **2.00** |
| 8½″ d, luncheon | **6.00** |
| 10″ d, dinner | **15.00** |
| Platter, 8 x 11″ | **25.00** |
| Popcorn Set, 10″ bowl, six 5⅓ x 2¼″ bowls | **70.00** |
| Punch Bowl, base, cups, 14 pcs | **70.00** |
| Punch Cup | **2.00** |
| Salad Bowl, 7″ d | **7.50** |
| Soup Bowl, sq | **16.00** |
| Sugar | **5.00** |
| Tumbler | |
| 11 oz | **4.00** |
| 15 oz | **5.00** |
| Vase | |
| 3″ h, ruffled | **4.00** |
| 6⅜″ h | **5.00** |
| 9″ h | **6.50** |

## NORMANDIE

"Bouquet and Lattice," Federal Glass Co., 1933–1940. Made in amber, crystal, iridescent, and pink.

| | Amber | Irid | Pink |
|---|---|---|---|
| Berry Bowl | | | |
| Individual, 5″ d | **4.00** | **4.00** | **6.00** |
| Master, 8½″ d | **15.00** | **12.00** | **20.00** |
| Cereal Bowl, 6½″ d | **11.00** | **6.00** | **18.00** |
| Creamer, ftd | **7.00** | **7.00** | **10.00** |
| Cup | **6.00** | **5.00** | **8.00** |
| Iced Tea Tumbler, 5″ h, 12 oz | **22.00** | — | **60.00** |
| Juice Tumbler, 4″ h, 5 oz | **18.00** | — | **40.00** |
| Pitcher, 8″ h, 80 oz | **65.00** | — | **95.00** |
| Plate | | | |
| 6″ d, sherbet | **3.00** | **2.50** | **3.00** |
| 8″ d, salad | **6.00** | **45.00** | **10.00** |
| 9¼″ d, luncheon | **6.00** | **8.00** | **12.00** |
| 11″ d, dinner | **20.00** | **15.00** | **90.00** |
| 11″ d, grill | **14.00** | **6.00** | **16.00** |
| Platter, 11¾″ l | **15.00** | **12.00** | **20.00** |
| Salt and Pepper Shakers, pr | **40.00** | — | **65.00** |
| Saucer | **3.00** | **2.00** | **2.00** |
| Sherbet | **5.00** | **5.00** | **6.00** |
| Sugar, cov | **85.00** | — | **130.00** |
| Tumbler, 4¼″ h, 9 oz | **12.00** | — | **50.00** |
| Vegetable Bowl, 10″ l, oval | **12.00** | **15.00** | **25.00** |

## PETALWARE

MacBeth-Evans Glass Co., 1930–1940. Made in cobalt blue, cremax, crystal, fired on red, green, monax, and yellow.

| | Cremax, Fired-OnDec, Monax Florette | Crystal | Monax Plain | Pink | Red Trim Floral |
|---|---|---|---|---|---|
| Berry Bowl, 9″ d | **24.00** | **7.50** | **15.00** | **12.00** | **90.00** |
| Cereal Bowl, 5¾″ d | **10.00** | **3.50** | **5.00** | **8.00** | **25.00** |
| Creamer, ftd | **10.00** | **3.00** | **5.00** | **6.50** | **25.00** |
| Cream Soup, 4½″ d | **10.00** | **4.00** | **9.00** | **10.00** | — |
| Cup | **8.00** | **2.50** | **5.00** | **6.00** | **20.00** |
| Plate | | | | | |
| 6″ d, sherbet | **5.00** | **1.50** | **2.00** | **2.00** | — |
| 8″ d, salad | **8.00** | **2.00** | **3.00** | **4.00** | — |
| 9″ d, dinner | **12.00** | **3.50** | **5.00** | **7.50** | **22.00** |
| Platter, 13″ l | **18.00** | **8.00** | **15.00** | **13.00** | — |
| Salver, 12″ d | **15.00** | **5.00** | **18.00** | **9.00** | **35.00** |
| Saucer | **2.50** | **1.00** | **1.50** | **1.50** | **5.00** |
| Sherbet, 4½″ h | **10.00** | **4.00** | **6.00** | **6.00** | **25.00** |
| Sugar, open, ftd | **9.00** | **3.00** | **5.00** | **6.50** | **25.00** |

## STARLIGHT

Hazel Atlas Glass Co., 1938–1940. Made in crystal, pink, and white.

| | Crystal | Pink | White |
|---|---|---|---|
| Bowl, 8½″ d, handles | **15.00** | **13.00** | **15.00** |
| Cereal Bowl, 5½″ d | **9.00** | **8.00** | **9.00** |
| Creamer | **8.00** | — | **8.00** |
| Cup | **7.00** | — | **7.00** |

| | Crystal | Pink | White |
|---|---|---|---|
| Plate | | | |
| 6″ d, bread and butter | 3.75 | — | 3.75 |
| 8½″ d, luncheon | 9.00 | — | 9.00 |
| 9″ d, dinner | 10.00 | — | 10.00 |
| Relish Dish | 12.00 | — | 12.00 |
| Salad Bowl, 11½″ d | 15.00 | — | 15.00 |
| Salt and Pepper Shakers, pr | 20.00 | — | 20.00 |
| Sandwich Plate, 13″ d | 12.00 | 14.00 | 12.00 |
| Saucer | 2.00 | — | 2.00 |
| Sherbet | 10.00 | — | 10.00 |
| Sugar, open | 5.00 | — | 5.00 |

## VITROCK

"Flower Rim," Hocking Glass Co., 1934–1937. Made in white and white with fired on colors.

| | Fired-On Colors | White |
|---|---|---|
| Berry Bowl, 4″ d | 4.50 | 4.00 |
| Cereal Bowl, 7½″ d | 5.50 | 5.00 |
| Creamer | 4.50 | 4.00 |
| Cream Soup, 5½″ d | 15.00 | 14.00 |
| Cup | 4.00 | 3.00 |
| Fruit Bowl, 6″ d | 5.00 | 5.00 |
| Plate | | |
| 7¼″ d, salad | 2.50 | 2.00 |
| 8¾″ d, luncheon | 5.00 | 4.00 |
| 10″ d, dinner | 8.00 | 6.00 |
| Platter, 11½″ l | 25.00 | 20.00 |
| Saucer | 2.50 | 1.50 |
| Soup Plate, 9″ d | 12.00 | 10.00 |
| Vegetable Bowl, 9½″ d | 12.00 | 10.00 |

## WATERFORD

"Waffle," Hocking Glass Co., 1938–1944. Made in crystal, pink, and yellow. Forest green made in 1950s.

| | Crystal | Pink |
|---|---|---|
| Ashtray, 4″ d | 7.00 | — |
| Berry Bowl | | |
| Individual, 4¼″ d | 5.00 | 10.00 |
| Master, 8¼″ d | 9.50 | 24.00 |
| Butter Dish, cov | 24.00 | 195.00 |
| Cake Plate, 10¼″ d | 9.00 | 15.00 |
| Cereal Bowl, 5½″ d | 15.00 | 24.00 |
| Coaster, 4″ d | 3.00 | — |
| Creamer | | |
| Miss America Style | 30.00 | — |
| Oval | 6.00 | — |
| Cup and Saucer | 8.00 | 15.00 |
| Goblet | | |
| 5¼″ h | 15.00 | — |
| 5½″ h, Miss America style | 28.00 | 125.00 |

**Petalware, plate, dinner, monax, 9″ d, $12.00.**

**Waterford, goblet, crystal, 5¼″ h, $15.00.**

| | Crystal | Pink |
|---|---|---|
| Juice Tumbler, 3½" h, 5 oz, Miss America style | — | 55.00 |
| Lamp, 4" h | 25.00 | — |
| Pitcher | | |
| 42 oz, tilted, juice | 27.00 | — |
| 80 oz, tilted, ice lip | 30.00 | 180.00 |
| Plate | | |
| 6" d, sherbet | 2.00 | 4.00 |
| 7½" d, salad | 5.00 | 7.00 |
| 9½" d, dinner | 8.00 | 16.00 |
| Relish, 13¾" d | 15.00 | — |
| Salt and Pepper Shakers, pr | 8.50 | — |
| Sandwich Plate, 13¾" d | 12.00 | 28.00 |
| Saucer | 2.50 | 4.50 |
| Sherbet, ftd | 3.50 | 10.00 |
| Sugar | | |
| Cov | 8.50 | 30.00 |
| Open, Miss America Style | 30.00 | — |
| Tumbler, 4⅞" h, 10 oz, ftd | 11.00 | 20.00 |

# DIONNE QUINTUPLETS

**Collecting Hints:** Almost all the doll companies in the 1930s released dolls resembling the Quints. The only "genuine" Dionne Quintuplet dolls are the Madame Alexander dolls dating from 1935 to 1939. They realized the highest prices.

**History:** The Dionne Quintuplets were born on May 28, 1934, on a small farm between Corbeil and Callander, Ontario, Canada. The five baby girls weighed a total of 10 lbs, 1¼ ozs. They were delivered by Dr. Dafoe and two midwives. They were named Yvonne, Annette, Cecile, Emilie, and Marie.

When they were just two days old, their father, Oliva Dionne, and the parish priest signed a contract to exhibit the babies at the Chicago World's Fair. The Canadian government passed "An Act For the Protection Of the Dionne Quintuplets" to prevent this. The girls became special wards of King George V.

A special house, the Dafoe Hospital, was built for them across the road from their place of birth. It had one–way glass through which visitors could view the children. People came by the thousands during the mid to late 30s. In this nursery they were attended by Dr. Dafoe and a staff of professionals. Newspapers gave daily reports and photographs of their progress. Souvenirs of every type were sold including rocks, called "Fertility Stones," from the farm which brought between 50¢ and $1.00.

Emilie died in a convent in August 1954 and Marie died February 27, 1970. Yvonne, Annette, and Cecile remain alive today.

**Reference:** John Axe, *The Collectible Dionne Quintuplets*, Hobby House Press, 1977, out–of–print.

**Collectors' Club:** Dionne Quint Collectors, P.O. Box 2527, Woburn, MA 01888.

Blotter, 4 x 9", cardboard, sepia photo, NEA Service, 1935 . . . . . . . . . . . . . . . **18.00**

Book, *The Story of the Dionne Quintuplets*, Whitman, 1935, 40 pgs . . . . . . **40.00**

Booklet, Lehn & Fink Products Corp, quintuplet photo on page 5, 1938 . . **15.00**

Calendar, 10 x 7", 1945, Harvest Days–Dionne Quintuplets, full pad . . . . . . **12.00**

Door Hanger, 5 x 7", Quintuplet Bread, diecut, bread loaf shape, blue silhouette pictures of quints . . . . . . . . . . . . . **50.00**

Fan, 8¼ x 8¾", cardboard, diecut, "Sweethearts of the World," 1936 copyright . . . . . . . . . . . . . . . . . . . . . . . **20.00**

Handkerchief, set of 3, 9" sq, different images on each one, orig box with full color group photo, c1937 . . . . . . **100.00**

Magazine, *Dionne Quints/Pictorial Review*, Feb, 1937, Karo Syrup adv with Quints . . . . . . . . . . . . . . . . . . . . . . . . **12.00**

Mirror . . . . . . . . . . . . . . . . . . . . . . . . . . . **20.00**

Paper Doll

Merrill, #3488, uncut, 1935 . . . . . . . **175.00**

Palmolive Soap Premium, book, five 6" h dolls on cov, four pgs uncut clothing, orig mailing envelope, 1937 . . . . . . . . . . . . . . . . . . . . . . . . **75.00**

Pinball Game, 3½ x 5", Place The Quintuplets In The Carriage, green tin frame . . . . . . . . . . . . . . . . . . . . . . . . . . **18.00**

Print, 16 x 22", girls each holding identical doll, 1935 . . . . . . . . . . . . . . . . . . **60.00**

Tray, souvenir, 2 x 3½", china, irid tan, soft brick pattern, colorful maple leaf, Quint figures on edge, marked "Souvenir of Callander," late 1930s . . . . . **100.00**

# DIRIGIBLES

**Collecting Hints:** All areas of dirigible material remain stable. Focus on one specific topic, e.g., material about one airship, models and toys, post cards, etc. The field is very broad, and a collector might exhaust his funds trying to be comprehensive. The most common collecting focus is material relating to specific flights.

**History:** The terms *airship* and *dirigible* are synonymous. Dirigible (Latin for directable) means steerable and can apply to a bicycle. Dirigible evolved through usage into a word for *airship*.

There are three types of dirigibles: (1) *Rigid*—a zeppelin, e.g., HINDENBURG, GRAF, SHENANDOAH; (2) *Non–Rigid*—a blimp, e.g., GOODYEAR BLIMPS and Navy blimps; and (3) *Semi–Rigid*—non–rigid with a keel, e.g., NORGE and ITALIA. Note: Hot air balloons, barrage balloons, hydrogen balloons, etc., are not dirigibles. They are not directable. They go where the wind takes them.

Prior to 1900 only non-rigid and semi–rigid dirigibles existed.

Zeppelins dated from 1900 to 1940, the last being the LZ130 sister ship to the HINDENBURG. The GRAF ZEPPELIN was the most successful zeppelin, flying between 1928 and 1940. The HINDENBURG was the most famous zeppelin, due to the spectacular fire that led to its demise in 1937. Its flying dates were 1936 to 1937.

America never used its four zeppelins for passenger travel. They were strictly military. The Naval Air Station at Lakehurst, New Jersey, where the well–known zeppelins docked, has remained open to this day. However, its name has been changed to the Naval Air Engineering Center. None of its present operations include lighter–than–air vehicles, except for an occasional blimp. The famous Hangar #1 has been refurbished, but the base is currently off limits to the general public. The last Navy blimp flew from Lakehurst in 1962.

**References:** Walter Curley, *The Graf Zeppelin's Flights to South America*, Spellman Museum, 1970; Arthur Falk, *Hindenburg Crash Mail*, Clear Color Litho, 1976; Sieger, *Zeppelin Post Katalog*, Wurttemberg, 1981, in German.

**Collectors' Club:** Zeppelin Collectors Club, c/o Aerophilatelic Federation, P. O. Box 1239, Elgin, IL 60121–1239.

**Advisor:** Arthur R. Bink.

**REPRODUCTION ALERT**

Baggage Tag, stiff paper, multicolored airship under German inscription "In Zeppelin Over The Ocean," Nazi swastika symbol on tail fins, mid 1930s, 4¼ x 6½" . . . . . . . . . . . . . . . . **125.00**

Bank, Goodyear blimp, porcelain, pedestal base, 8½" l . . . . . . . . . . . . . . . . **50.00**

Button, brass, airship, globe, and swastika . . . . . . . . . . . . . . . . **35.00**

Cap, souvenir, leather, Airship *Akron* . **125.00**

Charm, binoculars, miniature, white celluloid, brass fittings, black and white views of Graf Zeppelin and Empire State Building inside, France, late 1920s . . . . . . . . . . . . . . . . **100.00**

Flight Cover, Century of Progress, 50¢ zeppelin stamp . . . . . . . . . . . . . . . . **65.00**

Key Chain Token, Airship *Akron*, Duralumin . . . . . . . . . . . . . . . . **45.00**

Launch Souvenir, aluminum disk, Goodyear Zeppelin ZRS–4, emb US Navy airship, Goodyear logo, "Akron, Ohio, U.S.A. Oct. 31, 1929," 3" d . . . . . . . . . . . . . . . . **50.00**

Needle Book, Air Fleet, Zeppelin, Statue of Liberty cov . . . . . . . . . . . . . . . . **22.50**

Palm Puzzle, silvered tin frame, glass cov, airship launching scene, black cardboard underside, Germany, mid 1930s, 4" d . . . . . . . . . . . . . . . . **200.00**

Photograph, black and white, Goodyear Zeppelin dock and Airship *Macon*, text sticker on cardboard back, dated April 23, 1933, Duralumin frame, 8 x 10" . . . . . . . . . . . . . . . . **90.00**

Picture Frame, commemorative, title inscription "Winner, Park Service Station, Third Annual Goodyear Dealers Zeppelin Race July–August 1931," tag at bottom center reads "Made of Duralumin Used in Girder Construction of the United States Airship *Akron* Built by the Goodyear Zeppelin Corporation," 20¼ x 26" . . . . . . . . . . . . **100.00**

Pilot's Badge, German zeppelin, silver, hallmarked . . . . . . . . . . . . . . . . **375.00**

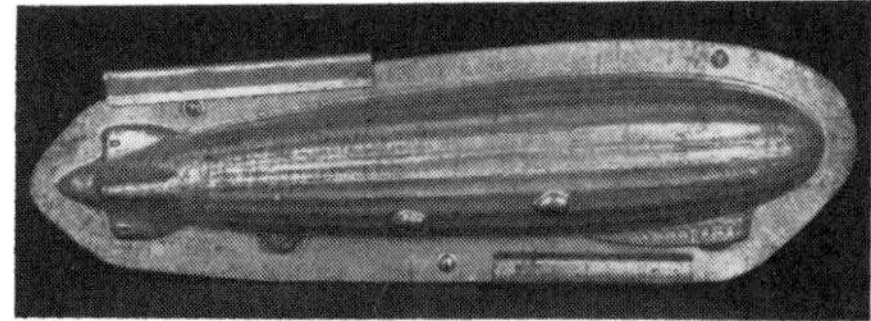

**Chocolate Mold, tin, Anton Reiche, #25647, 11¾" l, $125.00.**

Pin, figural airship
- Silver Plated Brass, Airship *D–LZ 130*, swastika symbols on upper and lower tail fins, mid 1930s, 1¾" l . **75.00**
- Sterling Silver, 3½" l . . . . . . . . . . . . . **85.00**

Pinback Button, Zeps, litho tin, Sunday school award, airship flying through clouds, red, white, and blue, 1930s, ⅝" d . . . . . . . . . . . . . . . . **15.00**

Plaque, Goodyear adv, cast iron, relief factory scene with blimp, buses, plane, trucks, and cars, painted gold, c1930, 12" w, 17" h . . . . . . . . . . . . . **130.00**

Playing Cards, Airship No. 909, Standard Playing Card Co, Chicago, orig box, dated 1894 . . . . . . . . . . . . . . . . **40.00**

Poster, "12 Hours at Sebring, Florida," racetrack scene, Goodyear blimp flying overhead, 1963, 27½ x 36" matted and framed . . . . . . . . . . . . . . . **240.00**
Sheet Music, *The Hindenburg* . . . . . . . . **18.00**
Soda Bottle, Zep, depicts airship . . . . . **85.00**
Tin, Zeppelin Motor Oil, 2 gal, Zeppelin flying over ocean, red and white lettering, 1925–45, 11½" h . . . . . . . . . . **85.00**
Toy, airship
  Aluminum, "Flying Airship," windup, brass rear props, string for hanging from ceiling, Strauss, c1925, orig box, 10" l . . . . . . . . . . . . . . . . . . . . **650.00**
  Celluloid, red, blue wooden wheels, raised "USA" on sides, Stasco, USA, 1930s, 5½" l . . . . . . . . . . . . . **125.00**
  Tin, "Airship," windup, string for hanging from ceiling, K & K, Japan, c1925, orig box and instructions, 7" l . . . . . . . . . . . . . . . . . . . . . . . . . . **575.00**

# DISNEYANA

**Collecting Hints:** The products from the 1930s command the most attention. Animated celluloids range in value from $100 into the tens of thousands of dollars depending on subject and complexity of scene. Disneyana is a popular subject, and items tend to be priced on the high side.

Make condition a key element in your purchase. An incomplete toy or game should sell for 40% to 50% less than a complete one in mint condition.

**History:** Walt Disney and the creations of the famous Disney studio hold a place of fondness and enchantment in the hearts of Americans and people throughout the world. The release of "Steamboat Willie" in 1928 heralded an entertainment empire.

Walt and his brother, Roy, showed shrewd business acumen. From the beginning they licensed the reproduction of Disney characters in products ranging from wrist watches to clothing.

The market in Disneyana has been established by a few determined dealers and auction houses. Hake's Americana and Collectibles has specialized in Disney material for over a decade. Sotheby's Collector Carousel auctions and Lloyd Ralston Toys auctions have continued the trend.

Walt Disney characters are popular throughout the world. Belgium is a leading producer of Disneyana along with England, France, and Japan. The Disney characters often take on the regional characteristics of the host country; don't be surprised to find a strange looking Mickey Mouse or Donald Duck. Disney has opened a new theme park in Japan; it will produce a wealth of new Disney collectibles.

**References:** Marcia Blitz, *Donald Duck,* Harmony Books, 1979; Robert Heide and John Gilman, *Cartoon Collectibles,* Doubleday & Co., Inc., 1984; Bevis Hillier, *Walt Disney's Mickey Mouse Memorabilia,* Harry Abrams, 1986; David Longest and Michael Stern, *The Collector's Encyclopedia of Disneyana,* Collector Books, 1992; Leonard Maltin, *The Disney Films,* Crown Publishers, 1973; Walton Rawls, *Disney Dons Dogtags: The Best of Disney Military Insignia From World War II,* Abbeville Press, 1992; Richard Schickel, *The Disney Version: The Life, Times, Art and Commerce of Walt Disney,* Avon Books, 1968; Michael Stern, *Stern's Guide to Disney Collectibles, First Series* (1989, 1992 value update) and *Second Series* (1990, 1993 value update), Collector Books; Tom Tumbusch, *Tomart's Illustrated Disneyana Catalog and Price Guide, Volume 1* (1985), *Volume 2* (1985), *Volume 3* (1985), *Volume 4* (1987), Tomart Publications; Tom Tumbusch, *Tomart's Illustrated Disneyana Catalog and Price Guide, Condensed Edition,* Tomart Publications, 1989.

**Periodicals:** *Mouse Club Newsletter,* 2056 Cirone Way, San Jose, CA 95124; *Storyboard Magazine For Disneyana Collectors,* 2512 Artesia Blvd, Redondo Beach, CA 90278; *Storyboard/The Art of Laughter,* 80 Main Street, Nashua, NH 03060.

**Collectors' Club:** National Fantasy Club For Disneyana Collectors, P. O. Box 19212, Irvine, CA 92713.

**Archives:** Walt Disney Archives, 500 South Buena Vista Street, Burbank, CA 91521.

**Advisor:** Ted Hake.

Alice in Wonderland
  Activity Book, *Alice in Wonderland Sticker Fun, Stencil and Coloring Book,* Whitman, 1951, 10½ x 12" **50.00**
  Belt, 24" l, vinyl, red, orig cardboard display card, Disney Productions copyright, 1950s . . . . . . . . . . . . . . . **40.00**
  Figure, plastic, stand–up, set of fifteen, orig box, 1951 . . . . . . . . . . . **17.00**
  Pinback Button, 2" d, black, white, red, blue, and yellow, attached ribbon and pair of silver metal skates, marked "Ice Capades Presents Alice In Wonderland," 1950s . . . . . . **25.00**
  Puzzle, 14 x 19", Alice chasing White Rabbit, orig box, Jaymar, Walt Disney Productions copyright, 1950s **15.00**
  Tea Set, 9 pcs, china, teapot, three teacups and saucers, creamer and sugar, orig box, unused, Walt Disney Productions copyright, 1970s **50.00**
Bambi
  Bank, 6½" h, Thumper, ceramic,

painted and glazed, incised "T" on back, Disney copyright, 1940s ... **35.00**
Book, *Walt Disney's Bambi Tell–A–Tale Book,* Whitman, 1972, 28 pgs **8.00**
Bookmark, 6" l, paper, Bambi, Thumper, and flower illus, US Department of Agriculture–Forest Service issue, 1940s .................. **15.00**
Card Game, 40 cards, Russell Mfg Co, 1965 Walt Disney Productions copyright ..................... **12.00**
Figure
Bambi, 8½" h, vinyl, movable head and legs, orig bag and cardboard tag, Dakin, 1970s ........... **25.00**
Thumper, 3¾" h, ceramic, painted and glazed, American Pottery, 1940s ..................... **50.00**
Tile, 6" sq, Thumper, ceramic, Kemper–Thomas, Disney copyright, 1940s ....................... **25.00**

Cinderella
Figure, porcelain, holding gold slipper, orig box, 1950s ............ **95.00**
Magazine, *Quick,* April 24, 1950, four page article with illus ....... **15.00**
Pattern, apron, 1952 ............. **10.00**
Toy, windup, Cinderella and Prince, orig box, 1940s ............... **150.00**

Davy Crockett
Clock, wall, orig box, 1950s ....... **250.00**
Game, Davy Crockett Frontierland Game, Parker Brothers, 1955 Walt Disney Productions copyright .... **55.00**
Lobby Card, 11 x 14", autographed, full color Fess Parker photo, 1956 film *The Great Locomotive Chase* **50.00**
T–shirt, child's, 1950s ........... **25.00**
Wristwatch, silvered metal case, off–white dial with illus, replaced adult size pigskin straps, US Time, c1950 **50.00**

Donald Duck
Bank, 6" h, ceramic, raised arm holding coin, 1940s ............... **50.00**
Better Little Book, *Donald Duck and The Green Serpent,* Whitman, #1432, 1947 ................. **25.00**
Big Little Book, *Donald Duck Hunting For Trouble,* #1478, Whitman, 48 pgs, 1949 .................... **25.00**
Camera, 3 x 4 x 3", plastic, black, orig black vinyl strap, circular metal plate with "Donald Duck/ Herbert–George Company, Chicago," Disney Productions copyright, 1950s ................... **50.00**
Feeding Dish, three parts, pink ..... **45.00**
Figure, 4" h, Donald playing accordion, bisque, 1930s ............ **200.00**
Game, Donald Duck Bean Bag Game, orig box and instruction sheet, Gardner, Disney Productions copyright, c1950 .............. **50.00**
Glass, 4¾" h, clear, blue image, 1930s ........................ **50.00**
Lamp, 7½" h, Donald standing on candle holder, 1940s ........... **75.00**
Little Golden Book, *Donald Duck and The Christmas Carol,* first edition, 1960 ........................ **15.00**
Puzzle, "Donald Duck's Diamond Jubilee," 18 x 23½" assembled, full color photo, Hallmark Cards Inc, Walt Disney Productions copyright, c1985 ........................ **12.00**
Roly Poly, 4" d, ball shape, plastic, musical, white top, yellow bottom, blue illus and star design, 1950s . **50.00**
Soaky Bottle, 9" h, soft plastic body, hard plastic head, Disney Productions copyright, 1960s .......... **25.00**
Sprinkling Can, 3" h, litho tin, Donald illus, Ohio Art Co, 1938 Walt Disney Enterprises copyright ........ **100.00**
Toy
Carpet Sweeper, 5 x 7", tin litho, wood wheels and sides, color illus, missing metal bracket and handle, Ohio Art, 1940 Disney Productions copyright ......... **75.00**
Pull, Donald Duck Choo Choo, Fisher–Price, c1942 .......... **75.00**
Stuffed, 18" h, felt beak, legs, and feet, Gund, copyright Walt Disney Productions ............. **85.00**
Valentine, 2½ x 4½", mechanical, Donald wearing sombrero holding guitar, 1939 Walt Disney Productions copyright ................ **30.00**
Walker, celluloid ................ **35.00**
Watering Can, litho tin, Ohio Art, Walt Disney Enterprises ......... **95.00**

Dumbo
Bank, 6" h, ceramic, painted and glazed, incised Walt Disney copyright, 1940s .................. **125.00**
Figure, 7" h, vinyl, movable head and legs, orig bag and cardboard tag, 1970s ....................... **25.00**
Puppet, 10½" h, cloth body, vinyl head, orig "Gund" tag, c1940 ... **15.00**
Salt and Pepper Shaker, pr, 3" h, figural, china, glazed, Leeds, 1940s **35.00**

Goofy
Toy
Goofy Pop–A–Part, 9" h, plastic, orig display card, Multiple Toymakers, 1965 Disney Productions ....................... **25.00**
Windup, 7½" h, plastic, built–in key, Marx, 1950s ............. **100.00**

Mickey Mouse
Advertising Display Sign, 4 x 5",

"Have You Seen The Mickey Mouse Pencil Boxes At The School Sale? Yours Truly Mickey Mouse," diecut cardboard, black, white, red, and yellow ............... **50.00**
Baby's Cup, 1¾" h, silver plated, Mickey playing saxophone, International Silver Co, 1934 ........ **50.00**
Bag, 10 x 16", red, fabric, plastic coating, Mickey illus on each side, c1970 ........................ **12.00**
Bank, 8" h, Mickey the Magician, plastic, orig shrink wrap, Paragon–Reiss, 1981 copyright ........... **15.00**
Better Little Book, *Mickey Mouse and The Lazy Daisy Mystery,* Whitman, 31433, 1947 .................. **25.00**
Big Little Book
 *Mickey Mouse,* #717, Whitman, 1933 ...................... **50.00**
 *Mickey Mouse, The Mail Pilot,* #2138, Whitman, 1933 ....... **50.00**
Clock
 Alarm, 6" h, windup, dark red case, brass bells, Bradley, 1970s .... **50.00**
 Wall, 6" d, quartz, red plastic case, black numerals, Bradley, 1970s **25.00**
 Windup, 4½" sq, green metal case, Ingersoll, 1930s ............. **400.00**
Doll, 13" h, Mickey and Minnie, plush, Gund, late 1940s, pr ..... **300.00**
Figure
 3¼" h, china, Mickey playing French horn, glazed, Germany, 1930s ..................... **300.00**
 3½" h, rubber, Seiberling, 1930s . **75.00**
Flashlight, interchangeable Mickey and Donald Duck heads, Arco ... **22.00**
Game
 Mickey Mouse Bowling Game, orig box, Artco Industries, c1980 ... **15.00**
 Mickey Mouse Old Maid, orig box, Whitman, 1930s ............ **75.00**
Hairbrush, 2 x 4", silver metal handle, Mickey illus, 1930s ............ **50.00**
Handbag, 9 x 11", child's, fabric, dark red flocked covering, Walt Disney Enterprises copyright, late 1930s ....................... **40.00**
Jigsaw Puzzle, Spirit of '76 ........ **15.00**
Pencil Holder, 4½" h, ceramic, Mickey standing beside cov barrel holder, metal and plastic sharpener on side, Enesco label .......... **25.00**
Planter, 3 x 6 x 6½", ceramic, figural Mickey holding sack planter, 1940s **50.00**
Plate, 7" d, china, pie-eyed Mickey and Horace Horsecollar, Patriot China, Walt Disney Enterprises ... **125.00**
Pocket Watch, 2" d, metal, Mickey image stamped on back, Ingersoll, early 1930s ................... **300.00**
Radio, Emerson, Model 411 ...... **1,200.00**
Rug, 26 x 44", Mickey Band Concert scene, Alexander Smith & Sons Carpet Co, 1935 .............. **200.00**
Target, 17½" d, cardboard, Marks Brothers, mid 1930s ............ **75.00**
Toothbrush, talking ............... **20.00**
Toothbrush Holder, 5" h, bisque, one movable arm ................. **200.00**
Toy
 Fire Truck, 6" l, 4" h, Mickey Mouse Fire Dept, rubber, red, Sun Rubber Co ............. **75.00**
 Pull, Mickey Mouse Puddle Jumper, wood, paper label, Fisher–Price, 1953 ........... **50.00**

**Mickey Mouse, pull toy, Fisher-Price, Mickey Mouse Safety Patrol, #733, litho paper on wood, 1956, $200.00.**

Valentine Card, 3½ x 4½", diecut "X" shape, orig canceled envelope, Hallmark, 1936 ............... **25.00**
Wristwatch, orig red plastic straps, Ingersoll, 1950 ................. **100.00**
Minnie Mouse
 Bank, 5" h, composition, house shape, Minnie standing in doorway holding broom, 1970–80 ........ **20.00**
 Bracelet, 6" l, brass links, diecut charm, Disney copyright, c1970 . **15.00**
 Figure, 5¾" h, Minnie, ceramic, glazed, American Pottery, orig foil sticker, 1940s ................. **200.00**
 Puppet, Minnie, red and white check fabric body, molded head, Gund, 1950s ...................... **25.00**
 Toothbrush Holder, 5" h, bisque, one movable arm ................. **200.00**
 Wristwatch, Minnie, orig white leather straps, Bradley, 1970s .... **25.00**
Miscellaneous
 Disneyland
  Christmas Ornaments, set of 6 balls, Mickey and Disney characters, orig box ............. **145.00**

Coloring Book
*A Visit To Walt Disney World,* Whitman, 1971, 8 x 11" .... **12.00**
*Disneyland,* 9 x 11", Whitman, 1961 .... **25.00**
Pennant, 28" l, felt, red, white logo, late 1950s .... **15.00**
Plate, 8½" d, characters standing by tree, castle background, inscribed "Christmas 1983 Tokyo Disneyland," orig styrofoam holder and cardboard slip case . **75.00**
Salt and Pepper Shaker, pr, 2½" h, ceramic, gold trim and "Disneyland" logo, castle and Tinkerbell illus, Japan foil sticker, late 1950s **25.00**
Souvenir Book, *Walt Disney's Disneyland/A Pictorial Souvenir and Guide,* 9 x 11½", 32 pgs, 1963 **25.00**
Ticket, 2¼ x 6½", CSEA Party, dated Oct 7, 1984 .... **15.00**

Fantasia
Souvenir Book, 9½ x 12½", *Walt Disney Presents Fantasia,* 1940 . **45.00**

Ferdinand The Bull, book, *Ferdinand The Bull,* 8½ x 12", Whitman, 1938, 12 pgs .... **25.00**

Jungle Book
Book, *Jungle Book,* Whitman, 1967, 24 pgs, hard cov .... **15.00**
Doll, 13" h, vulture, stuffed, Gund, Disney Productions 1966 copyright .... **15.00**
View–Master Reel, set of 3, booklet and catalog, orig envelope, 1966 Disney Productions copyright .. **20.00**

Lady And The Tramp, figure, 5" h, Lady, ceramic, painted and glazed, Walt Disney Productions copyright, 1960s .... **25.00**

Mary Poppins
Jigsaw Puzzle, Jaymar, 1964 .... **15.00**
Lunch Box, emb metal, color illus, metal thermos with white plastic cup, Aladdin Industries, 1964 Disney Productions copyright .. **75.00**

Mickey Mouse Club
Costume, vinyl face mask and vest, printed Mouseketeer logo, orig clear plastic bag, Ben Cooper, 1972 copyright .... **25.00**
Lunch Box, steel, emb, Mouseketeers on boat flying over earth on one side, Mouseketeers on stage on other, plastic thermos, Aladdin, 1970s .... **40.00**
Puzzle, 11½ x 14½", Jimmy Dodd playing guitar, Mouseketeers singing, Whitman, 1956 .... **30.00**

Pete's Dragon
Banner, theater, 24 x 96", white synthetic fabric, brass eyelets, yellow fringe, black lettering, green and orange dragon illus, c1977 .... **50.00**
Lunch Box, emb metal, color illus, Aladdin Industries, Disney Productions copyright, c1977 .... **45.00**

**Mickey Mouse Club, record, Walt Disney Presents Musical Highlights from the Mickey Mouse Club TV Show, Disneyland Records, DQ-1227, 33⅓ rpm, 1962, $15.00.**

Sleeping Beauty, game, Walt Disney's Sleeping Beauty, orig box, Whitman, 1958 Walt Disney Productions copyright .... **25.00**

Three Little Pigs
Birthday Card, 4 x 5", Three Pigs illus, silver background, Walt Disney Enterprises 1934 copyright .... **20.00**
Pail, 6½" d, 3" h, tin litho, Three Pigs, dancing, washing clothes, and ironing, 1930s .... **75.00**
Playing Cards, 52 cards, orig box with Three Pigs illus, marked "By Special Permission Walt Disney Enterprises," 1930s .... **75.00**
Salt and Pepper Shaker, pr, 4" h, one playing accordion, other holding saxophone, marked "Japan," 1930s .... **50.00**

Walt Disney
Book, *Through The Picture Frame,* 6½ x 8", Simon & Schuster, subtitled *Walt Disney's Little Library,* 1946 .... **25.00**
Magazine, *Walt Disney's Magazine,* Vol 4, #4, June, 1959 ... **15.00**

Peter Pan
Planter, 4" h, ceramic, painted and glazed, Peter Pan beside open treasure chest, incised "Peter Pan," Disney copyright, 1950s .... **75.00**
Puzzle, frame tray, 11½ x 15", Whitman, 1952 Walt Disney Productions copyright .... **20.00**

View–Master Reels, set of 3, orig envelope and booklet, Disney Productions copyright 1957 . . . . . . . . **25.00**

Pinocchio

Book, *Walt Disney's Pinocchio,* Whitman, #709, 1939 . . . . . . . . . . . . . . **75.00**

Card Game, 40 cards, orig box, Russell Mfg Co, 1965 Walt Disney Productions copyright . . . . . . . . . . . . . **15.00**

Doll

Jiminy Cricket, 8" h, wood, jointed body, Ideal, Disney copyright, c1940 . . . . . . . . . . . . . . . . . . . . . **300.00**

Pinocchio, 10½" h, composition, Knickerbocker, c1940 . . . . . . . . . **200.00**

Game, Walt Disney Presents Pinocchio, orig box, Parker Brothers, 1971 copyright . . . . . . . . . . . . . . . . **25.00**

Glass, 5" h, clear glass, weighted bottom, Pinocchio with apple, Jiminy Cricket holding umbrella, Disney copyright, 1940–50 . . . . . . . . . . . . **50.00**

Marionette, 14" h, composition head, hand, and feet, orig box, Peter Puppet Playthings, 1950s . . . . . . . . . . . **200.00**

Paint Book, 8¼ x 11", 48 pgs, Collins of London, 1940 Disney copyright **75.00**

Record, 45 rpm, "Hi–Diddle–Dee–Dee," orig paper sleeve, Little Golden Record, c1960 . . . . . . . . . . **15.00**

Sheet Music, 9 x 11¾", "When You Wish Upon A Star," 2 pgs, Pinocchio and Jiminy Cricket illus on front, copyright 1940 Bourne, Inc **25.00**

Snow Dome, 5" h, figural, seated Pinocchio holding clear plastic dome, marked "Made in Hong Kong," Disney copyright, 1970s . . . . . . . . **50.00**

Tea Set, 11 pcs, teapot, four cups and plates, creamer, and sugar, character illus, orange trim, Wade Heath, c1940 . . . . . . . . . . . . . . . . . . **250.00**

**Snow White and the Seven Dwarfs, rug, Alexander Smith & Co., NY, 45 x 60", $440.00. Photograph courtesy of James D. Julia Inc.**

Pluto

Figure, 6" l, 4" h, foam rubber, poseable, Disney Productions copyright, 1960s . . . . . . . . . . . . . . . . . . . **15.00**

Lamp, 6½" h, molded ceramic, doghouse, Pluto in doorway, Railley Corp, 1947 . . . . . . . . . . . . . . . . . . . . **100.00**

Soaky Bottle, 8½" h, plastic, orange, Disney Productions copyright, 1960s . . . . . . . . . . . . . . . . . . . . . . . . **15.00**

Toy, 9" l, Pluto Pop–A–Part, plastic, orig display card, Multiple Toymakers, Disney Productions copyright, 1965 . . . . . . . . . . . . . . . . . . . . . . . . **25.00**

Snow White and the Seven Dwarfs

Book, *Walt Disney's Famous Seven Dwarfs,* 12½ x 13", Whitman, 12 pgs, 1938 . . . . . . . . . . . . . . . . . . . . **55.00**

Cake Tin, Belgium . . . . . . . . . . . . . . . **250.00**

Figure, set of 8, 6½" h Snow White, seven 5" h dwarfs, bisque, c1938 **200.00**

Glass, 4⅜" h, Doc, clear, blue illus, c1938 . . . . . . . . . . . . . . . . . . . . . . . **45.00**

Lamp, figural, Snow White, composition, Walt Disney Enterprises, dated 1938 . . . . . . . . . . . . . . . . . . . **175.00**

Mask, 8 x 8¼", Snow White, stiff paper, red bow with inscription, marked "Par–T–Mask/Einson–Freeman Company Inc," Disney Enterprises copyright, 1937 . . . . . . . . . **50.00**

Pencil Holder, 4" h, Happy, figural, china, painted and glazed, marked "Disneyland," orig price sticker, c1960 . . . . . . . . . . . . . . . . . . . . . . . **35.00**

Puppet, hand, Dopey, Walt Disney Enterprises . . . . . . . . . . . . . . . . . . . **65.00**

Puzzle, frame tray, 8½ x 11½", Dopey, masonite board, "Judy Toys" decal, Disney Productions copyright, 1950s . . . . . . . . . . . . . . **30.00**

Rug, 22 x 45", Dwarfs carrying tools crossing bridge, Snow White setting at end . . . . . . . . . . . . . . . . . . . . . . . **200.00**

Toothbrush Holder, 4" h, Bashful, china figure, marked "Genuine Walt Disney Copyright," English, late 1930s . . . . . . . . . . . . . . . . . . . . **100.00**

Wristwatch, Snow White, silvered metal case, orig silver metal expansion band, US Time, c1958 . . . . . **25.00**

Zorro

Bowl, 5" d, plastic, color illus, Disney Productions copyright, c1960 . . . . **15.00**

Charm Bracelet, 6" l, silvered metal, charms with black, red, and white accents, late 1950s . . . . . . . . . . . . **25.00**

Game, Walt Disney's Zorro Game, orig box, Parker Brothers, Walt Disney Productions copyright, 1966 . **50.00**

Paint Set, Walt Disney's Zorro Oil Painting By Numbers, Hassenfield

Brothers, orig box, unused, late 1950s . . . . . . . . . . . . . . . . . . . . . . . . **75.00**
Puppet, 10″ h, fabric body, soft vinyl head, detachable cape, vinyl mask, and felt hat, orig Gund tag, Walt Disney Productions copyright, c1960 . . . . . . . . . . . . . . . . . . . . . . . . **50.00**
Puzzle, 11¼ x 14½″, Zorro on rearing horse, Whitman Publishing Co, Disney Productions copyright, 1965 . . . . . . . . . . . . . . . . . . . . . . . . **20.00**
Thermos, 6½″ h, metal, color illus, black plastic cup, Aladdin Industries, 1960s . . . . . . . . . . . . . . . . . . . . **40.00**
Wristwatch, black band with silver accents, black dial, white numerals, Walt Disney Productions copyright, US Time, 1957 . . . . . . . . . . . **50.00**

# DOG COLLECTIBLES

**Collecting Hints:** A collection of dog related items may be based on one particular breed. Another way to collect dog items is by items picturing a dog or even dog–shaped objects. With millions of dog owners in the United States, dog collectibles are very popular.

**History:** Dogs, long recognized as "Man's Best Friend," have been a part of human life since the early cavemen. The first dogs probably were used for hunting and protection against the wilder animals. After man learned that dogs could be trained to provide useful services, many types of dogs were bred and trained for specific purposes. Over 100 breeds of dogs have evolved from the first dog which roamed the earth over 15 million years ago. Today, dogs are still hunters, protectors, herders, and are trained to see and hear for people.

Man has continued to domesticate the dog, developing today's popular breeds. The American Kennel Club has divided the breeds into seven classifications: herding, hounds, sporting, non–sporting, terriers, toy breeds, and working dogs.

In 1859 in Newcastle, England, the first modern dog show was held. People enjoyed this show and many others were started. The breeding of prize dogs became important. The bloodlines of important dogs were established and recorded. Today, the dogs with the largest pedigrees command the highest prices.

As the dog's popularity grew, so did its appearance on objects. They became popular in literature, in paintings and other art forms.

**References:** Norman E. Martinus and Harry L. Rinker, *Warman's Paper,* Wallace–Homestead, 1993; Alice L. Muncaster and Ellen Sawyer, *The Dog Made Me Buy It!,* Crown Publishers, 1990; William Secord, *Dog Painting: 1840–1940: A Social History of the Dog in Art,* Antique Collectors Club, 1992.

**Collectors' Club:** Canine Collectibles Club of America, 736 N. Western Ave., Suite 314, Lake Forest, IL 60045.

**Museum:** The Dog Museum of America, Jarville House, St. Louis, MO.

**Advisor:** Jocelyn C. Mousley.

**Calendar Plate, white china, gold trim, 1910, 8⅝″ d, $45.00.**

Advertising
  Calendar, 1938, Lehigh Coal, hunting dogs, full color . . . . . . . . . . . . . . . . **20.00**
  Sign, Old Vitality Dog Food, 10 x 14″ **85.00**
Ashtray, Scottie, seated, marked "Nuart NYC" . . . . . . . . . . . . . . . . . . . . . . . . . **45.00**
Book
  A P Terkune, *Real Tales of Real Dogs,* illus by Diana Thorne, 1935 . . . . . **35.00**
  Ellis Parker Butler, *That Pup,* 1908 . . **15.00**
Bookends, pr, metal
  Scotties, 1929 . . . . . . . . . . . . . . . . . . **85.00**
  Setter, heads, incised marking, gold finish, 5½″ h, paper sticker marked "Reno Industries Inc" . . . . . . . . . . . **55.00**
Candy Container, Bull Dog, sitting . . . . **20.00**
Carnival Chalkware
  Dog holding ball, 7″ h . . . . . . . . . . . . **15.00**
  Spaniel type, black, white, and red, 11″ h . . . . . . . . . . . . . . . . . . . . . . . . . **30.00**
Cereal Bowl, puppy, sitting, marked "Roseville" . . . . . . . . . . . . . . . . . . . . . **35.00**
Cigarette Box, Scottie, dispenses cigarettes, wood . . . . . . . . . . . . . . . . . . . . **25.00**
Cookie Jar, puppy with sign, McCoy . . **50.00**
Creamer, puppy, sitting, marked "Roseville" . . . . . . . . . . . . . . . . . . . . . . . . . **95.00**
Creamer and Sugar, Scotties, black, ceramic, price for pair . . . . . . . . . . . . . **22.00**
Door Knocker, English Setter, bronzed metal, 4 x 5″ . . . . . . . . . . . . . . . . . . . **20.00**

Doorstop
- Boston Bull Terrier, iron, orig dark paint, some rust, c1920 **95.00**
- English Setter, iron, orig white and black paint **95.00**
- French Bull Dog, National Foundry **100.00**
- German Shepherd, Hubley **190.00**
- Setter, brown and black paint, Hubley **325.00**
- Whippet, orig black and cream paint **140.00**
- Wire Haired Terrier, facing front, Hubley **170.00**

Figure
- Airdale, wood, carved, two pups on chain **35.00**
- Boxer, reclining, Mortens Studios **55.00**
- Bull Dog, wood, carved **22.00**
- Cocker Spaniel, 4½″ l, charcoal, Mortens Studios **50.00**
- Collie, sitting, Mortens Studios **35.00**
- Dachshund, 3½″ h, German **20.00**
- English Bull Dog, German **40.00**
- German Shepherd, Royal Dux, pink triangle mark, 8¼″ l **120.00**
- Greyhounds, facing pair, chalkware, American, c1920, price for pair **100.00**
- Poodle, bisque, lying, white, Boehm **265.00**
- Scottie
  - Bronze, male **35.00**
  - Wood, carved **28.00**
- Spaniel, black, Royal Doulton, 3″ l **115.00**
- St Bernard, German **20.00**

**Figure, racing greyhound, cast bronzed metal, red fabric blanket with "Florida 5," 6⅛″ l, 2⅞″ h, $18.00.**

Inkwell, Whippet type dog, sitting by figural tree stump, painted white metal, orig glass insert **125.00**

Jewelry, pin, round, two Scotties **10.00**

Lamp, Scotties, pair, metal **75.00**

Music Box, Snoopy, dressed as astronaut, sitting on wood dog house, Schmid **125.00**

Needle Tin, RCA Victor, The Gramophone Co, Nipper, orig needles **35.00**

Nodder
- Beagle, puppies **20.00**
- Boston Terrier **12.00**

Nutcracker, St Bernard, gilded iron **65.00**

Paperweight, sitting dog, glass, 5″ h **20.00**

Pen Holder, Scottie, Goldscheider **45.00**

Pen Wiper, pug **25.00**

Pipe Holder, 5¼″ l, Scottie, syroco, figural **12.00**

Planter
- Bird Dog, McCoy Pottery **40.00**
- Scottie, 4 x 4″, Japan **18.00**

Poster, Sgt Preston and Yukon King, Contest Winner Award, 16 x 22″, 1950 **200.00**

Pounce Pot, pug, glass eyes, metal **100.00**

Powder Jar, Scottie, iridescent glass **20.00**

Print
- Atchison Fox, man with two hunting dogs **70.00**
- De Forest, Speak Rover, boy with dog **60.00**

Puppet, hand, Tramp, Disney **20.00**

Puzzle, Sgt Preston and Yukon King, Milton Bradley, 45 pieces, 1950s **25.00**

Salt and Pepper Shakers, pr, Bloodhound heads, Rosemeade **35.00**

Slipper, ceramic, 12¼″ l, dog's hind end sticking out, head in slipper **35.00**

Stuffed Toy
- Boston Terrier type, velvet covered straw, stitched nose, glass eyes, marked "Wagee Walker," c1920 **95.00**
- Dachshund, Steiff, 1950s **50.00**
- Poodle, mohair, glass eyes and nose, movable legs **20.00**
- Puppy, mohair, felt tongue, glass eyes, straw stuffing, c1920 **65.00**
- Sheep Dog, curly mohair, jointed head, glass eyes, orig collar and lead, sits or stands, 17″ h, c1930 **95.00**

Teapot, majolica, figural **125.00**

Textile, needlepoint, puppy in teacup, orig rustic wooden frame **45.00**

Tie Rack, wood, carved, seated Scottie, glass eyes **22.00**

Toothpick Holder, spaniel type, sitting next to cup, marked "Asbury Park, NJ" **18.00**

Towel Hanger, Cocker Spaniel, metal, painted gold, 3″ l **10.00**

Toy, windup
- Collie, Alps **45.00**
- Jumping Dog, white and brown fur, Japan, c1930, MIB **85.00**

Wall Plaque, Greyhound, two boys on unicycles, sculpted and incised figures, artist sgd, 8 x 10″ **125.00**

Whiskey Bottle, figural
- Great Dane, black and white, reclining, Jim Beam, 1976, 11″ l **18.00**
- Setter, Ezra Brooks
  - Brown and white, standing on point, 1974, 13″ l **18.00**
  - White, hunter in cap, gun, 1973 **25.00**

Whistle
- Hush Puppy Shoes, molded plastic,

figural, stamped "Hush Puppy" on back .......... **5.00**
Sgt Preston and Yukon King, nylon cord, 1950 .......... **35.00**
Wrist Watch, Snoopy, tennis style .......... **50.00**

# DOLL HOUSE FURNISHINGS

**Collecting Hints:** Doll house furnishings are children's toys. Some wear may be expected. It is possible to find entire room sets in original boxes. These sets will command a higher price.

**History:** Doll house furnishings are the tiny articles of furniture and accessories used to outfit a doll house. They may be made of many types of materials, from fine handmade wooden pieces to molded plastic. Furnishings were played with by children to decorate and redecorate their favorite dollhouse. Several toy manufacturers, such as Tootsietoy, Petite Princess, and Renwal, made doll house furnishings.

Doll houses and doll house furnishings are experiencing a current craze and are highly collectible. Many artists and craftsmen devote hours to making scale furniture and accessories. This type of artist–oriented doll house furnishing is not included in this listing. It does, however, affect the market by offering the buyer a choice of an old piece versus a present day handmade piece.

**References:** Flora Gill Jacobs, *Doll's Houses in America: Historic Preservation in Miniature,* Charles Scribner's Sons, 1974; Constance Eileen King, *Dolls and Dolls Houses,* Hamlyn; Von Wilckens, *Mansions in Miniature,* Tuttle.

**Periodical:** Miniature Collector, P. O. Box 631, Boiling Springs, PA 17007.

**Collectors' Clubs:** International Guild Miniature Artisans, P. O. Box 71, Bridgeport, NY 13030; National Association of Miniature Enthusiasts, P.O. Box 69, Carmel, IN 46032.

**Museums:** Kansas City Doll House Museum, Kansas City, MO; Margaret Woodbury Strong Museum, Rochester, NY; Mildred Mahoney Jubilee Doll House Museum, Fort Erie, Canada; Toy Museum of Atlanta, Atlanta, GA; Washington Dolls' House and Toy Museum, Washington, DC.

Bathinette, Renwal .......... **12.00**
Bathroom Set
Renwal, price for three piece set .......... **10.00**
Tootsietoy, orig box, price for ten piece set .......... **75.00**
Bed
Petite Princess .......... **18.00**
Renwal, twin size .......... **5.00**
Bedroom Suite
Biedermier, bed, marble topped stand, armoire, price for three piece set .......... **350.00**
Ideal, plastic, c1940, MIB, price for four piece set .......... **25.00**
Tootsietoy, orig box, price for six piece set .......... **60.00**
Buffet
Petite Princess, MIB .......... **15.00**
Tootiestoy, metal, c1920 .......... **25.00**
Candelabra, Petite Princess .......... **20.00**
Chair
Arm
Petite Princess, matching ottoman **20.00**
Tootsietoy .......... **12.00**
Side, Petite Princess, red satin, MIB .......... **14.00**
Wing Back, Petite Princess, MIB .......... **12.00**
Chaise Lounge, Petite Princess, MIB, c1964 .......... **20.00**
Chest of Drawers
Hand Made, walnut, 4 x 6 x 7" .......... **48.00**
Petite Princess, plastic, MIB, 1964 .......... **15.00**
Cradle, wood .......... **25.00**
Cup and Saucer, ironstone, ⅝" .......... **5.00**
Desk, maple, hinged front, royal blue and black int., 3½ x 6" .......... **100.00**
Dining Room
Chair, Tootiestoy, metal, c1920, price for pair .......... **25.00**
Suite
Arcade, Curtis, cast iron, white lacquer finish, two high backed benches, matching 4¾" l table, openwork legs, 1936, price for three piece set .......... **50.00**
Tootsietoy, Daisy, circular pedestal table, four chairs, buffet, sideboard, and tea cart, orig box, price for eight piece set .......... **65.00**
Table
Petite Princess, MIB .......... **20.00**
Tootiestoy, metal, c1920 .......... **25.00**
Table and Chairs, Renwal, four chairs, price for five piece set .......... **20.00**
Doll, bisque, shoulderhead, molded hair, painted facial features, muslin body
4½" h, girl, blonde hair, Kate Greenaway style cape and muff .......... **100.00**
5" h
Chauffeur, molded brown cap, brown felt suit .......... **70.00**
Maid, bobbed hair, short blue dress, lace trimmed apron .......... **60.00**
6¼" h, mother, molded upswept chignon, high collar dress, leg o'mutton sleeves, lace apron .......... **75.00**

7" h, father, brown hair and mustache, orig wool tweed suit, white shirt, tie . . . . . . . . . . **60.00**
Fernery, 4¼" h, tin, painted red and gold, two circular trays, fancy scrolled legs . . . . . . . . . . **175.00**
Foot Warmer, brass, working drawer, ¾" **35.00**
Ice Cream Set, 3½" circular table, twisted metal legs, four matching chairs, heart shaped backs, four blue lemonade glasses, matching blown pitcher, price for ten piece set . . . . . **100.00**
Ironing Board, folding, Kilgore, cast iron, c1930 . . . . . . . . . . **20.00**
Kitchen
Cupboard, Petite Princess, MIB . . . . **40.00**
Refrigerator
Arcade, cast iron, white lacquer, gray trim, 5¾" h, marked "Leonard" . . . . . . . . . . **35.00**
Tootiestoy, metal, c1920 . . . . . . . . **25.00**
Sink, Petite Princess, accessories, MIB **50.00**
Suite
German, finished hardwood, painted bright salmon, PA Dutch style dec of hearts and flowers in red, yellow, and brown, 4¼" hutch, 4" l domed trunk, sq table, three chairs, cradle, bench, oven, box marked "Seit 1912, Kuhn Operboyeriche Heimathust," orig box, price for eight piece set . . . . . . . . . . **50.00**
Ideal, plastic, orig box, c1940, price for seven piece set . . . . . . **30.00**
Tootsietoy, green, cupboard, table, chair, and stove, orig litho box, price for four piece set . . . . . . . . **40.00**
Lamp
Floor, 4" h, black, soft metal, gilded frame, glass beaded shade . . . . . . . **100.00**
Table, 3" h, blue painted base, bulbous milk glass shade . . . . . . . . . . . **42.00**
Living Room Suite
Arcade, cast iron, sofa, chair, deep pink, maroon trim, removable cushion, price for two piece set . . **165.00**
Tootsietoy, Daisy Doll House Furniture, gold, sofa, two chairs, library table, floor lamp, table lamp, and phonograph stand, price for seven piece set . . . . . . . . . . **60.00**
Patio Set, litho tin, round table, four chairs, floral design, price for five piece set . . . . . . . . . . **35.00**
Piano
Ideal, plastic, litho, mirror . . . . . . . . . **25.00**
Petite Princess, grand, MIB . . . . . . . . **20.00**
Renwal, matching bench . . . . . . . . . . **12.00**
Potty Chair, 3" h, gilt soft metal, spindled back, floral dec chamber pot, wheels, c1900 . . . . . . . . . . **24.00**
Radio, Renwal . . . . . . . . . . **30.00**
Rocking Chair, carved arms, fabric seat and back . . . . . . . . . . **25.00**
Rug, polar bear, white, royal purple velvet lining, glass bead eyes . . . . . . . . . **25.00**
Set, Nancy Forbes, wooden, general household furnishings, MIB . . . . . . . . **65.00**

**Set, Nancy Forbes, No. 4502, 18 pcs, Rapaport Bros., Chicago, orig box, $45.00.**

Settee, Arcade, cast iron . . . . . . . . . . . . **80.00**
Sink, Tootiestoy, pedestal, metal, c1920 **25.00**
Sofa
Petite Princess, green, MIB . . . . . . . . **18.00**
Tootsietoy, metal . . . . . . . . . . . . **35.00**
Stool, Tootsietoy, metal . . . . . . . . . . . . **12.00**
Stove, Tootiestoy, metal, c1920 . . . . . . **25.00**
Tea Cart
Petite Princess . . . . . . . . . . . . **20.00**
Tootiestoy, metal, c1920 . . . . . . . . . . **25.00**
Tea Set, porcelain, teapot, creamer, sugar, and tray, 6 pcs . . . . . . . . . . . . **50.00**
Television, Petite Princess, MIB . . . . . . **60.00**
Toilet, Tootiestoy, metal, c1920 . . . . . . **25.00**
Vanity
Renwal . . . . . . . . . . . . **8.00**
Tootiestoy, metal, c1920 . . . . . . . . . . **25.00**

# DOLLS

**Collecting Hints:** The most important criteria in buying dolls are sentiment and condition. The value of a particular doll increases if it is a childhood favorite or family heirloom.

When pricing a doll, condition is the most important aspect. Excellent condition means that the doll has all original parts.

The wig should not be soiled or restyled. The surface of the skin must be free of marks and blemishes. Original sleep eyes must be free moving. All mechanical parts should be operational. Original clothing means original dress, underclothes, shoes, and socks in excellent and clean condition, preferably with original tags and labels.

A doll that is mint in the original box is listed as "MIB." Many modern collectible doll prices depend on the original box. Mattel's original Barbie doll, for example, is valued over $1,000 MIB. However, without the original box, the doll is worth much less. Another pricing consideration is appeal. Only a collector knows how important and valuable a particular doll is to her collection.

Modern and early 20th century dolls are highly collectible. They offer many appealing features to collectors, one of which is price. A collector of modern dolls need not spend thousands of dollars. This type of doll collecting fits into the average person's budget.

Another feature is the sizes of dolls which enables collectors to artfully display them. Many dolls are made of materials easily cleaned and maintained. An attractive appeal of modern dolls is that they are easily available at flea markets, garage sales, swap meets, etc.

**History:** The history of modern doll manufacturers is long and varied. While competitors, these companies used similar procedures, molds, and ideas. When Effanbee was successful with the Patsy dolls, Horsman soon followed with a Patsy look–alike named Dorothy. Vogue's Ginny doll was imitated by Cosmopolitan's Ginger. Some manufacturers reused molds and changed sizes and names to produce dolls which were similar for many years.

Dolls have always been popular with Americans. The early Patsy dolls with their own wardrobes were a success in the 1930s and 1940s. During the 1950s Vogue's Ginny doll was very successful in generating sales of dolls, clothes, and accessories. The next decade of children enjoyed Mattel's Barbie. Collectors will determine what the collectible dolls of the 1970s and 1980s will be. Doll collecting has become a major hobby.

**References:** Johana Gast Anderton, *The Collector's Encyclopedia of Cloth Dolls: From Rag Baby to Art Object,* Wallace–Homestead, 1984; Johana Gast Anderton, *More Twentieth Century Dolls From Bisque to Vinyl, Volume A–H, Volume I–Z, Revised Edition,* Wallace–Homestead, 1974; John Axe, *The Encyclopedia of Celebrity Dolls,* Hobbie House Press, Inc. 1983; Julie Collier, *Official Identification and Price Guide to Antique and Modern Dolls, Fourth Edition,* House of Collectibles, 1989; Jan Foulke, *11th Blue Book Dolls & Values,* Hobby House Press, Inc., 1993; Carol Cast Glassmire, *Price Guide to The Collector's Encyclopedia of Cloth Dolls,* Wallace–Homestead, 1985; R. Lane Herron, *Herron's Price Guide to Dolls,* Wallace–Homestead, 1989; Polly Judd, *Cloth Dolls of the 1920s and 1930s,* Hobby House Press, 1990; Polly and Pam Judd, *Composition Dolls: 1928–1955,* Hobby House Press, 1991; Polly and Pam Judd, *Hard Plastic Dolls, Revised,* Vol. I (1989), Vol. II (1990); A. Glenn Mandeville, *Contemporary Doll Stars: Forty Years of the Best,* Hobby House Press, 1992; A. Glenn Mandeville, *Doll Fashion Anthology & Price Guide, 3rd Revised Edition,* Hobby House Press, 1992; A. Glenn Mandeville, *Ginny: An American Toddler Doll, 3rd Revised Edition,* Hobby House Press, 1992; Jeanne Du Chateau Niswonger, *That Doll, Ginny,* Cody Publications, 1978; Edward R. Pardella, *Shirley Temple Dolls and Fashion: A Collector's Guide To The World's Darling,* Schiffer Publishing, Ltd., 1992; Paris and Susan Manos, *The Wonder of Barbie,* Collector Books, 1987, 1993 value update; Paris and Susan Manos, *The World of Barbie Dolls,* Collector Books, 1983, 1992 value update; Myla Perkins, *Black Dolls: An Identification And Value Guide,* Collector Books, 1993; Joleen Ashman Robison and Kay Sellers, *Advertising Dolls: Identification & Value Guide,* Collector Books, 1980, 1992 value update; Patricia N. Schoonmaker, *Patsy Doll Family, Vol. I,* Hobby House Press, 1992; Patricia R. Smith, *Collector's Encyclopedia of Madame Alexander Dolls, 1965–1990,* Collector Books, 1991; Patricia R. Smith, *Madame Alexander Collector's Dolls Price Guide #17,* Collector Books, 1992; Patricia R. Smith, *Madame Alexander Collector's Doll Price Guide #18,* Collector Books, 1993; Patricia R. Smith, *Modern Collector's Dolls, Editions 1, 2, 3, 4, 5,* Collector Books, 1973, 1975, 1976, 1979, 1984, 1993 value update Vol. 1–5; Patricia R. Smith, *Patricia Smith's Doll Values, Ninth Series,* Collector Books, 1993; Patricia R. Smith, *Patricia Smith's Doll Values: Antique to Modern, Eighth Series,* Collector Books, 1992; Marjorie Victoria Sturges Uhl, *Madame Alexander, Ladies of Fashion,* Collector Books, 1982, out–of–print; Florence Theriault, *More Dolls: The Early Years, 1780–1910,* Gold Horse Publishing, 1992.

**Periodicals:** *Celebrity Doll Journal,* 5 Court Place, Puyallup, WA 98372; *Collectors United,* Master Key To The World of Dolls, P. O. Box 1160, Chatsworth, GA 30705; *Contemporary Doll Magazine,* Scott Publications, 30595 W. 8 Mile Road, Livonia, MI 48152; *Costume Quarterly for Doll Collectors,* 38 Middlesex Drive, Brentwood, MO 63144; *Doll Artisan,* Doll Artisan Guild, 35 Main Street, Oneonta, NY 13820; *Doll Collector's Price Guide,* P. O. Box 11310, Des Moines, IA 50340; *Doll Reader,* P. O. Box 467, Mount Morris, IL 61054; *Doll Times,* 218 West Woodin, Dallas, TX 75224; *Dolls–The Collector's Magazine,* 170 Fifth Ave., 12th Floor, New York, NY 10010.

**Collectors' Clubs:** Ginny Doll Club, 305 West Beacon Road, Lakeland, FL 33803; United Federation of Doll Clubs, P. O. Box 14146, Parkville, MO 64152.

**Museums:** Margaret Woodbury Strong Museum, Rochester, NY; Museum of Collectible Dolls, Lakeland, FL; Yesteryears Museum, Sandwich, MA.

**Note:** All prices listed here are for dolls in excellent condition and original clothes, unless otherwise noted.

## AMERICAN ARTISTS

Americans have been making dolls for children for centuries. During the past several decades, several artists began making dolls on a limited edition basis, emphasizing exquisite detailing and uniqueness. Today's doll artists offer a varied range of collectible dolls.

The listing below is a sampling of artist dolls which have been sold during the past year. Many artists currently producing dolls are not included because their works have not yet begun to appear in the secondary market. Speculation runs high in this area of doll collecting.

Appalachian Artworks, Inc., Xavier Roberts, orig Cabbage Patch
- Anna Ruby, 1989 ........ **300.00**
- Celebrity Girl, 1980 ........ **425.00**
- Irish boy and girl, price for pair .... **500.00**
- Mai Ling, porcelain, limited edition, marked "MLG–001" on neck, MIB **300.00**
- Mitzi, circus outfit, 1991 ........ **150.00**
- Sybil, 1982, MIB ........ **400.00**

Ball, Betty, Heidi ........ **80.00**

Clear, Emma, George and Martha Washington, 1947, orig clothes, 30" h, price for pair ........ **1,600.00**

Cochran, Dewees, 15", Cindy, latex, jointed neck, shoulders, and hips, human hair wig, painted eyes, character face, c1948 ........ **600.00**

DeHetre, Terre, Punkin, 1988 DOTY award ........ **155.00**

Middleton, Lee, Dear One, black porcelain ........ **425.00**

Sullivan, Elsie, 13" h, Trudy, composition head, flanged neck, muslin body, three painted faces, blonde mohair wisps, painted baby facial features, mohair flannel hooded pajamas, MIB; mark: An Elsie Sullivan Creation, Trudy 3 in 1 Doll, New York, c1940 **265.00**

Wellings, Norah
- 14½" h, Royal Canadian Mountie, velvet ........ **175.00**
- 15" h, girl, felt, blonde braids, wrist label ........ **220.00**
- 19" h, Pajama Bag Doll, velvet head, dark skin tone, pajama bag body, painted features, mohair wig, felt shoes, orig sticker on foot, c1928 **100.00**
- 39" h, Mexican Boy, pressed felt face, velvet body, inset brown glass eyes, yellow felt hat, c1935 ........ **100.00**

Woods, Robin, Clara, cloth ........ **150.00**

Zeller, Fawn, 17½" h, Jackie Kennedy, porcelain shoulderhead, slender neck, muslin body, bisque forearm, painted side parted bouffant hair, painted facial features, pink satin dress, applied seed pearls, c1962 .. **400.00**

## AMERICAN CHARACTER DOLL COMPANY

The American Character Doll Company was founded in 1918 and made high quality dolls. When the company was liquidated in 1968, many molds were purchased by the Ideal Toy Co. American Character Dolls are marked with the full company name, "Amer. Char." or "Amer. Char" in a circle. Early composition dolls were marked "Petite."

8" h
- Betsy McCall, hard plastic, jointed knees, brunette rooted hair, sleep eyes, orig red and white striped skirt, white organdy top, red shoes, c1960 ........ **45.00**
- Cartwright, Ben, Bonanza, Lorne Green, plastic, 1965 ........ **115.00**
- Little Joe, Bonanza, Michael Landon, vinyl, fully jointed body, painted brown hair and eyes, molded clothing, c1965 ........ **155.00**

10" h, Toni, collegiate outfit, orig booklet ........ **70.00**

10½" h, Tiny Toodles, vinyl, molded, painted hair, 1958 ........ **35.00**

11" h, Tiny Tears, hard plastic head, vinyl body, curly rooted hair, sunsuit, wood and plastic bathinette, c1955 . **85.00**

13" h, Bottle Tot, composition head, body mark, orig tagged clothes ..... **175.00**

16" h, Baby, composition head, stuffed cloth body and limbs, molded, painted brown hair, brown sleep eyes, c1925; mark: A. M. Char. Doll, c1925 ........ **125.00**

18" h
- Sally, composition head, cloth body, orig clothes ........ **185.00**
- Sweet Sue, plastic head, vinyl jointed body ........ **100.00**
- Toodle–Loo, fully jointed, magic foam plastic body, rooted blonde synthetic hair, painted brown eyes,

closed mouth; mark: American Doll & Toy Co, 1961 . . . . . . . . . . . **175.00**
20½" h, Little Ricky, I Love Lucy, vinyl, fully jointed, 1953 . . . . . . . . . . . . . . . **165.00**
23" h, Chuckles, all vinyl, rooted blonde saran hair, painted, brown eyes, closed mouth, elastic strung legs; mark: Amer. Doll & Toy Co/1961/ copyright . . . . . . . . . . . . . . . . . . . . . . . . **150.00**

## ARRANBEE

This company was founded in 1922. Arranbee's finest dolls were made in hard plastic. One of Arranbee's most popular dolls was Nancy, and later Nanette. The company was sold to Vogue Dolls, Inc., in 1959. Marks used by this company include "Arranbee," "R&B," and "Made In USA."

8" h, Little Dear, stuffed vinyl body, rooted hair, blue sleep eyes, c1956 . **80.00**
11" h, Littlest Angel, vinyl head, hard plastic body, jointed, rooted dark brown hair; mark: R & B on head, 1959 . . . . . . . . . . . . . . . . . . . . . . . . . . **40.00**
13" h, Angel Skin, stuffed soft vinyl head, stuffed magic skin body and limbs, molded, painted hair, inset stationary blue eyes, closed mouth; mark: R & B on head, orig tag: The R & B Family/Rock Me, Nanette/Little Angel, Angel Face/Littlest Angel, Dream Baby/Baby Bunting, Angel Skin/Taffy, MIB, c1954 . . . . . . . . . . . **80.00**
14" h, Nancy Lee, composition, blonde wig, blue sleep eyes, closed mouth, orig red and white taffeta dress; mark: R & B/Quality/Doll/Nancy Lee, c1947 **150.00**
15" h
- Baby Bunting, vinylite plastic head, stuffed magic skin body, molded, painted hair, pink fleece bunting; mark: 17BBS/R & B/D6 on head, orig tag reads: Head is of Vinylite Plastic by Bakelite Company . . . . . **60.00**
- Nanette, all hard plastic, glued on wig, sleep eyes, walker, cotton pinafore, straw hat, MIB, 1952 . . . . . **250.00**

17" l, Red Cross Nurse, composition, damaged finger . . . . . . . . . . . . . . . . . **160.00**
17½" h, child, all composition, jointed body, blue sleep eyes, brown wig, closed mouth; mark: R & B, c1940 . **70.00**
19" h
- Judy, hard plastic, nylon blonde wig, braids, metal knob to wind hair back into head, open mouth; mark: 210 on head, body, Pat. 2,537,598, c1951 . . . . . . . . . . . . . **75.00**
- Rosie, composition, swivel head, cloth body, molded hair, 1935 . . . **85.00**

20" h, Dream Baby, composition shoulderhead, cloth body, painted hair, redressed, c1925 . . . . . . . . . . . . . . . . . . **145.00**
21" h, Nanette, hard plastic fully jointed body, saran braided wig, blue sleep eyes, closed mouth, orig clothes, 1953 . . . . . . . . . . . . . . . . . . . . . . . . . . **125.00**
23" h, Taffy, plastic, socket head, blue eyes, brunette saran wig, straight walker legs, blue striped satin skirt, white organdy blouse, ruffled sleeves, straw hat, 1954 . . . . . . . . . . . . . . . . . . **175.00**

## CLOTH, PRINTED

Cloth Dolls were manufactured by several companies and became quite popular after the invention of the sewing machine. Dolls and animals were frequently sold by the yard. Uncut early examples can still be found.

Bear, stuffed . . . . . . . . . . . . . . . . . . . . . . . **55.00**
Cream of Wheat, stuffed . . . . . . . . . . . . **75.00**
Dutch Boy, stuffed . . . . . . . . . . . . . . . . . . **25.00**
Foxy Grandpa, stuffed . . . . . . . . . . . . . . **130.00**
Girl, 8" h, uncut . . . . . . . . . . . . . . . . . . . **65.00**
Hen and Chickens, uncut . . . . . . . . . . . **65.00**
Imperial Granum Co, 1915, gold curls, spit curls, flirty eyes, smiling, uncut **65.00**
Indian Girl, 1920s, stuffed . . . . . . . . . . . **40.00**
Kellogg's
- Crackle, 1940s, stuffed . . . . . . . . . . . . **40.00**
- Dandy Duck, Wheat Krispies, 1930s, uncut . . . . . . . . . . . . . . . . . . . . . . . . . **45.00**
- Freckles Frog, Wheat Krispies, 1930s, uncut . . . . . . . . . . . . . . . . . . . . . . . . . **45.00**
- Mama Bear, stuffed . . . . . . . . . . . . . . . **75.00**
- Pop
  - 1940s, stuffed . . . . . . . . . . . . . . . . . **40.00**
  - 1948, uncut . . . . . . . . . . . . . . . . . . . **45.00**

**Cloth, Mary Merritt, made by Chase Bag Co. for the Mary Merritt Doll Museum, c1974, 14" h, $4.00.**

Snap, 1940s, stuffed .............. **40.00**
Little Doggie, Saalfield, stuffed ....... **100.00**
Papoose, 8" h, stuffed ............... **25.00**
Puppy, stuffed ..................... **65.00**

## COSMOPOLITAN DOLL COMPANY

Little recorded history is available about this company. Dolls dating from the late 1940s through the 1960s are found with the mark of CDC. It is believed that the company made many unmarked dolls. One of their most popular dolls was Ginger, made in 1955–1956, which was a take off of Vogue Doll's Ginny. Many of these Ginger dolls are found with original clothes made by the Terri Lee Doll Company.

7½" h
- Ginger, hard plastic, glued on wig, walker, head turns, 1955
  - Bedtime Outfit ................. **35.00**
  - Bride Outfit .................... **40.00**
  - Ice Skating Outfit ............... **40.00**
  - Mousketeer Outfit .............. **45.00**
- Ginger, vinyl head, hard plastic body, arms, and legs, rooted medium blonde hair, closed mouth; mark: Ginger on head, 1956 .......... **35.00**

8½" h, Little Miss Ginger, vinyl head, hard plastic body, rooted ash blonde hair, closed mouth, high heel feet; mark: Little Miss Ginger, 1956 ..... **20.00**
14" h, Merri, plastic, rooted blonde hair, high heel feet, red gown, white fur trim; mark: AE1406/41, backward AE on lower back, 1960 ............. **20.00**
25" h, Emily, hard plastic swivel head shoulderplate, cloth body, composition arms and legs, glued on blonde wig, open mouth, two teeth, 1949 . **60.00**

## EFFANBEE DOLL CORPORATION

The Effanbee Doll Corporation was founded in 1912 by Bernard E. Fleischaker and Hugo Baum. Its most successful line was the Pasty Doll and its many variations. Patsy was such a success that a whole wardrobe was designed and it also sold well. This was the first marketing of a doll and her wardrobe.

Effanbee experimented with materials as well as molds. Rubber was first used in 1930; the use of hard plastic began in 1949. Today vinyl has replaced composition. Effanbee is still making dolls and last year's catalog contained over 170 specimens.

8" h
- Baby Tinyette, 1932 .............. **165.00**
- Button Nose, Betty, 1943 .......... **165.00**
- Fluffy, 1954 ..................... **40.00**

9" h, Fairy Princess, 1935 ........... **185.00**
10" h, Wolf, 1934 .................. **185.00**
11" h, Billy Boy, 1915 .............. **100.00**
11½" h, Babyette, composition head and hands, stuffed pink cloth body, molded painted brown hair, closed eyes and mouth, orig tags and box, c1945 ......................... **100.00**

12" h
- Baby Grumpy, 1988, MIB ......... **36.00**
- Butterball, all vinyl, molded blonde hair, orig box, 1969 ............ **60.00**
- Cupcake, 1963 .................. **40.00**
- Dy Dee Baby, caracal wig, orig wardrobe and trunk ................. **185.00**
- Miss Coquette, 1916 .............. **125.00**
- Newborn Baby, 1925 ............. **125.00**
- Red Cross Nurse, 1918 ........... **125.00**

14" h
- Cinderella, hard plastic, jointed, sleep eyes, orig clothes, MIB .... **115.00**
- My Fair Baby, 1968 .............. **45.00**
- Patricia Walker, 1952 ............. **125.00**

15" h
- Alice, 1958 ..................... **145.00**
- Baby Blanche, 1918 .............. **150.00**
- Mickey Baby, 1938 ............... **135.00**

16" h
- Beach Baby, 1923 ................ **145.00**
- Cookie, 1968 .................... **50.00**
- Dorothy Dainty, 1916 ............. **125.00**
- Eisenhower, Dwight, MIB ......... **70.00**
- Honey Walker, 1953 .............. **145.00**
- Li'l Darlin, 1947 ................ **75.00**
- MacArthur, General, MIB ......... **70.00**
- Truman, Harry S, MIB ............ **70.00**

17" h, Groucho Marx, vinyl, 1983 .... **60.00**

18" h
- Anne Shirley, composition, orig clothes ....................... **175.00**
- Baby Bright Eyes, orig red and blue plaid cotton dress, orig hairdo, orig pin, tagged "Baby Bright Eyes" .. **950.00**
- Cinderella, 1952 ................. **200.00**
- McCarthy, Charlie, composition head, hands, and feet, cloth body, orig suit ...................... **225.00**
- Prince Charming, 1952 ........... **225.00**
- School Girl Writing, 1963 ......... **80.00**
- Snowsuit Susan, 1967 ............ **85.00**
- Today's Girl, 1943 ............... **140.00**
- West, Mae, vinyl, fully jointed, 1982 **100.00**

20" h
- Dydee, MIB ..................... **365.00**
- Hammer, Rusty, Make Room For Daddy, vinyl, fully jointed, 1955 . **110.00**
- Sugar Plum, 1980 ................ **65.00**

21" h, Rootie Kazootie, 1954 ........ **125.00**
24", Boudoir Doll, 1938 ............ **125.00**
25" h, Bubbles, composition ......... **290.00**
29" h, Elizabeth, 1938 .............. **175.00**

## HASBRO

Hasbro is primarily a toy manufacturer. Among their most popular dolls were GI Joe and his friends. The detailed accessories made for GI Joe include military sets and numerous adventure pieces (camping, mountain climbing, etc.). Hasbro is also noted for their advertising and personality dolls.

4″ h, Peter Noone, Herman's Hermits, vinyl, jointed head, 1967 ......... **25.00**
4½″ h, Mama Cass, Mammas And The Papas, Cass Elliot, vinyl, jointed at head, 1967 ...................... **30.00**
5″ h, The Flying Nun, Sally Field, vinyl, fully jointed, 1967 ............... **30.00**
7½″ h, Junior Miss Sewing Kit, jointed arms, orig box contains doll patterns, material, dresses to sew, sewing implements, orig 11½ x 15½″ box, c1948 ......................... **25.00**
9″ h, Choo Choo Charlie, soft vinyl head, stuffed cotton bean bag body, rooted hair, painted eyes; mark: Copyright 1973 Quaker City Chocolate & Conf'y Co, Inc ............. **20.00**
12″ h, GI Joe, vinyl, flocked hair, beard, orig clothes, c1974 ............... **20.00**
17″ h, Amanda, Sweet Dreams, stuffed gingham head and body, yard hair, black felt eyes, button nose, embroidered smile, eyelet lace trimmed night cap, orchid print dress, 1974 . **12.00**

## HORSMAN DOLLS COMPANY INC.

The Horsman Dolls Company, Inc., was founded in 1865 by E. I. Horsman, who began by importing dolls. Soon after the founding, Horsman produced bisque dolls. It was the first company to produce the Campbell Kids. They invented Fairy Skin in 1946, Miracle Hair in 1952, and Super Flex in 1954. The Horsman process for synthetic rubber and early vinyl has always been high quality.

11″ h, Peterkin, composition, character face, molded hair, painted side glancing eyes, watermelon smile, c1915 . **215.00**
12″ h
Baby Bumps, negro, cloth body, arms, legs, painted hair, eyes, large well molded ears, orig romper, c1912 ........................ **250.00**
Mary Poppins, all vinyl, 5 pc body, black rooted hair, painted blue eyes, extra clothes, c1965 ....... **40.00**
12½″ h
Duke, Patty, vinyl, plastic body, orig telephone, 1965 ............... **50.00**
Ruthie, all vinyl rooted black hair, Oriental hair style, long straight legs, dimpled knees; mark: 12–6aa on upper legs, B–1 on upper arms **30.00**

**Horsman, Mary Poppins, vinyl head and arms, plastic body and legs, 1964, 11½″ h, $40.00.**

13″ h, Campbell Kid, composition head, painted at neck, shoulders, and hips, light brown hair, painted side glancing googly eyes, 2 pc brown knicker suit, c1940 ...................... **185.00**
14″ h, Bye–Lo, vinyl head, arms, and legs, cloth body, molded straight hair, painted eyes, christening outfit; mark: Horsman Doll/1972 on head, MIB .. **50.00**
15″ h
Dimples Toddler, redressed ........ **150.00**
Tynie Baby, composition head, cloth body, composition arms, sleep eyes, closed mouth ............. **250.00**
16″ h, Baby Dimples, composition, orig clothes .......................... **185.00**
17″ h, Ronald Reagan, vinyl, fully jointed .......................... **65.00**
18″ h
Ella Cinders, composition head, cloth body, composition arms and lower legs, molded black hair, painted facial features, orig dress, c1925 ... **225.00**
Joyce, composition shoulderhead, arms, and legs, cloth body, glued on bright red mohair hair ........ **50.00**
19″ h, Pram Baby, vinyl, jointed head, glass sleep eyes, closed mouth, coos **65.00**
20″ h, Rosebud, composition head, arms, and legs, cloth body, painted eyes, human hair wig ............. **100.00**
21″ h, Cindy Walker, all hard plastic, sleep eyes, open mouth, two teeth, 1950s, redressed in lace .......... **65.00**
22″ h, Baby Dimples, composition, cloth body, 1928, crazing on all composition parts .................... **180.00**

24″ h, Emmett Kelly Jr, vinyl head, moving mouth, cloth body, 1979 ....... **65.00**

## IDEAL TOY CORPORATION

The Ideal Toy Corp. was formed in 1902 by Morris Michtom to produce his teddy bear. By 1915 the company had become a leader in the industry by introducing the first sleep eyes. In 1939, Ideal developed magic skin. It was the first company to use plastic. Some of their most popular lines include Shirley Temple, Betsy Wetsy, and Toni dolls.

10″ h, Little Miss Revlon, vinyl, rooted saran hair, sleep eyes, orig clothes, c1957 .......................... **80.00**
11¾ h, Mitzi, all vinyl, jointed at neck and shoulders, rooted Saran hair, painted eyes, closed mouth, high heel feet, 1965 ....................... **25.00**
12″ h
  Abbott & Costello, orig "Who's On First" tape, shop worn box, price for pair ....................... **45.00**
  Betsy Wetsy, fully jointed vinyl, rooted Saran hair, sleep eyes, drink and wet mouth ............... **30.00**
  Dorothy Hamill, vinyl, #1290–6, 1977 ......................... **50.00**
  Shirley Temple, fully jointed vinyl, walker body, rooted blonde hair, brown sleep eyes, open–closed mouth
    Captain January, 1982, MIB ..... **45.00**
    Stand Up and Cheer, 1982, MIB . **100.00**
    Stowaway, 1982, MIB .......... **35.00**
14″ h
  Betsy McCall, vinyl head, hard plastic body, dark brown curly saran wig, round brown sleep eyes; mark: P–90 on head, orig clothes, c1953 . **100.00**
  Joan Palooka, 1958 ............... **40.00**
16″ h, Baby Giggles, vinyl head, arms, and legs, plastic body, rooted hair, blue eyes, MIB, 1965 ............. **45.00**
17″ h
  Miss Revlon, all vinyl, jointed at neck and shoulders, rooted Saran hair, sleep eyes, closed mouth, high heel feet .......................... **100.00**
  Shirley Temple, fully jointed vinyl, walker body, rooted blonde hair, brown sleep eyes, open–closed mouth, 1972 ................. **125.00**
18″ h
  Baby, composition head, lower arms, and legs, cloth body, molded hair, flirty eyes, closed mouth; mark: Ideal Doll, c1938 .............. **175.00**
  Betty Jane, composition, jointed neck, shoulders, and hips, lashed sleep eyes, open mouth, teeth, orig clothes; mark: Ideal 18, 1943 .... **200.00**
  Flossie Flirt, composition, cloth body, red wig, crier not working ....... **150.00**
  Judy Garland, composition, five pc body, red–brown mohair braids, brown sleep eyes, orig Wizard of Oz blue checked dress, c1939 ... **650.00**
  Shirley Temple, composition head and body, jointed at shoulders and hips, blonde mohair wig, blue sleep eyes, open mouth, c1935 .. **365.00**
19″ h
  Harmony, vinyl, sleep eyes, open–closed mouth, 1972 ............ **200.00**
  Diana Ross, vinyl, fully jointed, 1969 **150.00**
20″ h, Thumbelina, vinyl head, arms, and legs, cloth body, rooted dark blond hair, painted blue eyes, music box; mark: Ideal Toy Corp, 1962 ... **45.00**
21″ h, Princess Mary, vinyl head, plastic body, orig ball gown and wrist tags, 1952 .......................... **150.00**
23″ h, Saucy Walker, hard plastic, walker, rooted Saran hair, blue sleep eyes, closed mouth, orig dress, 1956 **95.00**
27″ h, Sister–Coos, composition head and shoulderplate, cloth stuffed body, composition arms and legs, brown mohair wig, brown sleep eyes, redressed, c1935 .................. **175.00**
36″ h, Patty Playpal, vinyl head, hard vinyl jointed body, orig clothes ..... **150.00**

## KNICKERBOCKER

This currently operating toy company has made some dolls which collectors are beginning to recognize. One of these biggest doll lines centers around Holly Hobbie and her accessories.

6″ h, Aileen Quinn, Annie, vinyl, fully jointed, 1982 .................... **10.00**
7″ h, Punjab, Annie, Geoffrey Holder, vinyl, fully jointed, 1982 .......... **18.00**
9″ h, Robbie Hobbie, rag, shirt, blue jeans, MIB ..................... **15.00**
12″ h, Mickey Mouse, Mouse Club ... **22.00**
13″ h, Soupy Sales, vinyl and cloth, 1966 .......................... **135.00**
15″ h, Raggedy Andy, orig clothes and tags, 1970s ..................... **25.00**
24″ h, Holly Hobbie ................ **12.00**
30″ h, Raggedy Ann and Andy, orig labels, price for pair ................ **90.00**

## MADAME ALEXANDER DOLL COMPANY

The Madame Alexander Doll Co was started in 1923 by Bertha Alexander. The dolls made by this company are beautifully done with exquisite costumes. They have made hundreds of dolls including several series such as the International Dolls and the Americana Dolls. Marks used by this company include "Madame Alexander," "Alexander," and "Alex," and many are unmarked on the body but can be identified by clothing tags. Today, Madame Alexander continues to make dolls which are very collectible. Many dolls are made for a limited time period of one year. Others are offered for several years before being discontinued.

**Madame Alexander, 21″ h, Portrait Series, plastic, 1966, left: Scarlett, #2061, Coco face, brunette hair, white tulle dress, $2,500.00; right: Lissy, #2051, Coco face, red hair, pink dress, $2,500.00.**

7″ h, Sonja Henie, composition, tagged dress, skates, extra ski outfit ....... **235.00**
7½″ or 8″ h, Alexanderkins, 1953, all hard plastic, jointed at neck, shoulders and hips, synthetic wig, sleep eyes, closed mouth, orig clothes
  Lady, pink lace trimmed dress ...... **200.00**
  Wendy, ballerina ................. **250.00**
8″ h
  Americana Series, hard plastic, orig clothes
    Amish Boy, c1965 .............. **450.00**
    Colonial Girl, c1962 ............ **350.00**
    Daniel Boone, MIB ............. **36.00**
  David and Dianna, twins, wagon, FAO Schwarz, MIB ............. **145.00**
  Dionne Quints, composition, set in orig box ...................... **995.00**
  Enchanted Doll House Series, Cissette
    #1, rick rack on pinafore, 1980, MIB ....................... **275.00**
    #2, eyelet pinafore, 1981, MIB .. **275.00**
  Friar Tuck, hard plastic, 1989, MIB . **45.00**
  International Series, hard plastic
    Austrian Girl, MIB .............. **80.00**
    Netherlands Boy, straight legs, 1975, MIB .................. **80.00**
    Spanish Girl, bent knee walker, black skin tone, 1962 ......... **55.00**
    Thailand, bent knee walker, 1966 **75.00**
  Little Women, hard plastic, straight legs, complete set, MIB ......... **300.00**
  Maggie Mix–Up, hard plastic, 1960, undressed ..................... **200.00**
  Melanie, hard plastic, Wendy Ann, 1956, MIB .................... **50.00**
  Scarlett Series, hard plastic, 1990
    Ashley, #628, MIB ............. **45.00**
    Mammy, #402, MIB ............ **45.00**
    Melanie, hard plastic, #627, MIB **50.00**
    Prissy, #630, MIB .............. **45.00**
    Rhett, #401, MIB .............. **45.00**
    Scarlett, straight leg, tiny floral print gown, MIB ................. **65.00**
  Storybook Series, hard plastic
    Goldilocks, MIB ............... **36.00**
    Huckleberry Finn, MIB .......... **45.00**
    Little Bo Peep, bent knee walker, #483, MIB ................. **55.00**
    Little Maid, straight legs, 1987, MIB **45.00**
    Maid Marian, 1989, MIB ........ **50.00**
    Mary, Mary, bent knee walker, 1965–72, MIB .............. **45.00**
    Miss Muffet, bent knee walker, #452, MIB .................. **60.00**
    Robin Hood, 1988, MIB ........ **45.00**
    Snow White, bent knee walker, 1990, MIB .................. **85.00**
    Tommy Tittlemouse, 1988, MIB .. **36.00**
    Tom Sawyer, 1989, MIB ........ **45.00**
12″ h
  Amy, Little Women, 1972, MIB .... **55.00**
  Little Huggums, molded hair, orig pajamas, 1981, shop worn box .... **60.00**
13″ h
  Bride, Wendy Ann, composition, MIB **300.00**
  First Lady
    Cleveland, Frances, Series IV, 1985, MIB ................. **135.00**
    Monroe, Elizabeth, Series I, 1976–78, MIB .................... **55.00**
    Randolph, Martha, Series I, 1976–78, MIB .................... **55.00**
  Sweet Tears, layette, blonde ....... **40.00**
14″ h
  Bride, blonde, #1570, MIB ........ **75.00**
  McGuffey Ana, 1944, MIB ........ **45.00**
  Portrait Child, Degas, 1967, MIB ... **45.00**
17″ h, Polly, bride, plastic and vinyl, 1965 .......................... **60.00**
18″ h, Elise, ballerina, vinyl, jointed, 1963 .......................... **300.00**
20″ h, Cissy, bridesmaid, trunk, fur coat set, two additional tagged outfits ... **550.00**
21″ h, Carnival in Rio, porcelain, 1989 **250.00**

## MATTEL, INC.

Mattel, Inc., was started in 1945. The most celebrated doll they made is Barbie, which was designed by one of the company's founders, Ruth Handler, in 1958. Barbie Dolls were dressed in bathing suits and sold in boxes. Her many outfits and accessories were also marketed successfully. Skipper, Ken, Midge, Skooter, and Francie are part of Barbie's extended circle of family and friends. Mattel has sponsored two trade–in programs for Barbie Dolls, the first in 1967. The purpose was to introduce the new bendable Barbie. This trade–in drew more than 1,250,000 dolls. In 1970, Mattel introduced Living Skipper with a trade–in deal.

3″ h, Little Kiddles
- Anabelle Autodiddle, hat, car, and pusher, 1968 .......... **30.00**
- Harriet Heliddle, without goggles ... **25.00**
- Orange Blossom Kologne, doll stand, bottle, 1969 .......... **20.00**
- Peter Paniddle, hat and tunic ...... **25.00**
- Santa Kiddle, 1969 .......... **35.00**

6″ d, Doctor Doolittle, Rex Harrison, Pushmi–pullyu and Polynesia, vinyl, fully jointed, #3579, 1967 ........ **65.00**

9″ h, Mork, Mork and Mindy, Robin Williams, talks, 1979 .......... **25.00**

9½″ h, Grizzly Adams, Dan Haggerty, vinyl, fully jointed, 1978 .......... **35.00**

10½″ h, Buffy and Mrs Beasley, vinyl head, plastic body, blonde ponytails, painted blue eyes, painted upper teeth, pull talk string, holding Mrs Beasley, MIB, c1969 .......... **125.00**

11½″ h, The Great Gretzky, Wayne Gretzky, vinyl, 1982 .......... **35.00**

12″ h
- Donnie and Marie Osmond, price for pair .......... **40.00**
- Cheerful Tearful, vinyl head and body, orig clothes, 1966 ........ **35.00**

16″ h, Bozo The Clown, vinyl head, cloth body, pull talk string, c1962 .. **65.00**

18″ h, Chatty Cathy, soft vinyl head, hard plastic body, rooted blonde dynel hair, blue sleep eyes, open mouth, two teeth, voice box, MIB, c1965 .. **60.00**

24″ h
- Charmin' Chatty, 1961, orig clothes **60.00**
- Mrs Beasley, glasses missing, silent . **30.00**

## REMCO

Remco Industries, Inc., was founded by Sol Robbins, and was the first company to advertise its products on television. Part of what made this company unique was that many products were related to television and promotional character dolls. The company closed in January, 1974.

4⅞″ h, Beatles, Paul, vinyl and plastic, 1964 .......... **150.00**

5″ h, Morticia, The Addams Family, Carolyn Jones, vinyl head, rooted black hair, plastic body, 1964 .......... **135.00**

6½″ h
- Herman Munster, vinyl and plastic, 1964 .......... **85.00**
- I Dream of Jeannie, Barbara Eden, vinyl, fully jointed .......... **25.00**
- Rocky, vinyl, fully jointed, 1983 ... **5.00**

19″ h, Laurie Partridge, The Partridge Family, Susan Dey, vinyl, plastic, 1973 .......... **100.00**

## SUN RUBBER COMPANY

The Sun Rubber Company produced all rubber or lasiloid vinyl dolls. Many have molded features and clothes.

7″ h, Happy Kappy, one piece rubber body, molded painted hair, painted blue eyes, open/closed mouth, yellow hat; mark: The Sun Rubber Co/Barberton, OH/Made in USA/Ruth E. Newton/New York/NY .......... **25.00**

9″ h, So Wee, rubber, Ruth Newton designer, good condition .......... **20.00**

10″ h, So Wee, bottle, booties, jacket, towel, soap, MIB .......... **35.00**

10½″ h, Tod–L–Dee, one piece rubber body, molded painted hair, open nurser mouth, molded diaper, shoes, and socks .......... **25.00**

11″ h
- Betty Bows, rubber, fully jointed, molded hair, blue sleep eyes, drinks and wets; mark: Betty Bows/Copyright The Sun Rubber Co/Barberton, OH USA/34A, c1953 .... **35.00**
- Gerber Baby, all rubber, molded, painted hair, open mouth, nurser, dimples, crossed baby legs; mark: Gerber Baby/Gerber Products Co on head .......... **45.00**

## VOGUE DOLLS

Vogue Dolls was founded by Mrs. Jennie H. Graves. She began a small doll shop which specialized in well made costumes. The original business of doll clothing led to a cottage industry which employed over 500 home sewers in 1950. This branch of the industry peaked in the late 1950s with over 800 home workers plus several hundred more at the factory. During World War II, the shortages created a market for an American doll source. Mrs. Graves created the Ginny doll and promoted her heavily. The Ginny Doll was the first doll created with a separate wardrobe and accessories. For many years Vogue issued one hundred new outfits each year for Ginny alone. They continued to produce their own dolls and clothing for others. Ginny Dolls reached their heyday in the 1950s and are still being made today.

**Note:** The Ginny doll was reproduced in 1985.

7″ h
- Hansel and Gretel, hard plastic, jointed at neck, shoulders, and hips, blonde mohair wigs, blue sleep eyes, orig clothes and booklet "The Vogue Doll Family," copyright 1958; mark: Ginny/Vogue Dolls, and Hansel/Vogue Dolls, pr **325.00**
- Toddles, composition, jointed neck, shoulders, and hips, molded hair, painted side glancing eyes, orig clothes; mark: Vogue on head, Doll Co on back, Toddles stamped on sole of shoe, MIB .............. **265.00**

7½″ h, Crib Crowd Baby, all hard plastic, curved baby legs, painted eyes, blonde synthetic ringlets wig, orig tagged dress, rubber pants, c1949 .. **425.00**

8″ h, Ginny
- 1948–1950, all hard plastic, painted eyes, molded hair, mohair wig; mark: Vogue on head, Vogue Doll on back
  - Cinderella ..................... **150.00**
  - Clown ........................ **225.00**
  - Coronation Queen, MIB ........ **1,100.00**
  - Springtime .................... **115.00**
  - Valentine ..................... **125.00**
- 1950–1953, moving eyes; mark: Vogue on head, Vogue Doll on back
  - Catholic Nun .................. **165.00**
  - Christmas ..................... **125.00**
  - Mistress Mary .................. **135.00**
  - Roller Skating .................. **200.00**
- 1954, walking mechanism; mark: Ginny on back, Vogue Dolls, Inc. Pat. Pend., Made in USA
  - Ballerina, poodle cut wig ........ **100.00**
  - Rainy Day ..................... **75.00**
  - School Dress ................... **75.00**
  - Springtime .................... **70.00**
- 1957, bending knees
  - Beach outfit ................... **75.00**
  - Davy Crockett ................. **80.00**
  - Southern Belle ................. **90.00**
- 1959
  - Country Fair, walker, floral print gown, black bodice, straw hat with flowers, straw basket ..... **265.00**
  - Nurse, hard plastic, straight legs, white uniform and hat, blue cape, white knit hose ......... **250.00**
- 1963, soft vinyl head, rooted hair
  - Bridesmaid ..................... **45.00**
  - Faraway Places, France ......... **50.00**
  - Mary Had A Little Lamb ......... **75.00**
- 1977, Bride, vinyl head and arms, plastic body, long black rooted hair, dark skin tone, almond shaped painted eyes, ornate Chinese costume, metal head gear with red tassels ........................... **50.00**

10″ h
- Jeff, orig clothes .................. **35.00**
- Jill, hand painted, bride's dress ..... **50.00**

11″ h, Ginny Baby, vinyl, undressed .. **8.00**

12″ h
- Baby Dear, all composition, bent baby limbs, 1961 .............. **40.00**
- Betty Jane, all composition, bent right arm, braided piglets, red plaid woven cotton dress, white eyelet trim; tag: Vogue Dolls Inc., 1947 . **85.00**

14″ h, Baby Burps, fully jointed vinyl, rooted black Afro hair, painted eyes, nurser mouth, 1975 .............. **35.00**

14½″ h, Picture Girl, vinyl head and arms, plastic body and legs, rooted blond hair, large painted black eyes, open hands, floral print dress, framed portrait, 1965 .................... **35.00**

17″ h, Star Brite, vinyl, rooted brown hair, large side glancing eyes with stars, long lashes, 1964 ........... **35.00**

18″ h
- Baby Dear, vinyl head, arms, and legs, cloth body, molded short hair, blue sleep eyes, nurser mouth, orig pajamas, 1964 ................. **25.00**
- Brickette, rooted curly strawberry blond hair, sleep eyes, polka dot dress, straw hat, 1979–80 ....... **65.00**

# DRUGSTORE COLLECTIBLES

**Collecting Hints:** There are several suggestions to consider when starting a drugstore collection: (1) buy the best that you can afford (it is wise to pay a bit more for mint/near mint items if at all possible); (2) look for excellent graphics on the packaging of items; (3) do not buy anything that is rusty or damp; (4) before purchasing an item, ask the dealer to remove price tags or written prices (if this isn't possible, consider how badly you really want the item); (5) buy a variety of items (consider placing several similar items together on a shelf for increased visual effect); and (6) purchase items from a variety of time periods.

**History:** The increasing diversity of health related occupations has also encouraged an awareness in collecting pharmaceutical material, items that appeared in old drugstores from the turn of the century through the 1950s. Products manufactured before the Pure Food and Drug Act of 1906 are eagerly sought by collectors. Patent medicines, medicinal tins, items from a specific pharmaceutical company, dental items, and shaving supplies are a few key collecting areas.

The copyright date on a package, graphics, style of lettering, or the popularity of a specific item at a particular period in history are clues to date a product. Other approaches to finding information are talking with a pharmacist who has been in the business for a number of years or checking old manufacturing directories at a regional library.

**References:** Al Bergevin, *Drugstore Tins & Their Prices,* Wallace–Homestead, 1990; Douglas Congdon–Martin, *Drugstore & Soda Fountain Antiques,* Schiffer Publishing, Ltd., 1991; Martin R. Lipp, *Medical Museums USA: A Travelguide,* McGraw Hill Publishing Co.

**Advisor:** Patricia McDaniel.

**Rexall Cold Cream, turquoise letters, red container, 4¼" d, 1¾" h, $11.00.**

## ASTHMA

Asthma Powder, E C Powers Co, Boston, MA, ignite powder, breathe in smoke, unused, 6 oz, 2½ x 3½ x 2½" tan and red cardboard and tin, tan and red letters, E C Powers signature ....... **8.00**

Devilbiss #42 Nebulizer, The Devilbiss Co, Somerset, PA, for aerosol therapy, boxed 2¾ x 2¼ x 7½" glass nebulizer, rubber bulb and stoppers, carrying case, spare jet .................. **16.00**

Haysma, Haysma Co, Chicago, IL, trial size, unused, 3 caps, 1⅛ x 2⅛ x ½", red and black letters ............. **3.75**

Nephenalin Asthma Relief, Thos Leeming & Co, Inc, New York, NY, half full, tablets, clear glass bottle, 1½ x 3½ x 1½", yellow and white label, blue letters ..................... **5.00**

## COLD, ALLERGY, HAY FEVER REMEDIES

Antomine Antihistamine Formula with Quinine, Grove Laboratories, Inc, St Louis, MO, unused, 36 tablets, 2 x 2½ x ½" blue and white cardboard box, red, white and blue letters, E W Grove signature, instruction sheet .. **5.25**

Cam–A One Day Internal Treatment, Chas E Lane & Co, St Louis, MO, sole owners & distributors, 10 tablets, 1¼ x 2 x ½" blue box, red and white letters, instruction sheet .......... **4.50**

CoVac, Ramon's, The Little Doctor, The Antihistamine Tablet, Brown Mfg Co, Distrs Leroy, New York, NY, unopened, 12 tablets, 2¼ x 3½" blue and white envelope, blue letters, picture of Little Doctor ................. **6.00**

Great Seal Cold Tablets, Distributed By The Styron–Beggs Co, Newark, OH, unopened, 24 tablets, 1¾ x 2½ x ⅛" yellow and green metal box, green and yellow letters ............... **8.00**

Histo–Plus Antihistamine Analgesic Compound, Anahist Co, Inc., Yonkers, NY, unopened, 30 tablets, 2 x 1¼" clear glass jar, blue metal lid, 2¼ x 1½ x 1½" gray and blue cardboard box, blue and white letters ........ **6.50**

Special Formula, Distributed by Woodruff's Pharmacy, Charles R Woodruff, Owensville, OH, Batavia 5218, unopened, 20 capsules, 3 x 1 x 1" clear glass bottle, black plastic lid, red and white label, black letters ......... **5.00**

Zero–10 Cold Tablets, Docus Drug Co, Portageville, MO, Owners–Distributors, unused, 16 tablets, 1¼ x 2⅛ x ½" red, white, and blue cardboard box, blue and white letters, instruction sheet ...................... **4.75**

## COUGH AND COLD SYRUPS

Creosoted Emulsion, J W Quinn Drug Co, Manufacturing Chemists, Greenwood, MS, ⅔ full, 12 oz, 8 x 2¾ x 1½" clear glass bottle, black metal lid, 9¼ x 3⅜ x 1½" red, black, and yellow cardboard box, red and black letters ............................ **12.00**

Fahrney's Cough Syrup, Distributed by Dr Peter Fahrney & Sons Co, Chicago, IL, and Winnipeg, Canada, ¾ full, 4 oz, 5⅜ x 2⅛ x 1" clear glass bottle with black metal lid, 5¾ x 2½ x 1⅝" blue and brown cardboard box, blue letters ......................... **12.00**

Liquid Center Cough Drop, Iodent Co, Detroit, MI, USA, empty, 12 drops, 5 x 2½ x ½" silver and metal box, red and black letters ................. **13.00**

Menthol Cough Mixture, Moore & Miller Drug Store, 221 Main St, Vincennes, IN, half full, 3 x 1⅜" clear glass bottle, black plastic lid, brown label, black letters ................ **3.00**

Smith Brothers Cough Drops, Smith Brothers Div of Warner–Lambert Pharmaceutical Co, Poughkeepsie, NY, unopened, 1⅜ oz, 1⅞ x 3¾ x ½" cellophane wrapped green and white cardboard box, black, white, and green letters, trademark picture of the Smith Brothers .................. **3.50**

St Joseph Pine Tar & Honey Compound, a product of Plough Inc, New York, NY, Memphis, TN, unused, 2 oz, 4½ x 1¾ x ¾" brown glass bottle, white metal lid, 4¾ x 2 x 1" white and orange cardboard box, brown letters .. **9.00**

Vicks Medi–trating Cough Syrup, Vicks Chemical Co, Greensboro, NC; New York, NY,

- 6 oz, 6⅜ x 2⅜ x ¾" brown glass bottle, red metal lid, 6⅝ x 2¾ x 1½" blue and red cardboard box, blue and white letters, instruction sheet **8.50**
- 8 oz, 6¾ x 2½ x 1⅛" brown glass bottle, red metal lid, 7¼ x 3¼ x 1¾" blue and red cardboard box, blue and white letters, instruction sheet ........................ **10.00**

Waterbury's Compound, distributed by Standard Laboratories Inc., unused, 14 oz, 7½ x 2¼ x 2¼" brown glass bottle, black plastic lid, white and orange label, black letters ........... **8.00**

## DIARRHEA

Kaomagma, Wyeth Laboratories Inc, Philadelphia, PA, 12 oz, unused, blue bottle, 3¼ x 7½", yellow box, dark blue and white letters ............. **12.00**

Wampole's Bismuth Compound, Henry K Wampole & Co, Inc, Philadelphia, PA, unused, bottle, 2⅜ x 5" tan sealed box, white and brown letters ...... **7.00**

## EYES

Adjust–O–Specs, Ever–Wear Seal Co, Lake Geneva, WI, Free Sample, 3 x 4⅞", paper package, white and blue, blue letters, drawing of lady with glasses .......................... **5.00**

Murine For Your Eyes, The Murine Co, Inc, Chicago, IL, 4 x 1½" green, black, white box, red and black letters, 4 dram, amber, stoppered bottle, instruction folder ................. **12.00**

Oval Eye Pad, Parke, Davis & Co, Detroit, MI, five individually wrapped pads, cellophane wrapped package . **10.00**

Tin Eye Cup, Manufacturer Unknown, 1 x 1¼" .......................... **10.00**

## FEMININE HYGIENE

Ceepryn, The William S Merrell Co, Cincinnati, OH, unused, 10 gram, bottle, 1¼ x 3½ x 1¼" white and navy box, light blue and navy letters .... **8.50**

Koromex, Holland–Rantos Co, Inc, New York, NY, unused, 8 oz, glass bottle, 2⅜ x 5 x 2⅜" white, maroon, gray box and letters, figure of lady draped in a towel ................ **6.50**

Kotex Slenderline Feminine Napkins, 1959, Kimberly–Clark Co, Neenah, WI, 9 x 8¼ x 2", pink, red, red and white letters, white rose corsage .... **12.00**

Lygel Vaginal Jelly, Lehn & Fink Products Corp, Bloomfield, NJ, unused, tube, 3 oz refill, 1¾ x 1½ x 6" blue and white box, blue letters, instruction sheet ....................... **7.25**

Pre–Mens, The Purdue Frederick Co, Yonkers, NY, for tension, pain, bloating, 18 capsules, unused, round brown bottle, 1½ x 2¾", pink and yellow label, black letters, drawing of unhappy woman ................. **4.75**

Progynon–DH, Schering Corp, Bloomfield, NJ, unused, 60 tablets, 5¼ x 2 x ¾" box, light blue, navy, white, white and navy letters ............ **6.00**

The Featherweight Sanitary Belt, non–elastic, pocket size, adjustable, ¾ x 2½ x 1½" box, navy, blue, white, white letters ..................... **7.00**

Virginia Douche Powder, Virginia Chemical Co, St Louis, MO, unopened, 3⅛ x 2⅛ x 1¼" white box, blue letters ...................... **12.00**

Zonitors Vaginal Suppositories, Dunbar Laboratories, Wayne, NJ, the douche in a capsule, 4, foil wrapped packs of three, 3¾ x 2¼ x 1½" pink, green, and white box, instruction sheet .... **4.50**

## FIRST AID

Chex–It, Styptic Sticks, Styptic Products Co, Glendale, CA, unused, 2¾ x 1¾", match book type, cardboard, white cover, red and white letters .. **3.75**

Curity Adhesive Tape, Bauer & Black, Division of The Kendall Co, Chicago, IL, Wet–pruf, 1½ yards, red and white tin, opening in middle ............ **5.75**

DeWitt's Antibiotic First Aid Powder, E C DeWitt & Co, Inc, Chicago, IL, unused, 1½ oz, round, plastic, squeeze bottle, 6½ x 1½", tan, gray, green label, pink and black letters ....... **5.50**

Gauze Bandage, Acme Cotton Products Co, Inc, New York, NY, sterilized bandage, 1" x 6 yards, unused, 1¼ x 1⅜ x 1¼" tan box, blue letters ..... **4.00**

Hydrosal, The Hydrosal Co, Cincinnati, OH, copyright 1931, unused, 8 oz, blue, round bottle, 2¾ x 6 x 2¾", pale blue, light blue and navy box, navy and white letters, tested and approved by Good Housekeeping Bureau, no lid on box ...................... **7.50**

Isodine Complex, Isodine Pharmacal Corp, Dover, DE, copyright 1958, half full, ½ oz, brown glass bottle, plastic applicator, 1⅜ x 1¼ x 3" pink and brown box, brown and white letters ............................ **6.00**

Mediplast Bandages, Duke Laboratories Inc, South Norwalk, CT, stretchable, form fitting adhesive bandages, 100 bandages, ¾ x 1½", flesh color, unused, 9⅜ x 1 x 3½" tan and navy outer box, tan and navy letters ..... **8.00**

Nurse Brand, Boric Acid U.S.P., Powdered, The DePree Co, Holland, MI, half full, 2 oz, round cardboard with metal ends, shaker top, 3¼ x 1⅞", white, blue and light blue label, light blue letters, picture of nurse ....... **8.00**

Penntest Witch Hazel, Pennex Products Co, Pittsburgh, PA, unused, 3 oz, clear glass bottle, 4¾ x 2 x 2", brown and yellow label, brown and white letters .......................... **5.50**

Rub–My–Tism, Monticello Drug Co, Jacksonville, FL, half full, 3 oz, clear glass bottle, navy and yellow box, navy and yellow letters ........... **10.00**

Unguentine First–Aid Spray, The Norwich Pharmacal Co, Norwich, NY, round fire extinguisher shaped plastic squeeze bottle, red and white bottle and letters ....................... **15.00**

Vaseline Petrolatum Gauze, Chesebrough–Pond's Inc, Professional Products Division, New York, NY, box of six, one remaining, 36" strips, aluminum individual packs, 7⅝ x 4 x 1½" navy and white box, navy and white letters, drawing of hands using strip . **9.00**

## FOOT

Blue Jay Moleskin Protect–O–Pads, Blue Jay Products, Division of Kendall Co, Chicago, IL, unused, 2¾ x 3½ x ½" navy, yellow, and white box, navy and white letters, drawing of bunion pad and foot, advertising sheet ..... **7.00**

Dr Scholl's Ball–O–Foot Cushion, The Scholl Manufacturing Co, Inc, Chicago, IL, tan and cream cushion, cellophane wrap, 3½ x 4¼" .......... **4.00**

Hy–Pure Powder, Hy–Pure Labs, Cincinnati, OH, medicated foot powder, unused, 3½ oz, cardboard cylinder, metal top and bottom, shaker top, green and white label and letters ... **10.00**

Icy–Cool Foot Stick, foil wrapped, almost empty, 3¾ x 2" round clear glass jar, emb horizontal lines, metal cap, green label, green and white letters . **8.00**

Jim Wade Foot Medicine, Jim Wade & Co, Shreveport, LA, half full, 1 oz, small glass bottle, 3¾ x 1 x 1¾" red and white box and letters ......... **9.00**

Perrigo's Corn Liquid, L Perrigo Co, Allegan, MI, unused, ¼ oz, 2¼ x ¾ x ¾", clear glass bottle, navy, red and white label and letters ........... **3.50**

T–4–L Foot Powder, Sorbol Co, Mechanicsburg, OH, unused, 1½ oz, 4 x 1¾", dark blue, yellow and white cardboard cylinder, dark blue and white letters, picture of stars on side **8.50**

## HERBS

Agrimony Herb, Murray & Nickell Mfg Co, Chicago, IL, mild tonic, alternative astringent, ⅞ x 2⅛ x 2⅛" white cardboard box with black letters ... **4.50**

Boneset Leaves & Tops, S B Penick & Co, Crude Drugs, New York, NY; Asheville, NC; Chicago, IL; Jersey City, NJ, emetic, cathartic, relieves indigestion, 1 oz, 2¾ x 2¾ x 1½" blue, gray, and white cardboard box, black and blue letters ................. **6.00**

Chamomile Flowers, Purepac Corp, New York, NY, anti–spasmodic, anti–infectives for numerous minor illnesses, 1 oz, 3 x 3 x 2" pink and maroon metal box, maroon and white letters .......................... **5.00**

Flax Seed, Hook's Dependable Drug Store, Indianapolis, IN, cough medicines, irritations of the urinary tract, laxative, 4 oz, 2¾ x 2¼", metal container, green and white label, green and black letters ................ **3.00**

Guaiac Gum, S B Penick & Co, New York, NY; Chicago, IL, stimulant, irritant, mild laxative, anti–inflammatory, 1 lb, 4¾ x 4 x 4" blue and white cardboard box, black letters ....... **9.00**

Leaf Sage, packaged by L Perrigo Co, Allegan, MI, 2 oz, 4½ x 2½", metal container, gray and blue label, blue and white letters .................. **4.00**

Sarsaparilla Root, Allaire, Woodward & Co, Peoria, IL, alterative, diuretic, tonic, 1 oz, 1½ x 3 x 2⅞" green and yellow cardboard box, green and yellow letters ...................... **7.00**

Senna Leaves N F, S B Penick & Co, New York, NY; Chicago, IL, powerful cathartic, 1 lb, 6 x 3½ x 3½", gold metal container, blue and white label, black letters .................... **10.00**

Wild Cherry Bark, S B Penick & Co, Crude Drugs, New York, NY; Asheville, NC; Chicago, IL; Jersey City, NJ, 1 oz, 2¼ x 2¼ x 1⅜" blue, gray, and white cardboard box, black letters .. **5.00**

## INFANTS AND CHILDREN

Baby Pacifier, Star Baby Toys, Star Mfg Co, Leominster, MA, latex filled pacifier, yellow, hard plastic, mouse handle, red, white, light blue, yellow cardboard adv, red and white letters, 8 x 3½" ........................ **5.00**

Chix, Chix Baby Products Division, Chicopee Mills, Inc, New York, NY, 1958, disposable diaper pads, medicated pads, soft non–woven fabric, box of 30 pads, pink, tan and black gift package box, pink ribbon drawing around box, pink stripes on box ends, 7½ x 6½ x 16½", black and pink letters ............................ **12.00**

Hall's Corated Baby Talc, Special Sale Products Co, Boston, MA, 1 lb, 6¾ x 3", dark blue, light blue, and white cardboard cylinder, dark blue and white letters, sketches of toys ...... **12.00**

Johnson's Cotton Buds, Johnson & Johnson, New Brunswick, NJ, 2 packs of 90 double tipped buds, unused, outer sleeve is 4½ x 3½ x 1¼", red, white, navy and dark blue box and letters . **6.50**

Ke Ko Baby Pants, Keko Products Div, Kennedy Car Liner & Bag Co, Inc, large size, 3½ x ¾ x 7¾" pink, white, dark blue box, dark blue letters, drawing of baby playing on the floor with striped ball ...................... **8.50**

Pamper Shampoo, by Toni, The Gillette Co, Chicago, IL, unused, 3½ oz, clear glass bottles, 5 x 1½ x 6", yellow, red, and white box, red, black and white letters, blue "Special Offer" stripe ...................... **12.00**

Protect–O–Pin, a Reliance Product, Diaper Pins, three stainless steel and plastic diaper pins on card, pink plastic heads on pins, 3¾ x 5", light blue, pink and white card, light blue, pink and black letters, drawing of a baby and teddy bear ................... **4.00**

## KIDNEY/URINARY

Balmwort Compound, The Blackburn Products Co, Dayton, OH, 3⅛ x 1¼", round, 1 oz, ¾ full, cork stoppered bottle, tan label, dark blue letters, boxed, folder enclosed ........... **15.00**

Clinitest, Ames Co, Inc, Elkhart, IN, 100 tablet, brown bottle, metal cap 4¾ x 2 x 1¼" tan box, black and red letters, directions and color chart enclosed . **5.50**

Doan's Pills, Foster–Milburn Co, Buffalo, NY, 85 pills, 3¼ x 1¼", round, empty, green tin, black and white letters, drawing of a leaf ............. **5.50**

Hexalith, Wayne Pharmacal Supply Co, 100 capsules, clear glass bottle, metal cap, 4⅞ x 1¾ x 1¾" ............. **8.50**

Kieffer's Pills, Kieffer Products Co, Kinston, NY, 25 pills in cellophane envelope, 2½ x 1½ x ½" maroon box, white letters ..................... **4.00**

Dr Rankin's Kidney Tablets, Rankin Drug Co, Chicago, IL, round vial, wood top, 1¼ cent US Revenue Stamp on bottom, white label, black letters, 12/31/1906 ............... **8.00**

Urotropin, William R Warner, Div of Warner–Hudnut, Inc, New York, Los Angeles, St Louis, 100 tablets, brown bottle, black plastic cap, 4¼ x 1¾ x 1¼", white and black label, white and black letters ..................... **6.00**

Vola–Vin Pills, Vola–Vin Medicine Co, Cincinnati, OH, empty, brown bottle, metal cap, 2¾ x 1½ x ¾" ......... **6.00**

## LAXATIVES

Adlerika, Chester–Kent Inc, St Paul, MN, 11 oz, 8 x 3 x 1½", brown glass bottle, maroon metal lid, white and black label, red and black letters ... **12.00**

Blackstone Tasty–Lax Chewing Gum, Monticello, IL, 6 tablets, 2⅞ x 1 x ¼" red, blue and yellow cardboard box, blue and red letters .............. **4.00**

Blue Seal Citrate of Magnesia, The Integrity Magnesia Corp, Philadelphia, PA, 11½ oz, 6½ x 2¼", clear glass bottle, metal lid, blue and red label, white and blue letters ............. **7.00**

Dr Edward's Olive Tablets, distributed by the Olive Tablet Co, Columbus, OH, a pleasant laxative, almost empty, 75 tablets, 2¼ x 1 x ¾", green metal container, green metal lid, green letters ..................... **5.75**

Foley Cathartic Tablets, Foley & Co,

Sole Distributors, Chicago, IL, empty, 40 tablets, 2⅝ x ½″, clear plastic bottle, cork stopper, 3 x 1 x 1″ yellow cardboard box, black letters, instruction sheet . . . . . . . . . . . . . . . . . . . . . . . **7.00**

Inner–Aid, Inner–Aid Medicine Co, Covington, KY, ¼ full, 8 oz, 8 x 2¾ x 1″, clear glass bottle, black metal lid, 8½ x 3 x 1½″ cardboard box, tan, brown and white letters, instruction sheet . . . . . . . . . . . . . . . . . . . . . . . . . **9.00**

Kruschen Salts, Sole US Distributors, E. Griffiths Hughes Inc, Rochester, NY, 4 oz, 3¾ x 7″, brown glass bottle, black metal lid, 4 x 2¼ x 2¼″ yellow cardboard box, black letters . . . . . . . **8.00**

Nite–lets, The Nitelets Co, Columbus, OH, unused, 30 tablets, 2¾ x 1″, wooden cylinder, white and green label, red and green letters . . . . . . . . . . **8.00**

Phillips Milk of Magnesia, Chas H Phillips Co, Division of Sterling Drug Inc, New York, NY, 4 oz, 5 x 2¼ x 1½″, blue glass bottle, blue metal lid, wrapped in white and blue cardboard paper, red and blue letters . . . . . . . . . **6.00**

**Saraka for Constipation, Schering Corporation, Bloomfield, NJ, orange, 3″ w, 4⅝″ h, $5.00.**

Sal Hepatica, Bristol–Myers Co, New York, Montreal, San Francisco, London, Sydney, unopened, glass vial, aluminum cap, 3 x ⅞ x ¾″ tan and black box, black letters, sample, instruction sheet . . . . . . . . . . . . . . . . . . . **10.00**

Sulphur & Cream of Tartar Lozenges, Hance Bros & White Co Pharmaceutical Chemist, Philadelphia, PA, orange, white and brown cardboard box, black and white letters, picture of volcano . . . . . . . . . . . . . . . . . . . . **10.00**

Zymenol, Hankscraft Co, Reedsburg, WI, for relief of constipation, 8 oz, 4¼ x 2¾ x 2″, brown glass jar, white metal lid, white label, brown letters **8.00**

## NASAL

Efedron–Hart Nasal Jelly, Hart Drug Corp, Miami, FL, 20 gram, green tube, green and yellow label, black letters, 4½ x 1 x ¾″ navy and white box, white letters, folder enclosed . . **8.00**

Marshall's Snuff, Williams Mfg Co, Cleveland, OH, ¾ oz, glass bottle, black metal cap, 2⅞ x 1¼ x 1¼″, tan and white label, maroon letters . . . . **6.00**

Neo–Efemist Solution, Hart Drug Corp, Miami, FL, empty, square brown bottle, dropper, 3¼ x 1¼ x 1¼″ pale green and black box, white and black letters, red heart, copyright 1933, folder . . . . . . . . . . . . . . . . . . . . . . . . . **13.00**

Rhinalgan HC, DoHo Chemical Corp, New York, NY, white plastic squeeze bottle, 1¾ x 1½ x 4⅜″ blue and tan box, blue, black, and orange letters **5.50**

Soltice Nose Drops, The Chattanooga, Medicine Co, Chattanooga, TN, brown glass bottle, 2¾ x 1¼″, black plastic cap and dropper, 1¾ x 3½ x 1″ maroon and yellow box, maroon and white letters . . . . . . . . . . . . . . . . **7.50**

## RECTAL

Airol Suppositories, Hoffman–LaRoche, Inc, Nutley, NJ, 6 foil wrapped suppositories, 3½ x 1¾ x ¾″ slide–top box, maroon, gold, gray, orange, and black letters . . . . . . . . . . . . . . . . . . . . **7.00**

Anusol–Hemorrhoidal Suppositories, William R. Warner, Div of Warner–Hudnut, Inc, 6 foil wrapped suppositories, 2½ x 1¾ x ⅝″ slide–top box, maroon and light gray, black letters . **5.75**

DeWitt's Manzan Ointment, E. C. DeWitt & Co, Inc, Chicago, IL, 1 oz, tube, 4⅜ x 1⅝ x 1″ pink and light gray box, black and white letters, instruction folder . . . . . . . . . . . . . . . . . . **8.00**

Dr Pierce's Suppositories, empty, 2⅜ x 2⅜ x ¾″, picture and signature of Dr Pierce . . . . . . . . . . . . . . . . . . . . . . . . . **6.00**

Rectone, Nyal Co. Distributors, Detroit, MI, 1 oz tube, 4½ x 1 x 1″ navy and light gray box . . . . . . . . . . . . . . . . . . . **5.75**

## RHEUMATISM

Citru–mix, Citru–Mix Co, Grand Rapids, MI, 2 oz, brown bottle, 3½ x 1¾″, blue, white, and orange label and letters . . . . . . . . . . . . . . . . . . . . . . **6.00**

Tysmol Absorbent, Tysmol Co, San Francisco, CA, tan aluminum tube, green letters, 4¼ x ¼ x 1¼″ orange box, black and red letters . . . . . . . . . **6.00**

### STOMACH

BiSoDol, Whitehall Laboratories Inc, New York, NY, for upset stomach due to excess stomach acidity, unused, 3 oz, 3⅞ x 2⅛ x 2⅛", white and yellow metal canister, metal lid, blue and white letters .................... **7.00**

Harvey's Tablets, distributed by The Harvey Co, Bloomington, IL, unopened, 48 tablets, 2⅝ x 4 x ¾", cellophane wrapped, beige and blue cardboard box, blue letters ........ **7.25**

Red Drops, distributed by Dr Hoffman Co, St Louis, MO, empty, 2 oz, 3 x 1 x 1", clear glass bottle, red metal lid, cork stopper, copper cork screw included, red and white, 3½ x 1⅛ x 1⅛" cardboard box, red letters, instruction sheet, translations in Spanish, German, and Italian .......... **10.00**

Tums Antacid Tablets, Lewis/Howe Co, St Louis, MO, unopened, 15 tablets, 2½ x ½", red and yellow foil roll, blue letters, lemon flavor .............. **3.00**

Von's Pink Tablets, New York Von Co, 48 tablets, 4⅛ x 2⅞ x 2⅜" red, tan and black cardboard box, black letters ............................ **7.50**

### THROAT

Dixi Throat Tablets, Dixi–Chem Co, Chattanooga, TN, 2¾ x ¾", plastic cylinder, black, red and yellow label and letters ...................... **5.50**

Okare, Drugmaster, Inc, St Louis, MO, ¾ full, round clear glass, pint size bottle, yellow, silver and blue label, silver, blue, and brown letters ...... **5.75**

Super Anahist, Anahist Co, Inc, Yonkers, NY, 16 lozenges, cylinder, white and blue box, red, white and blue letters .......................... **.75**

### VITAMINS, MINERALS, TONICS

Arsenoferratose, Rare Chemicals Inc, Flemington, NJ, 1 pt, yellow, black and white box, black and white letters **15.00**

Film Tab Optilets, Abbott Laboratories, 100 tablets, clear bottle, 1⅝ x 4⅜ x 1⅝" green, white and black box ... **6.00**

Hope Mineral Tablets, The Hope Co, St Louis, IL, 40 tablets, brown bottle, 1⅝ x 1 x 3⅞", green, white and red label, green and white letters ...... **6.50**

Oleum Per Comorphum, Mead Johnson & Co, Evansville, IN, 50 cc, bottle, dropper, unopened, 2¾ x 1⅝ x 3¾", yellow and dark blue, dark blue and white letters .................... **4.50**

White's Multi–Beta Liquid, White Laboratories Inc, Newark, NJ, 25 cc, round, brown bottle, dropper, 2⅛ x 1⅜ x 4⅛" white, yellow and dark brown box, dark brown letters ..... **8.00**

# ELECTRICAL APPLIANCES

**Collecting Hints:** Small electric appliances are still readily available and can be found at estate and garage sales, flea markets, auctions, and best of all, Grandma's attic. They generally cost very little, making them attractive to collectors on a limited budget.

Most old toasters, waffle irons, and other appliances still work. Construction was simple with basic, 2–wire connections. If repairs are necessary, it usually is simple to return an appliance to good working order.

Whenever possible ask to plug in the appliance to see if it heats. On "flip–flop" type toasters (the most numerous type), check to see if elements are intact around mica and not broken.

Most appliances used a standard size cord, still available at hardware stores. Some early companies did have strange plugs and their appliances will only accept cords made for that company. In such an instance, buy the appliance only if the cord accompanies it.

Do not buy an appliance that is in non–working order, in poor or rusted condition, or with missing parts unless you plan to strip it for parts. Dirt does not count. With a little care and time, most of the old appliances will clean up to a sparkling appearance. Aluminum mag wheel polish, available at auto parts stores, used with a soft rag will produce wonderful results. Also, a non–abrasive kitchen cleanser can be of great help.

As with most collectibles, the original box or instructions for any item can enhance the value and add up to 25%. Also beware of chrome, silver, and other plated articles stripped to their base metal, usually brass or copper. Devalue these by 50%.

**History:** The first all electric kitchen appeared at the 1893 Chicago World's Fair and included a dishwasher that looked like a torture device and a range. Electrical appliances for the home began gaining popularity just after 1900 in the major eastern and western cosmopolitan cities. Appliances were sold door to door by their inventors. Small appliances did not gain favor in the rural areas until the late 1910s and early 1920s. However, the majority of the populace did not trust electricity.

By the 1920s, competition among electrical companies was keen; innovations in electrical appliances were many. Changes were rapid. The electric servants were here to stay. Most small appliance companies were bought by bigger companies. These, in turn, have been swallowed up by the huge conglomerates of today.

Some firsts in electrical appliances are:

1882 Patent for electric iron (H. W. Seeley [Hotpoint])
1903 Detachable cord (G. E. Iron)
1905 G. E. Toaster (Model X–2)
1905 Westinghouse toaster (Toaster Stove)
1909 Travel iron (G. E.)
1911 Electric frying pan (Westinghouse)
1912 Electric waffle iron (Westinghouse)
1917 Table Stove (Armstrong)
1918 Toaster/Percolator (Armstrong "Perc–O–Toaster")
1920 Heat indicator on waffle iron (Armstrong)
1920 Flip–flop toasters appear (everyone)
1920 Mixer on permanent base (Hobart Kitchen Aid)
1920 Electric egg cooker (Hankscraft)
1923 Portable mixer (Air–O–Mix "Whip–All")
1924 Automatic iron (Westinghouse)
1924 Home malt mixer (Hamilton Beach #1)
1926 Automatic pop–up toaster (Toastmaster #1h–A–1)
1926 Steam iron (Eldec)
1937 Home coffee mill (Hobart Kitchen Aid)
1937 Automatic coffee maker (Farberware "Coffee Robot")
1937 Conveyance device toaster ("Toast–O–Lator")

**References:** Linda Campbell Franklin, *300 Years of Kitchen Collectibles, Third Edition*, Books Americana, 1991; Don Fredgant, *Electrical Collectibles, Relics of the Electrical Age*, Padre Productions, 1981; Howard Hazelcorn, *Hazelcorn's Price Guide To Old Electrical Toasters, 1908–1940*, H. J. H. Publications, no date, 1988–89 revised price list available; Greg Ivy (compiler), *Early Fans*, Kurt House, 1983; Norman E. Martinus and Harry L. Rinker, *Warman's Paper*, Wallace–Homestead, 1993; Gary Miller and K. M. Scotty Mitchell, *Price Guide To Collectible Kitchen Appliances*, Wallace–Homestead, 1991; Ellen M. Plante, *Kitchen Collectibles: An Illustrated Price Guide*, Wallace–Homestead, 1991.

**Collectors' Clubs:** American Fan Collector Association, P. O. Box 804, South Bend, IN 46624; Electric Breakfast Club, P. O. Box 306, White Mills, PA 18473.

**Advisors:** Gary L. Miller, K. M. Scotty Mitchell.

## BLENDERS

Drink Master Mixall, Chronmaster, NY, Chicago, Art Deco design, black metal stand, chrome motor housing, chrome knob on top, front switch, single shaft, clear glass with silver bands, mixes drinks, whips cream, 1934 patent, 14″ h . . . . . . . . . . . . . . . **30.00**

Home Malt Mixer, A C Gilbert, chrome, domed motor housing, crinkle green painted base, 1930s, 13″ h . . . . . . . . **65.00**

Silex, Philadelphia, PA, #D2606, cream sq metal base housing one speed motor, push button switch, four cup sq tapered glass top, Art Deco center vertical design and measure, soft black plastic lid, early 1940s . . . . . . **12.00**

## CHAFING DISHES

American Beauty, American Electrical Heater Co, Detroit, MI, nickel, 3 pcs, two plugs marked "fast" and "slow," black wood knob and handles, 1910 **50.00**

Manning Bowman, cat. #601, ser. #K–601, high style Art Deco design, chrome, round tray/hot plate, hot water dish, bowl, and lid, black bakelite handles, three prong hi–lo plug, 1925 . . . . . . . . . . . . . . . . . . . . . . . . . . **45.00**

Universal, Landers, Frary & Clark, #E–940, two quart copper body, hot water pan and lid, faceted base and lid, nickel plated, flat prongs, black wooden handles and knob, 1908–14 **50.00**

**Coffee Urn, Farberware, S.W. Farber Inc., Brooklyn, NY, No. 40, Bakelite handles, 8″ w, 14″ h, $60.00.**

## COFFEE MAKERS AND SETS

Farberware, SW Farber, Brooklyn, NY
Coffee Robot, chrome body with glass top bowl, thermostat keeps coffee warm, stirs, 1937 . . . . . . . . . . . . . **35.00**

Model #208, chrome with garland drape, black wooden handles, late 1930s, 12½" h ................. **15.00**

General Electric Dining Room Set, nickel bodies, wooden handles, paw feet, 1918–19

Chafing Dish ................... **50.00**

Hot Plate ........................ **25.00**

Percolator, glass top ............. **45.00**

Water Kettle ..................... **50.00**

Manning Bowman, Meriden, CT

Coffee Urn Set, cat. #C474–8, ser. #10–30, 15" h urn, creamer, sugar, and tray, nickel chrome tapered faceted body, ivory bakelite swing handles, short cabriole legs, 1910–25 ......................... **60.00**

Percolator, cat. #381/9, chrome Art Deco body, reeded band at neck and above stepped base, part of dining room set consisting of chafing dish and waffle maker, 1920s, 12" h ........................ **35.00**

Porcelier Breakfast Service, dining room type, Porcelier Mfg Co, Greensburg, PA, cream colored porcelain bodies and handles, basketweave texture, multicolored floral transfer designs, 1930–40

Complete Set .................... **250.00**

Creamer and Sugar, cov ........... **30.00**

Percolator, #5007 ................ **55.00**

Sandwich Grill, #5004 ........... **45.00**

Toaster, #5002 .................. **75.00**

Waffle Iron ...................... **45.00**

Royal Rochester Percolator, Rochester, NY, #366 B–29, nickel body over copper, black wooden handles, 1920s, 10" h .................... **15.00**

Silex Dripolator, #550 EC–8, rounded chrome and bakelite hot plate, two piece all glass pot and top, bakelite handle and stand, glass center, rubber connection center, 3 pcs, mid 1930s, 13" h .......................... **18.00**

Sunbeam Dripolator, Coffee Master, Chicago Flexible Shaft Co, chrome, Art Deco design on side, bakelite, 2 pcs, 1935–44, 12½" h ............ **20.00**

United Metal Goods Mfg Inc

Coffee Maker/Server, model 750, chrome pot with pierced tulip design, clear glass liner lights up when coffee is made, black wooden handle and feet, 1930s, 11½" h ...................... **45.00**

Percolator, cat. #760, urn shaped body and pierced tilting frame, dec mid body band, emb spout base, ornate handle, indicator light, 1940s, 17" w ................. **65.00**

Universal, Landers, Frary & Clark, New Britain, CT

Breakfast Set, porcelain, cream china bodies, blue and orange floral transfers, 1920–30s

Creamer and Sugar, cov ......... **25.00**

Percolator, chrome mounted, #E–6927 ....................... **60.00**

Syrup, chrome mounted ......... **20.00**

Waffle Iron, chrome, pierced stand, drop handle, china lid insert, #E–6324 .................... **60.00**

Complete Set .................. **200.00**

Coffee Service, 4 pcs

E–9119, nickel chrome, 16½" h classical urn on flared base, creamer, cov sugar, and tray, open handles with flat tops, large glass insert, black wooden handled spigot, 1912–24 ......... **125.00**

E–9189, nickel chrome, 14" h urn on flattened base, tri–form applied legs, drop reverse bail handles, creamer and cov sugar, rect tray with rounded corners, applied leaf banding, glass insert with etched leaf design, 1912 .. **50.00**

E–9239, 11" h classical squatty urn, nickel, upturned open scrolled handles, tall flared base on short feet, smaller top flared with wide opening, green depression glass insert, footed creamer, cov sugar, large oval tray, 1912–24 ...... **195.00**

Urn, classical design, nickel, cabriole legs, tall curved handles, flat top, lid with large swirled glass insert, 15½" h ...................... **35.00**

Westinghouse Dripolator, Mansfield, OH, cat. #CM–81, black bakelite handles, 2 pcs, 1940s, 14" h ...... **20.00**

## EGG COOKERS

Hankscraft, model 599, yellow ceramic, chrome lid, large yellow ceramic knob, instructions on base and cord tag, 1930s ...................... **15.00**

The Rochester, Rochester, NY, egg shaped nickel body, flared base, flat prongs, domed lid, int. fitted skillet/pan, sealed element in base, 4 pcs, 1912 ......................... **35.00**

## FOOD COOKERS

Betty Crocker Deep Fryer, General Mills, model 9–A, chrome body, rounded corners, black bakelite base with red control, chrome lid, aluminum basket, late 1940s, 11 x 7" .... **25.00**

Breakfaster, Calkins Appliance Co, Niles, MI, hot plate/toaster, model #T–2, Art Deco design, louvered, round corners on sq aluminum body, bakelite base and handles, small rect door in side for toast tray, hot plate on top, 1930s .................. **35.00**

Broiler Robot, Farberware, SW Farber, Brooklyn, NY, broiler/grill, round nickel body, two part with internal rack, domed lid with element and three top feet to reverse and turn from broiler to grill, heat indicated, 1938, 11″ d ......................... **30.00**

Electric Range, Eureka Vacuum Cleaner Co, Detroit, MI, Art Deco, cream painted body, black porcelainized trim, chamfered top, emb design with "Eureka" across at angle, black bakelite handle, int. racks, fold down sides with chrome surfaces and round hot plates, large red indicator light on lower front panel, black bakelite oven controls, hi–med–lo for hotplates and pre–warm and hi–med–lo control for oven, short feet made into sides of body, top carrying handle, restored, 1930s, 15 x 13 x 19″ h .......... **80.00**

Everhot Cooker, cat. #EC–JR–10, cylindrical body, chrome middle with emb "Everhot" and Art Deco design, black top and base, aluminum lock–on lid, fitted int. with three pans and lids, 1925 patent date, 9½″ d, 13″ h .... **50.00**

Hotpoint Table Top Stove, General Electric, nickel pierced base and frame holds elements, slots for poacher, broiler, griddle pan, late 1910s, 7″ sq **75.00**

Table Top Stove

- Armstrong Mfg Co, porcelain and nickel body, toaster rack, broiler pan and liner, waffle iron, skillet, four egg poacher with lid, black wooden handles, orig cord, 1917 **95.00**
- Lander, Frary & Clark, model #E–988, large control with white china selector, chrome and aluminum frame, pierced holder, broiler and rack, four egg poacher, skillet, lid, black wooden handles, 1924, 7″ sq **150.00**

Westinghouse, Mansfield, OH

- Frying Pan, steel, cord in wooden handle, six legged iron detachable base, inverts to make hot plate, first electric frying pan, 1911, 6″ d ... **150.00**
- Roaster Oven, white metal painted body, aluminum top with window and gray plastic handle, lift–out gray graniteware pan, griddle, three lids and marked glass baking dishes, matching stand with clock timer and storage, late 1940s .... **50.00**
- Toaster Stove, type "O" ser. #198158–B, low rect nickel body, removable cabriole legs, top with dark metal strip, serving tray and rack, coiled wire handles, orig box, paper guarantee, first Westinghouse toaster, unused, dated June 1904 and 1914, 9 x 5″ .............. **125.00**

## HOT PLATES

Disk Stove, General Electric, cat. #40101, heavy round iron top on chrome, three tall triangular pierced legs, lower shelf, wooden bun feet, 1920s, 6″ d ..................... **30.00**

Westinghouse, Mansfield, OH, cat. #PH–103, round plate, round green porcelainized metal top, hexagonal nickel base, three faceted legs, 1920s, 7″ d ........................... **20.00**

## IRONS

Adjust–O–Matic, Westinghouse, Mansfield, OH, cat. #LJG 4, early control, heat indicator, black wooden handle, detached cord, 1924 ............ **25.00**

Cord–Less–Matic, Brannon, Inc, Detroit, MI, cordless, pat. pend., plug–in detachable base and contacts in sole plate, black painted metal, bakelite handles, 1930s .............. **25.00**

Dover Co–Ed, Dover Mfg Co, Dover OH, child's, #27–1/2, 5″ plate, 2½ lb nickel body, green wooden handle **20.00**

Gad–A–Bout, Knapp–Monarch, travel, cat. #403–R, folding chrome and brown handle, flat chrome body, heat indicator, brown zippered bag, late 1930s ......................... **12.00**

Never Lift, Proctor Silex, #966–B, Art Deco style, work light in handle, attached cord, heat indicator, 1935–37 **25.00**

Steam–O–Matic, Waverly Products, Inc, Sandusky, OH, model B–300, hammered aluminum body, temperature control, 9 hole plate, black bakelite handle, orig box, paper, and funnel, unused, 1931–44 ........... **35.00**

Sunbeam, Chicago Flexible Shaft Co

- Dark green painted metal box, bail handle, fold down front, lift top, cord compartment, "Chicago Flexible Shaft Co, 34 Years of Quality" decal, stand, first all–over heat element, late 1920s–early 1930s .... **40.00**
- Iron Master, model #52, 2¾ lb chrome body, steam attachment #52–A, orig boxes, papers, and tags, unused, 1940s ........... **40.00**

Tru–Heat Iron and Steam Attachment, General Mills, Betty Crocker, model GM–1–B and GM–4–A, chrome body, side rest, black handles, red knob, orig box, late 1940s ........ **35.00**

## MISCELLANEOUS

Baby Bottle Warmer, Universal, Landers, Frary & Clark, #E–9930, cylindrical body, nickel, wooden side handle, bun feet, lid, 1912–14, 4¾" d . **8.00**

Bun Warmer, unmarked, 1930s, 10" d bowl, Art Deco style, chrome, domed cov, red, yellow, and green wood ball feet and finial, removable fitted wire basket, 1930s .................... **25.00**

Can Opener, Kitchen Pal, Union Die Casting, Whittier, CA, model #58, ser. #7–2031, bright yellow metal body, chrome trim, orig booklet, first electric can opener, unused, 1956 .. **25.00**

Clock Timer, Montgomery Ward & Co, cream body, flat swivel base, windup, electric plug in back, silver and red, 1940s ......................... **15.00**

Coffee Mill, Kitchen Aid, Hobart, model A–9, cream metal motor base, sloped sides, adjustment ring at top, clear glass top, open both ends, threaded black metal lid, first home coffee grinder, 1936, 13½" h ........... **60.00**

Flour Sifter, Miracle Electric Co, Chicago, IL, ivory metal body, push button above blue wooden handle, decal label, unused, 1930s ............ **35.00**

Home Motor, Hamilton Beach, #29650192, 1910s ............... **30.00**

Knife Sharpener, Handy Hannah, cat. #4950, red and cream body, low flat base, 1930s, 4½" d .............. **10.00**

Marshmallow Toaster, Campfire Bar–B–Q, Angelus, 2 pc lightweight metal body, sq base, pierced flattened pyramid top, loop wire legs with rubber encased cushion feet, three small metal 2–prong forks, 3" sq ......... **55.00**

Percolator and Toaster Combination, Perc–O–Toaster, Armstrong Mfg Co, model PT, nickel, two plug, sq base, cabriole legs, slip–out toast rack in base, 1918 ..................... **60.00**

Tea Kettle

- Mirro, domed shape, flat bottom, polished aluminum, whistle cover, bakelite handle, 1930–40s, 4 qt .. **20.00**
- Universal, Landers, Frary & Clark, #E– 973, low teapot shape, flared base, flattened top with tall handle and shaped, black wooden holder, top knob, 1910–20 ............. **45.00**

**Malt Mixer, Machine Craft, Los Angeles, CA, model B, 18¾" h, $60.00.**

## MIXERS

General Electric, cat. #149 M8, ser. #10–A, cream colored metal, black bakelite handle, work light in top, three beaters in row, white bowls, head folds down, 1938 ........... **30.00**

Hamilton Beach, 1930–40s, model G, ser. #366839, cream colored metal body, slip–off base, beaters in one unit, bakelite handle, white bowls .. **25.00**

Handy Hanna, Standard Products, Whitman, MA, cat. #495, natural wooden handle, single shaft, quart jar base, late 1930s ................ **22.00**

Handymix, Mary Dunbar, Chicago Elect Mfg Co, #D–121124, stand, push button, two beaters, late 1930s, 11½" h .............................. **16.00**

Kitchen Aid, Hobart Corp, Troy, OH, rounded cream colored body with heavy aluminum trim and handle, screw–down aluminum bowl, wire whisk beater, aluminum meat grinder, dough hook, 1939, 14 x 12" ....... **50.00**

Knapp–Monarch, St Louis, MO, cat. #6–501, white metal motor housing, louvered sides, red plastic handle, three cup white glass measuring base, mid 1930s, 9½" l ................ **20.00**

Mixmaster, Sunbeam, Chicago Flexible Shaft Co, model K, cream colored metal body, folding handle on stand, green glass bowl/juicer, 1930 ...... **40.00**

Polar Cub, A C Gilbert, hand mixer, #B–89, gray, blue wooden handle, single shaft, orig box, 1929, 9½" l .. **75.00**

Portable Hand Mixer, Sears Kenmore, Model 322–8220, cream colored plastic body, single shaft, orig box and booklet, early 1940s, 5" l ......... **25.00**

Unmarked, small, green metal encased motor, metal handle, green depression glass measured Vidrio cup, mid 1930s, 8" l ........ **25.00**

## POPCORN POPPERS

Dominion Elect Mfg Co, model #75, cylindrical, pierced nickel body, cabriole legs, hand crank, red wooden handles and knob, 1920s ........ **24.00**

Knapp–Monarch, St Louis, MO, cat. #12A–500B, oil, aluminum body, wire base, domed glass lid with vented sides, walnut handles, measuring cup, 1930–40 ........ **20.00**

Unmarked, mesh wire basket set in tin, hand crank, black wooden handle and knob, sets atop tin "can" which holds element, attached cord ...... **25.00**

US Mfg Co
- Dry, #1, two pc heater in base, lid, hand crank, silver painted metal body with red lid, three red wood vertical dowel legs, 1920–30s ... **18.00**
- Oil, model #10, 3 pcs, heater, pad, and lid, bakelite handles and knobs, hand crank, 1920–30s .... **36.00**

**Toaster, Universal, Landers, Frary & Clark, New Britain, CT, $50.00.**

## TOASTERS

Edison Electric Appliance Co, NY
- Cat. #214 T–5, nickel base, open sides, separate warming rack, tab holders, 1910 ........ **45.00**
- Cat. #E125 T22, flip–flop type, pierced geometric warming top and doors, large black wooden knobs, 1910–14 ........ **35.00**

Estate Stove Co, Hamilton, OH, model 177, nickel, sq body, canted, pierced door rack on four sides turn simultaneously with one button movement, 1922 ........ **75.00**

General Electric
- Model D–12, white china base, open wire frame, lift–off warming rack, screw–in china plug, first marketed toaster, 1908 ........ **125.00**
- Radio Toggle, two slice flip–over type, pierced nickel body, doors, and top, large radio knob on side to reverse toast, 1933 ........ **95.00**

Knapp–Monarch, cat. #21–501, rounded chrome Art Deco body, flip–flop type, bakelite handles, mechanical opening device, mid 1930s .... **20.00**

Manning Bowman, Meriden, CT
- #1225, nickel body, double wire mechanical turnover doors, bakelite knobs, pierced top, flat prongs, 1926 ........ **35.00**
- Ser. #11–27, Meriden Homelectrics, flip–flop type, thin pierced doors and top, tab feet, flat prongs, 1930s **25.00**

Merit Made Inc, Buffalo, NY, ser. #024146, unusual rounded design, Art Deco flip–flop type, painted silver gray body, black metal base, plunger opener on top, both sides open simultaneously, never used, 1930s ... **30.00**

Montgomery Ward & Co, model 9–4KW 2298– B, flip–flop type, sq body, rounded corners, chrome, bakelite handles, mechanical open, dec sides, mid 1930s ........ **18.00**

Sears Kenmore, model #307–6323–1, two slice automatic pop–up, mechanical clock timing mechanism, rounded chrome body and base, bakelite handles and knobs, early 1940s ........ **15.00**

Sunbeam, Chicago Flexible Shaft Co
- #4, rect bed 5 x 9" on flat L–shaped feet, chrome body, horizontal flip–flop cage, black handles, 1924 ... **45.00**
- #T–1E, Art Deco design, two slice top load automatic, chrome body, concentric lines, indicator light, bakelite base and handles, large rect glass divided relish tray with toaster compartment ........ **65.00**
- #T–9, Art Deco design, two slice top load automatic, rounded chrome body, bakelite handles, rect liner and four glass trays, 1932–40 .... **65.00**

Toastmaster, Waters Genter Co, Minneapolis, MN
- Model 1–A–1, single slice, mechanical clock mechanism, chrome, Art Deco style, thin sq body, one top rounded corner, louvered sides, slightly large base, bakelite controls, first automatic pop–up, 1927 **80.00**
- Model 1–A–3, Art Deco style, sq chrome body, one chamfered top

end, vertically fluted design on sides, third pop–up model, 1929 . **35.00**

Toast–O–Lator, Long Island, NY, model J, ser. #49, Art Deco style, chrome, tall rectangle with flat sides and top, rounded vertical ends, bakelite base, slot in each end, toast "walks" through past small round window, double mechanical track, on–off switch, 1938 .................... **40.00**

Universal, Landers, Frary & Clark

#E–7542, single slice automatic, mechanical clock mechanism, pop–out rack, slender sq chrome body, circle dec on sides, late 1920s–early 1930s .................... **50.00**

Flat, pierced top, concave sides, vertically hinged mechanical reversible wire doors, flat base, small wooden handle, 1912–20 ....... **60.00**

Trademark "LMP" in diamond, pat. 1905, pierced design on spring doors, slender chrome body, flat base, tab feet, curved warming rack, 1913–15 ................. **40.00**

Westinghouse, Mansfield, OH, style #231570, flip–flop type, nickel body, wire doors, pierced warmer top, cord with china plug, 1910s ........... **35.00**

**Waffle Iron, General Electric, catalog #119W4, chrome plated, Bakelite handles, cast aluminum int., 12" w, $35.00.**

## WAFFLE IRONS & SANDWICH GRILLS

Armstrong Mfg Co, waffle iron, model W, metal tag, black wooden handles, first heat indicator, early 1920s, 7" d plates .......................... **25.00**

Coleman Lamp & Stove Co, Wichita, KS, waffle iron, model 17, round chrome body, 14" oval base, Art Deco style, small china insert on lid, black and white gazelle motif, black bakelite handles, 7½" d plates ......... **30.00**

General Electric, waffle iron, solid iron, three short legs, coiled wire, heat dissipating handles, separate screw–in plugs for top and bottom, 1900 .... **95.00**

Hostess, sandwich toaster, All Rite Co, IN, sq, ftd, heavy aluminum body with screw–off black wooden handle, orig Art Deco orange and black box with "Suggestions" book, 1930, 5 x 5 x 4½" ........................ **40.00**

Knapp–Monarch, waffle iron, dessert size, low body, black wooden knobs, dec top, 1930s, 6" d plates ........ **15.00**

Landers, Frary & Clark

Pat. 1916, horizontal type, rect, nickel, round tapered legs, attached tray, black wooden handles, two–headed cord, 8 x 4¼" ...... **75.00**

Universal Sandwich Grill/Waffle Iron, #EA–8601, two waffles, attached tray with bakelite handles, wheat dec on top, reusable plates, 1940s, 10 x 5½" plates ................ **25.00**

Majestic Electric Appliance Corp, San Francisco, CA, hotcake/waffle iron, reversible plates, knob on top acts as foot for open two part grill, makes two cakes at once, nickel body, black wood knobs, 1923, 8" d plates ..... **45.00**

Manning Bowman, waffle iron

Cat. #1646, Ser. #11–55, Art Deco style, chrome, stepped bakelite feet, drop handles, reeded edges and top, booklet, 1930s, 7" d plates, 9½" sq base ............ **30.00**

Ser. #24, Art. 1605, 7" round plates, nickel body, domed faceted lid, cabriole legs and attached tray, 1920s ....................... **25.00**

Twin–O–Matic, ser. #6060, double, Art Deco style, chrome, round flip–over, chrome, bakelite cradle, heat indicator in middle top, orig booklet, 1924–40 ................. **65.00**

Unmarked

Sandwich Grill, triple, nickel body, angled legs, tab feet, black wooden handles, 1920s, 6 x 17" ......... **25.00**

Waffle Iron, child's, green handle, slender, tall legs, 1930s, 4" sq ... **25.00**

Westinghouse, Mansfield, OH, waffle iron, heavy nickel body, straight legs, mechanical open, front handle, first electric waffle iron found to date, 1905–21, 9 x 5¼" plates .......... **75.00**

# ELEPHANTS

**Collecting Hints:** There is a vast number of elephant shaped or elephant related items. Concentrate on one type of object (toys, vases, bookends, etc.), one substance (china, wood, paper), one chronological period, or one type of elephant—African or Indian. The elephants of Africa and India do differ, a fact not widely recognized by the lay reader.

Perhaps the most popular elephant collectibles center around Jumbo and Dumbo, the Disney character who was a circus outcast and the first flying elephant. The "GOP" material is usually left to the political collector.

Because of the large number of items available, stress quality. Study the market carefully before buying. Elephant collecting is subject to phases of popularity, with its level being modest at the current time.

**History:** The elephant held a unique fascination to early Americans. Early specimens were shown in barns and moved at night to avoid a free look. The arrival of Jumbo in England, his subsequent purchase by P. T. Barnum, and his removal to America brought elephant mania to new heights.

American zoological parks always have had an elephant as one of their main attractions. The popularity of the circus in the early 20th century also helped draw continual attention to the elephant, through posters, setup, the parade, and center ring.

Hunting elephants was considered "big game" sport; participants included President Theodore Roosevelt. The search always was for the largest known example. It is not unexpected that it is an elephant that dominates the entrance to the Museum of Natural History of the Smithsonian Institution in Washington, D.C.

Television, through shows such as "Wild Kingdom," has destroyed some of the fascination of a first encounter with all real wild animals, the elephant included. The elephant has become so well known that it is, alas, now considered quite commonplace.

**Collectors' Club:** The National Elephant Collector's Society, 380 Medford Street, Somerville, MA 02145.

**Advisor:** Richard W. Massiglia.

**Ice Cream Mold, pewter, S & Co., #45, 3 pint, $550.00.**

Advertising Trade Card
- Clark's Spool Cotton, Jumbo at the Opera, Buck & Binder Lith ...... **8.00**
- Fairbanks Scales, Weighing Barnum's White Elephant, color, Donaldson **10.00**

Bank
- China, figural, white elephant, red and blue lettering "C.O.P., Peace, Prosperity," 1950s, 6" l, 4" h ..... **25.00**
- Plastic, mechanical, 1950s ........ **10.00**

Book
- *Hitting the Trail With the Inky Boys,* F R Morgan, M A Donohue, Chicago, 1909, boy riding large elephant cov illus ................. **75.00**
- *Little Orphan Annie and Jumbo, the Circus Elephant,* pop–up, 1935, 8 x 9¼" ........................ **125.00**

Compact, goldtone, triangle shaped, raised elephants on cov ........... **35.00**

Charm Bracelet, brass link bracelet, elephant, tiger, and lion charms, Clyde Beatty premium, 1930s ........... **150.00**

Cookie Jar, ceramic, Babar the Elephant, Sorcha Boru, 12" h ............... **175.00**

Diecut, elephant playing drum, emb, color, 5 x 7" ..................... **20.00**

Figure
- Cast Iron, painted, 1930s .......... **50.00**
- Ceramic
  - Royal Doulton ................. **175.00**
  - Vernon Kilns, *Fantasia* elephant, wearing pink dress, 1940 Disney copyright 1940, 5" h .......... **200.00**

Glass, cartoon elephants, Big Top Circus, 5¾" h ...................... **10.00**

Keychain Puzzle, clown on elephant, plastic, multicolored, 1950s ....... **10.00**

Lapel Stud, white metal, walking elephant, "Coolidge," 1" l ........... **12.00**

Lunch Pail, oval, tin, elephants and other circus characters around sides, 8½" w .......................... **75.00**

Mask, Dumbo, starched linen, 1940s, 18" h .......................... **40.00**

Needle Book, GOP elephant on cov, "Work & Vote for the Republican Party and Prosperity," color ........ **12.00**

Paper Toy, diecut elephant, emb, easel back, rocking, Germany, 5½" h, pr . **8.00**

Paperweight
- Rosemeade, glossy blue, hand finished, 2¼ x 2¾" ............... **150.00**
- Van Briggle, turquoise, 3" l ........ **40.00**

Perfume Bottle, figural, brown and white .......................... **75.00**

Pez Dispenser, plastic, yellow elephant head, red body, 4" h .............. **18.00**

Pinback Button, Nixon campaign, large celluloid bobbing head elephant hanger, 1960 ...................... **20.00**

Pitcher, Dumbo, painted and glazed ceramic, c1941, 6" h .............. **50.00**
Rattle, sterling silver, figural, marked "925" .......................... **85.00**
Sheet Music, "When I See An Elephant Fly" Disney's *Dumbo,* red, white, and blue Dumbo illus cov, four pgs, 1941, 9 x 12" ......................... **30.00**
Sign, political, GOP, masonite, gray, red, and black, two sided, wear, 66" l ............................. **110.00**
Stuffed Toy, Steiff, beige, wooden tusks, ears repaired, 3½ x 5" ........... **40.00**
Tin, Tetley Tea, elephant logo ....... **45.00**
Toothbrush Holder, Dumbo, painted bisque, 1940s, 3½" h ............. **80.00**
Toy
On Barrel, windup, celluloid, Occupied Japan, 7¼" h ............. **70.00**
Riding Bike, windup, litho tin, balancing balls .................. **15.00**
Sitting, windup, litho tin, trunk spins balls, US Zone Germany, 1940s, 7½" h, orig box ............... **200.00**
Standing, Schoenhut, large, circus series .......................... **175.00**
Walking, windup, litho tin, Jumbo, name on riding blanket, black yarn tail, US Zone Germany, 1950s, 3½" h ........................... **225.00**
With Rider, celluloid, elephant with movable legs, rider with jointed arms and neck, Japan, 1930s, 5" l, 4" h ......................... **75.00**
Trivet, souvenir 1980 Republican convention, black metal frame, round ceramic tile with elephant holding flag image, 11½" l .................. **8.00**

# FARM COLLECTIBLES

**Collecting Hints:** The country look makes farm implements and other items very popular with interior decorators. Often items are varnished or refinished to make them more appealing, but in fact this lowers their value to the serious collector.

Farm items were used heavily; collectors should look for signs of use to add individuality and authenticity to the pieces.

**History:** Initially farm products were made by local craftsmen—the blacksmith, wheelwright, or the farmer himself. Product designs varied greatly.

The industrial age and the "golden age" of American agriculture go hand in hand. By 1880–1900 manufacturers saw the farm market as an important source of sales. Farmers demanded quality products, capable of withstanding hard use. In the 1940s urban growth began to draw attention away from the rural areas and consolidation of farms took place. Bigger machinery was developed. Farm collectibles after 1940 have not yet achieved great popularity.

**References:** Lar Hothem, *Collecting Farm Antiques: Identification and Values,* Books Americana, 1982; Douglas R. Hurt, *American Farm Tools from Hand–Power to Steam Power,* Sunflower University Press, 1982; Norman E. Martinus and Harry L. Rinker, *Warman's Paper,* Wallace–Homestead, 1993; Dana Gehman Morykan and Harry L. Rinker, *Warman's Country Antiques & Collectibles,* Wallace–Homestead, 1992.

**Periodical:** *Antique Power,* P. O. Box 838, Yellow Springs, OH 45387.

**Collectors' Club:** Cast Iron Seat Collectors Association, RFD #2, Box 40, Le Center, MN 56057.

**Museum:** Pennsylvania Farm Museum, Landis Valley, PA.

Almanac
Hazeltines, pocket type, 1893 ..... **5.00**
Hooflands, 1875 ................. **15.00**
Parkers Nerve & Bone Linament, 1906 ........................ **15.00**
Basket
Berry, 6" h, woven splint, handmade **50.00**
Egg, 3½ x 6 x 7", splint, buttocks bottom ......................... **80.00**
Bell, cow, 7" h, wood, handmade .... **40.00**
Blotter, De Laval ................... **10.00**
Book, *Mann's Farm Soil* ............. **5.00**
Booklet
Farm Poultry Buildings, Agriculture Experiment Station University of Wisconsin, 1921, 31 pgs ........ **4.00**
Hatchery, Poultry/Egg Farm: Cy and Zeb's Discussion on Care of Baby Chicks, 1922, 52 pgs ........... **5.00**
Oliver Farm Equipment Sales, 1936, 20 pgs, 8 x 9", Oliver Red River special threshers ............... **20.00**
Bookmark, 4½" l, John Deere Plows–White Elephant Vehicles, celluloid, black and white, 1903 ............ **30.00**
Branding Iron, 21" l, wrought iron, letter "D" .......................... **15.00**
Broadside, 12½ x 18", Pioneer Bean & Pea Thresher, c1930 ............. **6.00**
Calendar
1938, De Laval, full pad, pretty woman ....................... **35.00**
1955, John Deere, full pad, wildlife book ........................ **35.00**
Calendar Top
The Farmer's Daughter, Walt Otto, 16 x 19½" ...................... **10.00**
World's First Reaper–Public Test of

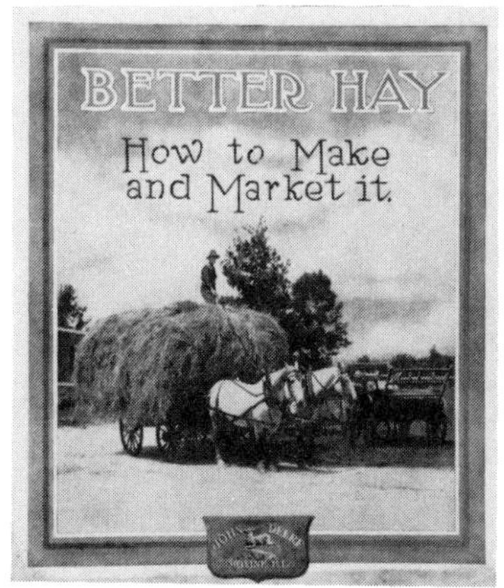


**Booklet, *Better Hay, How to Make and Market It,* John Deere, Moline, IL, 36 pgs., 7¾ x 8¾", 1916, $15.00.**

Cyrus Hall McCormick's Invention, c1930, 13¾" sq . . . . . . . . . . . . . . . . **16.00**

Catalog

American Harrow Co, Detroit, MI, c1904, 52 pgs, 5 x 7" . . . . . . . . . . . **38.00**

Ames Shovel & Tool Co, Boston, MA, 1926, 80 pgs, 4 x 6" . . . . . . . . . . . **35.00**

B G Pratt Co, New York, NY, 1915, 98 pgs, 4 x 7", equipment for fruit and truck growers . . . . . . . . . . . . . **30.00**

Bowker Fertilizer Co, Boston, MA, 1895, 32 pgs, 6 x 9", Stockbridge Special Manures . . . . . . . . . . . . . . **25.00**

Clay Equipment Corp, Cedar Falls, IA, 1931, 232 pgs, 6 x 9", barn equipment, barn and stable plans, fences, and gates . . . . . . . . . . . . . . . **40.00**

Gordon–Van Tine Farm Buildings, 1935, 12 pgs . . . . . . . . . . . . . . . . . **6.00**

Griffith & Turner Co, Baltimore, MD, 1909, 162 pgs, 7½ x 9¾", Catalog No 22, Farm and Garden Supplies **40.00**

Herschel–Roth Mfg Implement–Thresher & Tractor Supplies, 1920, 47 pgs, 4 x 9" . . . . . . . . . . . . . . . . **8.00**

International Harvester, Chicago, IL, 1919, 261 pgs, 6½ x 9½" . . . . . . . **25.00**

John Deere Manufacturing, Chicago, IL, c1920, 157 pgs, 5½ x 8" . . . . . **20.00**

J S Woodhouse Co, Inc, New York, NY, 1937, 82 pgs, 6¼ x 9½", agricultural implements and machines . . . . . . . . . . . . . . . . . . . . . . . **30.00**

McCormick Harvesting Co, Chicago, IL, 1894, 48 pgs, 7 x 9¼" . . . . . . . **45.00**

Moline Plow Co, Moline, IL, 1926, 12 pgs, 4 x 9" . . . . . . . . . . . . . . . . **15.00**

Our Latest Book of Practical Farm Buildings, Heinemann–Johnson Lumber Co, Wausau, WI, 1910, 96 pgs, 8½ x 11" . . . . . . . . . . . . . . . . **16.00**

Peerless Wire & Fence Co, Cleveland, OH, 1924, 104 pgs, 7 x 10", fences, gates, barbed wire . . . . . . . **20.00**

P P Mast & Co, Springfield, OH, cultivators and hayracks, illus . . . . . . **25.00**

Practical Farm Buildings, Miller–Piehl Co, c1930, 64 pgs . . . . . . . . . . . . **15.00**

Reliable Poultry, Quincy, IL, 1910, 96 pgs, 8¾ x 11¾", poultry houses and equipment . . . . . . . . . . . . . . . . **15.00**

S L Allen & Co, Philadelphia, PA, 1919, 72 pgs, 6 x 8½", tools, harrows, seeders . . . . . . . . . . . . . . . . . **25.00**

Smith Manure Spreader Co, Chicago, IL, 1903, 18 pgs, 9¾ x 14" . . . . . . **40.00**

The Cutaway Harrow Co, Higganum, CT, 39 pages, 6 x 9", implements, disks, harrows, cultivators, and plows . . . . . . . . . . . . . . . . . . . . . . . **45.00**

W Atlee Burpee & Co, Philadelphia, PA, 1894, 32 pgs, 6 x 9", manual of thoroughbred live poultry stock **30.00**

Certificate, Stockman Protective Assoc, Okalahoma, three farm scene vignettes, 1926 . . . . . . . . . . . . . . . . . . . **6.00**

Chicken Feeder, Full–O–Pep, large multicolored roosters . . . . . . . . . . . . **15.00**

Corn Cutter, hand forged blade, carved wood handle . . . . . . . . . . . . . . . . . . **12.00**

Egg Calculator, Fite's Peerless Calculator, c1900 . . . . . . . . . . . . . . . . . . . . . **95.00**

Egg Scale, metal egg cup, arm and weight . . . . . . . . . . . . . . . . . . . . . . . . . **8.00**

Feed Box, 42" h, hardwood, three vertical compartments . . . . . . . . . . . . . . **200.00**

Grain Scoop, metal, wood on top of handle . . . . . . . . . . . . . . . . . . . . . . . . . **10.00**

Hay Fork, three tines, 72" l handle . . . **12.00**

Lantern, barn, tin, blown glass chimney, brass burner, iron loop holder . . . . . . **55.00**

Lithograph, 12 x 18", Johnston Harvester Co, Batavia, NY, USA, Continental Mower No 6, multicolored . . **200.00**

Magazine

*Farm & Fireside,* November, 1920 . . **5.00**

*Farm Journal,* May, 1939, Grant Wood cov . . . . . . . . . . . . . . . . . . . . . **15.00**

*Successful Farming,* May, 1929 . . . . . **6.00**

Matchsafe, 2 x 3", silvered brass, Quality–John Deere Plow Co," 1910 . . . . **75.00**

Match Holder, 7½" h, Adriange Farm Machinery, multicolored . . . . . . . . . **165.00**

Medal, Schwarzschild & Sulzberger Co, beef and pork packer, 1906 International Livestock Exposition . . . . . . . . . **65.00**

Mirror, Jap Cultivator–Lehr Agricultural Co, Fremont, OH, multicolored . . . . **185.00**

Pin, 2½" l, Rumley Plowing & Threshing Co, c1900 . . . . . . . . . . . . . . . . . . . . . **8.00**

Pinback Button
- John Deere, Inventor of the Steel Plow, 1½" d, gold profile portrait, white background, blue lettering . **25.00**
- Morgan Cultivator, Bement, Lansing, MI, black and white, paper on reverse with farm implement adv . . . **45.00**
- Pennsylvania Farm Show Exhibitor, Harrisburg, 1932, blue, white, and yellow, 2⅛" d . . . . . . . . . . . . . . . . **12.00**
- The New Idea Manure Spreader, 1" d, multicolored, horsedrawn spreader and farm landscape scene, 1900s **75.00**

Stickpin, Oliver Farm Equipment Company, diecut, corporate flag, green red, black, and white, 1920s . . . . . . **18.00**

Wagon, hay, hardwood bed with stakes, iron rim wheels . . . . . . . . . . . . . . . . . . **100.00**

Yearbook, Agriculture, 1910, 711 pgs . **8.00**

# FARM TOYS

**Collecting Hints:** It is best to specialize in a single type of model, e.g., cast iron; models by one specific company; models of one type of farm machinery; or models in one size—1/16 scale being the most popular.

The tractor is the most popular vehicle. Accessories include wagons and trailers, manure spreaders, plows, disks, planters, and cultivators. Harvesting equipment also comes in model form.

**History:** The vast majority of farm models date from the early 1920s to the present. Manufacturers of farm equipment such as John Deere, International Harvester, Massey-Ferguson, Ford, and White Motors issued models to correspond to their full sized products. These firms contracted with America's leading toy manufacturers, such as Arcade Company, Dent, Ertl, Hubley, Killgore, and Vindex, to make the models.

The early models were cast iron, being replaced later by diecast, aluminum, and plastic. As production models were changed, so too were the toy models. Although most models are made in a scale of 1/16, other scales were used, e.g., 1/12, 1/20, 1/25, 1/32, and 1/50.

Toy manufacturers outside the United States have entered the picture. Firms such as Dinky, Corgi and Lesney produce models of American equipment as well as those of foreign manufacturers, among which are Deutz, Fiat, Leyland, and Porsche.

Limited edition models are being produced today to respond to the growing collector market. Controlled production is keeping their value high.

**References:** Raymond E. Crilley and Charles E. Burkholder, *International Directory of Model Farm Tractors,* Schiffer Publishing, Ltd, 1985; Dave Nolt, *Farm Toy Price Guide, 1988 Edition,* published by author, 1988; Richard Sonnek, *Dick's Farm Toy Price Guide & Checklist: Tractors and Machinery, 1886–1990,* published by author, 1990.

**Periodicals:** *Miniature Tractor & Implement,* 1881 Eagley Road, East Springfield, PA 16411; *The Toy Farmer,* H C 2, Box 5, LaMoure, ND 58458; *The Toy Tractor Times,* P. O. Box 156, Osage, IA 50461.

**Collectors' Club:** Ertl Replica Collectors' Club, Highways 136 and 20, Dyersville, IA 52040.

Baler, 1/16 scale
- International Harvester, diecast, four bales, Ertl, 1967 . . . . . . . . . . . . . . **20.00**
- John Deere, pressed steel, plastic teeth, Carter, 1952 . . . . . . . . . . . . . **80.00**
- Oliver . . . . . . . . . . . . . . . . . . . . . . . . . . **50.00**
- Tru–Scale, pressed steel, red, Carter, 1952 . . . . . . . . . . . . . . . . . . . . . . . . . **45.00**

Bulldozer, International Harvester, yellow, headlights, radiator, Ertl, 1960 . **45.00**

Combine, diecast, 1/16 scale, Ertl
- Case, plastic reel, 1974 . . . . . . . . . . . **75.00**
- International . . . . . . . . . . . . . . . . . . . . . **45.00**
- Massey Ferguson, yellow wheels, 1973 . . . . . . . . . . . . . . . . . . . . . . . . . **50.00**

Combine Gleaner, International Harvester, diecast, 1/32 scale, open reel supports, Ertl, 1966 . . . . . . . . . . . . . . . **45.00**

Conveyor, side, all steel, yellow cab, hood, bumper, and frame, white dump body and tailgate, red conveyor frame with chute, 20½" l, 1953, Buddy L . . . . . . . . . . . . . . . . . . . . . . . . **125.00**

Corn Picker, pressed steel, 1/16 scale, Carter
- John Deere, 1952 . . . . . . . . . . . . . . . . **100.00**
- Tru–Scale, 1971 . . . . . . . . . . . . . . . . . **70.00**

Corn Sheller, Minneapolis Moline
- Pull Type, decaled, 1/16 scale, rubber tires . . . . . . . . . . . . . . . . . . . . . . . . . **95.00**
- Truck Mounted, International Truck chassis, blower tube sock, shovels, corn rake . . . . . . . . . . . . . . . . . . . . **200.00**

Cream Separator, International Harvester, cast iron, 1/12 scale, black plated bowl and pail, Arcade, 1930 **250.00**

Disc, 1/16 scale
- International Harvester
  - Diecast, sure–lock hitch blades, Ertl, 1965 . . . . . . . . . . . . . . . . . . . **24.00**
  - Pressed Steel, four gang, red, Carter, 1950 . . . . . . . . . . . . . . . . . **65.00**
- Tru–Scale, pressed steel, Carter, 1952 **30.00**

Elevator, John Deere, pressed steel, 1/16 scale, Carter, 1960 . . . . . . . . . . . . . . . **85.00**

Grain Drill, pressed steel, 1/16 scale, Carter
- John Deere, 1960 . . . . . . . . . . . . . . . . **125.00**

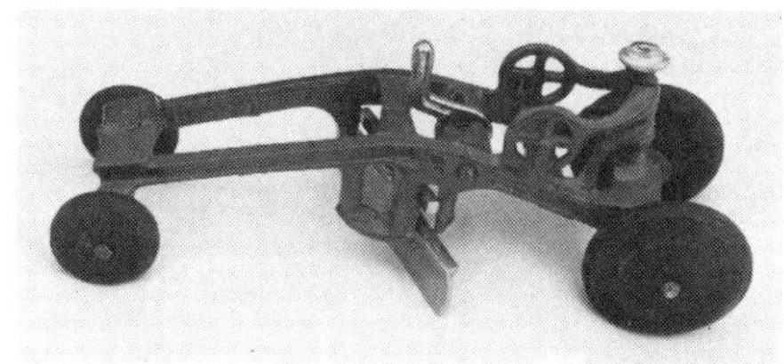

**Scraper, Kenton Toys, #151, cast iron, green, nickel plated blade, rubber tires, $145.00.**

Tru–Scale, 1972 ... **65.00**
Harrow, tandem disc, Corgi, 1967, MIB **12.00**
Hay Mower, John Deere, diecast, 1/16 scale, Ertl, 1961 ... **35.00**
Horse Trailer, Rice's Beaufort Double Horse Box, Corgi ... **20.00**
Manure Spreader
  Case, plastic, 1/16 scale, MP, 1950 .. **75.00**
  John Deere, diecast, 1/16 scale, tin wheels, Ertl, 1960 ... **40.00**
  Minneapolis Moline, aluminum, 1/32, Slik, 1950 ... **60.00**
  New Holland, high sides, Ertl ... **40.00**
Mower, Tru–Scale, pressed steel, 1/16 scale, Carter, 1970 ... **30.00**
Planter, White ... **15.00**
Plow
  Arcade, cast iron ... **150.00**
  John Deere
    Diecast, 1/16 scale, Ertl, 1960 ... **40.00**
    Pressed Steel, 1/16 scale, Carter, 1950 ... **75.00**
  McCormick–Deering, cast iron, 7¼", red, yellow wheels, Arcade, 1932 **65.00**
  Oliver, cast iron ... **50.00**
  Tru–Scale, pressed steel, 1/16 scale, Carter, 1970 ... **25.00**
Set
  Buddy L, cattle transport stake truck, six plastic steers, hydraulic farm supplies trailer dump truck, trailer, three farm machines, farm machinery trailer hauler truck, 1956 ... **150.00**
  Louis Marx Co, mechanical tractor and mower, 1940s, orig 6⅜ x 8½ x 2¾" red, yellow, and black box **250.00**
Threshing Machine
  John Deere, cast iron, Arcade, 1930 **125.00**
  McCormick–Deering, cast iron, Arcade, orig decal ... **100.00**
Tractor
  Allis Chalmers, cast iron
    6¼", emb name on rear wheels, Arcade, 1940 ... **175.00**
    7", painted driver, Dent, 1940 ... **250.00**
    Diecast, 1/16 scale, bar grill, Ertl, 1965 ... **200.00**
    Plastic, 1/25 scale, Beaver Falls Show insert, Yoder ... **75.00**
  Aveling–Barford ... **36.00**
  Case
    Diecast, 1/16 scale, Agri King, white, Ertl, 1974 ... **150.00**
    Plastic, 1/16 scale, Casomatic, Johan, 1956 ... **400.00**
  Ford, red, rubber tires, Tootsietoy .. **25.00**
  Husky, Buddy L, bright blue body, large rear fenders, black engine block, 13" l, 1969 ... **60.00**
  International Harvester, spun cast zinc, 1/16 scale, steerable, AT & T **70.00**
  John Deere, 1/16 scale
    Cast Aluminum, high lift, 1960 .. **145.00**
    Cast Iron, nickel plated man, rubber wheels, Arcade, 1940 ... **300.00**
  Lincoln Massey, 44 ... **95.00**
  Massey Ferguson, diecast
    1/16 scale, metal wheels, Ertl, 1965 **90.00**
    1/32 scale, Britains, 1978 ... **12.00**
  McCormick–Deering, Arcade ... **200.00**
  Minneapolis Moline
    Diecast, 1/25 scale, yellow, Ertl, 1965 ... **85.00**
    Rubber, 1/16 scale, red, Auburn, 1950 ... **24.00**
  Tru–Scale, diecast, 1/16 scale, Carter, 1975 ... **60.00**
  White, diecast, 1/16 scale, red decal **20.00**
Tractor and Spreader, Allis Chalmers, Arcade, 12" l ... **200.00**
Truck
  Dodge Farm Truck, Dinky, 1950s .. **25.00**
  Farm Supplies Hydraulic Dump Trailer, Buddy L, green tractor, cream body, fourteen rubber wheels, 26½" l, 1956 ... **150.00**
  Ford, Model T Pickup, Tootsietoy, c1916 ... **30.00**
  Mack, Farm Hauler, B–Line, Tootsietoy, c1955 ... **28.00**
  Stake, diecast, 4¼" l, blue, high sides, open cab, Hubley, c1936 ... **75.00**
Wagon
  John Deere
    Diecast, 1/16 scale, metal wheels, Ertl, 1960 ... **80.00**
    Wood, cast iron gears, 1/16 scale, Arcade, 1940 ... **275.00**
  Minneapolis Moline, pressed steel, 1/32 scale, rubber wheels, Slik, 1950 **24.00**

# FAST FOOD MEMORABILIA

**Collecting Hints:** Premiums, made primarily of cardboard or plastic and of recent vintage, are the mainstay of today's fast food collector. Other items sought are advertising signs and posters, character dolls, promotional glasses and trayliners. In fact, anything associated with a restaurant chain is collectible. The most sought after material is from McDonald's.

Collectors should concentrate only on mint items. Premiums should be unassembled or sealed in an unopened plastic bag.

Collecting fast food memorabilia has grown rapidly during the last half of the 1980s. Efforts are underway for a national convention of fast food collectors in 1990. More than ever before, the fast food chains continue to churn out an amazing array of collectibles.

**History:** During the period just after World War II, the only convenience restaurants were the coffee shops and diners located along America's highways or in the towns and cities. As suburbia grew, its young families created a demand for a faster and less expensive type of food service.

Ray A. Kroc responded by opening his first McDonald's drive–in restaurant in Des Plaines, Illinois, in 1955. By offering a limited menu of hamburgers, french fries, and drinks, Kroc kept his costs and prices down. This successful concept of assembly line food preparation soon was imitated, but never surpassed by a myriad of competitors.

By the mid–1960s the race was on with franchising seen as the new economic frontier. As the competition increased, the need to develop advertising promotions was imperative. A plethora of promotional give–aways entered the scene.

**References:** Ken Clee and Suzan Hufferd, *A Collector's Guide To Fast–Food Restaurant Kid's Meal Promotions (Other Than McDonalds),* published by authors, 1991; Gary Henriques and Audre DuVall, *McCollecting: The Illustrated Price Guide to McDonald's Collectibles,* Piedmont Publishing, 1992; Norman E. Martinus and Harry L. Rinker, *Warman's Paper,* Wallace–Homestead, 1993; Meredith Williams, *Tomart's Price Guide To McDonald's Happy Meal Collectibles,* Tomart Publications, 1992.

**Periodicals:** *Collecting Tips Newsletter,* P. O. Box 633, Joplin, MO 64802; *For Here or to Go,* 2773 Curtis Way, Sacramento, CA 95818.

**Collectors' Club:** McDonald's Collectors Club, 2315 Ross Dr., Stow, OH 44224.

**Note:** Prices are for mint condition items sealed in their original wrappers or packages and unassembled.

## ARBY'S

Glass
- Actors Collector Series, Laurel and Hardy, "Wrong Again," smoke colored glass, 1979 .......... **4.00**
- Monopoly Collector Series, Free Parking, 1985 .......... **6.00**
- The Wizard of Id, 5¼" h, tankard shape, Sir Rodney .......... **5.00**

Mug
- Pittsburgh Steelers, Steelers 50 Seasons Gold Cup, 5½" h .......... **4.00**
- Stained Glass Design, milk glass, Federal Glass, 3" h .......... **2.50**

## ARCTIC CIRCLE DRIVE INN, ACEY

Bank, 6" h, composition, 3" d base with decal, Japan, 1960s .......... **75.00**

Glass, 5½" h, black, white, and plum stained glass and filigree design, "Enjoy Coca–Cola" on front, reverse with "At Your/Arctic Circle" .......... **4.00**

## BIG BOY RESTAURANT

Activity Book, *Adventures of the Big Boy,* No 241, May, 1977, 7 x 10", full color .......... **20.00**

Ashtray, 3" d, glass, Frisch's boy holding up Big Boy hamburger, orange design **30.00**

Bank, 8½" h, hard plastic body, movable soft vinyl head with coin slot in back, 1960–70 .......... **25.00**

Cigarette Lighter, plastic and silvered metal, tan, brown Big Boy illus, c1960 .......... **25.00**

Doll, 10" h, plastic, 1974–78 .......... **15.00**

Figure, 8" h, hard vinyl, movable head, mid 1970s .......... **25.00**

Glass, Big Boy 50th Anniversary, 6¼" h, red, white, black, and gold .......... **3.00**

Lamp, 6½" h, vinyl, figural, marked "Big Boy Is A Reg U S Trademark," c1960 .......... **100.00**

Magic Slate, 2¾ x 3¾", Big Boy Mistic Slate, 1970s .......... **25.00**

Menu, 5½ x 8", cardboard, full color diecut cov, 1949 .......... **30.00**

Pinback Button, 1⅛" d, litho, orange, white, and brown, symbol trademark, 1960s .......... **15.00**

## BURGER KING

Car, Burger King Wind Car, plastic, 1979 .......... **1.00**

Doll, 16" h, cloth, 1972 .......... **20.00**

Eraser, pencil top, Burger King bust, 1979 .......... **1.00**

Glass
- American Football Conference Champions, Lyle Alzado, 1977 .......... **4.00**
- Have It Your Way Collector's Series 1776–1976, Liberty Bell, red lettering .......... **5.00**

Star Wars, Luke Skywalker, 1977 Twentieth Century–Fox Film Corporation, Limited Edition ........ **6.00**
Puppet, plastic, Burger King, 1977 ... **1.50**
Puzzle, 8½ x 10", frame tray, full color cartoon, 1973 .................. **10.00**
Tab, 1½" d, full color litho tin, 1970s . **3.00**
Whistle, plastic, pickle shape, green .. **1.25**

## CHUCK E CHEESE

Bank, 6½" h, hard plastic, figural, Pizza Time Theatre Inc, copyright 1980 .. **15.00**

## HARDEE'S

Doll, 14" h, cloth, Gilbert Giddy–Up, Chase Bag Co, 1971 .............. **7.00**
Glass
Hardee's, plum, black, and white design, "Hardee's" on one side, "Enjoy Coca–Cola" on other ........ **2.00**
Ziggy, Time for a Food Break, cartoon and caption, 1979 .............. **3.00**

## KENTUCKY FRIED CHICKEN, COLONEL SANDERS

Bank, 8" h, plastic, red, figural, holding bucket of chicken, 1977 .......... **20.00**
Doll, 13" h, Canada ................ **28.00**
Figure, 9" h, 1960s ................. **75.00**
Nodder, 7" h, early 1960s ........... **50.00**

**MacDonald's, glass mug, Garfield Characters series, "Use Your Friends Wisely," 1978, 3⅜" h, $4.00.**

## MCDONALD'S

Bank, die cast, delivery van, Ronald McDonald on side, 1992 Christmas Greetings ...................... **35.00**
Character Glasses
Garfield in hammock, 1978 ....... **3.50**
Happiness Hotel Bus, 1981 ........ **2.00**
Kermit with Fozzie in balloon, 1981 **2.00**
Kermit with bike friends, 1981 ..... **2.00**
Miss Piggy riding motorcycle, 1981 . **2.50**
Ronald McDonald, 1981 .......... **2.25**
Clock, 4½" d, alarm, windup, red case, two silver bells, metal round shape ringer, brass feet, marked "Robertshaw Controls, Luxtime division Lebanon, Tenn, USA" ............... **50.00**
Comb, figure handle, Ronald McDonald, 1980 .................. **2.25**
Comic Book, McDonaldland Comic Book No 101, 1976 ............. **25.00**
Doll, 6½" h, Big Mac, vinyl, wearing policeman's helmet, plastic whistle with gold cord around neck, c1976 . **20.00**
Game, The McDonald's Game, Milton Bradley ........................ **18.00**
Happy Meal Toys
Beach Ball, three panels with Grimace scenes, 1986 McDonald's Corporation .................. **2.00**
Bike Reflector, 3 x 1", Big Mac, 1978 **6.00**
Figure
Astrosniks I, ice skater, purple suit, red helmet with "M" and ice skates, green gloves, 1983 ..... **4.75**
Barney, Flintstone Kids, 1988 .... **3.25**
Clown, 2⅜" h, holding ball, big shoes, 1979 ................ **6.00**
Farmer, Old McDonald's Farm, movable head and arms ....... **3.00**
Mayor McCheese, The Adventures of Ronald McDonald series, 1981 ...................... **4.25**
Muppet Baby, Piggy, wearing roller skates, 1987 ................ **3.00**
Phantom F4E, Skybusters, target design on wings, marked "Matchbox, Lesney Prod Corp Ltd, Eng," 1982 ...................... **1.25**
Stegosaurus, Dinosaur Days, name and logo on tail, Diener Industry, 1981 ...................... **2.00**
Whale, Undersea series, raised head and tail, marked "Diener," 1980 ...................... **1.00**
Grimace Tubby Tubber, Ship Shape I, plastic, decals, 1983 ........... **8.00**
Happy Hat, fireman, red, Ronald McDonald, molded plastic, 1990 . **4.50**
Lego Building Set, helicopter, 1983 . **3.00**
Little Golden Book, *Poky Little Puppy,* Western Publishing Co, Inc, #301–32, 1982 ..................... **3.50**
Magni Finder, hidden case trick with Ronald McDonald, Birdie, and Fry Guy, 1983 .................... **7.00**
Mask, Zoo Face, monkey, soft plastic, elastic string, 1988 ............. **3.00**
Popoids, triangle, 1985 ........... **4.00**
Ring, plastic, character, Hamburglar, 1977 ....................... **3.00**

Sport Ball, football, red and yellow, 5″ l, 1988 .................... **6.50**
Straw, McDonaldland character head, 1977 .................... **2.75**

Happy Pail
McBunny, Fluffy, blue lid, yellow ear shape handle, 1989 ............ **3.00**
Treasure Hunt, handle, sand sifter lid, red rake, 1986 ................ **4.00**

Lunch Box, plastic, M shape handle, emb on one side with characters, other with bulletin board, sheet of stickers, red, 1988 ............... **2.00**
Magazine, *McDonaldland Fun Times,* 1984 to Present .................. **2.00**
Pin, Ken Griffey Jr, baseball, orig card, set of 3 ........................ **10.00**
Pinback Button, "I Guarantee It's Fast" **2.00**
Puppet, 12″ h, Big Mac, fabric body, soft vinyl head 1973 ................. **40.00**
Radio, Big Mac Box, red, yellow logo, General Electric .................. **45.00**
Sport Bottle, green, red basketballs ... **2.25**
Sticker, 9″ d, glossy paper, peel–off back, gold arches with red outline, blue border, inscribed "Licensee McDonald's System, Inc," Chicago Decal Co, c1962 ................ **25.00**
Tote Bag, Hamburglar, 10 x 13″, fabric, red, light blue vinyl edge, tag "Ronald McDonald Tote Bags" with 1982 copyright ....................... **18.00**

Toy
Frisbee, Big Mac, yellow, figure center, plastic .................... **4.00**
McDonald's Familiar Places Activity Set, Playskool Toys ............ **25.00**

Travel Bag, vinyl, lined, emb arches logo in square .................. **12.00**

### PIZZA HUT

Glass
Care Bears Collector's Series, Funshine Bear, Feeling Funtastic, 1983 **1.50**
Green Bay Packers National Football League Players, Vince Lombardi, MSA copyright ................ **5.00**
Popples, Puffball Popple, Steppin' out for fun!, 1986 ................ **3.00**

Napkin, paper, logo design .......... **.75**

### SAMBO

Coaster, Bicentennial ............... **3.00**
Doll, 10″ h, cloth, Dakin ............ **15.00**
Hand Puppet, plastic, Mother Tiger, holding spatula .................. **1.50**
Toy, 7″ h, stuffed, wearing chef's hat, fuzzy beard, felt facial features ..... **10.00**

### WENDY'S

Glass
New York Times Headlines, Nation and Millions in City Joyously Hail Bicentennial, July 3, 1976 ....... **7.00**
Where's the Beef, black line drawing of Clara Peller, round bottom, 1984 Wendy's Exclusive Licensee Pro Sports Inc .................... **5.00**

Mug, Wendy's Old Fashioned Hamburgers, ceramic, red, white, and black trademark, 1970s ........... **4.00**
Ring, 3½″ d, Fun Flyer, plastic ....... **1.25**
Wine Glass, 6⅝″ h, lead crystal, Wendy's/We've Got/The Future/10th Annual/Convention/Las Vegas/1985 ... **8.00**

# FENTON GLASS

**Collecting Hints:** During the past thirty years Fenton has produced some of the most beautiful glass ever made by this firm. Many pieces duplicate examples made by 19th century glass houses. Since that glass is so very difficult to find, the new collector has turned to this reproduction glass.

Carnival glass made by Fenton after 1970 has their logo in the glass. Milk glass made after 1973 and all Fenton glass made after 1974 is marked with their logo.

It is advisable for the beginning collector to understand and study Fenton glass and to purchase *Fenton Glass— The Third Twenty–Five Years* so that they can identify glass made from 1960 to 1980. The last ten identified years, while not covered by this book, can be studied by visiting gift shops and talking to dealers.

Many collectors begin collecting with the most recently made glass, then work their collecting back in time. For example, Fenton first started making Burmese in 1971. They made it almost continuously until 1990. By beginning with pieces in 1990, then 1989, and so on the collector will be lucky enough to put together a collection of all Burmese pieces.

**History:** The Fenton Art Glass Company began as a cutting shop in Martins Ferry, Ohio, in 1905. In 1906 Frank L. Fenton started to build a plant in Williamstown, West Virginia, and produced the first piece of glass in 1907. Early production included carnival, chocolate, custard, and pressed plus mold blown opalescent glass. In the 1920s stretch glass, Fenton dolphins, jade green, ruby, and art glass were added.

In the 1930s boudoir lamps, "Dancing Ladies," and various slags were produced. The 1940s saw crests of different colors being added to each piece by hand. Hobnail, opalescent, and two–color overlay pieces were popular items. Handles were added to different shapes, making the baskets they created as popular today as then.

Through the years Fenton has added beauty to their glass by decorating it with hand painting, acid etching, color staining, and copper wheel cutting. Several different paper labels have been used. In 1970 an oval raised trademark also was adopted.

**References:** Shirley Griffith, *A Pictorial Review Of Fenton White Hobnail Milk Glass,* published by author, 1984; William Heacock, *Fenton Glass: The First Twenty–Five Years,* O–Val Advertising Corp, 1978; William Heacock, *Fenton Glass: The Second Twenty–Five Years,* O–Val Advertising Corp, 1980; William Heacock, *Fenton Glass: The Third Twenty–Five Years,* O–Val Advertising Corp., 1989; Ferill J. Rice (ed.), *Caught In The Butterfly Net,* Fenton Art Glass Collectors of America, Inc., distributed by Antique Publications, 1991; Ellen Tischbein Schroy, *Warman's Glass,* Wallace–Homestead, 1992.

**Collectors' Club:** Fenton Art Glass Collectors Of America, Inc, P. O. Box 384, Williamstown, WV 26187.

**Additional Listings:** Carnival Glass.

**Advisor:** Ferill Jeane Rice.

Advertising Sign, irid green, 1980 .... **45.00**
Animal Dish, cov, hen, Rose Pastel, 9″ h .... **75.00**
Ashtray, Hobnail, Blue Opalescent, fan **32.50**
Banana Bowl, Silver Crest, low base .. **60.00**
Basket
  Peach Crest, 7″ h .... **75.00**
  Rose Crest, 5″ h .... **45.00**
  Silver Crest
    7″ h .... **30.00**
    8″ h .... **60.00**
Bonbon, cov, #643
  Jade .... **35.00**
  Stretch, irid, purple .... **50.00**
Bonbon Set, 5½″ d crimped bonbon, four 8½″ d plates, Emerald Crest ... **120.00**
Bowl
  Dolphin, 10½″ l, handle, jade .... **86.00**
  Mandarin Red, 12″ d, flare, #950 .. **85.00**
  Silver Crest, 8″ d, crimped, gold chrome cupid stand .... **25.00**
  Stiegel Blue, 7″ d, lace edge .... **26.00**
Cake Plate, 13″ d, ftd
  Emerald Crest .... **95.00**
  Hobnail, Yellow Opalescent .... **115.00**
  Silver Crest .... **35.00**
Candlesticks, pr, #848, black .... **35.00**
Champagne, Plymouth, red .... **12.50**
Compote
  Apple Blossom Crest, #7329 .... **60.00**
  Diamond Lace, French Opalescent, ftd, 1948 .... **75.00**
  Silver Crest, 8″ d, 6″ h .... **35.00**
Console Set
  Blue Ridge, ftd rose bowl, pr #1523 candlesticks, price for three piece set .... **250.00**
  Jade, #1600 dolphin bowl, pr #318 candlesticks, price for three piece set .... **125.00**
Cookie Jar, cov, Big Cookies, wicker handle
  Black Amethyst .... **95.00**
  Jade Green .... **95.00**
Creamer, Lincoln Inn, cobalt blue .... **37.50**
Creamer and Sugar
  Emerald Crest, price for pair .... **85.00**
  Hobnail, White Opalescent, tall, price for pair .... **27.50**

**Cruet, Hobnail, opalescent, cranberry, applied clear handle, ground stopper, $65.00.**

Cruet, Hobnail, Blue Opalescent, 3 oz **35.00**
Finger Bowl, Lincoln Inn, red .... **30.00**
Goblet
  Hobnail, White Opalescent .... **14.50**
  Plymouth, ruby .... **20.00**
Hat, top, Blue Overlay, 3¼″ h .... **24.00**
Ivy Bowl, Ruby Overlay, 9″ h .... **65.00**
Jug
  Beaded Melon, 5¼″ h, Green Overlay **85.00**
  Hobnail, Blue Opalescent, 5½″ h .. **35.00**
Juice Set, Hobnail, Yellow Opalescent, squatty juice pitcher, six matching tumblers, price for seven piece set .. **195.00**
Juice Tumbler, Plymouth, red .... **15.00**
Nut Dish, Lincoln Inn, dark green .... **65.00**
Olive, Lincoln Inn, green .... **12.50**
Petal Bowl
  #848, Jade .... **25.00**
  September Morn Nymph, Moonstone, orig flower frog .... **195.00**
Pitcher
  Button and Braids, Green Opalescent **175.00**
  Hobnail, Green Opalescent, 6½″ h . **42.00**

Plate
- Aqua Crest, 8½″ d ............... **30.00**
- Emerald Crest, 8″ d ............... **30.00**
- Silver Crest, 16″ d ............... **45.00**

Relish, Hobnail, Crystal, three parts .. **5.00**

Rose Bowl, Blue Overlay, Beaded Melon, 3½″ h ............... **30.00**

Salt and Pepper Shakers, pr
- Diamond Optic
  - Amber ............... **45.00**
  - Red ............... **135.00**
- Georgian, amber ............... **75.00**
- Hobnail, milk glass, white ......... **25.00**
- Hobnail, White Opalescent, plastic tops ............... **30.00**
- Lincoln Inn, black ............... **250.00**

Sherbet
- Hobnail, White Opalescent ........ **12.50**
- Silver Crest ............... **16.00**

Shoe, vaseline, sgd ............... **25.00**

Tidbit Server
- Emerald Crest, 8″ d and 12″ d tiers . **45.00**
- Silver Crest ............... **30.00**

Tumbler
- Hobnail
  - Blue Opalescent, flat, 9 oz ...... **14.50**
  - White Opalescent, ftd, 9 oz ..... **12.50**
- Lincoln Inn, red, ftd, 9 oz ......... **24.00**

Vanity Set, Blue Overlay, 192A, price for three piece set ............... **95.00**

Vase
- Aqua Crest, 8″ h, triangular ........ **37.50**
- Burmese, hp roses
  - 4″ h ............... **35.00**
  - 6″ h, bud ............... **40.00**
  - 7″ h ............... **45.00**
- Hobnail
  - 4″ h, rose pastel, fan ............ **12.00**
  - 4½″ h, Blue Opalescent, sq ..... **32.00**
- Lincoln Inn, 10″ h, jade ........... **175.00**
- Sophisticated Ladies, 10¼″ h, black, limited edition ............... **175.00**

# FIESTA WARE

**Collecting Hints:** Buy pieces without any cracks, chips, or scratches whenever possible. Fiesta ware can be identified by bands of concentric circles.

**History:** Fiesta ware is colorful pottery dinnerware made by the Homer Laughlin China Company. It was designed by Frederick Read. Production started in 1936. Fiesta ware was redesigned in 1969 and discontinued in 1972. In 1986 it was reintroduced.

**References:** Linda D. Farmer, *The Farmer's Wife's Fiesta Inventory & Price Guide*, privately printed, 1984; Sharon and Bob Huxford, *The Collectors Encyclopedia of Fiesta with Harlequin and Riviera, Seventh Edition*, Collector Books, 1987, 1992 value update.

Bowl
- 4¾″ d
  - Dark Green ............... **20.00**
  - Light Green ............... **15.00**
- 5½″ d, fruit
  - Cobalt Blue ............... **20.00**
  - Light Green ............... **15.00**
  - Red ............... **20.00**
  - Yellow ............... **18.00**
- 6″ d, dessert
  - Chartreuse ............... **50.00**
  - Gray ............... **50.00**
  - Light Green ............... **22.00**
  - Rose ............... **50.00**
  - Turquoise ............... **50.00**
- 8½″ d, Cobalt Blue ............... **30.00**

Candlesticks, pr, tripod, Yellow ...... **415.00**

Carafe
- Cobalt Blue ............... **225.00**
- Red ............... **225.00**
- Yellow ............... **115.00**

**Carafe, orange, $225.00.**

Casserole, cov
- Cobalt Blue ............... **125.00**
- Light Green, 8½″ d, Kitchen Kraft .. **40.00**
- Yellow ............... **200.00**

Chop Plate, 13″ d
- Chartreuse ............... **75.00**
- Cobalt Blue ............... **50.00**
- Light Green ............... **20.00**
- Turquoise ............... **20.00**
- Yellow ............... **35.00**

Coffeepot, cov
- Ivory ............... **90.00**
- Red ............... **180.00**
- Turquoise ............... **135.00**
- Yellow ............... **135.00**

Creamer
- Stick
  - Cobalt Blue ............... **30.00**
  - Red ............... **16.00**

Table
Cobalt Blue .................. **25.00**
Ivory .................. **14.00**
Turquoise .................. **14.00**
Cup
Chartreuse .................. **18.00**
Cobalt Blue .................. **20.00**
Dark Green .................. **18.00**
Gray .................. **24.00**
Turquoise .................. **18.00**
Yellow .................. **18.00**
Deep Plate
Gray .................. **35.00**
Light Green .................. **24.00**
Red .................. **27.00**
Turquoise .................. **22.00**
Yellow .................. **22.00**
Demitasse Cup and Saucer, Cobalt Blue **50.00**
Demitasse Pot, Red .................. **275.00**
Egg Cup
Cobalt Blue .................. **35.00**
Light Green .................. **30.00**
Yellow .................. **30.00**
Fork, Light Green, Kitchen Kraft ...... **65.00**
Gravy Boat, Cobalt Blue ............ **50.00**
Jar, cov, Red, Kitchen Kraft .......... **315.00**
Jug
Cobalt Blue, two pint ............ **75.00**
Green, cov, Kitchen Kraft .......... **170.00**
Juice Tumbler, Cobalt Blue .......... **30.00**
Mixing Bowl, nested set, #1 Turquoise, #2 Red, #3 Cobalt Blue, #4 Yellow, #5 Turquoise, #6 Red, #7 Turquoise, price for set .............. **550.00**
Mug, Cobalt Blue .................. **60.00**
Nappy
8½" d
Gray .................. **40.00**
Red .................. **32.00**
Rose .................. **45.00**
9½" d, Cobalt Blue ............... **60.00**
Onion Soup, cov, Ivory ............ **450.00**
Pie Baker, Green, Kitchen Kraft ...... **35.00**
Pitcher
Red, disc .................. **145.00**
Yellow, juice .................. **32.00**
Plate
6" d
Cobalt Blue .................. **5.00**
Ivory .................. **6.00**
Red .................. **4.50**
Rose .................. **9.00**
Turquoise .................. **5.00**
7" d
Gray .................. **10.00**
Rose .................. **10.00**
Turquoise .................. **6.00**
Yellow .................. **7.00**
9" d
Chartreuse .................. **10.00**
Cobalt Blue .................. **18.00**
Dark Green .................. **10.00**
Gray .................. **19.00**
Ivory .................. **18.00**
Light Green .................. **10.00**
Red .................. **12.50**
Rose .................. **18.00**
Turquoise .................. **10.00**
Yellow .................. **10.00**
10" d
Light Green .................. **20.00**
Red .................. **25.00**
10½" d, grill, Cobalt Blue ......... **40.00**
Platter, 15" d
Cobalt Blue .................. **40.00**
Red .................. **55.00**
Salad Bowl, ftd, Ivory .............. **150.00**
Salt and Pepper Shakers, pr
Dark Green .................. **40.00**
Red, Kitchen Kraft ................ **75.00**
Sauce Boat
Chartreuse .................. **55.00**
Gray .................. **80.00**
Saucer
Chartreuse .................. **4.00**
Cobalt Blue .................. **4.00**
Ivory .................. **3.00**
Red .................. **4.00**
Turquoise .................. **2.00**
Yellow .................. **3.00**
Spoon, Cobalt Blue, Kitchen Kraft .... **65.00**
Sugar, cov, Cobalt Blue ............ **25.00**
Syrup, Ivory .................. **195.00**
Teapot
Red, large, pinpoint flake on rim ... **100.00**
Yellow .................. **90.00**
Tumbler
Cobalt Blue .................. **40.00**
Red .................. **55.00**
Vase
8" h
Green .................. **295.00**
Ivory .................. **250.00**
Turquoise .................. **300.00**
10" h, Cobalt Blue ............... **500.00**

# FIREHOUSE COLLECTIBLES

**Collecting Hints:** It was fashionable for a period of time to put a date on the back of a fireman's helmet. This date is usually the date the fire company was organized, not the date the helmet was made.

Firehouse collectibles is a very broad area of collecting. The older, scarcer collectibles, such as helmets and firemarks, command high prices. The newer collectibles, e.g., cards and badges, are more reasonably priced. This area of collecting is continually growing and expanding.

**History:** The volunteer fire company has played a vital role in the protection and social growth of many towns and rural areas. Paid professional firemen are usually found in large metropolitan areas. Each fire company prides itself on equipment and uniforms. Annual conventions and parades give the individual fire companies a chance to show off their equipment. These conventions and parades have produced a wealth of firehouse related collectibles.

**References:** Chuck Deluca, *Firehouse Memorabilia: A Collectors Reference,* Maritime Antique Auctions, 1989; Charles V. Hansen, *The History of American Firefighting Toys,* Greenberg Publishing, 1990; Norman E. Martinus and Harry L. Rinker, *Warman's Paper,* Wallace–Homestead, 1993; Mary Jane and James Piatti, *Firehouse Collectibles,* The Engine House, 1979; Donald F. Wood and Wayne Sorenson, *American Volunteer Fire Trucks,* Krause Publications, 1993.

**Periodical:** *The Fire Mark Circle of the Americas,* 2859 Martin Drive, Chamblee, GA 30341.

**Collectors' Club:** Fire Collectors Club, P. O. Box 992, Milwaukee, WI 53201.

**Museums:** There are many museums devoted to firehouse collectibles. Large collections are housed at: Insurance Company of North America (I.N.A.) Museum, Philadelphia, PA; Oklahoma State Fireman's Association Museum, Inc., Oklahoma City, OK; San Francisco Fire Dept. Pioneer Memorial Museum, San Francisco, CA; The New York City Fire Museum, New York, NY.

Alarm Box
- Gamewell, aluminum .......... **125.00**
- Horni, aluminum .......... **85.00**
- Utica Fire Alarm & Telegraph, cast iron .......... **600.00**
- Western Electric .......... **50.00**

Badge
- Alison/Harrisburg, 1" silvered brass, center numeral "2," 1930s, threaded post fastener .......... **15.00**
- Columbia Firemans Relief Ass'n, 1", silvered brass, ladder, fire hose nozzles, c1930 .......... **15.00**
- Friendship 1, Harrisburg, PA, 1½ x 1¾", silvered brass, c1930 .......... **12.00**
- Good Will Fire Co
  - 1 x 1½", silvered rolled brass, unfinished brass numeral "7" over diecut center opening, early 1900s, back pin missing .......... **20.00**
  - 1½", silvered brass, ladder, hook, and hydrant symbols, Harrisburg, PA, c1920 .......... **18.00**
- Liberty 3, Lebanon, PA, 1" brass, fire hydrant, hook, and ladder, lightly worn finish, c1930 .......... **12.00**

Bell, American LaFrance, chrome .......... **400.00**

Book, *Footprints of Assurance,* Macmillan Co, New York, NY, 1953, 319 pages, 9 x 12", history and story of fire marks in America, eight colored plates, many black and white illus .......... **50.00**

Bucket, Franklin Hook & Ladder Co, 1823, rubber, price for pair .......... **250.00**

Catalog
- General Fire Extinguisher, Atlanta, GA, 1930, 669 pages, 5½ x 7½" .......... **30.00**
- J H Bunnell & Co, New York, NY, c1919, 4 pages, 4¾ x 7", Jove fire alarms, red ink, illus .......... **12.00**

Fire Extinguisher, 24" h, polished copper **95.00**

**Fire Extinguisher, Excelsior Fire Appliances, Homestead, PA, 21¾" l, $28.00.**

Gauge, 4" d, American LaFrance, brass, beveled glass .......... **100.00**

Gong, 6" h, turtle style, Gamewell Newton, Upper Falls, MA .......... **125.00**

Grenade
- Harden's Star, blue .......... **75.00**
- Hayward's, amber, orig contents .......... **150.00**

Helmet
- Aluminum, high eagle, leather front piece .......... **150.00**
- Fiberglass, leather front piece .......... **35.00**
- Leather, high eagle, leather front piece
  - Anderson & Jones .......... **235.00**
  - Cairns .......... **350.00**

Lantern, Dietz Fire King, brass, red globe, 1907 patent date .......... **165.00**

Magazine, Volunteer Fireman, Prof Journal of Vol Fireman's Section of Nat'l Fire Protection Assoc, lot of fourteen issues from 1935 through 1937 .......... **15.00**

Mirror, pocket, 2¾" oval, celluloid
- Rescue Fire Co, No 1, Annville, PA, black and white photo image of engine, logo for engine maker, Seagrave Co, Columbus, OH, c1920 **50.00**
- We Kick For Our Rights, Harrisburg, PA, 1914, blue, green, gold, and white fire symbols and keystone logo .......... **40.00**

Nozzle, brass
- Ashworth shut–off .......... **70.00**

Eureka, leather grips .............. **80.00**
Rockwood, bayonet applicator ..... **35.00**

Pin
Brass, figural, fireman, Hi–Glo, screw back .......................... **5.25**
Silver, USAF Fire Protection ....... **45.00**

Pinback Button, 1¼" d, celluloid
Black and white, horse drawn hose wagon, c1890, removable brass rosette frame .................... **18.00**
Multicolored, scene of firemen rescuing baby from burning window, early 1900s, removable brass rosette frame .................... **20.00**

Ribbon
Allison H & L Co, No. 12, 3 x 6" brass, celluloid, and fabric link badge, celluloid insert in hanger bar, inscribed "Entertaining Our Soldiers Who Were In The World War, Harrisburg, Pa, Oct 31–Nov 1, 1919," red, white, and blue fabric ribbon ..................... **35.00**
Citizen Steam Fire Engine Co, 2¾ x 6", fabric ribbon, gold fringe tassels, brass hanger bar holds ribbon, dark blue printing on pale blue ground, illus of horse drawn pumper, c1890 ................ **20.00**
Guests of Delaware Fire Co, No. 3, South Penn Hose Co, No. 31 of Philadelphia/Wilmington, Delaware, Oct 11, '93, 2½ x 7", purple fabric ribbon, gold lettering, bright brass hanger bar with emb fire symbols .......................... **18.00**
Reily Hose Co, No. 10, 2½ x 9", tin framed hanger bar, full color depiction of clasped handshake, blue fabric ribbon, matching overlay half ribbon, bright silver lettering, pumper, name, and Harrisburg, Pa, July 11, 1885 organization date, reverse with bright silver and black fabric with silvery gray trim stripes, back overlay of horse drawn ladder wagon and inscription .......... **40.00**

Sign, "No Smoking...By Order of Upper Peninsula Farmers Mutual Fire Ins Co, Rock, MI," early 1900s, 9 x 4" ..... **10.00**

Toy, firecracker, cardboard house, roof printed "House on Fire, Light the Chimney," 1928 ................ **35.00**

Watch Fob, Connecticut Tercentenary, 1935, 2nd Reg, convention delegate bar, silk ribbon .................. **35.00**

Whistle, 24" h, brass, building type, manual type lever ................ **300.00**

Wrench, 9½" l, Boston Coupling Co, combination spanner ............. **10.00**

# FIRE–KING

**Collecting Hints:** Anchor Hocking's Fire–King is a contemporary of Pyrex and other "oven-proof" glassware of the 1940s and 1950s. It is only within the past decade that collectors have begun to focus on this range of material. As a result, prices fluctuate. A stable pricing market is several years in the future.

Anchor Hocking introduced a line of children's dishes in 1938. These became part of the Fire–King line. A popular pattern is Little Bo Peep. Like all children's dishes, these objects command strong prices.

Some Fire–King collectors focus on a single color. Jane Ray, a jadite-colored pattern, was introduced in 1945. In 1948 the color was introduced in a series of restaurant wares. It was discontinued in 1963.

Fire–King was sold in sets. Add an additional 25% to 35% to the price of the individual pieces if a set remains intact in its original box.

**History:** Fire–King is a product of the Anchor Hocking Glass Company. In 1905 Isaac J. Collins founded the Hocking Glass Company along the banks of the Hocking River near Lancaster, Ohio. On March 6, 1924, fire completely destroyed the plant, but it was rebuilt in six months. Hocking produced pressed glass dinnerware, many patterns of which have the Depression Glass designation.

In 1937 Hocking Glass Company merged with the Anchor Cap Company and became Anchor Hocking Glass Corporation. Shortly thereafter the new company began to manufacture glass ovenware that could withstand the high temperatures of a kitchen oven.

Production of oven-proof glass marked "FIRE–KING" began in 1942 and lasted until 1976. Dinnerware patterns include: Alice, Charm, Fleurette, Game Bird, Honeysuckle, Jane Ray, Laurel, Primrose, Turquoise Blue, Swirl, and Wheat. Utilitarian kitchen items and ovenware patterns also were produced.

Housewives eagerly purchased Fire–King sets and could assemble large sets of matching dinnerware and ovenware patterns. Advertising encouraged consumers to purchase prepackaged sets, starter sets, luncheon sets, and snackware sets, as well as casseroles and baking sets. Oven glassware items included almost everything needed to completely stock the kitchen.

Fire–King patterns are found in azurite, forest green, gray, ivory, jadite, peach luster, pink, plain white, ruby red, sapphire blue, opaque turquoise, and white with an assortment of rim colors. Decals were applied to increase sales.

Fire–King pieces are found with two types of marks. The first is a mold mark directly on the piece. The second is an oval foil paper label.

**References:** Gene Florence, *Collectible Glassware From The 40's, 50's, 60's, An Illustrated Value Guide,* Collector Books, 1992; Gene Florence, *Kitchen Glassware of the Depression Years, Fourth Edition,* Collector Books, 1990; Gary and Dale Kilgo and Jerry and Gail Wilkins, *A Collectors Guide To Anchor Hocking's Fire–King Glassware,* K & W Collectibles Publisher, 1991; Glyndon Shirley, *The Miracle In Grandmother's Kitchen,* published by author, 1983; April M. Tvorak, *History and Price Guide to Fire–King,* VAL Enterprises, 1992.

**Periodical:** *The Daze,* 10271 State Rd., Box 57, Otisville, MI 48463.

**Collectors' Club:** The National Depression Glass Association, PO Box 69843, Odessa, TX 79769.

**Hot Plate, light blue, 10⅜" handle to handle, $15.00.**

## DINNERWARE

Alice, 1940–50s
- Cup and Saucer, jadite ........... **5.00**
- Plate, 9½" d, dinner
  - Jadite ........... **10.00**
  - White, blue trim ........... **12.00**

Charm, Azurite, sq
- Bowl, 4½" w ........... **4.25**
- Cup and Saucer ........... **6.00**
- Plate
  - 6¼" w ........... **3.25**
  - 8⅜" w ........... **4.50**
  - 9¼" w, dinner ........... **11.00**

Fruits, hand painted
- Bowl
  - 6" d ........... **4.00**
  - 8¾" d ........... **8.00**
- Casserole, cov, pint ........... **6.00**
- Refrigerator Dish, cov
  - 4 x 4" ........... **4.00**
  - 4½ x 8½" ........... **6.00**

Golden shell
- Creamer and Sugar
  - Irid luster ........... **5.00**
  - White, 22K gold edge ........... **6.00**
- Cup and Saucer
  - Irid luster ........... **4.25**
  - White, 22K gold edge ........... **4.00**
- Plate, dinner, white, 22K gold edge . **3.75**
- Platter, white, 22K gold edge ........... **6.00**
- Set, lunch, 16 pcs, orig box ........... **32.00**
- Soup Bowl, white, 22K gold edge .. **3.75**

Golden Wheat, 22K gold trim
- Cup and Saucer ........... **3.00**
- Creamer ........... **6.00**
- Dessert Bowl, 5⅜" d ........... **2.00**
- Gravy Boat ........... **9.00**
- Plate
  - 6" d, bread and butter ........... **1.00**
  - 7¼" d, salad ........... **2.00**
  - 9¼" d, dinner ........... **3.00**
- Platter, 9 x 12" ........... **8.00**
- Soup Bowl, 7½" d ........... **3.50**
- Sugar ........... **5.00**
- Vegetable Bowl, 8¾" d ........... **5.50**

Jane Ray, 1940–50s
- After Dinner Cup and Saucer
  - Jadite ........... **27.00**
  - White ........... **15.00**
- Berry Bowl, ivory ........... **3.00**
- Bowl
  - 4¼" d ........... **3.25**
  - 6" d ........... **7.00**
  - 8¼" d ........... **8.00**
- Creamer and Sugar, cov ........... **12.00**
- Cup and Saucer
  - Ivory ........... **4.00**
  - Jadite ........... **3.50**
- Oatmeal Bowl, Jadite ........... **10.00**
- Plate
  - Dinner ........... **3.50**
  - Salad ........... **8.00**
- Platter ........... **12.50**
- Saucer, Peach Lustre ........... **3.00**
- Soup Bowl ........... **10.00**
- Set, Starter, Jadite, 8½" d bowl, creamer, cov sugar, platter, four 4⅞" d bowls, cups, saucers, 7½" d plates, unused, some orig labels, orig box ........... **115.00**

Leaf Blossom, bowl, 4¾" d, jadite .... **6.50**

Meadow Green
- Baking Dish, 6 x 12" ........... **5.00**
- Bowl, 4⅝" d ........... **2.50**
- Casserole
  - 7¾" d, cov ........... **5.00**
  - 8½" d, open ........... **4.00**
  - 9½" d, cov ........... **7.00**
- Plate, 10" d ........... **4.25**
- Platter, 12½" l, oval ........... **4.25**
- Soup Bowl, 6⅝" d ........... **4.50**

Mosaic, blue
- Berry Bowl ........... **3.50**
- Creamer and Sugar ........... **15.00**
- Cup ........... **4.00**
- Plate
  - Dinner ........... **5.00**

Salad .......... **4.00**
Pink Swirl
Plate, 9⅛" d .......... **5.25**
Saucer .......... **1.25**
Sunrise
Bowl
4⅞" d .......... **2.50**
8¼" d .......... **9.00**
Creamer and Sugar, open .......... **8.00**
Cup and Saucer .......... **4.00**
Plate, 9⅛" d .......... **5.50**
Platter, 9 x 12" .......... **9.00**
Swirl White, 1955–60, brushed gold
Cup and Saucer .......... **2.75**
Mixing Bowls, nesting, set of five .......... **40.00**
Plate, 9" d .......... **4.50**
Platter .......... **10.00**
Turquoise Blue, 1950s
Ashtray .......... **6.50**
Bowl
4½" d .......... **6.00**
5" d .......... **8.00**
8" d .......... **12.00**
Coffee Mug .......... **7.00**
Creamer and Sugar .......... **7.50**
Cup and Saucer .......... **4.00**
Egg Plate .......... **10.00**
Mixing Bowl, 6¾" d, Spill Proof .......... **9.25**
Plate
7" d .......... **9.00**
9" d .......... **6.50**
10" d .......... **25.00**
Relish, oval, three part .......... **8.50**
Snack Set, orig box .......... **50.00**
Vegetable Bowl, 8" d .......... **12.00**

### KITCHENWARE

Bowl, Tulip
7½" d .......... **12.00**
8½" d .......... **16.00**
9½" d .......... **16.00**
Casserole, cov, Oven Glass, tab handle, 1 pint .......... **9.00**
Custard, Oven Glass .......... **3.00**
Drip Jar, cov, Tulip .......... **15.00**
Hot Plate, Oven Glass .......... **15.00**
Measuring Cup, sapphire blue, 2 cup .......... **18.00**
Pie Plate, Oven Glass
8" d .......... **7.00**
9" d .......... **9.00**
Popcorn Popper, Oven Glass .......... **38.00**
Skillet, jadite, 2 spout, lug handle .......... **35.00**
Utility Bowls, sapphire blue, nesting, rolled rim, set of three .......... **40.00**

### RESTAURANTWARE

Bowl, 4¾" d, 2¾" h, jadite, rolled lip .......... **9.00**
Cereal Bowl, 5" d, jadite .......... **3.75**
Cup, jadite .......... **4.00**
Cup and Saucer, jadite .......... **7.00**
Mug, jadite .......... **3.50**
Pie Plate, 6¾" d, jadite .......... **7.00**
Plate, jadite
5½" d .......... **4.00**
6¾" d .......... **2.75**
Grill, 5 part .......... **9.00**
Platter, jadite
9½" l .......... **18.00**
11½" x 8" .......... **8.00**

# FISHING COLLECTIBLES

**Collecting Hints:** The fishing collectibles category is rapidly expanding as the rare items are becoming more expensive and harder to locate. New categories include landing nets, minnow traps, bait boxes, advertising signs, catalogs, and fish decoys used in ice spearing. Items in original containers and in mint condition command top prices. Lures that have been painted over the original decoration or rods that have been refinished or broken have little collector value.

Early wooden plugs (before 1920), split bamboo fly rods made by the master craftsmen of that era, and reels constructed of German silver with special detail or unique mechanical features are the items most sought by advanced collectors.

The number of serious collectors is steadily increasing as indicated by the membership in the "National Fishing Lure Collectors Club" which has approximately 2,000 active members.

**History:** Early man caught fish with crude spears and hooks made of bone, horn, and flint. By the middle 1800s metal lures with hooks attached were produced in New York State. Later, the metal was curved and glass beads added for greater attraction. Spinners with wood–painted bodies and glass eyes appeared around 1890. Soon after, wood plugs with glass eyes were being produced by many different makers. A large number of patents were issued in this time period, covering developments of hook hangers, body styles, and devices to add movement of the plug as it was drawn through the water. The wood plug era lasted up to the mid–1930s, when plugs constructed of plastic were introduced.

With the development of casting plugs, it became necessary to produce fishing reels capable of accomplishing that task with ease. Reels first appeared as a simple device to hold a fishing line. Improvements included multiplying gears, retrieving line levelers, drags, clicks, and a variety of construction materials. The range of quality in reel manufacture varied considerably. Collectors are mainly interested in reels made with quality materials and workmanship, or those exhibiting unusual features.

Early fishing rods were made of solid wood and were heavy and prone to break easily. By gluing together strips of tapered pieces of split bamboo, a rod was fashioned which was light in weight and had greatly improved strength. The early split bamboo rods were round with silk wrappings to hold the bamboo strips together. With improvements in glue, fewer wrappings were needed, and rods became slim and lightweight. Rods were built in various lengths and thicknesses depending upon the type of fishing and bait used. Rod makers' names and models can usually be found on the metal parts of the handle or on the rod near the handle.

**References:** Jim Brown, *Fishing Reel Patents of The US, 1838–1940;* published by author; Silvo Calabi, *The Collector's Guide To Antique Fishing Tackle,* Wellfleet Press, 1989; Clyde A Harbin, *James Heddon's Sons Catalogues,* CAH Enterprises, 1977; Art and Scott Kimball, *Collecting Old Fishing Tackle,* Aardvark Publications, Inc., 1980; Art and Scott Kimball, *Early Fishing Plugs of the U. S. A.,* Aardvark Publications, Inc., 1985; Art and Scott Kimball, *The Fish Decoy,* Aardvark Publications, Inc.; Carl F. Luckey, *Old Fishing Lures and Tackle: Identification and Value Guide, Third Edition,* Books Americana, 1991; Norman E. Martinus and Harry L. Rinker, *Warman's Paper,* Wallace–Homestead, 1993; Albert J. Munger, *Those Old Fishing Reels,* published by author, 1982; J. L. Smith, *Antique Rods and Reels,* Gowe Printing, 1986; Bob and Beverly Strauss, *American Sporting Advertising, Volume 2,* L–W Book Sales, 1990, 1992 value update; Richard L. Streater, *Streater's Reference Catalog of Old Fishing Lures, Volume I and II;* Steven K. Vernon, *Antique Fishing Reels,* Stackpole Books, 1984; Karl T. White, *Fishing Tackle Antiques and Collectibles,* Holli Enterprises, 1990.

**Periodical:** *Antique Fishing Collectibles,* P. O. Box 627, Newtown, PA 18940.

**Collectors' Club:** National Fishing Lure Collectors Club, P.O. Box 0184, Chicago, IL 60690.

**Museums:** American Fishing Tackle Mfg. Assn. Museum, Arlington Heights, IL; Sayner Museum, Sayner, WI.

**REPRODUCTION ALERT:** Lures and fish decoys.

Advertising Sign, 15 x 22", "Live Bait For Sale," painted pickerel dec ..... **275.00**
Bait Bucket, marked "T J Conroy's Floating Bait Bucket" ................ **500.00**
Book
*Fishing Memories,* Dorothy N Arms, first edition, dj ................ **35.00**
*Just Fishing,* Ray Bergman, Philadelphia, 1932, first edition ......... **110.00**
*Lore of the Open,* Joe Godfrey, Jr and Frank Dufresne, Brown & Bigelow, 1949, 449 pgs, leather binding ... **20.00**
*Trout Fishing,* Joe Brooks, New York, 1972, first edition, dj ........... **40.00**
*You Can Always Tell A Fisherman,* New York, 1958, first edition, dj . **75.00**
Catalog
Allcock's Angler's Guide, 1938–39 . **30.00**
Bristol Rod Co, #39 .............. **140.00**
Orvis, Charles F Co, Finest Rods, Reels, Flies, & Fishing Tackle, c1902 ....................... **185.00**
Creel, split ash, wood spring woven front ............................ **170.00**

**Lure, Paw Paw, Wottafrog, yellow, black speckles, painted eyes, three treble, hair covered hooks, 3½" l, $10.00.**

Lure
Arbogast, Northern Pike Metal Bait, 2¾" l ......................... **275.00**
Creek Chub
Creek Chub Fin Tail Shiner, 4" l, red fiber fins and tail ......... **130.00**
Gar Minnow, #2900 ........... **110.00**
Husky Dinger, #5700, golden shiny finish, big tail .......... **180.00**
Eureka Bait Company, Eureka Little Giant Wiggler, 3¼" l, white, red hole dec ...................... **115.00**
Heddon
Dowagiac Minnow, #100, cup rig, slate back, hp gill ............ **42.00**
Heddon Musky Vamp, 8" l, green scale body .................. **175.00**
King Basser, #8500–5, blue herring scale ...................... **45.00**
River Runt, #110, 2 pc, dace scale finish ...................... **58.00**
Zaragossa, #6500, red head, frog scale finish .................. **165.00**
Lockhart, E J, Baby Wiggler, 2⅞" l, red, yellow holes ............... **95.00**
Paw Paw Bait Company
Baby Wottafrog, 3¼" l, green splatter finish, plain trebles ........ **35.00**
Jointed Musky Minnow, perch finish ........................ **38.00**

Pfluegei
Monarch Minnow, orig box, 1911 patent ...................... **325.00**
Neverfail Minnow, see through wire rig, three hooks, green crackle back ................. **95.00**
South Bend
Fish Oreno, yellow strawberry spots, orig box ............... **35.00**
Five Hook Panatella Minnow, red head, white body, tail cap ..... **65.00**
Peach Oreno, #502, metal, red head, white body, missing leader butt ........................ **25.00**
Three Hook Panatella Minnow, green scale finish ............. **30.00**
Winchester, Crusader Fluted Spinner, #9538, 7" l, nickel, red, treble hook ......................... **45.00**

Reel
B F Meek & Sons, Blue Grass, marked "Pat Jul 5, 04, Patent Pending" .. **180.00**
Edward Vom Hofe Model 621–4/0, ocean, six point star drag ........ **150.00**
Hardy, St George Junior, 2⁹⁄₁₆" d, orig box .......................... **525.00**
Heddon, Model 3–15, bait casting, German silver ................. **210.00**
Orvis, Battenkill trout, adjustable drag, zipper case ............... **40.00**
Pflueger Sal–Trout Model 100, ferris wheel design, brass ............. **35.00**
Thomas J Conroy, NY, 2⅛" d, bait casting, German silver .......... **225.00**
Winchester, Takapart 4350 ........ **80.00**

Rod, Split–Cane
Constable, 6' 9" l, R H Wood Classic, trout, 2:2, agate stripper guide, bag, and tube .................. **325.00**
Edwards, 7' l, Quadrate, spinning, 2:1, orig bag and tube .......... **200.00**
Granger, 9' l, Aristocrat, 3:2, varnished ........................ **250.00**
Orvis, 8' l, Battenkill, 2:2, orig bag and tube ...................... **200.00**
Thomas, F E, 9' l, Special Fly, 3:2, orig bag and tube .............. **325.00**

Tackle Box, Shakespeare Honor Built, lift out trays ..................... **170.00**

# FLAG COLLECTIBLES

**Collecting Hints:** Public Law 829, 77th Congress, approved December 22, 1942, describes a detailed set of rules for flag etiquette. Collectors should become familiar with this law.

The amount of material on which the American flag is portrayed is limitless. Collectors tend to focus on those items on which the flag enjoys a prominent position.

**History:** The Continental or Grand Union flag, consisting of 13 alternate red and white stripes with a British Union Jack in the upper left corner, was first used on January 1, 1776, on Prospect Hill near Boston. On June 14, 1777, the Continental Congress adopted a flag design similar to the Continental flag, but with the Union Jack replaced by a blue field with thirteen stars. The stars could be arranged in any fashion. Historical documentation to support the claim that Betsy Ross made the first Stars and Stripes is lacking.

On January 13, 1794, Congress voted to add two stars and two stripes to the flag in recognition of Vermont and Kentucky joining the Union. On April 18, 1818, when there were 20 states, Congress adopted a law returning to the original 13 stripes and adding a new star for each state admitted. The star would be added on the July 4th following admission. The 49th star, for Alaska, was added July 4, 1959; the 50th star, for Hawaii, was added July 4, 1960.

**Reference:** Boleslow and Marie–Louis D'Otrange Mastai, *The Stars and Stripes: The American Flag As Art And As History From The Birth Of The Republic To The Present,* Alfred Knopf, 1973.

**Collectors' Club:** North American Vexillological Association, P.O. Box 580, Winchester, MA 01890.

**Museums:** State capitals in northern states; Hardisty Flag Museum, Hardisty, Alberta, Canada; Tumbling Waters Museum of Flags, Prattville, AL.

**Advisor:** Richard Bitterman.

## FLAGS

29 star, 7 x 10", parade flag, coarse cotton material, Great Star pattern, used during Mexican–American War, discolored ....................... **125.00**
36 star
21½ x 36", parade flag, mounted on stick, five point star design, star pattern of 6,6,6,6,6,6 ............ **85.00**
25 x 22", parade flag, printed muslin **85.00**
37 star, 16 x 24", parade flag, 1867–1877, muslin, all printed .......... **40.00**
38 star, 12½ x 22", coarse muslin, mounted on stick, star pattern of 6,7,6,6,7,6 ...................... **12.00**
42 star, four flags on swatch, direct from flag manufacturer, uncut, were to be 11½ x 16¾" when cut up and mounted on a stick, flag makers prepared banners with 42 stars during the winter of 1889 for adoption on July 4, 1890; however, a last minute addition on July 3 of Idaho as a state made 43 stars necessary, so these ban-

ners never made it; $20 per flag on fabric swatch . . . . . . . . . . . . . . . . . . . . **100.00**

44 star, 3½ x 2¼", child's parade type, pattern of 8,7,7,7,7,8 and five point star . . . . . . . . . . . . . . . . . . . . . . . . . . . . . **15.00**

45 star, 32 x 47", 1896–1908, printed on silk, bright colors, black heading and no grommets . . . . . . . . . . . . . . . . **75.00**

46 star, 4 x 5', 1908–1912, stars sewn on, Oklahoma . . . . . . . . . . . . . . . . . . **35.00**

48 star, 5¾ x 4½", 1912–1959, printed on heavy canvas–type material, used on D–Day in Infantry invasion, men wore them under the camouflage net on their helmets . . . . . . . . . . . . . . . . . **47.00**

49 star, 4 x 5¾", 1959–1960, child's parade flag, silk, wood stick, Alaska **18.00**

**Stickpin, celluloid, promoting S. A. Cook for U. S. Senate, 48 stars, $4.00.**

## FLAG RELATED

Catalog, Detra Flag Company, Catalog #24, 6½ x 9", 1941, NY and Los Angeles . . . . . . . . . . . . . . . . . . . . . . . . . **40.00**

China and Glass

Button

½" d, glass dome, flag printed inside, 6 mounted on card . . . . . . **12.00**

1¾" d, horse button, glass dome with eagle and flag . . . . . . . . . . . **18.00**

Magic Lantern Slide, 42 star flag, c1889, hand tinted, mounted in wood . . . . . . . . . . . . . . . . . . . . . . . . **30.00**

Magnifying Glass, pocket, ¾ x 1¼", oval, Voorhees Rubber Mfg Co adv, American flag artwork . . . . . . . . . . **37.00**

Plate, 10" d, Washington's Headquarters, Newburg, NY, 1783–1883, crossed flags under house, brown printing on cream plate . . . . . . . . . **25.00**

Metal

Badge, Foresters of America, with red, white and blue ribbon . . . . . . **4.00**

Clock, Howard Miller Mfg, mantel, God Bless America, WWII vintage, small American flag waves back and forth as second hand . . . . . . . . **100.00**

Match Box, 1½ x 2¾", Civil War period, emb, picture of Stars and Stripes on one side, Miss Columbia on reverse . . . . . . . . . . . . . . . . . . . . . **65.00**

Pin Back, Our Flag . . . . . . . . . . . . . . . **3.00**

Stickpin

Celluloid, American flag, 48 stars, advertising, S A Cook for US Senator . . . . . . . . . . . . . . . . . . . . . . . . **4.00**

Metal, ⅜ x ⅝", 13 stars, c1925, 2" long pin . . . . . . . . . . . . . . . . . . . . **4.00**

Token, 3¾" d, Dix Token Coin, Civil War, commemorates the order of General John Adams Dix, Jan 29, 1861, "If anyone attempts to haul down the American flag, shoot him on the spot," copper–colored coin, picture of "The flag of our Union" on one side and quote on the other **10.00**

Paper

Advertising Trade Card

Hub Gore, 3½ x 6¼", Uncle Sam holding shoe, saying Hub Core Makers of Elastic For Shoes, It Was Honored at the World's Fair of 1893 . . . . . . . . . . . . . . . . . . . . . **9.00**

Major's Cement, 3 x 4¼", two American flags decorating display of 125 lb weights holding suspended object, full color, adv Major's Leather Cement–For Sale By Druggists and Crockery Dealers . . . . . . . . . . . . . . . . . . . . . . . . **9.00**

Merrick's Thread, 2¾ x 4½", two infant children, one beating Civil War type drum, other waving flag **5.00**

Certificate, Betsy Ross Flag Association, 1917, serial #38181, Series N, 12 x 16", C H Weisgerber painting . . . . . . . . . . . . . . . . . . . . . . . . . . **40.00**

Envelope

**Envelope, printed, 45 stars, $20.00.**

Civil War, angry eagle with shield hanging from his mouth and ribbon that reads "Liberty or Death," 34 large stars going around all four edges; each state has its name within its own star **28.00**

Printed semblances of Stars and Stripes with 45 stars covering address side .................. **20.00**

Post Card

Printed semblances of Stars and Stripes covering address side, picture of Wm H Taft for President ........................ **15.00**

Printed semblances of Stars and Stripes covering address side, picture of Wm H Taft for President, July 4, 1908, 46 stars, used **18.00**

Poster, 14 x 29", lithograph, History of Old Glory, Babbitt soap giveaway .......................... **145.00**

Print, Currier and Ives, The Star Spangled Banner, #481, 11¼ x 15½" . **165.00**

Sheet Music

*America Forever March,* E T Paull Music Co, Columbia draped in flag, shield, and eagle ........ **30.00**

*Miss America,* two step by J Edmund Barnum, lady with stars, red and white striped dress, large flowing flag ................ **20.00**

*Stars & Stripes Forever March,* John Phillip Sousa portrait in upper left hand corner, Old Glory in center, published by John Church Co .. **20.00**

*The Triumphant Banner,* E T Paull **25.00**

Song Sheet, published by Chas Magnus, NY, 5 x 8"

*The Female Auctioneer,* lady dressed in costume, waving flag **30.00**

*The Flag with The 34 Stars,* six verses and chorus, illus of soldiers marching with hand colored flag ................... **35.00**

*Traitor Spare That Flag,* four verses by Rev J P Lundy, illus of Columbia and her shield, waving flag . **35.00**

Thread Box, cov, black lacquer finish, decal, picture of spool of white thread and American flag, marked "Use Merricks Six Cord Thread For Hand and Machine Sewing"

2½ x 1½" ....................... **14.00**

3 x 1¾" ......................... **18.00**

Textile

Advertising Ribbon, Leonards Spool Silk, Northampton, MA, silk ..... **20.00**

Arm Band, WWII, 48 star flag, worn by paratrooper on D–Day invasion, two safety pins ................. **45.00**

Bandanna, 22 x 25", silk, flag inside wreath of 36 stars .............. **110.00**

Handkerchief, WWI, flags of US and France, embroidered

A Kiss from France ............. **5.00**

Souvenir France 1919 ........... **5.00**

To My Dear Sweetheart ......... **5.00**

Scarf, 17 x 15", silk, Chicago 1893 Expo, panorama of Expo overlaying American flag .................. **45.00**

# FLORENCE CERAMICS

**Collecting Hints:** Florence Ceramics pieces are well marked. Names of figures appear on the bottom of most pieces. A total of six backstamps were used, all containing a variation of the name of the company, location, and/or copyright mark.

Florence Ceramics is in the early stage of collectibility. As a result, stable national pricing has not yet been achieved. It pays to shop around.

Several figures have articulated fingers. In a few instances a figure was issued with both articulated and closed fingers. Figures with articulated fingers command a slight premium.

The company used a rich palette of colors. Look for figures with especially rich colors, elaborate decorations such as bows, flowers, lace, ringlets, and tresses, and gold trim. Aqua, beige, maroon, and gray, occasionally highlighted with green or maroon, are most commonly found on economy line figures. Yellow is a hard-to-find color.

**History:** In 1939, following the death of a young son, Florence Ward began working with clay as a way of dealing with her grief. Her first pieces were figures of children, individually shaped, decorated, and fired in a workshop in her Pasadena, California, garage. Untrained, she attended a ceramic class in 1942.

She continued to sell her pottery as a means of supplemental income during World War II. Her business grew. In 1946 the Florence Ceramics Company moved to a plant located on the east side of Pasadena. Clifford, Ward's husband, and Clifford, Junior, her son, joined the firm.

With the acquisition of increased production facilities, Florence Ceramics began exhibiting its wares at major Los Angeles gift shows. A worldwide business quickly developed. In 1949 a modern factory featuring a continuous tunnel kiln was opened at 74 South San Gabriel Boulevard in Pasadena. Over a hundred employees worked at the new plant.

Florence Ceramics produced semiporcelain figurines that featured historic couples in period costumes and ladies and gentlemen outfitted in costumes copied from late 19th century Godey fashions. Fictional characters and movie promotional figurines, e.g., Rhett and Scarlet from *Gone With The Wind*, were made. An inexpensive line of small figurines of children and figural vases also was manufactured.

Florence Ceramics offered a full line of period decorative accessories that included birds, busts, candle holders, clock frames, smoking sets, wall plaques, and wall pockets. Lamps utilizing some of the figural pieces were offered with custom shades.

In 1956 the company employed Betty Davenport Ford, a modeler, to develop a line of bisque–finished animal figures. The series included cats, dogs, doves, rabbits, and squirrels. A minimal airbrush decoration was added. Production lasted only two years.

Florence Ceramics was sold to Scripto Corporation following the death of Clifford Ward in 1964. Scripto retained the Florence Ceramics name but produced primarily advertising specialty wares. The plant closed in 1977.

**References:** Jack Chipman, *Collector's Encyclopedia of California Pottery,* Collector Books, 1992; Harvey Duke, *The Official Identification and Price Guide to Pottery and Porcelain, Seventh Edition* , House of Collectibles, 1989; Lois Lehner, *Lehner's Encyclopedia of U. S. Marks on Pottery, Porcelain & Clay,* Collector Books, 1988.

**Figure, Delia, maroon dress, gold trim, 7¾" h, $100.00.**

Figure
- Annabelle .......... **250.00**
- Birthday Girl, 9" h .......... **125.00**
- Blue Boy and Pinkey, pr .......... **500.00**
- Camille .......... **225.00**
- Charmain .......... **165.00**
- Choir Boy .......... **25.00**
- Delia .......... **100.00**
- Edith .......... **140.00**
- Elizabeth .......... **325.00**
- King Louis XIV and Marie Antoinette, pr .......... **550.00**
- Lady Pompadour .......... **300.00**
- Linda Lou, 8" h, pink .......... **75.00**
- Marilyn .......... **125.00**
- Martin .......... **175.00**
- Oriental Man and Woman, pr
  - Black and White .......... **125.00**
  - Green and Black .......... **125.00**
- Sarah, 7½" h, green .......... **75.00**
- Sue, 6" h, yellow .......... **50.00**
- Sue Ellen, 8" h, pink .......... **75.00**
- Victor .......... **200.00**
- Vivian .......... **350.00**

Plaque
- Mauve, green, and gray, pr .......... **225.00**
- Oval, gray, white, and green .......... **80.00**

# FOOTBALL CARDS

**Collecting Hints:** Condition is a key factor. Buy cards that are in very good condition, i.e., free from any creases and damaged corners. When possible strive to acquire cards in excellent to mint condition. Rob Erbe's *The American Premium Guide To Baseball Cards* (Books Americana, 1982) photographically illustrates in the introduction how to determine the condition of a card. What applies to a baseball card is equally true for a football card.

The football card market is just beginning to develop. Prices still are modest. Develop a collecting strategy, such as cards related to one year, one player, Heisman trophy winners, or one team. There are large numbers of cards available; a novice collector can be easily overwhelmed.

**History:** Football cards have been produced since the 1890s. However, it was not until 1933 that the first bubble gum football card appeared in the Goudey Sport Kings set. In 1935 National Chicle of Cambridge, Massachusetts, produced the first full set of gum cards devoted exclusively to football.

Both Leaf Gum of Chicago and Bowman Gum of Philadelphia produced sets of football cards in 1948. Leaf discontinued production after their 1949 issue. Bowman Gum continued until 1955.

Topps Chewing Gum entered the market in 1950 with its college stars set. Topps became a fixture in the football card market with its 1955 All–American set. From 1956 through 1963 Topps printed a card set of National Football League players, combining them with the American Football League players in 1961.

Topps produced sets with only American Football League players from 1964 to 1967. The Philadelphia Gum Company made National Football League card sets during this period. Beginning in 1968 and continuing to the present, Topps has produced sets of National Football League cards, the name adopted by the merger of the two leagues. Topps' only competition during this time came in 1970 and 1971 from Kellogg's Cereal, which issued sets of football related cards.

**References:** James Beckett, *The Sport Americana Football Card Price Guide, No. 9,* Edgewater Book Co., 1992; Jeff and Jane Fritsch, *The Sport Americana Team Football and Basketball Card Checklist No. 2,* Edgewater Book Co., 1993; Allan Kaye and Michael McKeever, *Football Card Price Guide, 1994,* Avon Books, 1993; Sports Collectors Digest, *Football, Basketball & Hockey Price Guide,* Krause Publications, 1991.

**Periodical:** *Sports Collectors Digest,* 700 E. State Street, Iola, WI 54990.

Bowman Gum Company

1948

| | |
|---|---|
| Complete Set (108) | **2,650.00** |
| 3 John Lujack | **110.00** |
| 23 Kon Kindt | **9.00** |
| 65 Mike Holovak | **20.00** |
| 72 Ted Fritsch Sr | **50.00** |
| 99 Harry Gilmer | **60.00** |
| Ernie Steele | **7.50** |

1951

| | |
|---|---|
| Complete Set (144) | **1,400.00** |
| Common Player | **6.25** |
| 20 Tom Landry | **200.00** |
| 75 Lou Groza | **30.00** |
| 96 Ernie Stautner | **35.00** |

1952, Large

| | |
|---|---|
| Complete Set (144) | **4,500.00** |
| Common Player (1–72) | **10.50** |
| Common Player (73–144) | **16.00** |
| 2 Otto Graham | **80.00** |
| 23 Gino Marchetti | **55.00** |
| 78 Bobby Layne | **65.00** |
| 137 Bob Waterfield | **42.50** |

1952, Small

| | |
|---|---|
| Complete Set (144) | **2,050.00** |
| Common Player (1–72) | **7.50** |
| Common Player (73–144) | **10.00** |
| 28 Kyle Rote | **20.00** |
| 46 Art Donovan | **37.50** |
| 85 Andy Robustelli | **37.50** |
| 142 Tom Landry | **125.00** |

1954

| | |
|---|---|
| Complete Set (128) | **750.00** |
| Common Player (1–64) | **3.00** |
| Common Player (65–96) | **6.00** |
| Common Player (97–128) | **3.00** |
| 23 George Blanda | **125.00** |
| 55 Frank Gifford | **60.00** |
| 118 Ernie Stautner | **9.00** |

1955

| | |
|---|---|
| Complete Set (160) | **675.00** |
| Common Player (1–64) | **2.00** |
| Common Player (65–160) | **2.50** |
| 14 Len Ford | **15.00** |
| 52 Pat Summerall | **22.50** |
| 101 Bob St Clair | **14.00** |

Collector's Edge, 1992

| | |
|---|---|
| Complete Set (175) | **6.00** |
| Common Player (1–175) | **.03** |

Fleer

1960

| | |
|---|---|
| Complete Set (132) | **300.00** |
| Common Player (1–132) | **1.00** |
| 7 Sid Gilman CO | **5.50** |
| 58 George Blanda | **16.00** |
| 118 Ron Mix | **16.00** |

1961

| | |
|---|---|
| Complete Set (220) | **600.00** |
| Common Player (1–132) | **1.00** |
| Common Player (133–220) | **1.75** |
| 11 Jim Brown | **60.00** |
| 59 John Brodie | **32.50** |
| 88 Bart Starr | **18.00** |
| 188 Tom Flores | **8.00** |
| 220 Sid Youngelman | **3.50** |

1963

| | |
|---|---|
| Complete Set (89) | **750.00** |
| Common Player (1–88) | **3.00** |
| 36 George Blanda | **25.00** |
| 62 Jim Otto | **12.00** |
| 72 Lance Alworth | **75.00** |

1990

| | |
|---|---|
| Complete Set (400) | **6.00** |
| Common Player (1–400) | **.01** |
| 5 Roger Craig | **.05** |
| 113 Jim Kelly | **.17** |
| 249 Marcus Allen | **.05** |
| 299 Mike Singletary | **.04** |
| 397 Super Bowl MVP's | **.10** |

1991

| | |
|---|---|
| Complete Set (432) | **5.00** |
| Common Player, (1–432) | **.01** |
| 22 Harold Green | **.07** |
| 110 Bo Jackson | **.10** |
| 228 Troy Aikman | **.17** |
| 363 Jerry Rice | **.17** |
| 453 Emmitt Smith | **.25** |

Leaf

1948

| | |
|---|---|
| Complete Set (98) | **2,650.00** |
| Common Player (1–49) | **7.50** |
| Common Player (1–98) | **37.50** |

1949

| | |
|---|---|
| Complete Set (49) | **650.00** |
| Common Player (1–49) | **8.00** |

Philadelphia

1964

| | |
|---|---|
| Complete Set (198) | **425.00** |
| Common Player (1–198) | **.65** |
| 51 Don Meredith | **15.00** |
| 79 Bart Starr | **14.00** |
| 117 Frank Gifford | **22.50** |
| 161 Jim Johnson | **2.10** |

1966

| | |
|---|---|
| Complete Set (198) | **425.00** |
| Common Player (1–198) | **.60** |
| 38 Gale Sayers | **100.00** |
| 69 Alex Karras | **4.00** |
| 114 Fran Tarkenton | **15.00** |
| 187 Bobby Mitchell | **2.50** |

Score

1989

- Complete Set (330) **90.00**
- Common Player (1–330) **.04**
- 1 Joe Montana **1.00**
- 43 Christian Okoye **.60**
- 105 Mark Rypien **10.00**
- 152 Andre Reed **.35**
- 211 Thurman Thomas **17.50**
- 225 Steve Largent **.35**

1990

- Complete Set (660) **6.00**
- Common Player (1–660) **.01**
- 10 Bo Jackson **.17**
- 136A Vai Sikahema **.30**
- 608 Blair Thomas **.20**
- 629 Eric Green **.22**

Topps Chewing Gum Inc

1956

- Complete Set (121) **750.00**
- Common Player (1–120) **2.50**
- 28 Chuck Bednarik **8.50**
- 61 Washington Redskins Team Card SP **25.00**
- 78 Elroy Hirsch **8.00**
- 109 Dale Atkeson SP **6.00**
- 115 Al Carmichael **2.50**

1958

- Complete Set (132) **600.00**
- Common Player (1–132) **1.25**
- 10 Lenny Moore **6.00**
- 42 Emlen Tunnell **4.00**
- 59 Mike McCormack **3.25**
- 90 Sonny Jurgensen **50.00**

1960

- Complete Set (132) **325.00**
- Common Player (1–132) **.80**
- 1 John Unitas **30.00**
- 54 Paul Hornung UER **15.00**
- 93 Bobby Layne **10.00**
- 113 Y A Tittle **12.50**

1962

- Complete Set (176) **700.00**
- Common Player (1–176) **1.00**
- Common Player SP **2.50**
- 17 Mike Ditka **55.00**
- 49 Dallas Cowboys Team Card **3.25**
- 152 John Brodie **7.50**
- 176 Checklist **10.00**

1964

- Complete Set (176) **600.00**
- Common Player (1–176) **1.25**
- Common Player SP **3.00**
- 68 George Blanda **30.00**
- 121 Don Maynard **10.50**
- 159 John Hadl **10.00**

1966

- Complete Set (132) **125.00**
- Common Player (1–132) **1.60**
- 26 Jack Kemp **60.00**
- 67 Len Dawson **10.50**
- 104 Fred Biletnikoff **25.00**

1968

- Complete Set (219) **300.00**
- Common Player (1–131) **.35**
- Common Player (132–219) **.50**
- 65 Joe Namath **40.00**
- 100 John Unitas **13.50**
- 127 Dick Butkus **16.00**
- 196 Bob Griese **45.00**

1970

- Complete Set (263) **225.00**
- Common Player (91–132) **.25**
- Common Player (133–263) **.35**
- 25 Jan Stenerud **5.00**
- 30 Bart Starr **9.00**
- 80 Fran Tarkenton **10.00**
- 114 Bubba Smith **12.50**
- 247 Fred Dryer **8.00**

**Topps, 1970, O. J. Simpson, #90, $75.00.**

1972

- Complete Set (351) **800.00**
- Common Player (1–132) **.22**
- Common Player (133-n263) **.30**
- Common Player (264–351) **7.50**
- 13 John Riggins **12.50**
- 101 L C Greenwood **6.00**
- 122 Roger Staubach IA **8.50**
- 235 George Blanda **4.25**
- 331 Mercury Morris **11.00**

1975

- Complete Set (528) **145.00**
- Common Player (1–528) **.15**
- 300 Franco Harris **5.50**
- 380 Ken Stabler **1.75**

1977

- Complete Set (528) **120.00**
- Common Player (1–528) **.07**
- 74 Joe Theisman **1.60**
- 177 Steve Largent **30.00**
- 245 Terry Bradshaw **2.25**

1979

- Complete Set (528) **60.00**
- Common Player (1–528) **.04**

1981
- Complete Set (528) ............. **110.00**
- Common Player (1–528) ........ **.03**

1983
- Complete Set (396) ............. **30.00**
- Common Player (1–396) ........ **.03**
- Common Player DP ............ **.02**

1985
- Complete Set (396) ............. **40.00**
- Common Player (1–396) ........ **.02**

1987
- Complete Set (396) ............. **25.00**
- Common Player (1–396) ........ **.02**

1990
- Complete Set (528) ............. **6.25**
- Common Player (1–528) ........ **.01**

# FRANCISCAN DINNERWARE

**Collecting Hints:** The emphasis on Franciscan art pottery and dinnerware has overshadowed the many other collectible lines from Gladding, McBean and Company. Keep your eye open for Tropico Art Ware, made between 1934 and 1937. This company made some very stylistic bird baths, florist vases, flowerpots, garden urns, and hotel cigarette snuffers. Catalina Art Ware (1937–41) also is attracting collector attention.

Most buyers of Franciscan's Big 3 patterns (Apple, Desert Rose, and Ivy) are seeking replacement pieces for sets currently in use. As a result, prices tend to be somewhat inflated, especially for hollow pieces. Keep in mind that these patterns enjoyed strong national popularity.

Early Franciscan lines are in the Bauer and Homer Laughlin Fiesta tradition. Stress shape and color as the principal means of separating them from their more popular counterparts. These pieces are more commonly found on the West Coast than in the East. Current collectible West Coast trendiness compensates for the scarcity in the East.

**History:** Gladding, McBean and Company, Los Angeles, California, produced the Franciscan dinnerware patterns at their Glendale, California, pottery. The company began in 1875 as a manufacturer of sewer pipe and terra cotta tile. In 1922 Gladding, McBean and Company acquired Tropico Pottery in Glendale, and the West Coast properties of American Encaustic Tile in 1933.

In 1934 the company began producing dinnerware and art pottery marketed under the name Franciscan Ware. Franciscan dinnerware had talc (magnesium silicate) rather than clay as a base. Early pieces used plain shapes and bright primary colors. Early lines include Coronado, El Patio, Metropolitan, Montecito, Padua, and Rancho. As the line developed, much more graceful shapes were introduced along with pastel colors.

Three patterns are considered Franciscan classics. The Apple pattern with its embossed body, hand decoration, and underglaze staining was introduced in 1940. The Desert Rose pattern (1941) is the most popular dinnerware pattern ever manufactured in the United States. Ivy, the third of the Big 3, was first made in 1948.

Franciscan comes in three distinct lines: (1) masterpiece china, a quality translucent ceramic; (2) earthenware, a cream–colored ware found in a variety of decal and hand decorated patterns; and, (3) whitestone or white earthenware.

Gladding, McBean and Company became Interpace Corporation in 1963. In 1979 Josiah Wedgwood and Sons, Ltd., acquired the company. In 1986 the Glendale plant was closed, marking the end of American production.

**References:** Jack Chipman, *Collector's Encyclopedia of California Pottery,* Collector Books, 1992; Lois Lehner, *Lehner's Encyclopedia of U. S. Marks on Pottery, Porcelain & Clay,* Collector Books, 1988.

**APPLE.** Introduced in 1940. Embossed earthenware body, hand decorated and underglazed stained.

- Ashtray, 9" l ........................ **30.00**
- Batter Jug ......................... **200.00**
- Bowl
  - 5" d, fruit ....................... **10.00**
  - 6" d, cereal ..................... **12.00**
  - 7½" d ........................... **20.00**
- Butter, cov ........................ **45.00**
- Candle Holder ..................... **40.00**
- Casserole, cov
  - 1 qt ............................ **125.00**
  - 1½ qt ........................... **85.00**
- Cigarette Box ..................... **85.00**
- Coffeepot, cov .................... **125.00**
- Compote, large .................... **65.00**
- Cookie Jar ........................ **190.00**
- Creamer .......................... **25.00**
- Creamer and Sugar, individual size ... **50.00**
- Cup and Saucer .................... **20.00**
- Demitasse Cup and Saucer .......... **42.00**
- Eggcup ........................... **15.00**
- Gravy Boat, underplate ............. **45.00**
- Marmalade, cov ................... **95.00**
- Mug, 7 oz ........................ **95.00**
- Pitcher
  - Milk, 1 qt ....................... **80.00**
  - Water, 2 qt ..................... **125.00**
- Plate
  - 6" d, bread and butter ............ **6.00**
  - 8" d, salad ...................... **12.00**
  - 9½" d, dinner ................... **16.00**
  - 10½" d ......................... **18.00**

Platter
- 12″ l .......... **38.00**
- 14″ l .......... **42.00**

Salad Bowl, large .......... **95.00**
Soup Bowl, 5½″ d, ftd .......... **25.00**
Sugar, cov .......... **35.00**
Teapot .......... **100.00**
Tidbit Server
- 2 tiers .......... **42.00**
- 3 tiers .......... **75.00**

Tumbler, 6 oz .......... **40.00**
Tureen, small, leaf handle .......... **395.00**
Vegetable Bowl, 9″ l .......... **45.00**
Wine Glass .......... **18.00**

**CORONADO SWIRL.** Dinnerware line produced from 1936 until 1956. Made in fifteen different colors with both satin and glossy glazes.

Celery Dish, yellow, satin .......... **15.00**
Cream Soup, coral, satin .......... **22.00**
Creamer, gray, satin .......... **22.00**
Cup and Saucer, maroon, glossy .......... **18.00**
Demitasse Creamer and Sugar
- Gray, satin .......... **15.00**
- Turquoise, glossy .......... **15.00**

Demitasse Cup and Saucer
- Coral, glossy .......... **35.00**
- White, satin .......... **35.00**
- Yellow, satin .......... **15.00**

Demitasse Pot, turquoise, glossy .......... **75.00**
Gravy, attached underplate, yellow, satin .......... **22.00**
Plate
- 6″ d, turquoise, glossy .......... **3.00**
- 7½″ d, coral, satin .......... **5.00**
- 10″ d, turquoise, glossy .......... **8.00**
- Chop, yellow, satin .......... **25.00**

Teacup, maroon, glossy .......... **9.00**
Vegetable, oval, yellow, satin .......... **22.00**

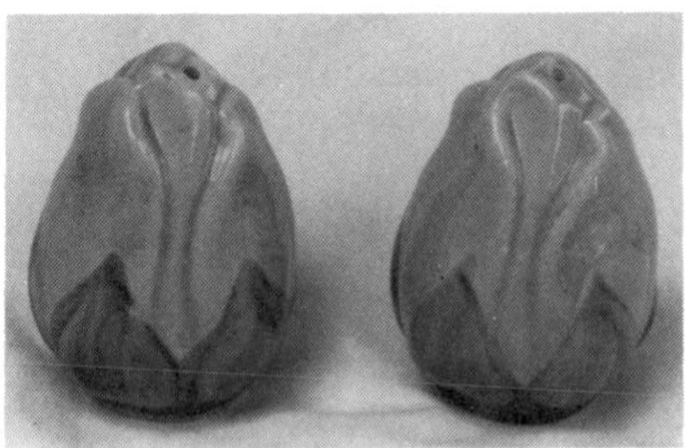

**Desert Rose, salt and pepper shakers, pr, rosebud, 2¾″ h, $14.00.**

**DESERT ROSE.** Introduced in 1941. Embossed earthenware with hand-painted underglazed decoration.

Ashtray, large .......... **65.00**
Baby Dish .......... **85.00**
Bone Dish, crescent shape .......... **27.00**
Bud Vase .......... **195.00**
Butter Dish, cov, ¼ lb .......... **40.00**
Cereal Bowl, 6″ d .......... **20.00**
Cigarette Box .......... **125.00**
Coffeepot .......... **125.00**
Compote .......... **195.00**
Creamer and Sugar, cov .......... **50.00**
Cup and Saucer .......... **15.00**
Demitasse Cup and Saucer .......... **35.00**
Fruit Bowl, 5″ d .......... **10.00**
Gravy .......... **45.00**
Marmalade .......... **125.00**
Mug, 12 oz .......... **45.00**
Napkin Ring .......... **50.00**
Pitcher, milk .......... **85.00**
Plate
- 6½″ d, bread and butter .......... **6.00**
- 8″ d, salad .......... **11.00**
- 9½″ d, luncheon .......... **12.00**
- 10½″ d, dinner .......... **15.00**
- 12″ d, chop .......... **45.00**
- 14″ d .......... **50.00**

Platter, 14″ l .......... **15.00**
Relish Dish
- Oval, 10¼″ l .......... **25.00**
- Three Part, 11″ l .......... **50.00**

Salt and Pepper Shakers, pr
- Rosebud .......... **14.00**
- Tall .......... **45.00**

Sherbet, ftd .......... **15.00**
Soup, flat .......... **14.00**
Syrup .......... **125.00**
Teapot .......... **115.00**
Tumbler, 10 oz .......... **40.00**
Vegetable Bowl
- 8″ l .......... **40.00**
- 9″ l .......... **45.00**

Wine Glass .......... **18.00**

**DUET.** Introduced in 1956.

Ashtray, individual .......... **12.00**
Butter Dish, cov .......... **25.00**
Canister, 10″ h .......... **95.00**
Creamer and Sugar, cov .......... **18.00**
Cup and Saucer .......... **7.00**
Gravy, underplate .......... **15.00**
Hostess Plate, cup ring .......... **20.00**
Plate
- 6″ d, bread and butter .......... **5.00**
- 7¼″ d, salad .......... **9.00**
- 10″ d, dinner .......... **12.00**
- 13″ d, chop .......... **18.00**

Platter, 15″ l .......... **20.00**
Relish, 7″ l, handled .......... **10.00**
Salt and Pepper Shakers, pr .......... **15.00**
Vegetable Bowl, divided .......... **22.00**

**IVY.** Introduced in 1948. Embossed earthenware with hand-painted underglazed decoration.

Ashtray, individual .................. **40.00**
Butter Dish, ¼ lb .................. **30.00**
Cereal Bowl, 7½" d ................ **25.00**
Compote .......................... **95.00**
Cup and Saucer, jumbo ............. **65.00**
Fruit Bowl, 5" d .................... **8.00**
Gravy, underplate .................. **30.00**
Mug, 4¼" h ........................ **22.00**
Pickle Dish, 10½" l ................. **35.00**
Pitcher, water ...................... **125.00**
Plate
  6" d, bread and butter ............ **6.00**
  14" d, chop ..................... **85.00**
Platter
  Oval, 13" l ...................... **45.00**
  Turkey .......................... **225.00**
Salad Bowl, 11¼" d ................ **85.00**
Salt and Pepper Shakers, pr .......... **30.00**
Sherbet ........................... **12.00**
Soup Bowl, flat .................... **30.00**
Sugar, cov ......................... **35.00**
Tea Tile ........................... **55.00**
Tumbler, Libbey, hp dec ............ **14.00**
Vegetable Bowl, 8¼" l .............. **40.00**

**STARBURST.** Introduced in 1954.

Ashtray
  Individual ....................... **20.00**
  Large, oval ...................... **65.00**
Baby Dish ......................... **75.00**
Bone Dish, crescent shape .......... **25.00**
Butter Dish, cov ................... **30.00**
Casserole, small .................... **35.00**
Creamer and Sugar, cov ............. **30.00**
Cup and Saucer .................... **18.00**
Fruit Bowl ......................... **12.00**
Gravy, ladle ....................... **45.00**
Mustard Jar ........................ **85.00**
Oil and Vinegar Cruets, pr .......... **100.00**
Pitcher
  Large ........................... **95.00**
  Medium ......................... **75.00**
Plate
  6" d, bread and butter ............ **8.00**
  7½" d, salad ..................... **10.00**
  10" d, dinner .................... **15.00**
Platter, oval
  13" l ............................ **25.00**
  15" l ............................ **22.00**
Relish
  6½" w, triangular, divided ......... **25.00**
  7½" w, handled .................. **25.00**
Salad Bowl
  Individual ....................... **45.00**
  Serving ......................... **85.00**
Salt and Pepper Shakers, pr, tall ...... **60.00**
Soup Bowl, 7¼" d .................. **15.00**
Teapot ............................ **195.00**
Vegetable Bowl
  Oval, 8" l ....................... **20.00**
  Round, 8¼" d, divided ............ **24.00**

**TRIO.** Square and rectangular shaped dinnerware from the Metropolitan line. Produced during the 1950s, Trio is decorated with a stylized leaf decal.

Bowl, fruit ........................ **9.00**
Cup and Saucer .................... **12.50**
Gravy ............................ **10.00**
Plate
  6" d, bread and butter ............ **6.00**
  8" d, salad ...................... **10.00**
  10" d, dinner .................... **15.00**
Platter, 14" l ....................... **16.00**
Saucer ............................ **4.00**
Vegetable Bowl
  Divided ......................... **18.00**
  Open ............................ **18.00**

# FRATERNAL ORGANIZATIONS

**Collecting Hints:** Fraternal items break down into three groups. The first focuses on the literature, pins and badges, and costume paraphernalia which belonged to individual members of each organization. This material can be found easily. The second group is the ornamentation and furniture used in lodge halls for ceremonial purposes. Many of these items were made locally and are highly symbolic. Folk art collectors have latched on to them and have driven prices artificially high.

The third group relates to the regional and national conventions of the fraternal organizations. Each meeting generally produces a number of specialized souvenir items. These conventions are one of the few times when public visibility is drawn to a fraternal group; hence, convention souvenirs are the most commonly found items.

Concentrate on one fraternal group. Since so much emphasis has been placed on Masonic and Shriner material, new collectors are urged to focus on one of the other organizations.

**History:** Benevolent and secret societies played an important part in American society from the late 18th century to the mid–20th century. Groups ranged from Eagles, Elks, Moose, and Orioles to Odd Fellows, Redmen, and Woodmen. These secret societies had lodges or meeting halls, secret ceremonies, ritualistic materials, and souvenir items from conventions and regional meetings.

Initially the societies were organized to aid members or their families in times of distress or death. They evolved from this purpose into important social clubs by the late 19th century. Women's auxiliaries were organized. In the 1950s, with the arrival of civil rights, an attack occurred on the secretiveness and often discriminatory practices of these societies. Americans had greater outlets for leisure and social life, and less need for the benevolent aspects of the groups. The fraternal movement, with the exception of the Masonic order, suffered serious membership loss. Many local chapters closed and sold their lodge halls. This has resulted in many items arriving in the antiques market.

**Note:** This category does not include the souvenir and other items related to the many service clubs of the 20th century, such as the Lions, Rotary, etc., who replaced the focus of many of the fraternal group members. Items from these service groups are not yet viewed as collectible by the general marketplace.

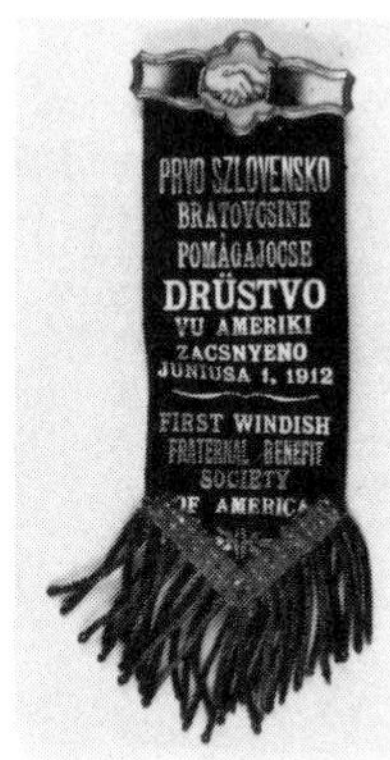


**First Windish Fraternal Benefit Society of America, pin, brass and celluloid, two ribbons, one black with silver lettering, other red, white, and green with gold lettering, gold and silver wire fringe, 1912, 2¼" w, 7¼" l, $15.00.**

Benevolent & Protective Order of Elks, BPOE
- Ashtray, brass, three elks illus . . . . . . **18.00**
- Badge, 1920 Chicago 56th Annual Reunion . . . . . . **15.00**
- Book, *National Memorial,* 1931, color illus . . . . . . **30.00**
- Flask, 4" h, elks tooth, opaque white **80.00**
- Note Pad and Pencil, Ladies Night, 1916 . . . . . . **35.00**
- Pinback Button
  - Elks Harvest Festival, AERIE 102, Nov–19–08, red, white, and blue, eagle illus . . . . . . **10.00**
  - Member Lodge No 481 State Ass'n BPOE, Belleville, 1921, multicolored, elk on hind legs illus . . . . . . **5.00**
- Pitcher, 6½" h, Louisville, 1911 . . . . **35.00**
- Plate, litho tin, Mt Hood, lodge, and elk by river illus, 1912 . . . . . . **75.00**
- Spoon, "Elks" and Elks building, Joplin, MO on bowl, "BPOE" on handle . . . . . . **18.00**
- Stein . . . . . . **85.00**
- Tie Tack, SS, jeweled dec . . . . . . **28.00**

Independent Order of Odd Fellows, IOOF
- Badge, Rebekah Lodge, 1894 memorial . . . . . . **25.00**
- Banner, 33 x 58", felt, red, white, and blue, 1910 . . . . . . **25.00**
- Certificate, 1916 . . . . . . **8.00**
- License Tag, multicolored logo, orig package . . . . . . **10.00**
- Mug . . . . . . **35.00**
- Pamphlet, Odd Fellows Fraternal Accident Association of America, 8 pgs, 1891 . . . . . . **4.00**
- Pin, Alpha Lodge No 611, hanging oval medal . . . . . . **15.00**
- Pinback Button
  - Field Day Point of Pines, June 29, 1907, red and white, chain link and eye dec . . . . . . **4.00**
  - One Hundredth Anniversary, Independent Order of Odd Fellows, 1818–1919, red, white, and blue, Thomas Widley photo, chain links, eye, and American flag . . . . . . **5.00**
- Souvenir Book, 1922 Convention . . . **25.00**
- Token, Lexington, KY, 1916 . . . . . . **15.00**
- Watch Fob, 94th Anniversary April 12, 1913 . . . . . . **25.00**

Knights of Pythias
- Pinback Button, Founder of the Order Knights of Pythias, Justus H Rathbone, black and white, Rathbone photo . . . . . . **4.00**
- Shaving Mug . . . . . . **160.00**
- Whirligig, 11⅝" h, carved Pythias . . **450.00**

Knights Templar
- Badge, brass link, enameled, 29th Triennial Conclave of Grand Encampment, 1904 . . . . . . **25.00**
- Book, *Grand Encampment of Knights Templar,* 1895, 160 pgs . . . . . . **40.00**
- Pinback Button, Ascalon Commandery No 59, Pittsburgh, PA, 1906, multicolored, chicken standing on sword and branch . . . . . . **12.00**
- Plate, 8" d, Pittsburgh Commandery, 1903, china . . . . . . **45.00**
- Tumbler, 4" h, 36th Conclave, glass **75.00**

Loyal Order of Moose
- Clock, figural, moose . . . . . . **50.00**
- Straight Razor, The Mighty, blade with

etched crown and two flags, moose and LOOM on handle .......... **15.00**

Masonic

Badge, brass link, 32nd Degree Mason, engraved name, dark red and blue enameled pendant, early 1900s ........................ **25.00**

Book, *History of the Most Ancient & Honorable Fraternity of Free 7 Accepted Masons in New York From the Earliest Date,* Charles T McClenachan, 1888, Grand Lodge, New York .................... **18.00**

Bowl, 5" d, El Riad Temple, 1911, brass ........................ **30.00**

Certificate, Third Degree Freemason, Penobscot Lodge, dated August 8, 1863 ........................ **165.00**

Cookie Mold, 4⅞" d, cast iron ..... **25.00**

Fez, Mohassen .................. **25.00**

**Masonic, watch fob, gold and enamel, $33.00. Photograph courtesy of Morton M. Goldberg Auction Galleries.**

Flask, aqua, qt, eagle dec, GIV–42 . **25.00**

Goblet, St Paul 1908, glass ........ **65.00**

Ice Cream Mold, 5½" d, pewter, figural emblem .................. **15.00**

Letter Opener, metal, symbols ..... **20.00**

Mug, china, Rising Star Lodge, 1903 **40.00**

Pinback Button

Bound For Washington, Morocco Temple 1900, From the Hot Sands of Florida, multicolored, man riding alligator ........... **15.00**

Hello Rube, Meet Me At The Masonic Fair & Bazaar, Nov 14–19, 1910, black and white ........ **8.00**

Oriental Troy, NY, compliments of International Shirts & Collar Co, multicolored ................ **12.00**

Pitcher, 12" h, 60th Anniversary, Newark, NJ, 1913 .............. **95.00**

Plate, 8" d, 64th Annual Conclave, Toledo, emblem border, marked "K & K," 1906 .................... **75.00**

Spoon, SS, Chicago Temple on bowl, Masonic emblem on handle ..... **25.00**

Trivet, brass, symbol .............. **35.00**

Watch Fob, J E King, Rockford, IL, 1919 ........................ **22.00**

Order of the Eastern Star

Demitasse Cup and Saucer, porcelain **18.00**

Jewelry

Earrings, pr, 1" d, enamel emblem center, two double rows of rhinestones ...................... **45.00**

Pin, 14K gold ................. **35.00**

Ring, Past Matron, star shape stone, diamond center, gold ......... **135.00**

Shrine

Champagne Glass, 4½" h, New Orleans–Syria, alligator dec, 1910 .. **90.00**

Change Tray .................... **45.00**

Cup and Saucer, Los Angeles, 1906, glass .......................... **70.00**

Goblet, Pittsburgh, PA, 1908, ruby flashed ....................... **65.00**

Medal, St Paul, MN, 1908 ........ **12.00**

Mug, Syria Temple, Pittsburgh, 1895, ceramic, gold dec .............. **110.00**

Nodder ........................ **45.00**

Pinback Button, Mystic Shrine Day, Pan–American, August 31, 1901, black, white, and red, buffalo wearing hat .................. **15.00**

Plate, ceramic, man with bandaged face ......................... **25.00**

Post Card, A Little Shriner Wearing His Frat Pin, child wearing shrine hat and diaper, copyright 1908 ... **10.00**

Tumbler, Pittsburgh, 1918, milk glass **50.00**

# FROGS

**Collecting Hints:** The frog is a popular theme in art work, but often enjoys a secondary rather than a primary position. As with other animal collectibles, the frog collector competes with collectors from other subject areas for the same object.

The frog has lent its name to several items—from flower frog to railroad frog switches to the attachment device holding a sword scabbard to a belt. True collectors usually include examples of these in their collection.

**History:** A frog is a small, tailless animal with bulging eyes and long back legs. The first frogs appeared about 180 million years ago; today there are more than 2,000 species.

Throughout history frogs have been a source of superstition. One myth says frogs fall from the sky during rain.

The frog in character form has appeared in cartoons, on television and in movies. Flip the Frog is one example. The Buster Brown show featured Froggy the Gremlin. Kermit the Frog is the star of the Muppets, both on television and in the movies.

**Collectors' Club:** The Frog Pond, P. O. Box 193, Beech Grove, IN 46107.

**Post Card, comic, $10.00.**

Ashtray, double, marked "Brush" ..... **50.00**
Chocolate Mold, tin, 5" h ........... **25.00**
Clicker, large, gold colored .......... **15.00**
Cookie Jar, ceramic, California Original #906 .......................... **35.00**
Dish, cov, dark amber, figural ........ **50.00**
Doorstop, cast iron, traces of old green paint, 4¾" l ..................... **55.00**
Figure
  Clay, prime male, marked "What Cheer, Iowa" .................. **75.00**
  Metal, large blue applied eyes, Salviati, paper label ............... **175.00**
  Porcelain, dressed, Occupied Japan **40.00**
  Sewer Tile
    4¼" l ......................... **220.00**
    5¼" l, black glass marble eyes, small chips, one back leg repaired ...................... **165.00**
Fish Bowl Stand, Art Deco style frog wearing tuxedo and top hat, ceramic **165.00**
Flower Frog, figural, white, green and yellow spray glaze, American Art Potteries .......................... **12.00**
Paperweight, "I Croak for the Jackson Wagon," old green paint, polychrome dec, 5¼" l ..................... **275.00**
Planter, frog on lily pad
  McCoy, 7½" w .................. **40.00**
  Niloak, 4" l ...................... **35.00**
Pull Toy, Slinky Frog, green hard plastic frog, metal wire mid section, 6" l, orig box, 1960s ..................... **10.00**
Salt and Pepper Shakers, pr, china, green, Japan ..................... **5.00**
Sign
  Buckeye Camp, Modern Cottages–Rooms, cutout plywood, orig polychrome paint, 35½" h .......... **185.00**
  Vanity Fair Cigarettes, paper, monochromatic frog image, Major & Knapp, 8½" w, 10½" h ......... **145.00**
Snowdome, figural, plastic, sitting up, 2½" d ball in middle, frogs and grass scene, "Puerto Rico" on plaque, 1980s ......................... **10.00**
Stuffed Toy, green velvet back, white satin underside, 9" l, c1960 ....... **12.50**
Trade Card, Ponk's Extract ........... **6.00**

# FRUIT JARS

**Collecting Hints:** Old canning jars can be found at flea markets, household sales, and antiques shows. Interest in fruit jars is stable.

Some collectors base their collections on a specific geographical area, others on one manufacturer or one color. Another possible way to collect fruit jars is by patent date. Over 50 different types bear a patent date of 1858. Note: The patent date does not mean the jar was made in that year.

**History:** An innovative Philadelphia glass maker, Thomas W. Dyott, began promoting his glass canning jars in 1829. John Landis Mason patented the screw type canning jar on November 30, 1858. The progress of the American glass industry and manufacturing processes can be studied through fruit jars. Early handmade jars show bits of local history.

Many ways were devised to close the jars securely. Lids of fruit jars can be a separate collectible, but most collectors feel it is more desirous to have a complete fruit jar. Closures can be as simple as cork or wax seal. Other closures include zinc lids, glass, wire bails, metal screw bands, and today's rubber sealed metal lids.

**References:** Alice M. Creswick, *Red Book No. 6: The Collector's Guide To Old Fruit Jars,* published by author, 1990; Dick Roller, *Standard Fruit Jar Reference,* published by author, 1987; Dick Roller, *Supplementary Price Guide to Standard Fruit Jar Reference,* published by author, 1987; Bill Schroeder, *1000 Fruit Jars: Priced And Illustrated, 5th Edition,* Collector Books, 1987.

**Periodical:** *Fruit Jar Newsletter,* 364 Gregory Avenue, West Orange, NJ 07052.

**Collectors' Club:** Ball Collectors Club, 22203 Doncaster, Riverview, MI 48192.

**Note:** Fruit Jars listed below are machine made unless otherwise noted.

All Right, aqua, qt, metal disc, wire clamp ......................... **75.00**
Anderson Preserving Co, clear, qt, metal lid ............................ **12.00**

**Mason's, aqua, qt., emb "Patent Nov 30th 1858," $8.00.**

Atlas E–2, seal, half pint, wire, glass lid **10.00**
Ball
Eclipse, Wide Mouth, clear, qt, glass lid, wire bail .................. **2.50**
Ideal, aqua, pt, glass lid, wire bail .. **2.00**
Mason, aqua, qt, emb backwards "s," zinc lid ....................... **4.00**
Perfection, aqua, qt, glass lid, zinc band, handmade ............... **18.50**
Bamberger's Mason Jar, blue, qt, glass lid, wire bail .................... **10.00**
Brockway Clear–Vu Mason, clear ½ pt, metal lid ....................... **2.50**
Calcutt's, clear, qt, glass screw lid, handmade ....................... **35.00**
Clarks Peerless, aqua, pt, glass lid .... **8.00**
Crown Mason, clear, qt, zinc lid ..... **1.50**
Cunningham & Ihmsen, aqua, qt, wax seal ........................... **15.00**
Dillon, aqua, qt, wax seal ........... **12.00**
Dunkley, clear, qt, hinged glass lid ... **5.00**
Easy Vacuum Jar, clear, qt, glass lid, wire clamp ..................... **25.00**
Everlasting Jar, Improved, clear, qt, glass lid, toggles ...................... **15.00**
Franklin Fruit Jar, aqua, qt, glass lid .. **3.50**
Gem, Wallaceburg, clear, pt, glass lid, screw band ..................... **5.00**
Globe, green, pt, glass lid, lever bail . **30.00**
Hansee's Palace Home Jar, clear, qt, glass lid ....................... **50.00**
Hazel Preserve Jar, clear, qt, glass lid . **8.50**
I G Co, aqua, qt, wax seal .......... **25.00**
Independent Jar, clear, qt, glass lid ... **35.00**
Jewell Jar, clear, ½ gallon, glass lid, screw band ..................... **8.00**
Johnson & Johnson, NJ, amber, qt, glass lid ............................ **20.00**
Keystone, clear, pt, zinc lid .......... **10.00**
Knox Mason, clear, qt, zinc lid ...... **4.00**
Leotric, aqua, ½ gallon, glass lid, wire bail ........................... **10.00**
Lustre, aqua, pt, glass lid, wire bail ... **8.00**
Mallinger, clear, qt, zinc lid ......... **4.00**
Mason
Improved, green, qt, glass lid, screw band ......................... **2.00**
Iron Cross, quart, blue ............ **12.00**
Keystone in circle, Patent Nov 30, 1858, green, qt, zinc lid ........ **8.00**
Root, aqua, qt, zinc lid ........... **4.00**
Mid West, Canadian Made, clear, qt, glass lid, screw band ............. **5.00**
Norge, clear, qt, glass lid, metal band **10.00**
Opler Brothers, clear, qt, glass lid, wire bail ........................... **5.00**
Peoria Pottery, gray pottery, brown glaze, pt ........................ **20.00**
Perfect Seal, clear, qt, rubber seal .... **3.00**
Presto Wide Mouth, clear, ½ pt, glass lid, wire bail ................... **2.50**
Rhodes, Kalamazoo, MI, aqua, pt, zinc lid ............................ **6.00**
Samco Genuine Mason, clear, 3 gallon, zinc lid ......................... **15.00**
SC & CO, Mason, half gallon ........ **10.00**
Standard, aqua, qt, wax seal ......... **20.00**
Tropical Canners, clear, pt, zinc lid ... **4.00**
Universal, clear, qt, zinc lid ......... **5.00**
White Crown Mason, aqua, qt, zinc lid **10.00**
Woodbury, aqua, glass lid, metal clip . **25.00**
Young's Pat May 27, 1902, stoneware, brown neck, metal clamp lid ...... **20.00**

# GAMBLING CHIPS, CHECKS, AND TOKENS

**Collecting Hints:** Almost all the different types of casino "money" used today are collected. In the gaming industry, "checks" refers to chips with a stated value. "Chips" do not have a stated value. Their value is determined at the time of play.

Two other collectible categories are free play and drink tokens. Gaming tokens have been issued in values from 50¢ to $500.

Many collectors display chips, checks, and tokens in albums similar to those used by coin collectors.

**History:** Gambling chips developed as a substitute for money in the riverboat days of America's frontier. The earliest chips, made from bone or ivory, are quite rare and command high values.

In the early 1880s clay composition materials were used to manufacture chips. Most of the chips of this period do not have values, but can be found with a wide variety of designs. In the early 1920s better technology produced a high quality heat compressed chip with inlaid designs.

Checks with stated values became popular as gambling became more established. Later, club names and addresses were added. Modern chips and checks may include different shaped inlays in the center and color edge spots called "inserts." Molds with designs were impressed into the checks.

Gaming tokens were introduced in 1965 to replace silver dollars for use in slot machines and on table games.

**References:** *Antique Gambling Chips*, Past Pleasures, 1984; *Harvey's Guide to Collecting Gaming Checks & Chips*, High Sierra Numismatics, 1984.

**Collectors' Club:** Casino Chips & Gaming Tokens Collector Club, 5410 Banbury Drive, Worthington, OH 43235.

## CHIPS AND CHECKS

CHIPCO molded check .......... **3.00**
Clay molded check .......... **4.00**
Coin inlay check .......... **7.50**
Crest & seal check .......... **15.00**
Inlaid clay check .......... **3.00**
Inlaid litho plain chip .......... **7.50**
Metal inlay check .......... **20.00**
Plastic molded slug core check .......... **5.00**
Roulette chip .......... **2.00**
Scrimshawed ivory chip .......... **35.00**

## GAMING TOKENS

1965–1989 $ value .......... **2.00**
1967 Sterling $5 .......... **12.00**
Proofs 1965–1969 .......... **15.00**
Special strikes, errors, and off metal strikes have higher values.

**Gaming Token, aluminum, Dunes Oasis, Las Vegas, free slot play, 4½" d, $2.00.**

# GAMBLING COLLECTIBLES

**Collecting Hints:** All the equipment used in the various banking games such as Chuck-A-Luck, Faro, Hazard, Keno, and Roulette are collected today. Cheating devices used by professional sharpers are highly sought.

A well rounded gambling collectibles display also includes old books, prints, postcards, photographs, and articles relating to the field.

**History:** American history reveals that gambling always has been a popular pastime for the general public, as well as a sure way to make a "quick buck" for the professional *sharper*.

In the late 18th and early 19th centuries, governmental agencies and other entities used lotteries to supplant taxes as a means to raise funds needed to construct schools, libraries, and other civic developments. Many of the state and city lotteries proved to be crooked and fixed, a fact which adds to the collecting appeal. Lottery tickets, broadsides, ads, and brochures are very ornate and display well when mounted and framed.

Most of the gambling paraphernalia was manufactured by "gambling supply houses" that were located throughout the country. They sold their equipment via catalogs. As the majority of the equipment offered was "gaffed," the catalogs never were meant to be viewed by the general public. The catalogs are sought by collectors for their information and are difficult to find.

Perhaps the most significant gambling collectibles are those relating to the American West. Many collectors of saloon and western "cowboy" items seek gambling paraphernalia traceable to the West. Equipment marked with a western manufacturer's name generally will fetch a higher price than a comparable eastern made piece.

**References:** *Old West Collectibles*, Great American Publishing Co.; Dale Seymour, *Antique Gambling Chips*, Past Pleasures, 1985.

## CHEATING DEVICES

Corner Rounder, lever style, solid brass, complete .......... **750.00**
Dice, weighted, black with white, always totals 12, set of three .......... **50.00**
Holdout
- Franks, Pat Nov 22, 1887 .......... **150.00**
- Wizard, 14", double Roulette type, carved cherry wood upper wheel with six holes, 20" lower wood wheel, controlled underneath, 1870 .......... **1,200.00**

## CHUCK–A–LUCK EQUIPMENT

Dice, ⅝", celluloid, used in cage, set of three .......... **15.00**
Dice Cage, nickel plated brass
- 11"h, 6" w, two celluloid dice .......... **175.00**
- 18½" h, 13" w, calfskin ends, 16 lbs, Mason & Co, Newark, NJ .......... **400.00**

Layout, 30½ x 9½ x ¾", vinyl, black, yellow painted numbers, pr . . . . . . . . **75.00**

## DICE

Celluloid, 1", red, white spots, round corners, set of five, MIB . . . . . . . . . . . **50.00**
Ivory, ⅝", pr . . . . . . . . . . . . . . . . . . . . . . **25.00**
Sterling Silver, ½", sq, marked "Sterling 925" . . . . . . . . . . . . . . . . . . . . . . . . . . **50.00**

**Dice Keno Cage, nickel plated iron and brass, hourglass cage, two dice, 16" w, 18" h, $220.00. Photograph courtesy of James D. Julia Inc.**

## FARO

Cards, sq corners, Samuel Hart & Co, New York, complete . . . . . . . . . . . . . **125.00**
Casekeeper
  Geo Mason & Co, Denver, CO, spade suit, walnut, composition beads, ace with crossed American flags . . **450.00**
  George W Williams, New York, heart suit, walnut closed box style, ivory blue and natural colored beads, cribbage board . . . . . . . . . . . . . . . . . **425.00**
Chip Rack, 18" l, 10" w, blue–green billiard cloth lined bottom . . . . . . . . . . . **85.00**
Dealing Box, German silver, straight, unmarked . . . . . . . . . . . . . . . . . . . . . . . **250.00**
Layout, felt, walnut trim, George Mason & Co, 1910 Laurence St, Denver . . . **600.00**

## HORSE RACE COLLECTIBLES

Catalog, Bookmaker's Supply Catalog, 1895, 19 pgs, illus . . . . . . . . . . . . . . **35.00**
Game, Derby Day With Hurdles, Parker Bros, boxed . . . . . . . . . . . . . . . . . . . . . **12.00**
Score Card, Grand Circuit Meet, Providence, RI, 1902 . . . . . . . . . . . . . . . . . . **15.00**
Stop Watch, 2" d, long chain, Meylan . **75.00**
Trade Stimulator, 3 x 10 x 8½", wood and metal case, glass top, two through twelve horses around outside, silver and black scenes, side lever spin dice . . . . . . . . . . . . . . . . . . . . **350.00**

## KENO EQUIPMENT

Cards, 136, wood, covered material and paper, H C Evans & Co, Chicago, Keno Cards . . . . . . . . . . . . . . . . . . . . . . **250.00**
Hopper, walnut, blue–green billiard cloth lined bowl, plated metal mouth, acorn finial, three carved feet . . . . . . **600.00**

## MISCELLANEOUS

Bingo Cage, 9" h, metal, red celluloid handle, eleven wood balls, 9 cards, 1941 copyright . . . . . . . . . . . . . . . . . **15.00**
Book
  *Card Games and How to Play Them,* 123 pgs, soft cov, 1900, copyright **25.00**
  *Gambler's Don't Gamble,* Michael MacDougall & J C Furnas, 167 pgs, illus, 1939 . . . . . . . . . . . . . . . . . . . . **30.00**
Bottle, figural, slot machine shape
  8 x 5", Liberty Bell, gray, 24 karat gold dec, Ezra Brooks . . . . . . . . . . . . . . . **25.00**
  9 x 9", Barney's, red . . . . . . . . . . . . . **15.00**
Card Counter, plated, imitation ivory face, black lettering . . . . . . . . . . . . . **20.00**
Card Press, 9½ x 4½ x 3", dovetailed, holds ten decks, handle . . . . . . . . . . . **175.00**
Catalog
  H C Evans & Co, Secret Blue Book, Gambling Supply, 1936, 72 pgs . . **75.00**
  K C Card Co, Blue Book No 520 Gambling Equipment, 68 pgs . . . . **50.00**
Chromolithograph, 16 x 24", men playing poker in hunting lodge, titled "Respecters of Limits," framed sgd "William Eaton" . . . . . . . . . . . . . . . . . **125.00**
Gambling Dirk, 9" l, mother–of–pearl, marked "Pookes Clarke" . . . . . . . . . . **125.00**
Shot Glass, ribbed dec, porcelain dice in bottom . . . . . . . . . . . . . . . . . . . . . . **15.00**
Sign, 11 x 30", Carlisle Whiskey adv, titled "A Bold Bluff," dogs gambling, silver and black background, orig frame impressed "Carlisle Rye" . . . . **75.00**
Tintype, 2¼ x 4", two men playing cards **15.00**
Tray, 11" d, tin, red, black, and white, martini center, card border . . . . . . . . **65.00**

## POKER

Arcade Game, 10 x 15 x 6", 1¢ draw, five play, counter top type, wood and metal case, orig graphics, c1930 . . . **400.00**
Book, *The Game of Draw Poker,* John Keller, NY, 1887, 84 pgs, 4½ x 4¼" **25.00**
Chip Holder, bakelite, pink and black, Art Deco, pressed red, white, and

blue composition chips, holds four sets of 50 chips, card rack ......... **75.00**

Chip Rack, 11½ x 4" h, revolving, wood, German silver handle, holds 400 chips and four decks of cards .. **50.00**

Chip Set

Bone, 37 rect and 39 round, geometric design, wood box ........... **150.00**

Composition, set of 24, emb horse and jockey pattern, red, white, and blue, double sided ............. **50.00**

Lighter, 2", poker dice set shape, marked "Old Crow The Greatest Name in Bourbon" ............... **45.00**

## ROULETTE

Ball, set of three, one metal, two composition ......................... **20.00**

Chip Rack, walnut, holds 1,500 chips . **125.00**

Game, Spear's Co, lithographed ...... **15.00**

Layout, 40 x 19", hp, oilcloth, black and red betting areas, wood trim ....... **150.00**

Tray, 13" d, metal, roulette wheel rim . **45.00**

Wheel, 8" d, wood and metal, single and double zero decal, four prong spinner, cloth layout, makers stamp on bottom ....................... **50.00**

## WHEEL OF FORTUNE

9½" d, 12" h, table top style, yellow, black, and red numbers and designs, black wood stand ................ **65.00**

20", 30 numbers, hp cutout painted center, yellow and white, red ground, unmarked ......................... **175.00**

# GAMES

**Collecting Hints:** Make certain a game has all its parts. The box lid or instruction booklet usually contains a full list of all pieces. Collectors tend to specialize by theme, e.g., western, science fiction, Disney, etc. Most television games fall into the ten to twenty–five dollar range, offering the beginning collector a chance to acquire a large number of games without a big capital outlay.

Don't stack game boxes more than five deep or mix sizes. Place a piece of acid free paper between each game to prevent bleeding from inks and to minimize wear. Keep the games stored in a dry location. Extreme dryness and extreme moisture are both undesirable.

**History:** A board game dating from 4,000 B.C. was discovered in ruins in Upper Egypt. Board games were used throughout recorded history, but reached popularity during the Victorian era. Most board games combine skill (from chess), luck and ability (from cards), and pure chance (from dice). By 1900 Milton Bradley, Parker Brothers, C. H. Joslin and McLoughlin were the leading manufacturers.

Monopoly was invented in 1933 and first issued by Parker Brothers in 1935. Before the advent of television, the board game was a staple in evening entertainment. Many board games from the 1930s and 1940s focused on radio personalities, e.g., Fibber McGee or The Quiz Kids.

In the late 1940s television became popular. The game industry responded. The golden age of the TV board game was from 1955 to 1968. The movies, e.g., James Bond, also led to the creation of games, but never to the extent of the television programs.

**References:** Avedon and Sutton–Smith, *The Study of Games,* Wiley & Son, 1971; Lee Dennis, *Warman's Antique American Games, 1840–1940, Second Edition,* Wallace-Homestead, 1991; Walter Gibson, *Family Games America Plays,* Doubleday & Co., 1970; Caroline Goodfellow, *A Collector's Guide To Games and Puzzles,* The Apple Press, 1991; Jefferson Graham, *Come on Down!!!, The TV Game Show Book,* Abbeville Press, 1988; Norman E. Martinus and Harry L. Rinker, *Warman's Paper,* Wallace–Homestead, 1993; Rick Polizzi and Fred Schaefer, *Spin Again, Board Games from the Fifties and Sixties,* Chronicle Books, 1991; Harry L. Rinker, *Collector's Guide To Toys, Games, and Puzzles,* Wallace–Homestead, 1991; Bruce Whitehill, *Games: American Boxed Games And Their Makers, 1822–1992, With Values,* Wallace–Homestead, 1992.

**Collectors' Club:** American Game Collectors Association, 4628 Barlow Drive, Bartlesville, OK 74006.

**Note:** Prices listed below are for games boxed and in mint condition.

All–Fair

1928, Captain Hop Across Junior ... **300.00**

1929, The Capital Cities Air Derby . **400.00**

1932, Cities ..................... **56.00**

1940, Ko–Ko the Clown .......... **50.00**

1943, Game of International Spy ... **135.00**

American Toy Works

1930, Magnetic Treasure Hunt ..... **40.00**

1940, Opportunity Hour .......... **55.00**

Avalon Hill

1966, Oh–Wah–Ree .............. **12.00**

1971, Luftwaffe .................. **40.00**

1982, Civilization ................ **20.00**

Beachcraft, Frederick H Beach

1937, Balloonio .................. **50.00**

1939, Fun Kit .................... **35.00**

1940, Oldtimers ................. **30.00**

Bettye–B Co
- 1955, Masquerade Party .......... **120.00**
- 1956, Big Time Operator .......... **70.00**

Cadaco Ltd
- 1935, Foto World ................ **240.00**
- 1953, Skip–A–Cross .............. **25.00**
- 1965, National Pro Football Hall of Fame Game .................. **40.00**
- 1975, Mostly Ghostly ............. **30.00**

Chaffee & Selchow
- 1899, Lee at Havana ............. **145.00**
- 1913, Pana Kanal, The Great Panama Canal Game .................. **175.00**

Corey Games
- 1939, Questo .................... **25.00**
- 1941, Barage .................... **50.00**
- 1947, Hippety Hop ............... **65.00**

Einson–Freeman Publishing Corp
- 1922, Comin' Round the Mountain . **80.00**
- 1933, Dick Tracy Detective Game .. **120.00**
- 1935, Pioneers of the Santa Fe Trail **65.00**
- 1942, Macy's Pirate Treasure Hunt . **55.00**
- 1944, Let's Go to College ......... **70.00**

Hasbro
- 1955, The Merry Milkman ......... **200.00**
- 1962, Frankenstein Game ......... **160.00**
- 1964, Superman Game ........... **120.00**
- 1967, Newlywed Game 1st Edition . **20.00**

Ideal
- 1965, Fishbait .................. **80.00**
- 1966, Fugitive .................. **240.00**
- 1967, The Case of the Elusive Assassin ......................... **105.00**
- 1969, Hang On Harvey ........... **30.00**
- 1976, Can You Catch It Charlie Brown? ...................... **20.00**
- 1982, Curse of the Cobras Game ... **32.00**

Lowell
- 1955, Dollar A Second ........... **50.00**
- 1958, Bat Masterson .............. **120.00**
- 1961, Mr Magoo Visits the Zoo .... **70.00**
- 1962, Bowl and Score ............ **15.00**

Mattel
- 1963, Godzilla Game ............. **80.00**
- 1967, Gentle Ben Animal Hunt Game **40.00**

McLoughlin Brothers
- 1899, Game of Phoebe Snow ...... **350.00**
- 1901, Chiromagica, or The Hand of Fate ......................... **600.00**
- 1902, Diamon Heart ............. **295.00**
- 1903, Game of Bang ............. **250.00**
- 1904, Game of District Messenger Boy ......................... **240.00**
- 1912, The Air Ship Game ......... **375.00**

Milton Bradley
- 1905, Hurdle Race ............... **200.00**
- 1909, Game of Robinson Crusoe ... **200.00**
- 1910, Cabin Boy ................ **160.00**
- 1911, Checkered Game of Life ..... **250.00**
- 1913, Honey Bee Game .......... **135.00**
- 1914, Round the World Game ..... **160.00**
- 1925, Auto Race Game ........... **225.00**

**Milton Bradley, The Fess Parker Trail Blazers Game, #4528, 1964, $25.00.**

- 1927, Little Orphan Annie Game ... **300.00**
- 1931, Through the Clouds ......... **200.00**
- 1932, Lotto ...................... **15.00**
- 1936, Monopoly, metal markers .... **25.00**
- 1937, The Game of Tom Sawyer ... **120.00**
- 1938, Go to the Head of the Class . **75.00**
- 1939, Pinocchio ................. **150.00**
- 1942, Adventures of Superman ..... **375.00**
- 1952, Captain Video Game ........ **200.00**
- 1955, Mr Bug Goes to Town ...... **175.00**
- 1956, Chutes and Ladders ......... **25.00**
- 1957, Bobbsey Twins ............ **70.00**
- 1959, Spot Cash ................ **20.00**
- 1960, Concentration 3rd Edition ... **32.00**
- 1963, Cut Up Shopping Spree Game **16.00**
- 1965, Call My Bluff ............. **30.00**
- 1966, Fang Bang ................ **25.00**
- 1968, Felix the Cat Game ......... **40.00**
- 1970, Cardino .................. **25.00**
- 1971, Emergency ............... **12.00**
- 1972, All in the Family .......... **15.00**
- 1973, Sealab 2020 Game ......... **15.00**
- 1974, Planet of the Apes .......... **45.00**
- 1975, Kojak ..................... **20.00**
- 1977, Lucan, The Wolf Boy ....... **15.00**
- 1978, Mighty Mouse ............. **30.00**
- 1981, Huckleberry Hound ......... **15.00**
- 1982, Leverage .................. **10.00**
- 1983, Centipede ................ **15.00**

Parker Brothers
- 1900, The Hen That Laid the Golden Egg ......................... **275.00**
- 1903, The Coon Hunt Game ..... **1,200.00**
- 1914, Peter Peter Pumpkin Eater ... **160.00**
- 1921, Polly Pickles, Queen of the Movies ...................... **200.00**
- 1922, The Game of Cottontail and Peter ......................... **192.00**
- 1923, Peggy .................... **90.00**
- 1924, Peg Base Ball ............. **275.00**
- 1929, Cats and Dogs ............ **300.00**
- 1930, Derby Day ............... **120.00**
- 1934, Peter Coddles Trip to New York **25.00**
- 1935, Hendrik Van Loon's Wide World Game .................. **100.00**
- 1936, Stock Exchange ........... **80.00**
- 1937, Boake Carter's Star Reporter . **285.00**
- 1938, Donald Duck Party Game ... **150.00**

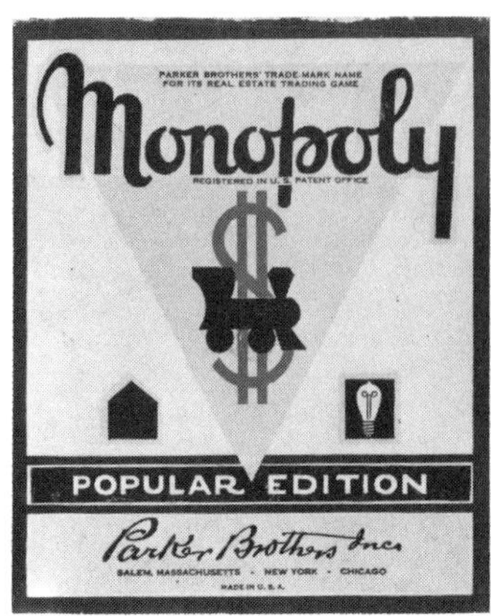


**Parker Brothers, 1936, Monopoly, $12.00.**

1940, Citadel .... **175.00**
1941, Flying the Beam .... **250.00**
1943, Famous Authors .... **25.00**
1948, Sunken Treasure .... **25.00**
1954, Steps of Toyland .... **55.00**
1960, Walt Disney's Swamp Fox Game .... **80.00**
1962, Finance .... **35.00**
1968, Formula One Car Race Game **100.00**
1971, Plotz! .... **55.00**
1972, Dealer's Choice .... **35.00**
1974, General Hospital .... **25.00**
1977, Escape From the Death Star .. **55.00**
1979, Fangface .... **13.00**
1981, Trust Me .... **13.00**
1983, Star Wars Wicket the Ewok .. **20.00**
1984, Super Powers .... **40.00**

Rosebud Art Co, Inc
1933, Popeye Ring Toss Game .... **135.00**
1938, Big Apple .... **80.00**

Saalfield Publishing Co
1925, Thorton W Burgess Animal Game .... **175.00**
1959, Casey Jones .... **70.00**

Samuel Gabriel Sons & Co
1939, Chee Chow .... **40.00**
1940, In and Out the Window .... **55.00**
1955, Mt Everest .... **40.00**

Samuel Lowe Co
1941, Hornet .... **70.00**
1941, Land and Sea War Games ... **100.00**

Schaper
1949, Cootie .... **50.00**
1965, Monkeys and Coconuts .... **20.00**
1974, Casper the Friendly Ghost ... **20.00**

Selchow & Righter
1937, Ed Wynn the Fire Chief .... **120.00**
1940, Cabby .... **100.00**
1941, The Elsie Game .... **200.00**
1957, Mr Ree .... **70.00**
1960, Ellsworth Elephant Game .... **70.00**
1965, Go For Broke .... **25.00**
1969, Behind the 8 Ball Game .... **65.00**
1970, Emily Post Popularity Game .. **35.00**
1977, Barbapapa Takes A Trip .... **8.00**

Standard Toycraft, Inc
1961, Dick Van Dyke Board Game . **120.00**
1962, My Fair Lady .... **65.00**
1963, Beverly Hillbillies .... **100.00**

Stoll & Edwares
1921, Black Beauty .... **110.00**
1923, Game of Alice in Wonderland **135.00**
1926, Pony Express .... **90.00**
1929, Game of Pegpin .... **70.00**
1935, Dog Sweepstakes .... **120.00**

The Embossing Co
1929, Flapper Fortunes .... **50.00**
1929, Neck and Neck .... **65.00**

Transogram
1937, Dog Race .... **100.00**
1955, Dragnet .... **95.00**
1960, Hawaiian Eye .... **250.00**
1961, Ben Casey MD Game .... **35.00**
1962, The Kennedys .... **100.00**
1963, Jetsons .... **225.00**
1964, Flintstone's Hoppy the Hopperoo Game .... **120.00**

Volume Sprayer Mfg Co
1939, Contack .... **56.00**
1942, Discretion .... **75.00**

Whitman
1938, Charlie McCarthy Put And Take Bingo Game .... **70.00**
1939, Charlie Chan Game .... **80.00**
1964, Kar–Zoom .... **35.00**
1968, Dark Shadows Game .... **104.00**
1977, Popeye's Treasure Map Game **15.00**
1979, Donald Duck Big Game Box . **20.00**

Wilder Mfg Co
1920, Tiddley Winks Game .... **105.00**
1922, Combination Board Games .. **100.00**
1925, Construction Game .... **200.00**
1927, Radio Game .... **70.00**

**Wilder, Throwing the Bull, $30.00.**

Wolverine Supply & Mfg Co
- 1926, Across the Channel ......... **135.00**
- 1930, Hoop–O–Loop ............. **50.00**

Zulu Toy Mfg Co
- 1926, City of Gold ............... **135.00**
- 1927, Covered Wagon ............ **136.00**

# GASOLINE COLLECTIBLES

**Collecting Hints:** There still is plenty of material in the storage area of old garages; try to find a cooperative owner. If your budget is modest, concentrate on paper ephemera, such as maps. Regionally related items will bring slightly more in their area of origin.

**History:** The selling of gasoline has come full circle. The general store, livery stable, and blacksmith were the first people to sell gasoline. Today the mini–market is a viable factor in gasoline sales. The gas crisis of 1973 brought the circle to a close. The gas station, whose golden era was from the 1930s to the 1960s, is beginning to disappear. The loss of the independently owned station is doubly felt because it also was the center of automobile repair.

The abolition of credit cards by ARCO marked another shift. Reduction in price for paying cash is a new marketing device. Elimination of free maps, promotional trinkets, and other advertising material already is a fact. As more and more stores in shopping centers sell oil, parts, and other related automobile products, it is doubtful whether the gasoline station will ever recover its past position.

**References:** Scott Anderson, *Check The Oil,* Wallace–Homestead, 1986; Mark Anderton, *Gas Station Collectibles,* Wallace–Homestead, 1993; Norman E. Martinus and Harry L. Rinker, *Warman's Paper,* Wallace–Homestead, 1993.

**Periodical:** *Hemmings Motor News,* Box 100, Bennington, VT 05201.

**Collectors' Clubs:** Automobile License Plate Collectors Association, Box 712, Weston, WV 26452; International Petroliana Collectors Association, P. O. Box 1000–F, Westerville, OH 43081; Spark Plug Collectors of America, 14018 NE 85th St, Elk River, MN 55330.

**REPRODUCTION ALERT:** Small advertising signs and pump globes have been extensively reproduced.

Advertising
- Print, Champion Lamps, clipper ship on high seas ................... **25.00**
- Radio, Sinclair, pump shape ....... **35.00**

Bank
- Mobiloil, glass, baseball shape, winged horse .................. **30.00**
- Sinclair Gasoline, 4" d, tin, figural, gas pump ..................... **35.00**
- Texaco, Ertl, #3 ................. **300.00**

Blotter, Texaco, automobile and service station illus, 1920s ............... **16.00**

Brochure, McKinley Brothers Gasoline Sales Station, Tours Through the Hudson Valley, 16 pgs, 1927 .......... **6.00**

Calendar, Texaco Sky Chief, 1940 .... **50.00**

**Road Map, Standard Oil, Florida, with pictorial guide, 1958, 4 x 8½" folded size, $3.00.**

Can, Cities Service Koldpruf Anti–Freeze, tin, logo and penguin, 1957–65 ............................ **40.00**

Catalog, Buick, 1955 ............... **20.00**

Display Rack, Standard Oil, factory labeled samples ................... **90.00**

Gargoyle, Mobil Oil, two sided ...... **350.00**

Gas Globe
- Cities Service, 15", metal frame .... **425.00**
- Esso Extra, 15", metal frame ....... **425.00**
- Mobilgas, milk glass, red winged horse, 1936–47 ................ **310.00**
- Pioneer Zipper, glass ............. **450.00**
- Red Crown, milk glass ............ **285.00**
- Signal Gasoline, 3 pcs, metal frame **400.00**
- Sinclair H–C, one piece ........... **415.00**
- Special ......................... **150.00**
- Super Shell, blue ................ **1,500.00**

Hood Ornament
- Dodge Ram ..................... **35.00**
- Fish ........................... **45.00**

Jar, 6" h, Coreco Motor Oil, glass, emb lettering, yellow label, metal screw lid, 1940s ....................... **25.00**

License Plate Attachment, 4½ x 7", litho tin, diecut, Tydol Oil & Gasoline, 1930s ......................... **50.00**

Notebook, aluminum hinged cov, emb "House of Better Values–Condon's Service Station, Charleston, SC," c1920 .......... 10.00
Oil Bottle
Mobil Gargoyle, flat sides, Artic, 1 qt 85.00
Seal Cap Oil Co, 15" h, raised logo and ribbed design, 1 qt .......... 30.00
Shell, 15" h, raised logo and ribbed design, 1 qt .......... 65.00
Oil Bottle Rack, Mobil Oil, holds eight diamond shape bottles .......... 85.00
Oil Can
Ace High Motor Oil, touring car illus, sunburst on red background, 1 qt 135.00
Barnsdall Motor Oil, 1 qt, 1932–35 145.00
Mobil Oil, 1920s .......... 15.00
Phillips 66 .......... 15.00
Oil Dispenser, copper, 1918 .......... 115.00
Padlock, brass, Ford Motor Co .......... 75.00
Plate, DX Marine Gasoline Pump, boat silhouette .......... 150.00
Poster, 17 x 22", Kissel's Garage, paper, tow truck on circular background .. 20.00
Premium, States of the Union Coins, bronze coins, orig frame, Shell Oil, 1969 .......... 25.00
Pump Sign, Ethyl Gasoline Corporation, porcelain, 1940 .......... 40.00
Radio, Shell, figural, gas pump .......... 40.00
Sign
Bruinoil Bruin Gasoline, oval, tin, diecut, mounting flange, 1920s . 1,600.00
Conoco Ethyl, 30" .......... 150.00
Indian Gasoline, 12 x 18", porcelain, 1940 .......... 335.00
Oilzum Motor Oil, 18 x 60", litho tin, orange, black and white letters ... 180.00
Pure Oil Co, 42" .......... 195.00
Quaker State Motor Oil, 29 x 27", porcelain, rounded top, square bottom, 1930s .......... 120.00
Sinclair, dinosaur, porcelain .......... 25.00
Texaco, 7 x 10", metal and glass, red, "Texaco 22¢ NY" .......... 35.00
Texaco Pipeline, porcelain .......... 55.00
Spark Plug, Champion, #V3, boxed, ¼" h .......... 25.00
Thermometer, Frigiking Auto Coolant, round .......... 85.00
Thimble
Buick .......... 7.00
Sinclair Oils, plastic, black dinosaurs and stars, butterscotch swirl background .......... 4.00
Toy Truck, Texaco
Fire Truck .......... 75.00
Tanker .......... 65.00
Upholstery Brush, Atlantic Gasoline, emb brass with service station scene, inscribed "Atlantic Gasoline Puts Pep In Your Motor," 1920s .......... 25.00

# GEISHA GIRL PORCELAIN

**Collecting Hints:** Check for enamel and gold wear as well as porcelain flakes, hairlines, etc. Buy only items in good to mint condition. Become familiar with the type of items produced so you are not fooled by a "pitcher" that actually is a lidless cocoa pot or a lidless sugar bowl which may appear to be a planter.

Check the designs on all items within a set. Be aware that a "set" contains items complementary in size and with the same pattern executed in the same manner on all pieces. Value depends upon condition, quality, pattern, border color, and type of piece. Teapots, cups and saucers, and red bordered items are the most common.

**History:** Geisha Girl porcelain is a Japanese export ware whose production commenced during the last quarter of the 19th century and continued heavily until WW II. Limited quantities were produced after WW II and are called "modern" Geisha ware.

Geisha Girl porcelain features over 150 different patterns focusing on the flora and fauna (both real and mythical) and people of pre–modern Japan. The name is derived from the fact that all the wares contain lovely kimono–clad Japanese ladies as part of the pattern. It was manufactured and decorated by over 100 different establishments.

Colors and design methods vary greatly. The most common examples bear a red–orange stencil design over which artists hand painted enamels. Other examples have a different color stencil, and may be wholly hand painted or decaled. In the majority of instances, items bear a border color of red, light green, pine green, cobalt blue, greenish blue, turquoise, brown, black, or a lovely combination of several colors. Borders themselves are often further embellished with lacing, flowers, diapering, dots, or stripings of gold or contrastingly colored enamels.

Although Geisha Girl was produced in an Oriental pattern, it was meant for export to the Western market. Therefore, most shapes represent those used in the West during the early days of the twentieth century. These forms include tea items, cocoa sets, luncheon sets, dresser sets, (powder jars, hair receivers, ring trees, etc.), and vases. Examples of children's and doll house sizes also exist.

Maker marks found on Geisha Girl porcelain include many of the famous Nippon trademarks, Japanese signatures (including Kutani), and post–Nippon indicators.

**Reference:** Elyce Litts, *The Collector's Encyclopedia of Geisha Girl Porcelain*, Collector Books, 1988.

**REPRODUCTION ALERT:** "Modern" Geisha ware was sold in Oriental import shops until the early 1980s. Reproduced forms, all having a red border, include bail handled tea sets, five piece dresser sets, sake sets, toothbrush holders, and ginger jars. Also produced was a children's set of demitasse cups, each having a different border color.

The chief characteristics of reproduction are very white porcelain, minimal background washes, sparse detail coloring, and no gold or occasionally very bright gold enameling. Old gold should show tarnish.

Also watch for Czechoslovakian reproductions made in the 1920s. Some will be marked with the country of origin, but others bear only a faux–Oriental mark. Generally these items are decaled or very simply hand painted. Faces of the geisha will be distinctively different than those on Japanese Geisha ware.

## BY LAND AND BY SEA

This is an example of diminutive Geisha ware, in that the geisha figures are very tiny when compared to the overall designed space. At the forefront of this pattern is a lady in a sampan. On a bridge above her rides a samurai on horseback, accompanied by a retainer. The underlying stencil is black. The border, also stenciled, is composed of alternating sections of stylized bamboo and diapering overlaid by floral vines. Tan and dark green colors predominate, accented by pinks and reds.

Cocoa Set, 6 pcs, cov chocolate pot, five cups and saucers .......... **85.00**
Luncheon Set, 13 pcs, hexagonal demitasse pot, six hexagonal cups and round saucers, six 7" plates ........ **165.00**
Plate, 7" .......... **12.00**
Tea Cup and Saucer .......... **12.00**

## CHILD REACHING FOR BUTTERFLY

There are several variations of this pattern which feature two geisha chatting while a child attempts to catch a butterfly alighting on a nearby plant. Another constant is a porch placed to the rear right of the scene. Variation A is the most common, displaying the child to the left of the geisha and a dark green porch of two sides. Variation B shows an uncolored bamboo porch with stairway access. Variation C shows the child between the two foremost geisha. The porch is overflowing with flowers and upper quadrant features a display of billowing fabric and dangling lanterns, all highly ornamented.

Egg Cup, red, Variation A .......... **12.00**
Mustard Jar, red, Variation A .......... **18.00**
Plate, 7", red
  Variation A .......... **12.00**
  Variation C .......... **15.00**
Salt and Pepper Shakers, pr, red, Variation A .......... **15.00**
Tea Cup and Saucer
  Variation A .......... **10.00**
  Variation B .......... **12.00**
  Variation C .......... **18.00**

## GARDEN BENCH

There seem to be endless varieties of this pattern series, the focal point of which are geisha seated around a bench in some lovely flower adorned garden. Variant letters refer to those described either in the *Collector's Encyclopedia of Geisha Girl Porcelain* or *The Geisha Girl Porcelain Newsletter*.

Box, 6", hexagonal, red, Variant B .... **26.00**
Cocoa Pot, blue, Variant B .......... **55.00**
Condiment Set, 4 pcs, salt and pepper shakers, mustard pot, and tray, multicolored border, Variant Q, marked "Royal Kaga Nippon" ..... **45.00**
Dresser Tray, clover shape, red and green geometrics, Variant F, marked "Plum Blossom, Hand Painted, Japan" .......... **75.00**
Pitcher, 2½", child's, red, Variant N .. **15.00**
Plate
  7¼", red, Variant B .......... **16.00**
  8½", green, Variant C .......... **25.00**
Ring Tree, gold hand shaped stem, multicolored border, Variant Q, marked "Kutani" .......... **65.00**
Tea Cup and Saucer, red and green geometrics, Variant S .......... **24.00**
Teapot, cov, melon ribbed, blue with red spout, Variant C, marked "Japan" **30.00**

## MEETING B

This variant of the Meeting series features two ladies who have stopped to chat. At least one child is present, often pulling at the hand of one of the women. This pattern is often found in reserves on beautifully decorated backgrounds of floral decor or completely covered with richly colored carp in a stream.

Cracker Jar, blue border, carp background .......... **95.00**
Creamer, green banded border, floral background .......... **24.00**
Demitasse Cup and Saucer, subject pattern, Shishi pattern and scenic reserves, border of alternating red and green semi-circles with gold, floral background, sgd "Tashiro" ........ **25.00**

Demitasse Pot, pedestal, red border, carp background . . . . . . . . . . . . . . . . . **65.00**
Ginger Jar, dark green border, carp background . . . . . . . . . . . . . . . . . . . . **85.00**
Sake Cup, red border, carp background **14.00**
Tea Cup and Saucer, green banded border, floral background . . . . . . . . . . . **28.00**

**Plate, 10" d, $25.00.**

## VARIOUS PATTERNS

Bon Bon Dish, red, Courtesy in reserve on floral ground . . . . . . . . . . . . . . . . . **20.00**
Candlesticks, pr, red, Parasol D . . . . . . **100.00**
Cheese and Cracker Dish, blue, Boat Festival, marked "Plum Blossom, Japan" . . . . . . . . . . . . . . . . . . . . . . . . . **50.00**
Condiment Set, 4 pcs, pine green, salt and pepper shakers, mustard pot, toothpick holder, and cherry blossom shape tray, Duck Watching B . . . . . . **48.00**
Cookie Jar, green, bell pepper shape, Battledore . . . . . . . . . . . . . . . . . . . . . . **70.00**
Creamer and Sugar, red with green geometrics, miniature cocoa pot and cracker jar shapes, River's Edge . . . . **65.00**
Demitasse Place Setting, 3 pcs, blue, cup, saucer, and plate, Fan A and Garden Bench A in reserves on crane and floral background, marked "Japan" . . . . . . . . . . . . . . . . . . . . . . . . . **27.00**
Ice Cream Set, 6 pcs, red, master bowl, plus five individual serving bowls, Fan A . . . . . . . . . . . . . . . . . . . . . . . . . **95.00**
Jar, cylindrical, cov, Temple A, green M in wreath mark . . . . . . . . . . . . . . . . . **65.00**
Powder Jar, red, Lantern Gateway . . . . **26.00**
Roll Tray, Chinese Coin, floret shape, green leaf handles . . . . . . . . . . . . . . . **45.00**
Sugar Shaker, red, hexagonal, handles, Prayer Ribbon, marked "Japan" . . . . **55.00**
Toothpick Holder, red, blue washed int., River's Edge, fauna and birds dec, marked "Kutani" . . . . . . . . . . . **65.00**
Vase, red, Cloud B, bulbous, trifooted, $3\frac{1}{2}$" h . . . . . . . . . . . . . . . . . . . . . . . . . **25.00**

# G.I. JOE COLLECTIBLES

**Collecting Hints:** It is extremely important to determine the manufacturing date of any G. I. Joe doll or related figure that you have. The ideal method is to discipline yourself to do a check point comparison with the dolls described and dated in the existing reference books. Be alert to subtle variations. You do not have a match until all checking points are identical. Also make a point to learn the proper period costume for each doll variation.

Accessory pieces can be every bit as valuable as the dolls themselves. Whenever possible, accessory pieces should be accompanied by their original packaging and any paper inserts.

G. I. Joe dolls and accessories were produced in the millions. Rarity is not a factor. Condition is. When buying dolls or accessories as collectibles, as opposed to acquiring for play, do not purchase any items in less than fine condition.

**History:** Hasbro Manufacturing Company produced the first G. I. Joe twelve–inch poseable action figures in 1964. The original line consisted of one male action figure for each branch of the military services. Their outfits were styled after military uniforms from World War II, the Korean Conflict, and the Vietnam Conflict.

In 1965 the first black figure was introduced. The year 1967 saw two additions to the line—a female nurse and Talking G. I. Joe. To keep abreast of changing times, Joe received flocked hair and a beard in 1970.

The creation of the G. I. Joe Adventure Team made Joe the marveled explorer, hunter, deep sea diver, and astronaut, rather than just an American serviceman. Due to the Arab oil embargo in 1976, the figure was reduced in size to eight–inches tall and renamed Super Joe. Production ceased in 1977.

In 1982 G. I. Joe staged his comeback. A few changes were made to the character line and in the way in which G. I. Joe was presented. "The Great American Hero" line now consists of $3\frac{3}{4}$" poseable plastic figures with code names corresponding to their various costumes. The new Joe deals with both current and futuristic villains and issues.

**References:** Jeff Killian and Charles Griffith, *Tomart's Price Guide to G. I. Joe Collectibles*, Tomart Publications, 1992; Paris and Susan Mano, *Collectible Male Action Figures: Including G. I. Joe Figures, Captain Action Figures and Ken Dolls,* Collector Books, 1990, 1992 value update; Carol Markowski and Bill Sikora, *Tomart's Price Guide to Action Figure Collectibles,* Tomart Publications, 1991; Vincent Santelmo, *The Com-*

*plete Encyclopedia To GI Joe,* Krause Publications, 1993.

**Collectors' Club:** GI Joe Collectors Club, 150 S. Glenoaks Blvd., Burbank, CA 91510.

## ACTION FIGURES

3¾" h
- 1st Series, 1st release, 1982, straight arms
  - Grunt Infantry Trooper .......... **60.00**
  - Rock & Roll Machine Gunner .... **75.00**
- 1st Series, 2nd release, 1982, Cobra Soldier, straight arms ........... **75.00**
- 2nd Series, 1983, swivel arms
  - Snake Eyes Commando ......... **65.00**
  - Stalker Ranger ................ **45.00**
- 3rd Series, 1984
  - Duke ......................... **50.00**
  - Recondo ..................... **40.00**
  - Road Block .................... **30.00**
  - Storm Shadow ................ **45.00**
- 4th Series, 1985
  - Airtight ...................... **25.00**
  - Barbecue ..................... **35.00**
  - Bazooka ...................... **20.00**
  - Ripper ....................... **30.00**
  - Snake Eyes, with wolf .......... **40.00**
- 5th Series, 1986
  - Dial–Tone .................... **12.00**
  - Hawk 2 ...................... **18.00**
  - Iceberg ...................... **15.00**
  - Wet–Suit ..................... **25.00**
- 6th Series, 1987
  - Chuckles ...................... **8.00**
  - Cobra Commander ............ **20.00**
  - Crazylegs .................... **12.00**
  - Fast Draw .................... **10.00**
  - Law & Order ................. **15.00**
- 7th Series, 1988
  - Shockwave .................... **8.00**
  - Storm Shadow 2 .............. **12.00**
- 8th Series, 1989
  - Gnawgahyde .................. **6.00**
  - Snake Eyes 3 ................. **10.00**
- 9th Series, 1990
  - Night Creeper ................. **4.00**
  - Rapid Fire, with video tape ...... **10.00**

12" h
- Action Pilot, 1964 ............... **225.00**
- Action Soldier, #7500, 1964 ...... **200.00**
- Sea Adventurer, kung–fu grip, Adventure Team, 1970 ............... **160.00**
- Talking Astronaut, Adventure Team, 1970 ......................... **350.00**

## ACCESSORIES

2nd Series, 1983, for 3¾" figures
- Battle Gear, pack #1 ............. **20.00**
- Pac Rat's Machine Gun ........... **15.00**
- Snake Armor, white .............. **45.00**

3rd Series, 1984, for 3¾" h figures
- CLAW Cobra .................... **7.00**
- Machine Gun Defense Unit ........ **7.00**

4th Series, 1985, for 3¾" h figures
- Ammo Dump .................... **8.00**
- SNAKE Blue ................... **55.00**
- Transportable Battle Platform ...... **65.00**
- Weapon Transport ................ **10.00**

5th Series, 1986, for 3¾" h figures
- LAW .......................... **7.00**
- Outpost Defender ................ **12.00**

6th Series, 1987, for 3¾" h figures
- Buzz Boar ...................... **7.00**
- Jet Pack ........................ **6.00**
- Motorized Back Packs ............ **5.00**

## VEHICLES

Adventure Team Series, jeep, with real motor noise, 1964 ................ **400.00**

1st Series, 1st release, 1982, for 3¾" figures
- Mobat Battle Tank, with steeler .... **85.00**
- Rapid Fire Motorcycle, #6073–1 ... **25.00**

1st Series, 2nd release, 1982, Vamp Attack Vehicle, with figure ......... **75.00**

2nd Series, 1983, for 3¾" figures
- Amphibious Personnel Carrier ...... **50.00**
- Cobra FANG .................... **20.00**
- Cobra HISS, with figure .......... **65.00**

3rd Series, 1984, for 3¾" figures
- CAT Tank ...................... **135.00**
- CLAW Cobra .................... **7.00**
- Night Attack Stinger, with figure .... **55.00**
- SHARC, with figure .............. **30.00**

4th Series, 1985, for 3¾" figures
- Cobra ASP ..................... **18.00**
- Night Landing .................. **10.00**
- Snow Cat, with figure ............ **35.00**
- USS Flagg, with figure ........... **200.00**

5th Series, 1986, for 3¾" figures
- Devil Fish ...................... **15.00**
- Dreadnok Thundermachine ........ **30.00**
- Hydro Sled ..................... **11.00**
- Tomahawk, with figure .......... **60.00**

6th Series, 1987, for 3¾" figures
- Defiant Shuttle Complex, with figure **125.00**
- Persuader, with figure ............ **18.00**
- Pogo–Ballistic Battle Ball .......... **15.00**
- Sea Ray, with figure ............. **25.00**

7th Series, 1988, for 3¾" figures
- BF 2000 Sky Sweeper ............ **10.00**
- Destro's Despoiler, with figure ..... **25.00**
- Skystorm X–Wing Chopper, with figure .......................... **18.00**
- Swampmaster ................... **8.00**

# GLASS COLLECTIBLES, MODERN

**Collecting Hints:** For the past several years, modern glass collectibles have been a source of speculation among collectors. Some new glass now is selling below initial retail as overstocked dealers are trying to unload. All this actually has resulted in a stabilization of prices.

The first issue in a series often brings the highest price. Collectors are urged to concentrate on assembling full sets of one figure. Focusing on a single color is difficult because of the large variances in color and different companies' interpretation of the same color.

Several series have been left off the price list since the companies did not press their promised amount. They stopped midway or just barely into the series. This practice, while cost effective, is deceptive to the collector.

**History:** The popularity of limited edition plates, the success of Degenhart Crystal Art Glass and a renewed interest in old glass forms in the 1960s and 1970s led several companies to produce modern glass collectibles. Leading firms include Boyd's Crystal Art Glass Company, Fenton, Vi Hunter, Mosser, Pisello Art Glass, and Summit Art Glass Company.

The modern glass collectible market is organized into three categories—limited edition series, limited edition single items, and collectible company colors.

The limited edition series usually has between 12 and 18 colors issued of a single pattern. The new colors appear monthly or bimonthly. The form generally is new.

The limited edition single item, often utilizing an early mold from an existing company, is issued in a color not previously used and in limited numbers from 100 to 1,000.

Collectible company colors are open stock. However, many smaller companies may make a limited amount of a color, e.g., shadings and slags. Once the color is used, it is not prepared again. Hence, some of these figurines have become collectible.

The recent closing of several glass factories, e.g., Imperial, Seneca, Tiffin, and Westmoreland, has resulted in the sale of their molds and a new collectible category within modern glass collectibles: reissues.

In the 1950s the Imperial Glass Company acquired over 10,000 molds when the Heisey and Cambridge glass factories closed. They used very few of these molds in production over the next thirty years. When Imperial Glass Company closed in early 1985, these molds, as well as their own, were sold. The Heisey Collectors of America, Inc., purchased 4,000 original Heisey molds, all except for sixty Old Williamsburg patterns. The Cambridge and Imperial molds were scattered to Michigan, Ohio, Pennsylvania, Texas, West Virginia, and Germany.

In late 1984 the Westmoreland Glass Company started selling their 20,000 molds, many from the mid–1880s. Collectors are concerned about repressings.

The big trend is miniatures. Several glass producers are offering miniature versions of their larger items or beginning a new item in miniature size.

## LIMITED EDITION SERIES

Items produced in limited amounts in a series. Usually not more than 1,000 per color for 12 to 16 variations. To distinguish between each collectible figurine a name is given to each color.

Edna Barnes, 5″ d, orange juice reamer. Made at Mosser from original Imperial Glass mold. A 2½″ d miniature version of the same in a series of 12. Each marked with Barnes's logo: "B".
- Black Amethyst
  - 2½″ d . . . . . . . . **4.50**
  - 5″ d . . . . . . . . **7.50**
- Custard
  - 2½″ d . . . . . . . . **4.50**
  - 5″ d . . . . . . . . **7.50**
- Lavender, 5″ d . . . . . . . . **7.50**
- Red Glow
  - 2½″ d . . . . . . . . **7.75**
  - 5″ d . . . . . . . . **10.00**

Guernsey Glass, Rocky, rocking horse. A reproduction of a 1915 Cambridge candy container, 4¼″ l, 3″ h, 12 issues. Each marked "B" in a triangle.
- Blue Boy . . . . . . . . **12.00**
- Carousel Slag . . . . . . . . **12.00**
- Hi–O–Silver . . . . . . . . **12.00**
- Holly Berry . . . . . . . . **10.00**
- Royal Prince . . . . . . . . **14.00**

Vi Hunter
- Carousel Horse, 4½″ h, six issues per year, beginning 1985, gold frost first issue . . . . . . . . **15.00**
- Jenny, 4¼″ h doll, 12 per year plus bell. First issued January 1979, in Cornflower Blue Slag.
  - 1979, set of 12, plus bell . . . . . . . . **500.00**
  - 1980, set of 12, plus bell . . . . . . . . **200.00**
  - 1981, set of 12 . . . . . . . . **150.00**
- Jenny Bell. Each Christmas a bell is issued.
  - 1979, No. 1, Cobalt Carnival . . . . **30.00**
  - 1980, No. 2, Pearl Carnival . . . . **25.00**
  - 1981, No. 3, Samurai Red . . . . **20.00**
  - 1982, No. 4, Mistletoe Slag . . . . **18.00**
- Josh, 4½″ h doll
  - First issue . . . . . . . . **18.00**

1981, set of 12, plus bell ........ **400.00**
1982, set of 12, plus bell ........ **300.00**
Mirror Images
Bear, ruby
Baby ........................ **40.00**
Mama ........................ **40.00**
Venus Rising, 6½" h, Cambridge mold of a lady flower frog (reworked for solid base). Series of 12, each color available solid or frosted, each marked "IG–81." First issued in Midnight Magic in early 1981.
Blue Bell Frosted .............. **35.00**
Midnight Magic ................ **38.00**
Sunmaid Frosted ............... **20.00**
Mosser. This company has produced three limited edition clown figurines.
Balloon Clown, 3½" h, sitting, holding balloons, 16 issues. Each individually named on back of clown. Introduced January 1981, with Arty.
Arty ........................ **100.00**
Bags ........................ **20.00**
Cleo ........................ **20.00**
Daisy ........................ **20.00**
Dealer Clown .................. **225.00**
Eros ........................ **15.00**
Flip ........................ **15.00**
Gabby–Maxi .................. **15.00**
McGoo ...................... **15.00**
Niki ........................ **15.00**
Orie ........................ **15.00**
Barrel Clown, 3½" h, sitting on a barrel. Issued January 1982, 12 issues in a continuation of the alphabet P through Z, the last one marked "The End."
Poko ........................ **25.00**
Quinn ...................... **25.00**
Rufus ...................... **25.00**
Fiddler Clown
Bim ........................ **12.00**
Dappy ...................... **12.00**
Randy ...................... **12.00**
Willy ...................... **12.00**
Pisello Art Glass
Chief Thundercloud Toothpick, 2½", each dated and sgd "P" in a circle, less than 1,000 of each, introduced 1983
Color 1, cobalt blue carnival .... **15.00**
Color 2, chocolate slag ......... **15.00**
Color 3, milk white ............ **15.00**
Flipper, 3½ x 2½", miniature, covered dolphin. Based on Greentown dolphin, introduced late 1982.
Chocolate .................... **12.00**
Marigold Carnival ............. **12.00**
Red Carnival ................. **14.00**
John and Sarah, The Amish Couple, 2½" h, sgd "P" in a circle, cobalt blue carnival, price for pair ...... **20.00**

Summit Art Glass Company
Clown Elephant, 4¾" h, elephant figurine. Reproduction of Cambridge candy container. 12 issues, introduced December 1982.
Jimmy, Ringling Red ............ **16.00**
Tommy, Calliope ............... **16.00**
Melanie, 5¼" h, doll. Copied from Cambridge figurine, two series of twelve dolls each plus a Mother's Day bell. First issued August 1980, in "Tom's Surprise." Mold destroyed June 10, 1983.
Autumn Glow ................ **15.00**
Canyon Whisper .............. **15.00**
Set of 24 dolls, plus 2 bells ...... **300.00**
Oscar, 4½" l, 2½" h, sitting lion. 12 issues, introduced June 1981.
Harvest Gold ................. **12.00**
Paradise Orchid ............... **12.00**

## LIMITED SINGLE ITEM

A single item, often from an old original mold, is made in a color not previously issued and in a limited number from 100 to 1,000. In this category also would be a mold used from a company or a custom–made mold used for a one–time special color run.

Cherished Editions
Love Bouquet, series of six items from Fenton. Burmese with hand painted flowers, artist signed and dated, 350 sets issued.
Basket, 5" h .................. **42.50**
Bud Vase, 6" h ................ **32.50**
Jack–In–The–Pulpit Vase
6½" h ...................... **32.50**
10" h ...................... **48.00**
Rose Bowl, 4½" h .............. **28.00**
Doris Lechler. A series of children's collectibles designed by Doris Lechler and made by Fenton Art Glass, limited to 500 sets per color, 3 colors per style.
Elizabeth Series
Lemonade set, 6" h ruffled pitcher, six 2" h tumblers, price for eight piece set
Amethyst, hp lilies of the valley dec ...................... **55.00**
Burmese, hp roses ........... **60.00**
Custard, hp violets .......... **50.00**
Tumble–Up, 5" h, price for two piece set
Custard, hp violets .......... **50.00**
Ruby Overlay ................ **50.00**
Grace Series, lemonade set, cobalt blue overlay, price for eight piece set ......................... **85.00**

## COLLECTIBLE COMPANY COLORS

Large glass companies have many molds and the amount of glass made is not limited. Smaller companies don't actually limit the amount of glass run, but certain items become "limited" because a given color will not be repeated.

Mosser Glass Company. Trademark is the letter "M."

Bear, solid, sitting, Violet D'Orr .... **24.00**

Candlestick, child's, opaque blue, Dutch boy and dog ............. **5.00**

Children's Dishes

Berry Set, Cherry Thumbprint, master berry, four serving bowls ... **35.00**

Butter Dish, cov, Cherry Thumbprint ........................ **15.00**

Cereal Set, Jennifer, pink, four cereal bowls, milk pitcher ........ **18.00**

Cracker Jar, cov, Cherry Thumbprint ........................ **18.00**

Creamer and Sugar, Cherry Thumbprint ........................ **18.00**

Cup and Saucer, Lindsey, blue ... **20.00**

Dessert Set, Jennifer, yellow, four plates, round divided relish dish **18.00**

Juice Set, Jennifer, green, pitcher, four tumblers ................ **18.00**

Pitcher and Tumbler, Lindsey, blue **20.00**

Spooner, Cherry Thumbprint ..... **9.00**

Table Set, Jennifer, yellow, cov butter, creamer, cov sugar ........ **15.00**

# GOLF COLLECTIBLES

**Collecting Hints:** Condition is very important as collectors grow in sophistication and knowledge. The more modern the item, the better the condition should be.

It is extremely rare to find a club or ball made before 1800, and any equipment made before 1850 is scarce. There were few books, with a couple of very rare exceptions, published before 1857. Few pieces of equipment made after 1895 are rare.

Some items, such as scorecards, ball markers, golf pencils, and bag tags are so common that their value is negligible.

Most American clubs and other items manufactured after 1895 are rather common. Some modern equipment, 1950–65, is in demand, but primarily for actual play rather than collection or display.

The very old material is found in Scotland and England, unless brought to this country early in this century. Christie's, Sotheby's, and Phillips' hold several major auctions of golf collectibles each year in London, Edinburgh, and Chester. Golf collectible sales often coincide with the British Open Championship each July. The English market is more established, but the American market is growing rapidly. Auctions of golf items and memorabilia now are held in the United States.

The prices of golf clubs escalated tremendously in the 1970s, but have stabilized in more recent years. The prices of golf books, which for many years remained static, have risen dramatically in the 1980s. Art prints, drawings, etchings, etc. have remained static, but pottery, china, glass, and other secondary items, especially Royal Doulton, have attracted premium prices.

**History:** Golf has been played in Scotland since the 15th century. Until 1850 it was a game played by gentry, with a few exceptions. With the introduction of the cheaper and more durable "guttie" ball in 1848, the game became more popular and spread to England and other countries, especially where Scottish emigrants settled.

There are documents indicating golf was played in America before the Revolution. The great popularity of golf began about 1890 in both England and the United States.

**References:** Henderson & Stark, *Golf In The Making;* Pat Kennedy, *Golf Club Trademarks,* privately printed; John M. and Morton W. Olman, *Olman's Guide To Golf Antiques & Other Treasures of the Game,* Market Street Press, 1992; Norman E. Martinus and Harry L. Rinker, *Warman's Paper,* Wallace–Homestead, 1993; Beverly Robb, *Collectible Golfing Novelties,* Schiffer Publishing, Ltd., 1992; Janet Seagle, *The Club Makers,* United States Golf Association; Shirley and Jerry Sprung, *Decorative Golf Collectibles: Collector's Information, Current Prices,* Glentiques, Ltd., 1991; Tom Wishon, *Golf Club Identification and Price Guide.*

**Collectors' Club:** Golf Collectors' Society, P. O. Box 491, Shawnee Mission, KS 66201.

**Museums:** Ralph Miller Memorial Library, City of Industry, CA; United States Golf Association, "Golf House," Far Hills, NJ; PGA World Golf Hall of Fame, Pinehurst, NC.

**Flask, sterling silver, 2¾ x 4½", $585.00.**

## BOOKS

Alger, Horatio Jr, *Strive and Succeed,* 1910 .......... **25.00**
Barnes, James M, *A Guide To Good Golf,* 1927, 5th edition, 137 pgs ... **17.50**
Bauer, Dave, *Golf Techniques of the Bauer Sisters,* Prentice–Hall, Inc, first edition .......... **15.00**
Collett, Glenna, *Ladies in the Rough,* Alfred A Knopf, England, 1929 ..... **35.00**
Cotton, Henry, *My Swing,* Vandyck Printers, England, third edition, 1954 **20.00**
Hogan, Ben, *Power Golf,* 1948, 166 pgs **10.00**
Jones, Robert Jr, *Rights and Wrongs of Golf,* Spalding Brothers, 1935 ...... **35.00**
MacDonald, Bob, *Golf at a Glance The Pocket "Pro,"* 1931 .......... **120.00**
Morrison, Alex J, *A New Way To Better Golf,* 1931 .......... **35.00**
Prentiss, Mrs E, *Little Susy Stories,* M A Donohue & Co, 1900 .......... **12.00**
Schoor, Gene, *Babe Didrickson, the World's Greatest Woman Athlete,* Doubleday, first edition, 1978 ..... **20.00**
Smith, Garden G, *Four Little Mischiefs,* Frederick A Stokes Co, 1900 ....... **15.00**
Vaile, P A, *Putting Made Easy, The Mark G Harris Method,* Reilly & Lee, first edition, 1935 .......... **25.00**
Vanderbeck, Mrs Clarence H, *Golf For Women,* Moffat, Yard and Co, first edition, 1916 .......... **45.00**
Watt, Alick A, *Collecting Old Golfing Clubs,* A A Watt & Sons, first edition, 1985 .......... **35.00**
Wethered, Roger and Joyce, *Golf From Two Sides,* Longmans, Green & Co, second edition, 1922 .......... **25.00**
Zaharias, Mildred Didrickson, *Championship Golf,* A S Barnes, first edition, 1948 .......... **65.00**

## EQUIPMENT

Ball
- Dino Brand, Dean Martin, Pro–Tel, USA, orig box, 1970s .......... **36.00**
- Reach Eagle Multidot Mesh, sq dimples, orig box, 1915 .......... **1,200.00**

Club (Note: w/s–wood shaft; s/s–steel shaft)
- Iron
  - Kroy Don, waffle face spade mashie, 1925 .......... **150.00**
  - Mills Driver, w/s, 1900 .......... **200.00**
  - Rollin Wilson Co, Midget Midiron, 16" l, w/s, c1900 .......... **30.00**
  - Seeley Mid Iron, w/s, 1912 ...... **75.00**
  - Smith Anti–Shank, mashie, w/s ... **175.00**
  - Spalding, Ded Stop, mashie niblick, 1925 .......... **100.00**
  - Tom Stewart, w/s, 1905 .......... **200.00**
- Putter
  - A G Spalding, rut niblick, 1900 .. **300.00**
  - Bryon Nelson Northwestern, s/s, brass head .......... **35.00**
  - J G Gourlay, lofter, 1895 .......... **100.00**
  - Ivora Perfection, w/s, ivory disc, 1915 .......... **200.00**
  - Lambert Bros Jewelers, 35" l, w/s, sterling head, marked "Walter Hagen, Putter," c1930 ....... **1,200.00**
  - Probst, 37" l, sterling silver head, marked West Point and Cyna Weight, 1950s .......... **850.00**
  - Shur Line, s/s, brass head ....... **40.00**
  - Spalding & Bros, w/s, Wry Neck B, leather wound handle .......... **45.00**
  - Wilson Guerspin, w/s, 1915 ..... **150.00**
- Wood
  - Buthcart, putter, 1900 .......... **200.00**
  - Scott, splice driver, 1905 .......... **500.00**

Tee
- Rite Hite, orig drawstring bag ...... **10.00**
- Super Golf Tees, orig package, 1920s **30.00**
- The Reddy Tee, orig package, 1920s **18.00**

**Cap, Arnold Palmer, Doubleday, Play Great Golf, green, white, and gold, ASI, one size fits all, $5.00.**

## MISCELLANEOUS

Advertising
- Box, 5¼ x 6¼", Wilson Putting Disc, The Putting Instructor, three men putting golf balls, two men seated, 1940s .......... **30.00**
- Sign, 13½ x 12", The Original Canadian Dry, cardboard, golfing scene, 1920s .......... **75.00**

Ashtray
- Chase .......... **65.00**
- Silver Plate, 6" d, Art Deco figure, marked "monarch Plate Brand," c1930 .......... **150.00**

Badge, caddie's, 2¼" d, Plum Hollow, 1962 .......... **12.00**
Belt Buckle, 3" l, pewter, "Golf" with clubs, shoe, ball, and golf bag, Siskiyou, 1985 .......... **10.00**
Booklet, *Rules of Golf,* 1947 .......... **10.00**
Cigarette Dispenser, Rookwood .......... **185.00**
Cigarette Lighter, chrome, golfing scene, Scripto Vu–lighter .......... **22.00**
Cuff Links, pr, metal, plated, crossed clubs with golf ball, Swank, 1960–80 **15.00**

Game
Miniature Golf Pocket Course, 4 x 7", orig box, 1930 .......... **45.00**
Tom Thumb 9 Hole Golf Game, orig box, Transogram, 1954 .......... **25.00**
Glove Box, 4 x 13", wood, pyrography, woman golfer .......... **95.00**
Golf Bag Tag, 2⅛" d, celluloid, "Wolfert's Roost Country Club," red, black lettering, leather strap, 1920–30 .......... **15.00**
Jewelry Set, pendant, brooch, and earrings, figural .......... **26.00**
Magazine
*American Golfer,* June, 1932 .......... **8.00**
*Golfing,* April, 1949 .......... **12.00**
*Golf World,* April 13, 1951 .......... **15.00**
Match Safe, 1½ x 3", aluminum, Art Nouveau, raised golfer swinging golf club, c1900 .......... **100.00**

Match Striker, Majolica .......... **195.00**
Medal, "I Beat Ben Hogan," 1952 .......... **65.00**
Mug, golf bag shape .......... **20.00**
Photo, Ben Hogan, autographed, 1955 **200.00**
Pin, golf club, sterling silver, 1959 ... **55.00**
Pin Tray, 3½" h, porcelain, figural, seated golfer, marked "7970," 1930s **75.00**
Playing Cards, Animal Snap, complete deck, Hong Kong, 1960 .......... **10.00**
Pocket Watch, 1½" d, golf ball form, brass case, white enamel finish, Intex, marked "17 Rubis," c1940 .......... **175.00**
Post Card
Golf Club House and Links, Hyannisport, MA, golfer, tennis court and club house background, 1911 ... **8.00**
It's A Great Game For Us Fat People, Isn't It?, multicolored fox illus, c1900 .......... **10.00**
Print
The Golf Girl, Howard Chandler Christy .......... **100.00**
Two Up, Harrison Fisher, 1909 .... **100.00**
Uncle Wiggily, matted and framed, 1919 .......... **18.00**
Program
Bob Hope Desert Classic, 1968 .... **15.00**
Fort Worth Open Golf Championship, Glen Garden Country Club, Fort Worth, TX, 1945 .......... **100.00**
Spoon, 4¼" l, sterling silver, enameled dec, inscribed "Kingussie Golf Club House, R C Birmingham, 1906 ..... **75.00**
Tie Rack, celluloid, 1937 .......... **20.00**
Toothpick Holder, 3½" h, porcelain, figure holding golf bag, marked "Made in Germany," 1930s .......... **150.00**
Trophy, 10" h, pewter, double handle stein, "Wesquetonsing Golf Club," Reed and Barton .......... **25.00**

# GONDER POTTERY

**Collecting Hints:** Learn to identify the Gonder glazes and forms. Once you do, you will have no trouble identifying the pieces. Since production is recent, many examples still can be found in basements and at garage sales. Dealers have been buying Gonder pieces and placing them in storage in anticipation of a future rise in prices.

**History:** Lawton Gonder purchased the Zane Pottery of Zanesville, Ohio, in 1941. Previously Gonder had worked for the Ohio Pottery, American Encaustic Tiling, Cherry Art Tile, and Florence Pottery. He was a consultant for Fraunfelter China and Standard Tile. Gonder renamed the Zane Pottery the Gonder Ceramic Arts, Inc.

Gonder's pottery was high priced for its time. Besides a mingled color glaze, the pottery made a flambe glaze, a gold crackle glaze, and a line of old Chinese crackle reproduction pottery. Many shapes followed the Rum Rill patterns from the Florence Pottery.

Almost all Gonder Pottery is marked. Some had paper labels, but the majority had one of the following impressed marks: "GONDER CERAMIC ART," "Gonder/Original" in script, "Gonder" in script, "GONDER/U.S.A.," "Gonder (script)/U.S.A.," and "GONDER" in a semicircle.

The company expanded in 1946 and opened the Elgee Pottery, which made lamp bases. The plant burned in 1954. A brief expansion occurred at the main plant, but production ceased in 1957.

**References:** Ron Hoopes, *The Collector's Guide and History of Gonder Pottery,* L–W Books, 1992; Ralph and Terry Kovel, *The Kovel's Collector's Guide To American Art Pottery,* Crown Publishers, 1974.

**Collectors' Club:** American Art Pottery Association, 125 E. Rose Ave., St. Louis, MO 63119.

Ashtray, free form, yellow, 10" l, #408 **12.00**
Basket, twisted handle, brown glaze, 13" w, 9" h, L–19 .......... **45.00**
Candleholders, pr
Crescent Moon, white, 6½" h, J–56 **35.00**
Lotus Flower, 5" w, E–14 .......... **20.00**

**Basket, pink and gray, H-39, 8¼″ w, 7″ h, $35.00.**

Creamer and Sugar, cov, large, ivory ground, brown speckles and drips .. **12.50**
Ewer, shell shape, green and brown glaze, 14″ h, #508 .......... **85.00**
Figure
  Oriental Man and Woman, 14″ h, price for pair .......... **75.00**
  Panther, 15″ l, #217 .......... **115.00**
  Two Deer, jumping over fronds, Art Deco style, brown, 11″ h, #690 . **25.00**
Planter
  Gondola, yellow and pink .......... **25.00**
  Swan, E–44 .......... **25.00**
Television Lamp
  Seagull, black, flying over yellow waves, 12″ h .......... **75.00**
  Ship, green and brown speckled glaze, 14″ h .......... **35.00**
Vase
  6″ h, urn with leaf shape, pink, H–80 **38.00**
  8½″ h, rectangular, yellow, H–74 .. **20.00**
  9″ h, ewer, brown and yellow glaze, H–33 .......... **35.00**
  10″ h, cornucopia, green and brown, H–14 .......... **25.00**

# GRANITEWARE

**Collecting Hints:** Old graniteware is heavier than new graniteware. Pieces with cast iron handles date from 1870 to 1890; wood handles date from 1900 to 1910. Other dating clues are seams, wood knobs, and tin lids.

**History:** Graniteware is the name commonly given to iron or steel kitchenware covered with enamel coating.

The first graniteware was made in Germany in the 1830s. It was not produced in the United States until the 1860s. At the start of World War I, when European manufacturers turned to the making of war weapons, American producers took over the market.

Colors commonly marketed were white and gray. Each company made their own special color, including shades of blue, green, brown, violet, cream, and red. Graniteware still is manufactured with the earliest pieces in greatest demand among collectors.

**References:** Dana Gehman Morykan and Harry L. Rinker, *Warman's Country Antiques & Collectibles,* Wallace–Homestead, 1992; Helen Greguire, *The Collector's Encyclopedia of Graniteware: Colors, Shapes & Values,* (1990, 1992 value update), Book 2 (1993), Collector Books; Vernagene Vogelzang and Evelyn Welch, *Graniteware, Collectors' Guide With Prices, Volume 1* (1981), and *Volume 2* (1986), Wallace–Homestead, out–of–print.

**Collectors' Club:** National Graniteware Society, P.O. Box 10013, Cedar Rapids, IA 52410.

Bacon Platter, brown and white, swirl . **195.00**
Baking Pan
  Blue and White, large swirl, small .. **95.00**
  Chrysolite, swirl .......... **125.00**
  Iris, swirl .......... **195.00**
Berry Set, gray, master bowl and five small bowls .......... **145.00**
Butter Dish, cobalt and white, mottled **195.00**
Cake Pan, robin's egg blue .......... **20.00**
Candle Holder, red, leaf shape .......... **55.00**
Canister Set, cobalt and white, veined, 6 pcs .......... **195.00**
Chamber Pot, white, blue trim .......... **10.00**
Chocolate Dipper, gray, tubular handle **155.00**

**Coffeepot, cov, cream colored, green trim, drip, two sections, 10″ h, $25.00.**

Coffee Boiler
  Chrysolite, swirl .......... **175.00**
  Gray .......... **25.00**
  Iris, swirl .......... **285.00**
  Red, swirl .......... **650.00**

Coffeepot
 Blue and White, large swirl ........ **95.00**
 Cobalt and White, chicken wire .... **95.00**
 Gray, Columbian label ............ **85.00**
Colander
 Blue, swirl ...................... **125.00**
 Blue and Gray, swirl .............. **75.00**
 Emerald, swirl ................... **150.00**
Cream Bucket, gray, mottled, tin lid, orig label ...................... **100.00**
Custard, cobalt and white, large swirl . **65.00**
Double Boiler
 Blue ........................... **115.00**
 Cobalt and White, large swirl, Brilliant Belle ..................... **295.00**
Dust Pan, gray, speckled ........... **100.00**
Eggcup, blue, cobalt and white checkerboard trim, pr ................. **95.00**
Funnel
 Blue Diamond Ware, 9″ d ......... **95.00**
 Gray, Acme ..................... **40.00**
Grater
 Cream and Green, flat ............ **95.00**
 Red, small ...................... **75.00**
Gravy Boat, blue and white, mottled .. **195.00**
Jelly Roll Pan, blue and white, large swirl ........................... **40.00**
Ladle, blue and white, large swirl .... **70.00**
Measure, 4 quart, gray, hanging ring, marked "4 Qt. NYC," L & G ...... **90.00**
Milk Pitcher
 Blue and White, large swirl, early .. **175.00**
 Bonnie Blue, small, marked ....... **175.00**
Molasses Jug, white, large, tin lid .... **35.00**
Muffin Pan, cobalt and white, 8 hole, large swirl ...................... **225.00**
Mug, cobalt and white, large swirl, child's, pr ...................... **98.00**
Pitcher and Bowl Set, gray .......... **125.00**
Platter, blue and white, mottled, large **70.00**
Rice Ball, white, small .............. **265.00**
Roaster, cov, cobalt, oval, small ...... **10.00**
Scoop, white, small ................ **70.00**
Spoon, Blue Diamond Ware, long handle ............................ **48.00**
Sugar Bowl, gray, tin lid, L & G ...... **295.00**
Syrup Pitcher, brown, Onyx Ware, bulbous .......................... **365.00**
Teapot
 Brown and White, swirl, gooseneck spout ........................ **145.00**
 Cream and Green, gooseneck spout, 8½″ w ...................... **75.00**
Tea Strainer
 Blue, star perforations ............ **55.00**
 Cream, circles ................... **40.00**
Tray, blue and white, mottled, corrugated, 19″ w, 25″ l, 1¼″ d ......... **125.00**
Tumbler
 Blue and White, mottled, 5″ d ..... **65.00**
 White, small .................... **10.00**

# HALL CHINA

**Collecting Hints:** Hall China Company named many of their patterns, but some of these pattern names are being gradually changed by dealers to other names. A good example of this is the Silhouette pattern, which is also known as Taverne. Many shapes are also referred to by more than one name, i.e., Radiance aka Sunshine; Terrace aka Stepdown; and, Pert aka Sani–Grid.

Due to its high quality, most Hall China pieces are still in wonderful condition. There is no reason to pay full price for imperfect pieces.

**History:** Hall China Company was born out of the dissolution of the East Liverpool Potteries Company. Robert Hall, a partner in the merger, died within months of forming the new company. Robert T. Hall, his son, took over.

At first, the company produced the same semi–porcelain dinnerware and toiletware that was being made at the other potteries in East Liverpool, Ohio. Robert T. Hall began to experiment in an attempt to duplicate an ancient Chinese one–fire process that would produce a non–crazing vitrified china, with body and glaze being fired at the same time. He succeeded in 1911. Hall has been made that way ever since.

Hall's basic products are institutional ware (hotel and restaurant) to the trade only. However, they also have produced many retail and premium lines, e.g. Autumn Leaf for Jewel Tea and Blue Bouquet for the Standard Coffee Co. of New Orleans. A popular line is the gold–decorated teapots that were introduced for retail sale in 1920. In 1931 kitchenware was introduced, soon followed by dinnerware. These lines were decorated in both solid colors and decals for retail and premium sales.

Hall is still producing china at its plant in East Liverpool, Ohio.

**References:** Harvey Duke, *Hall: Price Guide Update,* ELO Books, 1992; Harvey Duke, *Superior Quality Hall China,* ELO Books, 1977; Harvey Duke, *Hall 2,* ELO Books, 1985; Harvey Duke, *The Official Price Guide to Pottery and Porcelain,* House of Collectibles, 1989; Margaret and Kenn Whitmyer, *The Collector's Encyclopedia of Hall China,* Collector Books, 1989, 1992 value update.

**Periodicals:** Hall China Encore, 317 N. Pleasant St., Oberlin, OH 44074.

**Collectors' Club:** National Autumn Leaf Collector's Society, 7346 Shamrock Dr., Indianapolis, IN 46217.

**Note:** Hall has been reissuing many of its products in its new Americana retail line for several years now. They are all decorated in solid colors. If you are a new collector and are unsure if an item is new or old, you may want to buy only the items with decal or gold decorations, as these pieces have not been reissued and there is no intention of doing so. Because of this reissue, prices have dropped slightly on a few solid–colored items.

**Autumn Leaf, soup, flat, $10.00.**

**AUTUMN LEAF.** Premium for the Jewel Tea Company. Produced 1933 until 1978. Other companies made matching fabric, metal, glass, and plastic accessories.

Bowl, 5½" d, berry ................. **4.00**
Butter Dish, cov
  ¼ lb, wing knob ................. **450.00**
  1 lb, regular knob ................ **180.00**
Creamer and Sugar, cov, ruffled–D ... **26.00**
Cream Soup ........................ **18.00**
Cup and Saucer .................... **8.00**
Custard, Radiance .................. **5.50**
French Baker ...................... **8.00**
Gravy Boat ........................ **20.00**
Plate
  7¼" d ........................... **5.00**
  9" d ............................ **6.00**
Platter, 13½" l .................... **14.00**
Salt and Pepper Shakers, pr
  Handled, range ................... **22.00**
  Ruffled–D, small ................. **14.00**
Stack Set ......................... **75.00**
Sugar, cov, Radiance ............... **15.00**
Teapot, Aladdin, round infuser ....... **42.00**
Vegetable Bowl, oval ............... **18.00**
Autumn Leaf Accessories
  Coasters, set of 8 ................ **45.00**
  Coffeepot, metal ................. **75.00**
  Hot Pad, tin back, 7¼" ........... **30.00**
  Tablecloth, 54 x 72", sailcloth ..... **75.00**

**CARROT (a.k.a. Carrot and Beet).** Kitchenware line with vegetable decal on white ground. Some pieces available with gold decoration.

Baker, oval, 12½" l ................. **85.00**
Ball Jug, #4 ....................... **125.00**

Casserole
  Radiance ......................... **55.00**
  Thick Rim, 10½" l ................ **125.00**
Cookie Jar, Zeisel .................. **150.00**
Custard, thick rim .................. **20.00**
Salt and Pepper Shakers, pr, Novelty .. **95.00**
Teapot, Windshield ................. **195.00**

**Chinese Red, ball jug, $35.00.**

**CHINESE RED.** This pattern name refers to the bright red color found on various shapes of solid colored kitchenware. Chinese Red is the most commonly found color.

Ashtray, triangular .................. **30.00**
Ball Jug ........................... **35.00**
Batter Bowl, Five Band .............. **75.00**
Bean Pot, #5 ...................... **150.00**
Butter, Zephyr ..................... **185.00**
Casserole, #1, Sundial .............. **55.00**
Coffeepot, Terrace, 4 pcs, all china, 4 cup ........................... **250.00**
Coffee Server, Sundial .............. **250.00**
Cookie Jar, Sundial ................. **225.00**
Creamer and Sugar, cov
  Daniel .......................... **75.00**
  Morning ......................... **95.00**
Drip Jar, open, #1188 .............. **35.00**
Jar, cov, 3" h ..................... **35.00**
Jug, Radiance
  #1, no lid ....................... **35.00**
  #2, cov ......................... **75.00**
  #4, cov ......................... **75.00**
  #5, no lid ....................... **45.00**
Leftover, Zephyr ................... **155.00**
Pretzel Jar, cov, hairline crack in bottom **95.00**
Ramekin, #1 ....................... **50.00**
Water Bottle, Zephyr, missing stopper . **70.00**

**FANTASY.** Kitchenware line with gaudy floral decal. Most pieces are trimmed with a thin red band.

Ball Jug
  #1 ............................. **95.00**
  #3 ............................. **110.00**

Donut . . . . . . . . . . **200.00**
Batter Bowl, Sundial . . . . . . . . . . **350.00**
Casserole
Sundial
#1 . . . . . . . . . . **95.00**
#4 . . . . . . . . . . **45.00**
Thick Rim, 9″ d . . . . . . . . . . **35.00**
Cookie Jar, Five Band . . . . . . . . . . **225.00**
Creamer and Sugar, cov, Morning . . . . **75.00**
Custard, Thick Rim . . . . . . . . . . **20.00**
Jug, Five Band, 2 pt . . . . . . . . . . **75.00**
Leftover, loop handle . . . . . . . . . . **145.00**
Salt and Pepper Shakers, pr, handled . **32.00**
Tray, rect, 11½″ l, 10″ w . . . . . . . . . . **200.00**

**MULBERRY.** In the early 1950s, Eva Zeisel designed two futuristic dinnerware shapes for Hall. Both shapes, Century and Tomorrow's Classic, were backstamped "Hallcraft." The Mulberry pattern consists of a decal with purple mulberries and green leaves on a white ground.

Ashtray . . . . . . . . . . **22.00**
Berry Bowl, 5¾″ l . . . . . . . . . . **6.50**
Casserole, cov, 2 qt . . . . . . . . . . **45.00**
Celery Dish, oval, 11″ l . . . . . . . . . . **22.00**
Cereal Bowl, 6″ l . . . . . . . . . . **15.00**
Cup and Saucer . . . . . . . . . . **12.00**
Gravy Boat, ladle . . . . . . . . . . **25.00**
Plate
6″ l, bread and butter . . . . . . . . . . **5.00**
8″ l, salad . . . . . . . . . . **7.50**
11″ l, dinner . . . . . . . . . . **12.00**
Salt and Pepper Shakers, pr . . . . . . . . . . **18.00**
Sugar, cov . . . . . . . . . . **18.00**
Vegetable Bowl, open, 9″ sq . . . . . . . . . . **22.00**

**NO. 488.** Produced early 1930s until 1940. Accessory pieces only.

Custard . . . . . . . . . . **20.00**
Jug, Radiance, #5, no cov . . . . . . . . . . **50.00**
Pepper Shaker, Novelty . . . . . . . . . . **30.00**
Refrigerator Jar, cov, square . . . . . . . . . . **60.00**
Teapot
New York, bottom chip . . . . . . . . . . **55.00**
Radiance . . . . . . . . . . **225.00**

**ORANGE POPPY.** Premium for the Great American Tea Company. Introduced 1933. Discontinued in the 1950s. Dinnerware made in the C–style shape. Metal accessory pieces available, though scarce.

Bean Pot . . . . . . . . . . **60.00**
Cake Plate . . . . . . . . . . **15.00**
Casserole
Oval, small . . . . . . . . . . **45.00**
Round, 8″ d, cov . . . . . . . . . . **42.00**
Custard . . . . . . . . . . **5.25**
Leftover Dish, loop handle . . . . . . . . . . **38.00**
Pepper Shaker . . . . . . . . . . **15.00**
Platter, 13″ l . . . . . . . . . . **15.00**
Salad Bowl . . . . . . . . . . **11.00**
Salt and Pepper Shakers, pr, handled . **30.00**
Teapot, Boston . . . . . . . . . . **165.00**
Vegetable Bowl, round . . . . . . . . . . **20.00**

**PASTEL MORNING GLORY (a.k.a. Pink Morning Glory).** Dinnerware line produced in the late 1930s and readily found in northern Michigan, Wisconsin, and Minnesota. Design consists of large pink morning glories surrounded by green leaves and small blue flowers on a white ground.

Ball Jug . . . . . . . . . . **85.00**
Bean Pot, handled . . . . . . . . . . **150.00**
Berry Bowl, 5½″ d . . . . . . . . . . **8.50**
Bowl, oval . . . . . . . . . . **35.00**
Cake Plate . . . . . . . . . . **55.00**
Cereal Bowl, 6″ d . . . . . . . . . . **20.00**
Coffeepot, Medallion . . . . . . . . . . **95.00**
Creamer and Sugar, cov, D–style . . . . . **55.00**
Cup and Saucer . . . . . . . . . . **15.00**
Custard . . . . . . . . . . **20.00**
Drip Jar, #1188 . . . . . . . . . . **55.00**
Mixing Bowl, Radiance, #2 . . . . . . . . . . **55.00**
Plate
6″ d, bread and butter . . . . . . . . . . **6.00**
7″ d, salad . . . . . . . . . . **14.00**
9″ d, dinner . . . . . . . . . . **15.00**
Platter, 13½″ l . . . . . . . . . . **35.00**
Pretzel Jar, cov . . . . . . . . . . **150.00**
Salt and Pepper Shakers, pr, Teardrop . **35.00**
Soup, flat . . . . . . . . . . **20.00**

**RED DOT (a.k.a. Eggshell Polka Dot).** This pattern is found on the Eggshell Buffet Service. Red is the most commonly found Dot color, but the pattern was also produced in blue, green, and orange.

Baker, individual, handled . . . . . . . . . . **30.00**
Bean Pot, #2, one handle . . . . . . . . . . **125.00**
Bowl, 8¾″ d . . . . . . . . . . **25.00**
Casserole, cov
Oval . . . . . . . . . . **25.00**
Round, 9″ d . . . . . . . . . . **25.00**
Custard . . . . . . . . . . **18.00**
Jug, cov, #2 . . . . . . . . . . **85.00**
Onion Soup, cov . . . . . . . . . . **35.00**
Pitcher, Baron . . . . . . . . . . **95.00**
Punch Set, ftd punch bowl and 12 cups **350.00**
Shirred Egg Dish . . . . . . . . . . **25.00**
Teapot, Rutherford . . . . . . . . . . **195.00**

**RED POPPY.** Premium for Grand Union Tea Company. Produced from mid 1930s until mid 1950s. Complete line of D–style dinnerware and kitchenware in various forms. Red poppy and black leaves decals on white ground. Glass, metal, wood, and cloth accessory pieces were also marketed.

Cereal Bowl, 6″ d ........ **16.50**
Coffeepot, Daniel, metal dripper ........ **35.00**
Cup and Saucer ........ **13.50**
Custard, Radiance ........ **16.50**
Jug, Radiance, #5 ........ **35.00**
Plate, dinner, 10″ d ........ **13.50**
Soup, flat ........ **20.00**
Stack Set ........ **65.00**
Teapot, Aladdin, oval infuser ........ **110.00**

**SERENADE (a.k.a. Eureka Serenade).** Premium for the Eureka Tea Company, Chicago. Complete line of D–style dinnerware. Kitchenware found in various forms. Rust colored floral decal on white ground.

Berry Bowl, 5½″ d ........ **5.50**
Casserole, cov ........ **30.00**
Coffeepot, 4 pc, all china ........ **125.00**
Creamer and Sugar, cov ........ **29.00**
Cup and Saucer ........ **13.50**
Plate, dinner, 9″ d ........ **13.50**
Platter, 13½″ l ........ **20.00**
Salad Bowl, 9″ d ........ **20.00**
Soup, flat ........ **13.50**
Teapot, Boston ........ **110.00**

**Wildfire, gravy boat, ruffled D shape, gold trim, #85, 9″ l, 3⅜″ h, $30.00.**

**WILDFIRE.** Great American Tea Company premium, 1950s. D–style dinnerware. Various forms of kitchenware. Pattern consists of intertwining blue ribbon and floral swag decal on white ground.

Bowl
  Oval, 9″ l ........ **28.50**
  Straight Sided, 5″ d ........ **18.00**
Creamer and Sugar, D–style ........ **38.50**
Gravy Boat ........ **30.00**
Jug, Radiance, #5 ........ **55.00**
Plate
  7″ d, salad ........ **11.00**
  9″ d, dinner ........ **13.00**
Platter, oval, 11½″ l ........ **25.00**
Salad Bowl, 9″ d ........ **22.50**
Salt and Pepper Shakers, pr, Teardrop . **35.00**
Teapot
  Aladdin, round infuser ........ **95.00**
  Pert, cov ........ **200.00**
Tidbit Tray, 3 tiers ........ **45.00**

**WILD POPPY (a.k.a. Poppy and Wheat).** Kitchenware line introduced in the late 1930s and sold by Macy's.

Bean Pot, #5, one handle ........ **175.00**
Canister Set, cov, set of four ........ **600.00**
Casserole
  Oval
    9″ l ........ **55.00**
    13″ l, cov ........ **165.00**
  Radiance ........ **35.00**
Coffeepot, #691, 4 pc, all china ........ **325.00**
Cookie Jar, cov, Five Band ........ **225.00**
Creamer and Sugar, New York ........ **110.00**
Custard, Radiance ........ **20.00**
Jug, Radiance
  #3, no lid ........ **35.00**
  #4, cov ........ **75.00**
Leftover, sq ........ **125.00**
Salt and Pepper Shakers, pr, handled . **95.00**
Salt Shaker, canister style ........ **100.00**
Shirred Egg Dish
  5½″ l ........ **22.50**
  6½″ l ........ **25.00**
Stack Set, Radiance ........ **165.00**
Teapot, New York, 12 cup, missing lid **30.00**
Tea Tile, 6″ sq ........ **85.00**

## COFFEEPOTS

Deca Flip, Chinese red and white ........ **55.00**
Floral Lattice (a.k.a. Flowerpot) ........ **30.00**
Meltdown, green and ivory ........ **40.00**
Panel ........ **30.00**
Queen, Chinese red ........ **75.00**
Red Poppy, Daniel ........ **55.00**
Rounded Terrace, Rose White ........ **30.00**
Terrace, Gold Label line ........ **37.00**
Tulip ........ **35.00**
Waverly (a.k.a. Crest), large ........ **45.00**

## TEAPOTS

Aladdin
  Chinese Red, oval infuser ........ **100.00**
  Cobalt Blue, gold dec, oval infuser . **85.00**
  Emerald Green, gold dec, oval infuser **85.00**
Basket, emerald ground, platinum dec **175.00**
Basketball, Chinese red ........ **750.00**
Bowknot, pink ........ **45.00**
Car, maroon ........ **60.00**
Carroway, lettuce green ........ **65.00**
Football, maroon ........ **750.00**
French, Royal Rose ........ **50.00**
Hollywood, Chinese red, 8 cup ........ **200.00**
Hook Cover
  Chinese Red ........ **135.00**
  Cobalt Blue, gold dec ........ **95.00**
  Emerald Green, gold dec ........ **95.00**

Kansas, ivory, gold dec .......... **350.00**
Los Angeles
  Chinese Red, 4 cup .......... **275.00**
  Cobalt Blue .......... **35.00**
McCormick, maroon, 6 cup .......... **35.00**
Medallion (a.k.a. Colonial), Crocus ... **95.00**
Melody, Chinese red .......... **175.00**
Moderne, marine blue .......... **50.00**
Nautilus, maroon, gold dec .......... **175.00**
New York, Chinese Red, 6 cup .......... **125.00**
Parade
  Canary Yellow .......... **28.00**
  Emerald Green, gold dec .......... **175.00**
Philadelphia, Chinese Red, 6 cup .... **225.00**
Radiance, Chinese red, knob reglued . **125.00**
Rutherford (a.k.a. Alton)
  Chinese Red .......... **250.00**
  Orange Dot .......... **250.00**
Star
  Delphinium .......... **95.00**
  Ivory .......... **75.00**
  World's Fair, cobalt ground, gold dec **750.00**
Streamline, canary yellow .......... **95.00**
Surfside, emerald green, gold dec .... **125.00**
Thorley, Brilliant Series
  Harlequin, gold dec .......... **125.00**
  Windcrest, #1524, lemon yellow ground, gold dec .......... **125.00**
Washington, marine blue, 6 cup ..... **65.00**
Windshield
  Black, gold dec .......... **125.00**
  Cobalt Blue, gold dec .......... **175.00**
  Delphinium, gold dec .......... **110.00**
  Maroon .......... **35.00**
  Yellow .......... **95.00**

# HARKER POTTERY

**Collecting Hints:** In 1965 Harker China had the capacity to produce 25 million pieces of dinnerware each year. Hence, there is a great deal of Harker material available at garage sales and flea markets. Many patterns also were kept in production for decades.

Between 1935 and 1955 the Harker Company organized Columbia Chinaware, a sales organization used to market Harker products in small towns across the country. The line included enamel ware, glass and aluminum products. One pattern of Columbia Chinaware was "Autumn Leaf," eagerly sought by Autumn Leaf collectors.

Collectors should focus on Harker patterns by famous designers. Among these are Russel Wright's White Clover and George Bauer's Cameoware. Many patterns will be found with different color grounds. Other patterns were designed to have mass appeal. Colonial Lady was popular at "dish nites" at the movies or other businesses.

Shapes and forms did change through the decades. An interesting collection might focus on one object, e.g., a sugar or creamer, in a variety of patterns from different historical periods. Watch for unusual pieces. The Countryside pattern features a rolling pin, scoop and cake server.

**History:** The Harker Co. began in 1840 when Benjamin Harker, an English slater turned farmer in East Liverpool, Ohio, built a kiln and began making yellow ware products from clay deposits on his land. The business was managed by members of the Harker family until the Civil War when David Boyce, a brother–in–law, took over the operation. Although a Harker resumed management after the war, members of the Boyce family assumed key roles within the firm; David G. Boyce, a grandson of David, served as president.

In 1879 the first whiteware products were introduced. A disastrous flood in 1884 caused severe financial problems which the company overcame. In 1931 the company moved to Chester, West Virginia, to escape the flooding problems. In 1945 Harker introduced Cameoware made by the engobe process. The engobe or layered effect was achieved by placing a copper mask over the bisque and sand blasting to leave the design imprint. The white rose pattern on blue ground was marketed as "White Rose Carv–Kraft" in Montgomery Ward stores.

The Harker Company used a large variety of backstamps and names. Hotoven cookingware featured a scroll, draped over pots, with a kiln design at top. Columbia Chinaware had a circular stamp with the Statue of Liberty.

Harker made a Rockingham ware line in the 1960s. The hound handled pitcher and mugs were included. The Jeannette Glass Company purchased the Harker Company and the plant was closed in March, 1972. Ohio Stoneware, Inc., utilized the plant building until it was destroyed by fire in 1975.

**References:** Neva W. Colbert, *The Collector's Guide To Harker Pottery, U.S.A.: Identification and Values,* Collector Books, 1993; Jo Cunningham, *The Collector's Encyclopedia Of American Dinnerware,* Collector Books, 1982, 1992 value update.

**Periodical:** *The Daze,* 10271 State Rd., P.O. Box 57, Otisville, MI 48463.

**See:** Russel Wright

**COLONIAL LADY.** Black silhouette decal of colonial woman in various settings. White ground. Silver trim.

Cake Plate .......... **22.00**
Cereal Bowl .......... **10.00**
Creamer and Sugar .......... **20.00**
Cup and Saucer .......... **12.00**

Dessert Bowl .......... 7.00
Pie Baker and Server .......... 35.00
Plate
  Bread and Butter .......... 4.00
  Salad .......... 6.00
Salt and Pepper Shakers, pr, small .......... 16.00
Soup Bowl .......... 18.00
Vegetable Bowl .......... 22.00

**DECO–DAHLIA.** Red and black stylized flowers on white ground. Trimmed with red and black bands.

Baker, cov, individual, set of four on rotating rack .......... 50.00
Cake Lifter .......... 28.00
Jug, 6" h .......... 18.00
Pie Baker, 9" d .......... 17.00
Rolling Pin .......... 85.00
Utility Plate, 12" d .......... 15.00

**MALLOW.** Decal decoration of pastel pink, blue, and yellow flowers and green leaves on white ground. Black trim.

Bowl
  5" d .......... 15.00
  10" d .......... 30.00
Jug, cov .......... 25.00
Plate, 8" d .......... 10.00
Spoon, hairline crack .......... 10.00

**PANSY.** Similar to Mallow, this decal has pink, yellow, and blue pansies and green leaves on white ground. Also trimmed in black.

Ashtray .......... 30.00
Cereal Bowl .......... 10.00
Cup .......... 10.00
Pie Baker .......... 30.00
Plate, dinner .......... 10.00
Platter .......... 30.00
Salt Shaker .......... 15.00

**RED APPLE.** Decal of large red apple and yellow pear on white ground. Red band trim.

Custard .......... 6.00
Mixing Bowl, 10" d .......... 30.00
Pie Server .......... 20.00
Spoon .......... 25.00
Utility Plate .......... 20.00
Vegetable Bowl, 9" d .......... 28.00

### ROLLING PIN

Amy .......... 85.00
Basket of fruits and flowers .......... 75.00
Cameoware, pink .......... 110.00

**Colonial Lady, mixing bowl, pouring spout, $25.00.**

Countryside .......... 115.00
Fruit Basket .......... 85.00
Petit Point Rose .......... 100.00

# HOLIDAY COLLECTIBLES

**Collecting Hints:** The most common holiday item is the postcard. Collectors tend to specialize in one holiday. Christmas, Halloween, and Easter are the most desirable. New collectors still can find bargains especially in the Thanksgiving and Valentine's Day collectibles.

Holiday items change annually. Manufacturers constantly must appeal to the same buyer.

**History:** Holidays are an important part of American life. Many have both religious and secular overtones such as Christmas, St. Patrick's Day, Easter, and Halloween. National holidays such as the Fourth of July and Thanksgiving are part of one's yearly planning. There are regional holidays. Fastnacht day in Pennsylvania–German country is just one example.

Some holidays are the creation of the merchandising industry, e.g., Valentine's Day, Mother's Day, Father's Day, etc. The two leading forces in the perpetuation of holiday gift giving are the card industry and the floral industry. Through slick promotional campaigns they constantly create new occasions to give their products. Other marketing aspects follow quickly.

Holiday collectibles also keep pace with popular trends. Peanuts is now being challenged by Strawberry Shortcake, the Smurfs, and Star Wars.

**References:** Juanita Burnett, *A Guide To Easter Collectibles,* Collector Books, 1992; Helaine Fendelman and Jeri Schwartz, *The Official Pride Guide to Holiday Collectibles,* House of Collectibles, 1991; Dana Gehman Morykan and Harry L. Rinker, *Warman's Country Antiques & Collectibles,* Wallace–Homestead, 1992; L–W Book Sales (pub.), *Favors & Novelties: Wholesale Trade List No. 26, 1924–1925,* price list available; Herbert N. Schiffer, *Collectible Rabbits,*

Schiffer Publishing, Ltd., 1990; Margaret Schiffer, *Holidays Toys and Decorations,* Schiffer Publishing Ltd., 1985; Ellen Stern, *The Very Best From Hallmark: Greeting Cards Through The Years,* Harry N. Abrams, Inc., 1988.

**Periodicals:** *Trick or Treat Trader,* P. O. Box 499, Winchester, NH 03470.

Easter
- Advertising Box, Kauffman's Egg Dye, early 1900s .......... **75.00**
- Bank, figural, rabbit, plastic, red and white check top, orange felt skirt, marked "Roy Des of Fla," 1968 .. **20.00**
- Basket, woven cardboard, cellophane grass, cotton batting chicks ...... **25.00**
- Book
  - *Peter Cottontail,* 1940 ........... **10.00**
  - *The Tale of Peter Rabbit,* Edna M Aldredge and Jessie F McKee, Harter Publishing Co, 1931 .... **18.00**
  - *Uncle Wiggily Starts Off,* 1940s .. **12.00**
- Box, Swansdown Easter Eggs, clown, Blacks, and Mickey Mouse illus, 1940s .......... **45.00**
- Cake Mold, rabbit, Griswold ....... **275.00**
- Candy Container
  - Egg shape, litho tin, 1930 ....... **50.00**
  - Rabbit
    - Glass, seated, pink ribbon, J H Millstein Co, 1940s ......... **15.00**
    - Pressed Cardboard, 8″ h ....... **75.00**
- Cookie Cutter, Easter lily, tin, backplate, late 19th C ............. **18.00**
- Dinner Bell, ceramic, rabbit on top of bell, marked "Happy Easter 1979" **15.00**
- Egg, 6″ h, milk glass, marked "Easter Greetings" .................... **50.00**
- Figure, rabbit, chalk, pink, 1930–40 **12.00**
- Ice Cream Mold, pewter, Easter lily, early 20th C .................. **50.00**
- Lunch Pail, metal, Peter Rabbit, 1920s ...................... **75.00**
- Nodder, 5″ h, rabbit, wearing girl's clothing, papier mache ......... **275.00**
- Nut Cup, yellow crepe paper, cardboard cutout rabbit, name tag, 1940 ........................ **5.00**
- Pinata, Easter rabbit with carrot, standing, unused, Mexican, mid 20th C ........................ **35.00**
- Pip Squeak, egg, rabbit dec, Grand Toys, 1960s .................. **8.00**
- Post Card
  - Happy Easter, four chicks and flowers, one chick emerging from egg shell ....................... **10.00**
  - To Greet You on Easter Day, bunny discovering girl in basket, Raphael Tuck & Sons ........... **10.00**
- Roly Poly, celluloid, decorated egg

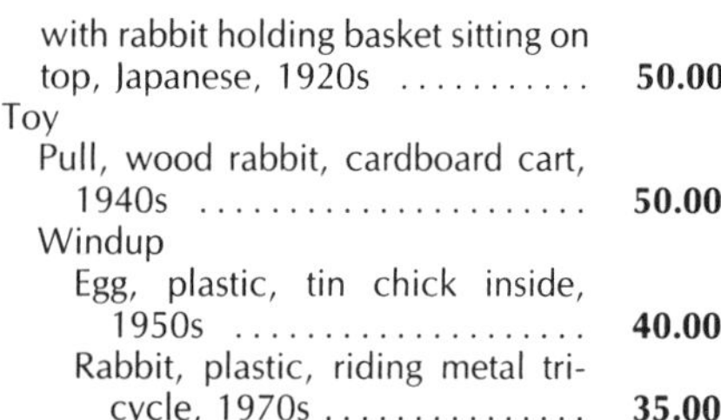

  with rabbit holding basket sitting on top, Japanese, 1920s ........... **50.00**
- Toy
  - Pull, wood rabbit, cardboard cart, 1940s ...................... **50.00**
  - Windup
    - Egg, plastic, tin chick inside, 1950s .................... **40.00**
    - Rabbit, plastic, riding metal tricycle, 1970s ............... **35.00**

**Easter, toy, Easter Copter, windup, litho tin, pink plastic propeller, Japan, 6″ l, 3½″ h, $12.00.**

Father's Day, pinback button, 1¾″ d, blue, white, and yellow, c1940 .... **15.00**

Fourth of July
- Bank, 7″ h, Liberty Bell, patinated white metal, wood closure ...... **110.00**
- Bottle Opener, Uncle Sam, cast iron, painted, early 20th C ........... **35.00**
- Candy Container, Uncle Sam, composition, removable base, 1920s . **175.00**
- Chocolate Mold, Liberty Bell, tin, early 20th C .................. **35.00**
- Needlework, "Stars & Stripes," punched paper, rect shape, orig grain painted frame, early 20th C . **275.00**
- Pinback Button
  - ⅞″ d, "Fourth of July 1919," red, white, and blue flag, white background ...................... **12.00**
  - 1¼″ d
    - Cleveland Independence Day Association 1911, Sane Fourth, multicolored, eagle and shield ................. **25.00**
    - Fire Department of Forest City issue, red, white, and blue, 1930s .................... **25.00**
    - July 4th Celebration, Homecoming And Made In LaCrosse Celebration, multicolored, c1912 **50.00**
- Post Card, Wishing You a Glorious 4th of July, children, dog, firecrackers, and flag, emb .............. **10.00**

**Independence Day, post card, emb, red, white, blue, and gold, divided back, International Art Publ. Co., 5¼ x 3¼", $4.50.**

- Sheet Music, Yankee Doodle Dandy, James Cagney, 1931 .......... **20.00**
- Tablecloth, paper, printed red, white, and blue flags and Liberty Bell, Dennison .......... **10.00**

Ground Hog Day, post card, two dressed ground hogs with shadows . **150.00**

Halloween
- Apron, crepe paper, orange and black, ruffled edge .......... **25.00**
- Bank, skeleton, laying in coffin, tin, Japan, mid 20th C .......... **45.00**
- Candle, pumpkin face, painted features, 1940 .......... **5.00**
- Candy Container
  - Black Cat, plastic, orange dec ... **5.00**
  - Devil's Head, papier mache, 1930s **225.00**
  - Jack–o'–lantern, composition, early 20th C .......... **75.00**
  - Witch, head, papier mache, early 20th C .......... **175.00**
- Chocolate Mold, four witches, Germany, early 20th C .......... **150.00**
- Cookie Cutters, metal, set of six, Halloween scene on orig box ....... **48.00**
- Costume, Wicked Witch, Wizard of Oz, orig box .......... **50.00**
- Fan, orange tissue, black cat, fold–out, Germany, 1920 .......... **20.00**

**Halloween, cat lantern, cardboard and paper, 7" w ear to ear, 5¾" h, $75.00.**

- Game, Cat and Witch, Whitman, party type, 1940s, unused, MIB .. **50.00**
- Horn, metal, marked "USA" ....... **18.00**
- Jack–o'–lantern
  - 3" h, face, German .......... **68.00**
  - 4" h, orig paper eyes .......... **45.00**
- Mask, clown face, papier mache, painted features, early 20th C .... **35.00**
- Noisemaker, litho tin, T Cohn Inc .. **20.00**
- Nut Cup, jack–o'–lantern, crepe paper and cardboard, 1940 ........ **35.00**
- Pinback Button, 1½" d, yellow, black, and white, Halloween symbols, 1930s .......... **25.00**
- Post Card
  - Halloween Greetings, woman bobbing for apples, jack–o'–lantern border, E C Banks, 1909 ...... **12.00**
  - Happy Halloween, witch on broom, early 20th C .......... **10.00**
  - Wishing You a Merry Halloween, black cat driving jack–o'–lantern carriage, pulled by six mice, checked border, 1912 ........ **15.00**
- Salt and Pepper Shakers, devils, 1930s .......... **52.00**
- Tambourine, pumpkin face
  - Metal .......... **25.00**
  - Paper over wood frame, German . **130.00**
  - Tin, 6½" d, people dancing illus . **75.00**
- Trick–or–Treat Bag, paper, litho pumpkin head and Happy Halloween, 1940 .......... **18.00**
- Wall Decoration, 2 x 6", jack–o'–lantern, cardboard cutout, black, orange tissue dec, double sided .... **55.00**

Mother's Day
- Pinback Button
  - ⅞" d, white carnation, red, background, white lettering, 1920s . **18.00**

**Mother's Day, magazine tear sheet, Whitman's Chocolates and Confections adv, Pioneer Woman statue illus, $8.00.**

1¾" d
Gimbels Mother's Day Reminder, black and white, pink carnations, green stems, 1940–50 .......... **12.00**
Whitman's Chocolates/Mother's Day, blue and white, 1930s . **12.00**

New Year's Day
Banner, "Happy New Year," paper, silver border, 1930 .......... **10.00**
Centerpiece, 9" h, Father Time, cardboard, scythe, emb "New Year's Greetings" .......... **25.00**
Hat, headband, silver, glitter dec, plume in center, 1920 .......... **10.00**
Noisemaker
Paper over cardboard, horn, silver and black, 1930 .......... **5.00**
Litho tin, wood handle, Kirchhof . **20.00**
Post Card
A Happy New Year, four pigs illus, hold to light type .......... **30.00**
Happy New Year, emb, flowers encircle 1912 .......... **10.00**

President's Day
Bank, bottle shape, glass, Abraham Lincoln, tin closure .......... **25.00**
Bookends, pr, Abraham Lincoln standing by chair, bronzed metal, early 20th C .......... **35.00**
Candy Container, bust, Washington, papier mache, early 20th C ...... **110.00**
Ice Cream Mold, Washington chopping cherry tree, iron, early 20th C **75.00**
Post Card
Liberty and Union Now and Forever, little girl and flag draped portrait of Washington, emb, gilded highlights .......... **10.00**
Lincoln Centennial Souvenir, Lincoln's Birthday Series 1, emb, gilded highlights, copyright 1908 **6.00**

St Patrick's Day
Candy Container, bust, Irishman, molded cardboard, hp .......... **75.00**
Handkerchief, linen, embroidered shamrock, crocheted green border **5.00**
Nut Cup, green and white crepe paper, double frill, cardboard shamrock .......... **5.00**
Pinback Button
⅞" d, "St Patrick's Day 1897," green and gold, white background with Irish harp and shamrock .......... **15.00**
1¼" d, multicolored, c1950 ..... **12.00**
Place Card, leprechaun with pot of gold and name tag .......... **5.00**
Post Card, The Charm of the Morn to You, Here's wishing you a bright and happy St Patrick's Day, little girl holding flower bouquet, 1916 **15.00**
Sheet Music, "When Irish Eyes Are Smiling," 1930s .......... **10.00**
Tablecloth, paper, printed leprechauns and shamrocks, green and white, orig cellophane package, mid 20th C .......... **10.00**

Thanksgiving Day
Advertising Trade Card, Acme Stove Co, Thanksgiving greetings, emb, 1936 .......... **7.00**
Apron, fabric, "Happy Thanksgiving," leaf border .......... **5.00**
Book, *Thanksgiving,* Dennison, 1930 **10.00**
Candy Container, 3½" h, turkey, composition, bottom closure, Germany **45.00**
Chocolate Mold, 8" h, turkey, German .......... **30.00**
Costume, Pilgrim, boy, handmade, 1940s .......... **15.00**
Greeting Card, "Happy Thanksgiving," turkey, mid 20th C ........ **5.00**
Ice Cream Mold, cornucopia, pewter, early 20th C .......... **22.00**
Menu, Hotel Astor, Thanksgiving dinner, early 20th C .......... **10.00**
Plate, 9" d, glass, emb turkey ...... **35.00**
Post Card
May Your Thanksgiving Pies Always Turn Out Well, little girl preparing pies for her dolls, emb, H B Griggs **15.00**
With Thanksgiving Greeting, maiden and turkey, John Winsch, copyright 1911 .......... **25.00**
Salt and Pepper Shakers, pr, turkey, pottery, brown and red, mid 20th C **10.00**
Tablecloth, paper, Pilgrims and Indians at feast, matching napkins, price for set .......... **25.00**

Valentine's Day
Banner, fabric, stenciled, hearts, "Happy Valentine's Day," 1930s . **75.00**
Candy Box, heart shape, red satin, gold lace dec, doves center ...... **35.00**
Cookbook, Valentine Queen of Hearts, Jell–O, early 20th C ..... **18.00**
Greeting Card
Easel back, children ice skating, Grace Drayton, early 20th C ... **25.00**
Fold–out
Floral "LOVE," paper lace dec . **25.00**
Girl's head in heart, flowers with white lace, 1940 .......... **15.00**
Mechanical
Automobile, children, flower festoons, movable wheels, 1930s **150.00**
Black boy, wearing soldier uniform, emb, 1930s .......... **50.00**
Boy on skis, winter scene, verse **25.00**
Snow White, 1938 .......... **50.00**
Pop–up Center, train filled with flowers and hearts, c1920 ..... **50.00**

Mold, aluminum, heart shape, "Happy Valentine's Day," 1940 .. **10.00**
Post Card
  Hearts with arrows, cupid, and flowers, early 20th C ......... **10.00**
  St Valentine's Greeting, Woman's sphere is in the Home, little girl sitting on rocker, Ellen H Clapsaddle ...................... **100.00**
  To My Dear Valentine, monk child with wings ................. **8.00**
  To My Valentine, naked boy with wings and fire hat and boots, putting out flaming heart ......... **6.00**
  Valentine Message, Aw, Don't Be Jealous Rags, child and dog, emb, gilded highlights ........ **8.00**
Sheet Music, "My Funny Valentine" **4.00**

# HOMER LAUGHLIN

**Collecting Hints:** The original trademark from 1871 to 1890 merely identified the products as "Laughlin Brothers." The next trademark featured the American eagle astride the prostrate British lion. The third marking featured a monogram of "HLC" which has appeared, with slight variations, on all dinnerware since about 1900. The 1900 trademark contained a number which identified month, year and plant at which the product was made. Letter codes were used in later periods.

So much attention has been placed on Fiesta that other interesting patterns have not achieved the popularity which they deserve. Prices still are moderate. Some of the patterns from the 1930 to 1940 period have contemporary designs that are highly artistic.

Virginia Rose is a shape, not a pattern name. Several different decals can be found, with delicate pink flowers the most common.

**History:** Homer Laughlin and his brother, Shakespeare, built two pottery kilns in East Liverpool, Ohio, in 1871. Shakespeare withdrew in 1879, leaving Homer to operate the business alone. Laughlin became one of the first firms to produce American–made whiteware. In 1896, William Wills and a Pittsburgh group led by Marcus Aaron bought the Laughlin firm.

Expansion followed. Two new plants were built in Laughlin Station, Ohio. In 1906, the first plant (#4) was built in Newall, West Virginia. In 1923 plant #6 was built at Newall and featured a continuous tunnel kiln. Similar kilns were added at the other plants. Other advances included spray glazing and mechanical jiggering.

In the 1930 to 1960 period several new dinnerware lines were added, including the Wells Art Glaze line. Ovenserve and Kitchen Kraft were the cooking ware lines. The colored glaze lines of Fiesta, Harlequin and Rhythm captured major market shares. In 1959 a translucent table china line was introduced. Today, the annual manufacturing capacity is over 45 million pieces.

**References:** Jo Cunningham, *The Collector's Encyclopedia of American Dinnerware,* Collector Books, 1982, 1992 value update; Joanne Jasper, *The Collector's Encyclopedia of Homer Laughlin China: Reference & Value Guide,* Collector Books, 1993.

**Periodical:** *The Daze,* 10271 State Rd., P.O. Box 57, Otisville, MI 48463.

**REPRODUCTION ALERT.** Harlequin and Fiesta lines were reissued in 1978 and marked accordingly.

**See:** Fiesta

**DOGWOOD.** Produced early 1960s. Dogwood decal on white ground. Gold trim.

Bowl, 5¾" d ....................... **3.00**
Creamer and Sugar ................. **10.00**
Plate, 9" d ........................ **5.00**
Platter, 11¾" l .................... **9.00**
Soup ............................. **6.00**
Vegetable, oval ................... **9.00**

**EPICURE.** Produced in the 1950s in four pastel colors: Charcoal Gray, Dawn Pink, Snow White, and Turquoise Blue.

Casserole, turquoise ............... **45.00**
Creamer, turquoise ................ **15.00**
Gravy Boat, turquoise .............. **20.00**
Sugar, cov, charcoal ............... **20.00**

**HARLEQUIN.** Sold by F. W. Woolworth Company. Introduced in the late 1930s in four colors: Bright Yellow, Spruce Green, Maroon, and Mauve Blue. Harlequin was eventually produced in all the Fiesta colors except Ivory and Cobalt Blue. The line was discontinued in 1964. It was reissued in 1979 in Turquoise, Yellow, Medium Green, and Coral. The reissued plates have a Homer Laughlin backstamp.

Ashtray, basketweave, Red .......... **25.00**
Ball Jug, 22 oz
  Gray ........................... **54.00**
  Maroon ......................... **60.00**
Bowl, 5½" d
  Maroon ......................... **10.00**
  Red ............................ **7.50**
Butter, cov, Maroon ................ **95.00**
Candle Holders, pr, Turquoise ....... **75.00**
Casserole, cov, Maroon ............. **135.00**
Cereal Bowl, Yellow ................ **7.00**

Creamer
  Individual
    Maroon ........ **22.00**
    Turquoise ........ **10.00**
    Yellow ........ **10.00**
  Large, Medium Green ........ **40.00**
Cream Soup, Turquoise ........ **15.00**
Cup, Maroon ........ **7.50**
Cup and Saucer, Gray ........ **9.50**
Demitasse Cup and Saucer, Turquoise **40.00**
Eggcup
  Double
    Gray ........ **28.00**
    Turquoise ........ **14.00**
  Individual
    Gray ........ **21.00**
    Mauve Blue ........ **20.00**
    Spruce Green ........ **30.00**
    Turquoise ........ **20.00**
Fish, Yellow ........ **72.00**
Gravy, Yellow ........ **10.00**
Nappy, Yellow ........ **30.00**
Nut Dish, three part, Mauve Blue ........ **6.60**
Pitcher, water, Medium Green ........ **70.00**
Plate
  6″ d, Maroon ........ **6.00**
  7″ d
    Chartreuse ........ **6.50**
    Gray ........ **6.50**
    Maroon ........ **9.00**
    Rose ........ **9.00**
  9¼″ d, Rose ........ **6.00**
  10″ d, Gray ........ **25.00**
Salad Bowl, individual, Yellow ........ **20.00**
Soup, flat, Rose ........ **14.00**
Teacup, Mauve Blue ........ **16.00**
Teapot, Medium Green ........ **60.00**

**JUBILEE.** Introduced in 1948 to celebrate the company's 75th anniversary. Original four colors were Celadon Gray, Cream Beige, Mist Green, and Shell Pink.

Coffee Server, Shell Pink ........ **35.00**
Mayonnaise, underplate, Shell Pink ... **70.00**
Plate, dinner
  Cream Beige ........ **5.00**
  Mist Gray ........ **5.00**
Saucer
  Celadon Green ........ **3.00**
  Shell Pink ........ **3.00**

**KITCHEN KRAFT.** Kitchenware line with floral decals produced from the early 1930s. Pieces are marked Kitchen Kraft and/or Oven–Serve.

Casserole, 8½″ d, metal stand ........ **65.00**
Jug, cov ........ **75.00**
Mixing Bowl, 8″ d ........ **20.00**
Pie Plate ........ **25.00**
Salt and Pepper Shakers, pr ........ **28.00**

**MEXICANA.** Introduced in 1937. Cactus and pottery decal. Produced in the Century shape although it is occasionally found on other shapes. Trimmed with red, blue, green, or yellow bands with red being the most common.

Baker, oval ........ **25.00**
Bowl, 5″ d ........ **10.00**
Creamer ........ **20.00**
Cup and Saucer ........ **12.00**
Nappy ........ **25.00**
Pie Baker, 9″ d ........ **35.00**
Plate
  7″ d ........ **10.00**
  9″ d ........ **15.00**
Soup, flat ........ **22.00**

**RHYTHM.** Produced from 1950 to 1960 in solid colors of Chartreuse, Forest Green, Gray, Harlequin Yellow, and Maroon. The Rhythm shape was also produced with decal decoration on a white ground.

Bowl, 5″ d, Maroon ........ **4.00**
Plate
  7″ d
    Gray ........ **3.00**
    Maroon ........ **3.00**
  9″ d, Chartreuse ........ **6.00**
Platter, 11½″ l, Forest Green ........ **13.00**
Saucer, Gray ........ **3.00**
Soup Bowl, 8″ d
  Chartreuse ........ **8.00**
  Forest Green ........ **8.00**
  Harlequin Yellow ........ **8.00**

**RIVIERA.** Introduced in 1938, this dinnerware line was sold by the Murphy Company. Though usually unmarked, it is occasionally found with

**Riviera, Century shape, creamer and covered sugar: $14.00; dinner plate: $12.00; luncheon plate: $10.00; salad plate: $8.00; bowl: $5.00; cup and saucer: $10.00.**

a gold backstamp. Produced in the Century shape in Dark Blue (rare), Light Green, Ivory, Mauve Blue, Red, and Yellow.

| Item | Price |
|---|---|
| Casserole, Mauve Blue | **60.00** |
| Creamer and Sugar, cov, Light Green | **14.00** |
| Cream Soup, Yellow | **30.00** |
| Cup | |
| Light Green | **7.50** |
| Mauve Blue | **7.50** |
| Deep Plate, Yellow | **15.00** |
| Nappy | |
| Red | **18.00** |
| Yellow | **18.00** |
| Plate, 7" d, Dark Blue | **20.00** |
| Platter, 11½" l, Yellow | **18.50** |
| Salt Shaker, Red | **8.00** |
| Sugar, cov, Mauve Blue | **10.00** |

**Virginia Rose, eggcup: $8.00; dinner plate: $6.00; flat soup: $7.00; fruit bowl: $4.50; cup and saucer: $3.50.**

**VIRGINIA ROSE.** This is the name of a shape rather than a decal pattern as the name might imply. It was produced from 1929 until the early 1970s and was decorated with numerous floral decals. Pieces were trimmed with either silver or gold bands.

| Item | Price |
|---|---|
| Cup and Saucer | **3.50** |
| Fruit Bowl, 5½" d | **4.50** |
| Plate, 9" d, dinner | **6.00** |
| Soup | **7.00** |
| Vegetable, cov | **45.00** |

# HORSE COLLECTIBLES

**Collecting Hints:** Horses have been a strong influence in most aspects of the American lifestyle. They have been immortalized in nearly every media possible, creating a wide variety of equine–related memorabilia for collectors.

There is almost no category of collecting that does not include some sort of horse collectible. Advertising featuring the horse abounds—from the earliest saddle catalogs to current offerings featuring the Budweiser Clydesdales. Some of the most popular 1990s collectibles are 1950s items such as lamps, china, and blankets decorated with Western themes.

Television cowboy collectibles continue to be very popular. Look for collectibles featuring famous show business horses like Hopalong Cassidy's Topper, Tom Mix's Tony, and Roy Rogers' Trigger. Tack, from the beautifully handcrafted, ornately decorated parade saddles to the simple mochilla carried by the pony express rider, is always collectible.

Decorative items, especially figurines, attract the collector. Ceramic figurines and the Breyer and Hartland plastic model horses are enthusiastically collected.

Old rodeo programs, horse show trophies, state fair ribbons, horse racing memorabilia, bridle rosettes, soft plush toys, and advertising signs are a few more examples of collector categories. Equine art has become popular.

Many horse enthusiasts, overwhelmed by the volume and variety of equine collectibles available to them, choose to specialize. A sports fan may collect memorabilia from the Olympic Equestrian Teams, while a racing fan may collect Kentucky Derby glasses. Memorabilia from specific breeds also is popular.

Carousel horses remain a high ticket item, although prices have leveled off for the more common examples. Many smaller horses can be purchased for less than $5,000. The best examples still sell well. In 1992, an outside row horse carved by the artist Daniel Muller, around 1905, set a new auction record for a Muller figure, selling at $79,500.

Horse related toys, especially horse–drawn cast iron fire trucks, buses, and grocery wagons continue to be desirable. Buy carefully. Many of these cast iron toys have been reproduced. Reproductions usually have rather gaudy paint schemes, and the pieces fit together poorly.

**History:** Since the earliest days of our nation's history, the horse has played a vital role in American growth and lifestyle. Even our language reflects our love and respect for the horse. If we make intelligent decisions, we are credited with having "horse sense."

The English colonists brought the horse with them to the New World for transportation, plowing, and even as a food source. A person's social status was determined by the number and quality of his horses. Remember the condescending term, "one horse town?"

As the country became more civilized, people could afford an occasional day of rest. It quickly became a day to show off your horses and compete with those of your neighbor. Organized horse races and shows evolved from these casual Sunday afternoon gatherings.

As the motorcar became more affordable, the need for the horse died out. Today's horses are likely to be pampered family pets, living a sheltered life that a hard–working draft animal of the 1800s could only dream about.

**Reference:** Jim and Nancy Schaut, *Horsin' Around: A Price Guide To Horse Collectibles*, L–W Books, 1990.

**Museums:** Harness Racing Hall of Fame, Goshen, NY; Gene Autry Western Heritage Museum, Los Angeles, CA; Pony Express Museum, Joplin, MO.

**Advisors:** Jim and Nancy Schaut.

## HORSE EQUIPMENT AND RELATED ITEMS

### Bells, worn leather strap

24" l, four graduated size brass bells, nail holes in leather, probably nailed to wagon shaft ........... **100.00**
84" l, over forty nickel bells, all the same size, tug hook ........... **200.00**
Blanket, saddle, Navajo Indian made, early 1900s ..................... **600.00**
Bit, eagle, marked "G. S. Garcia" .... **700.00**
Bridle
Horsehair ....................... **200.00**
Walla Walla Prison made .......... **900.00**
Brush, leather back, stamped "US" (cavalry), patented 1860, Herbert Brush Mfg Co ................... **60.00**
Catalog, James Bailey Co, Portland, ME, 1912 edition, carriage and sleigh trimmings ...................... **60.00**
Collar, draft horse, leather covered wood, some brass trim ........... **75.00**
Curry Comb, tin back, leather handle, early 1900s ..................... **20.00**
Harness Brass Decoration, prancing horse in center, tape on back reads "Laura Grey," worn smooth from use **50.00**
Hobbles, chain and leather, sideline type .......................... **75.00**
Hoof Pick, bone handle, patent date 1855, Wastenholm, Germany ...... **50.00**
Ice Delivery Wagon, two horse hitch, some wood needs restoring, orig sign painted on sides ................**1,200.00**
Lasso, rawhide covered tips, 1890s ... **250.00**
Mane and Tail Comb, 1940s, stamped "Oliver Slant Tooth" ............ **20.00**
Popcorn Wagon, Creators, good orig condition, needs minor cosmetic work ..........................**5,000.00**
Saddle
McClelland type, large fenders for leg protection, early 1900s ......... **600.00**
Tooled leather, F M Sterns, CA maker **80.00**
Sidesaddle, tapestry seat, pre–1920s, maker unknown .................. **500.00**
Spurs
Arrow shank, stamped "Crockett" .. **600.00**
Brass, stamped "CSA," very rare ... **650.00**
Wagon Seat, springs, new leather upholstery on padded seat ........... **75.00**
Watering Trough, 24 x 36" l, hollowed out log, lined with tin ............. **100.00**

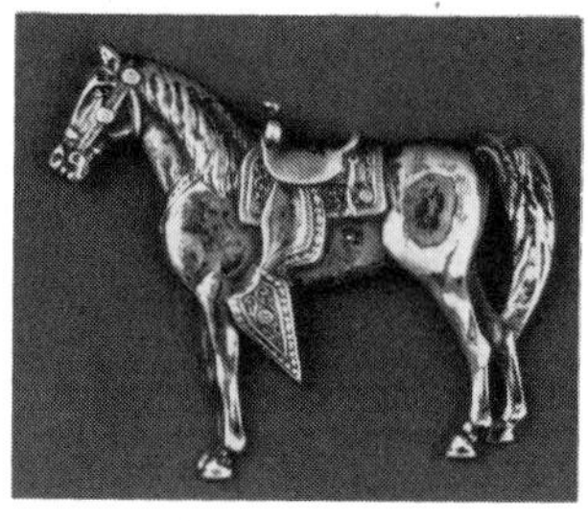

**Pin, sterling silver, 2¾" l, 2¼" h, $50.00.**

## HORSE THEME ITEMS

Bank, still
Arcade, horse and horseshoe, cast iron, Buster Brown shoe adv, 4½" h ............................ **250.00**
Ertl, horse and tank wagon, Texaco, #8 in series .................. **35.00**
Blanket, western theme, cowboys and horses on brown wool, 1950 ...... **95.00**
Book, Walter Farley, *The Black Stallion*, first edition, dust jacket ........... **15.00**
Bookends, pr, thoroughbred head, cast aluminum, signed "Bruce Cox" .... **150.00**
Calendar, 1907, Dousman Milling, cowgirl with horse, cardboard, 10 x 20" ........................... **50.00**
Carousel Horse, jumper, C W Parker, American flag on side, c1918 ......**4,500.00**
Catalog, D F Mangels Co, Carousel Works, Coney Island, NY, 28 pages, 1928 edition .................... **200.00**
Cookie Cutter, prancing horse, bobtail, 6½ x 7½", flat back ............. **100.00**
Cookie Jar, sitting horse, American Bisque .......................... **75.00**
Doorstop, racehorse, Virginia Metalcrafters, 1949 ................... **150.00**
Fan, adv, Moxie, rocking horse on front, 1920s .......................... **25.00**
Figurine
Breyer, plastic, Old Timer, Dapple gray, glossy finish, straw hat ..... **60.00**
Hagen Renaker, ceramic, miniature donkey, 2" h, 1986 ............. **10.00**
Heisey, glass, Clydesdale, amber ...**2,500.00**

Summit Art Glass, blue horse, short legs . . . . . . . . . . . . . . . . . . . . . . . . . . **25.00**
Vernon Kilns, ceramic, black unicorn from Disney Movie "Fantasia" . . . **250.00**
Wade, England, ceramic, miniature pony, Tom Smith artist . . . . . . . . . . **20.00**
Fruit Crate Label, Loop Loop, Washington State Apples, Indian chief on Palomino . . . . . . . . . . . . . . . . . . . . . . . . . . **10.00**
Game, Derby Day, Parker Bros, 72" game board, wooden horses, 1959 . **45.00**
Glass, Kentucky Derby, 1950 . . . . . . . . **85.00**
Hobby Horse, Tom Mix, wood, wheels on platform . . . . . . . . . . . . . . . . . . . . . . **500.00**
Lapel Pin, US Olympic Equestrian Team, 1988 . . . . . . . . . . . . . . . . . . . . . **5.00**
Liquor Decanter, Ezra Brooks, Man O'War, 1969 . . . . . . . . . . . . . . . . . . . . **25.00**
Magazine, *Western Horseman,* Volume 1, #1, 1935 . . . . . . . . . . . . . . . . . . . . . **15.00**
Mug, Frankoma, figural, ceramic, donkey, red, 1976 Democratic Party souvenir . . . . . . . . . . . . . . . . . . . . . . . . . . **35.00**
Paperweight, donkey, sgd "Louise Able, Rockwood," #6241 . . . . . . . . . . . . . . **125.00**
Plate, Syracuse China, Love The Rodeo pattern . . . . . . . . . . . . . . . . . . . . . . . . . . **50.00**
Post Card, three draft horses, heads shown, pre–1920, German . . . . . . . . **5.00**

**Post Card, Anheuser-Busch, Inc., double card, Clydesdales, color, 1944, 11 x 3½", $30.00.**

Poster, Beer Exhibitions, 1913, Dayton, OH Fairgrounds, "Saddle Horse Contests," nicely framed . . . . . . . . . . . . . . **300.00**
Salt and Pepper Shakers, pr, whimsical donkeys, one sitting, one kicking, Japan, 1950s . . . . . . . . . . . . . . . . . . . . . . **15.00**
Sheet Music, *Dan Patch March,* photo of Dan Patch on cov . . . . . . . . . . . . . . **60.00**
Sign, tin, Hunter Cigars, shows fox hunter with horse, c1915, 19 x 27" . **250.00**
Snowdome, Budweiser Clydesdales, 1988 edition, MIB . . . . . . . . . . . . . . . . **40.00**
Stuffed Toy, mule, collar inscription reads "One of the Twenty Mule Team," 1980s Boraxo promotion . . . **15.00**
Toy
Gibbs, hay cart, paper litho and painted wood, c1910, 19" l . . . . . **300.00**
Hubley, ice wagon, cast iron, 1920s, 9½" l . . . . . . . . . . . . . . . . . . . . . . . . . **250.00**
Tray, Genessee Twelve Horse Ale, shows horse team . . . . . . . . . . . . . . . . **75.00**
Windmill Weight, Dempster, Beatrice, NE, bob tail horse, 17" h . . . . . . . . . . **500.00**

# HULL POTTERY

**Collecting Hints:** Hull Pottery has distinctive markings on the bottom of its vases that help the collector identify them immediately. Early stoneware pottery has an "H." The famous matte pieces, a favorite of most collectors, contain pattern numbers. For example, Camelia pieces are marked with numbers in the 100's, Iris pieces have 400 numbers, and Wildflower numbers with a W– preceding their number. Most of Hull's vases are also marked with their height in inches, making determining their value much easier. Items made after 1950 are marked with "hull" or "Hull" in large script writing and are usually glossy.

**History:** In 1905 Addis E. Hull purchased the Acme Pottery Co. in Crooksville, Ohio. In 1917 A. E. Hull Pottery Co. began to make a line of art pottery for florists and gift shops. The company also made novelties, kitchenware, and stoneware. During the Depression, the company's largest production was tiles.

In 1950 the factory was destroyed by a flood and fire. By 1952 it was back in production, operating with the Hull Pottery Company name. At this time Hull added its newer glossy finish pottery plus developed Regal and Floraline as trade names for pieces sold in flower shops. Hull's brown House 'n Garden line of kitchen and dinnerware achieved great popularity and was the main line of pottery being produced prior to the plant closing its doors in 1986. Hull's Little Red Riding Hood kitchenware was manufactured between 1943 and 1957 and is a favorite of collectors, including many who do not collect other Hull items.

Hull collectors are beginning to seriously collect the glossy ware and kitchen items. Since the plant has closed, all Hull pieces have become desirable.

**References:** Joan Gray Hull, *Hull: The Heavenly Pottery,* published by author, 1993; Barbara Loveless Gick–Burke, *Collector's Guide To Hull Pottery, The Dinnerware Lines: Identification and Values,* Collector Books, 1993; Brenda Roberts, *Roberts Ultimate Encyclopedia Of Hull Pottery,* Walsworth Publishing Co., 1992; Brenda Roberts, *The Collectors Encyclopedia of Hull Pottery,* Collector Books, 1980, 1993 value update; Brenda Roberts, *The Companion Guide To Roberts' Ultimate Encyclopedia Of Hull Pottery,* Walsworth Publishing Co., 1992; Mark E. Supnick,

*Collecting Hull Pottery's Little Red Riding Hood,* L–W Book Sales, 1989, 1992 value update.

**Advisor:** Joan Hull.

## PRE-1950 PATTERNS

- Bow Knot
  - B–1–5½", pitcher **175.00**
  - B–5–6½", cornucopia **150.00**
  - B–10–10¼", vase **350.00**
  - B–25–6½", basket **250.00**
- Dogwood (Wild Rose)
  - 503–8½", vase **95.00**
  - 510–10½", vase **200.00**
  - 517–4¾", vase **50.00**
- Iris (Narcissus)
  - 401–8", pitcher **150.00**
  - 407–7", vase **95.00**
  - 414–10½", vase **300.00**
- Jack–in–the–Pulpit (Calla Lily)
  - 501–33–6", vase **65.00**
  - 510–33–8", vase **100.00**
  - 590–33–13", console bowl **150.00**
- Magnolia (Pink Gloss)
  - H–23, console bowl **75.00**
  - H–24, candleholders **75.00**
- Magnolia
  - 1–8½", vase **85.00**
  - 6–12", double cornucopia **100.00**
  - 13–4¾", vase **45.00**
  - 17–12½", winged vase **225.00**
- Open Rose (Camelia)
  - 102–8½", vase **95.00**
  - 110, 111, 112, tea set **450.00**
  - 120–6¼", vase **60.00**
  - 139–10½", lamp vase **400.00**
- Orchid
  - 302–4¾" **75.00**
  - 303–6½" **125.00**
  - 307–8" **195.00**
  - 308–10" **300.00**
- Poppy
  - 602–6½", planter **150.00**
  - 610–13", pitcher **650.00**
- Rosella
  - R–2–5", vase **30.00**
  - R–6–6½" **50.00**
  - R–13–8½", cornucopia **60.00**
- Stoneware
  - 536, H, jardiniere **50.00**
  - 39, H, 8", vase **85.00**
- Thistle, 52–6½" **125.00**
- Tile (Hull Cushion)
  - Designed **50.00**
  - Plain **20.00**
- Tulip (Sueno)
  - 100–33–6½", vase **90.00**
  - 102–33–6", basket **225.00**
  - 117–30–5", jardiniere **85.00**
- Waterlily
  - L–3–5½", pitcher **50.00**
  - L–11–9½", vase **100.00**
  - L–24–8½", jardiniere **200.00**
- Wildflower
  - W–9–8½", vase **75.00**
  - W–15–10½", fan vase **95.00**
  - W–19–13½", pitcher **450.00**
  - 52–5½" **125.00**
  - 65–7", low basket **600.00**
  - 71–12", vase **275.00**
- Woodland (Matte)
  - W–4–6½", vase **50.00**
  - W–13–7½", shell wall pocket **75.00**
  - W–17–7½", suspended vase **150.00**

## POST-1950 PATTERNS

- Blossom Flite
  - T–4–8½", basket **85.00**
  - T–7–10½", vase **60.00**
  - T–14,15,16, tea set **125.00**
- Butterfly
  - B–6–5½", candy dish **40.00**
  - B–9–9", vase **45.00**
  - B–24–25", Lavabo set **200.00**
- Capri
  - C–47–5¼" x 8", round flower bowl **40.00**
  - C–81, twin swan planter **75.00**
- Continental
  - C–53–8½", vase **40.00**
  - C–54–12½", vase **60.00**
- Ebbtide
  - E–2–7", twin fish vase **65.00**
  - E–11–16½", basket **200.00**

**Ebbtide, console bowl, E-12, 15¾" l, $100.00.**

- Figural Planters
  - 24, Madonna planter **35.00**
  - 62, 12", deer planter **55.00**
  - 98, 10", unicorn base **45.00**
- Parchment & Pine
  - S–4–10", vase **95.00**
  - S–5–10½", scroll planter **85.00**
- Serenade (Birds)
  - S–2–6", pitcher **35.00**
  - S–11–10½", vase **75.00**
- Sunglow (Kitchenware)
  - 54, salt and pepper **25.00**
  - 81, pitcher wall pocket **45.00**
  - 91, 6½", vase **35.00**

Tokay/Tuscany
  1–6½", cornucopia . . . . . . . . . . . . . . . **30.00**
  8–10, vase . . . . . . . . . . . . . . . . . . . . . . . **85.00**
  15–12", basket . . . . . . . . . . . . . . . . . . . **100.00**
Tropicania, 56–13½", pitcher . . . . . . . . **550.00**
Woodland
  W-3–5½", pitcher . . . . . . . . . . . . . . . **40.00**
  W-8–7½", vase . . . . . . . . . . . . . . . . . . **40.00**
  W-10–11", cornucopia . . . . . . . . . . . **45.00**

# HUMMEL ITEMS

**Collecting Hints:** A key to Hummel figures is the mark. Collectors are advised to get the early marks whenever possible. Since production runs were large, almost all figurines, no matter what the mark, exist in large numbers.

Prices fluctuate a great deal. Antiques newspapers, such as *The Antique Trader,* and dealers often run ads showing discounts on the modern pieces. The slightest damage to a piece lowers the value significantly.

Before World War II and for a few years after, the Goebel Company made objects, such as vases, for export. These often had the early mark. Prices are modest for these items because few collectors concentrate on them. The Hummel books do not list them. This aspect of the Goebel Company offers the chance for an excellent research project.

**History:** Hummel items are the original creations of the German artist, Berta Hummel. Born in 1909 in Massing, Bavaria, into a family where the arts were a part of everyday living, her talents were encouraged by her parents and formal educators from early childhood. At the age of 18, she was enrolled in the Academy of Fine Arts in Munich to further her mastery of drawing and the palette.

She entered the Convent of Siessen and became Sister Maria Innocentia in 1934. In this Franciscan cloister, she continued drawing and painting images of her childhood friends.

In 1935, W. Goebel Co. in Rodental, Germany, conceived the idea of reproducing Sister Berta's sketches into 3–dimensional bisque figurines. John Schmid discovered the German–made figurines. The Schmid Brothers of Randolph, Massachusetts, introduced the figurines to America and became Goebel's U.S. distributor.

In 1967, Goebel began distributing Hummel items in the U.S. and a controversy developed between the two companies involving the Hummel family and the convent. Lawsuits and counter suits ensued. The German courts finally effected a compromise. The convent held legal rights to all works produced by Sister Berta from 1934 until her death in 1964 and licensed Goebel to reproduce these works. Schmid was to deal directly with the Hummel family for permission to reproduce any pre–convent art work.

All authentic Hummels bear both the signature, M.I. Hummel, and a Goebel trademark. Various trademarks were used to identify the year of production. The Crown Mark (trademark 1) was used in 1935 until 1949; Full Bee (trademark 2) 1950–1959; Stylized Bee (trademark 3) 1957–1972; Three Line Mark (trademark 4) 1964–1972; Last Bee Mark (trademark 5) 1972–1980, Missing Bee Mark (trademark 6) 1979–1990; and the Current Mark or New Crown Mark (trademark 7) from 1991 to the present.

**References:** John F. Hotchkiss, *Hummel Art II,* Wallace–Homestead, 1981; John F. Hotchkiss, *Hotchkiss' Handbook To Hummel Art with Current Prices,* Wallace–Homestead, 1982; Carl F. Luckey, *Luckey's Hummel Figurines & Plates, 7th Edition,* Books Americana, 1987; Robert L. Miller, *The No. 1 Price Guide To M. I. Hummel: Figurines, Plates, More..., Fifth Edition* Portfolio Press, 1992; Lawrence L. Wonsch, *Hummel Copycats with Values,* Wallace–Homestead, 1987.

**Collectors' Clubs:** Goebel Collectors' Club, 105 White Plains Road, Tarrytown, NY 10591; Hummel Collectors Club, 1261 University Dr., Yardley, PA 19067; M. I. Hummel Club, Dept. O, Goebel Plaza, P.O. Box 11, Pennington, NJ 08534.

**Museum:** Goebel Museum, Tarrytown, NY.

Ashtray
  Joyful, 33, trademark 2 . . . . . . . . . . . **175.00**
  Let's Sing, 114, trademark 5 . . . . . . . **95.00**
Bell, annual
  1978, Let's Sing, 700, trademark 5 . **75.00**
  1980, Thoughtful, 702, trademark 6 **50.00**
  1984, Mountaineer, 706, trademark 6 **85.00**
  1987, With Living Greetings, 709, trademark 6 . . . . . . . . . . . . . . . . . . **125.00**
  1992, Whistler's Duet, 714, trademark 7 . . . . . . . . . . . . . . . . . . . . . . . **165.00**
Bookends, pr
  Bookworm, boy and girl, 14 A & B, trademark 5 . . . . . . . . . . . . . . . . . . **175.00**
  Feeding Time, 250 A & B, trademark 3 . . . . . . . . . . . . . . . . . . . . . . . . . . **250.00**
Candleholder
  A Gentle Glow, 439, trademark 7 . . **145.00**
  Angel With Trumpet, 1/40/0, trademark 1 . . . . . . . . . . . . . . . . . . . . . . . **80.00**
  Birthday Candle, 440, trademark 6 . **180.00**
  Little Band, 388, trademark 4 . . . . . . **200.00**
  Silent Night, 54, trademark 3 . . . . . . **275.00**
Candy Box
  Playmates, III/58, trademark 6 . . . . . **100.00**
  Singing Lesson, III/63, trademark 4 . **125.00**
Figurine
  A Fair Measure, 345, trademark 6 . . **175.00**
  Apple Tree Boy, 142/3/0, trademark 5 **95.00**

Artist, 304, trademark 4 ........... **275.00**
Baking Day, 330, trademark 6 ..... **175.00**
Band Leader, 129, trademark 3 .... **90.00**
Birthday Serenade, 218/2/0, trademark 4 ........................ **125.00**
Bookworm, 3/I, trademark 2 ....... **325.00**
Celestial Musician, 188/0, trademark 6 ............................ **130.00**
Congratulations, 17/0, trademark 2 . **200.00**
Coquettes, 179, trademark 4 ....... **175.00**
Culprits, 56/A, trademark 7 ........ **180.00**
Doll Bath, 319, trademark 6 ....... **200.00**
Evening Prayer, 495, trademark 7 .. **65.00**
Favorite Pet, 361, trademark 4 ..... **225.00**
Festival Harmony, with mandolin, 172/0, trademark 3 ............. **325.00**
For Father, 87, trademark 6 ........ **120.00**
Going Home, 383, trademark 7 .... **210.00**
Good Shepherd, 42/0, trademark 2 . **300.00**
Goose Girl, 47/II, trademark 6 ..... **325.00**
Guiding Angel, 357, trademark 5 ... **50.00**
Happy Days, 150/2/0, trademark 7 . **100.00**
Heavenly Lullaby, 262, trademark 6 **125.00**
Horse Trainer, 423, trademark 7 ... **150.00**
Is It Raining?, 420, trademark 6 .... **185.00**
Little Fiddler, 2/4/0, trademark 7 ... **60.00**
Little Hiker, 16/I, trademark 1 ...... **425.00**
Mountaineer, 315, trademark 4 .... **200.00**
Postman, 119, trademark 2 ........ **250.00**
Run–A–Way, The, 327, trademark 5 **175.00**
Shepherd's Boy, 64, trademark 3 ... **215.00**
Sing With Me, 405, trademark 6 ... **210.00**
Soloist, 135, trademark 4 .......... **95.00**
Stitch In Time, 255, trademark 5 ... **195.00**
Surprise, 94/3/0, trademark 3 ...... **135.00**
Sweet Greetings, 352, trademark 7 . **125.00**
Telling Her Secret, 196/0, trademark 2 ............................ **350.00**
Tuba Player, 437, trademark 6 ..... **175.00**
Umbrella Girl, 152/0/B, trademark 4 **400.00**
Wayside Harmony, 111/3/0, trademark 3 ....................... **100.00**
We Congratulate, 220, trademark 5 . **95.00**
Whistler's Duet, 413, trademark 7 .. **180.00**

Font
Angel Cloud, 206, trademark 4 .... **45.00**
Child With Flowers, 36/I, trademark 3 ............................ **85.00**
Good Shepherd, 35/0, trademark 7 . **20.00**
Heavenly Angel, 207, trademark 2 . **80.00**
Worship, 164, trademark 5 ........ **30.00**

Lamp Base
Good Friends, 228, trademark 4 ... **275.00**
She Loves Me, She Loves Me Not, 227, trademark 2 .............. **450.00**
To Market, 101, trademark 3 ...... **400.00**

Music Box, Little Band, candleholder on music box, 388M, trademark 5 .... **275.00**

Nativity Set Pieces
Angel Serenade, 214/D, trademark 2, color ......................... **90.00**
Donkey, 260L, trademark 6 ........ **80.00**
Flying Angel, 366, trademark 5, color **60.00**
Holy Family, 3 pcs, 214/A & B, trademark 3, color .................. **300.00**
Infant Jesus, 214/A/K, trademark 6, white ......................... **35.00**
Moorish King, 214L, trademark 4, color ......................... **150.00**
Ox, 260M, trademark 4 ........... **100.00**
Shepherd with Sheep, 214/F, trademark 3, white ................. **160.00**

Plate, annual
1972, Hear Ye, Hear Ye, 265, trademark 4 ........................ **50.00**
1975, Ride Into Christmas, 268, trademark 5 .................. **50.00**
1978, Happy Pastime, 271, trademark 5 ........................ **45.00**
1979, Singing Lesson, 272, trademark 5 ............................ **45.00**
1982, Umbrella Boy, 275, trademark 6 ............................ **90.00**
1984, Little Helper, 277, trademark 6 **50.00**
1987, Feeding Time, 283, trademark 6 ............................ **135.00**
1988, Little Goat Herder, 284, trademark 6 ........................ **100.00**
1991, Just Resting, 287, trademark 7 **150.00**

**1973 Annual Plate, Globe Trotter, orig box, $50.00.**

Wall Plaque
Child In Bed, 137, trademark 7 .... **35.00**
Little Fiddler, 93, trademark 6 ...... **95.00**
Merry Christmas, 323, trademark 5 . **75.00**
Quartet, 134, trademark 2 ......... **350.00**
Searching Angel, 310, trademark 7 . **70.00**
Swaying Lullaby, 165, trademark 5 . **120.00**
Vacation Time, 125, trademark 4 ... **145.00**

Wall Pocket
Boy and Girl, 360A, trademark 5 ... **100.00**
Girl, 360C, trademark 6 ........... **75.00**

# ICE CREAM COLLECTIBLES

**Collecting Hints:** The ice cream collector faces a wide range of competitors. One of the most difficult for the generalist ice cream collector is the regional collector, i.e., an individual who exclusively collects ice cream memorabilia related to a specific manufacturer or region. Because of this, highly distorted prices often are reported in trade periodicals.

Many ice cream collectibles are associated with a specific dairy, thus adding dairy collectors into the equation. Since most ice cream is made of milk, milk and milk bottle collectors also hover around the edge of the ice cream collecting scene. Do not forget to factor in the cow collector (ice cream advertising often features cows) and the collecting field becomes very crowded. Advertising, food mold, kitchen, and premium collectors are secondary considerations. The result is fierce competition for ice cream material, often resulting in higher prices.

When buying an ice cream tray, the scene is the most important element. Most trays were stock items with the store or firm's name added later. Condition is critical.

Beware of reproductions. They became part of the ice cream collectibles world in the 1980s. Many reproductions are introduced into the market as "warehouse" finds. Although these items look old, many are poor reproductions or fantasy pieces.

**History:** During the 1st century A.D. in ancient Rome, the Emperor Nero had snow and ice brought from the nearby mountains which he flavored with fruit pulp and honey. This fruit ice was the forerunner of ice cream. The next development occurred in the 13th century. Among the many treasures that Marco Polo brought back from the Orient was a recipe for a frozen milk dessert resembling sherbet.

In the 1530s Catherine de Medici, bride of King Henry II of France, introduced Italian ices to the French court. By the end of the 16th century, ices evolved and became similar to today's modern ice cream. By the middle of the 17th century, ice cream became fashionable at the English court.

Ice cream switched from being a luxury food for kings and their court to a popular commodity in 1670 when the Cafe Procope (rue de l'Ancienne) in Paris introduced ice cream to the general populace. By 1700 the first ice cream recipe book appeared. Ice cream was the rage of eighteenth century Europe.

Ice cream appeared in America by the early 18th century. In 1777 an advertisement by Philip Lenzi, confectioner, appeared in the New York *Gazette* noting that ice cream was available on a daily basis. George Washington was an ice cream enthusiast, spending over $200 with a New York ice cream merchant in 1790. Thomas Jefferson developed an eighteen step process to make ice cream and is credited with the invention of Baked Alaska.

By the mid–19th century, ice cream "gardens" sprang up in major urban areas. The ice cream street vendor arrived on the scene by the late 1820s. Ice cream remained difficult to prepare with production largely in commercial hands.

In 1846 Nancy Johnson invented the hand–cranked ice cream freezer. Ice cream entered the average American household. By 1850 ice cream was a basic necessity of American life. As the century progressed, the ice cream parlor arrived on the scene. Homemade ice cream competed with commercial products from local, regional, and national dairies.

The arrival of the home refrigerator/freezer and large commercial freezers in grocery stores marked the beginning of the end for the ice cream parlor. A few survived into the post–World War II era. The drug store soda fountain replaced many of them. They in turn passed away in the 1970s when drug store chain stores arrived upon the scene.

America manufactures and consumes more ice cream than any other nation in the world. But, Americans do not hold a monopoly. Ice cream reigns worldwide as one of the most popular foods known. In France it is called *glace*, in Germany *eis*, and in Russia marozhnye. No matter what it is called, ice cream is eaten and enjoyed worldwide.

**References:** Paul Dickson, *The Great American Ice Cream Book*, Galahad Books, 1972, out–of–print; Ralph Pomeroy, *The Ice Cream Connection*, Paddington Press, Ltd., 1975, out–of–print; Wayne Smith, *Ice Cream Dippers*, published by author, 1986.

**Note:** Also check general price guides to advertising and advertising character collectibles for ice cream related material.

**Collector's Club:** The Ice Screamers, PO Box 5387, Lancaster, PA 17601

**Museums:** Greenfield Village, Dearborn, MI; Museum of Science and Industry, Finigran's Ice Cream Parlor, Chicago, IL; Smithsonian Institution, Washington, D.C.

Ashtray, Roxco Ice Cream, Rockford, IL, brass . . . . . . . . . . **15.00**

Bingo Card, Butterman Ice Cream, 5 x 8", wood . . . . . . . . . . **5.00**

Book, *Let's Sell Ice Cream*, Ice Cream Merchandising Institute, 1947, 306 pgs, 9 x 11" . . . . . . . . . . **25.00**

Book Cover, 16 x 12", Breyers Ice Cream, spaceship and planets design **35.00**

**Parlor Rack, brass and copper, glass insert, 18″ d, 18″ h, $715.00. Photograph courtesy of James D. Julia, Inc.**

Catalog, Thomas Mills, 1900, 60 pages . . . **48.00**
Container, Chase's Ice Cream, cardboard, girl on skis, 1923 . . . **10.00**
Convention Badge, International Association of Ice Cream Manufacturers, gold, blue, black, and white, 1930s . . . **30.00**
Ice Cream Mold, pewter
  Boat, 5″ l, S & Co . . . **25.00**
  Football, 3 pcs, #381 . . . **30.00**
Ice Cream Scoop, cone shape . . . **45.00**
Letter Opener, MacGregor's Ice Cream, celluloid handle . . . **22.00**
Mirror, Better Made Ice Cream . . . **30.00**
Pin, 3½″ d, Sparkle Ice Cream Dessert, aqua and white, hanger, c1940 . . . **18.00**
Pinback Button
  Ben and Jerry's Ice Cream, black and white photo, red and white rim, 1960s . . . **8.00**
  Good Humor Safety Club, ⅞″ d, blue, white, and orange, 1930s . . . **20.00**
  Horton's Ice Cream Club, 1″ d, blue, white, and orange, 1930s . . . **15.00**
  Melorol Ice Cream, 1⅞″ d, red and white, 1930s . . . **15.00**
  Purity Ice Cream, black, white, and orange, c1930 . . . **25.00**
  Semon Ice Cream, 1¼″ d, red, white, and gold, 1920s . . . **25.00**
  Skippy Ice Cream, 1⅛″ d, litho, red, white, and blue, 1930s . . . **18.00**
  Spreckels Milk/Cream/Ice Cream, 1⅛″ d, crowing rooster, yellow background, black lettering, 1930–40 . . . **25.00**
  Stewart's Ice Cream, 2″ d, celluloid, lamb mascot, 1940s . . . **15.00**
Sheet Music, "I Scream–You Scream–We All Scream For Ice Cream," color cartoon cov, 1927 . . . **12.00**
Sign
  Binghamton OK Ice Cream, 36 x 24″, tin, emb, framed . . . **175.00**
  Darlene Ice Cream, 23 x 30″, tin, emb, blue and red lettering, lavender background . . . **45.00**
  Dolly Madison Ice Cream, 21 x 33″, tin, emb . . . **35.00**
  Jersey Ice Cream, 16 x 34″, tin, c1940 **40.00**
  Jones Ice Cream, rect, tin . . . **90.00**
  Redman's Ice Cream Double Malted Milk . . . **85.00**
  S & H Fro–Joy Ice Cream, 17½ x 24″, metal, c1930 . . . **70.00**
  Smith's Ice Cream, tin, rect, mounting flange, marked "Smith & Clark Co" on bottom . . . **140.00**

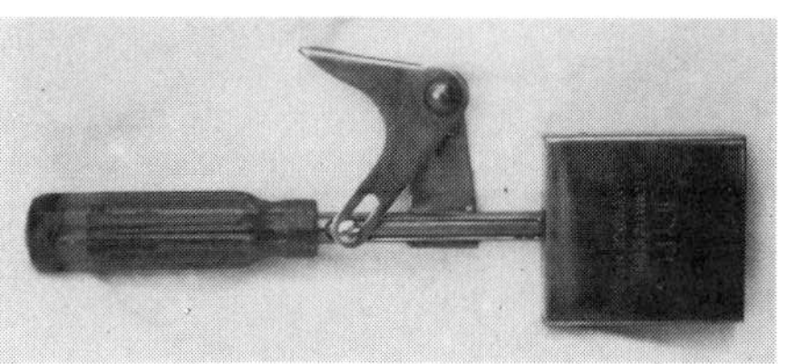

**Scoop, Icypi Automatic Cone Co., Cambridge, MA, amber plastic handle, $125.00.**

Tape Measure, Abbotts Ice Cream, black, white, and red illus . . . **15.00**
Tray
  Douglas Ice Cream, girl eating ice cream, wearing yellow dress, 1913 **140.00**
  Elmira Ice Cream, Cream Supreme, 12½″ d, 1920s . . . **225.00**
  Hall Co's Quality Ice Cream, 13 x 11″, woman and children . . . **375.00**
  Hershey's Superior Ice Cream, 13″ sq, ice cream and peaches illus . . . **115.00**
  Langenfeld's Ice Cream, 13″ sq, two Kewpies and Kewpie golfer . . . **275.00**
  Purity Ice Cream, sq, two Kewpies and dish of ice cream . . . **130.00**
  Weld's Ice Cream, 13″ d, boy playing drum . . . **50.00**

# INSULATORS

**Collecting Hints:** Learn the shapes of the insulators and the abbreviations which appear on them. Some commonly found abbreviations are: "B" (Brookfield), "B & O" (Baltimore and Ohio), "EC&M Co SF" (Electrical Construction and Maintenance Company of San Francisco), "ER" (Erie Railroad), "WGM Co" (Western Glass Manufacturing Company), and "WUT Co" (Western Union Telegraph Company).

The majority of the insulators are priced below $50.00. However, there are examples of threaded and threadless insulators which have exceeded $2,000. There has been little movement in the price of glass insulators for the past years. The top insulators in each category are:

Threaded

- CD 139, Combination Safety/Pat. Applied for, aqua .......... **2,500.00**
- CD 180, Liquid Insulator/blank, ice aqua .......... **2,500.00**
- CD 138–9, Patent Applied for/blank, aqua .......... **2,400.00**
- CD 176, Lower wire ridge, Whitall Tatum Co. No. 12 made in U.S.A./lower wire ridge, Patent No. 1708038, straw .......... **2,300.00**
- CD 181, no name and no embossing .......... **2,200.00**

Threadless

- CD 731, no name and no embossing, white milk glass .......... **3,000.00**
- CD 739, no name and no embossing, similar to jade green milk glass. .......... **3,000.00**
- CD 737, Leffert's/blank, green .......... **2,500.00**
- CD 790, no name and no embossing, known as Tea Pot, aqua .......... **2,200.00**
- CD 788, no name and no embossing, known as slash top .......... **2,200.00**

The six Fry Glass insulators are not counted in this survey. They are not common threadless insulators because they were made only between 1844 and 1865.

**History:** The invention of the telegraph in 1832 created the need for a glass or ceramic insulator. The first patent was given to Ezra Cornell in 1844. The principal manufacturing era was from 1850 to the mid–1900s. Leading companies include Armstrong (1938–69), Brookfield (1865–1922), California (1912–16), Gayner (1920–22), Hemingray (1871–1919), Lynchburg (1923–25), Maydwell (1935–40), McLaughlin (1923–25), and Whitall Tatum (1920–38).

Initially, insulators were threadless. Shortly after the Civil War, L. A. Cauvet received a patent for a threaded insulator. Drip points prevented water from laying on the insulator and causing a short. The double skirt kept moisture from the peg or pin.

There are about five hundred different styles of glass insulators. Each different style insulator has been given a "CD" (consolidated design) number which is found in N. R. Woodward's *The Glass Insulator In America.* Colors and names of the makers and all lettering found on the same style insulator have nothing to do with the CD number. Only the style of the insulator is the key to the numbering.

**References:** Bob Alexander, *Threaded Glass Insulator Price Guide . . . For The Year 1988,* A. B. Publishing Co., 1988; Gary G. Cranfill and Greg A. Kareofelas, *The Glass Insulator: A Comprehensive Reference,* published by author, 1973, separate price list; Michael G. Guthrie, *A Handbook For The Recognition & Identification Of Fake, Altered, and Repaired Insulators,* published by author, 1988; Paul Keating (ed.), *Milholland's Suggested Insulator Price Guide,* published by author, 1986; John and Carol McDougald, *Insulators: A History And Guide To North American Glass, Pintype Insulators, Volume 1* (1990), *Volume 2* (1990), published by authors; John and Carol McDouglad, *1991 Price Guide For Insulators: A History And Guide To North American Glass Pintype Insulators,* published by authors, 1991; Marion & Evelyn Milholland, *Glass Insulator Reference Book, 4th Revision,* published by authors, 1976; N. R. Woodward, *The Glass Insulator In America,* published by author, 1973.

**Collectors' Club:** National Insulator Association, 5 Brownstone Road, East Granby, CT 06026.

**Periodical:** *Crown Jewels of the Wire,* P.O. Box 1003, St. Charles, IL 60174.

**Museums:** Big Thicket Museum, Saratoga, TX; Edison Plaza Museum, Beaumont, TX.

**Insulator, ceramic, white, glazed, unmarked, 3½" h, 3¼" d, $2.00.**

## THREADED INSULATORS

CD 102
- BGM Co, smooth base, purple .......... **18.00**
- California/blank, blue .......... **15.00**

CD 112, New England Telegraph & Telephone, aqua .......... **35.00**

CD 122, Lynchburg No 30, light green **6.00**

CD 145
- Brookfield/New York
  - Aqua .......... **5.00**
  - Medium Green .......... **7.00**
- GNW Tel Co, deep purple .......... **25.00**
- GTP, dark aqua .......... **10.00**
- HG Co, petticoat, cornflower blue .. **25.00**

KCGW, aqua .................... **10.00**
Postal, light purple ............... **10.00**
CD 155, Armstrong's DPL, smooth base, smoky olive ................ **5.00**
CD 160
Hemingray 14/Made in USA
Aqua ......................... **5.00**
Clear ......................... **6.00**
Dark Smoke ................... **10.00**
CD 162, SS & Co, smooth base, lime green .......................... **150.00**
CD 168
Hemingray Made in USA/D510
Carnival ...................... **25.00**
Clear ......................... **4.00**
Green ........................ **7.00**
Ice Blue ....................... **6.00**
Whitall Tatum Co No 11/Made in USA
Ice Blue ....................... **15.00**
Light Aqua .................... **20.00**
Light Green ................... **30.00**
CD 317, Chambers, smooth base, lime green .......................... **150.00**
CD 320, Pyrex, smooth base, carnival **35.00**

### THREADLESS INSULATORS

CD 718, no name and no embossing
Aqua .......................... **200.00**
Black Glass ..................... **350.00**
Emerald Green .................. **300.00**
Olive Green .................... **300.00**
CD 724, Chester, smooth base, dark cobalt .......................... **600.00**
CD 728, Boston Bottle Works, smooth base, light aqua .................. **60.00**
CD 731, McKee, smooth base, aqua .. **150.00**
CD 734, McMicking, aqua .......... **55.00**
CD 735, Mulford & Biddle, UPRR, cobalt blue, repair to skirt ........... **250.00**
CD 1052, Hemi D–518, light flashed amber ......................... **20.00**

# IRONS

**Collecting Hints:** Heavy rusting, pitting, and missing parts detract from an iron's value. As a collector becomes more advanced, he may accept some of these defects on a rare and unusual iron. However, the beginning collector is urged to concentrate on irons in very good to excellent condition.

European, Oriental, and other foreign irons are desirable, since many unusual types come from these areas and some models were prototypes for later American–made irons.

**History:** Ironing devices have been in use for many centuries, with early references dating from 1100. Irons from the Medieval, Renaissance, and early industrial era can be found in Europe, but are rare. Fine brass engraved irons and hand-wrought irons dominated the period prior to 1850.

After 1850 the iron began a series of rapid evolutionary changes. New models were patented monthly. The housewife and tailor sought the latest improvement to keep "up–to–date."

The irons of the 1850 to 1910 period were heated in four ways—(1) a hot metal slug was inserted into the body, (2) a burning solid, such as coal or charcoal, was placed in the body, (3) a liquid or gas, such as alcohol, gasoline, or natural gas, was fed from an external tank and burned in the body, and (4) conduction heating, usually by drawing heat from a stove top.

Irons from the 1850 to 1910 period are plentiful and varied. Many models and novelty irons still have not been documented by collectors.

Electric irons are not being added to older collections. The more sought after are those with special features (temperature indicators, self–contained stands, sets) or those with Deco styling.

**References:** Esther S. Berney, *A Collectors Guide To Pressing Irons And Trivets,* Crown Publishers, Inc., 1977; A. H. Glissman, *The Evolution Of The Sad Iron,* privately printed, 1970; Brian Jewell, *Smoothing Irons: A History And Collectors Guide,* Wallace–Homestead, 1977; Judy (author) and Frank (illustrator) Politzer, *Early Tuesday Morning: More Little Irons and Trivets,* published by author, 1986; Judy and Frank Politzer, *Tuesday's Children,* published by author, 1977; Ted and V. Swanson, *The Swanson Collection,* published by authors.

**Collectors' Clubs:** Club of the Friends of Ancient Smoothing Irons, P. O. Box 215, Carlsbad CA 92008; Midwest Sad Iron Collectors Club, 2828 West Ave., Burlington, IA 52601.

**Museums:** Henry Ford Museum, Dearborn, MI; Shelburne Museum, Shelburne, VT; Sturbridge Village, Sturbridge, MA.

**Advisors:** David and Sue Irons.

**REPRODUCTION ALERT:** The most often reproduced irons are the miniatures, especially the swan's neck and flat irons. Reproductions of some large European varieties are available, but poor construction, use of thin metals, and the unusually fine condition easily identifies them as new. More and more European styles are being reproduced each year. Construction techniques are better than before and aging processes can fool many knowledgeable persons. Look for heavy pitting on the repros and two or more that are exactly alike. Few American irons have been reproduced at this time, other than the miniatures.

**Note:** The irons listed are American made unless otherwise noted.

Alcohol
German, "Feldmeyer," saw–grip handle, two rows of nine holes in base, Berney Fig. 144A .............. **160.00**
"Jubilee," rainbow handle, Glissman Fig. 318A ..................... **75.00**
Charcoal
"Acme," 1910, no spout, lift off top, large circular rear damper, Berney Fig. 134A ..................... **110.00**
"Bless & Drake," 1852, large spout, Vulcan head on damper, Berney Fig. 128B ..................... **110.00**
European, Dalli, brass, base line of holes, top latch, Berney Fig. 137B **110.00**
German, holes above base on sides, top hinged at rear, latch on front, common variety, Berney Fig. 135B **75.00**
Mexican, "Pagoel," c1950, hinged lid, front latch, Glissman Fig. 109B **45.00**
Siddons, right turn spout, lever latch, rear damper, Glissman Fig. 105 .. **95.00**

**Polishing Iron, P.J.O., $20.00.**

Children's
Block Grip
English, thin base, 3½", Tuesday's Children Fig. 49 ............. **60.00**
Three rib areas on handle, all cast, 2½", Tuesday's Children Fig. 44 **45.00**
Cylinder grip, two points, 2¾ to 3¼", all cast, Tuesday's Children Fig. 80 **50.00**
Diamond grip, two points, 3 3½", all cast, Tuesday's Children Fig. 97 .. **40.00**
"Dover Sad Iron," lift off tin cov, wood grip, two points, Tuesday's Children Fig. 272 ............. **65.00**
"Dover USA," wood handle, two points, Tuesday's Children Fig. 246 **50.00**
English, brass box, wood handle, 3½", Tuesday's Children Fig. 312 **150.00**
"Enterprise," rainbow handle, two points, holes in handle, Tuesday's Children Fig. 171 ............. **75.00**
"Ober," curved wood handle, two pieces, two points, Tuesday's Children Fig. 291 .................. **125.00**
"Our Pet," wood handle, Tuesday's Children Fig. 232 .............. **70.00**
Ribbon Goffering, brass barrel, dec cast base, Tuesday's Children Fig. 316 .......................... **150.00**
Round back, Tuesday's Children Fig. 177
French ....................... **55.00**
German ...................... **55.00**
"Sensible," two piece, two points, Tuesday's Children Fig. 283 ..... **75.00**
Swan, 1¾ to 3", Tuesday's Children Fig. 27
Blue, red, or yellow original paint and pin striping .............. **160.00**
No Paint ...................... **60.00**
"The Pearl," rainbow wood handle, two points, Tuesday's Children Fig. 257 .......................... **65.00**
Tri bump, three bulbous areas in handle, all cast, 1¾ to 3½", Tuesday's Children Fig. 58 .............. **45.00**
Wire handle with #1, #2, etc., cast base, Tuesday's Children Fig. 103 **30.00**
Wood grip, star on top, Tuesday's Children Fig. 229 ............. **70.00**

Flat or Sad Iron
All wrought iron, single point ...... **12.00**
Belgium, tear drop, flat strap handle **20.00**
"Enterprise," removable handle, two points ........................ **18.00**
French, thin base, recessed top, all cast
Fancy top design, people or animals in relief ............... **75.00**
Plain ......................... **25.00**
"Keystone 4", all cast ............ **15.00**
"Monitor," all cast, two points, Berney Fig. 30B .................. **75.00**
"Mrs Potts," removable handle, two points, Glissman Fig. 163 ....... **18.00**
Soapstone, "Hoods 1867," stone insulator above base, Berney Fig. 28 **165.00**

Flutter
Hand
"Clarks" roller, footed base, three pieces, Berney Fig. 96A ....... **95.00**
Fluting Scissors, five fingers, Berney Fig. 99B .................... **40.00**
"New Geneva" (common), rocker style, lead composition for plates **35.00**
Pleating Board, Berney Fig. 85A .. **30.00**
"The Erie," rocker, two pieces, like Berney Fig. 96C ............. **85.00**
Machine
"Companion," clamp–on flutter, Berney Fig 110A ............. **175.00**
"Crown," two 6" I rolls, cast base,

orig paint and stenciling, Berney Fig. 104A .................... **160.00**
English, open work cast frame, fine flutes compared to American flutters .......................... **175.00**

Gasoline
Coleman, green enamel, rear tank, Glissman Fig. B25D ............ **90.00**
Sears, rear tank, Glissman Fig. 326C **50.00**

Natural Gas
"Humphrey Gas Iron," curved heat shield, finds under handle, Berney Fig. 174B ..................... **65.00**
"I Wantu Comfort Gas Iron," hose coupling at rear, Berney Fig. 170A **55.00**

Slug/Box
Danish, brass, delicate iron posts, thin base about 1", small size, 4 to 5" long, hinge on rear door, Berney Fig. 12B ...................... **125.00**
English, brass box, turned posts, trap door back, Berney Fig. 15A ..... **120.00**
"Magic No. 1, N. R. Streeter," top lifts off to add hot slug, Berney Fig. 17A **150.00**
Scottish Box, very fancy turned posts, tear drop shaped base, brass and iron construction, top lifts off, Berney Fig. 131B ................. **350.00**

Specialty
Ball or egg iron, wood handle, Berney Fig. 203A ..................... **80.00**
Billiard Table Iron, English, Berney Fig. 241 ...................... **140.00**
Goffering
Double barrel, cast dec base ..... **425.00**
English, all brass, Queen Anne base **175.00**
"Kenrick," "S" wire style stand .. **80.00**
Hat
All cast, oval, Berney Fig. 226A .. **140.00**
All wood Tolliker, Berney Fig. 219B **150.00**
Gas Heated, large press, Berney Fig. 229 .................... **125.00**
Laundry Stove, holds eight irons around sides, Berney Fig. 292 ... **350.00**
Polisher, round bottom, "Siddons," English, cast iron, Berney Fig. 126A **125.00**
Pyramid Heater, Berney Fig. 283A .. **140.00**

# JEWELRY, COSTUME

**Collecting Hints:** Two diverse factors influence price—artistic merit and personal appeal. The result is that there is a wide fluctuation in market prices. Also, the changing values of gold and silver cause prices to vary.

Jewelry prices vary regionally, depending on what is popular in a given area. Costume jewelry, since it was mass produced, should be bought in very good or mint condition. Most stones in costume jewelry are not real. Advanced collectors generally can distinguish stones and metals; novice collectors should study carefully before trusting their eyes and a ten power loupe.

**History:** The design of jewelry closely followed costume design. Early inventions which influenced jewelry design were the pin making machine in 1832, the development of the electroplating process by the English firm of Elkington in the 1860s, and die stamping machinery.

The Art Deco and Art Nouveau eras made inexpensive costume jewelry acceptable. Mass production of tin–like pins, bracelets, rings, etc., followed. Newark (New Jersey), New York, and Philadelphia became centers for jewelry manufacturing, challenging Providence, Rhode Island, which had held the position in 1800. Coro Incorporated of Providence employed over 2,000 people in 1946.

Gold was removed from circulation in 1933, reducing the amount of gold related jewelry items. Scarcity of materials during World War II further aided the move to plastic and lesser metals. Precious stones were replaced by "gemstones" and glass imitations.

Mass produced jewelry employed the talents of many famous designers. Rapid communication of style changes through magazines and newspapers led to fads which quickly swept across the country. By the 1950s fine costume jewelry appeared on the market and received acceptance, even among the more sophisticated buyers.

**References:** Lillian Baker, *Fifty Years Of Collectible Fashion Jewelry: 1925–1975,* Collector Books, 1986, 1992 value update; Lillian Baker, *100 Years of Collectible Jewelry, 1850–1950,* Collector Books, 1978, 1993 value update; Lillian Baker, *Twentieth Century Fashionable Plastic Jewelry,* Collector Books, 1992; Jeanenne Bell, *Answers To Questions About 1840–1950 Old Jewelry, Third Edition,* Books Americana, 1992; Matthew L. Burkholz and Linda Lictenberg Kaplan, *Copper Art Jewelry: A Different Luster,* Schiffer Publishing, Ltd., 1992; Deanna Farneti Cera (ed.), *Jewels Of Fantasy: Costume Jewelry Of The 20th Century,* Harry N. Abrams, Inc., 1992; Corinne Davidov and Ginny Redington Dawes, *The Bakelite Jewelry Book,* Abbeville Press, 1988; Maryanne Dolan, *Collecting Rhinestone Jewelry, Third Edition*, Books Americana, 1993; Roseann Ettinger, *Popular Jewelry: 1840–1940,* Schiffer Publishing, Ltd., 1990; S. Sylvia Henzel, *Collectible Costume Jewelry, Second Edition*, Wallace–Homestead, 1987, 1990 value update; Susan Jonas and Marilyn Nissenson, *Cuff Links,* Harry N. Abrams, Inc., 1991; Lyngerdd Kelley and Nancy Schiffer, *Plastic Jewelry,* Schiffer Publishing Ltd., 1987; J. L. Lynnlee, *All That Glitters*, Schiffer Publishing, Ltd., 1986, 1993 value update; Sibylle Jargstorf, *Glass in Jewelry:*

*Hidden Artistry in Glass,* Schiffer Publishing, 1991; Harrice Miller, *The Official Identification and Price To Costume Jewelry,* House of Collectibles, 1990; Nancy N. Schiffer, *Costume Jewelry: The Fun of Collecting,* Schiffer Publishing Ltd., 1988, 1992 value update; Nancy N. Schiffer, *Rhinestones!,* Schiffer Publishing Ltd., 1993; Nancy N. Schiffer, *Silver Jewelry Treasures,* Schiffer Publishing Ltd., 1993; Sheryl Gross Shatz, *What's It Made Of: A Jewelry Materials Identification Guide,* published by author, 1991.

**Advisor:** Christie Romero.

Bar Pin, unknown maker
- Bakelite, red bar, red cherries, green leaves suspended from red Bakelite chain .......... **100.00**
- Silver, sterling, black Scottie paperweight type center .......... **25.00**

Beads, unknown maker
- Bakelite, brown faceted beads, 6.5 to 20 mm, c1920 .......... **40.00**
- Mother of Pearl, graduated elongated beads, 24" l .......... **45.00**
- Plastic, amber, transparent, 28" l .......... **65.00**

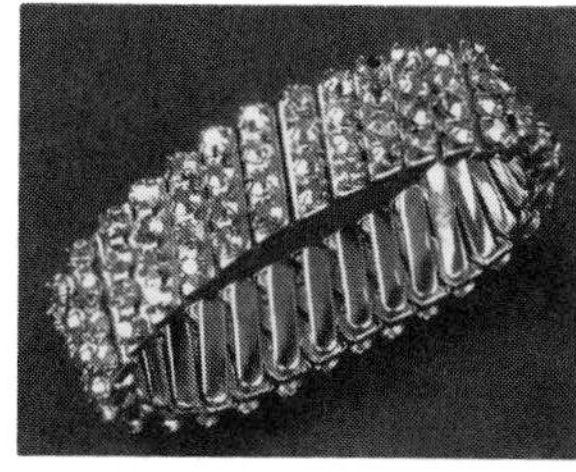

**Bracelet, flexible band, gold colored metal, rhinestones, early 1940s, $75.00.**

Bracelet
- Haskell, Miriam, pink rhinestones, Baroque type pearls .......... **165.00**
- Joseff of Hollywood, gold, cuff, shell and pearl dec, 1960s .......... **250.00**
- Ledos, rhinestone, six links, 1920s style pierced work, 1950 .......... **50.00**
- Monet
  - Bangle, plastic, lemon yellow .......... **25.00**
  - Link, silver, c1960 .......... **25.00**
- Napier, lantern .......... **125.00**
- Whiting Davis, rhinestones .......... **25.00**

Brooch/Pin
- Boucher, gold plated sterling, cultured pearls, sunburst, early mark **195.00**
- Carnegie, Hattie, dog and cat in basket .......... **32.50**
- Coro Craft
  - Bandstand, sterling .......... **225.00**
  - Lobster, sterling .......... **165.00**
  - Orchid .......... **22.00**
- Di Nicola, crown, gold tone, tiny rhinestones .......... **75.00**
- Eisenberg, leaf .......... **50.00**
- English, china, pink and yellow roses **25.00**
- Haskell, Miriam
  - Pansy, tiny gold beads and rhinestones, horseshoe signature .......... **125.00**
  - Swirls, gold tone, four pearls .......... **70.00**
- Monet
  - Flower Bud .......... **25.00**
  - Horse .......... **25.00**
- Orb, dachshund .......... **14.00**
- Schiaparelli, silver tone, blue/green irid rhinestones .......... **250.00**
- Schreiner, rhinestones, green, several shades and shapes .......... **85.00**
- Trifari, crown, sterling, light blue moonstone cabochons, 1¾" .......... **195.00**
- Unknown Maker
  - Clown, c1940 .......... **25.00**
  - Donkey, cactus, Mexican silver, turquoise inlay .......... **35.00**
  - Flower, round, abalone, cut–outs, Mexican silver fittings .......... **25.00**
  - Heart, sterling silver and rhinestones .......... **25.00**
  - Hummingbird .......... **35.00**
  - Monkey, palm tree, metal .......... **30.00**
  - Rose, rhinestones .......... **25.00**
  - Scatter, black devil, red devil, price for pair .......... **10.00**
  - Squirrel, rhinestones .......... **25.00**
- Weiss
  - Circular, aurora borealis, blue .......... **30.00**
  - Goose .......... **38.00**
  - Swan .......... **38.00**

Button Hook
- Steel, Potter & Culver, The Shoefitters **20.00**
- Sterling silver handle .......... **20.00**

Charm Bracelet, seven figural Disney characters .......... **25.00**

Charm
- Gold, yellow
  - Anniversary, diamond chip .......... **60.00**
  - Cat, enamel eyes .......... **35.00**
  - Thimble .......... **30.00**
  - Yacht .......... **40.00**
- Silver, Sterling
  - Baby Shoe, ¾" l .......... **25.00**
  - Banjo, mother of pearl disk, c1950 **10.00**
  - Clown, c1950 .......... **7.00**
  - Fish, body moves, c1950 .......... **15.00**
  - Outhouse, door opens, c1950 .......... **17.00**
  - Roller Skate, c1950 .......... **7.00**
  - Stein, lid opens, c1950 .......... **10.00**
  - Typewriter, carriage moves .......... **25.00**

Choker
- Coventry, Sarah, eight fine strands, silver colored .......... **12.00**
- Lane, Kenneth, crystal and rhinestones, gold setting, tassel drop .. **150.00**

- Clip, Eisenberg, rhinestones, clear .... **195.00**
- Cuff Links, pr
  - Hickok, fish .... **5.00**
  - Unknown maker, yacht, silver .... **30.00**
- Earrings, pr
  - Caviness, Alice, black irid .... **30.00**
  - Coro Craft
    - Clear, encased mustard seed .... **15.00**
    - Enamel, black flower petals, rhinestone cluster center, c1950 .... **40.00**
  - Eisenberg, clear rhinestones, drop .. **45.00**
  - Givenchy, rhinestone, dangle .... **15.00**
  - Haskell, Miriam, moon beads, pink . **30.00**
  - Hobe, light blue glass beads .... **27.00**
  - Joseff of Hollywood, pearl, paste and gold, metal drop .... **150.00**
  - Napier, molten ore .... **10.00**
  - Renoir, artist palette .... **15.00**
  - Trifari, sterling, flower .... **12.00**
  - Unknown maker
    - Abalone, silver fittings
      - Flowery .... **12.00**
      - Rectangular .... **12.00**
    - Mexican silver, abalone dec, hoops **15.00**
  - Weiss
    - Aurora Borealis, blue, clip on .... **20.00**
    - Clear rhinestones, dangle .... **35.00**
    - Pink, clear rhinestones .... **45.00**
    - Red rhinestones .... **35.00**
- Fur Clip
  - Eisenberg, orig box .... **150.00**
  - Trifari, fish, jelly belly, lucite, gold plated metal, rhinestones, 1941 design patent no., Norman Bel Geddes designer .... **1,500.00**
- Lapel Pin, man's, adv
  - Budweiser 3 Million Barrel Team, sterling, inset ruby, 1941 .... **25.00**
  - Ford Motor Co, ABC Bowling, St Paul **15.00**
- Locket, Hobe, cameo, holds four photos **95.00**

**Necklace and Earrings Set, necklace, pin, and earrings, light blue rhinestones, $10.00.**

- Necklace
  - Carnegie, Hattie, pearls with white stones, gold loops, dangles .... **55.00**
  - Danecraft, sterling silver, gold wash, lilies, 16" l .... **35.00**
  - Eisenberg, rhinestones, clear .... **90.00**
  - Hobe, crystal, double strand .... **45.00**
  - Unknown Maker
    - Bakelite, red and black geometric shapes, chrome links and spacers **95.00**
    - Celluloid, Art Deco, raspberries and leaves .... **75.00**
    - Mexican silver, drum shaped links, 24" l .... **75.00**
    - Rhinestone, aurora borealis, blue . **28.00**
- Pendant
  - Coventry, Sarah, large green stone surrounded by clear rhinestone leaflets .... **22.00**
  - Haskell, Miriam, massive gold colored, 36" l chain .... **35.00**
  - Razza, elephant head, orig chain ... **20.00**
  - Unknown Maker
    - Bakelite, cameo, sterling chain ... **28.00**
    - Mexican silver
      - Heart, abalone dec .... **20.00**
      - Oval, malachite stone dec .... **25.00**
    - Mustard Seed, gold filled chain .. **15.00**
    - Perfume, glass acorn shaped bottle, gold tone chain .... **25.00**
    - Rhinestone, sterling chain .... **12.00**
- Ring, garnet, diamond shape cluster, sixteen garnets, 10K .... **75.00**
- Suite
  - Haskell, Miriam, collar necklace, drop earrings, gold tone, green and blue translucent beads .... **275.00**
  - Hollycraft, bracelet, earrings, multicolored stones, dated 1950 . **65.00**
  - La–Rel, necklace and bracelet, emerald cut and round rhinestones .. **35.00**
  - Robert, Original By, brooch/pendant, earrings, gold tone, amber stones and pearls, large scale .... **125.00**
  - Schreiner, bracelet and brooch, colored stones .... **195.00**
  - Unknown Maker
    - Bracelet, necklace, earrings, Mexican silver, nickel size chunky links, turquoise studs .... **60.00**
    - Bracelet, three strand necklace, and earrings, pink crystal .... **50.00**
    - Brooch and earrings, Mexican silver, inlaid abalone, dancer shape **35.00**
    - Tie Clasp and cuff links, golfer emblem .... **5.00**
  - Weiss, bracelet, crown brooch, earrings, multicolored stones, orig box **195.00**
- Sweater Guard, rhinestone .... **25.00**
- Tie Bar
  - Advertising, Calvert's Reserve, plastic bottle on chain .... **10.00**
  - Anson, sword .... **7.00**
  - Hickok, fraternal, late 1940s .... **2.00**
  - Swank
    - Fishing Rod .... **7.00**
    - Hammer .... **7.00**
- Watch Fob, EC Atkins, saw, 10K .... **100.00**

# JUKEBOXES

**Collecting Hints:** Jukebox chronology falls into four distinct periods:

In the pre–1938 period jukeboxes were constructed mainly of wood and resembled a radio or phonograph cabinet. In this period Wurlitzer jukeboxes are the most collectible, but their value usually is under $600.00.

From 1938 to 1948 the addition of plastics and animation units gave the jukebox a more gaudy appearance. These jukeboxes played 78 RPM records. Wurlitzer jukeboxes are king, with Rock–Ola the second most popular. This era contains the most valuable models, e.g., Wurlitzer models 750, 850, 950, 1015, and 1080, plus others.

The 1940–1960 era jukeboxes are collected for the "Happy Days" (named for the TV show) feeling: drive–in food, long skirts, sweater girls, and good times. These jukeboxes play 45 RPM records. They rate in value second to those of the 1938–48 period. The period is referred to as the Seeburg era. Prices usually are under $1,500.00.

The 1961 and newer jukeboxes often are not considered collectible because the record mechanism is not visible, thus removing one of the jukebox's alluring qualities.

There are exceptions to these generalizations. Collectors should have a price and identification guide to help make choices. Many original and reproduction parts are available for Seeburg and Wurlitzer jukeboxes. In many cases incomplete jukeboxes can be restored. Jukeboxes that are in working order and can be maintained in that condition are the best machines to own.

Wait about three to four months after becoming interested in jukeboxes before buying a machine. Use this time to educate yourself about a machine's desirability and learn how missing components will affect its value.

**History:** First came the phonograph; the coin–operated phonograph followed. When electrical amplification became possible, the amplified coin–operated phonograph, known as a jukebox, evolved.

The heyday of the jukebox was the 1940s. Between 1946 and 1947 Wurlitzer produced 56,000 model 1015 jukeboxes, the largest production run of all time. The jukebox was the center of every teenage "hangout," from drug stores and restaurants to pool halls and dance parlors. They even invaded select private homes. Jukeboxes were cheaper than a live band, and, unlike radio, one could hear his or her favorite song when and as often as one wished.

Styles changed in the 1960s. Portable radios coupled with "Top 40" radio stations fulfilled the need for daily repetition of songs. Television changed evening entertainment patterns. The need for the jukebox vanished.

**References:** Frank Adams, *Wurlitzer Jukeboxes, 1934–1974,* AMR Publishing, 1983; Jerry Ayliffe, *American Premium Guide To Jukeboxes and Slot Machines, Third Edition,* Books Americana, 1991; Rick Botts, *A Complete Identification Guide To The Wurlitzer Jukebox,* privately printed, 1984; Rick Botts, *Jukebox Restoration Guide,* published by author, 1985; Stephan K. Loots, *The Official Victory Glass Price Guide To Antique Jukeboxes 1992,* published by author, 1992; Vincent Lynch, *American Jukebox: The Classic Years,* Chronicle Books, 1990; Scott Wood (ed.), *A Blast From the Past, Jukeboxes: A Pictorial Guide,* L–W Book Sales, 1992.

**Periodicals:** *Gameroom Magazine,* 1014 Mt. Tabor Rd, New Albany, IN 47150; *Jukebox Collector,* 2545 SE 60th Court, Des Moines, IA 50317; *Loose Change,* 1515 South Commerce St., Las Vegas, NV 89102-2703.

**Museums:** Jukeboxes have not reached the status of museum pieces. The best places to see approximately 100 or more jukeboxes in one place is at a coin–op show.

**Advisor:** Rick Botts.

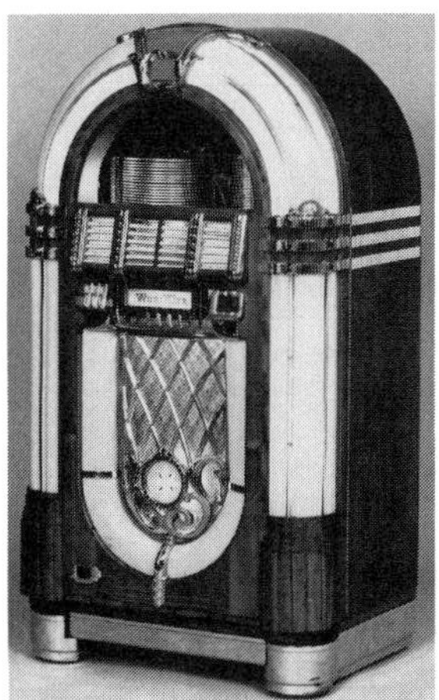

**Wurlitzer 1015, bubbler, Art Deco design, plays 78 rpm records, 24 selections, 1946, estimated price $3,500.00. Photograph courtesy of Morton M. Goldberg Auction Galleries, Inc.**

AMI, model

A .......... **900.00**
B .......... **750.00**
C .......... **500.00**
D .......... **400.00**
E .......... **500.00**

Mills, model
- Empress .......... **950.00**
- Throne of Music .......... **750.00**

Packard, Manhattan .......... **1,600.00**

Rock–Ola, model
- 1422 .......... **1,500.00**
- 1426 .......... **1,600.00**
- 1428 .......... **1,500.00**
- 1432 .......... **700.00**
- 1434 .......... **750.00**
- 1436 .......... **750.00**
- 1438 .......... **700.00**

Seeburg, model
- 147 .......... **600.00**
- HF100G .......... **810.00**
- HF100R .......... **860.00**
- M100B .......... **750.00**
- M100W .......... **650.00**
- V–200 .......... **810.00**

Wurlitzer, model
- 412 .......... **750.00**
- 600 .......... **850.00**
- 616 .......... **625.00**
- 700 .......... **1,620.00**
- 750 .......... **1,800.00**
- 780 .......... **2,500.00**
- 800 .......... **1,800.00**
- 850 .......... **5,500.00**
- 950 .......... **8,000.00**
- 1015 .......... **3,500.00**
- 1050 .......... **4.500.00**

# KEWPIES

**Collecting Hints:** Study the dolls carefully before purchasing. Remember that composition dolls were made until the 1950s; hence, every example is not an early one.

Many collectors concentrate only on Kewpie items. A specialized collection might include other O'Neill designs, such as Scootles, Ragsy, Kewpie–Gal, Kewpie–Kins and Ho–Ho.

The vast majority of Kewpie material is sold in the doll market where prices are relatively stable. Pricing at collectibles shows and malls fluctuates due to seller unfamiliarity with the overall Kewpie market.

**History:** Rose Cecil O'Neill (1876–1944) was a famous artist, novelist, illustrator, poet, sculptress, and creator of the Kewpie doll. O'Neill's drawing "Temptation" won her a children's art prize at the age of 14 and launched her career as an illustrator.

The Kewpie first appeared in art form in the December, 1909, issue of *Ladies Home Journal* in a piece entitled "Kewpies Christmas Frolic." The first Kewpie doll appeared in 1913. Assisting in the design of the doll was Joseph L. Kallus. Although Geo. Borgfeldt Co. controlled the production and distribution rights to Kewpie material, Kallus continued to assist in design and manufacture through his firm, the Cameo Doll Company.

Kewpie dolls and china decorated items rapidly appeared on the market. Many were manufactured in Germany. Twenty–eight German factories made products during the peak production years. Later other manufacturers joined in the effort.

O'Neill eventually moved to southwest Missouri, settling at Bonniebrook near Bear Creek. She died there in 1944. In 1947 Bonniebrook burned to the ground. Production of Kewpie items did not stop at O'Neill's death. Today Kewpie material still appears as limited edition collectibles.

**References:** John Axe, *Kewpies—Dolls and Art Of Rose O'Neill and Joseph L. Kallus,* Hobby House Press, 1987, out–of–print; Janet A. Banneck, *Antique Postcards Of Rose O'Neill,* Greater Chicago Productions, 1992; Lois Holman, *Rose O'Neill Kewpies And Other Works,* published by author, 1983; Maude M. Horine, *Memories of Rose O'Neill,* booklet, published by author; Ralph Alan McCanse, *Titans and Kewpies,* out–of–print; Rowena Godding Ruggles, *The One Rose,* out–of–print.

**Collectors' Club:** International Rose O'Neill Club, Box E, Nixa, MO 65714.

**Museum:** Shepherd of the Hills Farm and Memorial Museum, near Branson, MO.

**REPRODUCTION ALERT**

**Creamer, pale pink Kewpies, green ground, marked "copyrighted Rose O'Neill, Kewpie, Germany," $165.00.**

Action Doll, bisque, 3¾" h, Sweeper, attached broom and waste can, sgd "O'Neill" on foot, "C" mark .......... **350.00**

Bell, brass .......... **60.00**

Book, *Sing A Long Of Safety,* 1937 .......... **95.00**

Cake Decoration, wedding cake top, bride and groom .......... **40.00**

Candy Mold, 6" h, chocolate type, pewter .......... **70.00**

Children's Feeding Dish, 10" d, Kewpies and alphabet border .......... **150.00**

Coloring Book, Christmas ........... **25.00**
Crumb Tray, brass .................. **25.00**
Doll
6″ h, porcelain, movable arms, legs together, "O'Neill" incised on bottom of foot, copyright sticker on back .......................... **135.00**
14″ h, vinyl, fully jointed, orig clothes, Cameo Dolls Products, Port Allegheny ................ **65.00**
Figure
5″ h, Thinker, sgd ................ **25.00**
6″ h, bisque, set of three .......... **35.00**
Letter Opener, 7″ l, Kewpie finial, pewter ............................ **40.00**
Magazine Advertisement, Jello, *Ladies Home Journal,* 1917, color ........ **15.00**
Magazine Article, *Ladies Home Journal,* ten pages from 1925 through 1928 issues .......................... **100.00**
Pin Box, cov, 2½″ d, Kewpie with foot in air, marked "Goebel" .......... **450.00**
Pitcher, 3½″ h, jasperware, blue ground, white figures ............. **275.00**
Post Card, Christmas, Gibson, printed color illus, divided back .......... **20.00**
Powder Shaker, 7″ h, jointed arms, heart label on back, French label on feet . **70.00**
Salt and Pepper Shakers, pr, 2½″ h, marked "Paye & Baker, Trade Kewpie Mark" ......................... **250.00**
Tin, 5¾″ d, 3½″ h, round, nine Kewpies: two on tightrope, two on ground, five clinging to rope, c1935 **20.00**

# KEYS

**Collecting Hints:** The modern hobby of key collecting began with the publication of *Standard Guide To Key Collecting* which illustrates keys by function and describes keys by style and metal content. Most key collectors focus on a special type of key, e.g., folding keys, railroad keys, car keys, etc.

Very few, if any, American-manufactured keys can be called truly rare, although some may be currently very difficult to find. Little is known as to the quantity that was manufactured, how popular they were when first produced and marketed, or how many survived.

Some keys are abundant in certain areas of the country and scarce in others. Do not spend heavily just because you have never heard of or seen an example before. The best advice is to seek out other collectors and join a national organization.

**History:** The key as a symbol has held a mystical charm since Biblical times. The Catholic Church has keys in its coat of arms. During the Middle Ages, noblemen and women carried a large collection of keys hanging from their girdles to denote their status; the more keys the higher the status.

Many kings and other royal members practiced the art of key making. Presentation keys began during the earliest years when cities were walled enclaves. When a visitor was held in high esteem by the townspeople, he would be presented with a key to the city gate. Thus, we now have the honorary "Key To The City."

When it was popular to go on a Grand Tour of Europe in the 17th to 19th centuries, keys were among the most acquired objects. Unfortunately, many of these keys were fantasies created by the inventive local hustlers. Examples are King Tut's Tomb key, the key to the house where Mary stayed in Egypt, Bastille keys, Newgate Prison keys, and Tower of London keys.

**References:** Don Stewart, *The Charles J. McQueen Collection, Railroad Switch Keys, United States-Canada-World,* published by author; Don Stewart, *Collectors Guide, Antique Classic Marque Car Keys, United States 1915–1970,* published by author; Don Stewart, *Collectors Guide, Yale Jail/Prison Locks & Keys, 1884–1957,* published by author; Don Stewart, *Standard Guide To Key Collecting, United States-Canada 1850–1975, Second Edition* published by author.

**Collectors' Club:** Key Collectors International, P. O. Box 9397, Phoenix, AZ 85068.

**Museums:** Lock Museum of America, Terryville, CT; Mechanics Institute, New York, NY.

Cabinet, Barrel Type
Brass, decorative bow
1½″ .......................... **3.00**
2½″ .......................... **5.50**
3″ ............................ **9.00**
Brass, standard bow and bit
1½″ .......................... **1.50**
2″ ............................ **1.50**
3″ ............................ **3.50**
Bronze, gold plated bow
1½″, decorative ................ **8.50**
2″, Art Deco design ............ **12.00**
2½″, dolphin design ............ **12.00**
Iron, painted, 3″, plastic bow, Art Deco design ................... **9.50**
Nickel plated
2¼″, lyre design bow ........... **5.50**
2½″, Art Deco design bow ...... **5.00**
Steel
1½″, standard bow and bit ...... **.50**
2″, Art Deco design ............ **6.00**
3″, standard bow and bit ........ **.75**
Casting Plate, bronze
2½″ ............................ **15.00**
3″ .............................. **18.00**
4″ .............................. **22.00**
6″ .............................. **29.00**

**Studebaker, pen knife style, 2¾″ l, 1960s, $18.00.**

- Car
  - Auburn, logo, Yale, Jr — **2.00**
  - Basco
    - Early, flat steel — **1.50**
    - Set, #31–54, total of 24 keys — **25.00**
  - Chrysler Omega keys, brass, five piece set
    - 1933, Yale — **15.00**
    - 1934, Yale — **12.00**
  - CLUM, #DB76–DB99, set of 24 keys — **35.00**
  - Dodge
    - Any metal, no name — **.50**
    - Brass, reverse "Caskey–Dupree" — **1.25**
    - Nickel–Silver, reverse "Caskey–Dupree" — **1.50**
  - Dodge/Chevrolet, rear deck key — **2.00**
  - Edsel, two keys, any maker — **5.00**
  - Ford, Model "T"
    - Any Metal, no logo — **.75**
    - Brass, Ford logo
      - "B" in circle mark — **2.00**
      - C–D mark — **2.00**
      - Crown mark — **8.00**
      - Diamond mark — **2.00**
      - No mark — **1.50**
      - "V" in circle mark — **12.00**
    - Coil Switch Lever Key — **2.50**
    - Dealers Keys, set of 4 — **12.50**
    - Nickel–Silver, Ford Logo
      - "B" in circle mark — **1.75**
      - C–D mark — **1.75**
      - Diamond mark — **1.75**
  - Ford, rear deck key — **2.00**
  - Nash logo key, Ilco #132 — **5.00**
  - Omega, nickel–silver, 5 piece set, 1933 or 1934, Yale — **6.50**
  - Omega type, nickel–silver, any maker besides Yale — **.75**
  - Packard logo key, gold plated, 50th anniversary — **9.00**
  - Studebaker
    - Eagle Lock Co, logo key — **1.50**
    - Yale, aluminum — **1.50**
    - Yale, Jr, logo key — **1.50**
- Car, Special
  - Auto Dealer Presentation Keys
    - Diamond, Continental, gold — **75.00**
    - Gold Plated — **1.50**
    - Sterling Silver — **12.00**
  - Crest Key
    - Common Cars — **1.50**
    - Hudson, Frazer, Nash and Packard — **3.00**
  - OSCO Colt 45 Key, orig box — **25.00**
- Door
  - Brass, standard bow and bit
    - 3″ — **3.00**
    - 4″ — **5.00**
    - 5″ — **9.00**
    - 6″ — **12.00**
  - Bronze
    - 4″, Keen Kutter bow — **5.50**
    - 6″, special logo bow — **15.00**
  - Steel
    - 3″, Keen Kutter bow — **3.50**
    - 5″, standard bow and bit — **3.50**

**Folding Bow, Art Deco design, 2″ l, $12.00.**

- Folding, Jackknife
  - Bronze and Steel, bit cuts, 5″
    - Maker's name — **18.00**
    - No maker's name — **15.00**
  - Steel bit cuts, 5½″, maker's name
    - Branford, MW&CO — **9.00**
    - Ilco, Graham, etc. — **6.50**
  - Steel, uncut, 5½″
    - Maker's name — **6.00**
    - No maker's name — **4.00**
- Gate
  - Bronze, bit type
    - 4″ — **6.00**
    - 6″ — **12.00**
  - Iron, bit type
    - 6″ — **4.00**
    - 8″ — **6.00**
- Hotel
  - Bit Type, Bronze
    - 3″, Hotel name and room number on bow — **4.50**
    - 4″, Tag silhouette of hotel, white metal — **10.00**
  - Bit Type, Steel, 3″
    - Bronze Tag — **3.00**
    - Fiber Tag, room number and name — **2.25**
    - Hotel name and room number on bow — **3.75**
    - Large Tag, oval, silhouette, bronze — **9.00**
    - Standard Tag, room number, etc., bronze — **4.00**

- Bit Type, Steel, 4″
  - Bronze Tag **3.50**
  - Large Tag, oval, hotel founder, bronze **12.00**
  - Large Tag, rectangle, hotel name, white metal **6.50**
- Pin Tumbler
  - Large bow, hotel name and room number on bow **1.25**
  - Plastic or Fiber tag **1.50**

Jail (reproduction alert)

- Bronze, bit type with cuts
  - 4¼″, open oval bow, Newell **35.00**
  - 4½″, barrel type **28.00**
- Bronze, lever tumbler cut, 4½″, Folger–Adams, oval bow with "A" **18.00**
- Nickel–Silver, pin tumbler, Yale Mogul
  - Cut **15.00**
  - Uncut blank **12.00**
- Spike Key, 5½″
  - Bronze bow, steel bit, serial no., no maker's name **35.00**
  - Nickel plated steel, open oval bow, no maker's name, no serial no., bit cuts **30.00**
  - Steel plated bow, serial no, Yale, marked **40.00**
- Steel, flat, lever tumbler, Folger–Adams
  - Cut **18.00**
  - Uncut blank **12.00**

Keys To The City, Presentation

- 1½″, gold plated, small jewel, city and/or recipients name **9.00**
- 2″, iron, brass plated, Master Lock Co, 1933 Worlds Fair **7.50**
- 2½″, white metal, "Be A Golden Key For Happiness" **1.50**
- 6″, antique bronze, any city **14.00**
- 6 to 10″, gold plated, name engraved
  - Famous Person **32.00**
  - Historical Person **75.00**
  - Obscure Person **25.00**
- 7″, gold plated, presentation leatherette type folder **40.00**
- 8″, copper plated, 1933 Chicago Worlds Fair, Hall of Science **15.00**
- 8″, 22K gold plated, Cumberland, etc. **24.00**
- 10″, Chicago Worlds Fair, copper, thermometer **8.50**

Pocket Door, bow folds sideways

- Bronze
  - Art Deco, triangular bow **15.00**
  - "T" bow, cut, knurled nut **9.00**
- Nickel Plated
  - Art Deco, square bow **19.00**
  - Art Nouveau, oval bow **15.00**

Pocket Door, slide stem

- Bronze, "T" bow
  - Knurled nut **9.00**
  - Screw **8.00**
- Steel, "T" bow, screw **10.00**

Railroad (reproduction alert)

- A&S Abilene & Southern **25.00**
- ARR Alaska Railroad **20.00**
- AT&SF Atchison Topeka & Santa Fe **15.00**
- B&M RR Boston & Maine **20.00**
- C&O Chesapeake & Ohio **12.50**
- CM&ST P SIGNAL Chicago Milwaukee & St Paul **10.00**
- CRI & P RR Chicago Rock Island & Pacific **12.50**
- D&RGW RR Denver & Rio Grande Western **18.50**
- DT RR Detroit Terminal **18.50**
- ESS CO Eastern/Erie Steamship Co **19.00**
- FC NG RR Fulton County Narrow Gauge **85.00**
- GTW Grand Trunk Western **18.00**
- IC RR Illinois Central **10.00**
- LS&MS Lake Shore & Michigan South Steel **15.00**
- LM RR Little Miami Railroad **55.00**
- MC RR Michigan Central **18.00**
- MN RY Milwaukee Northern **45.00**
- NP RY Northern Pacific Railway **18.00**
- O&W RR Oregon & Washington **35.00**
- PENN RR Pennsylvania Railroad **18.00**
- FRISCO St Louis San Francisco **18.00**
- SPCO&CS Southern Pacific **9.00**
- SPTCO Southern Pacific **6.00**
- TT RR Toledo Terminal Railroad **18.00**
- UPRR Union Pacific **14.00**
- VGN Virginian **30.00**
- WPRR Western Pacific Railroad **12.50**

Ship, bit type

- Bronze, bit type
  - Foreign ship tags **6.00**
  - Ship name on bow **10.00**
- Bronze, tag, bit type, factory type tags
  - 2″ **6.00**
  - 3″ **9.00**
- Bronze, ship made tags, bit type, factory type tags
  - 2 to 3″ **4.50**
  - 4″ **5.00**
- Iron/steel, bronze tags, 3 to 4″ **3.00**
- Pin Tumbler Type
  - Passenger Liner Tags **9.00**
  - US Army Ship Tags **8.50**
  - US Coast Guard Tags **3.00**
  - USN Tag **2.00**

Watch

- Brass, 1″
  - Advertising type, ½ x¾″ **6.00**
  - Advertising type, shield **10.00**
  - Art Nouveau, loop bow **9.00**
  - Plain, swivel **2.00**
- Brass/gold plated, 1″, large number **4.00**
- Brass and Steel, 1″
  - Loop bow, folds **4.00**
  - Swivel **2.00**
- Gold, 14K, 1″, engraved **75.00**

Gold Plated, 1″

Advertising type ................ **12.00**

Decorated bow ................ **9.00**

Gold Plated and Silver, 1″

Cigar Cutter accessory .......... **25.00**

Plain ........................ **19.00**

Jewelers Key

Brass, 6 point .................. **18.00**

Steel and Brass

5 Point ..................... **12.00**

6 Point ..................... **15.00**

Set, #2 to #11, brass/gold plated, large numbers, 10 total ......... **75.00**

Sterling Silver 1″, rose on bow, etc. . **35.00**

# KITCHEN COLLECTIBLES

**Collecting Hints:** Bargains still can be found, especially at flea markets and garage sales. Look to the design of appliances for statements about a given age, e.g., the Art Deco design on toasters and coffee pots of the 1910–1920 period.

The country decorating craze has caused most collectors to concentrate on the 1860–1900 period. Kitchen products of the 1900–1940 period with their enamel glazes and dependability are just coming into vogue.

**History:** The kitchen was a central focal point in a family's environment until frozen food, TV dinners, and microwaves freed the family to concentrate on other parts of the house during meal time. Initially, food preparation involved both the long and short term. Home canning remained popular through the early 1950s.

Many early kitchen utensils were handmade and prized by their owners. Next came a period of utilitarian products of tin and other metals. However, the housewife did not wish to work in a sterile environment, so color was added through enamel and plastic while design began to serve both an aesthetic and functional purpose.

The advent of home electricity changed the type and style of kitchen products. Many products went through fads such as the toaster, electric knife, and now the food processor. The high technology field already has made inroads into the kitchen and another revolution seems at hand.

**References:** Jane H. Celehar, *Kitchens and Gadgets, 1920 To 1950,* Wallace–Homestead, 1982; Linda Campbell Franklin, *300 Years Of Housekeeping Collectibles*, Books Americana, 1992; Linda Campbell Franklin, *300 Years Of Kitchen Collectibles, Third Edition*, Books Americana, 1991; Bill and Denise Harned, *Griswold Cast Collectibles: History & Values,* published by author, 1988; Jan Lindenberger, *Black Memorabilia For The Kitchen: A Handbook And Price Guide,* Schiffer Publishing Ltd., 1992; Norman E. Martinus and Harry L. Rinker, *Warman's Paper,* Wallace–Homestead, 1993; Mary Lou Matthews, *American Kitchen And Country Collectibles,* L–W Promotions, 1984; Kathryn McNerney, *Kitchen Antiques, 1790–1940,* Collector Books, 1991, 1993 value update; Dana Gehman Morykan and Harry L. Rinker, *Warman's Country Antiques & Collectibles,* Wallace–Homestead, 1992; Ellen M. Plante, *Kitchen Collectibles: An Illustrated Price Guide,* Wallace–Homestead, 1991; Diane W. Stoneback, *Kitchen Collectibles: The Essential Buyer's Guide,* Wallace–Homestead, 1994; Frances Thompson, *Antiques From The Country Kitchen,* Wallace–Homestead, 1985, out–of–print.

**Periodicals:** *Kettles 'n Cookware,* P. O. Box B, Perrysville, NY 14129; *Kitchen Antiques & Collectibles News,* 4645 Laurel Ridge Dr., Harrisburg, PA 17110.

**See:** Advertising, Cookbooks, Kitchen Glassware, Reamers.

**Apple Peeler, Reading '78, Reading Hardware Co., cast iron, 1878, table mount, $60.00.**

Apple Parer, Goodall, orig box ....... **40.00**

Apple Peeler, Lightning ............. **135.00**

Apron, crocheted .................. **15.00**

Beater, Chicago, electric, motor on top, measure glass bottom ............. **25.00**

Booklet, Excelsior Fly Paper Mills, Chicago, IL, c1926, 5 x 7½″, six sheets of felt fly paper, yellow and black illus envelope, unused ................ **10.00**

Bread Board, wood, round, carved motto, "Give Us This Day Our Daily Bread," 9½″ d .................. **50.00**

Bread Maker, White House Bread Maker, table mount, 1902 ......... **125.00**

Bread Pan, Ideal, tin, double loaf, two tubes .......................... **30.00**

Butter Churn, Dazey, 4 quart ........ **125.00**

Butter Mold, R Hall, Burlington, NC,

star shape, cast aluminum, ½ lb, c1940, 3¾" d .................... **20.00**
Butter Paddle, wooden .............. **25.00**
Cabbage Cutter, wooden ............ **30.00**
Cake Decorator, aluminum and copper, eight design attachments .......... **10.00**
Cake Mold, lamb, cast iron .......... **55.00**
Cake Pan, angel food, dark tin, faceted sides, Star of David shaped ........ **30.00**
Canner, Iron Horse Cold Pack, Rochester Can Co, tin, wood handles, wire rack and lifter, 1930s, 13¾" d, 9" h . **65.00**
Catalog
D Eddy & Sons Co, Boston, MA, Eddy Refrigerators, 1925, 36 pgs, 6 x 9¼" ......................... **22.00**
Pittston Stove Co, Pittston, PA, stoves and ranges, 1921, 43 pgs, 7½ x 10½" ........................ **21.00**
Richardson & Boynton, Philadelphia, PA, stoves and ranges, 1921, 62 pgs, 7¾ x 10½" ................ **25.00**
The Brecht Co, St Louis, MO, 1918, sausage making equipment, 78 pgs, 7½ x 10½" .................. **40.00**
Westinghouse All Electric Kitchens, 1936, 20 pgs, 8½ x 11" ......... **10.00**
Cheese Slicer, Cut–Rite, Wagner Ware, OH, No. 300, aluminum, 7" l, 3⅛" w ........................... **35.00**
Cherry Pitter, Watt No. 15 ........... **60.00**
Chocolate Mold, tin, clamp type, 2 pcs
Basket, 1½ x 4" ................. **35.00**
Cat, sitting, #14, 2¼ x 3" ......... **20.00**
Rabbit, standing, Germany, 6¼" h .. **18.00**
Clothes Dasher, Ward Vacuum Washer **35.00**
Clothes Sprinkler, Siamese Cat ....... **30.00**
Coffee Grinder, Landers, Frary & Clark, clamp on, metal ................ **65.00**
Cookie Cutter, tin, lady, wearing hat and long dress, strap handle with rolled edges, 5¼" hp .................. **35.00**
Cookie Press, tin, star shape, wood plunger, 10½" l ................. **35.00**
Cookie Roller, Guirier, tin, wire, three rollers, c1930, orig box ........... **40.00**
Corkscrew, figural parrot, metal, corkscrew tail ...................... **25.00**
Corn Stick Pan
Griswold, #262, mini ............ **75.00**
Wagner Ware Krusty Korn Kobs, Pt'd July 6, 1920, cast iron .......... **75.00**
Crimper, Juice Tite Pie Sealer, aluminum, 5½" l ..................... **15.00**
Cutting Board, maple, figural pig, c1930, 9 x 19" .................. **15.00**
Danish Pan, Griswold, #32 ......... **60.00**
Deep Fryer, Griswold, basket, 1003 .. **90.00**
Dipper, cast iron, hand forged ....... **125.00**
Drying Rack, 27 x 6" folded size, wood and metal, 12 retractable arms, three legs ............................ **40.00**
Dutch Oven, cov, cast iron, Griswold
#6, large emblem ................ **150.00**
#8
Large emblem ................. **40.00**
Small emblem ................. **45.00**
#10, trivet, large emblem ......... **80.00**
Egg Beater, Holt, patented Aug 22, 1899 **65.00**
Egg Lifter, wire ..................... **6.00**
Egg Scale, Oakes Mfg Co, painted tin, 7" h ........................... **25.00**
Egg Timer, Alarm Whistle, aluminum insert, orig box and instructions ...... **15.00**
Egg Whisk
Spiral ........................... **10.00**
Wire ........................... **6.00**
Fish Scaler, Champion, cast iron ..... **12.00**
Flour Sifter, Kwik, tin, 5 cup, double ended, yellow wooden handle ..... **18.00**
Fly Trap, Sus–Ket–Vim, orig instructions **28.00**
Food Chopper, Kitchmaster, Chicago Flexible Shaft Co, plated metal, table mount, three discs, c1934 ......... **25.00**
Food Grinder, Keen Kutter, Simmons Hardware, model K110, tinned cast iron ........................... **25.00**
Food Mold, Turk's head, Rockingham glaze .......................... **145.00**
French Fry Cutter, Maid of Honor, tin, stamped, 1930s ................. **6.00**
French Roll Pan, cast iron, rect, 2 rows of 6, #11, 6½ x 12½" ........... **15.00**
Fruit Baller, hinged cutting ring, red handle, 1920s, 5¼" l ............ **5.00**
Glove Dryer, wire, pr ............... **20.00**
Grater, pierced tin, wood handle ..... **18.00**
Griddle, cast iron, Griswold, large emblem, round
#9 ............................ **20.00**
#10 ........................... **25.00**
Gypsy Kettle, cast iron, small, 3 ftd, wire bail handle, Wagner, 3 x 5" ... **28.00**
Hand Towel, fringed ................ **12.00**
Ice Cream Dipper, Mosteller #79 .... **195.00**
Ice Cream Disher, Mayer, adjustable shank .......................... **250.00**
Ice Cream Freezer, Kwik freeze, galvanized tin, blue, paper label ........ **50.00**
Ice Cream Mold, dressed turkey, pewter, 5" l ........................... **20.00**
Ice Cream Scoop, Gilchrist #33 ...... **145.00**
Ice Tongs, cast iron ................. **30.00**
Jar Wrench, Wilson Mfg Co, cast iron . **12.00**
Kitchen Saw, Keen Kutter, Simmons Hardware, carbon steel blade, wood handle, 13½" l .................. **12.00**
Kitchen Scale, Hanson .............. **24.00**
Lemon Squeezer
Cast Iron ...................... **35.00**
Wooden ....................... **38.00**
Match Safe, brass, snap lid, engraved fly rod, 2½ x1" ..................... **45.00**
Mayonnaise Mixer, Universal ........ **465.00**

Measuring Cup, adv, "Swans Down Cake Flour Makes Better Cakes," 1 cup, spun aluminum .............. **15.00**
Measuring Spoons, adv, Towles Log Cabin, set of four ................ **45.00**
Meat Grinder, Russvin, 1903 ........ **15.00**
Meat Slicer, Dandy, tin, wood handle . **12.00**
Mixing Spoon, adv, "Rumford Baking Powder," metal, slotted bowl, green wood handle, 10¾" l ............. **15.00**
Mouse Trap, wire mesh, 9" l ......... **45.00**
Muffin Pan, G F Filley No. 3, cast iron **100.00**

**Pitcher, chanticleer rooster, white, red comb, red and green dec, 10" w, 7½" h, $24.00.**

Noodle Cutter, The Ideal, Toledo Cooker Co, rolling type, wire handle and frame, 14 blades, c1910 ...... **15.00**
Nut Grinder, Climax, cast iron and tin, glass jar, threaded tin hopper, 1940s **12.00**
Nutmeg Grater, tin cylinder and barrel, wood plunger, 4" l ............... **85.00**
Pastry Blender, wire, marked "Omar Wonder Flour" .................. **8.00**
Pie Bird
  Black Bird, white base ............ **24.00**
  Rooster, Blue Willow ............. **18.00**
Pie Pan, Mrs Smith's, tin ............ **5.00**
Pineapple Snip ..................... **20.00**
Potato Masher, double grid .......... **50.00**
Potato Ricer, Handy Things, Ludington, MI, tinned metal presser and cup, iron handles painted red, c1940, 12" l .. **10.00**
Pot Scrubber, wire rings ............. **17.00**
Raisin Seeder, Everrit ............... **55.00**
Rolling Pin, maple, one piece, 14" l .. **25.00**
Sausage Stuffer, Wagner Stuffer Co 3, Salem Tool Co, Salem, OH, cast iron, crank type, mounted on board, c1900 **40.00**
Skillet, cast iron, Griswold, large emblem
  #3 ............................ **15.00**
  #4 ............................ **35.00**
  #5 ............................ **25.00**
  #6, lid ........................ **45.00**
  #8, lid ........................ **35.00**
  #9, smoke ring .................. **35.00**
  #10, smoke ring ................. **35.00**
Spatula, Rumford ................... **6.00**
String Holder
  Apple, ceramic .................. **20.00**
  Girl's Head, wearing bonnet, chalkware ......................... **45.00**
Teapot, Norge, iron, wall hanger ..... **25.00**
Toast Rack, SP, Art Deco design ...... **28.00**
Vegetable Slicer, A & J, Binghamton, NY, wood handle, twisted wire blade, c1930, 16" l ..................... **18.00**
Whisk Broom, Mammy handle, 4½" l . **18.00**

# KITCHEN GLASSWARE

**Collecting Hints:** Kitchen glassware was made in large numbers. Although collectors do tolerate signs of use, they will not accept pieces with heavy damage. Many of the products contain applied decals; these should be in good condition. A collection can be built inexpensively by concentrating on one form such as canister sets, measuring cups, reamers, etc.

**History:** The Depression era brought inexpensive kitchen and table products to center stage. Hocking, Hazel Atlas, McKee, U. S. Glass, and Westmoreland were companies which led in the production of these items.

Kitchen Glassware complemented Depression Glass. Many items were produced in the same color and style. Because the glass was molded, added decorative elements included ribs, fluting, arches and thumbprint patterns. Kitchen glassware was thick to achieve durability. The result were forms which were difficult to handle at times and often awkward aesthetically. After World War II, aluminum products began to replace Kitchen glassware.

**References:** Gene Florence, *Kitchen Glassware of the Depression Years, Fourth Edition*, Collector Books, 1990, 1992 value update; Shirley Glyndon, *The Miracle In Grandmother's Kitchen*, privately printed, 1983; Garry Kilgo and Dale, Jerry, and Gail Wilkins, *A Collectors Guide To Anchor Hocking's Fire–King Glassware*, K & W Collectibles Publisher, 1991; Susan Tobier Rogove and Marcia Buan Steinhauer, *Pyrex by Corning: A Collector's Guide*, Antique Publications, 1993; Diane W. Stoneback, *Kitchen Collectibles: The Essential Buyer's Guide*, Wallace–Homestead, 1994; April M. Tvorak, *Fire–King II*, published by author, 1993; April M. Tvorak, *History And Price Guide To Fire–King*, VAL Enterprises, 1992; April M. Tvorak, *Pyrex Price Guide*, published by author, 1992.

**Periodicals:** *Kitchen Antiques & Collectibles News*, 4645 Laurel Ridge Dr., Harrisburg, PA

17110; *The 50's Flea,* P. O. Box 126, Canon City, CO 81215.

**Collector's Club** Westmoreland Glass Society, 2712 Glenwood, Independence, MO 64052.

**Shaker, white, Frank Tea & Spice Co., 5¼″ h, $6.00.**

Bowl
  Cobalt Blue, Crisscross
    7¾″ d . . . . . . . . . . **70.00**
    9¾″ d . . . . . . . . . . **120.00**
  Custard, 4¼″ d, McKee . . . . . . . . . . **6.00**
Butter Dish, cov, ¼ lb, cobalt blue, Crisscross . . . . . . . . . . **95.00**
Drawer Knobs
  Crystal, ribbed . . . . . . . . . . **8.75**
  Moonstone, screw thru, 1½″ d
    Six sided . . . . . . . . . . **4.75**
    Ten sided . . . . . . . . . . **4.75**
  Peacock Blue, single . . . . . . . . . . **12.00**
Egg Separator, clambroth . . . . . . . . . . **55.00**
Grease Jar, cov, Vitrock, black circles and flowers . . . . . . . . . . **35.00**
Ice Bucket, amber, Decagon, Cambridge . . . . . . . . . . **25.00**
Ice Pail, pink, low, bail handle . . . . . . . . . . **15.00**
Iced Tea Server, frosted green, horizontal rib, "Frigidaire Iced Tea Server" . **20.00**
Knife
  Air–Flo, green . . . . . . . . . . **75.00**
  Block, crystal, 9″ l, orig box . . . . . . . . . . **30.00**
  Durex, Three Leaves, blue, 9¼″ l, orig box . . . . . . . . . . **25.00**
  Pinwheel, crystal, 8½″ l, orig box . . **45.00**
  Three Star, dark pink, 9½″ l . . . . . . . . . . **22.00**
Measuring Cup
  Amber, 1 cup, three spout, no handle, Federal . . . . . . . . . . **30.00**
  Green, 1 cup, three spout, Hazel Atlas . . . . . . . . . . **18.00**
  Jadite, ⅓ cup . . . . . . . . . . **8.50**
  Pearl, three spout, Fry . . . . . . . . . . **90.00**
  Seville Yellow, two spout . . . . . . . . . . **220.00**
Measuring Pitcher, pink, slick handle, U S Glass . . . . . . . . . . **40.00**
Mixing Bowl
  Custard, 9⅛″ d, Hamilton Beach, McKee . . . . . . . . . . **11.00**
  Green, 9″ d, slick handle . . . . . . . . . . **18.00**
  Vitrock, 10¼″ d, paneled, Anchor Hocking . . . . . . . . . . **13.00**
  White, aqua kitchen utensils decor, nested set of five, Pyrex . . . . . . . . . . **40.00**
Mustard Jar, white, hp dec . . . . . . . . . . **25.00**
Pepper Shaker
  Custard, black vertical lettering and stripes, McKee . . . . . . . . . . **15.00**
  Jadite, Hocking . . . . . . . . . . **15.00**
  White, lady watering . . . . . . . . . . **12.00**
Reamer
  Cobalt Blue, Crisscross . . . . . . . . . . **260.00**
  Jadite, emb Sunkist . . . . . . . . . . **45.00**
  Pink, emb Sunkist . . . . . . . . . . **75.00**
  Seville Yellow, emb Sunkist . . . . . . . . . . **55.00**
Refrigerator Dish, cov
  4 x 4″
    Cobalt blue, Crisscross . . . . . . . . . . **35.00**
    Chailane blue, Jeannette, two small chips . . . . . . . . . . **125.00**
    Pink, vegetable emb lid, Federal . **8.00**
  4 x 5″
    Jadite . . . . . . . . . . **15.00**
    seville yellow, McKee . . . . . . . . . . **15.00**
  8 x 8″, cobalt blue, Crisscross . . . . . . **120.00**
Refrigerator Jar, cov
  10 oz, Seville yellow, McKee . . . . . . **17.00**
  32 oz, jadite, Jeannette . . . . . . . . . . **24.00**
Rolling Pin, blown, light amber . . . . . . **145.00**
Salad Set, fork and spoon, clear, red teardrop handles . . . . . . . . . . **20.00**

**Salt, clear, hinged stainless steel cov, 4⅝″ d, 2¾″ h, $20.00.**

Salt Shaker, fired–on red, Roman Arch, McKee . . . . . . . . . . **7.00**
Salt and Pepper Shakers, pr, white
  Green Lettering, Hocking . . . . . . . . . . **40.00**
  Roosters, range, green lids . . . . . . . . . . **25.00**
Sugar Shaker, ⅝″ h, rings . . . . . . . . . . **24.00**
Towel Bar, jadite, 17″ l . . . . . . . . . . **25.00**
Water Bottle, cov, clear, Anchor Hocking . . . . . . . . . . **10.00**

# KNOWLES, EDWIN M.

**Collecting Hints:** Do not confuse Edwin M. Knowles China Company with Knowles, Taylor, and Knowles, also a manufacturer of fine dinnerware. They are two separate companies. The only Edwin M. Knowles China Company mark that might be confusing is "Knowles" spelled with a large "K".

Knowles dinnerware lines enjoyed modest sales success. No one line dominated. Among the more popular lines with collectors are: Deanna, a solid color line found occasionally with decals introduced in 1938; Esquire, designed by Russel Wright and manufactured between 1956 and 1962; and Yorktown, a modernistic line introduced in 1936 found in a variety of decal patterns such as Bar Harbor, Golden Wheat, Penthouse, and Water Lily.

When collecting decal pieces, buy only pieces whose decals are complete and still retain their vivid colors. Edwin M. Knowles China Company did make a Utility Ware line that has found some favor with kitchen collectibles collectors. Prices for Utility Ware range between half and two–thirds of the prices for similar pieces in the dinnerware patterns.

**History:** In 1900 Edwin M. Knowles established the Edwin M. Knowles China Company in Chester, West Virginia. Company offices were located in East Liverpool, Ohio. The company made semi–porcelain dinnerware, kitchenware, specialties, and toilet wares and was known for its commitment to having the most modern and best equipped plants in the industry.

In 1913 a second plant in Newell, West Virginia, was opened.

The company operated its Chester, West Virginia, pottery until 1931, at which time the plant was sold to the Harker Pottery Company. Production continued at the Newell pottery. Edwin M. Knowles China Company ceased operations in 1963.

The Edwin M. Knowles Company name resurfaced in the 1970s when the Bradford Exchange acquired rights to the company's name. The Bradford Exchange uses the Knowles name to front some of its collector plate series, e.g., Gone with the Wind and the Wizard of Oz. The name also has been attached to Rockwell items. Bradford Knowles marked pieces are made by offshore manufacturers, not in the United States at either of the old Knowles locations.

**References:** Jo Cunningham, *The Collector's Encyclopedia of American Dinnerware*, Collector Books, 1982, 1992 value update; Harvey Duke, *The Official Identification and Price Guide to Pottery and Porcelain, Seventh Edition*, House of Collectibles, 1989; Lois Lehner, *Lehner's Encyclopedia of U. S. Marks on Pottery, Porcelain & Clay*, Collector Books, 1988.

**DEANNA.** Introduced in 1938. This shape was available in both pastel and bright solid colors or designs using stripes, plaids, or decal decoration on white ground. Solid colors included green, light and dark blue, orange–red, bright and pastel yellow, turquoise, peach, burgundy, russet, and pink.

| | |
|---|---|
| Butter Dish, open, dark blue | **10.00** |
| Coffeepot, cov, red and blue stripes | **40.00** |
| Creamer and Sugar, cov, light blue | **25.00** |
| Cup and Saucer, yellow | **10.00** |
| Eggcup, double, turquoise | **12.00** |
| Plate | |
| 6″ d, bread and butter, yellow | **4.00** |
| 8″ d, salad, orange–red | **6.00** |
| 10″ d, dinner, dark blue | **10.00** |
| Platter, 12″ d, green | **15.00** |
| Vegetable Bowl, 8″ d, orange–red | **18.00** |

**Rose, platter, Tempo shape, gold trim, 13¾″ l, $12.00.**

**ESQUIRE.** Dinnerware line designed by Russel Wright. Made from 1956 until 1962, it was available in five colors and six designs. Each pattern was produced on a single colored ground. Botanica on beige, Grass on blue, Queen Anne's Lace on white, Seeds on yellow, Snowflower on pink, and Solar on white.

| | |
|---|---|
| Bowl | |
| 5½″ d, fruit, Snowflower | **8.00** |
| 6¼″ d, cereal, Queen Anne's Lace | **10.00** |
| Cup and Saucer, Snowflower | **18.00** |
| Plate | |
| 6¼″ d, bread and butter, Botanica | **6.00** |
| 8¼″ d, salad, Seeds | **9.00** |
| 10¾″ d, dinner, Grass | **12.00** |
| Platter, oval | |
| 13″ l, Queen Anne's Lace | **20.00** |
| 16″ l, Solar | **30.00** |
| Teapot, Botanica | **95.00** |
| Vegetable Bowl, divided, Seeds | **65.00** |

**YORKTOWN.** Dinnerware line introduced in 1936. Original four colors were burgundy, cadet blue, russet, and yellow. Later produced in Chinese red, green, orange–red, and pink. Also available with decal decoration on white ground.

Bowl, 6" d, cereal, green . . . . . . . . . . . 6.00
Casserole, yellow . . . . . . . . . . . . . . . . . . 35.00
Chop Plate, 10¾" d, burgundy . . . . . . . 15.00
Cup and Saucer, orange–red . . . . . . . . . 8.00
Custard Cup, green . . . . . . . . . . . . . . . . 6.00
Gravy Boat, pink . . . . . . . . . . . . . . . . . . 18.00
Plate
- 6" d, bread and butter, yellow . . . . . 5.00
- 8" d, salad, cadet blue . . . . . . . . . . . . 10.00
- 10" d, dinner, orange–red . . . . . . . . . 12.00

Platter, 12" d, russet . . . . . . . . . . . . . . . 20.00
Teapot, orange–red . . . . . . . . . . . . . . . . . 50.00

# LABELS

**Collecting Hint:** Damaged, trimmed or torn labels are less valuable than labels in mint condition.

**History:** The first fruit crate art was created by California fruit growers about 1880. The labels became very colorful and covered many subjects. Most depict the type of fruit held in the box. With the advent of cardboard boxes in the 1940s, fruit crate art ended and their labels became collectible.

**References:** Jerry Chicone, Jr., *Florida's Classic Crates,* privately printed, 1985; Joe Davidson, *Fruit Crate Art,* Wellfleet Press, 1990; Norman E. Martinus and Harry L. Rinker, *Warman's Paper,* Wallace–Homestead, 1993; Gordon T. McClelland and Jay T. Last, *Fruit Box Labels: A Collector's Guide,* Hillcrest Press, Inc., 1983; John Salkin and Laurie Gordon, *Orange Crate Art, The Story of Labels That Launched a Golden Era,* Warner Books, 1976.

**Collectors' Club:** Citrus Label Society, 16633 Ventura Blvd, No. 1011, Encino, CA 91436.

**Advisor:** Lorie Cairns.

Apple
- Bird Valley, blue crown perched on shield, orange background . . . . . . 2.00
- Blue Seal, blue seal with red apples, red background . . . . . . . . . . . . . . . 1.00
- Cascade, smiling little boy holding eaten red apple, blue background .50
- Columbia Belle, Columbia lady wearing patriotic dress, apple, blue and white background . . . . . . . . . . . . . 1.00
- Duckwall, wood duck by stone wall, blue background . . . . . . . . . . . . . . . 10.00
- Empire Builder, house and orchard scene, big red apple . . . . . . . . . . . 1.00
- Hula, topless hula girl, seated beneath palm tree, blue background 3.00
- Jackie Boy, little boy wearing sailor suit, blue background . . . . . . . . . . . 4.00
- James Parks, white setter dog, forest scene, blue border . . . . . . . . . . . . . 4.00

**Fireworks, Big Bear, blue, black, and yellow, 6 x 10", $5.00.**

- Luck Strike, hunter aiming at buck, lake and forest scene . . . . . . . . . . . 3.00
- Morjon, blue triangle with yellow apple, yellow background . . . . . . . . . 1.00
- Paradise, three big red apples, ranch scene . . . . . . . . . . . . . . . . . . . . . . . . 1.00
- Red Star, big red star, black background . . . . . . . . . . . . . . . . . . . . . . . 1.00
- Skookum, smiling cartoon Indian face, red and yellow apples . . . . . 2.00
- Snow Owl, fierce snowy owl, blue background . . . . . . . . . . . . . . . . . . . 2.00
- Swan, big white swan, black background . . . . . . . . . . . . . . . . . . . . . . . 5.00
- Triton, red Neptune holding trident and apple and pear . . . . . . . . . . . . 1.00
- Webster, big spider web, navy background . . . . . . . . . . . . . . . . . . . . . . . 2.00

Asparagus
- Caligras, men harvesting asparagus, horse drawn wagon . . . . . . . . . . . . 2.00
- Chickie, fluffy yellow chick, bunch of green asparagus, black background 2.00
- Kingfish, fish wearing crown, leaping from water . . . . . . . . . . . . . . . . . . . 1.50
- King O'Hearts, king of hearts playing cards, red heart, black background 1.00
- Kings Cadets, green and white uniformed marching cadets, yellow background . . . . . . . . . . . . . . . . . . . 1.00
- Mo Chief, big bundle of asparagus, scenic background . . . . . . . . . . . . . 1.00
- O Yes, We Grow The Best, two bunches of asparagus, blue background . . . . . . . . . . . . . . . . . . . . . . . 1.00
- Red Rooster, crowing red rooster, yellow, red, and navy . . . . . . . . . . . . . 1.00
- River Lad, Dutch boy and windmill . 2.00
- Singer, bird perched on G, green background . . . . . . . . . . . . . . . . . . . 1.00

Broom
- Capitol, capitol building, Washington, DC .50
- Giant, strong man flexing biceps .50
- Monarch, white haired bearded king holding scepter .50
- Winner, lady holding torch .50

**Food Can, Red Prince Salmon, red and blue, 4¼ x 9¾", $3.00.**

Broccoli, Ocean Mist, waves crashing rocks, shore scene, blue background .25

Cantaloupe
- Ekco, little boy shouting at red mountains, blue background .75
- Valley Queen, half of cantaloupe on plate and vase of flowers 1.00

Celery, Ligo, big bunch of celery, blue and green background .50

Cherries
- Brookside, orchard scene and big cherries .25
- Corvette, warship and three cherries, blue background .25
- G Saporito, maroon cherries, red background .15
- Marion, black bing cherries, white background .50
- Mountain, snowy Mt Hood, red cherries, red border .50
- San Ardo, cluster of red cherries, light blue background .25

Cigar
- Calsetta, woman wearing green bodice, gilt coins 1.00
- Epco, Egyptian lady with harp, seaside garden 3.00
- Flor De Cadiz, portrait of lady wearing mantilla 2.00
- Jewelo, romantic man and woman 1.00
- La Comporita, lady holding pink rose 3.00
- Merchants Queen, portrait of woman in plantation 1.00
- Our Kitties, black cat and white cat, woodgrain background 3.00
- Red Tips, horseshoe with horse head, white background 1.00
- Shoe Peg, black hightop shoe, red background 2.00
- Uncle Jake's Nickel Seegar, comical bearded man and cat, 1925 3.00
- White cat, fluffy white cat lying on cigar 1.00

Grape
- Baby Turtle, naked baby on turtle's back, blue grapes, red background .50
- Blue Hound, hound chasing rabbit .75
- Brunette, European girl carrying basket of grapes .50
- Carl's Special, smiling boy, blue purple grapes, red background .50
- Crystal, sparkling gemstone, orange background .25
- EFA, red and green grapes, lilac and yellow background .25
- Eperoors, purple grapes, green leaves, woodgrained background .25
- Four Sons, four boys admiring grape bunches .50
- Good Year, red and green–yellow grapes .25
- Jo–Vista, red and green grapes, blue background .25
- La Paloma, dove, green and red grapes, red and yellow background .25
- Lee, purple grapes, red background .25
- Old Mission, Spanish Mission scene, monks, green grape mission bells .50
- Pride of Dinuba, woman wearing yellow flowing gown, holding bunch of grapes, blue and red background .50
- Red Wagon, little boy pushing red wagon with grapes, red violet background .25
- Smiling Baby, little boy, yellow and purple grapes, glass of wine, blue background .50
- Try One, red and yellow bunches of grapes, blue background .25
- Valley Boy, little boy wearing cap, basket of grapes .75

Grapefruit
- Better 'N Ever, half slice grapefruit, blue background .50
- Dixie Boy, little black child eating half of grapefruit, 9" sq 3.00

Lemon
- Arboleda, ocean and ranch scene, Goleta 1.00
- Bridal Veil, Bridal Veil Falls, Yosemite Park, Santa Paula 5.00
- Cutter, cutter on choppy seas, orange–gold sky background, dated 1937, Oxnard 3.00
- Festival, two horses pulling cart, two lady passengers and driver, Santa Barbara 2.00
- Golden State, four lemons and map, Lemon Cove 1.00
- Kaweah Maid, Indian girl wearing turquoise beads, brown background, Lemon Cove 4.00

La Patera, blue pond and grove scene, Goleta ........................ 1.00
Limoneira Co, Sunkist lemon, red background, Santa Paula ........ 1.00
Mission, Santa Barbara mission and large lemon ................... 3.00
Oh–Cee, C in center, lemons, leaves, and blossoms, brown background, Orange Cove .................. 1.00
Parade, drum major leading parade, Saticoy ....................... 2.00
Red Ball California Lemons, red ball, yellow letters, black background, Los Angeles .................. 1.00
Sea Coast, lemons and blue triangle, brown background, Ventura ..... 2.00

**Fruit Crate, Doe Brand Carrots, dark blue ground, 7 x 10", $1.00.**

Selva, Sespe Canyon scene, maroon border, Fillmore ................ 2.00
Silver Cord, cord script, Santa Paula 1.00
Sunside, two lemons, orange and brown background, Santa Paula .. 1.00
Wave, two lemons, red background, Santa Paula ................... 1.00
Lettuce, Green Head, green duck's head and head of lettuce ............... 1.00
Orange
Airship, four propeller plane, royal blue background, Fillmore ....... 12.00
Annie Laurie, Scottish lassie, plaid background, Strathmore ......... 3.00
Belt, large orange encircled by tooled leather belt, E Highlands ........ 5.00
Blue Goose, blue goose, orange background, Los Angeles ............ 2.00
Brownies, Brownies preparing orange juice, yellow sun, blue background, Lemon Cove ........... 3.00
Caledonia, thistle sprays, tartan plaid background, Placentia .......... 1.00
Carefree, pretty blonde, blue background, Redlands .............. 2.00
Corona Lily, white and gold speckled lily, black background, Corona ... 2.00
Daisy, large white daisy, green leaves, black background, Covina ....... 2.00
Dash, orange in blue diamond, green background, Santa Paula ........ 1.00
Eat One, arrow pointing to juicy orange, aqua background, Lindsay . 2.00
Exeter, Tulare Co, map on orange, red and blue background, Exeter ..... 1.00
Gladiola, pink gladiola sprays, gold–tan background, Covina ......... 2.00
Golden Circle, wreath of oranges, Redlands ...................... 2.00
Green Mill, Dutch windmill, yellow skies, white clouds, red background, Placentia .............. 2.00
Have One, hand holding peeled orange, royal blue background, Lemon Cove .................. 2.00
Hill Choices, orchard scene, purple mountains, aqua background, Porterville ....................... 1.00
King David, king with white beard and crown, Placentia ........... 3.00
Linen, embroidered linen with diagonal lettering, black background, dated 1929, Irvine .............. 1.00
Loch Lomond, Scottish scene, blue and green plaid background, Strathmore .................... 2.00
Marvel, brass like letters on wood sign 1.00
Majorette, majorette in red and white, maroon and green background, Woodlake ..................... 2.00
National Orange Co, capitol buildings, blue background, Riverside . 2.00
Orbit, orange shape meteor, royal blue background, Exeter ........ 3.00
Orosi, large white graduated letters, blue background, Orosi ......... 1.00
Pala Brave, Indian chief wearing headdress, maroon background, Placentia ...................... 3.00
Polo, polo player and pony, red and green background, E Highlands .. 5.00
Rebecca, Rebecca with jug at well, Placentia ...................... 4.00
Rocky Hill Indian chief on horse, blue background, Exeter ............. 2.00
Satin, pink draped satin, Irvine ..... 1.00
Shamrock, large shamrock in sky over orange groves, Placentia ........ 1.00
Star of California, red star and map, Exeter ........................ 1.00
Sunny Cove, Spanish style ranch home, orange groves, Redlands .. 3.00
Talisman, three talisman roses, blue and black background, Redlands . 2.00
Treetop, twin Sequoia tree, yellow

lettering, blue background, Lemon Cove . . . . . . . . . . . . . . . . . . . . . . . . 1.00
Valley View, red tile roof home, orchards, snowy mountains, Claremont . . . . . . . . . . . . . . . . . . . . . . . . 2.00
Washington, Washington monument, pool, and trees, blue background, Exeter . . . . . . . . . . . . . . . . . . . . . . . 1.00
Yokohl, Indian brave fishing by stream, red background, Exeter . . 3.00

Pear
American Maid, navy blue silhouette, lady wearing floppy hat, orange background . . . . . . . . . . . . . . . . . . 1.00
Blue Goose, blue goose, orange background . . . . . . . . . . . . . . . . . . . . . . . 1.00
Camel, camel and master, sunrise in desert scene . . . . . . . . . . . . . . . . . . 2.00
Donner, snowy Lake Tahoe scene . . 2.00
El Rio Orchards, two yellow pears, blue background . . . . . . . . . . . . . . . .50
Forever First, red holly berries, plump juicy pears, blue background . . . . 2.00
High Hand, hand holding four aces, blue background . . . . . . . . . . . . . . . 1.00
Lake Wenatchee, mountain scene, three pears, blue border . . . . . . . . . 1.00
Magic Lake, snowy egrets wading in blue lake, mountain background . .50
Mopac, Indian portrait, blue background . . . . . . . . . . . . . . . . . . . . . . . 2.00
Our Pick, rooster pecking bowl of fruit, red background . . . . . . . . . . . 2.00
Peacock, male peacock . . . . . . . . . . . 1.00
Pirate's Cove, lake and country scene .50
River Maid, Dutch girl walking by canal, windmill . . . . . . . . . . . . . . . . .50
Stagecoach, stagecoach scene . . . . . 2.00
Sun Smile, smiling sun, rayed background . . . . . . . . . . . . . . . . . . . . . . . 2.00
Table Rock, pear orchard, Table Rock background . . . . . . . . . . . . . . . . . . 1.00
Violet, purple violets, black background . . . . . . . . . . . . . . . . . . . . . . . 4.00
Yuba Orchard, two yellow pears, blue background . . . . . . . . . . . . . . . . . . .50

Peas, Elkhorn, elks head, green peas in pods, brown background . . . . . . . . . .50

Tomato
Award, farmer holding big box tomatoes, ranch background . . . . . . .50
Big Chief, Indian chief and tomatoes .50
Bungalow, big tomato, bungalow home, and grounds . . . . . . . . . . . . . 1.50
Ekco, little boy shouting to red mountains and tomatoes, blue background . . . . . . . . . . . . . . . . . . . . . . . 1.00
Green Feather, green feather, black background . . . . . . . . . . . . . . . . . . .25
Little Boss, little boy wearing cap, tomato . . . . . . . . . . . . . . . . . . . . . . . . 1.00
Texus, cowboy wearing cowboy hat .50
White House, white columned house, black background . . . . . . . . . . . . . . .50
White Star, navy circle with big white star, red background . . . . . . . . . . . .25

Yam
Champ, two football players, blue background . . . . . . . . . . . . . . . . . . . 2.00
Deer Mark, stag's head over two sweet potatoes, red background . . 1.00
Gene–O, man wearing top hat and tails, holding diamond studded cane . . . . . . . . . . . . . . . . . . . . . . . . . .75
Hillview, farm scene . . . . . . . . . . . . . .50
Jack Rabbit, gray rabbit on red triangle and sweet potatoes, aqua background, green border . . . . . . . . . . . 1.00
Louise Anna, two big yams, yellow and aqua background . . . . . . . . . . . .50
Pride of the Farm, farm scene, red roofed homes, barn, and yams . . . 1.00
Sho–Am–Sweet, smiling black chef holding platter of cooked yams . . . 1.50
Smoky Jim's, smiling black man and crate of yams . . . . . . . . . . . . . . . . . . 2.00
Victorius, cowgirl riding white horse 2.00
White House, red yams, blue background . . . . . . . . . . . . . . . . . . . . . . . .50

# LAMPS

**Collecting Hints:** Be aware that every lamp has two values—a collectible value and a decorative value. Often the decorative value exceeds the collectible value. Most lamps are purchased as decorative accessories, often as accent pieces in a period room setting.

In the 1980s the hot lamp category was 1950s odd shaped lamps, some abstract and some figural. This craze is documented in Leland and Crystal Payton's *Turned On: Decorative Lamps of the 'Fifties*. While 1950s lamps continue to sell well as part of the 1950s~60s revival, prices have stabilized due largely to market saturation. A great many 1950s~60s lamps survived in attics and basements.

Lamp collectors specialize. In the 1970s and 1980s Aladdin was the magic name due in large part to the promotional efforts of J. W. Courter. One man can make a market.

Within the past five years, collector interest is spreading to other manufacturers and into electric lamps. One of the biggest drawbacks is the lack of a definitive lamp collecting manual and price guide that shows the full range of the lamp market. Far too many of the lamp books are nothing more than catalog reprints.

Just as post–World War II collectors discovered figural transistor and character radios, so also are they discovering motion lamps, many of which are character related. Look for a growing interest and rise in prices for character lamps once collectors begin to realize what a fertile territory this is for collecting.

The 1990s marks a major transitional period in lamp collecting. The kerosene lamp which dominated lamp collecting through virtually the entire twentieth century is slowly being upstaged by the electric lamp. By the twenty–first century, the electric, not the kerosene lamp, will dominate.

**History:** The dominant lamp during the nineteenth and first quarter of the twentieth century was the kerosene lamp. However, its death knell was sounded in 1879 when Thomas A. Edison developed a viable electric light bulb.

The success of the electric lamp depended on the availability of electricity. However, what we take for granted did not arrive in many rural areas until the 1930s.

Most electric lamps were designed to serve as silent compliments to period design styles. They were meant to blend, rather than stand out. Pairs were quite common.

Famous industrial designers lent their talents to lamp design. These are eagerly sought by collectors. Bradley and Hubbard and Handel are two companies whose products have attracted strong collector interest.

**References:** James Edward Black (ed.), *Electric Lighting of the 20s & 30s, Volume 2 with Price Guide*, L–W Book Sales, 1988, 1993 value update; J. W. Courter, *Aladdin, The Magic Name in Lamps, Wallace–Homestead, 1980, out–of–print; J. W. Courter, Aladdin Collectors Manual & Price Guide #14, Kerosene Mantle Lamps*, published by author, 1992; J. W. Courter, *Aladdin Electric Lamps Price Guide #1*, published by author, 1989; J. W. Courter, *Angle Lamps: Collectors Manual & Price Guide*, published by author, 1992; Nadja Maril, *American Lighting: 1840–1940*, Schiffer Publishing, 1989; Bill and Linda Montgomery, *Animation Motion Lamps: A Price Guide*, L–W Book Sales, 1991; Leland & Crystal Payton, *Turned On: Decorative Lamps of the 'Fifties*, Abbeville Press, 1989; *Quality Electric Lamps: A Pictorial Price Guide*, L–W Book Sales, 1992.

**Collectors' Clubs:** Aladdin Knights of the Mystic Light, Route 1, Simpson, IL 62985; Historical Lighting Society of Canada, 9013 Oxbox Road, North East, PA 16428.

Boudoir, figural French poodle, ceramic, pink, circular base, pink paper shade .......... **24.00**

Character

- Davy Crockett, 16″ h, Davy, tree, and bear ceramic base, Davy, Indians, and fort on shade, 1950s .......... **180.00**
- Fred Flintstone, 13 1/4″ h, painted vinyl, black metal base, missing shade .......... **45.00**
- Mickey Mouse, 4″ d, 6 1/2″ h, globular metal base, beige ground, three Mickey decals around sides, Soreng–Manegold Co .......... **75.00**

Children's

- Elephant, figural, ceramic, carousel beaded shade .......... **195.00**
- Football Player, 14 1/2″ h, hollow plaster, football player standing next to figural football standard, linen over cardboard shade, WK, Japan, Sears, Roebuck, 1978 .......... **20.00**

Lava, Lava Simplex Corp, c1968 .......... **80.00**

Motion

- Forest Fire, plastic, LA Goodman, 1956, 11″ h .......... **50.00**
- Niagara Falls, bronze frame, plastic sleeve, Rev–O–Lite, 1930s, 10″ h **85.00**
- Roy Rogers Rodeo, desk, rodeo scenes on shade, Pearson, c1950, 17″ h .......... **1,050.00**

**Lamp/Planter, gray ceramic base, plastic marbleized gray rect Venetian blind shade, 21½″ h, $65.00.**

**TV Lamp, gondola, ceramic, brown with gold trim, marked "copyright Premco Mfg Co, Chicago, Ill, 1954," 16″ w, 7″ h, $35.00.**

Statue of Liberty, plastic, Econolite, 1957, 11" h ..................... **75.00**
Television
Horse Head, 12 x 10 3/4" ......... **22.00**
Panther, black, 8 1/2 x 6 1/2" ...... **18.00**
Ship, 11 x 10 1/2", gold trim ...... **20.00**
Torchiere, blue flashed glass, ribbed and diamond beaded shade, circular ribbed base, 11 1/2" h ............ **25.00**
Vanity, glass, figural
Scottie Dog, with ball, fired on blue **125.00**
Tara, southern belle, fired on pink .. **60.00**

# LETTER OPENERS

**Collecting Hints:** The advertising and celluloid letter openers are the most eagerly sought. Most letter openers dating from 1940 to the present have little collector interest and value.

New collectors might focus on the openers issued from within a specific geographic region. Blanks were available that could be used to carry a local message.

**History:** The letter opener reflects the attributes of the period in which it was created. In the Colonial period elegant silver letter openers graced the desks of the middle and upper class. As letters became inexpensive to mail and a popular form of communication, the need for letter openers grew.

The late 19th century witnessed the popularity of the lithographed tin advertising letter opener. They usually were given away. By the 1920s brass and other metals captured the flowing lines of the Art Nouveau and Art Deco periods. The handcraft movements, e.g., Roycroft, produced some distinctively styled letter openers during the 1910 to 1930 period.

By the early 1950s letter openers lost their individuality. Americans phoned rather than wrote. Plastic openers of uniform design became standard. Letter openers were relegated from the desk top to the desk drawer.

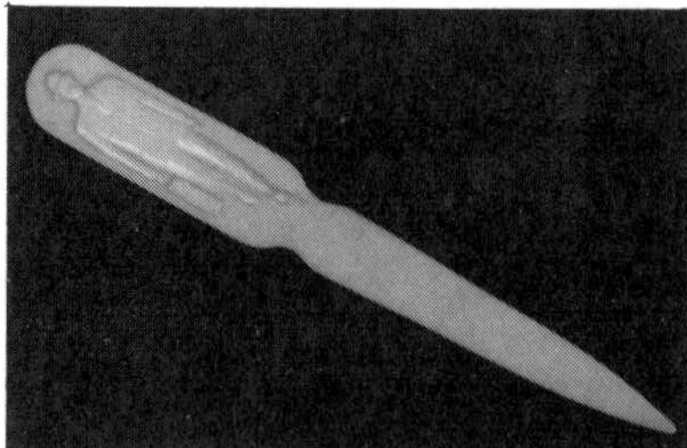

**Advertising, Fuller Brush Co., molded plastic, white, salesman one side, saleswoman other side, 8" l, $16.00.**

Advertising
Armstrong Cork Co, 6 1/2" l, celluloid, 5" printed rule on one side, printed cork gauge for measuring bottle neck sizes ............... **15.00**
Bastian Bros, 9" l, steel blade, silvered brass handle inscribed "Compliments of Bastian Bros Co, Metal and Celluloid Adv Specialities, Rochester, NY," single pocketknife blade in handle, c1900 ......... **40.00**
Coes Wrench Co, 7 1/2" l, celluloid, diecut, wrench shape, black printing of wrench holding nut and adv slogans on back, c1910 ......... **25.00**
Hoskins, Wm H, Office Supply Co, Philadelphia, PA, celluloid, white, blue printing on one side, red on reverse, c1900 ................. **18.00**
Humphrey Inverted, 7 1/2" l, celluloid, solid white blade, black and white handle shaped as gas operated ceiling lighting fixture, gold stripes ....................... **30.00**
Kellogg's Cereal, 9" l, celluloid, figural, white rooster's head, gray feathering, amber eye, bright red comb, inscribed "We Can't Help Crowing Once In A While – W K Kellogg," "Distributed Through The Jobbing Trade Only, Made In Germany" on back ................ **100.00**
Life Indemnity Insurance Company, sword ....................... **35.00**
MacGregor's Ice Cream, celluloid handle ....................... **22.00**
National Cash Register, 5 1/2" l, white metal, diecut, detailed illus in back of cash register, adv text, c1900 .. **45.00**
Whitehead and Hoag, 5" l, flat silvered brass opener, two celluloid inserts on handle, Art Nouveau drawing of Dutch girl with yellow tulip on one, other reads "Compliments of Whitehead & Hoag Co, Advertising Novelties with Merit, Branches In All Large Cities," c1900 ....................... **50.00**
Wilson, Jas G, New York City, 8 3/4" l, celluloid, black and white illus of blinds and shutters, white ground, 6" printed ruler, c1895 .......... **35.00**
Yellow Pages, celluloid, figural ..... **25.00**
Figural, celluloid
Alligator, 7" l, hollow beige alligator, small black and white eyes, 2 1/2" l black lead pencil with celluloid head of black man held in mouth, tail marked "St Augustine, FL," underneath marked "Germany," c1900 ....................... **75.00**
Elephant, 7 1/2" l, white and shaded

brown, black ink inscription "Kingston, Canada," marked "Depose–Germany," c1900 ......... **35.00**
Indian, 7" l, beige, black accents, seated, smoking pipe, red, white, and blue headpiece, 4" l thin black lead pencil .................... **60.00**
Owl, 9" l, white, owl's head handle, black textured feathers, blue tint eyes, metal tape measure attached to back, c1900 ................ **75.00**
Fraternal, Knights Templar, 6" l, diecut, white, souvenir of Grand Commandery of West Virginia 1910 Chicago conclave, multicolored masonic symbols ............................ **40.00**
World's Fair, 1933, Century of Progress **28.00**

# LIMITED EDITIONS OR COLLECTOR ITEMS

**Collecting Hints:** The first edition of a series usually commands a higher price. When buying a limited edition collectible be aware that the original box and/or certificates increase the value of the piece. Be alert to special discounts and sales.

**History:** Limited edition plate collecting began with the advent of Christmas plates issued by Bing and Grondahl in 1895. Royal Copenhagen soon followed. During the late 1960s and early 1970s, several potteries, glass factories, and mints began to issue plates, bells, eggs, mugs, etc. which commemorated special events, people, places, holidays. For a period of time these items increased in popularity and value. But in the late 1970s, the market became flooded with many collectibles and the market declined.

There are many new issues of collector items annually. Some of these collectibles can be found listed under specific headings, such as Hummel, Norman Rockwell, etc.

**References:** *The Bradford Book of Collector Plates, 12th Edition,* published by Bradford Exchange, 1987, supplements for 1988–1990; Gene Ehlert, *The Official Price Guide To Collector Plates, Fifth Edition,* House of Collectibles, 1988; Diane Carnevale Jones, *Collectors' Information Bureau's Collectibles Market Guide & Price Index, Eleventh Edition,* Collectors' Information Bureau, 1994; Diane Carnevale Jones, *Collectors' Information Bureau's Directory To Secondary Market Retailers: Buying And Selling Limited Edition Artwork,* Collectors' Information Bureau, 1992; Rosie Wells (ed.), *Official 1993 Secondary Market Price Guide For Precious Moments Collectibles, Eleventh Edition,* Rosie Wells Enterprises, 1993.

**Periodicals:** *Collector Editions,* 170 Fifth Ave., 12th Floor, New York, NY 10010; *Collectors Magazine,* P. O. Box 12830, Wichita, KS 67277; *International Collectible Showcase,* One Westminster Place, Lake Forest, IL 60045; *Plate World,* 9200 North Maryland Avenue, Niles, IL 60648; *Swan Seekers News,* 4118 East Vernon Ave., Phoenix, AZ 85008.

**Collectors' Clubs:** Lowell Davis Farm Club, 55 Pacella Park Drive, Randolph, MA 02368; Gorham Collectors Club, P. O. Box 6472, Providence, RI 02940; M. I. Hummel Club, Dept. O, Goebel Plaza, P.O. Box 11, Pennington, NJ 08534; Precious Moments Collector, RR 1, Canton, IL 61520; Precious Moments Collectors' Club, 1 Enesco Plaza, P. O. Box 1466; Elk Grove Village, IL 60009.

**Museum:** Bradford Museum, Niles, IL.

## BELLS

Anri, J. Ferrandiz, artist, wooden
1976, Christmas, FE .............. **50.00**
1977, Christmas ................. **42.00**
1978, Christmas ................. **40.00**
1979, Christmas ................. **30.00**
1980, The Christmas King ......... **18.50**
1981, Lighting the Way ........... **18.50**
1982, Caring .................... **18.50**
1983, Behold .................... **18.50**
1985, Nature's Dream ............ **18.50**
1987, The Wedding Bell, silver .... **25.00**
1988, Bride Belles, Caroline ....... **27.50**
1989, Christmas Pow–Pow ........ **25.00**
1990, Indian Brave ............... **25.00**
Bing & Grondahl, Christmas, annual
1980 .......................... **70.00**
1981 .......................... **15.00**
1982 .......................... **35.00**
1983 .......................... **45.00**
1984 .......................... **45.00**
1985 .......................... **45.00**
1986 .......................... **45.00**
1987 .......................... **48.00**
1988 .......................... **48.00**
1989 .......................... **50.00**
1990 .......................... **55.00**
1991 .......................... **55.00**
1992 .......................... **60.00**
1993 .......................... **60.00**
Danbury Mint, Norman Rockwell art
1975, Doctor and Doll ............ **50.00**
1976, No Swimming ............. **40.00**
1977, Santa's Mail ............... **40.00**
1979, Leapfrog .................. **30.00**
Enesco Corp, Precious Moments
1981, Prayer Changes Things ...... **40.00**
1982, Mother Sew Dear ........... **35.00**
1983, Surrounded With Joy ........ **60.00**

1984, Wishing You A Merry Christmas .......... **45.00**
1989, Your Love Is Special To Me .. **20.00**
1990, Here Comes The Bride ...... **25.00**
1991, May Your Christmas Be Merry **30.00**
1992, But The Greatest Of These Is Love .......... **25.00**
Franklin Mint, 1979, Unicorn, porcelain **35.00**
Gorham
1975, Sweet Song So Young ....... **50.00**
1976, Tavern Sign Painter ......... **30.00**
1977, Chilling Chore ............. **30.00**
1978, Currier & Ives .............. **20.00**
1979, Beguiling Buttercup ......... **30.00**
1980, Christmas ................. **25.00**
1981, Ski Skills .................. **27.00**
1982, Young Man's Fancy ......... **25.00**
1983, Christmas Medley .......... **30.00**
1984, Young Love ................ **28.00**
1985, Yuletide Reflections ......... **32.50**
1986, Home For The Holidays ..... **32.50**
1987, Merry Christmas Grandma ... **30.00**
1988, The Homecoming .......... **37.50**
Hummel, see HUMMEL
Hutschenreuther, 1978, Christmas .... **8.00**
Llardo, Christmas
1987 .......................... **90.00**
1988 .......................... **80.00**
1989 .......................... **90.00**
1990 .......................... **45.00**
1991 .......................... **40.00**
1992 .......................... **35.00**
Pickard
1977, The First Noel, FE .......... **75.00**
1978, O Little Town of Bethlehem .. **70.00**
1979, Silent Night ................ **80.00**
1980, Hark! The Herald Angels Sing **80.00**
Reco International
1980, I Love You, FE ............. **20.00**
1981, Sea Echoes ................ **20.00**
1982, Talk to Me ................ **20.00**
1988, Charity .................... **15.00**
1989, The Wedding ............. **15.00**
Reed and Barton
1980, Noel, musical .............. **45.00**
1981, Yuletide Holiday ........... **15.00**
1982, Little Shepherd ............. **14.00**
1983, Noel, musical .............. **45.00**
1984, Noel, musical .............. **48.00**
1985, Caroller ................... **17.50**
1986, Noel, musical .............. **25.00**
1987, Jolly St Nick .............. **15.00**
1988, Christmas Morning ......... **15.00**
1989, The Bell Ringer ............ **15.00**
1990, The Wreath Bearer ......... **15.00**
1991, A Special Gift .............. **20.00**
1992, My Special Friend .......... **20.00**
River Shore
1979, Allison .................... **48.00**
1980, Katrina .................... **45.00**
1981, Spring Flowers ............. **175.00**
1982, American Gothic ........... **50.00**

Schmid
Peanuts
1976, Christmas ............... **25.00**
1977, Christmas ............... **18.00**
1978, Mother's Day ............ **15.00**
1979, A Special Letter .......... **25.00**
1980, Waiting for Santa ......... **25.00**
1981, Mission for Mom ......... **20.00**
1982, Perfect Performance ...... **18.00**
1983, Peanuts in Concert ....... **12.00**
1984, Snoopy and the Beagle Scouts ...................... **12.00**
Walt Disney, Christmas
1985, Snow Biz ................ **18.00**
1986, Tree For Two ............ **16.00**
1987, Merry Mouse Medley ..... **17.50**
1988, Warm Winter Ride ........ **18.00**
1989, Merry Mickey Claus ...... **24.00**
1990, Holly Jolly Christmas ...... **25.00**
1991, Mickey & Minnie's Rockin' Christmas .................. **27.50**
Zemsky, 1978, Christmas .......... **20.00**
1979, Christmas, pewter ........ **25.00**
Towle Silversmiths, silverplated
1980, ball ....................... **17.50**
1982, musical ................... **27.50**
1984, musical ................... **25.00**
1986, ball ....................... **30.00**
1988, musical ................... **35.00**
Wedgwood, 1979, Penguins, FE ...... **48.00**
1981, Polar Bears ............... **40.00**
1982, Moose .................... **35.00**
1983, Fur Seals ................. **32.00**
1984, Ibex ...................... **50.00**
1985, Puffin ..................... **60.00**
1986, Ermine .................... **60.00**

## CHRISTMAS ORNAMENTS

Enesco
Memories of Yesterday
1988, Baby's First Christmas ..... **25.00**
1989, Christmas Together ....... **25.00**
1990, Moonstruck .............. **15.00**
1991, Star Fishing .............. **12.00**
Precious Moments
1982, Our First Christmas Together **25.00**
1983, Surround Us With Joy ..... **60.00**
1984, Peace On Earth .......... **30.00**
1985, Baby's First Christmas ..... **10.00**
1986, Rocking Horse ........... **20.00**
Goebel, Inc.
1978, Santa, glass ................ **12.00**
1980, Angel with Tree, glass ....... **12.00**
1981, Mrs. Santa, glass ........... **12.00**
1982, The Nutcracker, glass ....... **5.00**
1983, Clown, white .............. **18.00**
1984, Snowman ................. **15.00**
1985, Angel ..................... **18.00**
1986, Drummer Boy .............. **10.00**
1987, Rocking Horse ............. **20.00**
1988, Doll, white ................ **21.00**

1989, Love From Above, Hummel .. **75.00**
1990, Peace on Earth, Hummel .... **80.00**
1991, Hear Ye, Hear Ye, Hummel .. **35.00**
Gorham
1970, snowflake, sterling .......... **275.00**
1971, snowflake, sterling .......... **100.00**
1985, crystal .................... **25.00**
1988, Victorian heart ............ **50.00**
1990, snowflake, sterling .......... **50.00**
Lenox
1984, ball, crystal ............... **50.00**
1985, ball, crystal ............... **50.00**
1986, annual, china .............. **60.00**
1987, partridge bell .............. **45.00**
1988, angel bell ................. **40.00**
1989, Christmas Tree Top ......... **30.00**
1990, Christmas Goose ........... **25.00**
1991, Snowman ................. **18.00**
1991, Santa in Chimney .......... **25.00**

## DOLLS

Enesco Imports, Precious Moments
1981, Mikey, 18″ h ............... **225.00**
1982, Tammy, 18″ h .............. **650.00**
1983, Katie Lynne, 16″ h .......... **185.00**
1984, Kristy, 12″ h .............. **160.00**
1985, Bethany, 12″ h ............. **145.00**
1986, Bong Bong, 13″ h .......... **165.00**
1987, Angie, The Angel of Mercy .. **160.00**
1989, Wishing You Cloudless Skies . **115.00**
1990, The Voice of Spring ......... **150.00**
1991, You Have Touched So Many Hearts ....................... **90.00**
Gorham, 1981
Alexandria, 19″ h ............. **550.00**
Christina, 16″ h ............... **450.00**
Ellice, 18″ h ................... **400.00**
Melinda, 14″ h ................ **285.00**
1982
Baby, white dress, 18″ h ........ **350.00**
Jeremy, 23″ h .................. **650.00**
Mlle. Monique, 12″ h ........... **275.00**
Mlle. Yvonne, 12″ h ............ **375.00**
1983
Bride, Jennifer, 19″ h ........... **800.00**
Meg, 19″ h .................... **650.00**
1984
Holly, Christmas .............. **800.00**
Nicole ....................... **900.00**
Sweet Valentine, 16″ h .......... **300.00**
1985
Ariel, 16″ h ................... **475.00**
Linda, 19″ h .................. **450.00**
1986
Jessica ....................... **350.00**
Meredith ..................... **375.00**
Veronica, 19″ h ................ **750.00**
1987
Rachel, 17″ h ................. **800.00**
Silver Bell, 17″ h ............... **175.00**
Valentine Lady, Jane ............ **305.00**
1988
Christa, 19″ h .................. **1,000.00**
Madeline ...................... **350.00**
1989
Julianna ...................... **275.00**
Katrina ....................... **275.00**
Rose ......................... **225.00**
1990
Natalie, 16″ h ................. **375.00**
Peggy ........................ **90.00**
Victoria ...................... **375.00**
1991
Amanda ...................... **90.00**
Cherie ....................... **375.00**
Emily, 16″ h ................... **375.00**
Irene ........................ **125.00**
Hamilton Collection
1981, Hakata, Peony Maiden ...... **150.00**
1985, American Fashion Doll Collection, Heather ................. **125.00**
1986, Nicole ................... **50.00**
1987, Priscilla .................. **50.00**
1988, Mr Spock .................. **75.00**
1989, Scotty .................... **75.00**
Royal Doulton by Nisbet
Little Model .................... **185.00**
Pink Sash ...................... **145.00**
Royal Baby ..................... **350.00**
The Muffs ...................... **175.00**
Winter ........................ **180.00**
Seymour Mann, Connossieur Collection
1984, Miss Debutante ............ **180.00**
1985, Wendy ................... **150.00**
1986, Camelot Fairy ............. **225.00**
1987, Dawn .................... **175.00**
1988, Jolie ..................... **150.00**
1989, Elizabeth ................. **200.00**
1990, Baby Sunshine ............. **90.00**
1991, Dephine .................. **125.00**

## EGGS

Anri, 1979, Beatrix Potter ........... **5.00**
Cybis Studios, 1983, FE, 5″ h, Faberge style .......................... **300.00**
Ferrandiz
1978, FE ....................... **15.00**
1979 .......................... **12.00**
1980 .......................... **9.50**
1981 .......................... **9.00**
1982 .......................... **8.00**
1983 .......................... **18.00**
Franklin Mint, 1979, porcelain ....... **35.00**
Goebel
1978, Easter .................... **10.00**
1979, Easter .................... **8.00**
1980
Crystal ...................... **6.00**
Easter ....................... **12.00**
1981, Easter .................... **9.75**
1982, Easter .................... **8.00**
1983, Easter .................... **28.00**
Gorham, bone china, pink rose, 4¼″ **18.00**

Noritake
1971, Easter, FE .......... **75.00**
1972, Easter .......... **35.00**
1973, Easter .......... **18.00**
1974, Easter .......... **8.00**
1975, Easter .......... **10.00**
1976, Easter .......... **10.00**
1977, Easter .......... **12.50**
1978, Easter .......... **14.00**
1979, Easter .......... **14.00**
1980, Easter .......... **14.00**
1981, Easter .......... **15.00**
1982, Easter .......... **15.00**
1983, Easter .......... **28.50**
1984, Easter .......... **20.00**
Royal Bayreuth
1975 .......... **8.50**
1976 .......... **6.50**
1977 .......... **5.50**
1979 .......... **16.00**
1980 .......... **15.00**
Veneto Flair, 1975 .......... **14.50**
1976 .......... **14.50**
1977 .......... **15.00**
1983, FE, luster finish, new series .. **20.00**
Wedgwood, 1977 .......... **35.00**
1978 .......... **25.00**
1979 .......... **18.00**
1983 .......... **40.00**

## FIGURINES

Anri, Sarah Kay artist
1983, Morning Chores, 6″, FE .......... **475.00**
1984, Flowers for You, 6″ .......... **400.00**
1985, Afternoon Tea, 6″ .......... **325.00**
1986, Our Puppy, 1½″ .......... **90.00**
1987, Little Nanny, 4″ .......... **180.00**
1988, Purrfect Day, 6″ .......... **400.00**
1989, Garden Party, 4″ .......... **195.00**
1990, Season's Greetings, 4″ .......... **225.00**
1991, Season's Joy, 4″ .......... **250.00**
Burgues
1972, Canon Wren .......... **875.00**
1976, Anniversary Orchid .......... **120.00**
1978, Young Cottontail .......... **325.00**
1981, Joy .......... **85.00**
1982, Frosty .......... **75.00**
1983, Oscar, cat .......... **100.00**
1984, Cymbidium, Pink Blush .......... **80.00**
Cybis
1963, Magnolia .......... **400.00**
1964, Rebecca .......... **345.00**
1965, Christmas Rose .......... **750.00**
1967, Kitten, blue ribbon .......... **500.00**
1968, Narcissus .......... **500.00**
1969, Clematis with House Wren .. **315.00**
1970, Dutch Crocus .......... **750.00**
1971, Appaloosa Colt .......... **285.00**
1972, Pansies .......... **350.00**
1973, Goldilocks .......... **325.00**
1974, Mary, Mary .......... **750.00**
1975, George Washington Bust .......... **300.00**
1976, Bunny .......... **125.00**
1977, Tiffin .......... **400.00**
1978, Edith .......... **300.00**
1980, Little Miss Muffet .......... **350.00**
1982, Spring Bouquet .......... **750.00**
1985, Nativity Lamb .......... **125.00**
1986, Dapple Gray Foal .......... **185.00**
Department 56, Snowbabies
1986, Hold On Tight .......... **12.00**
1987, Down The Hill We Go .......... **20.00**
1988, Tiny Trio .......... **60.00**
1989, Icy Igloo .......... **35.00**
1990, A Special Delivery .......... **12.00**
1991, Just For You .......... **20.00**
Enesco Corp, Precious Moments
1979, Jesus Loves Me .......... **30.00**
1980, Come Let Us Adore Him .......... **90.00**
1981, But Love Goes On Forever ... **165.00**
1982, I Believe In Miracles .......... **90.00**
1983, Sharing Our Season .......... **100.00**
1984, Joy To The World .......... **40.00**
1985, Baby's First Christmas .......... **35.00**
1986, God Bless America .......... **50.00**
1987, This Is The Day The Lord Hath Made .......... **35.00**
1988, Faith Takes The Plunge .......... **30.00**
1989, Wishing You Roads of Happiness .......... **50.00**
1990, To My Favorite Fan .......... **15.00**
Goebel
1971, Fritz the Happy Boozer .......... **50.00**
1972, Bob the Bookworm .......... **50.00**
1973, Maid of the Mist, 14″ .......... **750.00**
1975, With Love .......... **125.00**
1978, Smiling Through, 5½″ .......... **75.00**
1979, Birthday .......... **45.00**
1982, The Garden Fancier .......... **40.00**
1984, On The Fairway .......... **45.00**
1985, Gentle Breezes .......... **45.00**
1987, Chuck on a Pig .......... **65.00**
1988, Beautiful Burden .......... **165.00**
1989, My First Arrow .......... **70.00**
1990, El Burrito .......... **60.00**
Hummel, see HUMMEL
Llardo
1971, Elephants .......... **475.00**
1973, Going Fishing .......... **90.00**
1974, Passionate Dance .......... **2,500.00**
1975, Wedding .......... **100.00**
1977, My Baby .......... **1,115.00**
1978, Chrysanthemum .......... **225.00**
1980, Reading .......... **175.00**
1983, California Poppy .......... **100.00**
1984, Torch Bearer .......... **125.00**
1985, Youthful Beauty .......... **800.00**
1986, Ragamuffin .......... **125.00**
1987, Spring Bouquets .......... **125.00**
1989, Reflecting Clown .......... **325.00**
River Shore
1978, Akiku, Baby Seal, FE .......... **145.00**
1979, Rosecoe, red fox kit .......... **50.00**

- 1980, Lamb **48.00**
- 1981, Zuela, elephant **60.00**
- 1982, Kay's Doll **90.00**

Rockwell, Norman, see NORMAN ROCKWELL

Royal Doulton

- 1969, HRH Prince Charles, bust **400.00**
- 1974, Lady Musicians, cymbals **475.00**
- 1976, Fledging Bluebird **450.00**
- 1977, Winter Wren **375.00**
- 1982, Sweet and Twenties, Monte Carlo **175.00**
- Series
  - Beatrix Potter
    - Benjamin Bunny **25.00**
    - Lady Mouse **20.00**
    - Mrs. Rabbit & Bunnies **25.00**
    - Old Mr. Brown **20.00**
    - Peter Rabbit **25.00**
    - Rebecca Puddle-duck **20.00**
  - Bunnykins
    - Autumn Days **17.00**
    - Clean Sweep **14.00**
    - Family Photograph **24.00**
    - Grandpa's Story **17.00**
    - Sleepy Time **12.00**
    - Springtime **18.00**
    - Tally Ho **15.00**
  - Dickens
    - Mrs. Bardell **24.00**
    - Scrooge **25.00**
  - Lord of Rings, Tolkien
    - Aragorn **45.00**
    - Bilbo **35.00**
    - Gandalf **50.00**
    - Gimli **45.00**
    - Gollum **35.00**
    - Legolas **45.00**

Royal Orleans Porcelain, Marilyn Monroe **80.00**

Schmid

- Lowell Davis, artist
  - 1979, Country Road **275.00**
  - 1980, Two's Company **45.00**
  - 1981, Plum Tuckered Out **225.00**
  - 1982, Right Church, Wrong Pew **80.00**
  - 1983, Stirring Up Trouble **165.00**
  - 1984, Catnapping Too **72.00**
  - 1985, Out of Step **45.00**

## MUGS

Bing & Grondahl

- 1978, FE **50.00**
- 1980 **25.00**

Franklin Mint, 1979, Father's Day **40.00**

Gorham, 1981, Bugs Bunny **8.00**

- 1981, Tom & Jerry, 4×4″ h **9.00**

Lynell Studios, 1983, FE, Gnome Series

- Mama Gnome **7.00**
- Gnome Sweet Gnome **6.50**

**Mug, John James Audubon, Cardinal, 4″ h, 24 k gold trim, $5.00.**

Royal Copenhagen, 1967, large **200.00**

- 1968, large **24.00**
- 1972, large **24.00**
- 1976, large **25.00**
- 1979, small **28.00**
- 1980
  - Large **65.00**
  - Small **25.00**
- 1981, Large **70.00**
  - Small **35.00**
- 1983, small **30.00**

Royal Doulton, Santa, second edition **75.00**

Schmid, Zemsky, musical, 1981, Paddington Bear **25.00**

Wedgwood, 1971, Christmas **35.00**

- 1972, Christmas **30.00**
- 1973, Christmas **40.00**
- 1974, Christmas **30.00**
- 1975, Christmas **30.00**
- 1976, Christmas **30.00**
- 1977, Father's Day **25.00**
- 1978, Father's Day **25.00**
- 1979, Christmas **25.00**
- 1980, Christmas **25.00**
- 1981, Christmas **35.00**
- 1982, Christmas **40.00**

## MUSIC BOXES

Anri

- Jemima **100.00**
- Peter Rabbit **100.00**
- Pigling **100.00**

Ferrandiz

- Chorale **125.00**
- Drummer **185.00**
- Flower Girl **150.00**
- Going Home **275.00**
- Letter, The **150.00**
- Proud Mother **140.00**
- Spring Arrivals **120.00**
- Wanderlust **110.00**

Gorham

- Cardinal, double, 6″ h, hp, sculptured, porcelain **30.00**

Happy Birthday, animals .......... **35.00**
Santa & Sleigh, 6″ h .............. **20.00**
Sesame Street, Big Bird & Snowman, 7″ h .......................... **24.00**
Schmid
Paddington Bear
1981, Christmas ............... **35.00**
1982 .......................... **22.00**
Peanuts
30th Anniversary ............... **18.00**
1981
Christmas ................... **28.00**
Mother's Day ............... **18.00**
1982
Christmas ................... **30.00**
Mother's Day ............... **20.00**
Raggedy Ann
1980 .......................... **15.00**
1981 .......................... **15.00**
1982, Flying High ............. **20.00**
Walt Disney
1980, Christmas, FE .............. **42.00**
1981, Christmas ................. **30.00**
1982, Christmas ................. **25.00**

## ORNAMENTS

Anri
Beatrix Potter Series
Hunca Munca ................. **12.00**
Jeremy Fisher ................ **12.50**
Mrs. Rigby ................... **10.00**
Pigling Bland ................. **12.00**
Tom Kitten ................... **12.75**
1982, Alpine Mother, pastel pink ... **14.00**
Danbury Mint, angel, 4″ ........... **45.00**
Davis, Lowell, R.F.D. Series, FE ...... **15.00**
Ferrandiz, 1978, FE ............... **22.00**
1979 .......................... **15.00**
1980 .......................... **15.00**
1981 .......................... **18.00**
Goebel
1978
Santa, colorful, FE .............. **12.00**
Santa, white, FE ................ **10.00**
1982, Santa ..................... **18.00**
Gorham
1972, Snowflake ................. **25.00**
1973, Snowflake ................. **35.00**
1979, Tiny Tim, FE ............... **8.00**
1980
Santa, FE, miniature series ....... **8.00**
Snowflake, SP ................. **8.00**
1981
Doll, Rosebud, china, 8″ h ...... **12.00**
Santa, miniature ............... **10.00**
Snowflake ..................... **30.00**
Toy Soldier, wooden, red jacket, blue hat .................... **4.50**
Hallmark, 1974, Mary Hamilton, orig Charmer Design .................. **7.50**
1975, Betsy Clark ................ **7.50**
1979, Special Teacher, satin ....... **4.50**
1980, Baby's First Christmas ....... **15.00**
1981
Candyville Express ............. **25.00**
Friendly Fiddler ................ **15.00**
St. Nicholas, tin ................ **10.00**
1982
Cookie Mouse .................. **17.50**
Cowboy Snowman ............. **10.00**
Jingling Teddy ................. **12.00**
Peeking Elf ................... **6.50**
Soldier, clothespin, FE .......... **25.00**
Haviland
1972 .......................... **8.00**
1973 .......................... **8.00**
1974 .......................... **12.00**
1975 .......................... **6.00**
1976 .......................... **6.00**
1977 .......................... **8.00**
1978 .......................... **7.50**
1979 .......................... **7.25**
1980 .......................... **18.00**
1981 .......................... **20.00**
1982 .......................... **22.00**
International Silver, Twelve Days of Christmas, SS, each .............. **25.00**
Lenox, 1982, FE, snowflake emb porcelain, 24K gold finials, date, 6″ h .. **40.00**
Lunt
1974, Trefoil .................... **20.00**
1980, Medallion ................. **18.00**
Reed & Barton
1980, Christmas Castle ............ **28.00**
1981
Bringing Home The Tree, SP ..... **15.00**
Cross ....................... **18.00**
1982, Little Shepherd Yuletide, SS .. **15.00**
Schmid
Paddington Bear, 1982
Ball ......................... **5.00**
Figural ...................... **10.00**
Raggedy Ann, 1976, FE ........... **6.00**
1977 ........................ **3.50**
1978 ........................ **3.00**
1979 ........................ **3.25**
1980 ........................ **3.00**
1982, Figural .................. **10.00**
Walt Disney, 1974, FE ............ **15.00**
1975 ........................ **5.00**
1976 ........................ **10.00**
1977 ........................ **4.50**
1978 ........................ **4.00**
1979 ........................ **4.00**
1980 ........................ **3.50**
1981 ........................ **3.00**
1982 Figural ................... **10.00**
Towle
1971, Twelve Days of Christmas, SP medallion ..................... **250.00**
1985, Poinsettia .................. **40.00**
1987, White Christmas ............ **35.00**
1988, Holly ..................... **40.00**

Wallace Silversmiths
- 1971, Sleigh Bell .......... **900.00**
- 1972, Sleigh Bell .......... **350.00**
- 1980, Snowman .......... **15.00**
- 1983, Boy Caroler .......... **15.00**
- 1985, Sleigh Bell .......... **45.00**
- 1987, Candy Cane .......... **35.00**

**Plate, Royal Copenhagen, Christmas, 1972, In The Desert, 7¼" d, $85.00.**

## PLATES

### Anri (Italy)

Christmas Plates, J Ferrandiz, 12" d
- 1972 Christ in the Manager .......... **230.00**
- 1973 Christmas .......... **220.00**
- 1974 Holy Night .......... **90.00**
- 1975 Flight Into Egypt .......... **80.00**
- 1976 Tree of Life .......... **60.00**
- 1977 Girl with Flowers .......... **175.00**
- 1978 Leading the Way .......... **165.00**
- 1979 The Drummer .......... **170.00**
- 1980 Rejoice .......... **150.00**
- 1981 Spreading the Word .......... **150.00**
- 1982 The Shepherd Family .......... **150.00**
- 1983 Peace Attend Thee .......... **150.00**

Mother's Day Plates, J Ferrandiz
- 1972, Mother Sewing .......... **200.00**
- 1973, Alpine Mother & Child .......... **150.00**
- 1974, Mother Holding Child .......... **150.00**
- 1975, Dove Girl .......... **150.00**
- 1976, Mother Knitting .......... **200.00**
- 1977, Alpine Stroll .......... **125.00**
- 1978, The Beginning .......... **150.00**
- 1979, All Hearts .......... **165.00**
- 1980, Spring Arrivals .......... **160.00**
- 1981, Harmony .......... **150.00**
- 1982, With Love .......... **150.00**

### Bareuther (Germany)

Christmas Plates, Hans Mueller artist, 8" d
- 1967 Stiftskirche, FE .......... **90.00**
- 1968 Kapplkirche .......... **25.00**
- 1969 Christkindlemarkt .......... **20.00**
- 1970 Chapel in Oberndorf .......... **18.00**
- 1971 Toys for Sale .......... **20.00**
- 1972 Christmas in Munich .......... **35.00**
- 1973 Christmas Sleigh Ride .......... **20.00**
- 1974 Church In The Black Forest .......... **20.00**
- 1975 Snowman .......... **25.00**
- 1976 Chapel in the Hills .......... **25.00**
- 1977 Story Time (Christmas Story) .......... **30.00**
- 1978 Mittenwald .......... **30.00**
- 1979 Winter Day .......... **40.00**
- 1980 Miltenberg .......... **38.00**
- 1981 Walk in the Forest .......... **40.00**
- 1982 Bad Wimpfen .......... **40.00**
- 1983 The Night Before Christmas .......... **45.00**
- 1984 Zeil on the River Main .......... **42.50**
- 1985 Winter Wonderland .......... **42.50**
- 1986 Christmas in Forchhe .......... **42.50**
- 1987 Decorating the Tree .......... **46.50**
- 1988 St Coloman Church .......... **80.00**
- 1989 Sleigh Ride .......... **50.00**
- 1990 The Old Forge in Rothenburg .......... **50.00**
- 1991 Christmas Joy .......... **55.00**
- 1992 Marketplace in Heppenheim .......... **55.00**

### Berlin (Germany)

Christmas Plates, various artists, 7¾" d
- 1970 Christmas In Bernkastel .......... **130.00**
- 1971 Christmas In Rothenburg On Tauber .......... **30.00**
- 1972 Christmas In Michelstadt .......... **50.00**
- 1973 Christmas In Wendelstein .......... **42.00**
- 1974 Christmas In Bremen .......... **25.00**
- 1975 Christmas In Dortland .......... **60.00**
- 1976 Christmas Eve In Augsburg .......... **30.00**
- 1977 Christmas Eve In Hamburg .......... **32.00**
- 1978 Christmas Market At The Berlin Cathedral .......... **55.00**
- 1978 Christmas Eve In Greetsiel .......... **55.00**
- 1980 Christmas Eve In Miltenberg .......... **55.00**
- 1981 Christmas Eve In Hahnenklee .......... **50.00**
- 1982 Christmas Eve In Wasserburg .......... **55.00**
- 1983 Chapel In Oberndorf .......... **55.00**
- 1984 Christmas in Ramsau .......... **50.00**
- 1985 Christmas Eve in Bad Wimpfen **55.00**
- 1986 Christmas Eve in Gelnhaus .......... **65.00**
- 1987 Christmas Eve in Goslar .......... **70.00**
- 1988 Christmas Eve in Ruhpolding .......... **100.00**
- 1989 Christmas Eve in Freidechsdadt **80.00**
- 1990 Christmas Eve in Partenkirchen **80.00**
- 1991 Christmas Eve in Allendorf .......... **80.00**

### Bing and Grondahl(Denmark)

Christmas Plates, various artists, 7" d
- 1895 Behind The Frozen Window . **3,400.00**
- 1896 New Moon Over Snow-covered Trees .......... **1,975.00**

1897 Christmas Meal Of The Sparrows .......... **725.00**
1898 Christmas Roses And Christmas Star .......... **700.00**
1899 The Crows Enjoying Christmas **900.00**
1900 Church Bells Chiming In Christmas .......... **800.00**
1901 The Three Wise Men From The East .......... **450.00**
1902 Interior Of A Gothic Church .. **285.00**
1903 Happy Expectation of Children **150.00**
1904 View of Copenhagen From Frederiksberg Hill .......... **125.00**
1905 Anxiety Of The Coming Christmas Night .......... **130.00**
1906 Sleighing To Church On Christmas Eve .......... **95.00**
1907 The Little Match Girl .......... **125.00**
1908 St. Petri Church of Copenhagen **85.00**
1909 Happiness Over The Yule Tree **100.00**
1910 The Old Organist .......... **90.00**
1911 First It Was Sung By Angels To Shepherds In The Fields .......... **80.00**
1912 Going To Church On Christmas Eve .......... **80.00**
1913 Bringing Home The Yule Tree . **85.00**
1914 Royal Castle of Amalienborg, Copenhagen .......... **75.00**
1915 Chained Dog Getting Double Meal On Christmas Eve .......... **120.00**
1916 Christmas Prayer Of The Sparrows .......... **85.00**
1917 Arrival Of The Christmas Boat **75.00**
1918 Fishing Boat Returning Home For Christmas .......... **85.00**
1919 Outside The Lighted Window . **80.00**
1920 Hare In The Snow .......... **70.00**
1921 Pigeons In The Castle Court .. **55.00**
1922 Star Of Bethlehem .......... **60.00**
1923 Royal Hunting Castle, The Hermitage .......... **55.00**
1924 Lighthouse In Danish Waters .. **65.00**
1925 The Child's Christmas .......... **70.00**
1926 Churchgoers On Christmas Day **65.00**
1927 Skating Couple .......... **110.00**
1928 Eskimo Looking At Village Church In Greenland .......... **60.00**
1929 Fox Outside Farm On Christmas Eve .......... **75.00**
1930 Yule Tree In Town Hall Square Of Copenhagen .......... **85.00**
1931 Arrival Of The Christmas Train **75.00**
1932 Lifeboat At Work .......... **90.00**
1933 The Korsor-Nyborg Ferry .......... **70.00**
1934 Church Bell In Tower .......... **75.00**
1935 Lillebelt Bridge Connecting Funen With Jutland .......... **65.00**
1936 Royal Guard Outside Amalienborg Castle In Copenhagen .......... **70.00**
1937 Arrival Of Christmas Guests .. **75.00**
1938 Lighting The Candles .......... **110.00**
1939 Ole Lock-Eye, The Sandman .. **150.00**
1940 Delivering Christmas Letters .. **170.00**
1941 Horses Enjoying Christmas Meal In Stable .......... **345.00**
1942 Danish Farm On Christmas Night .......... **150.00**
1943 The Ribe Cathedral .......... **155.00**
1944 Sorgenfri Castle .......... **120.00**
1945 The Old Water Mill .......... **135.00**
1946 Commemoration Cross In Honor Of Danish Sailors Who Lost Their Lives In World War II .......... **85.00**
1947 Dybbol Mill .......... **70.00**
1948 Watchman, Sculpture Of Town Hall, Copenhagen .......... **80.00**
1949 Landsoldaten, 19th Century Danish Soldier .......... **70.00**
1950 Kronborg Castle At Elsinore ... **150.00**
1951 Jens Bang, New Passenger Boat Running Between Copenhagen And Aalborg .......... **115.00**
1952 Old Copenhagen Canals At Wintertime With Thorvaldsen Museum In Background .......... **85.00**
1953 Royal Boat In Greenland Waters **95.00**
1954 Birthplace Of Hans Christian Andersen, With Snowman .......... **100.00**
1955 Kalundborg Church .......... **115.00**
1956 Christmas In Copenhagen .......... **140.00**
1957 Christmas Candles .......... **155.00**
1958 Santa Claus .......... **100.00**
1959 Christmas Eve .......... **120.00**
1960 Danish Village Church .......... **180.00**
1961 Winter Harmony .......... **115.00**
1962 Winter Night .......... **80.00**
1963 The Christmas Elf .......... **120.00**
1964 The Fir Tree And Hare .......... **50.00**
1965 Bringing Home The Christmas Tree .......... **65.00**
1966 Home For Christmas .......... **50.00**
1967 Sharing The Joy Of Christmas . **48.00**
1968 Christmas In Church .......... **45.00**
1969 Arrival Of Christmas Guests .. **30.00**
1970 Pheasants In The Snow At Christmas .......... **20.00**
1971 Christmas At Home .......... **20.00**
1972 Christmas In Greenland .......... **20.00**
1973 Country Christmas .......... **25.00**
1974 Christmas In The Village .......... **20.00**
1975 The Old Water Mill .......... **24.00**
1976 Christmas Welcome .......... **25.00**
1977 Copenhagen Christmas .......... **25.00**
1978 A Christmas Tale .......... **30.00**
1979 White Christmas .......... **30.00**
1980 Christmas In The Woods .......... **42.50**
1981 Christmas Peace .......... **50.00**
1982 The Christmas Tree .......... **55.00**
1983 Christmas in Old Town .......... **55.00**
1984 Christmas Letter .......... **55.00**
1985 Christmas Eve at the Farmhouse **55.00**
1986 Silent Night, Holy Night .......... **55.00**
1987 The Snowman's Christmas Eve **60.00**
1988 In The Kings Garden .......... **72.00**

1989 Christmas Anchorage . . . . . . . . **65.00**
1990 Changing of the Guards . . . . . . **60.00**
1991 Copenhagen Stock Exchange . **70.00**
1992 Christmas at the Rectory . . . . . **65.00**
1993 Father Christmas in Copenhagen . . . . . . . . . . . . . . . . . . . . . . **65.00**

Mother's Day Plates, Henry Thelander, artist, 6" d
1969 Dog And Puppies . . . . . . . . . . . **400.00**
1970 Bird And Chicks . . . . . . . . . . . . **35.00**
1971 Cat And Kitten . . . . . . . . . . . . . . **24.00**
1972 Mare And Foal . . . . . . . . . . . . . . **20.00**
1973 Duck And Ducklings . . . . . . . . **20.00**
1974 Bear And Cubs . . . . . . . . . . . . . **24.00**
1975 Doe And Fawns . . . . . . . . . . . . . **20.00**
1976 Swan Family . . . . . . . . . . . . . . . **22.00**
1977 Squirrel And Young . . . . . . . . . . **25.00**
1978 Heron . . . . . . . . . . . . . . . . . . . . . **25.00**
1979 Fox And Cubs . . . . . . . . . . . . . . **30.00**
1980 Woodpecker And Young . . . . . **35.00**
1981 Hare And Young . . . . . . . . . . . . **40.00**
1982 Lioness And Cubs . . . . . . . . . . . **45.00**
1983 Raccoon And Young . . . . . . . . . **45.00**
1984 Stork and Nestlings . . . . . . . . . . **40.00**
1985 Bear and Cubs . . . . . . . . . . . . . . **40.00**
1986 Elephant with Calf . . . . . . . . . . . **40.00**
1987 Sheep with Lambs . . . . . . . . . . . **42.50**
1988 Lapwing Mother with Chicks . **48.00**
1989 Cow with Calf . . . . . . . . . . . . . . **48.00**
1990 Hen with Chicks . . . . . . . . . . . . **50.00**
1991 The Nanny Goat and Her Two Frisky Kids . . . . . . . . . . . . . . . . . . . **70.00**
1992 Panda with Cubs . . . . . . . . . . . . **55.00**
1993 St. Bernard Dog and Puppies . **55.00**

## Franklin Mint (United States)

Audubon Society Birds
1972 Goldfinch . . . . . . . . . . . . . . . . . . **115.00**
1972 Wood Duck . . . . . . . . . . . . . . . . **110.00**
1973 Cardinal . . . . . . . . . . . . . . . . . . . **110.00**
1973 Ruffed Grouse . . . . . . . . . . . . . . **120.00**

Christmas Plates, Norman Rockwell, artist, etched sterling silver, 8"
1970 Bringing Home The Tree . . . . . **275.00**
1971 Under The Mistletoe . . . . . . . . . **125.00**
1972 The Carolers . . . . . . . . . . . . . . . . **125.00**
1973 Trimming The Tree . . . . . . . . . . **100.00**
1974 Hanging The Wreath . . . . . . . . **100.00**
1975 Home For Christmas . . . . . . . . . **125.00**

## Goebel (Germany), see Hummel

## Haviland (France)

Mother's Day (The French Collection),
1973 Breakfast . . . . . . . . . . . . . . . . . . . **25.00**
1974 The Wash . . . . . . . . . . . . . . . . . . **30.00**
1975 In The Park . . . . . . . . . . . . . . . . . **25.00**
1976 Market . . . . . . . . . . . . . . . . . . . . . **40.00**
1977 Wash Before Dinner . . . . . . . . . **35.00**
1978 Evening At Home . . . . . . . . . . . **40.00**
1979 Happy Mother's Day . . . . . . . . **30.00**
1980 Child & His Animals . . . . . . . . . **55.00**

1,001 Arabian Nights, Lillian Tellier artist
1979 Cheval Magique, Magic Horse **60.00**
1980 Aladin et Lampe . . . . . . . . . . . . **60.00**
1981 Scheherazade . . . . . . . . . . . . . . . **55.00**
1982 Sinbad the Sailor . . . . . . . . . . . . **55.00**

The Twelve Days Of Christmas Series, Remy Hetreau, artist, 8¾" d
1970 A Partridge In A Pear Tree, FE **115.00**
1971 Two Turtle Doves . . . . . . . . . . . **40.00**
1972 Three French Hens . . . . . . . . . . **35.00**
1973 Four Calling Birds . . . . . . . . . . . **35.00**
1974 Five Golden Rings . . . . . . . . . . . **30.00**
1975 Six Geese A'Laying . . . . . . . . . . **30.00**
1976 Seven Swans A'Swimming . . . . **30.00**
1977 Eight Maids A'Milking . . . . . . . **45.00**
1978 Nine Ladies Dancing . . . . . . . . **35.00**
1979 Ten Lords A'Leaping . . . . . . . . . **40.00**
1980 Eleven Pipers Piping . . . . . . . . . **50.00**
1981 Twelve Drummers Drumming . **55.00**

## Haviland & Parlon (France)

Christmas Series, various artists, 10" d
1972 Madonna And Child, Raphael, FE . . . . . . . . . . . . . . . . . . . . . . . . . . . . **80.00**
1973 Madonnina, Feruzzi . . . . . . . . . **95.00**
1974 Cowper Madonna And Child, Raphael . . . . . . . . . . . . . . . . . . . . . . . **55.00**
1975 Madonna And Child, Murillo . **45.00**
1976 Madonna And Child, Botticelli **50.00**
1977 Madonna And Child, Bellini . . **40.00**
1978 Madonna And Child, Fra Filippo Lippi . . . . . . . . . . . . . . . . . . . . . . . . **65.00**
1979 Madonna Of The Eucharist, Botticelli . . . . . . . . . . . . . . . . . . . . . . **150.00**

Lady And The Unicorn Series, artist unknown, 10" d
1977 To My Only Desire, FE . . . . . . **60.00**
1978 Sight . . . . . . . . . . . . . . . . . . . . . . **40.00**
1979 Sound . . . . . . . . . . . . . . . . . . . . . **50.00**
1980 Touch . . . . . . . . . . . . . . . . . . . . . **110.00**
1981 Scent . . . . . . . . . . . . . . . . . . . . . . **60.00**
1982 Taste . . . . . . . . . . . . . . . . . . . . . . **80.00**

Tapestry Series, artist unknown, 10" d
1971 The Unicorn In Captivity . . . . . **145.00**
1972 Start Of The Hunt . . . . . . . . . . . **70.00**
1973 Chase Of The Unicorn . . . . . . . **120.00**
1974 End Of The Hunt . . . . . . . . . . . . **120.00**
1975 The Unicorn Surrounded . . . . . **75.00**
1976 The Unicorn Is Brought To The Castle . . . . . . . . . . . . . . . . . . . . . . . **55.00**

## Edwin M. Knowles (United States)

Americana Holidays Series, Don Spaulding, artist, 8½" d, 1978 Fourth Of July, FE . . . . . . . . . . . . . . . . . . . . . . **35.00**
1979 Thanksgiving . . . . . . . . . . . . . . . **35.00**
1980 Easter . . . . . . . . . . . . . . . . . . . . . . **30.00**

1981 Valentine's Day ............ **25.00**
1982 Father's Day ................ **35.00**
1983 Christmas .................. **35.00**
1984 Mother's Day ............... **20.00**

Annie Series
1983 Annie And Sandy, FE ........ **25.00**
1983 Daddy Warbucks ............ **20.00**
1983 Annie & Grace ............. **19.00**
1984 Annie and the Orphans ...... **20.00**
1985 Tomorrow .................. **21.00**
1986 Annie, Lily, and Rooster ...... **24.00**
1986 Grand Finale ............... **24.00**

Gone With The Wind Series, Raymond Kursar, artist, 8½" d
1978 Scarlett, FE ................ **300.00**
1979 Ashley ..................... **225.00**
1980 Melanie .................... **75.00**
1981 Rhett ...................... **50.00**
1982 Mammy Lacing Scarlett ...... **60.00**
1983 Melanie Gives Birth ......... **85.00**
1984 Scarlett's Green Dress ....... **50.00**
1985 Rhett and Bonnie ........... **35.00**
1985 Scarlett and Rhett: The Finale . **30.00**

Wizard Of Oz Series, James Auckland, artist, 8½" d
1977 Over The Rainbow, FE ....... **65.00**
1978 If I Only Had A Brain ........ **30.00**
1978 If I Only Had A Heart ....... **30.00**
1978 If I Were King Of The Forest .. **30.00**
1979 Wicked Witch Of The West .. **35.00**
1979 Follow The Yellow Brick Road **35.00**
1979 Wonderful Wizard Of Oz .... **50.00**
1980 The Grand Finale (We're Off To See The Wizard) .............. **60.00**

## Lalique (France)

Annual Series, lead crystal, Marie-Claude Lalique, artist, 8½" d
1965 Deux Oiseaux (Two Birds), FE **800.00**
1966 Rose de Songerie (Dream Rose) **215.00**
1967 Ballet de Poisson (Fish Ballet) . **200.00**
1968 Gazelle Fantaisie (Gazelle Fantasy) ........................ **70.00**
1969 Papillon (Butterfly) .......... **80.00**
1970 Paon (Peacock) ............ **50.00**
1971 Hibou (Owl) ............... **60.00**
1972 Coquillage (Shell) .......... **55.00**
1973 Petit Geai (Jayling) .......... **60.00**
1974 Sous d'Argent (Silver Pennies) . **65.00**
1975 Due de Poisson (Fish Duet) ... **75.00**
1976 Aigle (Eagle) ............... **100.00**

## Lenox (United States)

Boehm Bird Series, Edward Marshall Boehm, artist, 10½" d, 1970 Wood Thrush, FE ..................... **175.00**
1971 Goldfinch .................. **65.00**
1972 Mountain Bluebird .......... **65.00**
1973 Meadowlark ................ **60.00**
1974 Rufous Hummim ............ **50.00**
1975 American Redstart .......... **50.00**
1976 Cardinal ................... **58.00**
1977 Robins ..................... **55.00**
1978 Mockingbirds ............... **60.00**
1979 Golden-Crowned Kinglets .... **65.00**
1980 Black-Throated Blue Warblers . **75.00**
1981 Eastern Phoebes ............ **100.00**

Boehm Woodland Wildlife Series, Edward Marshall Boehm, artist, 10½" d
1973 Raccoons, FE .............. **80.00**
1974 Red Foxes .................. **50.00**
1975 Cottontail Rabbits .......... **60.00**
1976 Eastern Chipmunks .......... **60.00**
1977 Beaver ..................... **60.00**
1978 Whitetail Deer ............. **60.00**
1979 Squirrels ................... **75.00**
1980 Bobcats .................... **90.00**
1981 Martens .................... **100.00**
1982 Otters ..................... **100.00**

## Llardo (Spain)

Christmas, 8" d, undisclosed artists
1971 Caroling .................. **30.00**
1972 Carolers .................. **35.00**
1973 Boy & Girl ................ **50.00**
1974 Carolers .................. **75.00**
1975 Cherubs .................. **60.00**
1976 Christ Child ............... **50.00**
1977 Nativity ................... **70.00**
1978 Caroling Child ............. **50.00**
1979 Snow Dance ............... **80.00**

Mother's Day, undisclosed artists
1971 Kiss of the Child ........... **75.00**
1972 Birds & Chicks ............. **30.00**
1973 Mother & Children .......... **35.00**
1974 Nursing Mother ............ **135.00**
1975 Mother & Child ............ **55.00**
1976 Vigil ...................... **50.00**
1977 Mother & Daughter ......... **60.00**
1978 New Arrival ............... **55.00**
1979 Off to School .............. **90.00**

## Reco International Corp. (United States)

Days Gone By, Sandra Kuck artist
1983 Sunday Best ............... **55.00**
1983 Amy's Magic Horse ......... **30.00**
1984 Little Anglers .............. **30.00**
1984 Little Tutor ................ **30.00**
1984 Easter at Grandma's ......... **30.00**

McClelland Children's Circus Series, John McClelland, artist, 9" d
1981 Tommy The Clown, FE ...... **30.00**
1982 Katie The Tightrope Walker ... **31.00**
1983 Johnny The Strongman ....... **31.00**
1984 Maggie The Animal Trainer ... **29.50**

McClelland's Mother Goose Series, John McClelland, artist, 8½" d
1979 Mary, Mary, FE ............. **250.00**
1980 Little Boy Blue ............. **100.00**

1981 Little Miss Muffet ............ **30.00**
1982 Little Jack Horner ........... **30.00**
1983 Little Bo Peep .............. **40.00**
1984 Diddle, Diddle Dumpling .... **30.00**
1985 Mary Had A Little Lamb ..... **42.00**
1986 Jack and Jill ................ **25.00**

## Reed & Barton (United States)

Christmas Series, Damascene silver, 11" d through 1978, 8" d 1979 to 1981
1970 A Partridge In A Pear Tree, FE **200.00**
1971 We Three Kings Of Orient Are **65.00**
1972 Hark! The Herald Angels Sing **60.00**
1973 Adoration Of The Kings ...... **75.00**
1974 The Adoration Of The Magi .. **60.00**
1975 Adoration Of The Kings ...... **65.00**
1976 Morning Train ............. **60.00**
1977 Decorating The Church ...... **60.00**
1978 The General Store At Christmas Time ........................ **67.00**
1979 Merry Old Santa Claus ....... **65.00**
1980 Gathering Christmas Greens .. **75.00**
1981 The Shopkeeper At Christmas . **75.00**

## Rockwell, see Norman Rockwell

## Rosenthal (Germany)

Christmas Plates, various artists, 8½" d
1910 Winter Peace ............... **550.00**
1911 The Three Wise Men ........ **325.00**
1912 Shooting Stars .............. **250.00**
1913 Christmas Lights ............ **235.00**
1914 Christmas Song ............ **350.00**
1915 Walking To Church .......... **180.00**
1916 Christmas During War ....... **235.00**
1917 Angel Of Peace ............. **210.00**
1918 Peace On Earth ............. **210.00**
1919 St. Christopher With The Christ Child ........................ **225.00**
1920 The Manger In Bethlehem .... **325.00**
1921 Christmas In The Mountains .. **200.00**
1922 Advent Branch .............. **200.00**
1923 Children In The Winter Wood **200.00**
1924 Deer In The Woods ......... **200.00**
1925 The Three Wise Men ........ **200.00**
1926 Christmas In The Mountains .. **175.00**
1927 Station On The Way ......... **200.00**
1928 Chalet Christmas ............ **175.00**
1929 Christmas In The Alps ....... **225.00**
1930 Group Of Deer Under The Pines **225.00**
1931 Path Of The Magi ........... **225.00**
1932 Christ Child ............... **195.00**
1933 Through The Night To Light .. **190.00**
1934 Christmas Peace ............ **200.00**
1935 Christmas By The Sea ........ **185.00**
1936 Nürnberg Angel ............. **185.00**
1937 Berchtesgaden .............. **195.00**
1938 Christmas In The Alps ....... **190.00**
1939 Schneekoppe Mountain ...... **195.00**
1940 Marien Church In Danzig .... **250.00**
1941 Strassburg Cathedral ......... **250.00**
1942 Marianburg Castle ........... **300.00**
1943 Winter Idyll ................ **300.00**
1944 Wood Scape ................ **275.00**
1945 Christmas Peace ............ **400.00**
1946 Christmas In An Alpine Valley **250.00**
1947 The Dillingen Madonna ...... **975.00**
1948 Message To The Shepherds ... **875.00**
1949 The Holy Family ............ **185.00**
1950 Christmas In The Forest ...... **185.00**
1951 Star Of Bethlehem ........... **450.00**
1952 Christmas In The Alps ....... **190.00**
1953 The Holy Light .............. **185.00**
1954 Christmas Eve .............. **185.00**
1955 Christmas In A Village ....... **190.00**
1956 Christmas In The Alps ....... **190.00**
1957 Christmas By The Sea ........ **195.00**
1958 Christmas Eve .............. **185.00**
1959 Midnight Mass .............. **195.00**
1960 Christmas In Small Village .... **195.00**
1961 Solitary Christmas ........... **225.00**
1962 Christmas Eve .............. **185.00**
1963 Silent Night ................ **185.00**
1964 Christmas Market In Nürnberg **225.00**
1965 Christmas In Munich ........ **185.00**
1966 Christmas In Ulm ........... **250.00**
1967 Christmas In Regensburg ..... **185.00**
1968 Christmas In Bremen ........ **195.00**
1969 Christmas In Rothenburg ..... **220.00**
1970 Christmas In Cologne ........ **165.00**
1971 Christmas In Garmisch ....... **100.00**
1972 Christmas Celebration In Franconia ........................ **90.00**
1973 Christmas In Lubeck-Holstein . **110.00**
1974 Christmas In Wurzburg ...... **100.00**
Bjorn Wiinblad (artist) Christmas Plates Series, 1971 Maria and Child ......**1,250.00**
1972 Caspar ..................... **550.00**
1973 Melchior ................... **450.00**
1974 Balthazar .................. **500.00**
1975 The Annunciation ........... **200.00**
1976 Angel With Trumpet ......... **200.00**
1977 Adoration Of The Shepherds .. **250.00**
1978 Angel With Harp ............ **275.00**
1979 Exodus From Egypt .......... **310.00**
1980 Angel With A Glockenspiel ... **360.00**
1981 Christ Child Visits Temple .... **375.00**
1982 Christening of Christ ......... **375.00**

## Royal Copenhagen

Christmas Plates, various artists, 6" d 1908, 1909, 1910; 7" 1911 to present
1909 Danish Landscape ........... **150.00**
1910 The Magi .................. **120.00**
1911 Danish Landscape ........... **135.00**
1912 Elderly Couple By Christmas Tree ....................... **120.00**
1913 Spire Of Frederik's Church, Copenhagen ..................... **125.00**

1914 Sparrows In Tree At Church Of The Holy Spirit, Copenhagen .... **100.00**
1915 Danish Landscape ........... **150.00**
1916 Shepherd In The Field On Christmas Night ................ **85.00**
1917 Tower Of Our Savior's Church, Copenhagen .................. **90.00**
1918 Sheep and Shepherds ........ **80.00**
1919 In The Park ................ **80.00**
1920 Mary With The Child Jesus ... **75.00**
1921 Aabenraa Marketplace ....... **75.00**
1922 Three Singing Angels ........ **70.00**
1923 Danish Landscape ........... **70.00**
1924 Christmas Star Over The Sea And Sailing Ship .............. **100.00**
1925 Street Scene From Christianshavn, Copenhagen ............ **85.00**
1926 View of Christmas Canal, Copenhagen ..................... **75.00**
1927 Ship's Boy At The Tiller On Christmas Night ................ **140.00**
1928 Vicar's Family On Way To Church ...................... **75.00**
1929 Grundtvig Church, Copenhagen **100.00**
1930 Fishing Boats On The Way To The Harbor .................... **80.00**
1931 Mother And Child ........... **90.00**
1932 Frederiksberg Gardens With Statue Of Frederik VI ........... **90.00**
1933 The Great Belt Ferry ......... **110.00**
1934 The Hermitage Castle ........ **115.00**
1935 Fishing Boat Off Kronborg Castle .......................... **145.00**
1936 Roskilde Cathedral .......... **130.00**
1937 Christmas Scene In Main Street, Copenhagen .................. **135.00**
1938 Round Church In Osterlars On Bornholm ..................... **200.00**
1939 Expeditionary Ship In Pack-Ice Of Greenland .................. **180.00**
1940 The Good Shepherd ......... **300.00**
1941 Danish Village Church ....... **250.00**
1942 Bell Tower of Old Church In Jutland ....................... **300.00**
1943 Flight Of Holy Family To Egypt **425.00**
1944 Typical Danish Winter Scene . **160.00**
1945 A Peaceful Motif ............ **325.00**
1946 Zealand Village Church ...... **150.00**
1947 The Good Shepherd ......... **210.00**
1948 Nodebo Church At Christmastime ......................... **150.00**
1949 Our Lady's Cathedral, Copenhagen ....................... **165.00**
1950 Boeslunde Church, Zealand .. **175.00**
1951 Christmas Angel ............ **300.00**
1952 Christmas In The Forest ...... **120.00**
1953 Frederiksborg Castle ......... **120.00**
1954 Amalienborg Palace, Copenhagen ....................... **150.00**
1955 Fano Girl .................. **185.00**
1956 Rosenborg Castle, Copenhagen **160.00**
1957 The Good Shepherd ......... **115.00**
1958 Sunshine Over Greenland .... **140.00**
1959 Christmas Night ............. **120.00**
1960 The Stag ................... **140.00**
1961 Training Ship Danmark ...... **155.00**
1962 The Little Mermaid At Wintertime ......................... **200.00**
1963 Hojsager Mill ............... **80.00**
1964 Fetching The Christmas Tree .. **75.00**
1965 Little Skaters ................ **60.00**
1966 Blackbird At Christmastime ... **55.00**
1967 The Royal Oak ............. **45.00**
1968 The Last Umiak ............. **40.00**
1969 The Old Farmyard ........... **35.00**
1970 Christmas Rose And Cat ...... **95.00**
1971 Hare In Winter ............. **80.00**
1972 In The Desert ............... **85.00**
1973 Train Homeward Bound For Christmas ..................... **85.00**
1974 Winter Twilight ............. **80.00**
1975 Queen's Palace ............. **85.00**
1976 Danish Watermill ........... **80.00**
1977 Immervad Bridge ............ **75.00**
1978 Greenland Scenery .......... **80.00**
1979 Choosing The Christmas Tree . **60.00**
1980 Bringing Home The Christmas Tree ......................... **60.00**
1981 Admiring The Christmas Tree . **55.00**
1982 Waiting For Christmas ....... **65.00**
1983 Merry Christmas ............ **60.00**
1984 Jingle Bells ................. **55.00**
1985 Snowman .................. **55.00**
1986 Wait for Me ............... **55.00**
1987 Winter Birds ................ **58.00**
1988 Christmas Eve in Copenhagen . **70.00**
1989 The Old Skating Pond ....... **50.00**
1990 Christmas at Tivoli .......... **50.00**
1991 The Festival of Santa Lucia ... **65.00**
1992 The Queen's Carriage ........ **65.00**
1993 Christmas Guests ........... **65.00**

Mother's Day Plates, various artists, 6¼" d
1971 American Mother ........... **125.00**
1972 Oriental Mother ............. **60.00**
1973 Danish Mother .............. **60.00**
1974 Greenland Mother ........... **55.00**
1975 Bird In Nest ................ **50.00**
1976 Mermaids .................. **50.00**
1977 The Twins .................. **50.00**
1978 Mother And Child ........... **25.00**
1979 A Loving Mother ............ **30.00**
1980 An Outing With Mother ...... **35.00**
1981 Reunion ................... **40.00**
1982 The Children's Hour ......... **45.00**

## Royal Doulton (Great Britain)

Beswick Christmas Series, various artists, earthenware in hand-cast bas-relief, 8" sq
1972 Christmas In England, FE ..... **40.00**
1973 Christmas In Mexico ......... **25.00**
1974 Christmas In Bulgaria ........ **40.00**

1975 Christmas In Norway ........ **54.00**
1976 Christmas In Holland ........ **45.00**
1977 Christmas In Poland ......... **100.00**
1978 Christmas In America ........ **45.00**

Mother And Child Series, Edna Hibel artist, 8″ d
1973 Colette And Child, FE ........ **450.00**
1974 Sayuri And Child ............ **150.00**
1975 Kristina And Child ........... **125.00**
1976 Marilyn And Child .......... **120.00**
1977 Lucia And Child ............ **100.00**
1978 Kathleen And Child ......... **95.00**

Portraits Of Innocence Series, Francisco Masseria artist, 8″ d
1980 Panchito, FE ................ **160.00**
1981 Adrien ..................... **110.00**
1982 Angelica ................... **100.00**
1983 Juliana ..................... **145.00**

Valentine's Day Series, artists unknown, 8¼″ d 1976 Victorian Boy And Girl **60.00**
1977 My Sweetest Friend .......... **40.00**
1978 If I Loved You .............. **40.00**
1979 My Valentine ............... **40.00**
1980 On A Swing ................ **40.00**
1981 Sweet Music ................ **35.00**
1982 From My Heart ............. **40.00**
1983 Cherub's Song .............. **45.00**
1984 Love In Bloom .............. **40.00**
1985 Accept These Flowers ........ **40.00**

## Schmid (Japan)

Christmas, J Malfertheiner, artist
1971 St Jakob in Groden, FE ....... **125.00**
1972 Pipers at Alberobello ........ **120.00**
1973 Alpine Horn ................ **375.00**
1974 Young Man and Girl ......... **100.00**
1975 Christmas In Ireland ......... **90.00**
1976 Alpine Christmas ............ **200.00**
1977 Legend of Heligenblut ....... **125.00**
1978 Klockler Singers ............. **175.00**
1979 Moss Gatherers ............. **130.00**
1980 Wintry Churchgoing ......... **165.00**
1981 Santa Claus in Tyrol ......... **160.00**
1982 The Star Singers ............. **160.00**
1983 Unto Us A Child Is Born ..... **150.00**
1984 Yuletide in the Valley ........ **150.00**
1985 Good Morning, Good Year ... **160.00**
1986 A Groeden Christmas ........ **75.00**
1987 Down From The Alps ........ **175.00**

Disney Christmas Series, undisclosed artists, 7½″ d
1973 Sleigh Ride, FE ............. **400.00**
1974 Decorating The Tree ......... **175.00**
1975 Caroling .................. **20.00**
1976 Building A Snowman ........ **35.00**
1977 Down The Chimney ......... **25.00**
1978 Night Before Christmas ...... **20.00**
1979 Santa's Surprise ............. **20.00**
1980 Sleigh Ride ................. **30.00**
1981 Happy Holidays ............ **18.00**
1982 Winter Games .............. **20.00**
1987 Snow White Golden Anniversary .......................... **48.00**
1988 Mickey Mouse & Minnie Mouth 60th .......................... **50.00**
1989 Sleeping Beauty 30th Anniversary .......................... **75.00**
1990 Fantasia Relief .............. **25.00**

Disney Mother's Day Series
1974 Flowers For Mother, FE ...... **80.00**
1975 Snow White And The Seven Dwarfs ........................ **45.00**
1976 Minnie Mouse And Friends ... **20.00**
1977 Pluto's Pals ................ **25.00**
1978 Flowers For Bambi .......... **20.00**
1979 Happy Feet ................. **25.00**
1980 Minnie's Surprise ............ **20.00**
1981 Playmates .................. **25.00**
1982 A Dream Come True ........ **20.00**

Peanuts Christmas Series, Charles Schulz, artist, 7½″ d, 1972 Snoopy Guides The Sleigh, FE ............ **90.00**
1973 Christmas Eve At The Doghouse **120.00**
1974 Christmas Eve At The Fireplace **65.00**
1975 Woodstock, Santa Claus ..... **15.00**
1976 Woodstock's Christmas ...... **30.00**
1977 Deck The Doghouse ......... **15.00**
1978 Filling The Stocking ......... **20.00**
1979 Christmas At Hand .......... **20.00**
1980 Waiting For Santa ........... **50.00**
1981 A Christmas Wish ........... **20.00**
1982 Perfect Performance ......... **35.00**

Peanuts Mother's Day Series, Charles Schulz, artist, 7½″ d
1972 Linus, FE .................. **50.00**
1973 Mom? ..................... **45.00**
1974 Snoopy And Woodstock On Parade ........................ **40.00**
1975 A Kiss For Lucy ............ **38.00**
1976 Linus And Snoopy .......... **35.00**
1977 Dear Mom ................. **30.00**
1978 Thoughts That Count ........ **25.00**
1979 A Special Letter ............ **20.00**
1980 A Tribute To Mom .......... **20.00**
1981 Mission For Mom ........... **20.00**
1982 Which Way To Mother? ...... **20.00**

Peanuts Valentine's Day Series, Charles Schulz, artist, 7½″ d
1977 Home Is Where The Heart Is, FE ........................... **25.00**
1978 Heavenly Bliss .............. **28.00**
1979 Love Match ................ **20.00**
1980 From Snoopy, With Love ..... **24.00**
1981 Hearts-A-Flutter ............. **20.00**
1982 Love Patch ................. **18.00**

Raggedy Ann Annual Series, undisclosed artist, 7½″ d
1980 The Sunshine Wagon ........ **65.00**
1981 The Raggedy Shuffle ......... **25.00**
1982 Flying High ................ **20.00**
1983 Winning Streak ............. **20.00**
1984 Rocking Rodeo ............. **22.50**

## U. S. Historical Society (United States)

Stained Glass Cathedral
1978 Canterbury .................. **175.00**
1979 Flight into Egypt ............ **175.00**
1980 Washington Cathedral/Madonna ......................... **160.00**
1981 The Magi .................. **160.00**
1982 Flight Into Egypt ............ **160.00**
1983 Shepherds at Bethlehem ...... **150.00**
1984 The Navitity ................ **145.00**
1985 Good Tidings of Great Joy, Boston ........................... **125.00**
1986 The Nativity from Old St. Mary's Church, Philadelphia ........... **165.00**
1987 O Come, Little Children ..... **160.00**

## Wedgwood (Great Britain)

Calendar Series
1971 Victorian Almanac, FE ....... **20.00**
1972 The Carousel ............... **15.00**
1973 Bountiful Butterfly ........... **14.00**
1974 Camelot .................... **65.00**
1975 Children's Games ........... **18.00**
1976 Robin ...................... **25.00**
1977 Tonatiuh ................... **28.00**
1978 Samurai .................... **32.00**
1979 Sacred Scarab .............. **32.00**
1980 Safari ...................... **40.00**
1981 Horses ..................... **42.50**
1982 Wild West ................. **50.00**
1983 The Age of the Reptiles ...... **50.00**
1984 Dogs ...................... **55.00**
1985 Cats ....................... **55.00**
1986 British Birds ................ **50.00**
1987 Water Birds ................ **50.00**
1988 Sea Birds ................... **50.00**
Christmas Series, jasper stoneware, 8" d, 1969 Windsor Castle, FE ........ **225.00**
1970 Christmas In Trafalgar Square . **30.00**
1971 Piccadilly Circus, London .... **40.00**
1972 St. Paul's Cathedral .......... **40.00**
1973 The Tower Of London ....... **45.00**
1974 The Houses Of Parliament .... **40.00**
1975 Tower Bridge ............... **40.00**
1976 Hampton Court ............. **46.00**
1977 Westminster Abbey .......... **48.00**
1978 The Horse Guards ........... **55.00**
1979 Buckingham Palace ......... **55.00**
1980 St. James Palace ............ **70.00**
1981 Marble Arch ................ **75.00**
1982 Lambeth Palace ............. **80.00**
1983 All Souls, Langham Palace ... **80.00**
1984 Constitution Hill ............ **80.00**
1985 The Tate Gallery ............ **80.00**
1986 The Albert Memorial ........ **80.00**
1987 Guildhall .................. **80.00**
Mothers Series, jasper stoneware, 6½" d
1971 Sportive Love, FE ........... **25.00**
1972 The Sewing Lesson .......... **20.00**
1973 The Baptism Of Achilles ..... **20.00**
1974 Domestic Employment ....... **30.00**
1975 Mother And Child ........... **35.00**
1976 The Spinner ................ **35.00**
1977 Leisure Time ............... **30.00**
1978 Swan And Cygnets .......... **35.00**
1979 Deer And Fawn ............. **35.00**
1980 Birds ...................... **48.00**
1981 Mare And Foal .............. **50.00**
1982 Cherubs With Swing ......... **55.00**
1983 Cupid And Butterfly ......... **55.00**
1984 Musical Cupids ............. **55.00**
1985 Cupids and Doves ........... **55.00**
1986 Anemones ................. **55.00**
1987 Tiger Lily .................. **55.00**
Queen's Christmas, A Price artist
1980 Windsor Castle ............. **30.00**
1981 Trafalgar Square ............ **25.00**
1982 Piccadilly Circus ............ **35.00**
1983 St. Pauls .................... **32.50**
1984 Tower of London ............ **35.00**
1985 Palace of Westminster ....... **35.00**
1986 Tower Bridge ............... **35.00**

# LITTLE GOLDEN BOOKS

**Collecting Hints:** Little Golden Books offer something for everybody. Collectors can pursue titles by favorite author, illustrator, or their favorite television show, film, or comic strip character. Disney titles enjoy a special place with nostalgia buffs. An increasingly popular goal is to own one copy of each title and number.

Books published in the forties, fifties, and sixties are in the most demand at this time. Books from this period were assigned individual numbers usually found on the front cover of the book, except for the earliest titles, where one must check the title against the numbered list on back of the book.

Although the publisher tried to adhere to a policy of one number for each title during the first thirty years, old numbers were assigned to new titles as old titles were eliminated. Also, when an earlier book was re–edited and/or re–illustrated, it was given a new number.

Most of the first thirty–six books had blue paper spines and a dust jacket. Subsequent books were issued with a golden–brown mottled spine. This was replaced in 1950 by a shiny gold spine.

Early books had 42 pages. In the late 1940s the format was gradually changed to 28 pages. Early 42 and 28 page books had no price on the cover. Later the price of 25¢ appeared on the front cover, then 29¢, followed by 39¢. In the mid–fifties the number of pages was changed to 24. In the early fifties books were produced with two lines that formed a bar across the top of the front cover. This bar was eliminated in the early sixties.

Little Golden Books can still be found at yard sales and flea markets. Other sources include friends, relatives, and charity book sales, especially if they have a separate children's table. Also attend doll, toy, and book shows. These dealers are sources for books with paper dolls, puzzles, and cut outs. Toy dealers are also a good source for Disney, television, and cowboy titles.

Look for books in good or better condition. Covers should be bright with the spine paper intact. Rubbing, ink and crayon markings, or torn pages lessen the value of the book. Pencil markings are fairly easy to remove, unless extensive. Stroke gently in one direction with an art gum eraser. Do not rub back and forth.

Within the past two years competition has increased dramatically, thus driving up prices for the most unusual and hard–to–find titles. Prices for the majority of titles are still at a reasonable level.

**History:** Simon & Schuster published the first Little Golden Books in September, 1942. They were conceived and created by the Artists & Writers Guild Inc., which was an arm of the Western Printing and Lithographing Company. The initial twelve, forty–two page titles, priced at 25¢ each, sold over 1.5 million books within five months of publication. By the end of WWII thirty–nine million Little Golden Books were sold.

A Disney series was begun in 1944, and Big and Giant Golden Books followed that same year. In 1949 the first Goldencraft editions were introduced. Instead of side–stapled cardboard, these books had cloth covers and were sewn so that they could hold up under school and library use. In 1958 Giant Little Golden Books were introduced, most combining three previously published titles together in one book.

1958 also marks Simon & Schuster selling Little Golden Books to Western Printing and Lithographing Company and Pocket Books. The books then appeared under the Golden Press imprint. Eventually Western bought out Pocket Books' interest in Little Golden Books. Now known as Western Publishing Company, Inc., it is the parent company of Golden Press, Inc.

In 1986 Western celebrated the one–billionth Little Golden Book by issuing special commemorative editions of some of its most popular titles, such as *Poky Little Puppy,* and *Cinderella.* In 1992 Golden Press celebrated the 50th birthday of Little Golden Books.

**Note:** Prices are based on the first printing of a book in mint condition. Printing is determined by looking at the lower right hand corner of the back page. The letter found there indicates the printing of that particular title and edition. "A" is the first printing and so forth. Occasionally the letter is hidden under the spine or was placed in the upper right hand corner, so look closely. Early titles will have their printings indicated in the front of the book.

Any dust jacket, puzzles, stencils, cutouts, stamps, tissues, tape, or pages should be intact and present as issued. If not, the book suffers a drastic reduction in value—up to 80 percent less than the listed price. Books that are badly worn, incomplete, or badly torn are worth little. Sometimes they are useful as temporary fillers for gaps in a collection.

**References:** Barbara Bader, *American Picture Books from Noah's Ark to the Beast Within,* Macmillan, 1976; Rebecca Greason, Tomart's Price Guide To Golden Book Collectibles, Wallace–Homestead Book Company, 1991; Dolores B. Jones, *Bibliography of the Little Golden Book,* Greenwood Press, 1987; Norman E. Martinus and Harry L. Rinker, *Warman's Paper,* Wallace–Homestead, 1993; Steve Santi, *Collecting Little Golden Books,* Books Americana, 1989.

**Periodical:** *Pokey Gazette,* 19626 Ricardo Ave, Hollywood, CA 94541.

**Advisor:** Kathie Diehl.

***This World of Ours,* Giant Little Golden Book, #5026, Golden Press, NY, 1959, $10.00.**

Activity

| | |
|---|---|
| #A17, *Stop and Go,* Loyta Higgins, illus Joan Walsh, Anglund, c1957, with wheel | **15.00** |
| #A26, *Trains Stamp Book,* Kathleen N. Daly, illus E Joseph Dreany, with stamps | **15.00** |
| #A31, *Mike and Melissa,* Jane Werner Watson, illus Adriana Mazza Saviozzi, c1959, with paper dolls | **20.00** |

#86, *The Color Kittens,* Margaret Wise Brown, illus Alice and Martin Provenson, c1949, with puzzle .. **30.00**
#441, *Bunny's Magic Tricks,* Janet and Alex D'Amato, illus Judy and Barry Martin, c1962, with pages that fold into tricks ............ **5.00**

Advertising
#129, *Tex and His Toys,* Elsa Ruth Nast, illus Corinne Malvern, c1952, Texcell Cellophane Tape . **25.00**
#139, *Fun With Decals,* Elsa Ruth Nast, illus Corinne Malvern, c1952, Meyercord decals ....... **10.00**
#203, *Little Lulu and Her Magic Tricks,* written and illus Marge Henderson Buell, 1954, orig Kleenex . **50.00**
#399, *Doctor Dan at the Circus,* Pauline Wilkins, illus Katherine Sampson, c1960, Johnson & Johnson Band-Aids .................... **17.00**
#550, *The Good Humor Man,* Kathleen N Daly, illus Tibor Gergely, c1964, Good Humor Ice Cream .. **6.00**

Disney
#A10, *Mickey Mouse Club Stamp Book,* Kathleen N Daly, illus Julius Svendsen, c1956, with stamps ... **20.00**
#D1, *Through the Picture Frame,* Walt Disney Studios, c1944, with dust jacket .................. **40.00**
#D47, *Davy Crockett's Keelboat Race,* Irwin Shapiro, illus Mel Crawford, c1955 .............. **7.50**
#D50, *Jiminy Cricket Fire Fighter,* Annie North Bedford, illus Samuel Armstrong, c1956 ............. **14.00**
#D54, *Perri and Her Friends,* Felix Salten, illus Annie North Bedford, c1956 ....................... **5.00**
#D68, *Zorro,* Charles Spain Verral, illus Walt Disney Studios, c1958 . **10.00**
#D75, *Manni The Donkey In The Forest World,* Emily Brown, illus Walt Disney Studios, c1959 ..... **5.00**
#D83, *Goliath II,* written and illus Bill Peet, c1959 .................. **14.00**

General Interest
#13, *The Golden Book of Birds,* Hazel Lockwood, illus Feodor Rojankovsky, c1943, with dust jacket .. **20.00**
#23, *The Shy Little Kitten,* Cathleen Schurr, illus Gustaf Tenggren, c1946, with dust jacket ......... **22.00**
#49, *Mr. Noah and His Family,* Jane Werner, illus Alice and Martin Provensen, c1948 ............. **14.00**
#56, *Our Puppy,* Elsa Ruth Nast, illus Feodor Rojankovsky, c1948 ...... **10.00**
#92, *I Can Fly,* Ruth Krauss, illus Mary Blair, c1950 ............. **12.00**
#119, *A Day at the Playground,* Miriam Schlein, illus Eloise Wilkin, c1951 ........................ **10.00**
#144, *The Road To Oz,* Peter Archer, illus Harry McNaught, c1951 .... **22.00**
#149, *Indian, Indian,* Charlotte Zolotow, illus Leonard Weisgard, c1952 ........................ **18.00**
#159, *The Tin Woodman of Oz,* Peter Archer, illus Harry McNaught, c1952 ........................ **18.00**
#167, *Animal Friends,* Jane Werner, illus Garth Williams, c1953 ..... **5.00**
#174, *Bible Stories of Boys and Girls,* Jane Werner, illus Rachel Taft Dixon, c1953 .................. **3.00**
#185, *Laddie The Superdog,* William P Gottlieb, c1954 .............. **5.50**
#208, *Tiger's Adventure,* William P Gottlieb, c1954 ................ **5.50**
#210, *The Kitten Who Thought He Was A Mouse,* Miriam Norton, illus Garth Williams, c1954 .......... **9.00**
#227, *The Twins,* Ruth and Harold Shane, illus Eloise Wilkin, c1955 . **18.00**
#229, *Houses,* Elsa Jane Werner, illus Tibor Gergely, c1955 ........... **6.50**
#238, *5 Pennies To Spend,* Miriam Young, illus Corinne Malvern, c1955 ....................... **7.50**
#243, *Numbers,* Mary Reed and Edith Oswald, illus Violet LaMont, c1955 ....................... **2.50**
#251, *Cars,* Kathryn Jackson, illus William J Dugan, c1956 ........ **5.00**
#257, *Counting Rhymes,* illus Corinne Malvern, c1947 ........... **5.00**
#317, *More Mother Goose Rhymes,* illus Feodor Rojakovsky, c1958 .. **10.00**
#388, *Our Flag,* Carl Memling, illus Stephen Cook, c1960 ........... **4.50**
#443, *Puff the Blue Kitten,* illus Pierre Probst, c1961 ................. **8.00**
#460, *My Little Golden Book of Manners,* Peggy Parish, illus Richard Scarry, c1962 ................. **4.00**
#479, *Rusty Goes to School,* Pierre Probst, c1962 .................. **5.00**

Television/Cartoons
#150, *Rootie Kazootie Detective,* Steve Carlin, illus Mel Crawford, c1953 ....................... **10.00**
#204, *Howdy Doody and Mr. Bluster,* Edward Kean, illus Elias Marge, c1954 ....................... **10.00**
#223, *It's Howdy Doody Time,* Edward Kean, illus Art Seiden, c1955 **12.00**
#226, *Rootie Kazootie Joins the Circus,,* Steve Carlin, illus Mel Crawford, c1955 .................. **11.50**

#356, *Steve Canyon,* Milton Caniff, c1959 ........................ **5.50**
#372, *Woody Woodpecker Drawing Fun for Beginners,* Carl Buettner, illus Harvey Eisenberg and Norman McGary, c1959 ................ **7.50**
#378, *Ruff and Ready,* Ann McGovern, illus Harvey Eisenberg and Al White, c1959 ............... **6.50**
#408, *Rocky and His Friends,* Ann McGovern, illus Ben DeNunez and Al White, c1960 ............... **12.00**
#474, *Touche Turtle,* Carl Memling, illus Al White, Norman McGary, Bill Lorencz, c1962 ............ **6.50**
#458, *Huckleberry Hound Safety Signs,* Ann McGovern, illus Al White, c1961 .................. **7.00**
#476, *Little Lulu,* Gina Inoglia Weiner, illus Woody Kimbrell and Al White, c1962 .................. **6.50**
#483, *Mister Ed The Talking Horse,* Barbara Shook Hazen, illus Mel Crawford, c1962 ............... **9.00**
#502, *Wally Gator,* Tom Golberg, illus Hawley Pratt and Bill Lorencz, c1963 ....................... **7.00**
#546, *Fireball XL5,* Barbara Shook Hazen, illus Hawley Pratt and Al White, c1964 .................. **18.00**

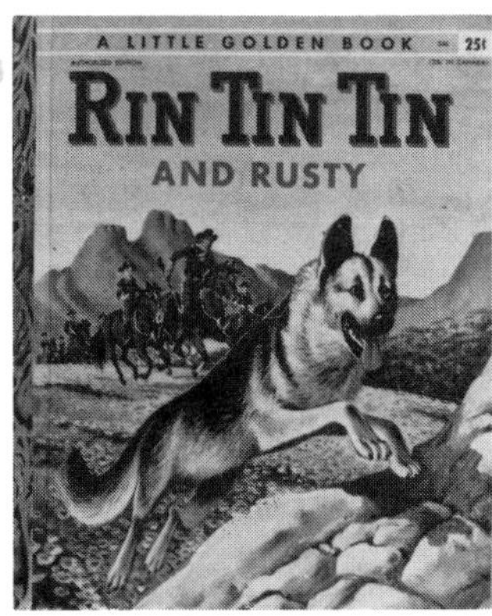


***Rin Tin Tin and Rusty*, #246, Simon & Schuster, NY, 1955, $8.00.**

Western
#195, *Roy Rogers and Cowboy Toby,* Elizabeth Beecher, illus Mel Crawford, c1954 .................. **10.00**
#213, *Dale Evans and the Lost Gold Mine,* Monica Hill, illus Mel Crawford, c1955 .................. **8.00**
#231, *Roy Rogers and the Mountain Lion,* Ann McGovern, illus Mel Crawford, c1955 ............... **9.00**
#246, *Rin Tin Tin and Rusty,* Monica Hill, illus Mel Crawford, c1955 .. **6.50**
#263, *The Lone Ranger,* Steffi Fletcher, illus Joseph Dreany, c1956 ........................ **12.00**
#297, *The Long Ranger and Tonto,* Charles Spain Verral, illus Edwin Schmidt, c1957 ................ **10.00**
#328, *Tales of Wells Fargo,* Leon Lazarus, illus John Leone, c1958 .... **15.00**
#354, *Maverick,* Carl Memling, illus John Leone .................... **7.50**

# LITTLE RED RIDING HOOD

**Collecting Hints:** Little Red Riding Hood is a "hot" collectible. Prices for many pieces are in the hundreds of dollars. Prices for the advertising plaque and baby dish are in the thousands.

A great unanswered question at this time is how many Little Red Riding Hood pieces have survived. Attempts at determining production levels have been unsuccessful. This category has the potential for an eventual market flooding, especially for the most commonly found pieces. New collectors are advised to proceed with caution.

Undecorated blanks are commonly found. Value them between 25% and 50% less than decorated examples.

**History:** On June 29, 1943, the United States Patent Office issued design patent #135,889 to Louise Elizabeth Bauer, Zanesville, Ohio, assignor to the A. E. Hull Pottery Company, Incorporated, Crooksville, Ohio, for a "Design for a Cookie Jar." Thus was born Hull's Little Red Riding Hood line. It was produced and distributed between 1943 and 1957.

The traditional story is that A. E. Hull only made the blanks. Decoration of the pieces was done by the Royal China and Novelty Company of Chicago, Illinois. When decoration was complete, the pieces were returned to Hull for distribution. Recent scholarship suggests a somewhat different approach.

Mark Supnick, author of *Hull Pottery's "Little Red Riding Hood": A Pictorial Reference and Price Guide* feels that A. E. Hull only made the blanks for early cookie jars and the dresser jar with a large bow in the front. They can be identified by their creamy off-white pottery. The majority of pieces have very white pottery, a body Supnick attributes to The Royal China and Novelty Company, a division of Regal China. Given the similarity in form to items in Royal China and Novelty Company's "Old McDonald's Farm" line, Supnick concludes that Hull contracted with Royal China and Novelty for production as well as decoration.

Great hand painted and decal variation is encountered in pieces, e.g., the wolf jar is found with bases in black, brown, red, or yellow.

**References:** Harvey Duke, *The Official Identification and Price Guide to Pottery and Porcelain, Seventh Edition*, House of Collectibles, 1989; Mark E. Supnick, *Collecting Hull Pottery's "Little Red Riding Hood": A Pictorial Reference and Price Guide*, L–W Book Sales, 1989, 1992 value update.

**REPRODUCTION ALERT:** Be alert for a Mexican produced cookie jar that closely resembles Hull's Little Red Riding Hood piece. The Mexican example is slightly shorter. Hull's examples measure 13″ high.

Bank, standing .......... **600.00**
Batter Pitcher .......... **425.00**
Butter Dish, cov .......... **350.00**
Canister, cov
  Coffee .......... **650.00**
  Flour .......... **650.00**
  Salt .......... **1,000.00**
  Sugar .......... **650.00**

**Cookie Jar, gold trim, floral decals, marked "Little Red Riding Hood, patent DES No 135889 USA," 13″ h, $350.00.**

Cookie Jar
  Closed basket .......... **300.00**
  Open basket, gold stars on apron, pink flowers on skirt .......... **325.00**
  Round basket, poinsettias on apron . **350.00**
Cracker jar, cov, 8½″ h .......... **500.00**
Creamer, pour through head .......... **275.00**
Creamer and Sugar, side pour .......... **325.00**
Lamp .......... **2,150.00**
Milk Pitcher, standing, 8″ h .......... **275.00**
Mustard, cov, orig spoon, 5½″ h .......... **350.00**
Salt and Pepper Shakers, pr
  Large, 5½″ h .......... **125.00**
  Small, 3¼″ h .......... **50.00**
Sugar, cov
  Crawling .......... **225.00**
  Standing .......... **450.00**
Teapot, cov .......... **325.00**
Wall Pocket .......... **450.00**

# LUNCH KITS

**Collecting Hints:** The thermos is an intregal part of the lunch kit. The two must be present to have full value. However, there has been a tendency in recent years to remove the thermos from the lunch box and price the two separately. The wise collector will resist this trend.

Prices on lunch kits have increased significantly in the last couple of years, largely due to the publicity generated by the manipulative efforts of Scott Bruce and others. Prices now appear to be stabilizing as the lunch box craze of the 1980s nears its end.

The values listed reflect realistic prices for a kit with thermos, both in near mint condition. Scratches and rust detract from a metal kit's value and lower value by more than fifty percent.

**History:** Lunch kits date back to the 19th century when tin boxes were used by factory workers and field hands. The modern child's lunch kit, the form most sought by today's collector, began in the 1930s. Gender, Paeschke & Frey Co. of Milwaukee, Wisconsin, issued a No. 9100 Mickey Mouse lunch kit for the 1935 Christmas trade. An oval lunch kit of a streamlined train, marked "Decoware," dates from the same period.

Television brought the decorated lunch box into a golden age. Among the leading manufacturers are: Aladdin Company; Landers, Frary and Clark; Ohio Art (successor to Hibbard, Spencer, Bartlett & Co.) of Bryan, Ohio; Thermos/King-Seeley; and Universal.

**References:** Larry Aikins, *Pictorial Price Guide To Metal Lunch Boxes & Thermoses*, L–W Book Sales, 1992; Larry Aikins, *Pictorial Price Guide To Vinyl & Plastic Lunch Boxes & Thermoses*, L–W Book Sales, 1992; Scott Bruce, *The Fifties and Sixties Lunch Box*, Chronicle Books, 1988; Scott Bruce, *The Official Price Guide To Lunch Box Collectibles, First Edition*, House of Collectibles, 1989; Philip R. Norman, *1993 Lunch Box & Thermos Price Guide*, published by author, 1992; Allen Woodall and Sean Brickell, *The Illustrated Encyclopedia of Metal Lunch Boxes*, Schiffer Publishing Ltd., 1992.

**Periodical:** *Hot Boxing*, P.O. Box 87, Somerville, MA 02143.

Action Jackson, metal, color illus, thermos, Okay Industries, copyright 1973 Mego Corp .......... **200.00**
Addams Family .......... **85.00**
Alvin and the Chipmunks, vinyl, dark green, color illus, thermos, copyright 1963 Ross Bagdasarian and Thermos **150.00**
Barbie and Francie, vinyl, black, color illus, King–Seeley Thermos Co, copyright 1965 Mattel Inc .......... **125.00**
Bugaloos, emb metal, color illus, Aladdin Industries, copyright 1971 Sid & Marty Krofft Productions Inc .......... **50.00**
Cabbage Patch Kids, metal, color illus, thermos, King–Seeley Thermos Co, copyright 1983 Original Appalachian Art Works Inc .......... **35.00**
Cable Car, metal, dome top, color illus, 6½" h metal thermos, Aladdin Industries, c1962 .......... **100.00**
Casey Jones, metal dome, Universal, 1960–61 .......... **200.00**
Central Union .......... **85.00**
Davy Crockett, American Thermos Bottle Co, 1955 .......... **140.00**
Debutante, metal, pink and tan basketweave design, 6" metal thermos, Aladdin Industries, c1958 .......... **55.00**
Denver Broncos, plastic, orange, helmet illus and logo, 1980s .......... **25.00**
Dinomutt, metal, color illus, 6½" yellow plastic thermos, blue plastic cup, King–Seeley, copyright 1976 Hanna–Barbera Productions Inc copyright .. **50.00**
Drag Strip, emb metal, color illus, thermos, Aladdin Industries, c1975 .... **75.00**
Dr Doolittle, emb metal, color illus, 6½" h metal thermos, red plastic cup, Aladdin Industries, copyright 1967 20th Century Fox Film Corp copyright **60.00**
Dragon's Lair, emb metal, color illus, 6½" h plastic thermos, Aladdin Industries, 1983 Don Bluth copyright .... **50.00**
Dukes of Hazzard .......... **10.00**

**The Dukes of Hazzard, emb metal, plastic thermos, Aladdin, 1980, $10.00.**

Fritos Brand Corn Chips, metal, King–Seeley Thermos Co, c1975 .......... **75.00**
Ghost Land, metal, color illus, Ohio Art, 1970s .......... **35.00**
Gremlins .......... **15.00**
Hansel & Gretel, metal, color illus, Ohio Art, early 1980s .......... **40.00**
Junior Miss, metal, color illus, 6½" h metal thermos, Aladdin Industries, late 1960s .......... **40.00**
Lidsville, emb metal, color illus, Aladdin Industries, copyright 1971 Sid & marty Krofft Television Productions Inc .......... **50.00**
Little Red Riding Hood, metal, color illus, unused, Ohio Art, early 1980s . **55.00**
Miss America, emb metal, color illus, 6½" h, plastic thermos, Aladdin Industries copyright 1972 Miss America Pageant .......... **45.00**
NFL, metal, color illus, 6½" h, plastic thermos, white plastic cup, King–Seeley, 1975 National Football League Properties Inc copyright .......... **40.00**
Pac–Man, metal, color illus, metal carrying handles, copyright 1980 Bally–Midway Mfg Co, Chein .......... **40.00**
Pee Wee's Playhouse, purplish–pink, 6" h plastic thermos, Thermos Co, copyright 1987 Herman Toys Inc .......... **50.00**
Plaid, metal, 8" h metal thermos, American Thermos Bottle Co, 1950s ..... **45.00**
Popples, emb metal, color illus, plastic thermos, Aladdin Industries, copyright 1986 Those Characters From Cleveland Inc .......... **30.00**
Rose Petal Place, emb metal, color illus, Aladdin Industries, copyright 1983 David Kirschner Productions .......... **25.00**
Roy Rogers and Dale Evans .......... **40.00**
Scooby Doo, metal, color illus, plastic thermos, King–Seeley, copyright 1973 Hanna–Barbera Productions Inc .... **25.00**
See America, metal, color illus, road map designs, Ohio Art, early 1970s **20.00**
Sesame Street, vinyl, yellow and white plaid, color illus, 6½" plastic thermos, Aladdin Industries, copyright 1981 Children's Television Workshop **50.00**
Skipper, vinyl, color illus, King–Seeley Thermos Co, copyright 1965 Mattel Inc .......... **110.00**
Strawberry Shortcake, vinyl, red and white, color illus, 6½" h, plastic thermos, Aladdin Industries, copyright 1980 American Greetings Corp .... **20.00**
US Mail, metal, 6½" h, plastic thermos, Aladdin Industries, 1970s .......... **25.00**
Washington Redskins, metal, 7½" h metal thermos, white plastic cup, Okay Industries, 1970s .......... **100.00**

# MAGAZINE COVERS AND TEAR SHEETS

**Collecting Hints:** A good cover should show the artist's signature, have the mailing label nonexistent or in a place that does not detract from the design element, and have edges which are crisp, but not trimmed.

When framing vintage paper use acid free mat board and tape with a water soluble glue base such as brown paper gum tape or linen tape. The tape should only be affixed to the back side of the illustration. The rule of thumb is do not do anything that can not be easily undone.

Do not hang framed vintage paper in direct sunlight which causes fading or in a highly humid area (such as a bathroom or above a kitchen sink) which causes wrinkles in both the mat and art work.

**History:** Magazine cover design attracted some of America's leading illustrators. Maxfield Parrish, Erte, Leyendecker, and Norman Rockwell were dominant forces in the 20th century. In the mid–1930s photographic covers gradually replaced the illustrated covers. One of the leaders in the industry was *Life,* which emphasized photojournalism.

Magazine covers are frequently collected by artist signed covers, subject matter, or historical events. Artist signed covers feature a commercially printed artist signature on the cover, or the artist is identified inside as "Cover by..." Most collected covers are in full color and show significant design elements. Black memorabilia is often reflected in magazine covers and tear sheets. It is frequently collected for the positive effect it has on African–Americans. However, sometimes it is a reflection of the times in which it was printed and may represent subjects in an unfavorable light.

Many of America's leading artists also illustrated magazine advertising. The ads made advertising characters such as the Campbell Kids, the Dutch Girl, and Snap, Crackle and Pop world famous.

**References:** Patricia Kery, *Great Magazine Covers of The World,* Abbeyville Press, 1982; Norman E. Martinus and Harry L. Rinker, *Warman's Paper,* Wallace–Homestead, 1993; check local libraries for books about specific illustrators such as Parrish, Rockwell, and Jessie Wilcox Smith.

**Periodical:** *PCM (Paper Collector's Marketplace),* P. O. Box 128, Scandinavia, WI 54977.

**Note:** Prices of covers and complete magazines have remained stable the last few years, but those of tear sheets have declined as more and more magazines have glutted the market. While only a short time ago magazines were thrown away when attics and garages were cleaned, now they are offered for sale. The public has been educated by seeing many magazine tear sheets being offered for sale at flea markets and mall shows. Dealers prefer to purchase complete magazines and gleen their profit from the contents.

As more and more magazines are destroyed for the tear sheets, complete magazines rise in value as the supply decreases. If a magazine is in mint condition, it should be left intact. We do NOT encourage removing illustrations from complete magazines. Only the complete magazine can act as a tool to interpret that specific historical time period. Editorial and advertising together define the spirit of the era.

## ARTIST SIGNED

| Item | Price |
|---|---|
| Armstrong, Rolf | **25.00** |
| Benito, Herbert | **10.00** |
| Bevans, Torre | |
| Children | **15.00** |
| Pictorial Review, April, 1920 | **18.00** |
| Others | **12.00** |
| Cassandre, A. M. | **10.00** |
| Christy, Howard Chandler | **10.00** |
| Coffin, Haskell | **12.00** |
| Crane, S. W. | **6.00** |
| Drayton, Grace (also Weiderseim) | |
| Illustrated Stories | **1.00** |
| Paper Dolls | |
| Large format | **18.00** |
| Small format | **8.00** |
| Tear Sheet | |
| Black and white | **1.00** |
| Colors | **4.00** |
| Covers | **30.00** |
| Eastman, Ruth, The Designer, Aug, 1913 | **10.00** |
| Erte, Harper's Bazaar Covers | **50.00** |
| Fisher, Harrison | |
| Ladies Home Journal, Dec, 1913 | **25.00** |
| Large format | **18.00** |
| Small format | **12.00** |
| Flagg, James Montgomery, color | **6.00** |
| Greer, Blanche, Woman's Home Companion, June, 1907 | **20.00** |
| Gunn, Archie | |
| Truth, June 20, 1896 | **15.00** |
| Others | **10.00** |
| Gutmann, Bessie Pease | **25.00** |
| Hays, Mary A., McCall's, May, 1915 | **5.00** |
| Hoff, Guy, The Woman's Magazine, Dec, 1918 | **15.00** |
| King, Hamilton, Coca Cola girl illustrator | **12.00** |
| Leyendecker | **15.00** |
| Marsh, Lucille Patterson | **15.00** |
| Mayer, My, Truth, Aug 15, 1896 | **25.00** |
| McClelland, Barclay | **6.00** |
| Mucha, Alphonse | |
| Century | **100.00** |
| Literary Digest | **40.00** |

O'Neill, Rose
 Illustrated articles ................ **4.00**
 Kewpies Covers
  Ladies Home Journal, Dec, 1910 . **35.00**
  Ladies Home Journal, Dec, 1927 . **35.00**
  The Designer, Aug, 1911 ........ **35.00**
  The Pictorial Review, Jan, 1914 .. **22.00**
 Kewpies Stories, some several pages
  Large format, Woman's Home Companion, 1911–1912 ...... **12.00**
  Medium format, Good Housekeeping, 1916–1919 .............. **10.00**
  Small format, Good Housekeeping, 1914–1916 ................. **8.00**
 Woman/Children Covers
  Metropolitan, Feb, 1900 ........ **20.00**
  Woman's Home Companion, Jan, 1924 ...................... **20.00**
 Tear Sheet
  Full page, color ................ **6.00**
  Jello adv, black and white ....... **3.00**
  Rock Island Line ............... **4.00**
Outcault, Truth, Feb 15, 1896 ....... **15.00**
Parkhurst, McCall's
 Dec, 1916 ...................... **15.00**
 March, 1918 .................... **8.00**
Parrish, Maxfield
 Cover, Ladies Home Journal, Dec, 1912 ........................ **60.00**
 Story illustration headlines ......... **3.00**
 Tear Sheet, Jello adv .............. **35.00**
Penfield, Edward, Harper's Weekly, Dec, 1898 ..................... **35.00**
Phillip, Coles
 Cover, McCall's, June, 1918 ....... **15.00**
 Tear Sheet, Community Silver ...... **6.00**
Ralph, Lester ...................... **6.00**
Robinson, Robert ................... **8.00**

**Phillip Coles illustration, *Ladies Home Journal,* 1919, Luxite Hosiery adv, 9½ x 14½", full color, $10.00.**

Rockwell, Norman
 Cover
  Prior to 1920 .................. **35.00**
  Prior to 1940 .................. **25.00**
  After 1940 ..................... **10.00**
 Tear Sheet, color ................. **8.00**
Smith, James Calvert, McCall's, Nov, 1921 ........................... **8.00**
Smith, Jessie Wilcox
 Cover
  Good Housekeeping ............ **20.00**
  Others, large format, pre–1920 .. **25.00**
 Tear Sheet, Seven Stages of Childhood ......................... **15.00**
Stanlaws, Penny ................... **8.00**
Twelvetrees, Charles
 Covers
  Capper's Farmer, 1930s ......... **5.00**
  Collier's, 1930s ................ **5.00**
  Pictorial Review
   Large format, pre–1930 ....... **15.00**
   Small format, pre–1930 ....... **10.00**
   Suffrage, Jan, 1921 ........... **25.00**
 Illustrated Stories ................. **3.00**
Usobal, McCall's, March, 1921 ...... **8.00**
Wireman, H. E., Woman's Home Companion, Dec, 1915 ............... **12.00**
Wood, Lawson
 Monkey images .................. **6.00**
 Other .......................... **4.00**

### BLACK MEMORABILIA

Covers feature African–American personalities
 Armstrong, Louis ................ **10.00**
 Clay, Cassius ................... **7.00**
 Davis, Jr., Sammy ............... **7.00**
 King, Martin Luther ............... **8.00**
 Life Magazine, 1956, Slave Auction cover ......................... **15.00**
 Saturday Evening Post, Black images **12.00**
Stories on Black History ............ **2.00**
Tear Sheet, adv
 Aunt Jemima ................... **2.00**
 Cream of Wheat
  General ....................... **10.00**
  Needlecraft Magazine ........... **6.00**
 Gold Dust Twins ................. **8.00**

# MAGAZINES

**Collecting Hints:** A rule of thumb for pricing general magazines without popular artist–designed covers is the more you would enjoy displaying a copy on your coffee table, the more elite the publication, and the more the advertising or editorial content relates to today's collectibles, the higher the price. *Life* magazine went into millions of homes each week, *Harper's Bazaar* and *Vogue* did not. Elite families had a greater tendency to discard last month's publication while middle–class families found the art on the *Saturday Evening Post* and *Collier's* irresistible and saved them. The greater the supply, the lower the price.

**History:** In the early 1700s general magazines were a major means of information for the reader. Literary magazines, such as *Harper's,* became popular in the 19th century. By 1900, the first photo–journal magazines appeared. *Life,* the prime example, was started by Henry Luce in 1932.

Magazines created for women featured "how to" articles about cooking, sewing, decorating, and child care. Many were entirely devoted to fashion and living a fashionable life, such as *Harper's Bazaar* and *Vogue.* Men's magazines were directed at masculine skills of the time, such as hunting, fishing, and woodworking, supplemented with appropriate "girlies" titles.

**References:** Jack Bramble, *The Playboy Collectors Guide & Price List, 5th Edition,* Budget Enterprises, 1982; David K. Henkel, *Magazines: Identification and Price Guide,* Avon Books, 1993; Marjorie M. and Donald L. Hinds, *Magazine Magic,* The Messenger Book Press, 1972; Denis C. Jackson, *Men's 'Girlie" Magazines: The Only Price Guide: Newstanders, Third Edition,* published by author, 1991; Norman E. Martinus and Harry L. Rinker, *Warman's Paper,* Wallace–Homestead, 1993

**Note:** The prices for general magazines are retail prices. They may be considerably higher than what would be offered for an entire collection filling your basement or garage. Bulk prices for common magazines such as *Life, Collier's,* and *Saturday Evening Post* are generally from fifty cents to one dollar per issue. Dealers have to sort, protect with plastic covering, discard ones that have items clipped from the interior, or have marred covers, and make no money on those which they never sell. The end result is that a lower price is paid for magazines purchased in bulk.

American Art Student & Commercial Artist, 1924, June ........ **4.00**
American Legion Weekly, 1926, April 16, Percy Crosby cartoon cov ...... **7.00**
American Machinist, 1913 .......... **14.00**
American Weekly, 1945, Henry Clive Cov ........ **5.00**
Argosy, January, 1940 ........ **10.00**
Arizona Highways, 1970, June ....... **2.00**
Art Magazine, 1922, December, G H Lockwood ........ **3.00**
Autocar, The, London, 1928, June .... **6.00**
Automobile Quarterly, 1962, Vol 1, No 1 ........ **20.00**
Automotive Magazine, 1917, Rolf Armstrong cov ........ **38.00**
Billboard, 1944 ........ **10.00**
Boys Home Weekly, 1911, Vol 1, No 22 ........ **22.00**
Catholic Digest, 1950, September, Tommy Henrich cov ........ **4.00**
College Football Illustrated, 1946 ..... **12.00**
Collier's, 1925, Dionne Quints ....... **15.00**

***Collier's,* Nov. 12, 1921, sgd Charles Livingston Bull illus, orange and black color wash, 10½ x 14", $18.00.**

Coronet, 1946, April, Norman Rockwell "How Yankee Doodle Went To Town" illus ........ **8.50**
Cosmopolitan
 1889, September, Rosie O'Neill illus and story ........ **10.00**
 1910, July, Weber–Ditzler color cov **10.00**
 1974, Brown/Davidson centerfold .. **5.00**
Country Gentleman, 1935 ........ **12.00**
Current Opinion, 1924, February, Roycrofters ad on back cov ........ **4.00**
Democratic Digest, 1955, December, 96 pgs ........ **4.00**
Dodge News, 1957, Lawrence Welk issue ........ **10.00**
Domestic Monthly, 1885, May, lady's and children's costumes, millinery .. **12.00**
Ebony, 1955 ........ **8.00**
El Morocco, 1957, Judy Garland, Jackie Gleason, and other stars ........ **12.00**
Esquire, 1934, September ........ **12.00**
Extension–National Catholic Monthly, 1943, September ........ **1.50**
Farm and Fireside
 1920, November, Frederick Stanley cover ........ **4.00**
 1929, December ........ **5.00**
Film Fun, 1923, January ........ **12.00**
Flair, 1950 ........ **10.00**
Fortune, 1937, March, Paramount

Movie studios and stars, four color posters by Cassandra ............ 12.50
Gags, 1941, July ................... 5.00
Gentleman, 1929 .................. 6.00
Glamour of Hollywood, 1940, December, Joan Bennett cov ............ 10.00
Harper's Bazaar, 1937, March ....... 6.00
Harper's Weekly, 1909 .............. 12.00
Hollywood Guys and Gals, 1955, 70 pgs, Monroe, Brando ............ 10.00
Horse Review, 1910, December ...... 40.00
Horse World, 1910, December ...... 40.00
House & Garden, 1940, August ...... 7.00
House & Garden Floor Plans, 1940, August ........................... 12.00
Hunting & Fishing, 1945, November .. 8.00
Illustrated London News, 1967, July 8, Jack Nicklaus cov ............... 5.00
Ladies Home Journal, 1973, Minnie Mouse needlepoint pattern ........ 15.00
Leslies, 1915 ..................... 10.00
Liberty, 1941, October 25, Hitler cov . 8.00
Life Magazine
1909, September 9, Henry Hutt on front cov ..................... 8.00
1938, May 23, Errol Flynn cov ..... 30.00
1939, September 11, Benito Mussolini cov ...................... 45.00
1950, June 12, Hopalong Cassidy cov 25.00
1966, March 11, Batman .......... 7.00
Literary Digest, 1909, Penfield cov ... 20.00
Look
1956, December 25, Lucille Ball cov 12.00
1966, four Rockwell illus .......... 15.00
1968, Bobby Kennedy, Rockwell illus 15.00
Mademoiselle, October, 1939 ....... 5.00
McCall's
1942, June ...................... 9.00
1943, October ................... 9.00
1946, December ................ 9.00
1963, F Scott Fitzgerald's letters .... 15.00
Mentor, The, 1923, October, lengthy article by C D Gibson .............. 5.00
Modern Priscilla, 1930, March ....... 3.00
Motion Picture, 1946, July, Maureen O'Hara cov .................... 7.00
Motor, 1948, December, Robert Robinson cov ......................... 5.00
Motor Mechanics, London, c1918, 172 pages .......................... 8.00
Nature Magazine, 1940 ............ 1.50
Needlecraft, 1926, color cov, Helen Grant .......................... 19.00
Newsweek, 1978, April 24, Woody Allen cov ........................ 5.00
New Yorker, 1944, June 10, Continental edition, 6¼ x 8¾" ............... 8.00
New York Times Midweek Pictorial, 1918 .......................... 10.00
Our World, 1948 .................. 8.00
Outdoor Life, 1953, February ........ 10.00
Outdoor World Recreation, 1924 ..... 28.00
Outlook & Independent, 1931 ....... 5.00
Pacific Monthly, Portland, OR, 1911, Feb ............................ 8.00
Penthouse, 1973 ................... 2.00
People's Home Journal
1920, November ................. 5.00
1929 .......................... 6.00
Personality Annual, 1964, Vol 1, #1, 66 pgs, black and white Beatles photos, 9 x 12" ..................... 30.00
Peterson's Pro Football, 1950 ........ 12.00
Photoplay
1935, July, Joan Bennett cov, Shirley Temple article ................ 12.50
1954 .......................... 6.00
Pictorial Review .................... 12.00
Playboy, 1942, December ........... 15.00
Popular Photography, 1937 .......... 5.00
Popular Science, 1927 .............. 6.00
Post, 1943, JFK In Memoriam, Rockwell cov ............................ 15.00
Pro Football Illustrated, 1943 ........ 12.00
Radio Guide, 1939, February 25, Charlie McCarthy cov ................ 8.50
Ring, 1963, August ................ 2.00
Rocky Mountain Sportsman & Western Wild Life, 1938 .................. 2.00
Saturday Evening Post
1938, May 28, Black drum major with black cat, cover by S N Abbott 8.50
1977, August, Special 250th Anniversary, Rockwell portfolio covers ... 8.50
Saturday Review, 1951 ............. 2.50
School Arts Magazine, 1933 ......... 5.00
Scientific American, 1917 ........... 14.00
Screenland, 1954, May ............. 6.00
Screen Stories, 1952, January ........ 7.00
Scribners, 1929 .................... 8.00
Sea Power, Magazine of Navy League of US, 1925, July ................ 4.00
S.E.P., 1910 ...................... 10.00
Showmen's Trade Review, 1948, July 10 6.00
Song Hits, 1941, March, Gene Autry cov ............................ 6.00
Sports Illustrated, 1987, swimsuit issue 5.00
Sports Review, 1958 ................ 12.00
St Nicholas, 1915, May, T Burgess story, Rockwell illus ................... 12.50
Street and Smiths Pro Football, 1962 .. 12.00
Success, July, 1904 ................. 6.00
Successful Farming, 1933 ........... 5.00
The Beatles are Back, 1964, 72 pgs, black and white photos, 9 x 12" .... 30.00
The Farmers Wife, 1930 ........... 12.00
The Independent, 1911, January 19, 7 page article on Japanese baseball ... 4.00
The Kourier, 1929 ................. 20.00
The Nation, 1945 .................. 4.00
The Pacific Monthly, 1911, February .. 10.00
Time
1945 .......................... 6.00
1946 .......................... 6.00

***Success*, April, 1903, sgd J. C. Leyendecker illus, full color, 10 x 13¾", $45.00.**

| | |
|---|---|
| 1947 | **6.00** |
| 1948, June 28, Jean Simmons cov | **6.00** |
| Today, 1937 | **4.00** |
| Today's Housewife, 1920, November | **5.00** |
| Today's Woman, 1946, December | **10.00** |
| True Confessions, 1935, July, Norma Shearer cov | **8.00** |
| True Romances, 1935, August, Mozart cov | **5.00** |
| Vanity Fair, 1933, March | **20.00** |
| Wide Awake, An Illustrated Magazine, 1887 | **7.00** |
| Wisconsin Motor News, 1925, February, Vol 1, No 1 | **5.00** |
| Woman's Day, 1945, N C Wyeth cov | **7.00** |
| Woman's Home Companion | |
| 1919, July | **10.00** |
| 1935, Diane Thorne dog cov | **15.00** |
| World's Events Magazine, 1906, February | **5.00** |
| Year Review, 1936 | **10.00** |
| Youth Companion, 1926 | **10.00** |

# MARBLES

**Collecting Hints:** Hand–made glass marbles usually command higher prices than machine–made glass, clay, or mineral marbles. There are a few notable exceptions, e.g., machine–made comic strip marbles were made for a limited time only and are highly prized by collectors. Care must be taken in purchasing this particular type since the comic figure was stenciled on the marble. A layer of glass was to be overlaid on the stencil. However, many examples exist that were not overlaid, and the stencils rub or wear off.

Some of the rarer examples of hand–made marbles are Clambroth, Lutz, Indian Swirls, Peppermint Swirls, and Sulphides. Marble values are normally determined by their type, size, and condition. Usually, the larger the marble, the more valuable it is within each type.

A marble in mint condition is unmarred and has the best possible condition with a clear surface. It may have surface abrasions from rubbing in its original package. A marble in good condition may have a few small surface dings, scratches, and slight surface cloudiness. However, the core must be easily seen, and the marble must be without large chips or fractures.

**History:** Marbles date back to ancient Greece, Rome, Egypt, and other early civilizations. In England, Good Friday is known as "Marbles Day" because the game was considered a respectable and quiet pastime for the hallowed day.

During the American Civil War, soldiers carried marbles and a small board to play "solitaire," a game whose object was to jump the marbles until only one is left in the center of the board.

In the last few generations, school children have identified marbles as peewees, shooters, commies, and cat's eyes. A National Marbles Tournament has been held each year, beginning in 1922, in June. Wildwood, New Jersey, is its current site.

**References:** Paul Baumann, *Collecting Antique Marbles, Second Edition* Wallace–Homestead, 1991; Jeff Carskadden and Richard Gartley, *Chinas: Hand–Painted Marbles of the late 19th Century,* Muskingum Valley Archaeological Society, 1990; Everett Grist, *Antique and Collectible Marbles, Identification and Values,* Collector Books, 1992; Everett Grist, *Everett Grist's Big Book of Marbles,* Collector Books, 1993; Everett Grist, *Everett Grist's Machine Made and Contemporary Marbles,* Collector Books, 1992; Marble Collectors Society of America, *Identification and Price Guide,* privately printed, 1989; Mark E. Randall, *Marbles As Historical Artifacts,* Marble Collectors Society; Mark E. Randall and Dennis Webb, *Greenberg's Guide to Marbles,* Greenberg Publishing Co., 1988.

**Collectors' Clubs:** Marble Collectors' Unlimited, P. O. Box 206, Northboro, MA 01532; Marble Collectors Society of America, P. O. Box 222, Trumbull, CT 06611; National Marble Club of America, 440 Eaton Road, Drexel Hill, PA 19026.

**Museums:** Corning Museum of Glass, Corning, NY; Sandwich Glass Museum, Sandwich, MA; Smithsonian Institution, Museum of Natural History, Washington, D.C.; Wheaton Village Museum, Millville, NJ.

**Advisor:** Stanley A. Block and Bob Block.

**REPRODUCTION ALERT:** Comic marbles are being reproduced.

## AGATE

A form of chalcedony quartz with banded or irregular appearance; it is usually a translucent stone found in all shades of earth colors, the most common being tones of brown with tan to white bands. Agate can be artificially dyed.

| Sizes | Mint | Good |
|---|---|---|
| To 7/8″ | 20.00 | 10.00 |
| 1″ to 1½″ | 80.00 | 25.00 |
| 1⅝″ to 1⅞″ | 100.00 | 40.00 |

## CLAMBROTH

Milk glass marbles in a solid color having many thin outer swirl lines of a different color running from pontil mark to pontil mark.

| Sizes | Mint | Good |
|---|---|---|
| To 7/8″ | 225.00 | 75.00 |
| 1″ to 1½″ | 600.00 | 125.00 |

## CLAYS

Marbles made of clay which may or may not be colored or glazed.

| Sizes | Mint | Good |
|---|---|---|
| To 7/8″ | .10 | .05 |
| 1″ to 1½″ | 3.00 | 1.00 |
| 1⅝″ to 1⅞″ | 10.00 | 4.00 |
| 2″ and over | 15.00 | 5.00 |

## COMIC

Marbles manufactured by the Peltier Glass Co. 1927 to 1934 with one of twelve comic strip character faces stamped on the marble and fired so as to be permanent.

| Sizes | Mint | Good |
|---|---|---|
| To 7/8″ | 65.00 | 25.00 |

## END–OF–DAY

Usually composed of a solid multicolored inner surface coated with an outer covering of clear glass; also known as Cloud Marbles.

| Sizes | Mint | Good |
|---|---|---|
| To 7/8″ | 30.00 | 15.00 |
| 1″ to 1½″ | 200.00 | 60.00 |
| 1⅝″ to 1⅞″ | 250.00 | 100.00 |
| 2″ and over | 350.00 | 150.00 |

## INDIAN SWIRL

Handmade, opaque black glass marble with very colorful swirls applied next to or on top of surface.

| Sizes | Mint | Good |
|---|---|---|
| To 7/8″ | 100.00 | 45.00 |
| 1″ to 1½″ | 300.00 | 120.00 |

## LATTICINIO CORE SWIRL

Inner part of the marble has a latticinio or lace center; usually with outer swirls of varying colors running from pontil mark to pontil mark.

| Sizes | Mint | Good |
|---|---|---|
| To 7/8″ | 12.00 | 5.00 |
| 1″ to 1½″ | 55.00 | 20.00 |
| 1⅝″ to 1⅞″ | 100.00 | 40.00 |
| 2″ and over | 175.00 | 75.00 |

## LUTZ (BANDED)

Handmade glass marbles usually with colored swirls, some of which contain copper flecks; also called Goldstone swirls. Other types of Lutz (end of day, ribbon, and opaque banded Lutz) are worth two to three times the values shown for banded Lutz.

| Sizes | Mint | Good |
|---|---|---|
| To 7/8″ | 125.00 | 65.00 |
| 1″ to 1½″ | 300.00 | 150.00 |
| 1⅝″ to 1⅞″ | 500.00 | 200.00 |
| 2″ & over | 1,100.00 | 225.00 |

**Banded Lutz, 1⅞″ d, polished, $500.00.**

## MACHINE MADE TYPES (U.S.)

Akro Agate Company: King of Machine made marbles for forty years. Founded in 1911, dissolved in 1951, located in Clarksburg, VA. All types are 5/8″.

| | Mint | Good |
|---|---|---|
| Brick | 50.00 | 20.00 |
| Corkscrew (two color) | 1.00 | .10 |

| | Mint | Good |
|---|---|---|
| Corkscrew (multicolor) | 15.00 | 3.00 |
| Egg Yoke Oxblood | 100.00 | 30.00 |
| Helmet Patch | 2.00 | .25 |
| Moonstone | 10.00 | 2.00 |
| Popeye Corkscrew | 10.00 | 2.00 |
| Slag | 1.00 | .10 |
| Swirl Oxblood | 15.00 | 3.00 |

Christensen Agage Co: Produced the finest colors in machine made marbles. Only produced marbles for eighteen months, beginning in 1927. Located in Cambridge, OH. (all numbers are ⅝")

| | Mint | Good |
|---|---|---|
| Cobra | 600.00 | 200.00 |
| Flame | 50.00 | 20.00 |
| Guinea | 300.00 | 125.00 |
| Swirl | 30.00 | 10.00 |

Other Machine Made: There were a dozen or so American manufacturers from the 1930s through the 1970s. All marble sizes are ⅝".

| | Mint | Good |
|---|---|---|
| Bumblebee, Marble King | 1.00 | .25 |
| Cat's Eye, various makers | .02 | .01 |
| Common Swirl, various makers | .05 | .01 |
| Girl Scout, Marble King | 6.00 | 1.00 |
| Victory, Vitro Agate | 1.00 | .10 |
| Wire Pull, unknown maker | 10.00 | 2.00 |
| Watermelon, Marble King | 200.00 | 75.00 |

Peltier Glass Company: Another large producer of machine made marbles. Founded in 1886 and still in existence. Located in Ottawa, IL. All marbles are ⅝".

| | Mint | Good |
|---|---|---|
| Christmas Tree | 50.00 | 20.00 |
| Patriot | 30.00 | 10.00 |
| Peerless Patch | 2.00 | .25 |
| Peerless | | |
| Patch with adventurine | 20.00 | 3.00 |
| Rainbow | 10.00 | 2.00 |

Transitional: Slag-glass, single pontil marbles. Hand-gathered on a punty and either individually handmade or made in an early, semi-automatic machine. Classified by pontil type. "Melted Pontil" are most common. Other types command two to five times the value.

| Sizes | Mint | Good |
|---|---|---|
| ⅝" to ⅞" | 30.00 | 10.00 |
| ⅞" to 1" | 50.00 | 20.00 |
| Over 1" | 80.00 | 30.00 |

## MICAS

Mineral silicates occurring in thin sheet and usually reflective of silver in appearance; handmade glass marbles of various types (usually clear colored glass) having silvery flakes inside.

| Sizes | Mint | Good |
|---|---|---|
| To ⅞" | 20.00 | 10.00 |
| 1" to 1½" | 300.00 | 75.00 |
| 1⅝" to 1⅞" | 600.00 | 400.00 |

## OPEN CORE SWIRL

Handmade glass swirl marble with open colored bands in center of marble.

| Sizes | Mint | Good |
|---|---|---|
| To ⅞" | 15.00 | 2.00 |
| 1" to 1½" | 65.00 | 22.00 |
| 1⅝" to 1⅞" | 120.00 | 45.00 |
| 2" and over | 200.00 | 75.00 |

## PEPPERMINT SWIRL

Swirl glass marble resembling peppermint stick candy, usually incorporating red, white, and blue colors.

| Sizes | Mint | Good |
|---|---|---|
| To ⅞" | 100.00 | 50.00 |

## POTTERY

Earthenware as distinguished on the one hand from porcelain and stoneware, and on the other hand from brick and tile.

| Sizes | Mint | Good |
|---|---|---|
| To ⅞" | 1.00 | .50 |
| 1" to 1½" | 10.00 | 4.00 |

**Divided Core Swirl, 2¼″ d, $200.00.**

### SOLID CORE SWIRL

Glass marble having a solid one–color or varicolored center looking like a piece of candy with outer swirls running from pontil mark to pontil mark.

| Sizes | Mint | Good |
|---|---|---|
| To ⅞″ | 18.00 | 8.00 |
| 1″ to 1½″ | 70.00 | 30.00 |
| 1⅝″ to 1⅞″ | 130.00 | 65.00 |
| 2″ and over | 300.00 | 150.00 |

### SULPHIDES

Objects made of china clay and supersilicate of potash for inserting in marbles and a variety or other glass objects, usually three dimensional; marbles are of clear glass containing a sulphide object, usually an animal figure. Antique sulphides with numbers, human figures, or colors are worth three to ten times the value shown.

| Sizes | Mint | Good |
|---|---|---|
| 1″ to 1½″ | 150.00 | 100.00 |
| 1⅝″ to 1⅞″ | 175.00 | 125.00 |
| 2″ & over | 250.00 | 150.00 |

**Sulphides, 1½″ d lamb, 1¾″ d duck, price each, $125.00.**

## MATCHCOVERS

**Collecting Hints:** Matchcovers generally had large production runs; very few are considered rare. Most collectors remove the matches, flatten the covers, and mount them in albums by category. They prefer the covers be unused.

Trading is the principal means of exchange among collectors, usually on a one for one basis. At flea markets and shows matchcovers frequently are seen marked for $1.00 to $5.00 for categories such as beer covers or pin–up art (girlies) covers. Actually these purchasers are best advised to join one of the collector clubs and get involved in swapping.

**History:** The book match was invented by Joshua Pusey, a Philadelphia lawyer, who also was a chemist in his spare time. In 1892 Pusey put 10 cardboard matches into a cover of plain white board. Two hundred were sold to the Mendelson Opera Company who, in turn, hand–printed messages on the front.

The first machine made matchbook was made by the Binghamton Match Company, Binghamton, New York, for the Piso Company of Warren, Pennsylvania. The only surviving cover is now owned by the Diamond Match Company.

Few covers survive from the late 1890s–1930s period. The modern craze for collecting matchcovers was started by a set of ten covers issued for the Century of Progress exhibit at the 1933 Chicago World's Fair.

The Golden Age of matchcovers was the mid–1940s through the early 1960s when the covers were a popular advertising medium. Principal manufacturers included Atlas Match, Brown and Bigelow, Crown Match, Diamond Match, Lion Match, Ohio Match and Universal Match.

The arrival of throw–away lighters, such as BIC, brought an end to the matchcover era. Manufacturing costs for a matchbook today can range from below a cent to seven or eight cents for a special die–cut cover. As a result, matchcovers no longer are an attractive "free" give–away item.

Because of this, many of the older, more desirable covers are seeing a marked increase in value. Collectors have also turned to the small pocket type boxes as a way of enhancing and building their collections.

**References:** Yosh Kashiwabara, *Matchbook Art,* Chronicle Books, 1989; Norman E. Martinus and Harry L. Rinker, *Warman's Paper,* Wallace–Homestead, 1993; Bill Retskin, *The Matchcover Collectors Resource Book and Price Guide,* published by author, 1988; H. Thomas Steele, Jim Heimann, Rod Dyer, *Close Cover Before Striking, The Golden Age of Matchbook Art,* Abbeville Press, 1987.

**Periodical:** *The Front Striker Bulletin,* 3417 Clayborne Avenue, Alexandria, VA 22306; *The Match Hunter,* 740 Poplar Boulder, Co, 80304.

**Collectors' Clubs:** Rathkamp Matchcover Society, 1359 Surrey Road, Vandalia, OH 43577; Trans–Canada Matchcover Club, Box 219, Caledonia, Ontario, Canada NOA–1A0. There are 33 regional clubs throughout the United States and Canada.

**Advisor:** Wray Martin.

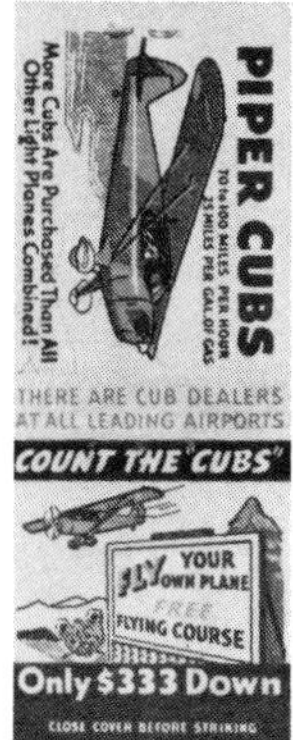


**Aviation, Piper Cubs adv, printed color plane illus, 1940s, 1½ x 3¾", $8.00.**

## SPECIAL COVERS

| | |
|---|---|
| Advertising, Stoeckle Select Beer, Giant, Stoeckle Brewery | **6.00** |
| Apollo Flights 8–17, Cameo's, each | **5.00** |
| Dwight D. Eisenhower, 5 Star General | **15.00** |
| Economy Blue Print, girlies, set of 6, 1950s | **45.00** |
| Joe Louis & Max Schmeling Championship Fight, (Giant) | **18.00** |
| Presidential Yacht, *Patricia* | **10.00** |
| Presidential Helicopter, "Marine One" | **10.00** |
| Pull for Willkie, Pullquick Match | **28.00** |
| Racquel Welch, color photo, made in South Africa | **15.00** |

## TOPICS

| | |
|---|---|
| Airlines | **.25** |
| Americana | **.05** |
| Atlas Four color | **.05** |
| Banks | **.02** |
| Beer and Brewery | **.75** |
| Best Western | |
| Non Stock | **.15** |
| Stock Design | **.10** |
| Bowling Alleys | **.02** |
| Cameo's, Universal trademark | **.05** |
| Canadian Four Color | **.05** |
| Casinos | **.05** |
| Chinese Restaurants | **.04** |
| Christmas | **.04** |
| Classiques | **.40** |
| Colleges | **.05** |
| Contours, diecut | **.10** |
| Conventions | **.03** |
| Country Clubs | **.07** |
| County Seats | **.05** |
| Dated | **.10** |
| Diamond Quality | **.50** |
| Elks | **.10** |
| Fairs | **.10** |
| Features | **.15** |
| Foilites, Universal trademark | **.05** |
| Foreign | **.05** |
| Fraternal | **.05** |
| Giants | **.50** |
| Girlies | |
| Non Stock | **.40** |
| Stock Design | **.15** |
| Group One, non–advertising | |
| New | **.03** |
| Old | **.40** |

**Note:** Group One items consist of matches with no advertising. The older matchcovers were sold in tobacco stores during the 1930s and contained personalities, football, baseball and other sport figures, city scenes, and state scenes. The usual buyer bought 16 matchbooks for a dime. The new items represent matchcovers purchased from a local supermarket. These are sets (clocks, railroads, etc.) and are found in packages of fifty matchbooks for sixty cents to over a dollar.

| | |
|---|---|
| Hillbillies | **.05** |
| Holiday Inns | |
| Non Stock | **.15** |
| Stock Design | **.10** |
| Jewelites | **.05** |
| Jewels | **.05** |
| Knot Holes | **.20** |
| Matchorama's, Universal trademark | **.08** |
| Matchtones, Universal trademark | **.10** |
| Midgets | **.15** |
| Navy Ships | **.30** |
| Odd Strikers | **.20** |
| Patriotic | **.05** |
| Pearltone | **.05** |
| Personalities | **1.00** |
| Political | **1.00** |
| Pull Quick | **1.00** |
| Radio & Television | **.05** |
| Railroads | **.25** |
| Rainbows, Universal trademark | **.10** |
| Restaurants | **.02** |
| Savings & Loan | **.02** |
| Service | |
| New | **.05** |
| Old | **.15** |
| Shiplines | **.10** |
| Signets, Universal trademark | **.05** |
| Small Towns | **.05** |
| Soft Drinks | **.75** |
| Souvenir | **.20** |
| Sports | |
| New | **.15** |
| Old | **1.00** |
| Ten Strikes | **.05** |

Transportation .... **.15**
Travelodges .... **.05**
Truck Lines .... **.10**
Trust Companies .... **.02**
Veterans Administration Hospitals .... **.15**
Whiskey .... **.30**

# McCOY POTTERY

**Collecting Hint:** Several marks were used by the McCoy Pottery Co. Take time to learn the marks and the variations. Pieces can often be dated by the mark used.

**History:** The J. W. McCoy Pottery Co. was established in Roseville, Ohio, in September, 1899. The early McCoy Company produced both stoneware and some art lines, including Rosewood. In October, 1911, three potteries in the Roseville area merged, creating the Brush-McCoy Pottery Co. This company continued to produce the original McCoy lines and added several new art lines. Much of the early pottery is not marked.

In 1910, Nelson McCoy and his father, J. W. McCoy, founded the Nelson McCoy Sanitary Stoneware Co. In 1925, the McCoy family sold their interest in the Brush-McCoy Pottery Co. and started to expand and improve the Nelson McCoy Company. The new company produced stoneware, earthenware specialties and artware. Most of the pottery marked McCoy was made by the Nelson McCoy Co.

**Reference:** Sharon and Bob Huxford, *The Collectors Encyclopedia of McCoy Pottery,* Collector Books, 1980, 1993 value update; Harold Nichols, *McCoy Cookie Jars: From The First To The Last, Second Edition,* Nichols Publishing, 1991; Martha and Steve Sanford, *The Guide To Brush–McCoy Pottery,* published by authors, 1992.

**Periodical:** *Our McCoy Matters,* 12704 Lockleven Lane, Woodbridge, VA 22192.

**REPRODUCTION ALERT:** The Nelson McCoy Pottery Co. is currently producing reproductions of their original work. This may add to the confusion about this company's products and will probably affect prices.

Ashtray, cupped hands, yellow, 1941 . **15.00**
Ball Jug, yellow, unmarked, 1950s .... **20.00**
Bank
- Dog and Barrel .... **35.00**
- Savings .... **27.00**
- Seaman's Savings, sailor with sea bag **50.00**

Basket
- Basketweave, green and white ext., white int., marked "McCoy USA," 1957 .... **25.00**
- Oak Leaves and Acorns, marked "McCoy USA," 1952 .... **30.00**

Bird feeder, hanging, brown, 1975 .... **12.00**
Bookends, pr, lily, marked "McCoy Made in USA," 1948 .... **50.00**
Compote, Garden Club, coral, marked "McCoy USA," 1957 .... **12.00**
Console Bowl, leaf, brown, 1960s .... **10.00**

Cookie Jar
- Apple, red .... **42.00**
- Cookie Stove, black .... **22.00**
- Dalmatian .... **425.00**
- Duck, yellow, shortbill, 1976 .... **60.00**
- Happy Face, orig box .... **45.00**
- Indian Head, commemorative issue . **195.00**
- Lamb, basketweave base .... **45.00**
- Little Miss Muffet .... **65.00**
- Mother Goose .... **98.00**
- Mr & Mrs Owl .... **160.00**
- Nabisco .... **125.00**
- Nursery Rhymes .... **65.00**
- Pineapple .... **90.00**
- Puppy with sign .... **50.00**
- Raggedy Ann .... **90.00**
- Stump, frog finial .... **38.00**
- Touring Car .... **75.00**

Crab Baking Set, set of six dishes, orig box .... **30.00**

Creamer, sitting dog, green, 1950s .... **28.00**
Flower Bowl, oblong free form, grape cluster, burgundy, marked "McCoy USA," 1954 .... **18.00**
Flowerpot, paneled, slightly flared at top, pink, saucer, marked "McCoy USA," 1959 .... **6.00**
Grease Jar, cabbage head, 1954 .... **35.00**
Hanging Basket
- Early American, marked "McCoy USA," 1967 .... **15.00**
- Ivy Leaves, emb design, green, 1950 **18.00**

Jardiniere
- Leaves, emb, green, blue grapes, 7" h, 7½" w .... **60.00**
- Pine Cone, 6½" h, 7½" w .... **20.00**
- Springwood, marked "McCoy USA," 1961 .... **15.00**

Lamp Base, boots .... **25.00**
Mixing Bowl, jadite
- 6" d .... **12.00**
- 7" d .... **12.00**

Mug
- Davy Crockett, marked "Brush" .... **35.00**
- Stoneware, grape pattern, 1926 .... **110.00**

Pitcher
- Cloverleaves, emb design, yellow, 1948 .... **20.00**
- Elephant, white, marked "NM USA," 1940s .... **45.00**
- Vegetable, transfer dec .... **35.00**

Planter
- Basinet, blue, marked "McCoy" .... **10.00**
- Chinese .... **11.00**
- Duck with umbrella .... **75.00**

- Fish, pink, green fins, and tail, marked "McCoy USA," 1955 .... **40.00**
- Hunting Dog, Sidney Cope design .. **75.00**
- Lamb, blue bow, marked "McCoy USA," 1953 .......... **15.00**
- Pelican, turquoise, marked "NM USA," 1941 .......... **20.00**
- Rooster, gray, marked "McCoy USA," 1951 .......... **18.00**
- Shell .......... **9.00**
- Tulip, double, bird, 10" d, small chip **15.00**
- Village smithy, Sidney Cope design, 1954 .......... **95.00**
- Wishing Well .......... **7.00**

Reamer, green, 8" w, 1948 .......... **40.00**
Spoon Rest, penguin shape, 1953 .... **35.00**
Sprinkler Bottle, turtle .......... **15.00**
Strawberry Jar, Bird of Paradise, brown and beige, #4, 1950 .......... **32.00**

**Strawberry Pot, mottled brown glaze, #3021, 10" w, 7" h, $32.00.**

Tea Set, Pine Cone .......... **40.00**
Vase
- Basket .......... **23.00**
- Blossomtime, two handled, marked "McCoy," 1946 .......... **20.00**
- Cala Lily, marked "McCoy USA," 1947 .......... **20.00**
- Fawn and Cornucopia, brown, marked "McCoy USA" 1954 ..... **25.00**
- Ginger Jar, cobalt blue, marked "NM USA," 1940 .......... **10.00**
- Magnolia, marked "McCoy USA," 1953 .......... **30.00**
- Pitcher .......... **18.00**
- Sunflower, 1954 .......... **30.00**
- Uncle Sam, green .......... **25.00**

Wall Pocket
- Apple, 1953 .......... **35.00**
- Mailbox, blue, marked "McCoy USA," 1951 .......... **45.00**
- Turtles, 5" h .......... **40.00**
- Violin, turquoise, marked "McCoy USA," 1957 .......... **30.00**

# McKEE GLASS

**Collecting Hint:** McKee Glass was mass produced in most colors. Therefore, a collector should avoid chipped or damaged pieces.

**History:** The McKee Glass Company was established in 1843 in Pittsburgh, Pennsylvania. In 1852 they opened a factory to produce pressed glass. In 1888, the factory relocated in Jeannette, Pennsylvania, and began to produce many types of kitchenwares. The factory was among several located there to make Depression era wares. The factory continued until 1951 when it was sold to the Thatcher Manufacturing Co.

The McKee Glass Company produced many types of glass including glass window panes, tumblers, tablewares, Depression glass, milk glass, and bar and utility objects.

McKee named its colors Chalaine Blue, Custard, Seville Yellow, and Skokie Green. They preferred Skokie Green to jadite which was popular with other manufacturers at the time. McKee also made several patterns on these opaque colors, including dots of red, green, and black and red ships. A few items were decaled. Most of the canisters and shakers were lettered in black for the purpose they were made for.

**References:** Gene Florence, *Kitchen Glassware of the Depression Years, Fourth Edition,* , Collector Books, 1990; M'Kee and Brothers, *M'Kee Victorian Glass,* Dover Publications, 1981; Ellen Tischbein Schroy, *Warman's Glass,* Wallace–Homestead, 1992.

**Salt and Pepper Shakers, pr, black, Roman Arch sides, script "S" and "P," range size, 4¼" h, $12.00.**

## KITCHEN WARE

Baker, 7" l, 5" w, oval, Skokie Green . **16.00**
Beer Mug, Bottoms Down, Seville Yellow, handle .......... **120.00**

Bowl
- 4" d, 2¾" h, French Ivory ......... **3.50**
- 6" d, Skokie Green, double scallop . **13.00**

Butter Dish, cov, rect
- Chalaine Blue .................... **75.00**
- Clear top, custard base ............ **20.00**
- Custard .......................... **45.00**
- Seville Yellow ................... **65.00**
- White, plain ..................... **38.00**

Canister, 10 oz, round, custard ...... **16.00**
Egg Beater Bowl, Skokie Green ...... **10.00**
Egg Cup, Skokie Green, ftd .......... **12.00**
Flour Shaker, sq, Skokie Green ....... **25.00**
Grease Jar, cov, Seville Yellow ....... **37.50**
Ice Bucket, transparent green ........ **20.00**
Measuring Cup, two cup
- Clear, Glasbake .................. **32.00**
- Fired On, red .................... **20.00**

Mixing Bowl
- 7" d, Skokie Green, pouring spout .. **15.00**
- 8" d, Hamilton Beach, custard ..... **10.00**

Pepper Shaker, sq, Skokie Green ..... **18.00**
Pitcher, custard, red dots, two cup ... **25.00**
Reamer, juice
- French Ivory ..................... **50.00**
- Seville Yellow ................... **165.00**

Refrigerator Dish, cov, 8 x 5, Skokie Green .......................... **16.00**
Refrigerator Water Dispenser, 11" l, 5" w, 4" h, Skokie Green, orig spigot .. **90.00**
Rolling Pin, Delphite Blue, shaker end **225.00**
Salt Shaker, range, sq, Skokie Green .. **18.00**
Spice Condiment Set, custard, labeled jars, metal lids, orig rack .......... **50.00**
Sugar Shaker, transparent green, bullet shape .......................... **85.00**
Towel Bar, Skokie Green ............ **25.00**
Tumbler, French Ivory, ftd ........... **12.00**

## STEM WARE

Cordial
- Gothic pattern, clear .............. **20.00**
- Rock Crystal pattern, clear ......... **22.50**

Goblet
- French Ivory ..................... **30.00**
- Puritan pattern, pink stem ......... **25.00**
- Queen pattern, amber ............ **25.00**
- Rock Crystal pattern, clear ......... **17.50**
- Star Rosetted pattern, clear ........ **35.00**

Sherbet
- Laurel pattern, Skokie Green ....... **12.00**
- Rock Crystal pattern, clear ......... **10.00**

Tumbler, ftd
- Rock Crystal pattern, clear ......... **20.00**
- Strigil pattern, clear ............... **20.00**

Wine
- Colonial pattern, green ............ **40.00**
- Queen pattern, canary yellow ...... **30.00**
- Rock Crystal pattern, clear ......... **45.00**
- Sunk Buttons pattern, blue ......... **38.00**

# METLOX POTTERY

**Collecting Hints:** The choices of patterns and backstamps is overwhelming. Collectors should concentrate on one specific line and pattern. Among the most popular Poppytrail patterns are California Ivy, Homestead Provincial, and Red Rooster.

The recent cookie jar craze has attracted a number of collectors to Metlox's cookie jar line. Most examples sell with a narrow range. The Little Red Riding Hood jar is an exception, often selling at two to three times the price of other cookie jars.

**History:** In 1921 T. C. Prouty and Willis, his son, founded Proutyline Products, a company designed to develop Prouty's various inventions. In 1922 Prouty built a tile plant in Hermosa Beach to manufacture decorative and standard wall and floor tiles.

Metlox (a contraction of metallic oxide) was established in 1927. Prouty built a modern all steel factory in Manhattan Beach to manufacture outdoor ceramic signs. The Depression impacted strongly on the sign business. When T. C. Prouty died in 1931, Willis reorganized the company and began to produce a line of solid color dinnerware similar to that produced by Bauer. In 1934 the line was fully developed and sold under the Poppytrail trademark. The poppy is the official state flower for California. Fifteen different colors were produced over an eight year period.

Other dinnerware lines produced in the 1930s include Mission Bell, sold exclusively by Sears & Roebuck, Pintoria, based on an English Staffordshire line, and Yorkshire, patterned after Gladding–McBean's Coronado line. Most of these lines did not survive World War II.

In the late 1930s Metlox employed the services of Carl Romanelli, a designer whose work appeared as figurines, miniatures, and Zodiac vases. A line called Modern Masterpieces featured bookends, busts, figural vases, figures, and wallpockets.

During World War II Metlox devoted its manufacturing efforts to the production of machine parts and parts for the B–25 bombers. When the war ended, Metlox returned its attention to the production of dinnerware.

In 1947 Evan K. Shaw, whose American Pottery in Los Angeles had been destroyed by fire, purchased Metlox. Dinnerware production with hand painted patterns accelerated. The California Ivy pattern was introduced in 1946, California Provincial and Homestead Provincial in 1950, Red Rooster in 1955, California Strawberry in 1961, Sculptured Grape in 1963, and Della Robbia in 1965. Bob Allen and Mel Shaw, art directors, introduced a number of new shapes and lines in the 1950s among which are Aztec, California Contempora, California Free Form, California Mobile, and Navajo.

When Vernon Kilns ceased operation in 1958 Metlox bought the trade name and select dinnerware molds. A separate Vernon Ware branch was established. Under the direction of Doug Bothwell the line soon rivaled the Poppytrail patterns.

Artware continued to flourish in the 1950s and 60s. Harrison McIntosh was among the key designers. Two popular lines were American Royal Horses and Nostalgia, scale model antique carriages. Between 1946 and 1956 Metlox made a series of ceramic cartoon characters under license from Walt Disney.

A line of planters designed by Helen Slater and Poppets, doll–like stoneware flower holders, were marketed in the 1960s and 70s. Recent production includes novelty cookie jars and Colorstax, a revival solid color dinnerware pattern.

Management remained in the Shaw family. Evan K. was joined by his two children, Ken and Melinda. Kenneth Avery, Melinda's husband, eventually became plant manager. When Evan K. died in 1980, Kenneth Avery became president. In 1988 Melinda Avery became the guiding force. The company ceased operations in 1989.

**References:** Jack Chipman, *Collector's Encyclopedia of California Pottery*, Collector Books, 1992; Harvey Duke, *The Official Identification and Price Guide to Pottery and Porcelain, Seventh Edition*, House of Collectibles, 1989; Lois Lehner, *Lehner's Encyclopedia of U. S. Marks on Pottery, Porcelain & Clay*, Collector Books, 1988.

**AZTEC.** Poppytrail line.

| Item | Price |
|---|---|
| Bowl, 9½″ d | **18.00** |
| Creamer | **18.00** |
| Fruit Bowl | **10.00** |
| Gravy Boat | **40.00** |
| Platter, 13″ l | **32.00** |
| Soup, dark int. | **8.00** |
| Sugar, cov | **35.00** |

**CALIFORNIA IVY.** Poppytrail line.

| Item | Price |
|---|---|
| Bowl | |
| 5¼″ d | **6.50** |
| 9″ d | **25.00** |
| Coaster | **10.00** |
| Creamer and Sugar, cov | **15.00** |
| Cup and Saucer | **5.40** |
| Demitasse Cup and Saucer | **18.00** |
| Gravy, underplate | **25.00** |
| Pitcher, ice lip | **35.00** |
| Plate | |
| 6″ d | **3.00** |
| 15″ d, chop | **25.00** |
| Salt and Pepper Shakers, pr | **12.00** |

**CALIFORNIA PROVINCIAL.** Poppytrail line.

| Item | Price |
|---|---|
| Bowl, 6″ d | **3.50** |
| Bread Tray | **40.00** |
| Coaster | **12.00** |
| Creamer | **6.00** |
| Cup and Saucer | **8.00** |
| Fruit Bowl, 6″ d | **6.00** |
| Gravy | **15.00** |
| Mug, large | **25.00** |
| Plate | |
| 6″ d, bread and butter | **4.00** |
| 8″ d, salad | **8.00** |
| 10″ d, dinner | **10.00** |
| 12″ d, chop | **18.00** |
| Platter, 13½″ l | **25.00** |
| Salt and Pepper Shakers, pr | **15.00** |
| Saucer | **1.00** |
| Soup, flat, 8½″ d | **7.00** |
| Vegetable Bowl, 10″ d | **20.00** |

**FREE FORM.** Poppytrail line.

| Item | Price |
|---|---|
| Berry Bowl | **9.50** |
| Cup | **10.50** |
| Plate | |
| 6″ d | **4.50** |
| 8″ d | **7.50** |
| 10″ d | **10.50** |
| Platter | **28.00** |
| Soup Bowl, lug handle | **14.00** |

**HOMESTEAD PROVINCIAL.** Poppytrail line.

| Item | Price |
|---|---|
| Bread Tray | **25.00** |
| Casserole, cov, 10″ d | **25.00** |
| Cereal Bowl, handle | **10.00** |
| Coffeepot | **30.00** |
| Creamer and Sugar, cov | **25.00** |
| Cup and Saucer | **8.00** |
| Gravy | **20.00** |
| Jewelry Box | **45.00** |
| Match Holder | **30.00** |
| Mug | **20.00** |
| Plate | |
| 10″ d, dinner | **8.00** |
| 12″ d, chop | **12.00** |
| Platter, 13½″ l | **20.00** |
| Salad Bowl, 11″ d | **22.00** |
| Salt and Pepper Shakers, pr | **15.00** |
| Sprinkling Can | **25.00** |
| Teapot | **28.00** |
| Vegetable Dish | |
| 8½″ l, two part, stick handle | **22.00** |
| 13″ l, three part, handled | **22.00** |
| Wall Pocket | **42.00** |

**NAVAJO.** Poppytrail line.

| | |
|---|---|
| Bowl, 13″ d | **45.00** |
| Butter Dish | **30.00** |
| Creamer and Sugar, cov | **30.00** |
| Gravy, underplate | **30.00** |
| Plate, 12″ d, chop | **30.00** |
| Platter, 11¾″ l | **30.00** |
| Teapot | **50.00** |

**PROVINCIAL FRUIT.** Poppytrail line.

| | |
|---|---|
| Bowl | |
| 5″ d, tab handled | **4.00** |
| 6″ d | **4.00** |
| 7″ d, deep | **8.00** |
| 10″ d | **18.00** |
| Butter Dish | **25.00** |
| Coffeepot | **45.00** |
| Creamer | **7.00** |
| Cup and Saucer | **8.00** |
| Gravy, handled | **12.00** |
| Pepper Shaker | **4.00** |
| Plate | |
| 6½″ d, bread and butter | **4.00** |
| 7¾″ d, salad | **8.00** |
| 10½″ d, dinner | **9.00** |
| Platter, 13½″ l | **18.00** |
| Relish, rect, divided, handled | **12.00** |
| Salt and Pepper Shakers, pr | **7.00** |
| Soup, 8½″ d | **8.00** |
| Vegetable Bowl, 10″ d | **18.00** |

**RED ROOSTER.** Poppytrail line.

| | |
|---|---|
| Butter, cov | **30.00** |
| Canister, flour | **40.00** |
| Cereal Bowl, 7″ d | **12.00** |
| Coffeepot, cov | **40.00** |
| Cup | **8.00** |
| Oil and Vinegar Cruets | **22.00** |
| Pitcher, 6″ h | **40.00** |
| Plate | |
| 7½″ d, salad | **6.00** |
| 10″ d, dinner | **10.00** |
| 12″ d, chop | **13.00** |
| Platter, 13½″ l | **20.00** |
| Salt and Pepper Shakers, pr, handled | **12.00** |
| Sugar, open | **12.00** |
| Vegetable Bowl, 10″ d | **15.00** |

**STRAWBERRY.** Poppytrail line.

| | |
|---|---|
| Bowl | |
| 7″ d | **12.00** |
| 9″ d | **15.00** |
| Creamer | **15.00** |
| Cup and Saucer | **15.00** |
| Plate | |
| 8″ d | **10.00** |
| 10″ d | **15.00** |
| Sugar, cov | **18.00** |

**VINEYARD.** Vernon Ware.

| | |
|---|---|
| Cereal Bowl, 7½″ d | **5.00** |
| Cup and Saucer | **7.00** |
| Plate | |
| 6¼″ d | **4.00** |
| 7½″ d | **6.00** |
| 10½″ d | **7.00** |
| Soup, flat, 8½″ d | **6.00** |

# MILITARIA

**Collecting Hints:** Militaria is any item that was used or relates to the act of warfare. Tools, clothes, weapons, and items that fulfill that requirement are found in many different places and in varying quantities. Saving militaria may be one of the oldest collecting traditions. Militaria collectors tend to have their own special shows and view themselves outside the normal antiques channels. However, they haunt small indoor shows and flea markets in hopes of finding additional materials.

**History:** Wars always have been part of history. Until the mid–19th century, soldiers often had to fill their own needs, including weapons. Even in the 20th century, a soldier's uniform and some of his gear is viewed as his personal property, even though issued by a military agency.

Conquering armed forces made a habit of acquiring souvenirs from their vanquished foes. They brought home their own uniforms and accessories as badges of triumph and service.

**References:** Thomas Berndt, *Standard Catalog of U. S. Military Vehicles: 1940–1965,* Krause Publications, 1993; Ray A. Bows, *Vietnam Military Lore 1959–1973,* Bows & Sons, 1988; Robert Fisch, *Field Equipment of the Infantry 1914–1945,* Greenberg Publishing, 1989; *North South Trader's Civil War Magazine's Civil War Collectors' Price Guide, 5th Edition,* North South Trader, 1991; Norman E. Martinus and Harry L. Rinker, *Warman's Paper,* Wallace–Homestead, 1993; Jack H. Smith, *Military Postcards 1870–1945,* Wallace–Homestead Book Company, 1988; Sydney B. Vernon, *Vernon's Collector's Guide to Orders, Medals, and Decorations,* published by author, 1986.

**Periodicals:** *Military Collector Magazine,* P. O. Box 245, Lyon Station, PA, 19536; *Military Collectors' News,* P. O. Box 702073, Tulsa, OK 74170; *North South Trader,* P.O. Drawer 631, Orange, VA 22960.

**Collectors' Clubs:** American Society of Military Insignia Collectors, 526 Lafayette Ave., Palmerton, PA 18701; Association of American Military Uniform Collectors, P. O. Box 1876, Elyria, OH 44036; Company of Military Historians, North

Main Street, Westbrook, CT 06498; Imperial German Military Collectors Association, 82 Atlantic St., Keyport, NJ 07735.

**Additional Listings:** See World War I, World War II, and *Warman's Antiques And Their Prices* for information about firearms and swords.

## CIVIL WAR

Kepi, Union, brass crossed rifles and 2, torn leather bill and strap .......... **75.00**
Medal, Woman's Relief Corps ........ **15.00**
Pay Voucher, Capt J Wilson, CS, 1864 **50.00**
Print, framed
"Camp Huntington, Rome, NY," 18 x 24", fair condition .............. **80.00**
"Camp Schuyler, Herkimer, NY," 28 x 19", poor condition ........... **55.00**
Roster, "C0. G 20th Regiment NY Cavalry Volunteers," framed, faded, 20 x 24" ........................... **85.00**
Sketch, Pvt Longley, Fredericksburg, 1862 .......................... **140.00**
Tintype, Union soldier .............. **30.00**

**Civil War, envelope, angry eagle, shield hanging from mouth, "Liberty or Death" banner, 34 large stars with state names, $12.50.**

## SPANISH AMERICAN WAR

Bayonet, 45–70 Springfield, scabbard marked "US," frog marked "Rosett" **110.00**
Canteen, steel, canvas cov, marked "US," cov dated 1901 ............ **75.00**
Cartridge Box, 45–70 Springfield, McKeever Pat, leather canvas, loop inserts .......................... **75.00**
Hat, campaign, vented, Banca of Service cord ........................ **120.00**
Haversack, khaki .................. **10.00**
Holster, leather, black, emb, dated 1870 **100.00**
Letter, Lt M Curry, US Army, Philippine Rebellion, May–Sept, 1900, set of 12 **160.00**
Medal, campaign, Philippine, US Army, bronze, red and blue ribbon ....... **150.00**
Poster, "Home Support," 1898 ....... **125.00**

## KOREAN WAR

Ammunition Magazine, 30 round, M1 Carbine, black painted steel ....... **7.00**
Coveralls, tanker's, US, olive green, 9th Div patch, worn ................ **30.00**
Helmet, M1, US, steel, canvas chin strap, liner ..................... **25.00**
Machete, shoulder, taken from Japanese officer, carved handle, tooled leather sheath .......................... **60.00**
Spade, entrenching, folding type, 1952 **15.00**

## VIETNAM WAR

Cigarette Lighter, Zippo, marked "SP/4 L B Parker" ...................... **50.00**
Crossbow, wood and bamboo, Vietnamese ......................... **325.00**
Jungle Fatigues, shirt and trousers, size large, Marshall, marked "US Navy" **250.00**

**Souvenir Program, U.S. Government War Exposition, Lake Front Chicago, Sept. 2–5, 1917, black and white photos, 32 pages, 6 x 9", $15.00.**

## MISCELLANEOUS ITEMS

Cartridge/Belt Plate, brass, eagle and arrows, filled lead back, two rusty wire loops .......................... **25.00**
Catalog
Francis Bannerman Sons, New York, NY, July Wholesale, Export, and Retail Price List, Military Goods Catalogue, 1925, 20 pgs, 8¾ x 11¾" ......................... **25.00**
Harold M Bennett, New York, NY, Carl Zeiss Binoculars and Field Glasses, 1920, 46 pgs, 4¾ x 7" .. **35.00**

Over Hohnson Arms & Cycle, Fitchburg, MA, "Catalog A–29 of Reliable Fire Arms," 1929, 20 pgs, 6 x 9" .......... **22.00**
W Stokes Kirk, Philadelphia, PA, military goods, guns, carbines, rifles, tents, 1929, 64 pgs, 5¼ x 7¼" ... **22.00**

Flag
13 stars, circled, 35 x 56", all applied stitching, bunting .......... **40.00**
48 stars, 24 x 34", applied stitching . **20.00**

Photograph, 9 x 15", "Camp McQuade Saratoga Sprigs, 1857," named officers, men, cannons, women, and horses .......... **120.00**

# MILK BOTTLES

**Collecting Hints:** Many factors influence the price—condition of the bottle, who is selling, the part of the country in which the sale is transacted, and the amount of desire a buyer has for the bottle. Every bottle does not have universal appeal. A sale of a bottle in one area does not mean that it would bring the same amount in another locale. For example, a rare Vermont pyro pint would be looked upon as only another "pint" in Texas.

A general trend indicates the growing popularity for pyroglaze (painted bottles) over embossed bottles. Pyro bottles display better at home or at shows.

**History:** Hervey Thatcher is recognized as the father of the glass milk bottle. By the early 1880s glass milk bottles appeared in New York and New Jersey. A. V. Whiteman had a milk bottle patent as early as 1880. Patents reveal much about early milk bottle shape and manufacture. Not all patentees were manufacturers. Many individuals engaged others to produce bottles under their patents.

The Golden Age of the glass milk bottle is 1910 to 1950. Leading manufacturers include Lamb Glass Co. (Mt. Vernon, Ohio), Liberty Glass Co. (Sapulpa, Oklahoma), Owens–Illinois Glass Co. (Toledo, Ohio), and Thatcher Glass Co. (New York).

Milk bottles can be found in the following sizes: gill (quarter pint), half pint, 10 ounces (third quart), pint, quart, half gallon (two quart), and gallon.

Paper cartons first appeared in the early 1920s and 30s and achieved popularity after 1950. The late 1950s witnessed the arrival of the plastic bottle. A few dairies still use glass bottles today, but the era has essentially ended.

**References:** Don Lord, *California Milks*, published by author; John Tutton, *Udder Delight: A Guide To Collecting Milk Bottles and Related Items*, published by author, 1980.

**Periodical:** *The Udder Collectibles,* HC73 Box 1, Smithville Flats, NY 13841.

**Collectors' Club:** National Association of Milk Bottles Collectors, Inc., 4 Ox Bow Road, Westport, CT 06880.

**Museums:** The Farmers Museum, Cooperstown, NY; Southwest Dairy Museum, Arlington, TX; Billings Farm Museum, Woodstock, VT.

**Half Pint, square, Dairylea, pyro-glazed red and black Hopalong Cassidy illus, 5½" h, $30.00.**

Half Pint
Embossed, round
Brookside Dairies, Inc, Waterbury, CT, First National Stores .......... **20.00**
Dairyland Creamery, Coos Bay, OR, Pasteurized Milk and Cream **25.00**
Lackawanna Dairy Co, 420 Electric Avenue, Lackawanna, NY ..... **14.00**
Pyro–glazed, round, Carpenters Dairy, Springvale, ME, orange ... **12.00**
Pyro–glazed, square, Korters Pasteurized Milk, Moscow, ID, yellow .. **16.00**

Pint
Embossed, round
American Oyster Co, Providence, RI, AO logo both sides .......... **27.50**
Chestnut Farms Dairy, Washington, DC, seal and ribbon on reverse, ribbed neck .......... **12.00**
Coo's Bay Ice & Cold Storage Co, Marshfield, OR .......... **27.50**
Our Own Dairies, Inc, Los Angeles, six point star is slug plate ...... **20.00**
Racy Cream Co, Knoxville, TN, bowling pin bottle .......... **24.00**
Pyro–glazed, tall, round
Hunts Dairy, Skowhegan, ME, Drink More Milk for Health, red **15.00**
Litchfield Dairy Association, Litchfield, MI, Use Litchfield Butter, black and orange .......... **12.00**
Mountain Lily Dairy, Alturas, CA,

mountain scene illus on front, dairy farm illus on reverse, green **24.00**
T & M Dairy, Hanover, NM, bowl of ice cream, arrow, and target illus, T & M Ice Cream Really Hits the Spot, brown .......... **16.00**
Valley Dairy, Yerington, NV, Drink Milk for Health, maroon ...... **27.50**
Vons Dairy Farm, Monroe, MI, dairy farm illus, Fresh from the Farm, red and blue ........... **14.00**

Quart

Embossed, cream–top, round
Bartholomay Co, 24, Rochester, NY ........................ **16.00**
Cheyenne Creamery, Cheyenne, WY ....................... **38.00**
Meadow Gold ................. **30.00**
Round Top Farms, Damariscotta, ME ......................... **24.00**

Embossed, tall, round
Blue Grass Dairy, Lawrence Gallenstein, Maysville, KY .......... **24.00**
Connors Dairy, Wilmington, DE, large diagonal script .......... **34.00**
Harding Dairy, Magna, UT ...... **32.00**
Illinois Dairy, Pasteurized, Peoria, IL ......................... **20.00**
Indian Hill Farm, Greenville, ME . **30.00**
K–C Dairy Inc, Kingsport, TN, beaded neck ................. **16.00**
Lone Star Creamery Company, Houston, TX, boy's head and Honey Boy Ice Cream/Gee It's Good emb on shoulder, star, ribbed neck ................. **38.00**
Newfair Dairy, Honolulu, diagonal script, ribbed neck ........... **75.00**
Simmons Dairy, Vernon Center, NY **30.00**

Pyro–glazed, cream–top, round
Cloverleaf Store Bottle, Blue Ribbon Farms, Stockton, CA, grocer illus, Buy Milk from your Careful and Courteous Grocer, red .... **38.00**
Producers Dairy, pasteurization/temperature scale illus, No Substitution for Quality, black ..... **24.00**

Pyro–glazed, tall, round
Almhurst Dairy, Westwood 83, Denver, CO, cow kicking up heels illus, orange ............ **32.00**
Dolly Madison Dairy Products, Denver, CO, Mrs Madison eating ice cream illus, The Highest Peak of Quality, red ............... **27.50**
Forest Dairy Co, Kansas City, MO, child holding bottle illus, Yours for Health/They Need the Best, black ....................... **30.00**
Home Owned Dairies, Inc, Salt Lake City, UT, child illus and Building America in shield on front, milkman illus on reverse, red ......................... **35.00**
JA Kelso & Son, Boscawen, NH, dairy cow illus, Pure Ayrshire Milk/Clearbrook Farm, black ... **30.00**
Markwell Milk & Ice Cream, Pasteurized, Sulphur, OK, housewife cooking meal illus, Everything is Better with Butter/Enrich your Favorite Dishes with Natural Vitamins, orange .......... **32.00**
Michigan State College Creamery, M Circle logo on side, dairy products list on reverse, green . **55.00**
Model Dairy, Pueblo, CO, dairy barn illus, Golden Quality Ice Cream, green ................ **27.50**
Modern Dairy, Fallon, NV, dairy farm and cows illus and Direct from Farm to You on front, crossing guard illus and Be Careful on reverse, green ............... **42.00**
Shadow Brook Dairy, Tunkhannock, PA, dairy barn and silo illus, maroon ................. **17.50**
Stedland Jersey Farms, Grade A Pasteurized Milk, Memphis, TN, dairy farm and milking parlor illus, orange .................. **27.50**

War Slogan, pyro–glazed, tall, round
Braden's Milk, It's Pasteurized, US map, stars, and Statue of Liberty illus, America is a Great Place to Live, Let's Keep it that Way, red **55.00**
Emmett's Dairy, Central, NM, milkman milking cow illus, We're All Pulling for Uncle Sam/Milk Plays a Vital Part in Maintaining the Health of Our Armed Forces and Defense Workers, orange ...... **75.00**
Mullan Store Bottle, 10 Cents Deposit, arc welder illus, America at Work/Our Army is Fighting for Us/Let Us Work for Them, yellow **48.00**
Producers Dairy, fighter plane illus, stars between letters VIM, Keep 'Em Flying and V for Victory/M for Milk, orange .............. **75.00**
Valley Gold, Albuquerque's Favorite Milk, milkman delivering milk illus, To Save our Freedom We Must Save our Materials/America Saves/Save this Bottle and Return to Dairy, red ................. **45.00**

# MODEL KITS

**Collecting Hints:** Model kits, assembled or unassembled, are one of the hot collectibles of the 1990s. Even assembled examples, provided they are done well, have value.

In many cases, a kit's value is centered more on the character or object it represents than on the kit itself. The high value of monster related kits is tied directly to the current monster collecting craze. When kit prices are craze related, a portion of the value is speculative.

Box art can influence a kit's value. When individual boxes sell in the $40 to $100 range, it becomes clear that they are treated as "objet d'art," a dangerous pricing trend. The value of the box is easily understood when you place an assembled model beside the lid. All too often, it is the box that is more exciting.

**History:** The plastic scale model kit originated in England in the mid–1930s with the manufacture of 1/72 Frog Penguin kits. The concept caught on during World War II when scale models were used in identification training. After the war companies such as Empire Plastics, Hawk, Lindberg, Renwal, and Varney introduced plastic model kits into the American market. The 1950s witnessed the arrival of Aurora and Monogram in the United States, Airfix in the United Kingdom, Heller in France, and Hasegawa and Marusan in Japan.

The 1960s was the "golden" age of the plastic kit model. Kits featured greater detail and accuracy. Three scale sizes dominated 1/48, 1/72, and 1/144. The oil crisis in the 1970s caused a temporary set back in the industry.

A revival of interest in plastic scale model kits occurred in the late 1980s. At the same time, collector interest began to develop. The initial collecting focus was on automobile model kits from the 1950s and early 1960s. By the end of the 1980s interest had shifted to character and monster kits.

**References:** Paul A. Bender, *1990 Model Car Promotional and Kit Guide*, Brasilia Press, 1990; Bill Bruegman, *Aurora: History and Price Guide*, Cap'n Penny Productions, 1992; C & C Collectibles, *Fantasies in Plastic: Directory of Old and New Model Car Kits, Promotionals, and Resin Cast Bodies*, C & C Collectibles, 1991; Gordy Dutt, *Aurora: A Collection of Classic Instruction Sheets, Vol. 1, Figures*, published by author, 1992.

**Periodicals:** *Kit Builders and Glue Sniffers*, Box 201, Sharon Center, OH 44274; *Model and Toy Collector*, 137 Casterton Avenue, Akron, OH 44303.

**Collectors' Club:** Society for the Preservation and Encouragement of Scale Model Kit, 3213 Hardy Drive, Edmond, OK 73013.

Alfred E Neuman, MADD, Aurora, #802, 1965 .......... **225.00**
American Astronaut, Aurora, #409, 1967 .......... **60.00**
American Buffalo, Aurora, #402, 1964 **20.00**

**Batman, Aurora, Kit No. 467–149, 1964, unassembled, orig instruction sheet and box, $175.00.**

Aston Martin, James Bond, Airfix, #823, 1965 .......... **175.00**
Black Fury, Aurora, #400, 1958 ..... **25.00**
Bride of Frankesntein, Horizon, 1988 . **35.00**
Captain Action, Aurora, #480, 1966 . **240.00**
Castro, Born Losers, Parks, 1965 ..... **125.00**
Charlie's Angels Van, Revell, 1977 ... **15.00**
Cro Magnon Man, Aurora, #730, 1971 **20.00**
Daddy the Suburbanite, Weird–Ohs, Hawk, 1963 .......... **65.00**
Deputy Sheriff, Pyro, 1956 .......... **40.00**
Dracula, Aurora, Monsters of the Movies, #656, 1975 .......... **150.00**
Drag–u–la, Munsters, AMT, 1965 .... **200.00**
Dr Jekyll, Aurora, Glow Kit, #482, 1969 .......... **85.00**
Dr Zira, Planet of the Apes, Addar, #105, 1974 .......... **25.00**
Dutch Girl, Aurora, #414, 1957 ..... **20.00**
Flintstones Rock Crusher, AMT, #487, 1974 .......... **50.00**
Flipper and Sandy, Revell, 1968 ...... **80.00**
George Harrison, Revell, 1965 ....... **120.00**
Green Beret, Aurora, #413, 1966 .... **125.00**
Hulk, Aurora, Comic Scenes, #184, 1974 .......... **75.00**
Indian Warrior, Pyro, 1960 .......... **35.00**
Invisible Man, Horizon, 1988 ........ **25.00**
James Bond, Aurora, #414, 1966 .... **275.00**
Jesse James, Aurora, #408, 1966 ..... **150.00**
King Arthur of Camelot, Aurora, #825, 1967 .......... **65.00**
Mad Barber, Aurora, #455, 1972 .... **125.00**
Mars Probe Space Station, Lindberg, 1969 .......... **70.00**
Monkeemobile, Airfix, 1967 ......... **240.00**
Mr Spock, AMT, #956, large box, 1973 **125.00**
Penguin, Aurora, #416, 1967 ....... **400.00**
Sonny & Cher Mustang, AMT ........ **250.00**
Space Taxi, Monogram, 1959 ........ **25.00**

Steel Plunkers, Frantics, Hawk, 1965 . **30.00**
Sunbeam Car, Get Smart, AMT, 1968 . **250.00**
Susie Whoozis, Aurora, #210, 1966 .. **65.00**
Tarzan, Comic Series, Aurora, #181, 1974 .......... **30.00**
Tonto, Aurora, #809, 1967 .......... **125.00**
Wacky Woodie, Krazy Kar Kustom Kit, AMT, 1968 .......... **70.00**
Willie Mays, Aurora, #860, 1965 .... **250.00**
Zorro, Aurora, #801, 1965 .......... **225.00**

# MONSTERS

**Collecting Hints:** This is a category rampant with speculative fever. Prices rise and fall rapidly depending on the momentary popularity of a figure or family group. Study the market and its prices carefully before becoming a participant.

Stress condition and completeness. Do not buy any item in less than fine condition. Check carefully to make certain that all parts or elements are present for whatever you buy.

Since the material in this category is of recent origin, no one is certain how much has survived. Hoards are not uncommon. It is possible to find examples at garage sales. It pays to shop around before paying a high price.

While an excellent collection of two dimensional material, e.g., comic books, magazines, posters, etc., can be assembled, stress three dimensional material. Several other crazes, e.g., model kit collecting, cross over into monster collecting, thus adding to price confusion.

**History:** Collecting monster related material began in the late 1980s as a generation looked back nostalgically on the monster television shows of the 1960s, e.g., Addams Family, Dark Shadows, and the Munsters, and the spectacular monster and horror movies of the 1960s and 1970s. Fueling the fire was a group of Japanese collectors who were raiding the American market for material relating to Japanese monster epics featuring reptile monsters such as Godzilla.

It did not take long for collectors to seek the historic roots for their post–World War II monsters. A collecting revival started for Frankenstein, King Kong, and Mummy material. Contemporary items featuring these characters also appeared.

**References:** Ted Hake, *Hake's Guide To TV Collectibles,* Wallace–Homestead Book Company, 1990; Carol Markowski and Bill Sikora, *Tomart's Price Guide To Action Figure Collectibles, Revised Edition,* Tomart Publications, 1992.

## ADDAMS FAMILY

Book, *The Addams Family,* Pyramid Publications Inc, 1965 Filmways TV Productions Inc, paperback, 4 x 7" . **20.00**
Costume, Morticia, molded plastic mask, one piece fabric outfit, orig box, Ben Cooper, copyright 1965 Filmways TV Productions, Inc ...... **75.00**
Figure, 5½" h, Lurch, hard plastic body, soft molded vinyl head, Remco, copyright 1964 Filmways TV Productions, Inc .......... **75.00**
Lunch Box, metal, color illus, 6½" h green plastic thermos, King–Seeley copyright 1974 Hanna–Barbera Productions .......... **75.00**
Puzzle, The Addams Family Mystery Jigsaw Puzzle, titled "Ghost At Large," 14 x 24", orig box, Milton Bradley, copyright 1965 Filmways TV Productions Inc .......... **75.00**
Record, 33⅓ rpm, RCA Victor label, six orig music themes, 12¼" cardboard album with full color family photo, 1965 copyright .......... **22.00**

## DRACULA

Doll, 8" h, glow–in–the–dark eyes, removable cape, marked "Copyright Mego 1974" .......... **25.00**
Model Kit, orig box and instruction sheet, assembled, Aurora, 1964 .... **250.00**
Paint Set, Dracula Oil Painting By Numbers, 12 x 16" canvas panel, 14 oil paints, paint brush, orig box, Hasbro, 1963 Universal Pictures Corp copyright .......... **100.00**
Puzzle, 200 pcs, American Publishing Corp, 1974 copyright, 5½" h cardboard and tin canister .......... **15.00**

## FRANKENSTEIN

Costume, plastic mask, fabric one piece suit, orig box, Ben Cooper, Universal Pictures copyright 1960s .......... **50.00**
Figure, Official Universal Studios Frankenstein, 8" h, plastic, poseable, orig box, Remco copyright 1980 Universal City Studios Inc .......... **22.00**
Glass, 6½" h, clear, purple, black, and green illus, copyright Universal Pictures Co Inc, late 1960s .......... **40.00**
Notebook, 10 x 11", three ring binder, vinyl, black, full color illus, late 1960s .......... **50.00**
Soaky Bottle, 10" h, plastic, Colgate–Palmolive Co, 1960s .......... **25.00**

## GODZILLA

Costume, plastic mask, one piece suit with vinyl top and synthetic bottom, orig box, Ben Cooper, copyright 1978 Toho Co Ltd .......... **25.00**

**Godzilla, model kit, Aurora, #149, 1964, $425.00.**

Figure, 18" h, plastic, dark green, hand fires dart, movable legs and arms, copyright 1977, Mattel ............ **125.00**
Game, Godzilla Game, 18½ x 19" playing board, orig box, Ideal, copyright 1963 .......................... **100.00**
Model, 8½" h, olive green, forest green fins, red accents, assembled and painted, Aurora, 1964 ........... **75.00**
Puzzle, titled "City Rampage," Godzilla breathing fire, orig box, HG Toys, copyright 1978 Toho Co Ltd ....... **15.00**
View Master Reel, set of 3, booklet, copyright 1978 Toho Co Ltd ....... **20.00**

## KING KONG

Bank
7½" h, plastic, black, red and white accents, marked "Japan," copyright 1953 S & O Merchandise Co .... **50.00**
16" h, hollow molded plastic, black, red and white accents, A J Renzi Corp, c1970 .................. **20.00**
Bubble Gum Card, Donruss, 1965, color puzzle back .................. **1.25**
Game, King Kong Game, unused, sealed box, Ideal, copyright 1976 Dino De Laurentis Corp .......... **25.00**
Lunch Box, metal, color illus, 6½" h light blue thermos, dark blue plastic cup, King–Seeley copyright 1977 Dino De Laurentis Corp .......... **50.00**
Model, 9" h, glossy dark brown, red and white accents, assembled and painted, Aurora, 1964 ........... **75.00**
Mug, 3½" h, plastic, white, color illus, Deka copyright 1976 Dino De Laurentis Corp ..................... **12.00**
Poster, movie, 24 x 28", stiff paper, 1963 Universal Pictures ................ **50.00**
Puzzle, titled "Python," King Kong and gigantic python illus, orig box, HG Toys, copyright 1976 Dino De Laurentis .......................... **15.00**

## MISCELLANEOUS

Bagatelle, Haunted Castle, hard plastic cov, tin litho bottom, bottom panel illus of monsters, skeleton, ghost, and haunted house, copyright 1972 Steven Mfg Co .................... **50.00**
Book
*Monsters,* Wonder Book, 1965, 48 pages, 8¼ x 11" .............. **25.00**
*Zacherly For President,* McCauley Co Publishers, 1960, 80 pages ...... **15.00**
Card Game, Monster Oil Maid, 39 cards, instruction card, orig box, Milton Bradley, 1964 ................ **50.00**
Eye Glasses, 6" l, molded plastic, green, black hair, one lens vampire, other Frankenstein type monster, 1960–70 **20.00**
Figure, 3" h, Cyclops, plastic, Palmer, 1962 .......................... **52.00**
Game, Mystic Skull, The Game Of VooDoo, orig box, Ideal, copyright 1965 .......................... **75.00**
Glass, 5" h, Friendly Freddy Fright, blue and orange image and lettering, 1960–70 ........................ **15.00**
Magazine
*Box Office,* March 6, 1943, Frankenstein Meets Wolfman ad ......... **40.00**
*Theater Art,* November, 1950, Vol 34, #11, Boris Karloff cov, 8½ x 11" . **22.00**
Mask, Cousin Eerie, soft rubber, Warren Publications, late 1960s ........... **75.00**
Model Kit
Gruesome Goodies, orig box, Aurora, 1971, unused .................. **75.00**
The Strange Changing Vampire, orig box, MPC, 1970s .............. **25.00**
Necklace, black vinyl necklace, molded plastic monster head, orig display bag with header card, 1970s .......... **25.00**
Nodder, 6" h, Phantom of the Opera, 1963 .......................... **80.00**
Poster
Advertising, 13 x 22", cardboard, Ghost Basketball Game adv, "Played In Entire Darkness/Firey Balls Floating In Air/Local Ghosts Come to Life" text, four illus, 1960s **25.00**
Movie, 27 x 41", *The Hairy Ape,* Susan Hayward and William Bendix, Film Classics Inc, 1944 ......... **25.00**
Toy
Candlemaking Set, Famous Monsters Candlemaking Set, plastic molds, orig box and instructions, Rapco, 1974 Universal Pictures copyright **30.00**

Fright Factory Maker–Pak, seven metal molds, orig box, instruction sheet and accessories, Mattel Inc, copyright 1966 ............... **100.00**
Triple Thingmaker, metal Thingmaker, fourteen molds, paint, flocking, handle, and cooling tray, instructions, two small color catalogs, Mattel Inc, copyright 1968 .. **75.00**

Trading Card, set of 8, monster cards and action flasher screen, 5 x 8½" blister pack, Knight Toy and Novelty Inc, 1960s ..................... **50.00**

View Master Reel, *Battle of the Monsters from the Animal World,* set of 3, Warner Bros Pictures, copyright 1956 .. **25.00**

Vomit Bag, *Mark of the Devil,* photo and text "This Vomit Bag And The Price Of One Admission Will Enable You To See . . . The First Film Rated V For Violence" and "Guaranteed To Upset Your Stomach," copyright Hallmark Releasing Corp, 1960s ........... **15.00**

## MUMMY

Magazine, *Weekly Film Review,* December 15, 1932, Vol 22, #3, *The Mummy* and Boris Karloff ad, 9¼ x 12½" ......................... **45.00**

Model Kit, unassembled, MIB, Aurora, 1963 .......................... **300.00**

Puzzle, jigsaw, orig box, Jaymar, 1963 **130.00**

Soaky Bottle, 10" h, soft plastic body, hard plastic head, white body, green head, red accents, 1960s .......... **75.00**

## MUNSTERS

Book, *The Munsters and the Great Camera Caper,* Whitman, 1965, 212 pages, hard cover, 5½ x 8" ........ **15.00**

Doll

8" h, Lily Munster, plastic and vinyl, Ideal tag, copyright 1965 ........ **100.00**
8½" h, Herman, plastic and vinyl, Ideal tag, copyright 1965 ........ **125.00**

Game, The Munster Card Game, 42 cards, eight plastic markers, 14 x 19½" paper playing board, orig box, Milton Bradley, copyright 1964 Kayro–Vue Productions ........... **50.00**

Puppet, 12" h, Herman, molded vinyl face and hands, fabric body, voice box, orig tag, Mattel, 1964 Kayro–Vue Productions ................ **100.00**

Sticker Book, Whitman, 1965, 8½ x 12" **68.00**

## WOLFMAN

Comic Book, *The Wolfman,* #1, June–August, 1963, Dell Publishing Co .. **20.00**

Figure, 4" h, plastic, brown, movable head, blue cloth pants, 1960s ...... **18.00**

Model Kit, orig box, instruction sheet, Aurora, Canadian issue, copyright 1964 .......................... **200.00**

Soaky Bottle, 10" h, soft plastic body, hard plastic head, metallic body, 1960s ......................... **75.00**

# MORGANTOWN GLASS

**Collecting Hints:** Two well known lines of Morgantown Glass are recognized by most glass collectors today—the much sought after etching known as #758 Sunrise Medallion, and the #7643 Golf Ball Stem Line. #758 was originally identified as "Nymph" when Economy introduced it in 1928. By 1931, the Morgantown front office had renamed it "Sunrise Medallion." Recent publications erred in labeling it a "dancing girl." Upon careful study of the medallion, you can see she is poised on one tip–toe, musically saluting the dawn with her horn. #7643 Golf Ball, the second well known line, was patented in 1928 and production commenced immediately and continued throughout the entire history of the company until the final closing in 1971. More Golf Ball is found on the market today than any other Morgantown product. It is plentiful and readily available in most markets.

**History:** The Morgantown Glass Works, Morgantown, West Virginia, was founded in 1899. Reorganized in 1903, it operated as the Economy Tumbler Company for twenty years. In 1923, the word "Tumbler" was dropped from the corporate title and the company was then known as The Economy Glass Company until reversion to its original name, Morgantown Glass Works, Inc., in 1929. The company name held until its first closing in 1937. In 1939, the factory was reopened under the aegis of a guild of glassworkers and operated from that time, until its final closing, as the Morgantown Glassware Guild. Purchased by Fostoria in 1965, the factory operated as a subsidiary of the Moundsville based parent company until 1971 when Fostoria opted to terminate production of glass at the Morgantown facility. Today, collectors use the generic term, Morgantown Glass, to include all periods of production from 1899 to 1971.

Morgantown was a 1920s leader in the manufacture of colorful wares for table and ornamental use in American homes. The company pioneered the process of iridization on glass as well as gold, silver, and platinum encrustation of patterns. They enhanced crystal offerings with contrasting handle and foot of India Black, Spanish Red (ruby), and Ritz Blue (cobalt blue) as well as pastel colors for which they are famous. They conceived the use of contrasting shades of fired enamel to add color to their etchings. They were the only American company to use a chromatic silk–screen printing process on glass, their two most famous and collectible designs being Queen Louise and Manchester Pheasant.

The company is justly famous for ornamental "open stems" produced during the late 1920s. Open stems are stems separated to form an open design midway between the bowl and foot, e.g., an open square, a "Y", and two "diamond" type designs. Many of these open stems were purchased and decorated by Dorothy C. Thorpe in her California studio, and her signed open stems command high prices from today's collectors. Morgantown also produced figural stems for commercial clients such as Koscherak Bros, and Marks & Rosenfeld. Chanticleer (rooster) and Mai Tai (Polynesian bis) cocktails are two of the most popular figurals collected today.

Morgantown is best known for its diversity of design in stemware patterns as well as the use of their four patented optics, Festoon, Palm, Peacock, and Pineapple. These designs were used to embellish stems, jugs, bowls, liquor sets, guest sets, salvers, ivy and witch balls, vases, and smoking items.

**References:** Gene Florence, *Elegant Glassware of the Depression Era, Revised Fifth Edition,* Collector Books, 1993; Jerry Gallagher, *Handbook of Old Morgantown Glass,* Morgantown Collectors of America, Inc., 1993; Jerry Gallagher, *Old Morgantown Catalogue of Glassware, 1931,* Morgantown Collectors of America, Inc., 1970; Ellen Tischbein Schroy, *Warman's Glass,* Wallace–Homestead, 1992.

**Periodical:** *The Morgantown Newscasters,* Morgantown Collectors of America, 420 First Ave., N.W., Plainview, MN 55964.

**Collectors' Clubs:** Morgantown Collectors of America Club, 420 First Ave, N.W., Plainview, MN 55964; Old Morgantown Glass Collectors' Guild, P. O. Box 894, Morgantown, WV 26507.

**Advisor:** Jerry Gallagher.

Bowl, #4355 Janice, 14K Topaz, Carlton/Madrid dec, 13″ d . . . . . . . . . . . **95.00**
Candleholders, pr
#81 Bravo, Thistle, 4½″ h . . . . . . . . . **95.00**
#7643 Golf Ball, Spanish Red and Crystal, two styles . . . . . . . . . . . . . **140.00**
#9931 Florentine, Bristol Blue Opaque, 5½″ h . . . . . . . . . . . . . . . . **65.00**
#9935 Barton, Peach Opaque, 5″ h **70.00**
#9962 Contessa, Steel Blue, 4½″ h . **48.00**
Candy Jar
#14½ Fairway, India Black, Crystal golf ball finial, 22 oz . . . . . . . . . . . **125.00**
#63½ Lorelei, ftd, 8″ h
Burgundy . . . . . . . . . . . . . . . . . . . . . **36.00**
Evergreen, Spiral Optic . . . . . . . . . **45.00**
#86½ Urn, Bristol Blue Opaque, Crystal lid, 6″ h . . . . . . . . . . . . . . . . **35.00**
#7858 Leora, Ritz Blue, Crystal foot and finial, 5½″ h . . . . . . . . . . . . . . . **145.00**
Champagne
#7565 Astrid, Anna Rose, American Beauty etch, 6 oz . . . . . . . . . . . . . . **37.50**
#7606½, Athena, Crystal, black filament stem, Baden etch, 6 oz . . . . **67.50**
#7630 Ballerina, Azure, Elizabeth etch, 6 oz . . . . . . . . . . . . . . . . . . . . **55.00**
#7640 Art Moderne, Crystal, India Black stem . . . . . . . . . . . . . . . . . . . **58.00**
#7643 Golf Ball, 5½ oz
Ritz Blue . . . . . . . . . . . . . . . . . . . . . . **45.00**
Spanish Red . . . . . . . . . . . . . . . . . . **38.00**
Stiegel Green . . . . . . . . . . . . . . . . . **28.00**
#7664 Queen Anne, Aquamarine, Sunrise Medallion etch, 6½ oz . . . **68.00**
#77942 Pygon, Crystal, satin stem, sgd "D. C. Thorpe," 5½ oz . . . . . **135.00**
Cocktail
Chanticleer, Crystal rooster stem and foot, 4 oz
Cobalt Blue bowl . . . . . . . . . . . . . . **78.00**
Pink Champagne bowl . . . . . . . . . . **35.00**
Old Crow, Crystal, 6⅛″ h, 5½ oz . . **70.00**
#7577 Venus, Venetian Green, Palm Optic, 3 oz . . . . . . . . . . . . . . . . . . . . **22.00**
#7638 Avalon, Anna Rose, Peacock Optic, 3½ oz . . . . . . . . . . . . . . . . . . **24.00**
#7643 Golf Ball, 3½ oz
Ritz Blue . . . . . . . . . . . . . . . . . . . . . . **42.00**
Spanish Red . . . . . . . . . . . . . . . . . . **38.00**
Stiegel Green . . . . . . . . . . . . . . . . . **25.00**
#7678 Old English, 3½ oz
Ritz Blue . . . . . . . . . . . . . . . . . . . . . . **42.00**
Spanish Red . . . . . . . . . . . . . . . . . . **38.00**
Stiegel Green . . . . . . . . . . . . . . . . . **28.00**
Compote, #12½ Woodsfield, Crystal, Nanking Blue threaded rim and foot, 12″ d . . . . . . . . . . . . . . . . . . . . . . . . . **165.00**
Cordial
#7643 Golf Ball, Ritz Blue, 1½ oz . **48.00**
#7654 Lorna, Crystal, Nantucket etch, 1½ oz . . . . . . . . . . . . . . . . . . **55.00**
#7668 Galaxy, Crystal, Mayfair etch, 1½ oz . . . . . . . . . . . . . . . . . . . . . . . **38.00**
#7678 Old English, Stiegel Green, 1¾ oz . . . . . . . . . . . . . . . . . . . . . . . **55.00**
Goblet
#7577 Venus, 9 oz
Anna Rose, Palm Optic . . . . . . . . . **38.00**
Nanking Blue, Pillar Optic . . . . . . **67.50**
#7604½ Heirloom, 14K Topaz, Adonis etch, 9 oz . . . . . . . . . . . . . . **58.00**
#7614 Hampton, 9 oz
Crystal, silk screen–color printed Queen Louise design, Anna Rose stem . . . . . . . . . . . . . . . . . . . . . . . **175.00**

**Goblet, Athena, Adonis etching, Venetian Green stem and foot, 9 oz, $95.00.**

Golden Iris (amber) Virginia etch . **50.00**
#7630 Ballerina, Azure, Elizabeth etch, 10 oz .................... **80.00**
#7638 Avalon, Venetian Green, Peacock Optic, 9 oz ............... **37.50**
#7643 Golf Ball, 9 oz
Ritz Blue ...................... **55.00**
Spanish Red .................. **42.00**
Stiegel Green ................. **40.00**
#7678 Old English, 10 oz
Ritz Blue ...................... **58.00**
Spanish Red .................. **55.00**
Stiegel Green ................. **45.00**
#7659 Cynthia, Crystal, Sonoma etch, 10 oz .................... **60.00**
#7644½ Vernon, Meadow Green, Pineapple Optic, 9 oz .......... **50.00**
#7664 Queen Anne, 10 oz
Aquamarine, Sunrise Medallion etch ....................... **85.00**
Crystal, silk screen–color printed Manchester Pheasant design ... **210.00**
#7690 Monroe, Golden Iris (amber), 9 oz ......................... **68.00**
#77842 Morgantown Square, Crystal, flared, 10 oz ............... **195.00**
#77943½ Paragon, Crystal, India Black stem, 5½ oz ............ **80.00**

Ivy Bowl
#7643 Kennon, Ritz Blue, Crystal Golf Ball stem and foot, 4″ h .... **75.00**
#7643 Kimball, Stiegel Green, Crystal Golf Ball stem and foot, 4″ h .. **70.00**

Jug
#37 Barry, Crystal, Anna Rose handle and foot, Palm Optic, 48 oz ..... **260.00**
#1933 Del Rey, El Mexicano Ice, 50 oz ......................... **255.00**
#1933 Ockner, El Mexicano, 54 oz
Hyacinth ...................... **350.00**
Ice ........................... **185.00**
Rose Quartz .................. **325.00**
Seaweed ...................... **225.00**
#1962 Crinkle Line, Amethyst, 64 lemonade tankard ............. **75.00**
#1962 Ockner, Crinkle Line
Amethyst, 54 oz .............. **87.50**
Pink Frosted ................... **165.00**

Plate
#1500 Anna Rose, Bramble Rose etch, luncheon/salad, 8½″ d ..... **32.00**
#7668 Galaxy, Crystal, Sear's Lace Bouquet etch, dessert, 7″ d ...... **20.00**

Sherbet
#1962 Crinkle, 6 oz
Pink ......................... **20.00**
Ruby ......................... **22.50**
#7640 Art Moderne, Ritz Blue, Crystal stem, 5½ oz ............... **65.00**
#7643 Golf Ball, 5½ oz
Ritz Blue ...................... **35.00**
Spanish Red .................. **32.00**
Stiegel Green ................. **24.00**
#7678 Old English, 6½ oz
Ritz Blue ...................... **42.00**
Spanish Red .................. **40.00**
Stiegel Green ................. **32.00**
#7654 Lorna, Crystal, Meadow Green stem, Nantucket etch, 5½ oz **48.00**
#7654½ Legacy, Crystal, silk screen–color printed Manchester Pheasant design, 6½ oz ................ **85.00**
#7690 Monroe, Old Amethyst, Crystal stem, 6 oz .................. **70.00**
#7780 The President's House, Crystal, 6 oz ...................... **15.00**

Torte Plate, #1500 Crystal Hollywood Line, platinum and red band, 14″ d . **220.00**

Tumbler
#1962 Crinkle
Amberina, flat water, 10 oz ...... **68.00**
India Black, flat juice, 6 oz ...... **28.00**
#7643 Golf Ball, 12 oz
Ritz Blue ...................... **48.00**
Spanish Red .................. **40.00**
Stiegel Green ................. **35.00**
#7678 Old English, 13 oz
Ritz Blue ...................... **48.00**
Spanish Red .................. **48.00**
Stiegel Green ................. **45.00**
#7664 Queen Anne, Aquamarine, Elizabeth etch, 11 oz ........... **85.00**
#7668 Galaxy, Crystal, Carlton etch, 9 oz ......................... **22.00**
#7703 Sextette, Ritz Blue/Alabaster Old Bristol, ftd tea, 11 oz ....... **145.00**
#9074 Belton
Golden Iris, Virginia etch, 12 oz . **40.00**
Primrose (Vaseline), Pillar Optic, 9 oz ....................... **95.00**

Vase
#26 Catherine
Anna Rose, Sunrise Medallion etch, bud, 10″ h ................. **365.00**

Azure, Sunrise Medallion etch, bud, 10" h .................. **235.00**
Jade Green, enamel floral dec, bud, crimped rim, 10" h ........... **180.00**
#35½ Electra, Continental Old Amethyst, Crystal handles and foot, 10" h .............................. **345.00**
#53 Serenade, bud, 10" h
Opaque Yellow ................ **240.00**
Spanish Red ................... **135.00**
Venetian Green, Tinker Bell etch . **295.00**
#54 Media, Golden Iris, Pillar Optic, bud, 10" h .................... **130.00**
#1933 El Mexicano, Seaweed, 6½" h **80.00**
Water Set, #20069 Melon, Alabaster, Ritz Blue trim, jug and six 11 oz tumblers, price for set ................ **650.00**
Wine
#7643 Golf Ball, 2½ oz
Ritz Blue ...................... **55.00**
Spanish Red .................. **50.00**
Stiegel Green .................. **50.00**
#7678 Old English, 3½ oz
Ritz Blue ...................... **55.00**
Spanish Red .................. **50.00**
Stiegel Green .................. **45.00**
#7690 Monroe, 3 oz
Golden Iris .................... **75.00**
Old Amethyst .................. **95.00**
Ritz Blue ...................... **80.00**
Spanish Red .................. **80.00**

# MORTON POTTERIES

**Collecting Hints:** The potteries of Morton, Illinois, used local clay until 1940. The clay fired out to a golden ecru color which is quite easy to recognize. After 1940 southern and eastern clays were shipped to Morton. These clays fired out white. Thus, later period wares are sharply distinguished from the earlier wares.

Few pieces were marked by the potteries. Incised and raised marks for the Morton Pottery Works, the Cliftwood Art Potteries, Inc., and the Morton Pottery Company do surface at times. The Cliftwood, Midwest, Morton Pottery Company, and American Art Pottery all used paper labels in limited amounts. Some of these have survived, and collectors do find them.

Glazes from the early period, 1877–1920, usually were Rockingham types, both mottled and solid. Yellow ware also was standard during the early period. Occasionally a dark cobalt blue was produced, but this color is rare. Colorful drip glazes and solid colors came into use after 1920.

**History:** Pottery was produced in Morton, Illinois, for 99 years. In 1877 six Rapp brothers, who emigrated from Germany, began the first pottery, Morton Pottery Works. Over the years sons, cousins, and nephews became involved in the production of pottery. The other Morton pottery operations were spin-offs from the original pottery and brothers. When it was taken over in 1915 by second generation Rapps, Morton Pottery Works became the Morton Earthenware Company. Work at that pottery was terminated by World War I.

The Cliftwood Art Potteries, Inc., operated from 1920 to 1940. One of the original founders of the Morton Pottery Works and his four sons organized it. They sold out in 1940, and the operation continued for four more years as the Midwest Potteries, Inc. A disastrous fire brought an end to that operation in March 1944. These two potteries produced figurines, lamps, novelties and vases.

In 1922 the Morton Pottery Company, which had the longest existence of all of the Morton's potteries, was organized by the same brothers who had operated the Morton Earthenware Company. The Morton Pottery Company specialized in beer steins, kitchenwares, and novelty items for chain stores and gift shops. They also produced some of the Vincent Price National Treasures reproductions for Sears Roebuck and Company in the mid-1960s. The Morton Pottery closed in 1976, thus ending the 99 years of pottery production in Morton.

By 1947 the brothers who had operated the Cliftwood Art Potteries, Inc., came back into the pottery business. They established the short-lived American Art Potteries. The American Art Potteries made flower bowls, lamps, planters, some unusual flower frogs, and vases. Their wares were marketed by florists and gift shops. Production at American Art Potteries was halted in 1961. Of all the wares of the Morton potteries, the products of the American Art Potteries are the most elusive.

**Reference:** Doris and Burdell Hall, *Morton's Potteries: 99 Years,* published by authors, 1982.

**Museums:** Illinois State Museum, Springfield, IL; Morton Public Library (permanent exhibit), Morton, IL.

**Advisors:** Doris and Burdell Hall.

## MORTON POTTERY WORKS AND MORTON EARTHENWARE COMPANY, 1877–1917

Baker, 1¾" h, 5½" d, brown Rockingham mottled glaze ............. **35.00**
Coffeepot, 5 pt, brown Rockingham, ornate emb top and bottom ......... **90.00**
Jar, stoneware, Albany slip glaze, marked on side, 2 gal ............. **65.00**
Miniature
Coffeepot, 3" h, brown glaze ...... **75.00**
Pitcher

1¾″ h, bulbous, green glaze ..... **25.00**
3¼″ h, cobalt blue glaze ........ **55.00**
Mixing Bowl, 12½″ d, yellowware, wide white band, narrow blue stripes top and bottom .................. **45.00**
Pie Plate
9″ d, brown Rockingham mottled glaze ......................... **100.00**
11″ d, yellowware ................ **80.00**
Spittoon, 15″ d, scalloped dec top and bottom, brown Rockingham mottled glaze .......................... **55.00**
Teapot, 4½″ h, 1 cup, brown Rockingham glaze
Acorn shape ..................... **30.00**
Pear shape ...................... **35.00**

## CLIFTWOOD ART POTTERIES, INC., 1920–1940

Beer Set, pitcher and six steins, barrel shape, yellow .................... **100.00**
Bookends, pr, 6 x 5 x 3½″, elephant, blue mulberry drip glaze .......... **85.00**
Candlesticks, pr, 11″ h, chocolate drip glaze, sq base .................. **50.00**
Clock, 7″ h, octagonal shape, two inkwells and pen tray in base, chocolate drip glaze ...................... **140.00**
Compote, 6″ h, 8½″ d, four dolphins support bowl, old rose glaze ....... **75.00**
Creamer, 4″ h, 3″ d, chocolate drip glaze .......................... **35.00**
Figurine, 4½″ l, 1½″ w, reclining cat, cobalt blue glaze ................ **25.00**
Flower Insert
Turtle #1, 4″ l, blue–mulberry drip glaze ......................... **12.00**
Turtle #2, 5½″ l, dark green glaze . **12.00**
Lamp
7½″ h, owl on log, yellow ........ **35.00**
12″ h, donut shape, clock base, blue–mulberry drip glaze ............. **125.00**
Wine Decanter, 6½″ h, spherical, molded swirl design, mottled green glaze, matching stopper ........... **25.00**

## MIDWEST POTTERIES, INC., 1940–1944

Figurine
Bear, 6 x 10″, brown spray glaze ... **30.00**
Deer, 12½″ h, Art Deco, antlers, head faces tail, brown, green spray glaze **25.00**
Dog, 6 x 4″, cocker spaniel, black gloss glaze ................... **25.00**
Female Dancer, 8½″ h, Art Deco, white, gold dec ................ **25.00**
Goose, 5¾″ h, long neck, white, yellow dec ....................... **8.00**
Hen, 7″ h, rooster, 8″ h, white, gold painted combs, pr .............. **35.00**
Heron, 12″ h, stylized, blue, green, yellow spray glaze ............. **22.00**
Parrot on Stump, 4½″ h, blue, yellow, brown spray glaze on white ..... **12.00**
Roadrunner, 8″ h, stylized, white, gold dec ...................... **12.00**
Stallion, 10¾″ h, rearing on hind legs, gold ......................... **25.00**
Flower Bowl
7½″ h, two orbs, nude figure, platinum ......................... **35.00**
10″ d, 5½″ h, circular, brown, yellow drip glaze, 2 pcs ............... **16.00**
11″ d, 2½″ deep, flat, matt turquoise **15.00**
Mask, wall type, 18th C English male bust, white, 5 x 4½″, right side view, braided hair, bangs ............... **20.00**
Miniature
Bird, 2″ h, blue .................. **5.00**
Camel, 2½″ h, brown, yellow spray glaze ........................ **7.00**
Goose, 2″ h, white, gold dec ...... **6.00**
Sailboat, 2″ h, light blue .......... **6.00**
Swan, 2½″ h, matt white .......... **5.00**

**Morton Pottery Company, wall pocket, harp, 10″ h, $15.00.**

## MORTON POTTERY COMPANY, 1922–1976

Miniature
Bear, 2½″ h, brown .............. **10.00**
Deer with antlers, 5″ h, white ...... **7.50**
Elephant, trunk over head, gray .... **6.50**
Kangaroo, 2½″ h, burgundy ....... **6.50**
Squirrel, 2½″ h, brown ........... **6.50**
Swordfish, 5″ h, yellow ........... **7.50**
Wren on stump, 7″ h, natural colors **8.50**
Pie Bird, 5″ h, white, multicolored wings and back .................. **22.00**
Pie Duckling, 5″ h, white, pink base and wings .......................... **25.00**
Planter
Art Deco, female bust, broad brim hat, matt white, 7½″ h .......... **30.00**

Cowboy and Cactus, 7″ h, natural colors .......................... **12.00**
Mother Earth Line, natural colors
Apple .......................... **3.00**
Banana .......................... **3.00**
Orange .......................... **3.00**
Pineapple .......................... **5.00**
Plum .......................... **3.00**
Rabbit, 9½″ h
Female with umbrella, pink blouse, egg planter .......................... **12.00**
Male with top hat, blue vest, egg planter .......................... **12.00**
Shoe House Variations, 9½″ h, yellow
Bank, cold paint red roof .......... **20.00**
Lamp, cold paint red roof .......... **25.00**
Planter, green glazed roof .......... **18.00**
Wall Plaque, green glazed roof ..... **12.00**
Vase
6″ h, bud, bulbous, long neck, multicolor .......................... **6.00**
8½″ h, cornucopia on shell base, blue **14.00**
20″ h, cylinder, emb crane and bamboo dec, white .......................... **20.00**
Wall Pocket
6½″ h, teapot, white, red apple dec, red finial .......................... **12.00**
7½″ h, Mary Quite Contrary, red dress, blue apron .......................... **10.00**
8½″ h, parrot on bunch of grapes, natural colors .......................... **18.00**
8¾″ h, violin, two musical notes, white, hp dec, pr .......................... **20.00**
10″ h, harp, white, hp underglaze floral dec .......................... **14.00**
Woodland Glaze Items, yellowware, brown and green spatter over transparent glaze
Coffee Server, 8 cup .......................... **85.00**
Milk Jug, 4½″ h, adv .......................... **80.00**
Pie Plate, 9″ d .......................... **100.00**
Salt and Pepper Shakers, pr, 5″ h ... **110.00**

**American Art Potteries, vase, mottled brown glaze, $18.00.**

## AMERICAN ART POTTERIES, 1947–1961

Bowl
5″ d, 3″ h, inverted umbrella shape, gold bisque, bronze spatter ...... **10.00**
10 x 4 x 2″, octagonal, elongated, green, yellow int. .......................... **8.00**
Compote, 10″ d, 6″ h, ftd, dark green bisque, high gloss spatter .......... **15.00**
Dinnerware
Creamer and Sugar, 3″ h, stylized flowers, blue, peach spray glaze . **18.00**
Demitasse Cup and Saucer, 3″ h, stylized flower on cup, flat blossom on saucer, gray, pink spray glaze .... **14.00**
Sugar, 3″ h, bulbous, handled, blue, gray spray glaze .......................... **10.00**
Doll Part, miniature, 1¼″ h head, hp features, yellow hair, 1½″ arms and legs .......................... **40.00**
Lamp, TV
7 x 10″, conch shell, purple, pink spray glaze .......................... **18.00**
9 x 12″, horse and colt, running, gray, mauve spray glaze .......................... **30.00**
12 x 10″, leopard, crouched on tree limb, black, gray spray glaze .... **25.00**
14 x 6″, panther, slinking position, black spray glaze .......................... **20.00**
Planter
5″ h, 5½″ l, fish, purple, pink spray glaze .......................... **14.00**
6″ h, cowboy boot, blue, pink spray glaze .......................... **12.00**
7″ h, log, applied squirrel figure, gray spray glaze .......................... **15.00**
9½″ h, quail, natural color spray glaze .......................... **22.00**
Vase
8″ h, bud, blue, pink spray glaze ... **8.00**
10½″ h, cornucopia, gold, white int. **10.00**
12½″ h, bulbous, blue, encircled by molded pink blossoms .......... **30.00**
Wall Pocket, 5″ h, tree stump, applied woodpecker, brown spray glaze .... **15.00**

# MOVIE MEMORABILIA

**Collecting Hints:** Collectors tend to focus on the blockbuster hits with *Gone With The Wind* and *Casablanca* among the market leaders. The cartoon image, especially Disney material, also is very popular.

Much of the material is two dimensional. Collectors have just begun to look for three dimensional objects, although the majority of these are star and personality, rather than movie related.

The market went crazy in the mid–1970s when people sought to speculate in movie memorabilia. A self disciplining has taken place with prices falling in the 1980s. The area was compounded further by the large number of reproductions, many made in Europe, which flooded the market.

**History:** The golden age of movie memorabilia was the 1930s and 1940s. The star system had reached its zenith and studios spent elaborate sums promoting their major stars. Initially, movie studios and their public relations firms tightly controlled the distribution of material such as press books, scripts, preview flyers, costumes, props, etc. Copyright has expired on many of these items, and reproductions abound.

The current interest in Hollywood memorabilia can be traced to the pop art craze of the 1960s. Film festivals increased the desire for decorative film–related materials. Collecting movie posters was "hot."

Piracy always has plagued Hollywood and is responsible for the release of many items into the market. Today the home video presents new challenges to the industry.

**References:** Tony Fusco, *The Official Identification and Price Guide To Posters,* House of Collectibles, 1990; John Hegenberger, *Collector's Guide To Movie Memorabilia,* Wallace–Homestead Book Company, 1991; Leslie Halliwell, *The Filmgoer's Companion,* Avon, 1978; Ephraim Katz, *The Film Encyclopedia,* Perigee Books, 1979; Leonard Maltin (ed.), *TV Movies and Video Guide,* New American Library, 1987; John Margolies, *Palaces of Dreams: Movie Theater Postcards,* Bullfinch Press, 1993; Norman E. Martinus and Harry L. Rinker, *Warman's Paper,* Wallace–Homestead, 1993; Patrick McCarver, *Gone With The Wind Collector's Price Guide,* Collector's Originals, 1990; Jay Scarfone and William Stillman, *The Wizard of Oz Collector's Treasury,* Schiffer Publishing, Ltd., 1992; Jon R. Warren, *Warren's Movie Poster Price Guide, 1993 Edition,* Collector's Exchange, 1992; Dian Zillner, *Hollywood Collectibles,* Schiffer Publishing, 1991.

**Periodicals:** *Big Reel,* Route 3, P. O. Box 83, Madison, NC 27025; *Classic Images,* P. O. Box 809, Muscatine, IA 52761; *Hollywood Movie Archives,* P. O. Box 1566, Apple Valley, CA 92307; *Movie Collectors' World,* P. O. Box 309, Fraser, MI 48026; *Nostalgia World,* P. O. Box 231, North Haven, CT 06473.

**Collectors' Club:** Hollywood Studio Collectors Club, Suite 450, 3960 Laurel Canyon Blvd, Studio City, CA 91604.

**See:** Cartoon Characters, Disneyana, Movie Personalities, and Posters.

Advertisement
- *Harvey Girls,* Judy Garland ........ **12.00**
- *Heat's On,* Mae West ............. **12.00**
- *The Chase,* Peter Lorre ............ **12.00**

Almanac, Motion Picture, 1945 ...... **40.00**

Book
- *Gone with the Wind,* Margaret Mitchell, signed by author, June, 1936 **2,750.00**
- *The Emerald City of Oz,* L Frank Baum, illus John R Neill, copyright 1910 ........................ **135.00**
- *The Land of Oz,* L Frank Baum, illus by John R Neill, copyright 1932, dj **65.00**
- *The Wizard of Oz,* illus by Evelyn Copelman, published by Bobbs–Merrill Co, copyright 1944 ...... **35.00**

Booklet, *Ben Hur,* MGM, 1926 ...... **15.00**

Christmas Stocking, *ET,* cotton ....... **15.00**

Cookbook, *Gone With The Wind,* 5½ x 7¼", soft cover, 48 pgs, Pebeco Toothpaste premium, c1939 ....... **40.00**

Cup and Saucer, 20th Century Fox Film Corp, brown and white company logo **20.00**

Display, stand–up, *Ghostbusters* ...... **30.00**

Film, *The King and I,* 16 mm, cinemascope, two tins with show's logo ... **450.00**

Handbill
- *Men Are Not Gods,* Miriam Hopkins, 6 x 9", 1930s ................. **15.00**
- *Spellbound,* Gregory Peck and I Bergman, 8 x 11", 4 pgs ........... **20.00**

Handkerchief, *Gone With The Wind,* 13" sq, Scarlet O'Hara, floral design, yellow, rose, green, black, white, and gold, black diecut foil sticker ...... **55.00**

Legal Files, *Miracle on 34th Street,* 20th C Fox, copy infringement, 1947–48 **45.00**

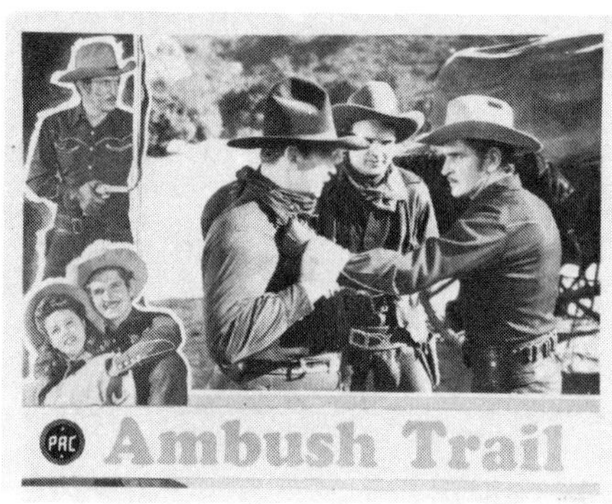


**Lobby Card, *Ambush Trail,* Bob Steele, color photo, 1946, 11 x 14", $15.00.**

Lobby Card
- *Berlin Express,* set of 8, RKO Radio Pictures, 1948 ................. **50.00**
- *Curse of the Living Corpse* ......... **22.00**
- *Horror of Beach* ................. **22.00**
- *Miss Tatlock's Millions,* Robert Stack, Dorothy Wood, 1948, framed .... **40.00**
- *Parade of Comedy,* 1964 .......... **25.00**

*Rawhide Rangers,* Johnny Mack Brown, Universal . . . . . . . . . . . . . **15.00**
*Reap Wild Wind,* octopus scene . . . . **15.00**
*Target,* Tim Holt, RKO, 1952 . . . . . . **18.00**
*Teenage Monster* . . . . . . . . . . . . . . . . . **20.00**
*Titanic #8* . . . . . . . . . . . . . . . . . . . . . . **15.00**
*Yogi Bear,* 1964 . . . . . . . . . . . . . . . . . **20.00**

Magazine
Everyday Science and Mechanics, Feb, 1934, full color cov art and article, *The Invisible Man,* 8½ x 11½", 64 pgs . . . . . . . . . . . . . . . . . **25.00**
Private Lives of Movie Stars, 8½ x 11", Arco Publishing Co, 50 pgs, 1945 . . . . . . . . . . . . . . . . . . . . . . . . **20.00**
Science and Invention Magazine, May, 1925, full color cov art and article, *The Lost World,* 8½ x 11½", 104 pgs . . . . . . . . . . . . . . . . . . . . . . **30.00**

Movie Folder, Son of the Sheik, Valentino . . . . . . . . . . . . . . . . . . . . . . . . . . **22.00**
Note Cards, Gone with the Wind, set of eight . . . . . . . . . . . . . . . . . . . . . . . . . **5.00**
Paint Set, *Tom Sawyer,* Paramount, 1931 . . . . . . . . . . . . . . . . . . . . . . . . . **30.00**
Pinback Button, *The Phantom,* 3½", celluloid, Universal Pictures, c1960 . . . **12.00**
Paper Dolls, *Gone with the Wind,* M3405, 1940 . . . . . . . . . . . . . . . . . . . **300.00**
Playbill, *Laffing Room Only,* Olsen and Johnson, 1945 . . . . . . . . . . . . . . . . . . **6.00**

**Poster, *Apache Rifles,* Audie Murphy, Admiral Pictures, 1964, $20.00.**

Poster
*Arson, Inc,* 22 x 28", Lippert Productions, 1949 . . . . . . . . . . . . . . . . . . . **30.00**
*Avenging Rider,* Tim Holt, 27 x 40", 1942 . . . . . . . . . . . . . . . . . . . . . . . . **100.00**
*Beach Blanket Bingo,* Frankie Avalon, 22 x 22" . . . . . . . . . . . . . . . . . . . . . **20.00**
*Black Fury,* Paul Muni, 23 x 43", 1935 **175.00**
*Dirty Dozen,* Lee Marvin, 27 x 41" . **15.00**
*Empire Strikes Back,* Mark Hamill, 27 x 41" . . . . . . . . . . . . . . . . . . . . . . . . . **25.00**
*Harlow,* Carol Baker, 27 x 41" . . . . . **10.00**
*Raiders Of The Seven Seas,* 27 x 41", United Artist, 1953 . . . . . . . . . . . . . **30.00**
*Shine On Harvest Moon,* Ann Sheridan, 27 x 40", 1943 . . . . . . . . . . . . **100.00**
*The High and The Mighty,* John Wayne, 27 x 41" . . . . . . . . . . . . . . . **75.00**
*To Have and Have Not,* Humphrey Bogart, 22 x 28" . . . . . . . . . . . . . . . **225.00**
*The Sound of Fury,* 14 x 36", United Artist, 1950 . . . . . . . . . . . . . . . . . . . **25.00**

Press Book
*Circus World,* John Wayne, 14 pg . . **20.00**
*Girl Happy,* Elvis Presley, 1965 . . . . . **20.00**
*Mary Poppins,* Julie Andrews . . . . . . **10.00**
*The Caine Mutiny,* Humphrey Bogart, 18 pgs . . . . . . . . . . . . . . . . . . . . . . . **30.00**

Program, souvenir
*Ben Hur,* MGM, 1926 . . . . . . . . . . . . **30.00**
*Gone with the Wind,* 1939 . . . . . . . . **95.00**
*White Shadows in the South Seas,* MGM, 1928 . . . . . . . . . . . . . . . . . . . **35.00**

Souvenir Book
*Lawrence of Arabia,* Peter O'Toole, colored photos, two foldout double page maps . . . . . . . . . . . . . . . . . . . **15.00**
*Since You Went Away,* 1944 Selznick film, 9 x 12", 20 pgs . . . . . . . . . . . **25.00**
*The Sea Hawk,* Milton Sills, silent version . . . . . . . . . . . . . . . . . . . . . . . . . **50.00**
*The Song of Bernadette,* 9 x 11½", 20 pgs, 1944 religious movie, full color cov Norman Rockwell illus of Jennifer Jones . . . . . . . . . . . . . . . . . **35.00**

Stein, *Butch Cassidy,* Jesse James boot, 1981, marked "Ceramarte" . . . . . . . . **85.00**
Studio Photo, boy on high wheeled cart, dog, harness . . . . . . . . . . . . . . . . . . . . **20.00**

Window Card
*High Noon,* Gary Cooper, 14 x 22", 1952 . . . . . . . . . . . . . . . . . . . . . . . . . **75.00**
*On The Waterfront,* Marlon Brando, 14 x 22", 1954 . . . . . . . . . . . . . . . . **125.00**

# MOVIE PERSONALITIES

**Collecting Hints:** Focus on one star. Today, the four most popular stars are Humphrey Bogart, Clark Gable, Jean Harlow, and Marilyn Monroe. Many of the stars of the silent era are being overlooked by the modern collector. Nostalgia appears to be a key to the star on which a person focuses.

Remember that stars have big support staffs. Not all autograph items were or are signed by the star directly. Signatures should be checked carefully against a known original.

Many stars had fan clubs and the fans tended to hold on to the materials they assembled. The collector should be prepared to hunt and do research. A great deal of material rests in private hands.

**History:** The star systems and Hollywood are synonymous. The studios spent elaborate sums of money promoting their stars. Chaplin, Valentino, and Pickford gave way to Garbo and Gable.

The movie magazine was a key vehicle in the promotion. *Motion Picture, Movie Weekly, Motion Picture World,* and *Photoplay* are just a few examples of this genre. *Photoplay* was the most sensational.

The film star had no private life and individual cults grew up around many of them. By the 1970s the star system of the 1930s and 1940s had lost its luster. The popularity of stars is much shorter lived today.

**References:** Leslie Halliwell, *The Filmgoer's Companion,* Avon, 1978; Ephraim Katz, *The Film Encyclopedia,* Perigee Books, 1979; Leonard Maltin (ed.), *TV Movies and Video Guide,* New American Library, 1987; Norman E. Martinus and Harry L. Rinker, *Warman's Paper,* Wallace–Homestead, 1993; Patrick McCarver, *Gone With The Wind Collector's Price Guide,* Collector's Originals, 1990; Edward R. Pardella, *Shirley Temple Dolls and Fashions: A Collector's Guide To The World's Darling,* Schiffer Publishing, Ltd., 1992; Jay Scarfone and William Stillman, *The Wizard Of Oz Collector's Treasury,* Schiffer Publishing, Ltd., 1992; Anthony Slide, *A Collector's Guide to Movie Memorabilia With Prices,* Wallace–Homestead, 1983; Jon R. Warren, *Warren's Movie Poster Price Guide, 1993 Edition,* American Collector's Exchange, 1992.

**Periodicals:** *Big Reel,* Route 3, P. O. Box 83, Madison, NC 27025; *Classic Images,* P. O. Box 809, Muscatine, IA 52761; Hollywood Movie Archives, P. O. Box 1566, Apple Valley, CA 92307; *Movie Collectors' World,* P. O. Box 309, Fraser, MI 48026; *Nostalgia World,* P. O. Box 231, North Haven, CT 06473.

**Collectors' Club:** Hollywood Studio Collectors Club, Suite 450, 3960 Laurel Canyon Blvd, Studio City, CA 91604.

**See:** Autographs, Magazines, and Posters.

Astaire, Fred
- Autographed Letter, 8½ x 11" RKO letterhead, March, 1937 ........ **20.00**
- Sheet Music, *My Shining Hour* ..... **5.00**

Bardot, Brigitte, book, *Brigitte Bardot,* Francoise Sagan, 1976, 100 pgs, 12½ x 9½" ........ **9.00**

Blyth, Ann, coloring book, unused, 1952 ........ **35.00**

Bogart, Humphrey, sheet music, *Passage to Marseille* ........ **5.00**

Brando, Marlon
- Book, *Brando,* Charles Higham, hard back ........ **10.00**
- Magazine, *Look,* May 17, 1955, Brando cov ........ **4.00**

Bushman, Francis X, magazine, *Motion Picture Classic,* May, 1917, color cov portrait ........ **35.00**

Chaney, Lon, movie book, *The Mocking Bird,* 5½ x 8", paperback, 138 pgs, 1925, MGM Movie ........ **35.00**

Chaplin, Charlie
- Book, cartoon, *Charlie Chaplin in the Movies,* 1917 ........ **68.00**
- Figure, 2½ x 8", stuffed leather, full length portrait image inked in black on natural tan leather, black felt back, 1920s ........ **65.00**
- Jewelry Box, musical, dancing plastic figure, marked "Hong Kong," 1981 **30.00**
- Magazine, *Film Fun,* Nov, 1918, Chaplin on cov ........ **75.00**
- Pencil Box, 2 x 8", full figure illus .. **50.00**

**Cigarette Card, Marlene Dietrich, Wills Cigarettes, actual photo, 1930s, 1¼ x 2⅝", $12.00.**

Coogan, Jackie
- Clicker, metal, adv for peanut butter **20.00**
- Pencil Box, minor rust on bottom .. **12.00**

Crawford, Joan
- Sheet Music, *Sadie McKee* ........ **5.00**
- Window Card, 10½ x 13½", cardboard, Joan at dinner table, c1940 **18.00**

Crosby, Bing, game, Call Me Lucky, Parker Bros, 1954, black and white portrait on box lid and 19½" sq playing board ........ **25.00**

Davis, Bette
- Coloring Book, 10 x 13", Merrill, 1942 ........ **20.00**

Movie Poster, *Hush, Hush Sweet Charlotte,* 27 x 41" ............. **35.00**
Press Book, *The Catered Affair,* 20 pgs **25.00**
Sheet Music, *Now Voyager* ........ **5.00**
Dean, James, magazine, *Spectator Illustrated,* 1950s, James Dean cov story **8.00**
DeHavilland, Olivia
Autograph, letter, sgd ............. **12.00**
Magazine, *Time,* December 20, 1948 **6.00**
Sheet Music, *To Each His Own,* DeHavilland and John Lund, 1946 **7.00**
Durbin, Deanna
Catalog, flowers .................. **25.00**
Folio, song ...................... **25.00**
Tablet, pencil, unused ............ **25.00**
Fairbanks, Douglas, Sr, press book, *Don Q, Son of Zorro,* 10 x 13", soft cov, "Exhibitors Campaign Book," 1925 silent film ...................... **80.00**
Farrow, Mia, magazine, *Life,* May 5, 1967, Farrow cov and story ....... **6.00**
Flynn, Errol
Magazine, *Movie and Radio Guide,* April 6, 1940, 10½ x 13½", 58 pgs **30.00**
Movie Book
*Adventures of Robin Hood,* Conklin Publishing Co, 1938, 8½ x 11", soft cover, 175 black and white glossy photos from Warner Bros movie ..................... **80.00**
*The Sea Hawk,* Whitman, 1940, 8 x 11", soft cover, 64 pgs, black and white photos from Warner Bros movie ................. **75.00**

**Post Card, premium, eight cowboy star photos, red, white, and blue, divided back with Exhibit coupon, 1930s, 5⅜ x 3⅜", $35.00.**

Gable, Clark
Book, *Clark Gable–A Personal Portrait,* Kathleen Gable, 1961, 151 pgs, dj ....................... **6.00**
Newspaper supplement, Philadelphia, 8 x 10" ................. **12.00**
Garbo, Greta, magazine, *Life,* January 10, 1955 ....................... **5.00**

**Puzzle, Movie-Land Puzzle, "Your Favorite Stars in scenes from Famous Photo Plays," Milton Bradley, 1926, $35.00.**

Garland, Judy, book, *Judy,* Gerold Frank, hard back ................. **10.00**
Gish, Lillian, autograph, card ........ **40.00**
Grable, Betty, sheet music, *I'm Always Chasing Rainbows,* Grable and June Haver, 1934 .................... **7.00**
Harlow, Jean
Magazine Cov, *Life,* 1937 ......... **30.00**
Sheet Music, *A New Star Shines in Heaven,* 1938 ................ **15.00**
Hayward, Susan, pocket mirror ...... **21.00**
Hayworth, Rita
Magazine, *Silver Screen,* September, 1952, Hayworth cov ........... **4.00**
Paper Doll, book, Saalfield, #2712, *Carmen,* 1948 ................ **50.00**
Henie, Sonja, program, *Hats Off To Ice,* Arthur Wirtz Production, c1945 .... **10.00**
Hepburn, Katharine, book, *Kate,* Charles Hingham, hard back ....... **10.00**
Hudson, Rock, Christmas card, fan club, photo pin, 1954 ........... **18.00**
Hurt, William, book, *William Hurt, The Man The Actor,* Toby Goldstein, hard back .......................... **10.00**
Laurel & Hardy
Movie Poster
*Four Clowns,* 27 x 41" .......... **35.00**
*Further Perils of Laurel & Hardy,* 27 x 41" ...................... **25.00**
Salt and Pepper Shakers, ½ x 2½ x 4" white china tray, 4" Laurel with black derby, 3" Hardy with brown derby, Beswick, England, 3 pcs .. **100.00**
Lombard, Carole, magazine, *Picturegoer,* 1935 ..................... **25.00**
MacDonald, Jeanette
Christmas Card, 1937 ............ **25.00**
Funeral Notice, 1965 ............ **20.00**
Mansfield, Jayne
Baby Announcement, 1965 ........ **30.00**
Christmas Card, family photo, 1965 **30.00**

Miranda, Carmen, doll, orig clothing, used ........ **97.50**
Monroe, Marilyn
Cologne Spray, 1983, MIB ........ **45.00**
Curves Protractor, orig envelope .... **115.00**
Doll, Tristar, 11½" h ........ **45.00**
Magazine, *Pageant,* December, 1957, Monroe article ........ **3.00**
Newspaper Supplement, New York, Sunday, 1982 ........ **20.00**
Tray, nude ........ **300.00**
Newman, Paul, magazine, *Us,* May 3, 1977, Newman cov ........ **4.00**
Novak, Kim, fan club kit, wallet, photos, and Christmas card, 1966 ..... **20.00**
O'Hara, Maureen, Christmas card, autographed, 1957 ........ **20.00**
Pickford, Mary, portrait, autographed, 1930 ........ **52.00**
Rogers, Ginger, 5 x 7" color photograph, Alhambra Theatre 1940 roster on back ........ **12.00**
Sheen, Charlie, silk scarf, autographed **50.00**
Sothern, Ann
Advertisement, Panama Hattie ..... **6.00**
Tablet, pencil, unused ........ **25.00**
Taylor, Elizabeth
Jewelry, 1¼ x 4½ x 7" gray flocked suede display case, gold colored necklace, rhinestones and simulated pearls, matching earrings, black and white photo, c1950 ... **50.00**
Movie Poster, *Cleopatra,* 27 x 41", small mend ........ **50.00**
Three Stooges, punch out book, 7½ x 13", Golden Press, 1962 ........ **75.00**
Tierney, Gene, magazine cover, *Photoplay* ........ **10.00**
Travolta, John, autographed pair of shoes worn in *Staying Alive,* sgd in each shoe ........ **150.00**
West, Mae, magazine, *Song Hits,* August, 1935, full page photo ........ **25.00**
Wood, Natalie, book, *Natalie,* Lana Wood ........ **10.00**

# MOXIE

**Collecting Hints:** A general rule is the older the Moxie item, the more expensive the price. Due to the vagaries of the Moxie Company's various managements, some recent items have acquired value. A large, 16 page, multicolored brochure published in 1929 by the soon defunct Moxie Company of America is one example. The short lived, New Moxie venture made New Moxie bottles scarce. "The Great New Taste" debacle of the late 1960s was not successful. Its dimpled bottles are unknown to many Moxie collectors.

Moxie items, especially those associated with Ted Williams, have risen dramatically in value. Baseball collectors are constantly outbidding Moxie collectors for the Williams' advertising items for Moxie and for Ted's Root Beer items. Lately, Moxie has been marketed in other soda–pop bottles, even beer bottles. For more information write Don Wortham, 179 Orchard Drive, Pittsburgh, PA 15235.

**History:** At the height of its popularity, 1920 to 1940, Moxie was distributed in approximately 36 states and even outsold Coca–Cola in many. It became so popular that the word "moxie," meaning nervy, became part of the American language.

Moxie is the oldest continuously produced soft drink in the United States, celebrating its 100th anniversary in 1984. It originated as Moxie Nerve Food, a nostrum concocted by Dr. Augustin Thompson from Union, Maine. It was first produced in Lowell, Massachusetts.

Moxie's fame is due in large part to the promotion efforts of Frank Morton Archer, an intrepid entrepreneur armed with charisma, wizardry, and a magnificent imagination. With a genius for showmanship and prophesying profits galore, Archer uncorked an advertising phenomenon by blazing a trail with eye– catching advertising vehicles and new benchmarks in unabashed barnstorming.

Bottle wagons were replaced by horseless carriages. Some folks called cars "Moxies," since the first automobile they saw had MOXIE lettered on its side. Next, Archer mounted a saddled, dummy pony in the sidecar of a motorcycle and put his TNT Cowboy Outfit on the road. He followed with an even more amazing machine—a dummy horse mounted on an automobile chassis driven from the horse's saddle.

Scarcely an event occurred in the first half of the 20th century which Archer did not exploit for Moxie. It was not by accident that the well remembered Uncle Sam poster, "I Want You For The U. S. Army," closely resembled another that already was familiar to the public—a steely–eyed Moxie man pointing at his viewers and commanding them to "Drink Moxie."

Moxie continues today, remaining especially popular in the New England area. A mountain of memorabilia surrounds the Moxie legend, much of which its aficionados claim are superior to Coke's both in quality and investment potential.

There are many firms which attempted to play upon the Moxie name. During the late 1920s the Moxie Company published a 64–page pamphlet entitled *This Book About Substitution* which contained "A Little History of Many Big Cases." Among the names imitative of Moxie were: Proxie, Hoxie, Noxie, Noxie Nerve Tonic, Noxall, Nerv–E–Za, Non–Tox, Appetizer, Visner, Puro, Nickletone, Neurene, Nerve Food (East India, Excelsior, Imperial, Standard), Miller, Man-ola, Modox, Rixie, Toxie, two Canadian Moxies and several others. Since only a limited amount of each spurious products was produced and many imitative bottles destroyed "whether full or empty" by court order, those which remain are eagerly sought by collectors.

**References:** Q. David Bowers, *The Moxie Encyclopedia,* Vestal Press, 1985; Frank N. Potter, *The Book of Moxie,* Collector Books, 1987, out–of–print; Frank N. Potter, *The Moxie Mystique—The Word, The Drink, The Collectible,* published by author, 1981.

**Collectors' Club:** Moxie Enthusiasts Collectors Club of America, Route 375, Box 164, Woodstock, NY 12498.

**Museums:** Clark's Trading Post, North Woodstock, NH; Matthews Museum of Maine Heritage, Union, ME.

**REPRODUCTION ALERT:** Modern Moxie items are being produced and sold by Kennebec Fruit Company, 2 Main Street, Lisbon Falls, ME 04252.

Ashtray, ceramic, white, Moxie man .. **25.00**
Belt Buckle, bronze finish ........... **17.50**
Book, Archer, *The TNT Cowboy,* 1919, purple cover, 81 pgs ............. **125.00**
Bottle
Diet Moxie, emb neck, paper label . **15.00**
Foxy Moxie, green, dumbbell shape, fox label, 1950s ............... **50.00**
Moxie
10 oz, clear, dimpled, ACL "Moxie," 1960s ............. **30.00**
26 oz, green tint, emb high shoulder ........................ **7.50**
Moxie Nerve Food, emb "Lowell, Mass," clear .................. **22.50**
New Moxie, ACL, 7 oz .......... **10.00**
Pureoxia, green ................. **10.00**
Bottle Case, wood, "It's Always A Pleasure," holds 12 bottles ............ **20.00**
Bottle Carrying Bag, paper
Kid Moxie, 6 bottle, 7 oz ......... **7.00**
Moxie/Pureoxia, 3 bottle, 26 oz, red semicircles ................... **6.50**
Bottle Hangers, paper and cardboard
Attached Moxie shoulder patch .... **5.00**
Bottle Cap drawing, 6 for 37¢ ..... **2.00**
Crown upper left, 10 oz bottle, king size ........................ **6.00**
The 3 Moxie–teers, 3 bottle, 7 oz .. **6.00**
Bottle Opener, Moxie/Pureoxia, wire, straight handle ................... **2.50**
Bumper Sticker
I've Got Moxie, red and orange, black lettering ...................... **5.00**
What This Country Needs Is Plenty of Moxie ........................ **2.00**
Butter Dish, cov ................... **60.00**
Calendar, 1962, Old Fashion Moxie .. **5.00**
Cereal Bowl ....................... **20.00**
Clicker, marked "Mfg by Whitehead & Hoag Co" ....................... **50.00**
Clock
Mantel, Moxie man .............. **275.00**
Pendulum, wall, banjo shape ...... **500.00**
Plastic, lighted, round ........... **17.50**
Clothing
Cap, historic, Moxie Festivals ...... **10.00**
Mitten, pr ....................... **8.00**
Scarf .......................... **10.00**
Sweatshirt ...................... **18.00**
T shirt, historic, Moxie Festivals .... **15.00**
Cuff Links, pr ..................... **25.00**
Cup and Saucer .................... **20.00**
Egg Cup, large .................... **50.00**
Glass
Flared top, red band .............. **12.50**
Frosted label, syrup line .......... **17.50**
Ice Pick and Opener, "Moxie 5/ The Best Drink in the World" .......... **44.00**
Lap Board, Moxie/Pureoxia .......... **10.00**
Mirror, purse size, Zodiac signs ...... **8.00**
Mug, ceramic ...................... **20.00**
Napkin, boy and dog ............... **20.00**
Novelty, Hitchy Koo, carved head .... **250.00**
Pendant, sterling silver ............. **100.00**
Pinback Button
Moxie man, pointing ............ **25.00**
Uncle Sam's hat ................ **35.00**
Pitcher, small ...................... **65.00**
Plate
Dinner ......................... **25.00**
Luncheon ....................... **25.00**
Platter ........................... **35.00**
Playing Cards, Moxie man ........... **6.50**
Post Card, two children with cutouts and sign ....................... **27.50**
Poster
Bathing Beauty, white swimsuit, paper ......................... **150.00**
Bottle, cardboard, diecut .......... **20.00**
Drink Moxie, 21 x 35", squarecut, cardboard, corrugated .......... **7.50**
Let's Get Acquainted, six–pack 5¢, squarecut, cardboard ........... **9.00**
Moxie League, baseball offer, paper **20.00**

**Sign, enameled, yellow and red, 18 x 9", $35.00.**

Serving Tray, Moxie Centennial, 1984 . **35.00**
Sheet Music, *Moxie Song,* one–step, 1921 . . . . . . **10.00**
Sign
Drink Moxie 100%, octagonal, diecut **75.00**
Pureoxia, squarecut, red oval on rectangle . . . . . . **75.00**
Yes! We Sell Moxie, Moxie Nerve Food, diecut, round, "X" . . . . . . **200.00**
Sugar, cov . . . . . . **60.00**
Tape
Cassette, Moxie Monarch NuGrape Co . . . . . . **25.00**
Open Reel, Mad about Moxie, jingles, 1967 . . . . . . **25.00**
Thermometer
New England's Own Soft Drink, white **7.50**
Remember Those Days, metal, round, orange . . . . . . **20.00**
Ya Gotta Have Moxie, yellow, kid boxer . . . . . . **25.00**
Tip Tray, girl's face . . . . . . **100.00**
Tray
Boy's face, glass . . . . . . **325.00**
Our Idol, Moxie man . . . . . . **175.00**

# MUSIC BOXES

**Collecting Hints:** Any figurine or box–shaped object has the potential for insertion of a music box. The following list of music boxes deals with objects in which the music box is secondary to the piece. Antique music boxes are covered in *Warman's Antiques And Their Prices.*

Collectors often tend to focus on one tune, trying to collect all the variety of ways it is used. Others concentrate on a musical toy form, such as dolls or teddy bears. A popular item is the musical jewel box, prevalent during the 1880 to 1930 period.

**History:** The insertion of a small music box into toys and other products dates back to the 18th century. Initially these were limited to the children of the aristocracy; but the mass production of music boxes in the late 19th century made them available to everyone.

The music box toy enjoyed greater popularity in Europe than in America. Some of the finest examples are of European craftsmanship. After World War II there was an influx of cheap music box toys from the Far East. The popularity of the musical toy suffered as people reacted negatively to these inferior products.

**Reference:** H. A. V. Bulleid, *Cylinder Musical Box Design and Repair,* Almar Press, 1987.

**Collectors' Club:** Musical Box Society International, R. D. #3, Box 205, Morgantown, IN 46160.

**Museums:** Bellms Car and Music of Yesterday, Sarasota, FL; Lockwood Matthews Mansion, Norwalk, CT.

Ballerina, 9" h, bisque, glass eyes, cylinder base, French . . . . . . **300.00**
Bank, plastic, Gorham
Acrobat, 7½" h, green . . . . . . **18.00**
Cyclist, 7½" h, red . . . . . . **18.00**
Barrel organ, 5½" h, Ohio Art . . . . . . **5.00**
Bear, hand carved . . . . . . **65.00**
Bird, figural, ceramic
Cardinal, 6½" h . . . . . . **18.00**
Dove, 6¼" h . . . . . . **15.00**
Owl, 6" h . . . . . . **20.00**
Box
1¼ x 4¼ x 3½", Thorens cylinder, grained wood case plays Bicycle Built for Two . . . . . . **45.00**
2½" h, Santa, white, plays Jingle Bells **8.00**
2½" h, snowman and lady, red, plays Frosty the Snowman . . . . . . **8.00**
2½ x 3½ x 6½", leather, porcelain plaque painting of five mallards on cov . . . . . . **70.00**
3 x 3 x 5", Manivelle, three tunes, litho on cov, children feeding swan, tune sheet on bottom, Swiss . . . . . . **80.00**
Children on Merry Go Round, 7¾" h, wood, figures move, plays Around the World in 80 Days . . . . . . **22.00**
Children on See Saw, 7" h, wood, figures move in time to music . . . . . . **20.00**
Christmas Tree Stand, revolving, Germany . . . . . . **65.00**
Church, 4 x 6", tin, hand crank, Germany . . . . . . **125.00**
Cigar holder, 15" h, wood and brass . . **75.00**
Clown, 5½" h, plastic, dome Gorham **18.00**
Coffee Grinder shape, 3" h . . . . . . **30.00**
Dog, 12" h, Nipper, ceramic . . . . . . **45.00**
Doll
Drum Major, 15" h, blue uniform, plays Cecile . . . . . . **100.00**
Sammy Kay, 11" h, composition, sways . . . . . . **65.00**
Dove, figural, ceramic . . . . . . **18.00**
Easter Egg, tin . . . . . . **15.00**
Kitten with ball, 5½" h, ceramic . . . . . **18.00**
Lamp, night, 6½" h, merry–go–round, c1950 . . . . . . **30.00**
Man, leaning against lamp post, cast iron, plays How Dry I Am, New York City souvenir . . . . . . **18.00**
Merry–Go–Round, three horses and riders, 1904 . . . . . . **45.00**
Mess Cart, two horses, tin, painted . . . **30.00**
Phonograph, 5¾ x 3¼ x 3¼", miniature, upright, wind–up, Swiss . . . . . . **78.00**
Powder Box, 3½ x 4¼", metal, silver, litho cov, c1940 . . . . . . **25.00**

Snowball, glass, wood base
- Frosty the Snowman, 5″ h, red base **10.00**
- Mr and Mrs Santa, 5″ h, green base . **10.00**
- Santa and Rudolph, 5″ h, green base **10.00**

Statue, Elvis Presley on music box base, plays Love Me Tender ............ **75.00**

**Elvis Presley, ceramic, plays "Love Me Tender," $75.00.**

Stein, 5″ h, porcelain, diamond dec .. **35.00**

Toy
- Bear, hand carved, spin with hand . **65.00**
- Chimp, jolly .................... **35.00**
- Clock, Hickory Dickory, Mattel, 1952 **25.00**
- Ferris Wheel, moving, cardboard, c1940, MIB .................. **15.00**
- Santa Claus, 14″ h, head moves .... **35.00**
- Three Little Pigs, Jaymar ........... **45.00**

# NAPKIN RINGS

**Collecting Hints:** Concentrate on napkin rings of unusual design or shape. This is one collectible which still can be used on a daily basis. However, check for the proper cleaning and care methods for the type of material you have. Many celluloid items have been ruined by storage in too dry an area or by washing in too hot water.

An engraved initial or other personalizing mark detracts, rather than adds value to a napkin ring. Many collectors and dealers have these marks removed professionally if it will not harm the ring.

**History:** Napkin rings enjoyed a prominent role on the American dinner table during most of the 19th and early 20th centuries. Figural napkin rings were used in the upper class households. However, a vast majority of people used the simple napkin ring.

The shape does not mean that the decorative motif could not be elegant. Engraving, relief designs, and carving turned the simple ring into works of art. When cast metal and molded plastic became popular, shaped rings, especially for children, were introduced.

The arrival of inexpensive paper products, fast and frozen foods and a quickened pace of American society reduced American's concern for elegant daily dining. The napkin ring almost has disappeared from the dining table.

Brass, two elves, dog, dragon and leaf dec, emb ...................... **20.00**

Celluloid, grapes, emb .............. **10.00**

China, blue and pink floral dec, white ground .......................... **15.00**

Cloisonne
- Dragon, white ground ............ **25.00**
- Floral, dark blue dec, white ground . **50.00**

Cut Glass
- Harvard Pattern .................. **75.00**
- Hobstars and Bow Tie Fans ........ **85.00**

Ivory, carved
- Medallions ...................... **38.00**
- Openwork ...................... **20.00**

Metal, lady holding stick, c1942 ..... **15.00**

Nippon
- Floral, blue and gold, white ground **35.00**
- Rose, gold trim, cream ground ..... **60.00**
- Scene, forest and lake, beaded trim . **75.00**

Noritake
- Flowers and Butterfly ............. **15.00**
- Man, Art Deco design ............ **30.00**
- Rose Azalea ..................... **45.00**

Porcelain, owl, seated on ring ....... **20.00**

Sabino Glass, bird, opalescent ....... **40.00**

Silver, plated
- Birds and tulips, beaded base and ring, Rockford Silver Plate Co .... **80.00**
- Bulldog, Dirigo Boy ............. **125.00**
- Cat, arched back ................. **120.00**
- Children and goats, etched ........ **15.00**
- Dog, pulling sled, emb greyhounds on sides, engraved "Sara," Meriden **165.00**
- Floral bouquets, Victorian, 1½″ .... **15.00**
- Man, nude, running holding torch, sq base ......................... **150.00**
- Oriental Fans, repousse flowers and hummingbird dec ............. **75.00**

**China, dog, 2″ d, 2¾″ h, marked "Japan," $19.00.**

Parrot, rect base, Rogers Mfg Co ... **50.00**
Ring, etched dogwood branch, 1¾" w ... **20.00**
Silver, sterling
Art Nouveau, girl with flowing hair, 1½" ... **25.00**
Cherubs, two seated ... **65.00**
Eagles, two ... **55.00**
Hen, sgd "Meriden" ... **195.00**
Koala Bear, 2 x 3", Australian ... **65.00**
Mickey Mouse ... **75.00**
Nursery rhyme figures ... **25.00**
Peacock, standing ... **55.00**
Scotty ... **35.00**
Windham Pattern, Tiffany & Co ... **70.00**
Souvenir
Grand Rapids, MI, scenic ... **10.00**
Louisiana Purchase ... **15.00**
Mt Washington, NH, 1880 ... **18.00**
St Louis World's Fair, 1904, enameled **40.00**

# NEW MARTINSVILLE VIKING

**Collecting Hints:** New Martinsville glass predating 1935 appears in a wide variety of colors. Later glass was only made in crystal, blue, ruby, and pink.

Look for cocktail, beverage, liquor, vanity, smoking and console sets. Amusing figures of barnyard and sea animals, dogs, and bears were produced. Both Rainbow Art Glass and Viking glass are handmade and have a paper label. Rainbow Art Glass pieces are beautifully colored and the animal figures are more abstract in design than New Martinsville. Viking makes plain, colored, cut and etched tableware, novelties, gift items. Viking began making black glass in 1979.

**History:** The New Martinsville Glass Manufacturing Company, founded in 1901, took its name from its West Virginia location. Early products were opal glass decorative ware and utilitarian items. Later productions were pressed crystal tableware with flashed-on ruby or gold decorations. In the 1920s innovative color and designs made vanity, liquor, and smoker sets popular. Dinner sets in patterns such as Radiance, Moondrops, and Dancing Girl, as well as new colors, cuttings and etchings were produced. The 40s brought black glass formed into perfume bottles, bowls with swan handles and flower bowls. In 1944 the company was sold and reorganized as the Viking Glass Company.

The Rainbow Art Glass Company, Huntington, West Virginia, was established in 1942 by Henry Manus, a Dutch immigrant. This company produced small, hand fashioned animals and decorative ware of opal, spatter, cased and crackle glass. Rainbow Art Glass also decorated for other companies. In the early 1970s, Viking acquired Rainbow Art Glass Company and continued the production of the small animals.

**Reference:** Lee Garmon and Dick Spencer, *Glass Animals of the Depression Era,* Collector Books, 1993; Ellen Tischbein Schroy, *Warman's Glass,* Wallace–Homestead, 1992; Hazel Marie Weatherman, *Colored Glassware of the Depression Era, Book 2,* Glassworks, Inc., 1982.

Animal
Bear
Baby ... **40.00**
Mama ... **165.00**
Papa ... **195.00**
Chick, baby ... **45.00**
Horse, head up ... **90.00**
Piglet, standing ... **150.00**
Police Dog ... **65.00**
Seal with ball ... **75.00**
Squirrel ... **35.00**
Ashtray, Moondrops, green, 3" d ... **12.00**
Basket, Janice, crystal ... **20.00**
Batter Set, cobalt blue ... **425.00**
Bonbon, Meadow Wreath etch, crystal, two handles, 6" d ... **13.00**
Bookends, pr
Elephant ... **95.00**
Sailboat, crystal ... **45.00**
Bowl
Moondrops, amber, concave, 8½" d, ftd ... **24.00**
Prelude, crystal
5¾" d, handle ... **27.50**
9" d, ruffled ... **45.00**
10¾" d, ftd ... **28.50**
12" d, ruffled, scalloped ... **50.00**
Cake Stand, Prelude, crystal, 11" d, ftd **45.00**
Candlesticks, pr
Prelude, crystal, 6" h ... **40.00**
Swan, dark green ... **25.00**
Cheese and Cracker, Moondrops, slight use marks ... **30.00**
Cocktail, #125, ruby, platinum bands . **6.50**
Compote, Prelude, crystal, 5" d, ftd ... **16.00**
Console Set, three piece set
Florentine Etch, crystal, 11½" d #29 bowl, pair #4450/29 double candlesticks, price for set ... **45.00**
Prelude, crystal, 12" d ruffled bowl, pair double candlesticks, price for set ... **62.00**
Swan, dark green center swan, pair swan candleholders, price for set . **24.75**
Cordial
Moondrops
Amber ... **22.50**
Ruby ... **15.00**
Prelude, crystal ... **15.00**

Creamer and Sugar
- Janice, light blue .......... **25.00**
- Moondrops, cobalt blue .......... **10.00**
- Prelude, crystal .......... **15.00**
- Radiance
  - Amber .......... **15.00**
  - Light Blue .......... **24.00**

Cup
- Moondrops
  - Amber .......... **6.00**
  - Ruby .......... **12.00**
- Radiance, dark amber .......... **11.00**

Cup and Saucer, Janice, light blue .... **15.00**

Figure, drunk man .......... **90.00**

Flower Frog, shawl dancer, pink ..... **375.00**

Goblet
- Georgian, ruby, 5⅝" h .......... **12.00**
- Mt Vernon, ruby, 6" h .......... **7.50**

Juice Tumbler, Moondrops, cobalt blue, ftd .......... **15.00**

Mustard, cov, Janice, blue .......... **55.00**

Nut Bowl, Florentine Etch, #4429, crystal, center handle, 11" d .......... **18.00**

Pitcher, Radiance, amber .......... **150.00**

Plate
- Florentine Etch, crystal, 13¾" d .... **12.00**
- Moondrops, emerald green, 9¼" d . **18.00**
- Prelude, crystal, 7" d .......... **10.00**
- Radiance
  - Amber, 8" d .......... **10.00**
  - Crystal, cut design, 8¼" d ....... **15.00**

Relish
- Moondrops, amber, three parts ..... **50.00**
- Prelude, crystal, 10" l, three parts .. **40.00**

Salt and Pepper Shakers, pr, Prelude .. **30.00**

Saucer, Radiance, blue .......... **3.75**

Serving Plate
- Prelude, crystal, 10½" d, two handles **35.00**
- Princess, crystal, center handle ..... **20.00**

Shell, Nautilus, crystal .......... **35.00**

Sherbet
- Georgian, ruby .......... **8.50**
- Janice, blue .......... **25.00**
- Mt Vernon, golf ball stem, ruby .... **7.50**

Shot Glass, Moondrops, handle, 2 oz
- Amber .......... **9.00**
- Ruby .......... **13.00**

Sugar
- Janice, light blue .......... **30.00**
- Moondrops, cobalt blue .......... **10.00**
- Prelude, crystal .......... **18.00**
- Radiance, light blue .......... **22.00**

Swan, Janice, crystal, 12" h .......... **35.00**

Torte Plate, Prelude, crystal, 14" d .... **45.00**

Tumbler
- Hostmaster, ruby, 4¼" h .......... **10.00**
- Oscar, amber, platinum trim ....... **5.50**
- Radiance, amber .......... **20.00**

Vanity Set, light blue, two diamond shaped cologne bottles, matching puff box, price for set .......... **62.00**

Vase, Prelude, crystal, 10½" h ....... **95.00**

Wine
- Hostmaster, ruby, 2 x 2½" ......... **10.00**
- Silver Overlay, cobalt blue ........ **5.00**

# NEWSPAPERS, HEADLINE EDITIONS

**Collecting Hints:** All newspapers must be complete with a minimal amount of chipping and cracking. The post–1880 newsprint is made of wood pulp and deteriorates quickly without proper care. Pre–1880 newsprint was composed of cotton and rag fiber and has survived much better than its wood pulp counterpart.

Front pages only of 20th century newspapers command about 60% of the value for the entire issue, since the primary use for these papers is display. Pre–20th century issues are collectible only if complete, as banner headlines were rarely used. These papers tend to run between four and eight pages.

Major city issues are preferable, although any newspaper providing a dramatic headline is collectible. Banner headlines, those extending completely across the paper, are most desirable. Also desirable are those from the city in which the event happened and command a substantial premium over the prices listed. Complete series collections carry a premium as well, such as all 20th century election reports, etc.

Twentieth century newspapers are easily stored. Issues should be placed flat in polyethylene bags, or acid free folders that are slightly larger than the paper, and kept from high humidity and direct sunlight.

Although not as commonly found, newspapers from the 17th through the 19th century are highly collectible, particularly those from the Revolutionary War, War of 1812, Civil War, and those reporting Indian and "desperado" events.

Two of the most commonly reprinted papers are the *Ulster County Gazette,* of January 4, 1800, dealing with Washington's death and the *N.Y. Herald,* of April 15, 1865, dealing with Lincoln's death. If you have either of these papers, chances are you have a reprint.

**History:** America's first successful newspaper was *The Boston Newsletter,* founded in 1704. The newspaper industry grew rapidly, experiencing its golden age in the early 20th century. Within the last decade many great evening papers have ceased publication, and many local papers have been purchased by the large chains.

Collecting headline edition newspapers has become popular during the last twenty years, largely because of the decorative value of the headlines. Also, individuals like to collect newspapers related to the great events which they have witnessed or which have been romanticized through the movies, television, and other media, especially those reporting events, the Old West, and the gangster era.

**References:** Harold Evans, *Front Page History,* Salem House, 1984; Robert F. Karolevitz, *From Quill To Computer: The Story of America's Community Newspapers,* National Newspaper Foundation, 1985; Jim Lyons, *Collecting American Newspapers,* published by author, 1989; Norman E. Martinus and Harry L. Rinker, *Warman's Paper,* Wallace–Homestead, 1993.

**Periodicals:** *Collectible Newspapers,* P. O. Box 19134-C, Lansing, MI, 48901; *PCM (Paper Collectors' Marketplace),* P.O. Box 128, Scandinavia, WI 54977.

**Advisor:** Tim Hughes.

**Note:** The listing concentrates on newspapers of the 20th century. The date given is the date of the event itself. The newspaper coverage usually appeared the following day.

| | |
|---|---|
| 1865, April 15, Lincoln Assassinated | **485.00** |
| 1869, May 9, Transcontinental Railroad Completed | **90.00** |
| 1871, Chicago Fire | **70.00** |
| 1886, October 28, Statue Of Liberty Dedicated | **60.00** |
| 1898, February 15, The Maine Is Sunk | **50.00** |
| 1898, front page, Spanish–American war battle reports | **10.00** |
| 1901, September 6, McKinley Is Shot | **55.00** |
| 1903, December 17, Wright Bros Fly | **255.00** |
| 1906, April 18, San Francisco Earthquake | **85.00** |
| 1912, April 15, Titanic Sinks | **250.00** |
| 1915, May 7, Lusitania Sunk | **175.00** |
| 1917, April 6, US Declares War | **30.00** |
| 1917–18, front page, World War II reports | **8.00** |
| 1918, November 11, Armistice Signed | **65.00** |
| 1920, January 16, Prohibition Goes In Effect | **35.00** |
| 1920, August 26, 19th Amendment Ratified (women vote) | **25.00** |
| 1921, July 14, Sacco & Vanzette Convicted | **10.00** |
| 1922, May 26, Babe Ruth Suspended | **15.00** |
| 1927, May 21, Lindbergh Flies The Atlantic | **50.00** |
| 1929, February 14, St Valentine's Day Massacre | **95.00** |
| 1929, October 28, Stock Market Crash | **75.00** |
| 1932, March 1, Lindbergh Baby Kidnapped | **25.00** |
| 1932, November 8, Franklin Roosevelt Elected | **25.00** |
| 1933, January 31, Hitler Named Chancellor | **20.00** |

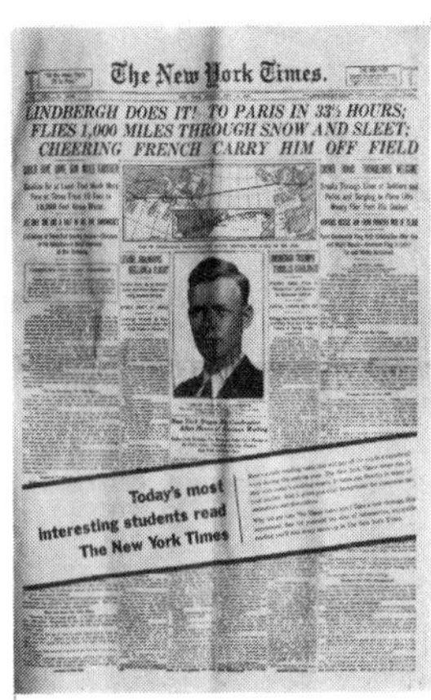
The New York Times.

LINDBERGH DOES IT! TO PARIS IN 33½ HOURS; FLIES 1,000 MILES THROUGH SNOW AND SLEET; CHEERING FRENCH CARRY HIM OFF FIELD

Today's most interesting students read The New York Times

**Lindbergh Does It!, *The New York Times,* May 22, 1927, Vol. 76, No. 25,320, $40.00.**

| | |
|---|---|
| 1933, December 5, Prohibition Repealed | **35.00** |
| 1934, May 23, Bonnie & Clyde Killed | **95.00** |
| 1934, July 22, Dillinger Shot & Killed | **55.00** |
| 1937, May 6, Hindenberg Crashes | **65.00** |
| 1939, September 1, Germany Invades Poland | **30.00** |
| 1941, December 7, Japan Attacks Pearl Harbor | **40.00** |
| 1941, December 11, U S Declares War On Italy & Germany | **20.00** |
| 1942–45, major World War II headline | **4.00** |
| 1945, May 7, War In Europe Ends | **30.00** |
| 1945, August 6, First Atomic Bomb Dropped In Japan | **30.00** |
| 1945, August 14, Japan Surrenders–War Over | **30.00** |
| 1948, November 3, "Dewey Defeats Truman," Chicago Tribune Error Headline | **700.00** |
| 1953, July 26, Truce Signed Ending The Korean War | **18.00** |
| 1955, May 17, Court Bans School Segregation | **18.00** |
| 1955, December 1, Rosa Parks Bus Incident | **18.00** |
| 1958, June 30, Alaska Joins The Union | **20.00** |
| 1959, March 12, Hawaii Joins The Union | **20.00** |
| 1963, November 22, Kennedy Assassinated | **25.00** |
| 1968, April 5, Martin Luther King Slain | **20.00** |
| 1969, July 20, Man Walks On The Moon | **20.00** |
| 1977, August 16, Elvis Presley Dies | **18.00** |
| 1986, January 28, Challenger Explodes | **5.00** |
| 1989, November 10, Berlin Wall Falls | **5.00** |
| 1991, January 16, War In The Gulf Begins | **5.00** |
| 1991, February 28, Gulf Cease Fire Declared | **5.00** |

# NILOAK POTTERY

**Collecting Hints:** Mission ware pottery is characterized by swirling layers of browns, blues, reds and cream. Very few pieces are glazed on both the outside and inside. Usually only the interior is glazed.

**History:** Niloak Pottery was made near Benton, Arkansas. Charles Dean Hyten, the founder of this pottery, experimented with the native clay and tried to preserve the natural colors. By 1911 he had perfected a method that produced this effect. The result was the popular Mission ware. The wares were marked Niloak, which is Kaolin, the type of fine porcelain clay used, spelled backwards.

After a devastating fire the pottery was rebuilt and named Eagle Pottery. This factory included the space to add a novelty pottery line which was introduced in 1929. This line continued until 1934 and usually bears the name Hywood–Niloak. After 1934 the name Hywood was dropped from the mark. Mr. Hyten left the pottery in 1941. In 1946 the operation closed.

**Reference:** David Edwin Gifford, *The Collector's Encyclopedia of Niloak,* Collector Books, 1993.

Ball Pitcher, medium green, low relief mark, 7½″ h .......... **30.00**
Basket, blue, low relief "N" mark, 4″ h **24.00**
Candlesticks, pr, Hywood Art Pottery, double cornucopia, white, unmarked, 6¾″ h .......... **75.00**
Console Bowl, 12¼″ d lotus flower shaped bowl, 7¼″ h crane shaped flower frog, white, low relief mark and Potteries stickers .......... **85.00**
Console Set, 14″ l oblong bowl, two 8⅜″ h bud vases, petal design, Ozark Dawn II .......... **100.00**
Cookie Jar, cov, hand thrown, blue, ear handles, 9½″ h .......... **80.00**
Creamer, cow, blue, Potteries sticker, 4½″ h .......... **60.00**
Ewer, Hywood line, dark brown, Potteries sticker, 6¾″ h .......... **15.00**
Flower frog
Duck, flying Ozark Dawn II, unmarked, 6″ h .......... **35.00**
Turtle, yellow, block letters mark, 4¾″ l, 1½″ h .......... **25.00**
Flowerpot, white, block letters mark, 3¼″ h .......... **20.00**
Humidor, cov, Mission Ware, second art mark, 5″ d, 7″ h .......... **400.00**
Jug, Ozark Dawn II, unmarked, 3″ h .. **15.00**
Lamp Base, Mission Ware, 9¾″ h .... **350.00**
Pin Dish, flower shaped, Ozark Dawn II, unmarked, 4″ d .......... **18.00**
Pitcher, ribbed neck, cobalt blue, Potteries sticker, 2¾″ h .......... **10.00**
Planter
Duck, wings extended, green, 4½″ h **25.00**
Elephant, standing on drum, light blue, incised mark, 6″ h .......... **20.00**
Scottie Dog, pink .......... **10.00**
Relish Dish, tree section, brown tones, unmarked, 9¾″ w .......... **50.00**
Salt and Pepper Shakers, pr, ball with "S" or "P" shaped handles, medium green, Potteries sticker, 2¼″ h ...... **20.00**
Strawberry Jar, tulips, medium brown, Niloak low relief mark, 7¼″ h ..... **30.00**

**Vase, olive green matte finish, 6″ h, $18.00.**

Vase
Fan, light blue, incised mark, 5¼″ h **10.00**
Mission Ware, 9¾″ h .......... **250.00**
Wall Pocket
Bouquet pattern, brown, low relief mark, 5″ h .......... **40.00**
Mission Ware, conical, unmarked, 6″ h .......... **225.00**

# NIPPON CHINA, 1891–1921

**Collecting Hints:** Examine each item carefully. Try not to purchase items with chips, cracks, hairlines, spiderwebs, or that have been restored. The condition of each item, in relationship to selling price, should be taken into consideration.

Also try to avoid buying sets which are incomplete. No matter what people say, you do not easily find the lid which is missing from your humidor, the cup and saucer to complete your chocolate set or the creamer to match your sugar bowl. Know what constitutes a complete set.

Beginning collectors should try to purchase only Nippon marked items. Learn the difference between the authentic marks and the reproduction marks. There are unmarked pieces from the Nippon era, but the purchase of these items should be put off until the collector has a commanding knowledge of Nippon.

**History:** Nippon, Japanese hand painted porcelain, was made for export between the years of 1891 and 1921.

In October 1891, the McKinley Tariff Act was passed by Congress, proclaiming that "All articles of foreign manufacture, be stamped, branded, or labeled, and all packages containing such or their imported articles, shall, respectively, be marked, stamped, branded, or labeled in legible English words, so as to indicate the country of their origin; and unless so marked, stamped, branded, or labeled they shall not be admitted to entry."

The Japanese chose to use "Nippon," which is the English equivalent of Japan, as their marking.

The McKinley Tariff Act also set rules and regulations on the marking system, stating that "all articles of foreign manufacture which are capable of being marked without injury shall be marked with the country of origin in legible English words and marking shall be nearly indelible and permanent as the nature of the article will permit." Paper labels were accepted. In the case of small articles shipped together, only the inside and outside packages were marked with the country of origin.

In 1921 the Government reversed its position and decided that: "Nippon" was no longer in compliance with the law. "After examination into the history and derivation of the word 'Nippon' and its treatment by lexicographers of recognized standing, the department is constrained to the conclusion that 'Nippon' is a Japanese word, the English equivalent of which is 'Japan', and the weight of authority does not support the earlier view that the word has become incorporated into the English language." All Japanese items now had to be marked "Japan," thus ending the Nippon era.

Nippon marks were applied by two methods: an under the glaze decal sticker or direct imprinting.

There are over 221 recorded Nippon backstamps or marks known to collectors today. The three most readily found and widely recognized are the "M" in Wreath, Maple Leaf and Rising Sun marks.

The majority of all marks are found in three color variations: green, blue, and magenta. The color of the mark indicates the quality of the porcelain used: green denotes first grade quality of porcelain; blue denotes second grade; and magenta denotes third grade.

**References:** Gene Loendorf, *Nippon Hand Painted China,* McGrew Color Graphics, 1975; Joan Van Patten, *The Collector's Encyclopedia Of Nippon Porcelain, Series One,* (1979, 1991 value update), *Series Two,* (1982, 1991 value update), *Series Three,* (1985, 1991 value update), Collector Books; Kathy Wojciechowski, *The Wonderful World of Nippon Porcelain: 1891–1921,* Schiffer Publishing, Ltd., 1992.

**Collectors' Clubs:** Great Lakes Nippon Collectors Club, P. O. Box 230, Peotone, IL 60468; International Nippon Collectors Club, 46-45 8 St, New York, NY 11358; Long Island Nippon Collectors Club, 3372 Hewlett Ave, Merrick, NY 11566; New England Nippon Collectors Club, 145 Londonderry Rd, Windham, NH 03087.

**Advisor:** Kathy Wojciechowski.

**REPRODUCTION ALERT:** Most so called Nippon reproductions do not even resemble the Nippon era wares; but, there is a "Nippon" backstamp found on them, thus fooling many collectors and dealers.

The pattern often found and on the biggest variety of pieces is "Wildflower." These items have a bisque finish, outside edges are highlighted with gold, and pink to lavender flower blossoms are used as the decoration. All wares in this pattern are marked with a bogus hourglass in a wreath mark.

The "Green Mist" pattern items are reminiscent of Limoges pieces in shape, have a bisque finish, a light to medium green background, pink flowers, and gold trim. The mark found on these pieces is similar to the familiar Nippon rising sun mark except that the rays are connected rather than open as in the genuine mark.

The "Antique Rose" pattern is one of the newest patterns being reproduced. This can be found in a variety of shapes and bears the bogus maple leaf mark, which is almost a duplicate of the genuine mark except that it is much larger in size.

Most reproduction Nippon wares are manufactured in Japan and have a "Nippon" mark of some type under the glaze and a small paper label on the bottom saying "Made in Japan." Dealers buy wholesale from the importing firms. First, they discard the shipping boxes, then the paper label, resulting in a genuine marked "Nippon" item for the market.

Ashtray, triangular shape, palm trees scene, moriage trim, Wreath mark .. **85.00**
Basket
  6½" l, maroon and pink roses, white background, gold handle ........ **215.00**
  10" h, red and white roses, foliage, gold trim, Leaf mark ............ **265.00**
  11" h, bisque, scenic, wreath mark . **225.00**
Bowl
  Blue roses and gold, open pierced gold handle, Wreath mark ....... **85.00**

**Ashtray, relief dec, reclining dog, continuous scene, 5¾″ d, 2¼″ h, $150.00.**

Pink roses and gold, gold loop handles, 5″ d, Rising Sun mark ...... **65.00**
Red roses, blown–out mold, gold bands, scalloped edges, unmarked **135.00**
Roses outlined in gold, blown–out shape, dark green background, scalloped edges, Wreath mark ... **245.00**

Cake Set, master and six small plates, orange and black flowers, TEOH mark .......................... **95.00**

Candlestick
8½″ h, roses, gray and green background, gold beaded top and bottom bands, Wreath mark ........ **65.00**

Celery Set, master and four small, yellow roses, white background, TEOH mark .......................... **65.00**

Chocolate Set
Floral and gold, pot, four cups and saucers, cobalt background, Leaf mark ........................ **850.00**
Scenic medallion top bands, outlined in gold, white background, narrow pot, Wreath mark ............. **375.00**

Cracker Jar
Red and white roses, gold outline, gold bead centers, melon ribbed body, ftd, Pagoda mark ......... **195.00**
White flowers, gold trim, deep green background, Wreath mark ....... **135.00**

Cup and Saucer
Birds in flight scene, bisque, Rising Sun mark .................... **35.00**
Pink rose garland, green foliage, white background, Wreath mark . **45.00**

Doll, bisque
4¼″ h, policeman, incised mark ... **135.00**
7″ h, jointed arms and legs, incised mark ........................ **135.00**
13″ h, red cloth body, bisque hands and feet, turned head, shoulder plate, blue painted ribbon in hair, incised mark .................. **235.00**

Dresser Set
4 pcs, tray, powder box, hair receiver, and pin tray, pink and blue flower bands, green foliage, white background, Rising Sun mark ........ **95.00**
8 pcs, 13″ tray, hatpin holder, candle holder, ftd powder box, hair receiver, two cov boxes, and pin tray, swans on lake, sunset on water, beige, Sho–Fu mark ........... **295.00**

Dutch Shoes
Moriage dragon, glass eyes, gray background, unmarked ......... **65.00**
Scenic, lake, trees, and house, bisque, Wreath mark ........... **175.00**

Egg Cup, double, pink and yellow floral bands, white background, 5″ h ..... **25.00**

Egg Warmer, stopper, holds four eggs, Rising Sun mark
Floral band, gold and white trim ... **125.00**
Scenic, trees and lake ............. **135.00**

Ewer
9″ h, pink roses, white moriage, marbleized pastel background, handle bolted base, unmarked .......... **285.00**
10″ h, lacy white moriage, gold trim, fancy spout and handle, unmarked **385.00**

Fruit Bowl, 11″ w, orchids, gold outline, ftd, Wreath mark ................ **165.00**

Hat Pin Holder
Center medallion with swans on lake, turquoise background, Wreath mark ........................ **85.00**
Light and dark pink roses top and bottom bands, gold trim, white center and background, 3½″ h ......... **55.00**
Rows of pink roses, gold outline, white background ............. **95.00**

Humidor
Blown out horse heads, rect, cov, .. **475.00**
Egyptian sailing ship, full sail, small sailing ships background, earth tones, 7″ h, Leaf mark .......... **375.00**
Geometric outlined panels, women carrying milk pails, front medallion of woman milking cow, 6″ h, 47 mark ....................... **350.00**
Hexagonal, bisque finish, black slip trailing, blue jewels, rocky island and sailboat, sailboats background, 6¾″ h, Maple Leaf mark ........ **245.00**
Scenic, black trees, lane, and house, bisque, Wreath mark ........... **300.00**

Lemonade Set, pitcher and six mugs, TEOH mark
Bisque, purple violets, pale green background .................. **160.00**
Dutch sailing ships and windmill ... **175.00**

Mug, 5½″ h, moriage dragon, blue enameled eyes, gray bisque background, green M in Wreath mark ... **225.00**

Napkin Ring
Owl on tree stump, figural, 4″ h, Wreath mark ................. **375.00**
Windmill scene, blue background, Wreath mark ................. **125.00**

Nappy, 5 x 5″, cottage scene, beaded handle, matte finish, Wreath mark .. **25.00**
Nut Set, pedestal master bowl and six small bowls, colorful nuts int., moriage flowers and leaves edges, Leaf mark .......................... **185.00**
Pancake Server, 9″, round, pink and green roses, pink and green jewels, bisque finish, gold overlay design, Maple Wreath mark .............. **325.00**
Pitcher, 7″ h, moriage sea gulls, slate gray background, Maple Leaf mark . **250.00**

Plaque
- 6″ h, man, Egyptian symbols and animals, sgd .................... **125.00**
- 10″
  - Arab by campfire, Art Deco rim, Wreath mark ................ **275.00**
  - Three dancing children, animals, rim, Wreath mark ............ **350.00**
- 10 x 8″, two Indians on horseback, sunset, bisque, Indian deco design band, Wreath mark ............. **475.00**
- 10½″, collie and terrier, relief molded, Wreath mark .......... **950.00**

Plate
- 10″ d, center medallion portrait, gold overlay design and jewel bands, Maple Leaf mark ............... **325.00**
- 11″ d, white center, gold beaded red and pink roses bunches, gold border, Maple Leaf mark ........... **65.00**

Potpourri, bisque, windmill, house, and lake scene, Wreath mark .......... **95.00**

Punch Bowl
- 11″ d, 2 pcs, gold scenic medallions on green, gold overlay design, ftd pedestal base .................. **550.00**
- 12″, d, man and boat scene, cobalt blue trim, cobalt and white base, gold loop handles, stand, Maple Leaf mark ..................... **300.00**
- 12½″ d, bisque, scenic center, rose bouquets, gold and jewels dec rim, stand, Wreath mark ............ **395.00**

Ramekin, grape bunches and leaves band, Maple Leaf mark ........... **35.00**

Salt and Pepper Shakers, pr
- Cobalt and red roses, gold overlay and beads, Maple Leaf mark ..... **55.00**
- Pastel floral top band, white background, Rising Sun mark ........ **25.00**

Sandwich Set, 17″ master tray, four 6″ small plates, iris bands, Wreath mark **145.00**
Serving Tray, 11″ d, gold and burgundy medallions in gold fluted rim, multicolored roses and leaves center, gold open pierced handles, Royal Kinran mark .................... **195.00**

Shaving Mug
- Pale green, floral design ........... **110.00**
- Red and green floral, white background, Rising Sun mark ........ **45.00**

Smoke Set
- 3 pcs, 7″ tray, cigar holder, and ashtray, bisque, playing card design, deep brown and cream background, Wreath mark ........... **185.00**
- 4 pcs, 11″ tray, cigarette holder, match holder, and ashtray, pastel and sunset colored rural scene, Wreath mark .................. **255.00**

Spoon Holder, 7¾″ w, yellow florals, black and green leaves ............ **35.00**

Stickpin Holder
- Cobalt and gold, white background, Wreath mark .................. **135.00**
- Multicolored roses, gold trim, 1½″ h, Wreath mark .................. **100.00**

Tankard, 12″ h
- Forest scene, matte finish, unmarked **165.00**
- Pink and white poppies, Maple Leaf mark ........................ **265.00**

Tea Set
- 3 pcs, teapot, creamer, and sugar, flying blue birds, white background, gold handles, finials, and rims, Wreath mark ............. **95.00**
- 12 pcs, teapot, creamer, sugar, and four cups and saucers, cobalt background, gold wash, Pagoda mark . **350.00**

Tea Strainer, bisque, scenic, white underplate, Maple Leaf mark ......... **65.00**

Urn
- 9½″ h, white flowers outlined in gold, turquoise background, handles, dome lid, pedestal base, Royal Kinran mark ...................... **425.00**
- 12″ h, Queen Louise portrait center medallion, turquoise background, gold and jewels, dome lid, Maple Leaf mark .....................**1,200.00**
- 16″ h, cows drinking from pond center medallion, gold overlay floral,

**Vase, tan, brown beaded deer, light green M in wreath mark surrounded by HP and Nippon, 4½″ h, $85.00.**

bolted base, gold stand–up handles, Wreath mark .............. **575.00**

Vase

5½" h, double handles, lake scene, wreath mark with M ............ **135.00**

7" h, multicolored floral and foliage front and back, shaded bisque background, gold overlay collar and base, coralene, marked "Patent Applied For" ............... **195.00**

8" h, floral medallions, heavy gold beading, wreath mark with M .... **125.00**

8½" h, double handles, country scene, foreground lake scene, large trees, wreath mark with M ....... **225.00**

9" h, magenta and pink roses center medallion with turquoise beads, gold background, Maple Leaf mark **425.00**

10" h, Indian and canoe scene, Wreath mark .................. **525.00**

11¼" h, orchids and foliage outlined in gold, bisque to brown background, gold reticulated handles, Maple Leaf mark ............... **325.00**

12½" h, cobalt and swan scene, gold overlay, Maple Leaf mark ........ **450.00**

Whiskey Jug

Egyptian Nile scene, bisque, gold handle, stopper, and lip rim, 7½" h, Wreath mark ................ **425.00**

Palm trees and lake scene, raised moriage trim ................... **450.00**

# NORITAKE AZALEA CHINA

**Collecting Hints:** There are several backstamps on the Azalea pattern of Noritake China. The approximate dates are:

| | |
|---|---|
| Prior to 1921: | Blue rising sun, printed "Hand painted NIPPON" |
| 1921–1923: | Green wreath with M, printed "Noritake, Hand painted, Made in Japan" |
| 1923–1930s: | Green wreath with M, printed "Noritake, Hand painted, Made in Japan 19322" |
| 1925–1930s: | Red wreath with M, printed "Noritake, Hand painted, Made in Japan 19322" |
| 1935–1940: | Red azalea sprig, printed "Noritake Azalea Patt., Hand painted, Japan No. 19322/252622" |

Most of the saucers and underplates do not have a backstamp, except those stamped "Azalea 19322/252622."

Most collectors assemble sets and are not concerned with specific marks. Those concentrating on specific marks, particularly the NIPPON one, may pay more. There presently are individuals who offer replacement service.

**History:** The Azalea pattern of Noritake China, made of fine china, was produced first in the early 1900s. Each piece was hand painted. The individuality of each artist makes it almost impossible to find two pieces with identical painting.

In the early 1900s the Larkin Company of Buffalo, New York, sold many household items to the American public through their catalog (similar to the Sears, Roebuck catalog). In the 1924 Larkin catalog a basic, Azalea pattern serving set was advertised. The set included the larger coffee cups with the blue rising sun backstamp.

Two forces came together in the 1920s to make the Azalea pattern of Noritake China one of the most popular household patterns in this century. First, the Larkin Company initiated their "Larkin Plan," in which housewives could sign up to become "Larkin Secretaries." Each Larkin Secretary formed a small neighborhood group of five or more women who would buy Larkin products for their homes. The Larkin Secretary earned premiums based on the volume of sales she obtained. Household items, including Azalea china, could then be purchased either for cash or premiums.

Second, many households in the 1920s could not afford a complete set of fine china in a single purchase. The Larkin Club Plan enabled them to obtain items in the Azalea pattern one or a few at a time.

Over the years, and to provide more enticements, additional pieces, such as the nut/fruit shell shaped bowl, candy jar, and child's tea set were added. Glassware, originally classified as crystal, was introduced in the 1930s but was not well received.

It became somewhat of a status symbol to "own a set of Azalea." The Azalea pattern china advertisement in the 1931 Larkin catalog claimed, *"Our Most Popular China."*

Some Azalea pieces were advertised for sale in the Larkin catalogs for 19 consecutive years, while others were advertised for only 4 or 5 years. These latter pieces are more scarce, and more sought after by collectors, resulting in a faster appreciation in value.

The ultimate goals of most serious collectors are the child's tea set, which we believe was advertised in only two Larkin Fall catalogs, and the so-called salesmen's samples, which were never advertised for sale.

The Larkin Company ceased operations as a distributor in 1945. Due to the quality and popularity of the Azalea pattern, this beautiful china remains cherished and highly collectible.

**Reference:** Larkin catalogs from 1916 through 1941.

**Note:** The Larkin catalog numbers are given in parentheses behind each listing. If arranged numerically, you will notice gaps in the numbering. For example, numbers 41 through 53 are missing. The "Scenic" pattern, presently called "Tree in the Meadow," of Noritake China also was popular during this same time period. Many of the missing Azalea numbers were assigned to the Scenic pattern.

**Vegetable, cov, handled, gold finial, $375.00.**

## CHINA

Basket (193) . . . . . . . . . . . . . . . . . . . . . . . **145.00**
Bonbon 6¼" d (184) . . . . . . . . . . . . . . . . **45.00**
Bouillon Cup, underplate, 5¼" d (124) **20.00**
Bowl (12) . . . . . . . . . . . . . . . . . . . . . . . . **33.00**
Butter Pat, 3¼" d, (312) . . . . . . . . . . . . **10.00**
Butter Tub (54) . . . . . . . . . . . . . . . . . . . . **25.00**
Cake Plate, 9¾" d, (10) . . . . . . . . . . . . **50.00**
Casserole, cov, gold finial, (372) . . . . . **525.00**
Celery Dish, 10" l (444) . . . . . . . . . . . . **250.00**
Coffeepot (182) . . . . . . . . . . . . . . . . . . . **475.00**
Creamer and Sugar (7) . . . . . . . . . . . . . **30.00**
Cup and Saucer (2) . . . . . . . . . . . . . . . . **15.00**
Demitasse Cup and Saucer (183) . . . . . **125.00**
Egg Cup (120) . . . . . . . . . . . . . . . . . . . . **55.00**
Fruit Bowl (9) . . . . . . . . . . . . . . . . . . . . **10.00**
Grapefruit Bowl, 4½" d (185) . . . . . . . . **115.00**
Gravy Boat (4) . . . . . . . . . . . . . . . . . . . . **35.00**
Lemon Dish (121) . . . . . . . . . . . . . . . . . . **25.00**
Marmalade Set (125), price for three piece set . . . . . . . . . . . . . . . . . . . . . . . . **135.00**
Mayonnaise Set (453), price for three piece set . . . . . . . . . . . . . . . . . . . . . . . . **425.00**
Milk Jug (100) . . . . . . . . . . . . . . . . . . . . **165.00**
Mustard Jar (191) . . . . . . . . . . . . . . . . . . **55.00**
Plate
6¼" d, bread and butter (8) . . . . . . . . **9.50**
7½" d, salad (4) . . . . . . . . . . . . . . . . . . **10.00**
8½" d, breakfast (98) . . . . . . . . . . . . . **18.00**
9¾" d, dinner (13) . . . . . . . . . . . . . . . **22.50**
Platter, 16" l (186) . . . . . . . . . . . . . . . . . **375.00**
Relish, 8½" l, oval (18) . . . . . . . . . . . . . **20.00**
Salad Bowl, 9½" d (12) . . . . . . . . . . . . . **45.00**
Salt and Pepper Shakers, pr, 3" h, bulbous . . . . . . . . . . . . . . . . . . . . . . . . . . . **25.00**
Soup Plate, (19) . . . . . . . . . . . . . . . . . . . . **18.00**
Spoon Holder, 8" l (189) . . . . . . . . . . . . **70.00**
Syrup, cov, underplate (97) . . . . . . . . . . **125.00**
Teapot, cov, (15) . . . . . . . . . . . . . . . . . . . **85.00**
Tile, 6" w (169) . . . . . . . . . . . . . . . . . . . . **35.00**
Toothpick Holder (192) . . . . . . . . . . . . . **80.00**
Vase, fan, ftd (187) . . . . . . . . . . . . . . . . **125.00**
Vegetable, oval, 10½" l (101) . . . . . . . . **33.00**
Whipped Cream Set (3) . . . . . . . . . . . . . **25.00**

## GLASSWARE, HAND PAINTED

Cake Plate, 10½" d (124) . . . . . . . . . . . . **40.00**
Candlesticks, pr, (114) . . . . . . . . . . . . . . **35.00**
Cheese and Cracker Set (111) . . . . . . . . **60.00**
Compote, 10" d (113) . . . . . . . . . . . . . . . **55.00**
Fruit Bowl, 8½" d (11) . . . . . . . . . . . . . . **50.00**
Tray, 10" l (112) . . . . . . . . . . . . . . . . . . . . **45.00**

# NUTCRACKERS

**Collecting Hints:** The most popular modern nutcrackers are the military and civilian figures which are made in East Germany. These are collected primarily for show and not for practical use.

Nutcracker design responded to each decorating phase through the 1950s. The figural nutcrackers of the Art Deco and Art Nouveau periods are much in demand. Concentrating on 19th century models results in a display of cast iron ingenuity. These nutcrackers were largely utilitarian and meant to be used.

Several cast iron animal models have been reproduced. Signs of heavy use is one method to tell an older model.

**History:** Nuts keep well for long periods, up to two years, and have served as a dessert or additive to cakes, pies, bread, etc., since the colonial period. Americans' most favorite nuts are walnuts, chestnuts, pecans, and almonds.

The first nutcrackers were crude hammers or a club device. The challenge was to find a cracker that would crack the shell but leave the nut intact. By the mid–19th century cast iron nutcrackers in animal shapes appeared. Usually the nut was placed in the jaw section of the animal and the tail pressed as the lever to crack the nut.

The 19th and early 20th century patent records abound with nutcracker inventions. In 1916 a lever–operated cracker which could be clamped to the table was patented as the Home Nut Cracker, St. Louis, Missouri. Perhaps one of the most durable designs was patented on January 28, 1889, and sold as the Quakenbush plated model. This hand model was plain at the top where the grip teeth were located and had twist–style handles on the lower half of each arm with the arms ending in an acorn finial.

**Reference:** Judith A. Rittenhouse, *Ornamental and Figural Nutcrackers: An Identification and Value Guide,* Collector Books, 1993.

**Cast Iron, Negroid features, red hat, mouth, and collar, white highlights, 5½" h, $225.00.**

Alligator, brass .......... **25.00**
Bear, wood, hand carved, glass eyes, German .......... **100.00**
Cat, nickel covered brass, 4½" .......... **45.00**
Couple, brass, sailor and lady, kisses when handles squeeze together, 6¼" **65.00**
Dog
- Brass, 10", 5¼" h .......... **65.00**
- Bronze, whippet, running, 7¾", 3¾" h .......... **75.00**
- Cast Iron, old paint, 4⅝" .......... **65.00**

Elephant, orig paint, c1920, 10" l, 5" h **70.00**
Hand, wood, holding cup, hand carved, 7⅝" .......... **110.00**
Jester, brass, head .......... **75.00**
Lady's Leg, 7", wood .......... **30.00**
Man, wood, bust, hand carved, 9" h .. **65.00**
Monkey, wood, carved, 6¾" .......... **90.00**
Parrot, brass, 5½" .......... **15.00**
Pheasant, bronze, France .......... **100.00**
Pliers Type
- Cast iron, Torrington .......... **4.00**
- Silver, double .......... **30.00**
- Steel, adjustable, c1890, 5½" .......... **12.00**

Punch & Judy, brass, figural .......... **100.00**
Rabbit, wood, head, hand carved, glass eyes, German .......... **100.00**
Ram, wood, carved, glass eyes, 8½" l **65.00**
Skull and Cross Bones, cast iron, 6" .. **85.00**
Squirrel
- Bronze, sitting on branch .......... **50.00**
- Cast Iron, sitting on leaf .......... **45.00**
- Wood, eating nut, carved, twist and screw type, 7" .......... **60.00**

Table Type, Perfection Nut Cracker Co, Waco, TX, patented 1914, clamp and turn buckle .......... **20.00**

# OCCUPIED JAPAN

**Collecting Hints:** Buyers should be aware that a rubber stamp can be used to mark "Occupied Japan" on the base of objects. Finger nail polish remover can be used to test a mark. An original mark will remain since it is under the glaze; fake marks will disappear. This procedure should not be used on unglazed pieces. Your eye is your best key to identifying a bad mark on an unglazed item.

Damaged pieces have little value unless the piece is extremely rare. Focus on quality pieces which are made well and nicely decorated. There are many inferior examples.

**History:** At the end of World War II, the Japanese economy was devastated. To secure needed hard currency, the Japanese pottery industry produced thousands of figurines and other knick knacks for export. From the beginning of American occupation until April 28, 1952, these objects were marked "Japan," "Made in Japan," "Occupied Japan," and "Made in Occupied Japan." Only pieces marked with the last two designations are of strong interest to Occupied Japan collectors. The first two marks also were used at other time periods.

The variety of products is endless—ashtrays, dinnerware, lamps, planters, souvenir items, toys, vases, etc. Initially it was the figurines which attracted the largest number of collectors; today many collectors focus on non–figurine material.

**References:** Florence Archambault, *Occupied Japan For Collectors,* Schiffer Publishing, Ltd., 1992; Gene Florence, *The Collector's Encyclopedia Of Occupied Japan Collectibles, 1st Series* (1976, 1992 value update), *2nd Series* (1979, 1993 value update), *3rd Series* (1987), *4th Series* (1990), and *5th Series,* (1992), Collector Books.

**Collectors' Clubs:** Occupied Japan Collectors Club, 18309 Faysmith Ave., Torrance, CA 90504; The O. J. Club, 29 Freeborn Street, Newport, RI 02840.

Ashtray
- Coal Hod, china, white, floral dec . **10.00**
- Florida, china, state shaped, black lettering, "FLORIDA," gold trim .... **12.00**
- Pikes Peak, metal, emb scene, oval . **3.00**

Badge, Special Police .......... **12.00**
Basket, china, miniature, floral dec ... **4.00**
Bell, chef holding wine bottle and glass, 3" h .......... **24.00**
Bookends, pr, sailing ships, emb wood **75.00**
Box, book shaped, metal .......... **12.00**
Cigarette Box, cov, china, rect, blue floral dec, gold trim .......... **15.00**
Cigarette Set, plated metal, cov box, with Scottie dog, matching lighter .. **20.00**

**Needle Book, New York, five needle packages, 1940s, 3½ x 6″, $15.00.**

| | |
|---|---|
| Clicker, beetle, silver colored | 5.00 |
| Coaster Set, papier mâché box, six coasters, floral dec | 18.00 |
| Compass, pocket watch shape | 20.00 |
| Cornucopia, china, white, pink roses, gold trim | 35.00 |
| Creamer, figural, cow | 25.00 |
| Crumb Tray, metal, emb New York scenes | 10.00 |
| Cup and Saucer | |
| Checkered Borders, black and white | 6.00 |
| Floral Dec, blue | 12.50 |
| Demitasse Cup and Saucer, white, yellow and red flowers | 10.00 |
| Dish, china, fish shape | 10.00 |
| Doll, celluloid, baby wearing snowsuit, jointed | 40.00 |
| Doll House Furnishings, china | |
| Couch, white, pink roses, 3″ l | 15.00 |
| Lamp, white base, green shade, gold trim | 10.00 |
| Refrigerator, Philco, white, 2½″ h | 18.00 |
| Figure | |
| Ballerina, bisque, 4¾″ h | 32.00 |
| Cherub with Horn, bisque, nude | 25.00 |
| Donkey, china | 8.00 |
| Duck, wearing hat, china | 6.00 |
| Elf, standing behind log, china | 15.00 |
| Flamingo | 22.50 |
| Frog, playing accordion, china | 12.50 |
| Horses, jumping, 5″ h | 10.00 |
| Hula Dancer, celluloid, MIB | 120.00 |
| Lady, china, hp, 8½″ h | 145.00 |
| Santa, china, 6½″ h | 65.00 |
| Harmonica, Butterfly, orig box | 17.50 |
| Head Vase, Oriental girl, china | 18.00 |
| Honey Jar, bee hive, bee finial | 25.00 |
| Incense Burner, woman | 20.00 |
| Kazoo, litho tin, set of 3, MIB | 5.00 |
| Lamp Base, colonial couple, bisque, gold trim, 7¼″ h | 45.00 |
| Lighter, pistol shape, metal, pearl grips | 15.00 |
| Mirror, pocket, round, lady portrait on back | 8.00 |
| Mug, china | |
| Boy Handle | 14.00 |
| Indian Chief | 35.00 |
| MacArthur | 55.00 |
| Napkins, damask, orig paper labels, price for set of six | 45.00 |
| Necklace, pearls, double strand, orig paper label | 12.00 |
| Nodder, donkey, celluloid | 30.00 |
| Noise Maker, horn, gold | 25.00 |
| Parasol, multicolored, 32″ d | 50.00 |
| Perfume Bottle, glass, blue, 4″ h | 15.00 |
| Piano Baby, hp | 65.00 |
| Pincushion, metal, grand piano shape, red velvet cushion | 15.00 |
| Pistol, plastic, black | 7.00 |
| Planter, china | |
| Baby Booties, blue trim | 8.00 |
| Cat, sitting up | 10.00 |
| Dog, with basket | 20.00 |
| Donkey Pulling Cart | 10.00 |
| Plate | |
| Cabin Scene, chickens in yard | 18.00 |
| Cherries, lacy edge | 25.00 |
| Geisha, Girls | 20.00 |
| Platter, Blue Willow pattern, oval, 12″ l | 35.00 |
| Powder Jar, cov, Wedgwood style, blue and white, 3″ d | 15.00 |
| Rooster, inflatable, rubber | 20.00 |
| Salt and Pepper Shakers, pr | |
| Hat, one brown, one black | 15.00 |
| Pigs, large ears | 12.00 |
| Shelf Sitter, Little Boy Blue | 15.00 |
| Silent Butler, metal | 20.00 |
| Stein, man and woman with dog, 8½″ h | 40.00 |
| Tape Measure, figural, pig, flowered dec | 35.00 |
| Teapot, china, colonial couple dec | 20.00 |
| Tea Set, miniature, china, floral dec | 25.00 |
| Toby Pitcher, barkeeper, holding mugs, 5″ h | 30.00 |
| Toothpick holder, puppy in barrel | 6.00 |

**Trapeze Toy, windup, celluloid figure marked "My Friend" in globe on back, inspection sticker on leg, 1930s, 8¼″ h, $60.00.**

Toy
- Boy on Sled, windup, litho tin, MIB . . . 150.00
- Camel, walker, celluloid, MIB . . . . . 120.00
- Cherry Cook, windup . . . . . . . . . . . . . 90.00
- Dancing Couple, celluloid, MIB . . . . 95.00
- Minstrel Monkey, celluloid, MIB . . . 175.00
- Monkey, windup, plays banjo, orig box . . . . . . . . . . . . . . . . . . . . . . . . 75.00
- Trick Seal, windup . . . . . . . . . . . . . . . 80.00

Tray, rect, papier mâché, black ground, gold floral dec . . . . . . . . . . . . . . . . . . 8.00

Vase
- Boy, skiing . . . . . . . . . . . . . . . . . . . . . 9.00
- Wedgwood style, pink rose . . . . . . . . 7.50

Wall Pocket, violin . . . . . . . . . . . . . . . . 10.00

Water Pistol, white, bird emb on side . 8.00

# OCEAN LINER COLLECTIBLES

**Collecting Hints:** Don't concentrate only on ships of American registry. Many collectors do favor material from only one liner or ship line. Objects associated with ships involved in disasters, such as the *Titanic,* often command higher prices.

**History:** Transoceanic travel falls into two distinct periods: the era of the great Clipper ships and the era of the diesel powered ocean liners. The latter craft reached their "Golden Age" in the period between 1900 and 1940.

An ocean liner was a city unto itself. Many had their own printing rooms to produce a wealth of daily memorabilia. Companies such as Cunard, Holland–America, and others encouraged passengers to acquire souvenirs with the company logo and ship name. Word–of–mouth was a principal form of advertising.

Certain ships acquired a unique mystique. The *Queen Elizabeth, Queen Mary,* and *United States* became symbols of elegance and style. Today the cruise ship dominates the world of the ocean liner.

**References:** John Adams, *Ocean Steamers: The History of Ocean Going Steam Ships,* New Cavendish Books, 1992; Norman E. Martinus and Harry L. Rinker, *Warman's Paper,* Wallace–Homestead, 1993; Karl D. Spence, *How To Identify and Price Ocean Liner Collectibles,* published by author, 1991; Karl D. Spence, *Oceanliner Collectibles,* published by author, 1992.

**Collectors' Clubs:** Steamship Historical Society of America, Inc., Suite #4, 300 Ray Drive, Providence, RI 02906; Titanic Historical Society, P. O. Box 51053, Indian Orchard, MA 01151.

Ashtray
- Everett (WA) Yacht Club, brass . . . . . 20.00
- *RMS Queen Elizabeth I,* Cunard Line, wooden ship's wheel, glass insert over color center photo . . . . . . . . . 30.00
- *Pacific Far East Steamship,* china . . . 25.00

Baggage Tag, French Line, France funnel, first class . . . . . . . . . . . . . . . . . . . . 5.00

Belt Buckle, *Queen Elizabeth II,* Cunard Line, chrome plated solid brass, black outline of ship, name in red . . . . . . . 14.00

Booklet
- *Independence,* American Export Lines, 1966 Gala Springtime Cruise, itinerary and deck plan inserts . . . . . . . . . . . . . . . . . . . . . . . . . 20.00
- *St Lawrence Route to Europe,* Canadian Pacific 1930, 8 x 11", 16 pgs 24.00

Change Tray, American Line Ship . . . . 100.00

Cigarette Lighter, *Queen Mary* . . . . . . . 32.00

Coffee Cup, *SS United States* . . . . . . . . 32.00

Compact, *Empress of Canada,* Canadian Pacific Line, Stratton, line flag logo, ship's name in enameled front medallion . . . . . . . . . . . . . . . . . . . . . . . . . 40.00

Cruise Book, *Scythia,* 1929 . . . . . . . . . . 30.00

Deck Card, Concordia Lines, Norway . 18.00

Deck Plan
- *MV Westerdam,* 1950, multicolored 15.00
- *RMS Samaria,* Cunard Line, Plan of Tourist Accommodation . . . . . . . . . 15.00
- *SS Hamburg,* 1930, fold out . . . . . . . 35.00

Dish, *Queen Mary,* Cunard Line, ceramic, 5" l, oval, color portrait, gold edge, Staffordshire . . . . . . . . . . . . . . . . 35.00

Excursion Announcement, *SS Cuba* . . . 20.00

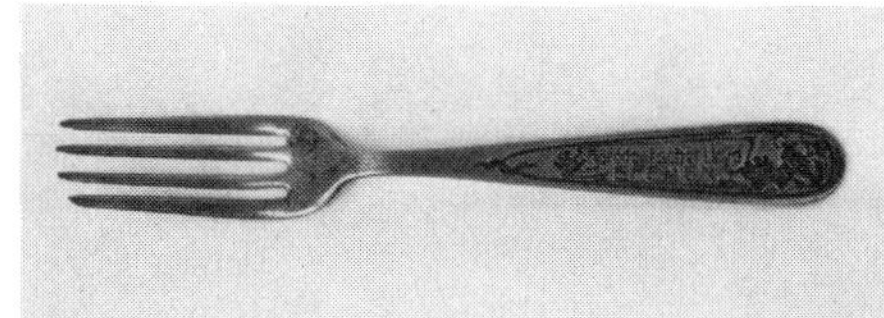

**Fork, *Bremen,* Norddeutscher Lloyd Lines, 7¾" l, $50.00.**

Goblet, *Queen Elizabeth II,* Cunard Line, souvenir, etched image and name, mfd by Stuart Crystal, #1305 225.00

Log Extract, Quebec to London
- *Aurana,* Cunard Line, 1938 . . . . . . . . 6.00
- *Scythia,* Cunard Line, 1949 . . . . . . . . 6.00

Menu
- Cosulich Lines, 1929 . . . . . . . . . . . . 8.00
- *RMS Samaria,* Cunard Line, 1953 . . 5.00
- *Scythia,* Cunard Line, 1949 . . . . . . . . 5.00
- *SS Lurline,* March 1960, cover art by L Macouillard . . . . . . . . . . . . . . . . . . 15.00

Paper Ephemera, loose leaf activity schedules and menus, *RMS Maureta Seas,* West Indies cruise, Feb 18 through March 8, 1954 . . . . . . . . . . . 40.00

**Passenger List, *R.M.S. Aquitania,* Cunard Line, sailing from Southampton to New York via Cherbourg, Saturday, 20th June, 1925, 32 pgs, 5 x 7½", $30.00.**

Passenger List
- *RMS Aquitania,* full color illus of ship **50.00**
- *SS Leviathan,* 1924 . . . . . . . . . . . . . . . **15.00**
- *St Louis,* American Line, eastbound trip, Feb 10, 1906 . . . . . . . . . . . . . **35.00**

Passport Cover, Red Star Line, fabric, ship illus . . . . . . . . . . . . . . . . . . . . . . . **25.00**

Pinback Button
- Carnival Cruises . . . . . . . . . . . . . . . . . **3.00**
- *RMS Queen Elizabeth I,* Cunard Line, 1¾", photo, "World's Largest Liner" at bottom . . . . . . . . . . . . . . . **8.00**

Playing Cards
- *Alaska Steamship* . . . . . . . . . . . . . . . . **15.00**
- Holland America Line, double deck **25.00**
- *SS Badger,* double deck . . . . . . . . . . . **20.00**
- *SS Spartan,* double deck . . . . . . . . . . . **20.00**
- Swedish American Lines, orig slip case . . . . . . . . . . . . . . . . . . . . . . . . . **18.00**

Post Card
- *Andania,* Cunard Line . . . . . . . . . . . . **6.00**
- *Aurania,* Cunard Line . . . . . . . . . . . . **6.00**
- Cosulich Lines, 1929 . . . . . . . . . . . . **6.00**

Poster, Grace Line, Caribbean, 1949, C Evers, illus of tourists, ship, cars, and boats, 23 x 30" . . . . . . . . . . . . . . . . . . **200.00**

Print
- Moor–McCormack Lines . . . . . . . . . . **85.00**
- *Titanic,* 15 x 22½", black and white, text of sinking, published by Tichnor Bro, Boston . . . . . . . . . . . . . . . . **60.00**

Replica, glass, *Sovereign of the Seas* . . **20.00**

Schedule, Cunard Lines, Programme of Events, embarkation notice, stationery, 1929 . . . . . . . . . . . . . . . . . . . . . . **17.00**

Shopping List, *RMS Queen Mary,* chrome, Art Deco styling . . . . . . . . . . **40.00**

Souvenir Spoon
- Cunard *White Star,* demitasse, silver plated, hallmark . . . . . . . . . . . . . . . **18.00**
- *Transylvania* Anchor Line, silver plated, twisted handle, blue enameled ring, flag, and crest . . . . . . . . **75.00**

Stationery
- *Queen Mary,* Cunard Line, note paper, matching envelope, color portrait, line, and ship name, 5 x 7" . **10.00**
- Royal Mail Steamer, two sheets of paper, matching envelope . . . . . . . . . **20.00**
- *Sylvania,* Cunard Line, beige, color portrait, line, and ship name, 5¼ x 6¾" . . . . . . . . . . . . . . . . . . . . . . . . . **8.00**

Steamer Directory, Clyde–Mallory Lines, c1920 . . . . . . . . . . . . . . . . . . . . **12.00**

Tie Clasp, *Queen Mary,* Cunard Line, goldtone, red, white, and blue enameled ship . . . . . . . . . . . . . . . . . . . . . . . **15.00**

Whiskey Bottle, *RMS Titanic* . . . . . . . . . **60.00**

# OWL COLLECTIBLES

**Collecting Hints:** If you collect the "creature of the night" or the "wise old owl," any page of this book might conceivably contain an owl–related object since the owl theme can be found in hundreds of collectible categories. A sampling of these categories includes advertising trade cards, books, buttons, postcards, etc. But, don't confine yourself to these categories. Let your imagination be your guide.

Don't confine yourself just to old or antique owls. Owl figurines, owl themes on limited edition collectors' plates, and handcrafted items from modern artisans are plentiful. There are many examples available in every price range.

**History:** Owls have existed on earth for over sixty million years. They have been used as a decorative motif since before Christ. An owl was used with Athena on an ancient Greek coin.

Every culture has superstitions surrounding the owl. Some believe the owl represented good luck, others viewed it as an evil omen. The owl has remained a popular theme in Halloween material.

Of course, the owl's wisdom is often attached to scholarly pursuits. Expanding this theme, the National Park Service uses "Woodsey" to "Give A Hoot, Don't Pollute."

**References:** Allan W. Eckert and Karl E. Karalus, *The Owls Of North America*, Doubleday & Company, Inc. 1974; Faith Medlin, *Centuries Of Owls In Art And The Written Word*, Silvermine Publishers Incorporated, 1967; Heimo Mikkola, *Owls Of Europe*, Buteo Books, 1983; Jozefa Stuart, *The Magic Of Owls*, Walker Publishing Co., Inc., 1977; Krystyna Weinstein, *Owls, Owls: Fantastical Fowls*, Buteo Books, 1985.

**Periodical:** *The Owl's Nest*, Howards Alphanumeric, P. O. Box 5491, Fresno, CA 93755.

**REPRODUCTION ALERT:** Recently reproduction fruit crate labels with an owl motif have been seen at several antiques and collectibles dealers who wholesale to dealers. These labels are appearing at flea markets and in shops where they are being passed as originals.

The Westmoreland molds have been sold to several different manufacturers. The owl sitting on two books is being reissued with the original "W" still on top of the books. The three owl plate mold also was sold.

The Imperial owl molds have also found new owners. Again, no reproductions have been seen, but chances are good they will appear in the near future.

**Collectors' Club:** Westmoreland Glass Society, 2712 Glenwood, Independence, MO 64052.

**Fruit Crate Label, red and yellow, 8½ x 10½", $5.00.**

Ashtray, 5½" w, tricorner, china, Nippon, green mark .......... **165.00**
Bank
  2 x 2½", tin, child size, owl pictured on side .......... **50.00**
  7" h, glass, ruby .......... **100.00**
Barometer, 11" h, carved, walnut, English .......... **50.00**
Bell, 4" h, brass, emb feathers and features .......... **45.00**
Book
  Lavine, Sigmund, *Wonders Of The Owl,* Dodd, Mead & Co, NY, 1971 **1.50**
  Mowat, Farley, *Owls In The Family,* Little, Brown & Co, 1961 .......... **.35**
Bookends, pr
  Brass, Frankart .......... **35.00**
  Bronze, head, sgd "M Carr" .......... **120.00**
  Van Briggle, green, matte finish .......... **135.00**
Book Rack, expanding .......... **55.00**
Calendar Plate, 1912, owl on open book, Berlin, NE .......... **25.00**
Calling Card Tray, 8½ x 7", quadruple plate, emb music staff and "Should Owl's Acquaintance Be Forgot," two owls sitting on back of tray .......... **85.00**
Candy Container, 4⅜" h, glass, screw cap closure .......... **125.00**
Clock, 6½" h, wood, hand carved .......... **110.00**
Cookie Jar, ceramic
  11" h, cream, one winking eye, Shawnee .......... **50.00**
  12" h, Woodsey Owl, green hat lid . **65.00**
Decoy, 13", papier mache, double faced, glass eyes, brown, small white area on chest .......... **65.00**
Degenhart
  Custard .......... **35.00**
  Holly Green .......... **20.00**
  Red Carnival .......... **80.00**
  Vaseline .......... **45.00**
Fairy Lamp
  3⅜" d, 4⅛" h, double faced figure, pyramid size, frosted cranberry glass, lavender enameled eyes, Clarke base .......... **200.00**
  4" h, painted eyes, Clarke base .......... **225.00**
Figure
  3" h, carnival glass, Fenton .......... **18.00**
  4" h, carnival glass, Mosser .......... **20.00**
  8½" h, orange, Viking .......... **100.00**
  9" h, turquoise, Van Briggle .......... **60.00**
Humidor, 6¾" h, octagonal, Nippon .. **375.00**
Inkwell, 8 x 4", brass, glass inset, hinged lid, pen tray, 2" owl figure .......... **75.00**
Lamp, candle, 5¼", snow white china, owl shaped shade, stump shaped base, fitted candleholder, marked "R S Germany" .......... **225.00**
Letter Opener, bronze .......... **30.00**
Mask, papier mache, c1915 .......... **90.00**
Match Holder
  2½" h, dark green, Wetzel Glass Co **5.00**
  8" h, 3" w, metal, hanging type .......... **18.00**
Medal
  Leeds International Exhibition, 1890, 2¼", metal, white bust of Queen Victoria on one side .......... **25.00**
  Natural History Society of Montreal, 1¾", bronze, cast, owl with branch in beak .......... **20.00**
Mustard Jar, cov, 5" h, milk glass, screw top, glass insert, Atterbury .......... **165.00**
Napkin Ring
  Nippon, owl sitting on stump .......... **225.00**
  Silver Plated, owl standing .......... **145.00**
Owl Drug Co
  Bottle, 3½" h, cork top, clear, Oil of Sweet Almond label, 1 oz .......... **4.00**
  Shot Glass, clear .......... **14.00**
  Tin, 4¼" d, 3" h, "Theatrical Cold Cream," orange ground, black print **24.50**
Paperweight, Kosta, sgd "D Lindstrand" **95.00**

Pin, blue, green, and gold enamel, amber eyes with rhinestone eye disks, pearl tail feathers . . . . . . . . . . . . . . . . . **15.50**
Pitcher
8″ h, 6″ d top, pressed glass, owl shape . . . . . . . . . . . . . . . . . . . . . . . **110.00**
9½″ h, cov, china, semi–vitreous, Edwin M Knowles China Co . . . . . . . **37.50**
Plate
China, barn owl, 1976 Wildlife, Goebel . . . . . . . . . . . . . . . . . . . . . . . . . . **38.00**
Milk Glass
Owl Lovers, 7½″ d . . . . . . . . . . . . **40.00**
Three owl heads, 6″ d, fluted open work edge, gold paint . . . . . . . . **65.00**
Three owls, Westmoreland . . . . . . **25.00**
Quilt, cigar silks, 5¢ Owls, single bed size . . . . . . . . . . . . . . . . . . . . . . . . . . . **450.00**
Ring Tree, 3¼″ d, 4″ h, shallow brown dish, blue lining, brown and tan owl perched on back, marked "Doulton Stoneware" . . . . . . . . . . . . . . . . . . . . . **325.00**
Salt and Pepper Shakers, pr, 3¼″ h, china, brown and white, mortarboard hats, scholarly expression, horn rim glasses . . . . . . . . . . . . . . . . . . . . . . . . . **6.50**
Sheet Music
*Beautiful Ohio*, owl on cover . . . . . . **3.50**
*The Pansy and the Owl* . . . . . . . . . . . **4.50**
*The Wise Old Owl* . . . . . . . . . . . . . . . **3.50**
Thermometer, 6″ h, plaster body . . . . . **75.00**
Toothbrush Holder, figural, Syroco . . . **12.50**
Trivet, Frankoma Pottery . . . . . . . . . . . **4.00**
Valentine, 15″ l, girl and boy riding balloon, owl sitting on moon above, "Nobody's looking but the owl and the moon!" . . . . . . . . . . . . . . . . . . . . . **8.00**
Vase
7″ h, gold owls, white ground, Phoenix Glass . . . . . . . . . . . . . . . . . . . . . . **125.00**
8¼″ h, Knifewood, Weller . . . . . . . . . **150.00**

# PADEN CITY

**Collecting Hints:** All Paden City glass was handmade and unmarked. The early glassware was of non–descript quality, but in the early 1930s quality improved dramatically. The cuttings were unpolished "gray cuttings," sometimes mistaken for etchings.

Paden City is noted for its colors: opal (opaque white), ebony, mulberry, Cheriglo (delicate pink), yellow, dark green (forest), crystal, amber, primrose (reddish–amber), blue, rose, and the ever popular red. No free–blown or opalescent glass was produced. Quantities of blanks were sold to decorating companies for gold and silver overlay and for etching.

**History:** Paden City Glass Manufacturing Co. was founded in 1916 in Paden City, West Virginia. David Fisher, formerly of the New Martinsville Glass Manufacturing Co., operated the company until his death in 1933 when his son, Samuel, became president. The additional financial burden placed on the company by the acquisition of American Glass Co. in 1949 forced Paden City to close in 1951.

**References:** Jerry Barnett, *Paden City, The Color Company,* published by author, 1978; Lee Garmon and Dick Spencer, *Glass Animals Of The Depression Era,* Collector Books, 1993; Ellen Tischbein Schroy, *Warman's Glass,* Wallace–Homestead, 1992.

Animal
Chinese Pheasant
Cobalt Blue . . . . . . . . . . . . . . . . . . . **125.00**
Crystal . . . . . . . . . . . . . . . . . . . . . . . . **65.00**
Pony, standing, 12″ l . . . . . . . . . . . . . . **55.00**
Squirrel on log . . . . . . . . . . . . . . . . . . . **25.00**
Berry Bowl, 5¼″ sq, Crows Foot, amber **7.00**

**Bowl, apple green, wide gold overlaid dec, 11¼″ d, 3″ h, $25.00.**

Cake Plate
Ardith Cherry etch, topaz, low, ftd . **50.00**
Silver Overlay, crystal ground, three toes, 12″ d . . . . . . . . . . . . . . . . . . . . **15.00**
Candy Dish, cov, Gazebo Etch, crystal, three part divided int. . . . . . . . . . . . . . **45.00**
Cocktail Shaker, Party Line, ruby . . . . . **20.00**
Compote
Ardith Cherry etch, topaz . . . . . . . . . **55.00**
Crows Foot, ruby, 7″ d, 6¾″ h . . . . . **45.00**
Peacock Rose, green, ruffled edge . . **55.00**
Console Bowl, Party Line, Gypsy cutting, green, 14″ d, ruffled edge . . . . . **38.00**
Console Set, Gazebo Etch, crystal, flared bowl, two double candlesticks, price for three piece set . . . . . . . . . . . **95.00**
Cotton Dispenser, rabbit, frosted, ftd . . **85.00**
Cream Soup, Crows Foot, amber, ftd . . **8.00**
Creamer and Sugar, Luli, ruby, price for pair . . . . . . . . . . . . . . . . . . . . . . . . . . **40.00**
Cup and Saucer, Crows Foot, amber, sq **7.00**
Goblet
Cupid . . . . . . . . . . . . . . . . . . . . . . . . . . **15.00**
Penny Line, 6″ h
Green . . . . . . . . . . . . . . . . . . . . . . . . **12.00**
Ruby . . . . . . . . . . . . . . . . . . . . . . . . . **20.00**

Gravy Boat, underplate, pink, gold encrusted rim . . . . 40.00
Ice Bucket
- Cupid, pink . . . . 135.00
- Party Line, amber . . . . 25.00

Iced Tea Tumbler, Popeye & Olive, ruby, 5" h . . . . 12.00
Juice Tumbler, Popeye & Olive, ruby, 3" h . . . . 8.00
Mayonnaise Set, #300 Line, green, orig ladle, price for three piece set . . . . 35.00
Napkin Holder, Party Line, black . . . . 90.00
Pitcher
- Lazy Daisy, pink, jug style, 60 oz . . 45.00
- Popeye and Olive, green . . . . 25.00

Plate
- Chavalier Line 90, ruby, 8" d . . . . 15.00
- Crows Foot, amber
  - Dinner, 9" . . . . 10.00
  - Salad, 6" sq . . . . 2.50
- Largo, 12" d, crystal, sterling trim . . 15.00
- Penny Line, 7½" d, amethyst . . . . 5.00
- Popeye and Olive, 12" d, ruby . . . . 20.00
- Wotta Line, 8" d, ruby . . . . 7.00

Reamer, Party Line, frosted turquoise, metal reamer top . . . . 90.00
Relish, Sunset pattern, three part, amber 20.00
Salt and Pepper shakers, pr, Penny Line, cobalt blue, flat base . . . . 50.00
Sandwich Tray, swan handle, crystal . . 30.00
Serving Plate, Gazebo Etch, 11¼" d . . 38.00
Sherbet, Peacock Reverse . . . . 25.00
Sugar, cov
- Nora Bird, Cheriglo . . . . 35.00
- Wotta Line, ruby . . . . 8.00

Syrup, green, metal lid, plain . . . . 20.00
Tumbler
- Peacock Reverse, ruby . . . . 35.00
- Penny Line, 5¼" h, amethyst . . . . 8.00

Vase
- Black Forest, 10" h, black . . . . 110.00
- Lela Bird, 8¼" h, green, eliptical . . . 80.00
- Utopia, 10½" h, green . . . . 125.00

Whiskey, Party Line, turquoise, floral cutting . . . . 6.00

# PADLOCKS

**Collecting Hints:** Padlocks must be more than just old and scarce to attract collector interest. They also must have some kind of appeal, e.g., historical, elaborate design, or intricate mechanism. Desirable padlocks are embossed in raised letters with the name or initial of a defunct company or railroad, a logo, an event, such as an exposition, or shapes such as a heart, figure, floral motif, or scroll design. Other desirable types include unique construction, unusual size, intricate and trick mechanism, or made and used during the early days of old companies.

The name or initial of a manufacturer is usually just stamped on a lock. This adds to value, especially if the lock is not embossed with other identification. A lock made by a small company in the 1850s can be worth many times more than a similar lock made by a large, prolific manufacturer. There always are exceptions. For example, "Smokies" do not have much value no matter how old or scarce.

The difference in value between types of padlocks is inexplicable. The round "Lever Push Key" locks can be valued at several times more than other locks with identical embossments. Locks classified as "Story" are worth many times more than similar locks classified as "Warded."

Regardless of the value of unmarked locks, collectors are challenged by the task of identifying them. Old hardware and lock catalogs help. A comprehensive book on United States lock companies, their padlocks, and padlock construction remains to be published.

Some collectors specialize in just one type of padlock (combination, logo, etc.) or a specific manufacturer. The reason is the breadth of the field and the wealth of locks made by the 200–plus manufacturers. The Eagle Lock Co., for example, made about 400 types and variations between 1880 and 1930. The most competitive collecting is in the embossed brass locks from defunct short line railroads or the very early locks from larger railroads.

Collectors will not knowingly buy padlocks if they are repaired, cracked, corrosion pitted, damaged internally, or appreciably dented. A rare lock at a greatly reduced price can be an exception. An original key increases the value of a padlock, but other keys have no value to most collectors.

Most collectors prefer American manufactured padlocks.

**History:** Padlocks of all shapes and sizes were made in Europe and Asia from the 1600s. The mass production of identifiable padlocks was pioneered in the United States in the mid–1800s. Almost all padlock mechanisms were adapted from earlier door and safe lock patents.

Over 200 United States padlock manufacturers have been identified. Six of the most prolific are:

Adams & Westlake, 1857– , "Adlake" trademark started c1900, made railroad locks.

Eagle Lock Co., 1833–1976, a general line of padlocks from 1880, with padlock patent dates from 1867.

Mallory, Wheeler & Co., 1865–1910, partnership history started in 1834, predominant manufacturer of wrought iron lever (smokies) padlock.

Miller Lock Co. (D. K. Miller from 1870 to c1880, Miller Lock Co. to 1930), general line of padlocks.

Star Lock Works, 1836–1926, largest manufacturer of Scandinavian padlocks.
Yale & Towne Mfg. Co., 1884– , Yale Lock Mfg. Co. from 1868 to 1884, started c1840 by Linus Yale, Sr., as the "Yale Lock Shop," started making padlocks c1875.

Railroad, express, and logo locks are identified with the names of the companies that bought and used them. A series of odd and heart–shaped cast iron padlocks produced from about 1880 to 1900 with various decorative or figural embossments are called "Story Locks."

Thousands of companies had locks custom made with their names to create logo locks. Logo locks are not to be confused with locks that are embossed with the names of jobbers. This applies particularly to the round six lever push key locks. If "6–Lever" is included with the name, it is not a logo lock. Since 1827 there have been over 10,000 railroad companies in the United States, not counting trolleys and interurbans. Most of these companies used at least two types of locks; some used dozens of types.

**Padlock Types:** Padlocks are categorized primarily according to tradition or use: Story, Railroad, etc. The secondary listing theme is according to the type of construction. For example: if a brass lever lock is marked with a railroad name, it is called a railroad lock. Scandinavian locks have always been called "Scandinavians." "Story" locks became a common usage term in the 1970s. In the 1880s they were listed in various ways.

**References:** Franklin M. Arnall, *The Padlock Collector, Illustrations and Prices of 1,800 Padlocks of the Last 100 Years, Fifth Edition,*The Collector, 1988; Jack P. Wood, *Town–Country Old Tools And Locks, Keys, And Closures,* L–W Books, 1990.

**Collectors' Club:** American Lock Collectors Association, 36076 Grennada, Livonia, MI 48154.

**Museum:** Lock Museum of America, Terryville, CT.

**Advisor:** Franklin M. Arnall.

**REPRODUCTION ALERT:** Beware of brass story locks, locks from the Middle East, railroad switch locks from Taiwan, and switch lock keys from the US Midwest. Early story locks should be embossed cast iron. However, beware. There are excellent iron reproductions of the skull and crossbones story lock.

Screw key, trick, iron lever, and brass lever locks are being imported from the Middle East. The Taiwan switch locks are rougher and lighter in color than the old brass ones. The crudely cast new switch keys are obvious. The high quality counterfeits are expertly stamped with various railroad initials, tumbled to simulate wear, and aged with acid. They can be detected only by an expert.

Authentic railroad, express, and logo locks will have only one user name or set of initials. The size and shape will be like other locks that were in common use at the time, except for a few modified locks made for the US government.

All components of an old lock must have exactly the same color and finish. The front, back, or drop of an old lock can be expertly replaced with a reproduced part embossed with the name or initials of a railroad, express company, or other user.

**Note:** The prices shown are for padlocks in original condition and without keys.

Combination
- Barrett Keyless, brass and steel, 3" h **10.00**
- Brass lettered dials, 1¾" w ........ **50.00**
- Dot Lock, brass, 3¼" h ........... **40.00**
- Junkunc Bros Mfrs, patent 1912 .... **10.00**
- Miller Lock Co, steel, 3⅛" h ....... **8.00**
- Mill's Keyless, patented, iron ...... **125.00**
- Slaymaker, laminated steel, 2⅞" h .. **10.00**
- Steel case, brass dial, 2¾" h ....... **3.00**
- The Edwards Mfg Co, No–Key, brass **30.00**
- Turman's, patent Mar 9, 1886, brass **175.00**

Commemorative
- AYPEX, Alaska Yukon Pacific Expo, 1909, Seattle, emb, steel, 3⅛" h . **350.00**
- Dan Patch, horseshoe emb on back, iron, 2" h ..................... **125.00**
- Man riding a buffalo, 1901 Pan–American Expo, emb, brass ...... **85.00**
- Missouri Seal, emb, brass, 1904 Expo **75.00**
- St Louis, 1904 World's Fair, Louisiana Purchase Exposition on reverse ... **500.00**

Lever
- Brass
  - Ames Sword, patent 1882, 3¼" h **15.00**
  - Corbin, emb, 3" h .............. **8.00**
  - Johnson Rotary Lock Co, patent 1861 ....................... **550.00**
  - Leader, emb, 2" h .............. **4.00**
  - Mercury, emb, 2¾" h ........... **20.00**
  - Pye's Patent, heart shape ........ **30.00**

**Lever, brass, emb "Good Luck," $50.00.**

Simmons, emb, heart shape ..... **10.00**
W Bochannon, patent Apr 18, 1860 ..... **15.00**
Yale, Y & T, rect, emb
1½ to 2″ w ..... **3.00**
3″ w ..... **65.00**
Iron
Heart shape, 3¼″ h, several manufacturers ..... **10.00**
Pye's Patent, Sep 8, 1958, Oct 16, 1860, 3¼″ h ..... **25.00**
Steel
Eagle, emb
2″ h ..... **2.00**
2¾″ h ..... **5.00**
3¼″ h ..... **10.00**
4⅜″ h ..... **40.00**
Indian Chief Head, emb ..... **35.00**
R & E, hatchet shape, steel case, 3¾″ h ..... **150.00**
Rugby, emb, 3″ h ..... **10.00**
S Andrews, 3″ h ..... **300.00**
Yale & Towne, lion head emb on front, 3″ h ..... **65.00**
Wrought Iron, (Shield, Smoke House, Smokies), brass drop
DM & CO, 3½″ h ..... **10.00**
Dog head, emb, 4½″ h ..... **45.00**
NW & Co, 3⅜″ h ..... **5.00**
R & E, 4″ h ..... **12.00**
Warranted, VR, 5″ h ..... **25.00**
WW & CO, 3½″ h ..... **5.00**

**Lever, iron and steel, Flag, 1½″ w, 2″ h, $6.00.**

Lever Push Key, brass, emb, 2¼″ d
Aztec Six Lever ..... **140.00**
Champion Six Lever, emb, brass, 2¼″ d ..... **3.00**
C M & D Six Lever ..... **200.00**
Columbia Six Lever ..... **15.00**
Cyclone Six Lever ..... **45.00**
Miller, Six Secure Levers, iron and brass, 3½″ h ..... **2.00**
Logo
Bell System, Best ..... **12.00**
BIR, Yale ..... **15.00**
Canada Excise, Yale, iron case ..... **160.00**
DNG Co, emb, brass, 2¼″ d ..... **250.00**
Hudson Motor Car Co, Yale ..... **75.00**
Metropolitan Water District, Yale ..... **10.00**
Milwaukee Tank Works, brass case ..... **10.00**
Ordance Dept, emb cannons, Yale ..... **5.00**
Texaco, Best ..... **10.00**
University of Colorado, Yale ..... **40.00**
US Customs, American Seal Lock Co **300.00**
U S Mail, 1852, H C Jones Patent, iron ..... **150.00**
USN, Chicago Lock Co ..... **5.00**
West Baking Co, emb, brass, 2¼″ d **175.00**
Pin Tumbler
Corbin, brass
1½ to 2″ w ..... **1.00**
3″ w ..... **50.00**
Keyhole in front ..... **25.00**
Steel case ..... **4.00**
Segal, brass, keyhole in front ..... **35.00**
SH Co, Simmons, brass case ..... **5.00**
Unit, brass ..... **35.00**
WB, brass ..... **4.00**
Yale
Brass case, emb ..... **1.00**
Iron case, brass panels, round ..... **5.00**
Railroad, GP and Signal
B & O, Yale, emb ..... **15.00**
C & El, brass, pin tumbler ..... **8.00**
Erie Railroad, emb, 2¼″ d ..... **95.00**
KCS, Yale, emb ..... **30.00**
P & R, emb, lever push type ..... **125.00**
Raco, screw key type ..... **6.00**
Santa Fe, emb, 2¼″ d ..... **250.00**
Southern Pacific, with sunset logo, emb ..... **65.00**
SP Co, emb on drop ..... **25.00**
Union Pacific CS–21, Roadway and Bridge, emb, brass lever ..... **30.00**
Railroad, Switch, brass lever
CP RR of CA, stamped on back ..... **110.00**
CRI & P RR
Emb on panel ..... **225.00**
On shackle, Union Brass ..... **40.00**
GB & W RR on shackle, Bochannon **30.00**
Illinois Traction System, emb in panel **150.00**
NP RR, emb in panel ..... **110.00**
N & W RY Co, emb on back ..... **35.00**
NWP RR, Switch, CS8, emb on back **550.00**
OSL RR, Switch, CS2, emb on back **200.00**
Penna Co, emb in panel ..... **80.00**
PRR, emb across back ..... **100.00**
SO PAC Co, emb on back and drop **75.00**
TRRA, stamped on shackle ..... **20.00**
Union Pacific, emb in panel ..... **75.00**
VGN Ry Co, emb across back ..... **450.00**
Railroad, Switch, steel
AT & SF RY and other common railroads ..... **4.00**
NC & STL, Yale, figure eight lock ..... **20.00**
T & G RR, A & W on laminated shackle ..... **100.00**

Scandinavian
- R & E, emb, iron, 2⅛" h .......... **25.00**
- Star emb on bottom, iron
  - 2¾" h .......... **18.00**
  - 4½" hp, short shackle .......... **100.00**
  - 5¼" h, long shackle .......... **120.00**
- Yale Junior, emb, brass, 2½" h .......... **100.00**
- 999, emb, brass, 2½" h .......... **30.00**

Six Lever and Eight Lever
- Armory Eight Lever, steel .......... **12.00**
- Corbin Iron Clad, steel .......... **4.00**
- Oak Leaf Six Lever, emb, steel .......... **8.00**
- Reese Eight Lever, steel .......... **10.00**
- Steel State Six Lever, steel .......... **4.00**
- Stilleto Six Lever, steel .......... **12.00**

Story, emb cast iron
- Aztec pattern, R & E, 2¼" d .......... **300.00**
- Mail Box, R & E, aluminum finish .. **475.00**
- Skull and Crossbones, emb, floral back .......... **175.00**

Warded
- Floral and scroll, rect cast, emb, iron or brass .......... **12.00**
- Fordloc, emb, brass case .......... **10.00**
- Lucky, emb, brass case .......... **4.00**
- Navy, emb, iron, 2¼" d .......... **12.00**
- SE Co, 1877, iron, 3⅛" h .......... **110.00**
- Texas, emb, iron, 2¼" d .......... **75.00**
- Winchester, brass case with panels . **100.00**

# PAPER DOLLS

**Collecting Hints:** Most paper dolls are collected in uncut books, sheets, or boxed sets. Cut sets are priced at 50% of an uncut set providing all dolls, clothing, and accessories are present.

Many paper doll books have been reprinted. An identical reprint is just slightly lower in value. If the dolls have been redrawn, the price is reduced significantly.

Barbara Ferguson's *The Paper Doll* has an excellent section on the care and storage of paper dolls.

**History:** The origin of the paper doll rests with the jumping jacks (pantins) of Europe. By the 19th century famous dancers, opera stars, Jenny Lind, and many general subjects were available in boxed or die–cut sheet form. Raphael Tuck in England began to produce ornate dolls in series form in the 1880s.

The advertising industry turned to paper dolls to sell products. Early magazines, such as *Ladies's Home Journal, Good Housekeeping,* and *McCall's,* used paper doll inserts. Children's publications, like *Jack and Jill,* picked up the practice.

The paper doll books first appeared in the 1920s. The cardboard covered books made paper dolls available to the mass market. Leading companies were Lowe, Merrill, Saalfield, and Whitman. The 1940s saw the advent of the celebrity paper doll books. Celebrities were drawn from screen and radio, followed later by television personalities. A few comic characters, such as Brenda Starr, also made it to paper doll fame.

The growth of television in the 1950s saw a reduction in the number of paper doll books produced. The modern books are either politically or celebrity oriented.

**References:** Marian B. Howard, *Those Fascinating Paper Dolls: An Illustrated Handbook For Collectors*, Dover, 1981; Martha K. Krebs, *Advertising Paper Dolls: A Guide For Collectors*, two volumes, privately printed, 1975; Norman E. Martinus and Harry L. Rinker, *Warman's Paper,* Wallace–Homestead, 1993; Mary Young, *A Collector's Guide To Paper Dolls: Saalfield, Lowe, and Merrill*, Collector Books, 1980, out–of–print; Mary Young, *A Collector's Guide To Paper Dolls, Second Series,* Collector Books, 1984, out–of–print; Mary Young, *A Collector's Guide To Magazine Paper Dolls: An Identification & Value Guide,* Collector Books, 1990; Mary Young, *Tomart's Price Guide To Lowe and Whitman Paper Dolls,* Tomart Publications, 1993.

**Collectors' Club:** United Federation of Doll Clubs, P. O. Box 14146, Parkville, MO 64152.

**Periodicals:** *Celebrity Doll Journal*, 5 Court Place, Puyallup, WA 98372; *Doll Reader,* P. O. Box 467, Mount Morris, IL 61054; *Midwest Paper Dolls & Toys Quarterly*, P.O. Box 131, Galesburg, KS 66740; *Paper Doll News*, P.O. Box 807, Vivian, LA 71082; Original Paper Doll Artist Guild, P. O. Box 176, Skandia, MI 49885.

**Museums:** Children's Museum, Indianapolis, IN; Detroit Children's Museum, Detroit, MI; Kent State University Library, Kent, OH; Museum of the City of New York, New York, NY; Newark Museum, Newark, NJ; The Margaret Woodbury Strong Museum, Rochester, NY.

**Notes:** Prices are based on uncut, mint, original paper dolls in book or uncut sheet form. It is not unusual for two different titles to have the same number in a single company.

- Amy Carter, MIB .......... **20.00**
- Ann Sheridan, uncut sheet .......... **110.00**
- Arlene Dahl, 4311, Saalfield, 5 dolls, 8 pgs, 1953 .......... **50.00**
- Baby Merry, 4350, Merry Mfg, 1964 .. **8.00**
- Baby Sandy, 4326, Merrill, 1941 .......... **185.00**
- Barbie's Boutique, 1954, Whitman, 1973 .......... **7.50**
- Betsy McCall, Biggest Paper Doll, D90, Gabriel & Sons, Samuel, 1955 .......... **20.00**
- Big Sister, Londy Card Corp, 1932 .... **5.00**
- Buffy, 1985, Whitman, 1 doll, 6 pgs, 1969 .......... **18.50**
- Carol & Her Dresses, D117, Gabriel & Sons, Samuel .......... **18.00**

**Tricia Paper Doll, Artcraft, six pgs, 1970, 8¼ x 12¼", $18.00.**

Cinderella, 1730, Saalfield, 4 dolls, 4 pgs ... **15.00**
Corinne, 203, American Colortype Co, 13" ... **30.00**
Daisy & Donald, 1986, Whitman, 4 dolls, 4 pgs, Walt Disney Productions, 1978 ... **15.00**
Dainty Dollies & Their Dresses, 3159, EP Dutton ... **45.00**
Deanna Durbin, 3480, Merrill, 1940 . **170.00**
Design A Doll, 11, Dennison Mfg, 1950 **8.50**
Dionne Quints, 3488, Merrill, 1940 .. **235.00**
Dionne Quints—Let's Play House, 3500, Merrill, 1949 ... **80.00**
Dolly's Wardrobe, Dean & Son, folder, chromolithograph, c1910 ... **75.00**
Doris Day, 1952, Whitman, 2 dolls, 1956 ... **25.00**
Dotty & Danny on Parade, 875, Burton Playthings, 1935 ... **25.00**
Fairliner Paper Doll Book, 1560, Merrill, 2 dolls, 8 pgs, 1953 ... **7.50**
Gale Storm, 2061, Whitman, 2 dolls, 6 pgs ... **45.00**
Glamour Models, 177, Stephens Publishing Co ... **8.00**
Gloria Jean, 1661, Saalfield, 1940 .... **165.00**
Gone With The Wind, 3404, Merrill, c1940 ... **250.00**
Gone With The Wind, M3405, uncut sheet, 1940 ... **300.00**
Greer Garson, uncut sheet ... **90.00**
Hollywood Fashion, S2242, uncut sheet, 1939 ... **40.00**
Jack & Jill, uncut sheet
  Easter, March 1921, Barbara Hale artist, 2 dolls, c1921, uncut sheet .. **12.00**
  Folk Festival, Philadelphia Mummers, Jan, 1951, Janet Smalley artist, uncut sheet ... **10.00**
Janet Leigh Cutouts & Coloring, 2554, Merrill, 2 dolls ... **45.00**
Joan Caulfield, 2725, Saalfield, 2 dolls, 6 pgs, 1953 ... **40.00**
Julia, 5140, Artcraft, 5 dolls, 4 pgs, 1971 ... **25.00**
June Allyson, 1173, Whitman, 8 pgs, 1953 ... **60.00**
Let's Play Paper Dolls, McLoughlin, 1938 ... **20.00**
Little Folks Army Book, McLoughlin Bros, folder, c1895 ... **85.00**
Lizzie, McLoughlin Bros, folder, 1 doll, c1870 ... **150.00**
Lucille Ball & Desi Arnaz, 2101, Whitman, uncut sheet, 1953 ... **75.00**
Margaret O'Brien, uncut sheet ... **145.00**
Margy & Mildred, 102, American Colortype Co, 1927 ... **18.00**
Mary Pickford, uncut page from Ladies World Magazine, 1916, five movie costumes ... **15.00**
Mary's Trousseau, 1180, Saalfield, cut, c1918 ... **8.00**
Minnie Warren, McLoughlin, complete, orig envelope ... **110.00**
Miss America Magic Doll, Parker Bros, 1953 ... **18.00**
Moving Eye Dolly, Toddling Tom, D112, Gabriel & Sons, Samuel, 1920 **25.00**
Nanny & Professor, 5114, Artcraft, 6 dolls, 4 pgs, 1971 ... **20.00**
Oliver, 4330, Artcraft, 4 pgs, 1968 ... **10.00**
Our Gang, Whitman, 1931, clothes uncut ... **55.00**
Our Happy Family, D141, Gabriel & Sons, Samuel, 6 dolls, 1929 ... **25.00**
Pat Crowley, 2050, Whitman, 2 dolls, 8 pgs, 1955 ... **42.00**
Patty's Party, 175, Stephens Publishing Co ... **8.00**
Paul, McLoughlin Bros, folder, 1 doll, c1870 ... **90.00**
Playtime Fashions, 135, Stephens Publishing Co, 1946 ... **7.50**
Pony Tail, D116, Gabriel & Sons, Samuel ... **15.00**
Raggedy Ann, uncut sheet, 1980 ... **5.00**
Real Sleeping Doll, McLoughlin, 1939 **25.00**
Roy Rogers and Dale Evans, 1950, Whitman, 2 dolls, 1956 ... **35.00**
Sabrina and The Archies, 1978, Whitman, 6 dolls, 6 pgs, 1971 ... **12.00**
Sally Dimple, 975, Burton Playthings, 1935 ... **25.00**
Shari Lewis, Treasure Books, 5 pgs ... **32.00**
Shirley Temple Masquerade Costumes, 1787, Saalfield, 1940 ... **185.00**
Teena The Teenager, Avalon Industries **5.00**
The Wedding Party, D132, Gabriel & Sons, Samuel ... **30.00**
This Is Margie, Whitman, 1939 ... **45.00**
Toddler Twins, D134, Gabriel & Sons, Samuel ... **25.00**

Triplet Dolls, 176, Stephens Publishing Co . . . . . . **8.00**
Valentine's Day Boy and Girl, Feb 1921, Barbara Hale artist, uncut sheet . . . . **15.00**
Wedding of the Paper Dolls, 3497, Merrill, Lucille Webster artist, 10 dolls . **85.00**
Welcome Back Kotter, MIB . . . . . . . . . . **30.00**

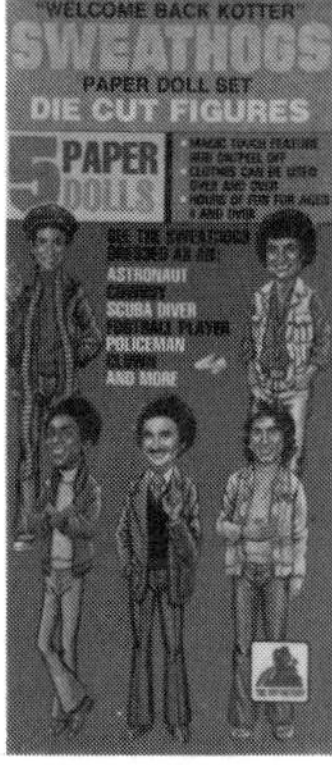


**Sweat Hogs, Welcome Back Kotter TV show, 5 diecut cardboard dolls, "Magic Touch" clothes, The Toy Factory, #108, 1977, $30.00.**

Wendy Walks, 6504, Merry Mfg, 1965 **10.00**
Your Own Quintuplets, 275, Burton Playthings, 1935 . . . . . . . . . . . . . . . . . **25.00**

# PAPERBACK BOOKS

**Collecting Hints:** For collecting or investment purposes, books should be in fine or better condition because many titles are common in lesser condition as well as being less desirable. Unique items, such as paperbacks in dust jackets or in boxes, often are more valuable and desirable.

Most collections are assembled around one or more unifying themes. Some common themes are: author (Edgar Rice Burroughs, Dashiell Hammett, Louis L'Amour, Raymond Chandler, Zane Grey, William Irish, Cornell Woolrich, etc.); fictional genre (mysteries, science fiction, westerns, etc.); publisher (early Avon, Dell and Popular Library are most popular); cover artist (Frank Frazetta, R. C. M. Heade, Rudolph Belarski, Roy Krenkel, Vaughn Bode, etc.); and books with uniquely appealing graphic design (Dell mapbacks and Ace double novels).

Because quantity lots of paperbacks still turn up, many collectors are cautious as they assemble their collections. Books in the highest condition grades remain uncommon. Many current dealers try to charge upper level prices for books in lesser condition, arguing that top condition is just too scarce. This argument is not valid, just self–serving.

**History:** Paperback volumes have existed since the 15th century. Mass–market paperback books, most popular with collectors, date from the post 1938 period. The number of mass market publishers in the 1938–50 period was much greater than today. These books exist in a variety of formats, from the standard size paperback and its shorter predecessor to odd sizes like 64 page short novels for 10¢ and 5¼" x 7½" volumes known as digests. Some books came in a dust jacket; some were boxed.

The "golden" period for paperback books was from 1939 to the late 1950s, a period generally characterized by a lurid and colorful graphic style of cover art and title lettering not unlike that of the pulp magazines. A lot of early paperback publishers had been or were publishers of pulps and merely moved their graphic style and many of their authors to paperbacks.

**References:** Kenneth Davis, *Two–Bit Culture: The Paperbacking of America,* Houghton Mifflin, 1984; Kevin Hancer, *The Paperback Price Guide, Third Edition,* Wallace–Homestead, 1989; Norman E. Martinus and Harry L. Rinker, *Warman's Paper,* Wallace–Homestead, 1993; Piet Schreuders, *Paperbacks USA, A Graphic History, 1939–1959,* Blue Dolphin, 1981; Jon Warren, *The Official Price Guide to Paperbacks,* House of Collectibles, 1991.

**Periodical:** *Paperback Parade,* P. O. Box 209, Brooklyn, NY 11228.

**Museum:** University of Minnesota's Hess Collection of Popular Literature, Minneapolis, MN.

**Note:** The prices given are for books in fine condition. Divide by 3 to get the price for books in good condition; increase price by 50% for books in near mint condition.

Adventure
- Burroughs, Edgar Rice, *Tarzan and the Lost Empire*, Ace, F–169 . . . . . **4.00**
- Fox, Gardner, F, *Woman of Kali*, Gold Medal, 438 . . . . . . . . . . . . . . . . . . . **4.00**
- Horner, Lance, *Rogue Roman*, Gold Medal, T1978, cov by Frazetta . . . **3.00**
- Raddall, Thomas, *Roger Sudden*, Harlequin, 141 . . . . . . . . . . . . . . . . . . . **9.00**
- Siegel, Jerry, *High Camp Superheroes*, Blemont, B50–695, comic book reprints from the co–creator of Superman . . . . . . . . . . . . . . . . . . . . . . . . **4.00**

Biography
- Donovan, B, *Eichman—Man of Slaughter*, Avon, T–464 . . . . . . . . . **2.00**
- Martin and Miller, *The Story of Walt Disney*, Dell, D266 . . . . . . . . . . . . **3.00**

Thomas, T T, *I, James Dean*, Popular Library, W400 ........ **6.00**

Combat

Bartlett and Lay, *Twelve O'Clock High*, Bantam, 743 ........ **4.00**

Busch, Harold, *U–Boats at War*, Ballantine, 120 ........ **4.00**

Tiempo, E K, *Cry Slaughter*, Avon, T–179 ........ **2.00**

Uris, Leon, *Battle Cry*, Bantam, F1996 ........ **3.00**

Erotica/Esoterica

Cargo, Francis, *Perversity*, Berkley, G–33 ........ **4.00**

Farmer, Philip Jose, *Fire and the Night*, Regency, 118 ........ **6.00**

Swados, Felice, *House of Fury*, Avon, 298 ........ **20.00**

Thayer, Tiffany, *One Man Show*, Avon, 327 ........ **6.00**

Van Vechten, Harold, *Nigger Heaven*, Avon, 314 ........ **28.00**

Woodford, Jack, *The Abortive Hussy*, Avon, 146 ........ **4.00**

Horror

Avallane, Michael, *The Coffin Things*, Lancer, 74–942 ........ **5.00**

Bradbury, Ray, *The Autumn People*, Ballantine, EC, comic reprints with Frazetta cov ........ **8.00**

Finney, Jack, *The Body Snatchers*, Dell, 42 ........ **10.00**

Lovecraft, H P, *Weird Shadow Over Innmouth*, Bart House, 4 ........ **25.00**

Humor

Capp, Al, *L'il Abner*, Ballantine, 350K, tie–in with movie ........ **4.00**

Gaines, William (ed.), *The Brothers Mad*, Ballantine, 267K ........ **4.00**

Kurtzman, Harvey, *Help!*, Gold Medal, K 485 ........ **3.00**

***Get Smart!*, William Johnston, Tempo Books, Grosset & Dunlap, 1965, 160 pgs, 4⅛ x 7", $4.50.**

Links, Marty, *Bobby Sox*, Popular Library, 678 ........ **3.00**

Mystery

Adams, Cleve, *And Sudden Death,*, Prize Mystery, 5 ........ **6.00**

Bliss, Tip, *The Broadway Butterfly Murders*, Checkerbook, 2 ........ **15.00**

Carter, Nick, *Death Has Green Eyes*, Vital Book, 3 ........ **6.00**

Hammett, Dashiell, *Hammett Homicides*, Best Seller, B81 ........ **10.00**

Lyon, Dana, *I'll Be Glad When You're Dead*, Quick Reader, 132 ........ **5.00**

Non–fiction

Blackstone, Harry, *Blackstone's Tricks Anyone Can Do*, Permabook, 15 . **7.50**

Disney, Walt, *Our Friend the Atom*, Dell, LB117 ........ **1.50**

Hershfield, Harry, *Book of Jokes*, Avon, 65 ........ **10.00**

Sinclair, Gordon, *Bright Path to Adventure*, Harlequin, 288 ........ **9.00**

Vagts, Alfred, *Hitler's Second Army*, Penguin, S214 ........ **3.00**

Romance

Bronte, Emily, *Wuthering Heights*, Quick Reader, 122 ........ **8.00**

Christian, Paula, *Edge of Twilight*, Crest, 267 ........ **7.00**

Gaddis, Peggy, *Dr Prescott's Secret*, Beacon, B302 ........ **6.00**

Kerr, Jean, *Please Don't Eat the Daisies*, Crest, S263 ........ **2.00**

Science Fiction

Campbell, John W, *Who Goes There?*, Dell, D–150 ........ **3.00**

Heinlein, Robert A, *Beyond This Horizon*, Signet, 1891 ........ **4.00**

Hubbard, L Ron, *Return to Tomorrow*, Ace, S–66 ........ **6.00**

Jones, Raymond, *The Deviates*, Beacon, 242 ........ **8.00**

Lafferty, R A, *Space Chantey*, Ace,H–56, Vaughn Bode cov ........ **4.00**

Orwell, George, *Animal Farm*, Signet, 1289 ........ **5.00**

Sports

DiMaggio, Joe, *Lucky To Be A Yankee*, Bantam, 506 ........ **4.00**

Robinson, Ray (ed.), *Baseball Stars of 1961*, Pyramid, G–605 ........ **2.50**

Scholz, F Jackson, *Fighting Coach*, Comet, 25 ........ **2.50**

Tully, Jim, *The Bruiser*, Bantam ........ **2.00**

Western

Fisher, Clay, *War Bonnet*, Ballantine, 11 ........ **4.00**

Grey, Zane, *Nevada*, Bantam, 3 ........ **3.50**

L'Amour, Louis, *Hondo*, Gold Medal, 347, tie–in with John Wayne movie **8.00**

Robertson, Frank C, *Red Rustlers*, Readers Choice Library, 24 ........ **4.00**

***It's Hell to be a Ranger,* Caddo Cameron, Thrilling Novels, Popular Library, 1937, 128 pgs, 5½ x 7½", $4.00.**

Sperry, Armstrong, *Wagons Westward,* Comet, 1 ................ **2.50**
Striker, Fran, *The Lone Ranger and the Secret of Thunder Mountain,* Bantam, 14 ....................... **60.00**

# PATRIOTIC COLLECTIBLES

**Collecting Hints:** Concentrate on one symbol, e.g., the eagle, flag, Statue of Liberty, Uncle Sam, etc. Remember that the symbol is not always the principal character on items. Don't miss examples with the symbol in a secondary role.

Colored material is more desirable than non-colored material. Much of the material is two dimensional, e.g., posters and signs. Seek three dimensional objects to add balance to a collection.

Much of the patriotic material focuses around our national holidays, especially the Fourth of July. Other critical holidays include Flag Day, Labor Day, Memorial Day, and Veterans' Day.

Finally, look to the foreign market. Our symbols are used abroad, both positively and negatively. One novel collection would be how Uncle Sam is portrayed on the posters and other materials from communist countries.

**History:** Patriotic symbols developed along with the American nation. The American eagle, among the greatest of our nation's symbols, was chosen for the American seal. As a result, the eagle has appeared on countless objects since that time.

Uncle Sam arrived on the American scene in the mid–19th century. He was firmly established by the Civil War. Uncle Sam did have female counterparts—Columbia and the Goddess of Liberty. He often appeared together with one or both of them on advertising trade cards, buttons, posters, textiles, etc.

Uncle Sam achieved his modern appearance largely through the drawings of Thomas Nast in *Harper's Weekly* and James Montgomery Flagg's famous World War I recruiting poster, "I Want You." Perhaps the leading promoter of the Uncle Sam image was the American toy industry. The American Centennial in 1876 and Bicentennial in 1976 also helped. A surge of Uncle Sam related toys occurred in the 1930s led by American Flyer's cheap version of an earlier lithographed tin, flatsided Uncle Sam bicycle string toy.

**Reference:** Norman E. Martinus and Harry L. Rinker, *Warman's Paper,* Wallace–Homestead, 1993.

**See:** Flag Collectibles.

**Pillow Cover, silk, souvenir of "Tennessee Maneuvers, 1944," red and blue flocking, white ground, red fringe border, 17½" sq, $25.00.**

Columbia, advertising trade card, "The President Suspender," Columbia depicted as sales clerk selling suspenders to President McKinley, 3⅝ x 5½" **20.00**
Eagle
- Architectural Element, roof bird, cast iron, black .................... **35.00**
- Bookends, pr, cast white metal, worn, 5½" w ........................ **45.00**
- Cookie Cutter, tin, 6½" l .......... **85.00**
- Figure, pot metal, gold paint, standing, 6" h ...................... **25.00**
- Pinback Button
  - Century Tire, celluloid, gold, red, white, and blue, 1½" d ....... **50.00**
  - National Cycle, red, white, and blue, star studded shield, 1" d . **25.00**
  - NRA Consumer, "We Do Our Part," red, white, and blue, 1¼" d .......................... **6.50**
- Tray, change, Hebburn House Coal, eagle in center, holding banner, wood grain ground, 4" l ......... **42.50**

Franklin, Benjamin
- Bookends, pr, cast white metal, bronzed .......... **35.00**
- Cuff Links, pr, emb figure, gold color, Franklin Life Insurance .......... **25.00**
- Pinback Button, Franklin Life Insurance co, sepia, bust portrait, red rim, white lettering, c1910, 1¼" d **12.00**

Flags and Shields
- Beer Tray, Jacob Metzger, American Brewing Co, Indianapolis, IN, trademark on star in center of flag, 12" d .......... **150.00**
- Automobile Set, five 4 x 5½" flags on 11" rods, 4 x 4" litho metal red, white, and blue diecut eagle shield flag holder, mounting clamp, orig 4 x 12" box, marked "Liberty Flags Sets For Automobiles, Jaymer Specialty Co," c1920 .......... **25.00**
- Match Safe, celluloid cov silvered brass, black and white bull dog standing on American flag, warships in background, "What We Have We'll Hold," reverse with black and white photo of Philadelphia businessman, 1½ x 1½" .... **80.00**
- Paper Dolls, Liberty Fair Dressing Doll, blue and white box, Miss Liberty cardboard doll, flags on wood stick, cut, c1900, 7 x 13" ....... **45.00**
- Pin, diecut celluloid, red, white, and blue shield design, dark gold eagle, raised flipper inscribed "Hupmobile The Car Of The American Family On United America Tour," c1910, 1 x 1¼" .......... **35.00**
- Pinback Button, ⅞" d
  - Americanism Club, red, white, and blue flag, white ground, blue letters .......... **12.00**
  - Hop Ale, American flag and shield, c1907 .......... **12.00**
- Stickpin, adv, diecut celluloid, red, white, and blue American flag on front, black and white text on reverse, brass, early 1900s, ¾ x 1"
  - Artistic Pianos .......... **10.00**
  - Eagle Mop Ringers and Ohio Detachable Mops .......... **12.00**
  - Grande Andes Kitchen Ranges ... **12.00**
- Watch Fob, silvered brass, shield shape, attached silvered brass horseshoe, raised eagle on front, red, white, and blue enameled name "American Badge Co," c1900, 1" w .......... **25.00**

Liberty Bell
- Bank, pot metal and wood, brown, marked "USA, 1947," 4½" h .... **32.00**
- Bread Plate, glass, clear, Constitution signers' names, emb 1776–1876 . **80.00**
- Paperweight, cast iron, figural, 6" h . **50.00**
- Pinback Button
  - General Accident Insurance, Philadelphia, blue and white, center bell, c1901, ¾" d .......... **10.00**
  - National Reflied Assurance Co, Philadelphia, multicolored eagle and bell, dark blue ground, c1900, ¾" d .......... **12.00**
  - Philadelphia Sesqui–Centennial, 1776–1926, gold, red, white, and blue, small red, white, and blue flag, yellow and blue ribbon, ⅞" d .......... **10.00**
  - St Louis 1904/Phila 1776, sepia, center bell, 1¼" d .......... **25.00**
- Post Card
  - Independence Hall, Philadelphia, sepia .......... **5.00**
  - Liberty Bell Trolley, insignia on front .......... **7.50**
- Sheet Music, *Liberty Bell Time To Ring Again,* 1918 .......... **3.50**
- Tape Measure, celluloid case, blue and white design, logo and inscription for Missouri and Kansas Telephone Company, "When You Telephone, Use The Bell," on reverse, cloth tape, c1900, 1¾" d ........ **35.00**

Pilgrims
- Advertising, pocket mirror, Pilgrim Specialty Company, pilgrim image **30.00**
- Booklet, Sermon Preached at Plymouth, 1621, 1851 facsimile reprinted by T G Bangs, Boston, Ma, beige cord binding, 30 pgs ...... **50.00**

Statue of Liberty
- Advertising Trade Card, Pratts Astrol Oil, night scene .......... **18.00**
- Bookmark, silk, Paris, 1878 ....... **65.00**
- Hat, heavy paper, "Liberty," red, white, and blue, picture of Statue, c1918 .......... **20.00**
- Mirror, pocket, round, tin, emb Statue of Liberty, reverse with American eagle, easel and ring, mirror inside, 2½" d .......... **65.00**
- Night Light, white metal, dark copper finish, wooden base, battery operated, c1920, 5½" h .......... **35.00**
- Pinback Button, Liberty Hotel, New York City, Statue of Liberty illus, green text, white ground, c1912, 1¼" d .......... **8.00**
- Playing Cards, "606," US Playing Card Co, Cincinnati, Oh, picture of Statue of Liberty and flags of nations, gold edges, complete, orig box .......... **18.00**
- Tie Slide, Boy Scout, emb brass, detailed raised Statue, scroll banner at base, c1930, 1¼ x 2" .......... **20.00**

Tin, Wiles Biscuits, octagonal, picture on cov . . . . . . . . . . . . . . . . . . . . . . . . **20.00**

Uncle Sam

Advertising Trade Card

Frank Millers Blacking, Uncle Sam type shaving with straight razor, using polished boot as mirror, eagle looking at reflection in other boot, 3½ x 5¼" . . . . . . . . . . . . . . **18.00**

Hub Gore, Uncle Sam holding she, saying "Hub Gore Makers of Elastic For Shoes . . . It Was Honored At The World's Fair of 1893," 3½ x 6¼" . . . . . . . . . . . . **9.00**

Bank, litho cardboard, red, white, and blue, silvered tin cap and bottom, issued by Poll Parrot Shoes, 2¼ x 3" . . . . . . . . . . . . . . . . . . . . . . . **65.00**

Figure, plaster

10" h, holding defense gun and binoculars, white pants, red stripe, blue belt, c1917 . . . . . . . **35.00**

16" h, rolling up sleeves . . . . . . . . **30.00**

Magazine Tear Sheet, Uncle Sam holding a "Health Bill" under his arm, looking at Cream of Wheat advertising billboard, copyright 1915, 5½ x 8½" . . . . . . . . . . . . . . . **20.00**

Mirror, pocket, Watertown Times Newspaper . . . . . . . . . . . . . . . . . . . . **75.00**

Pinback Button

Bound For Cuba, multicolored, black ground, white rim lettering, Uncle Sam with rifle and knapsack marching past sign, c1898, 1¼" d . . . . . . . . . . . . . . . . **35.00**

Dental Health For Victory, oval, red, white, and blue, blue rim, 1" w . . . . . . . . . . . . . . . . . . . . . . . **12.00**

East End Improvement Society, multicolored, Uncle Sam in center surrounded by firecrackers, July 4th 1920 celebration, black lettering, 1¾" d . . . . . . . . . . . . . **75.00**

Federal Casualty Insurance, Detroit, multicolored, Uncle Sam, money pouring from horn of plenty, c1907, ¾" d . . . . . . . . . . **20.00**

Good Teeth, Cincinnati Schools dental care program, red, white, and blue, 1930s, 1" d . . . . . . . . . **15.00**

Onkel Gem Club, red, white, and blue figure, yellow ground, Nov 6, 1895, 1¼" d . . . . . . . . . . . . . **30.00**

Uncle Sam's Citizenship Training Corps, multicolored, lieutenant rank, c1920, ⅞" d . . . . . . . . . . . **18.00**

Post Card, multicolored . . . . . . . . . . **6.00**

Puzzle, Uncle Sam's Tar Soap, Uncle Sam's National Puzzle, 10 cards, advertising slogans, c1900, orig 4 x 4" box . . . . . . . . . . . . . . . . . . . . . **30.00**

**Puzzle, United States Puzzle Map, Parker Brothers, wood, 8 x 13" box, $25.00.**

Salt and Pepper Shakers, pr, painted plaster, glossy white, black, and red accents, red, white, and blue top hat, 1½ x 2½ x 2" . . . . . . . . . . . . . **45.00**

Stickers, "Patriotic Decorations," diecut gummed seals, each 1 x 1½", red, white, and blue, 2 x 2¼" cardboard packet, Dennison, ten of orig 25 seals, c1925 . . . . . . . . . . . . . . . **15.00**

Sheet Music, *Wake Up, America!*, lyrics by George Graff Jr and music by Jack Glogau . . . . . . . . . . . . . . . . . . . **18.00**

Sign

Uncle Sam Selling US Paint, canvas, National Sign Co, Dayton, OH, c1910, 36 x 24" . . . . . . . . . **650.00**

Use Jaxon Soap, Uncle Sam leaning on fence, jack knife in hand, whittling on stick, easel back, 4½ x 8" . . . . . . . . . . . . . . . . . . . . **25.00**

Stickpin, diecut, white metal, tinted cherry red trousers and hat, blue coat, marching pose, c1898, 1" w **20.00**

Tobacco Tin, Union Leader brand, pocket size . . . . . . . . . . . . . . . . . . . **50.00**

Tray, Cascade Beer, San Francisco, Uncle Sam and five ethnic people **650.00**

Watch Fob

Brass, raised profile portrait of Uncle Sam above VFW symbol, inscribed "Dedication Uncle Sam Oakwood Cemetery," 1930s, 1¼ x 1½" . . . . . . . . . . . . . . . . . . . . . . **20.00**

Silvered Brass, raised portrait of Uncle Sam and IOOF Grand Lodge of NY State symbol, 1946 convention, Troy, NY, 1½ x 1½" **24.00**

Washington, George

Pinback Button, multicolored, portrait of Washington, dark red shaded to olive green ground, black inscription for Cherry Smash soft drink, c1912, 1¼" d . . . . . . . . . . . . . . . . . **40.00**

Post Card, multicolored . . . . . . . . . . . **3.75**

Sheet Music, *Father of the Land We Love*, lyrics and music by George

M Cohan, cover artist James Montgomery Flagg, 1931 ............ **8.50**
Tray, porcelain, portraits of George and Martha Washington, Mt Vernon, VA, "Washington's Home, Mt Vernon, VA" in center, multicolored, enhanced enameling, sq corners, gold trim, marked "Germany," 7½ x 11" ............... **75.00**

# PENNSBURY POTTERY

**Collecting Hints:** Concentrate on one pattern or type. Since the pieces were hand carved, aesthetic quality differs from piece to piece. Look for pieces with a strong design sense and a high quality of execution.

Buy only clearly marked pieces. Look for decorator and designer initials that can be easily identified.

Pennsbury collectors are concentrated in the Middle Atlantic states. Many of the company's commemorative and novelty pieces relate to businesses and events in this region, thus commanding their highest price within that region.

**History:** Henry and Lee Below established Pennsbury Pottery, named for its close proximity to William Penn's estate "Pennsbury", three miles west of Morrisville, Pennsylvania, in 1950. Henry, a ceramic engineer and mold maker, and Lee, a designer and modeler, had previously worked for Stangl Pottery in Trenton, New Jersey.

Many of Pennsbury's forms, motifs, and manufacturing techniques have Stangl roots. A line of birds similar to those produced by Stangl were among the earliest Pennsbury products. The carved design technique is also Stangl in origin. High bas–relief molds did not originate at Stangl.

Pennsbury products are easily identified by their brown wash background. The company also made pieces featuring other background colors. Do not make the mistake of assuming that a piece is not Pennsbury because it does not have a brown wash.

Pennsbury motifs are heavily nostalgic, farm, and Pennsylvania German related. Among the most popular lines were Amish, Black Rooster, Delft Toleware, Eagle, Family, Folkart, Gay Ninety, Harvest, Hex, Quartet, Red Barn, Red Rooster, Slick–Chick, and Christmas plates (1960–70). The pottery made a large number of commemorative, novelty, and special order pieces.

In the late 1950s the company had 16 employees, mostly local housewives and young girls. In 1963 employees numbered 46, the company's peak. By the late 1960s, the company had just over 20 employees. Cheap foreign imports cut deeply into the pottery's profits.

Marks differ from piece to piece depending on the person who signed the piece or the artist who sculptured the mold. The identity for some initials has still not been determined.

Henry Below died on December 21, 1959, leaving the pottery in trust for his wife and three children with instructions that it be sold upon the death of his wife. Lee Below died on December 12, 1968. In October 1970 the Pennsbury Pottery filed for bankruptcy. The contents of the company were auction on December 18, 1970. On May 18, 1971, a fire destroyed the pottery and support buildings.

**References:** Lucile Henzke, *Pennsbury Pottery*, Schiffer Publishing, 1990; Dana Gehman Morykan and Harry L. Rinker, *Warman's Country Antiques & Collectibles,* Wallace–Homestead, 1992.

**Look Alike Alert:** The Lewis Brothers Pottery, Trenton, New Jersey, purchased fifty of the lesser Pennsbury molds. Although they were supposed to remove the Pennsbury name from the molds, some molds were overlooked. Further, two Pennsbury employees moved to Lewis Brothers when Pennsbury closed. Many pieces similar in feel and design to Pennsbury were produced. Many of Pennsbury's major lines including the Harvest and Rooster patterns, plaques, birds, and highly unusual molds were not reproduced.

Glen View, Langhorne, Pennsylvania, continued marketing the 1970s Angel Christmas plate with Pennsbury markings. The company continued the Christmas plate line into the 1970s utilizing the Pennsbury brown wash background. In 1975 Lenape Products, a division of Pennington, bought Glen View and continued making products with a Pennsbury feel.

Ashtray
Amish People .................... **15.00**
Don't Be So Doppish, 5" l ......... **20.00**
Doylestown Trust ................ **15.00**
Outen the Light .................. **15.00**
Such Schmootzers ................ **15.00**
What Giffs ...................... **15.00**
Bank, jug, pig, "Stuff Me," 7" h ...... **100.00**
Beer Mug, Amish .................. **18.00**
Cake Stand, Amish ................. **75.00**
Candleholder, pr, roosters, 4" h ...... **75.00**
Canister Set, cov, black rooster, 9" h flour and sugar, 8" h tea and coffee . **400.00**
Coaster, Shultz ..................... **15.00**
Creamer, 2" h
Amish Woman's Head ............ **13.00**
Red Rooster ...................... **15.00**
Cup and Saucer
Black Rooster ..................... **12.00**
Red Rooster ...................... **15.00**
Desk Accessory, bucket, National Exchange Club ..................... **18.00**

Figure, Blue Jay, #108, sgd "D. Parker," 10½" h . . . . . **350.00**
Mug
- Eagle . . . . . **20.00**
- Sweet Adeline . . . . . **20.00**

Pie Plate, Mother Serving Pie . . . . . **75.00**
Pitcher
- Amish man, miniature, 2" h . . . . . **12.00**
- Amish man at fence, miniature, 2" h **8.00**
- Amish Woman, 5" h . . . . . **45.00**
- Red Rooster, 4" h . . . . . **27.00**

Plaque
- Lafayette, B & O Railroad . . . . . **45.00**
- NEA Centennial . . . . . **24.00**

Plate
- Black Rooster, 10" d, dinner . . . . . **13.00**
- Hex Sign
  - 8" d . . . . . **18.00**
  - 10" d, dinner . . . . . **20.00**
- Mother's Day
  - 1972 . . . . . **9.00**
  - 1975 . . . . . **9.00**
- Red Rooster, 10" d, dinner . . . . . **18.00**
- Yuletide, 1970, first edition . . . . . **9.00**

**Plate, 8" d, red, yellow, and green dec, tan ground, green and brown border band, $48.00.**

Pretzel Bowl, eagle, 8 x 11" . . . . . **50.00**
Salt and Pepper Shakers, pr, Amish heads . . . . . **55.00**
Snack Tray and Cup, red rooster . . . . . **20.00**
Vegetable Dish, red rooster, divided . . **30.00**
Vinegar and Oil Jars, jug shape, Amish man and woman, pr . . . . . **135.00**
Wall Pocket, bellows, eagle dec, 10" h **45.00**

# PENS AND PENCILS

**Collecting Hints:** Any defects seriously affect the price downward. Defects include scratches, cracks, dents, warping, missing parts, bent levers, sprung clips, nib damage, and mechanical damage. Engraved initials or names do not detract seriously from the price.

**History:** The steel pen point or nib was invented by Samuel Harrison in 1780. It was not commercially produced in quantity until the 1880s when Richard Esterbrook entered the field. The holders became increasingly elaborate. Mother–of–pearl, gold, Sterling silver, and other fine materials were used to fashion holders of distinction. Many of these pens can be found intact with their velvet lined presentation cases.

Lewis Waterman invented the fountain pen in the 1880s. Three other leading pioneers in the field were Parker, Sheaffer (first lever filling action, 1913), and Wahl–Eversharp.

The mechanical pencil was patented in 1822 by Sampson Mordan. The original slide–type action developed into the spiral mechanical pencil. Wahl–Eversharp was responsible for the automatic "clic" or repeater type pencil which is used on ball points today.

The flexible nib that enabled the writer to individualize his penmanship came to an end when Reynolds introduced the ball point pen in October, 1945.

**References:** Glen Bowen, *Collectible Fountain Pens,* L–W Book Sales, 1992; George Fischler and Stuart Schneider, *Fountain Pens and Pencils,* Schiffer Publishing, Ltd., 1990; Cliff Lawrence, *Fountain Pens: History, Repair & Current Values, Second Edition,* Pen Fancier's Club, 1985; Cliff and Judy Lawrence, *The 1992 Official P. F. C. Pen Guide,* Pen Fancier's Club, 1991.

**Periodical:** *Pen World,* World Publications, 2240 Northpark Drive, Kingwood, TX 77339.

**Collectors' Clubs:** American Pencil Collectors Society, 2222 S. Milwood, Wichita, KS 67213; Pen Fancier's Club, 1169 Overcash Drive, Dunedin, FL 34698.

**Advisor:** Dick Bitterman.

Conklin
- Cushion Point, pen, silver–pink stripes, gold filled trim, NOZAK filler, 1945 . . . . . **50.00**

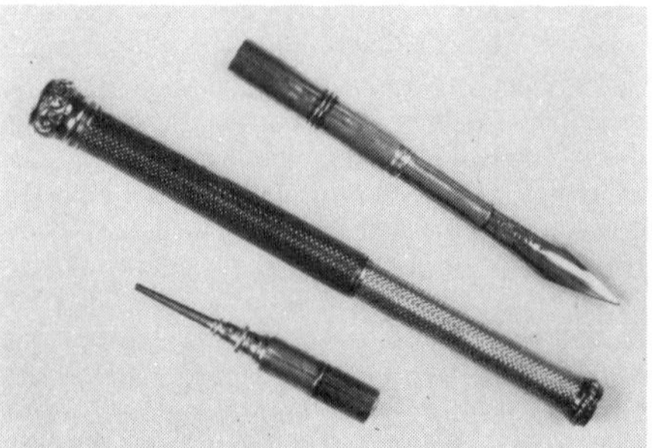

**B. T. Benton, NY, combination pen and pencil, brass, telescoping, 4¼" l extended, $65.00.**

Endura Model, desk set, two pens, 7¾" l, black marble base, side lever fill, double narrow gold color bands, marked "Patent Nov 17, 1925" on pen barrel, black–brown overlay color .................. **120.00**
Model 20, pen, 5⁵⁄₁₆" l, #2 Conklin point–nib, black crescent filler #20, gold clip, narrow gold band on cap, patent date May 28, 1918 stamped on clip ................ **65.00**
Model 25P, pen, ladies filigree cap ribbon, black, crescent filler, 1923 **60.00**
Model 30, pen, black hard rubber, 1903 ........................ **65.00**

Dunn, pen, black, red barrel, gold plated trim, 1920 ................ **35.00**

Epenco, pen, black case, gold plated trim ............................ **20.00**

Eversharp
Pen
C A Model, ball point, black, gold filled cap, 1946 .............. **40.00**
Doric
Desk, gold seal green marble cov, lever fill, large adjustable nib, 1935 ................. **50.00**
Lady's, Eversharp Gold Seal, green marble color, 14 carat point, twelve sided cap and barrel, 1931 ............... **95.00**
Pencil
Green marbleized base, upper half gold color metal cap, first of the repeater pencils, 1936 ........ **20.00**
Silver Plated, 1920 ............. **18.00**

Laughlin, pen, silver overlay case, eyedropper filled, 1905 .............. **135.00**

Marvel, black chased hard rubber, eyedropper, 1906 .................. **70.00**

Moore
Desk Set, gray and black marble base, black pen, 12 carat NIB, side lever fill .......................... **65.00**
Pen, rose color, fancy band around cap, warranted nib, side lever filler **60.00**
Ribbon Pen, lady's, black, three narrow gold bands on cap, lever filler, patent nib #2 ................. **65.00**

Onoto, Ink Pencil Stylographic, pen, black chased hard rubber, eyedropper, 1924 ....................... **37.50**

Parker
Blue–Diamond—51, pen, black, goldplated cap, button filled, 1942 **60.00**
Blue–Diamond—Vacumatic, pen, blue and black, goldplated trim, button filled, 1944 ............. **60.00**
Duofold, Model 78M, pencil, ladies, fuchsia color, gold color cap and tip, originally sold for $3, 1927 .. **95.00**
Duofold Deluxe, pen and pencil set, black and pearl, three narrow gold color bands on cap, push button fill, 1929 ...................... **450.00**
Duofold Senior, pen, Flashing Black, 1923 ......................... **150.00**
Duofold Streamline, burgundy and black, double narrow band on cap, 1932 ......................... **110.00**
Lucky Curve
Pen, push button filler, 1917 ..... **90.00**
Ring Pen, black hard rubber, gold filled trim, 1921 ............ **80.00**
Model 48, pen, ring top, gold filled barrel and cap, button filled, 1915 **140.00**
Model 51, pen, maroon, stainless steel cap, chrome plated trim, aerometic filler, 1950 ............... **30.00**
Model 61, pen, first edition, 1956 .. **45.00**
No 42, pen, gold filled metal mounted, 1927 ................ **85.00**
Vacumatic, gray–black, arrow clip, arrow design engraved on nib, silver color clip and band on cap, oversized model, 1932 .......... **100.00**

Pick, Exceptional, pen, black chased hard rubber, gold filled trim, lever filled, 1922 ...................... **60.00**

Reynolds, Model 2, pen, orig ball point, 1945–46 ........................ **65.00**

Sheaffer
Fineline 4000, pencil, novel point, platinum plating, 1946 .......... **18.00**
Strato Writer, pen, ballpoint, gold filled metal mounted, 1948 ...... **50.00**
Triumph Lifetime, desk set, green marble base, two black snorkel design pens, 1940s ............... **85.00**
White Dot, pen, green jade, goldplated trim, lever filled, 1923 .... **80.00**
White Dot Lifetime, pen, classic torpedo design cap and body, lever filler on side, 1930 ............ **95.00**

Security, pen, check protector, red hard rubber, gold filled trim, 1923 ...... **70.00**

Swan (made by Mabie, Todd & Co, NY and London)
Eternal
Model 4, pen, black, gold filled trim, marked "44 E.T.N., Model 4," nib marked 14 carat ....... **55.00**
Model 54, pen, red ripple, band at top and bottom of cap, marked "Model 54 Eternal" on barrel, nib marked 14 carat .......... **70.00**

Wahl
Lady's, ribbon pen, double narrow band on cap, 14 carat #2 nib, lever fill, 1928 ...................... **65.00**
Tempoint No 305A, pen, gold filled metal mounted, eyedropper, 1919 **125.00**
Wahl–Eversharp

Pen, gold seal, black, gold filled trim, lever filled, 1930 ........ **100.00**
Pencil
Gold filled metal mounted, 1919 **25.00**
Ring top, goldfilled case, 1923 . **40.00**
Sterling Silver, engraved case, 1924 .................... **95.00**
Waterman
Lady Patricia, pen, gray mottled finish, lever fill, 1936 ............ **45.00**
Model #12, pen, mottled brown, 14 carat gold bands, 1886 ......... **110.00**
Model #71, pen, ripple red hard rubber case, goldplated trim, wide clip, lever filled, 1925 .......... **120.00**
Safety Pen, Model 42½V, gold filigree, retractable screw action nib, 3½" l, 1906 .................. **100.00**
Taperite, pen, black, gold filled metal mounted cap, gold filled trim, lever filler, 1949 .................... **50.00**
100 Year Model, pen, black, gold color clip, nib marked "100 Year Pen–1944" ........................ **45.00**

# PEPSI

**Collecting Hints:** Pepsi, Hires, and a number of other soft drink companies became hot collectibles in the 1980s, fueled in part by the pricey nature of Coca–Cola items. The Pepsi market is still young; some price fluctuations occur.

Pepsi–Cola enjoys a much stronger market position in many foreign countries than it does in the United States. As a result, the best sales market for Pepsi items may be outside the United States. Look for major developments in this area in the decade ahead.

Reproductions, copycats, and fantasy items are part of the Pepsi collecting scene. Be on the alert for the Pepsi and Pete pillow issued in the 1970s, a 12" high ceramic statue of a woman holding a glass of Pepsi, a Pepsi glass front clock, a Pepsi double bed quilt, and a set of four Pepsi glasses. These are just a few of the items, some of which were done under license from Pepsi–Cola.

**History:** Pepsi–Cola was developed by Caleb D. Bradham, a pharmacist and drugstore owner in New Bern, North Carolina. As in many drugstores of its time, Bradham provided "soda" mixes for his customers and friends. His favorite was "Brad's Drink."

In 1898, Bradham named "Brad's Drink" Pepsi–Cola. Its popularity spread. In 1902 Bradham turned the operation of his drugstore over to an assistant and devoted his full time energies to perfecting and promoting Pepsi–Cola. He sold 2,008 gallons of Pepsi–Cola syrup his first three months. By 1904 Bradham was bottling Pepsi–Cola for mass consumption. Within a short time, he sold his first franchise.

By the end of the twentieth century's first decade, Bradham had organized a network of over 250 bottlers in twenty–four states. The company's fortunes sank shortly after World War I when it suffered large losses in the sugar market. Bankruptcy and reorganization followed. Roy Megargel, whose Wall Street firm advised Bradham, helped keep the name alive. A second bankruptcy occurred in 1931; but, the company survived.

In 1933 Pepsi–Cola doubled its bottle size, but still held to its nickel price. Sales soared. Under the direction of Walter Mack, 1938–1951, Pepsi challenged Coca–Cola for market dominance. In the 1950s Pepsi advertising became slogan oriented – "Pepsi Cola Hits The Spot, Twelve Full Ounces That's A Lot."

PepsiCo. is currently a division of Beatrice. It has a worldwide reputation and actually is the number one soft drink in many foreign countries.

**References:** Ted Hake, *Hake's Guide To Advertising Collectibles: 100 Years of Advertising from 100 Famous Companies*, Wallace–Homestead, 1992; Norman E. Martinus and Harry L. Rinker, *Warman's Paper*, Wallace–Homestead, 1993; Bill Vehling and Michael Hunt, *Pepsi–Cola Collectibles, Vol. 1* (1990, 1993 value update), *Vol. 2* (1990), and *Vol. 3* (1993), L–W Book Sales.

**Collectors' Club:** Pepsi–Cola Collectors Club, PO Box 1275, Covina, CA 91722.

**Museum:** Pepsi–Cola Company Archives, Purchase, NY.

Ashtray
Bakelite, 6" d, Yuba City, CA, 1950s **50.00**
Glass, 4 x 4", Pepsi Beats The Others Cold!, clear, colored center, 1960s **25.00**
Award, Volume Award, Durham, NC, 1953, 12 x 12" .................. **75.00**
Bathroom Scale, 14 x 10", Diet Pepsi Can Help, 1970s ................ **15.00**
Bedspread, c1960 .................. **35.00**
Bottle
8 oz, emb "No Return," 1950s .... **100.00**
32 oz, applied color label, c1960 .. **50.00**
Bottle Carrier
Cardboard, 6 bottle, c1960 ........ **25.00**
Metal, 6 bottle, c1930 ............ **125.00**
Wood, 24 bottle, c1910 ........... **100.00**
Bottle Opener, bottle shape .......... **7.00**
Cake Carrier, tin, Pepsi logo ......... **95.00**
Cake Tin .......................... **25.00**
Calendar
1950, paper, full pad, 11 x 24" .... **600.00**
1955, cardstock, 12 x 20" ......... **400.00**
Change Mat, 8 x 8", Say Pepsi Please, rubber, 1960s .................... **20.00**
Cigarette Lighter, 1 x 4", metal, bottle cap illus on side, 1950s ........... **150.00**

**Bottle, 12 oz, painted label, red and white logo, emb "Pepsi-Cola" around shoulder, Duraglas 951-G, 9¾" h, $10.00.**

Clock
- Glass, light–up, Drink Pepsi–Cola, Ice–Cold, 15" d, c1950 ......... **325.00**
- Plastic, metal frame, diamond shape, Pepsi, 16 x 16", c1960 .......... **125.00**

Coaster, 4" sq, cardboard, bottle cap illus, 1950s ....................... **20.00**
Cooler, picnic type, metal, orig box, 24 x 18 x 14", c1960 ............... **175.00**
Coupon, 3 x 2", Pepsi–Cola, 5 Cents, c1950s ........................ **25.00**
Fan, 10 x 10", cardboard, wood handle, c1940 .......................... **75.00**
Glass, 10 oz, applied color label, Pepsi–Cola, c1950 ..................... **35.00**
Golf Bag, 48" h, allover Pepsi logo, 1970s .......................... **25.00**
Letterhead, Pepsi–Cola Bottling Works, Greensboro, NC, 1916, 8½ x 11" .. **100.00**
Magazine, WEEI Boston, CBS Radio, Pepsi Home Carton Contest Issue ... **25.00**
Napkin, 19" sq, cloth, c1940 ........ **25.00**
Notepad, 2½ x 4½", cardboard cov, red and black logo, 1914 calendar ..... **30.00**
Paperweight, 3 x 3", glass, Delicious Pepsi–Cola, c1940 ............... **75.00**
Patch, 2 x 2", Pepsi, cloth, c1960 .... **10.00**
Pen, 5" l, plastic, c1960 ........... **15.00**

Pinback Button
- 1" d, Pepsi Day for Crippled Children, celluloid and tin, 1970s ......... **25.00**
- 2" d, I Drank A Pepsi, Did You?, tin, 1970s ....................... **10.00**
- 3" d, Be Sociable, Have a Pepsi, celluloid and tin, c1950 ........... **50.00**

Playing Cards, Pepsi–Cola Bottling Co, Quincy, IL, orig yellow box, c1940 . **100.00**
Program, Pepsi–Cola, Evervess 1947 Convention, Atlantic City, November 12–15, 6 x 12" ................. **75.00**
Record, Pepsi, Armed Service Man, 45 rpm ........................... **12.00**
Ruler, 12" l, tin, 1950s .............. **20.00**
Salt and Pepper Shakers, 75th Anniversary, pepper mill, MIB ............ **55.00**

Sign
- Come Alive, cardboard ........... **40.00**
- Drink Pepsi–Cola, 24 x 28", tin, bottle cap illus, 1950s ................ **50.00**
- Have A Pepsi, 22 x 7", paper, man, woman, and bottle cap illus, 1950s **25.00**
- Ice Cold Pepsi–Cola Sold Here, 9" d, celluloid and tin, 1930s ......... **275.00**
- It's A Great American Custom!, 28 x 11", family seated in front of fireplace drinking product, orig frame, 1940s ....................... **375.00**
- Out, 2 x 3", tin .................. **75.00**
- Pepsi, 13 x 15½", thin steel, red, white, blue, and gray bottle cap, yellow ground, double sided, c1950 ....................... **80.00**
- Pepsi–Cola, The Big Picnic Drink, 18 x 27", picnicing family, easel back, 1940s ....................... **450.00**
- Take Home Pepsi, 12 x 8", plastic, light–up, bottle cap illus, 1950s .. **150.00**

Spoon Rest, 5 x 6", plastic, figural, man, c1950 ......................... **25.00**
Sun Visor, 12" l, Say Pepsi Please, 1950s **35.00**
Tape Measure, 2 x 2", Drink Pepsi–Cola, 1950s .................... **20.00**

Thermometer
- Any Weather's Pepsi Weather!, 2 x 8", cardboard, 1950s .............. **50.00**
- Bouncy To Ounce, 26" d, 1950s ... **160.00**
- Pepsi, tin, 1950s ................ **25.00**

Toy, Pepsi–Cola Delivery Truck, 2½ x 7½ x 3", white, plastic body, black wood wheels, red, white, and blue Pepsi decal, three white plastic cases with 24 plastic bottles, Marx Toys, c1940 ......................... **85.00**

Tray
- Have a Pepsi, 13" d, 1950s ........ **75.00**
- Pepsi–Cola, Hits the Spot, 1940s ... **15.00**

# PEZ

**Collecting Hints:** PEZ developed as a hot collectible in the late 1980s. Its rise was due in part to PEZ's use of licensed cartoon characters as heads on their dispensers. Initially PEZ containers were extremely affordable. Generic subjects often sold for less than $5.00, character containers for less than $10.00. This changed when PEZ developed its own collecting category. It is one of the 1990s' "hot" collectibles.

Before investing large amounts of money in PEZ containers, it is important to recognize that: (1) PEZ containers are produced in large quantities—millions, (2) PEZ containers have a high saveability potential, and (3) no collecting category stays hot forever. PEZ prices fluctuate. Advertised and field prices for the same container can differ by as much as fifty percent depending on who is selling.

Starting a PEZ collection is simple. Go to a local store that sells PEZ and purchase the current group of products. Your initial cost will be less than $3.00 a unit.

**History:** Vienna, Austria, is the birthplace of PEZ. In 1927 Eduard Haas, an Austrian food mogul, invented PEZ and marketed it as a cigarette substitute, i.e., an adult mint. He added peppermint oil to a candy formula, compressed it in small rectangular bricks, and named it PEZ, an abbreviation for the German word *Pfefferminz*. Production of PEZ was halted by World War II. When the product appeared again after the war, it was packaged in a dispenser that resembled a BIC lighter. These early 1950s dispensers had no heads.

PEZ arrived in the United States in 1952. PEZ–HAAS received U.S. Patent #2,620,061 for its "table dispensing receptacle." The public response was less than overwhelming. Rather than withdraw from the market, Haas repositioned his product for the children's market. First, fruit flavors were added. Second, novelty dispensers, e.g., a space gun, and the addition of heads to the top of the standard rectangular containers combined the dual elements of a candy and a toy in one product. PEZ's success was assured.

PEZ carefully guards its design and production information. As a result, collectors differ on important questions such as dating and variation. Further complicating the issue is PEZ production outside the United States. A company in Linz, Austria, with PEZ rights to the rest of the world, including Canada, frequently issues PEZ containers with heads not issued by PEZ Candy, Inc., an independent privately owned company which by agreement manufactures and markets PEZ only in the United States. PEZ Candy, Inc., is located in Connecticut.

There is a communication link between the American and Austrian companies producing PEZ. Both use a common agent to manage the production of dispensers. The result is that occasionally the same container is issued by both companies. However, when this occurs, the packaging may be entirely different.

PEZ Candy, Inc., issues generic, seasonal, and character licensed containers. Container design is continually evaluated and upgraded. The Mickey Mouse container has been changed more than a dozen times.

Today PEZ candy is manufactured at plants in Austria, Hungary, Yugoslavia, and the United States. Previously, plants had been located in Czechoslovakia, Germany, and Mexico. Dispensers are produced at plants in Austria, China, Hong Kong, Hungary, and Slovenia.

**Reference:** David Welch, *A Pictorial Guide to Plastic Candy Dispensers Featuring PEZ*, Bubba Scrubba Publications, 1991.

**Periodicals:** *Plastic Candy Dispenser Newsletter*, 3851 Gable Lane Drive, #513, Indianapolis, IN 46208. Between 1990 and early 1992 Mike Robertson (PO Box 606, Dripping Springs, TX 78620) issued *The Optimistic PEZZIMIST*, a bimonthly newsletter. A bound 1990 annual was published and may still be available.

| Item | Price |
|---|---|
| Angel, 1960s | **5.00** |
| Annie, 1970s | **20.00** |
| Baloo, 1980s | **10.00** |
| Baseball Glove, 1960s | **100.00** |
| Bat Girl, soft head, 1970s | **40.00** |
| Betsy Ross, 1976 | **35.00** |
| Big Top Elephant, 1970s | **10.00** |
| Boy, Pez Pal, 1960–70 | **5.00** |
| Bozo, 4" h, light blue base, red and white head, 1952–68 | **40.00** |
| Brutus, 1960s | **100.00** |
| Bugs Bunny, 4½" h, yellow base, gray and white head, 1978 | **25.00** |
| Bullwinkle, 1960s | **150.00** |
| Casper, 1960s | **70.00** |
| Chick In Egg, 1960s | **1.00** |
| Chip, 1980s | **8.00** |
| Creature, 1960s | **75.00** |
| Crocodile, 1970s | **30.00** |
| Daffy Duck, 1970–80 | **2.00** |
| Daniel Boone, 1976 | **100.00** |
| Doctor, Pez Pal, 1960–70 | **20.00** |
| Donald Duck, NF | **12.50** |
| Donky Kong, Jr, premium, 1980 | **200.00** |
| Droopy Dog, 1980s | **10.00** |
| Dumbo, 1960s | **5.00** |
| Fireman, Pez Pal, 1960–70 | **10.00** |
| Fozzie Bear, 1991 | **1.00** |
| Garfield, 1980s | **2.00** |
| Goofy, 1960s | **1.00** |
| Gorilla, 1970s | **10.00** |
| Incredible Hulk, 1970s | **5.00** |
| Indian Squaw, 1976 | **50.00** |
| Jerry, 1980s | **10.00** |
| Kermit the Frog, 1991 | **1.00** |
| Knight, Pez Pal, 1960–70 | **75.00** |
| Lamb, 1960s | **1.00** |
| Lion, 1970s | **10.00** |
| Mexican Boy, unopened orig package | **75.00** |
| Mickey Mouse, 1950s | **50.00** |
| Miss Piggy, 1991 | **1.00** |
| Nurse, Pez Pal, 1960–70 | **10.00** |
| Panda Bear, 1970s | **1.00** |
| Peter Pan, 1960s | **75.00** |
| Peter Pan, 4" h, green base, copyright Walt Disney Productions | **25.00** |
| Pluto, 1960s | **1.00** |
| Pony, 4½" h, blue base, 1952–68 | **22.00** |

Pumpkin, 1960s .................... **1.00**
Road Runner, 1970–80 .............. **10.00**
Sailor, Pez Pal, 1960–70 ............ **50.00**
Santa Claus, 1950s ................. **1.00**
Scare Wolf, 1960s .................. **50.00**
Scrooge McDuck, 1970s ............ **10.00**
Sheriff, Pez Pal, 1960–70 ........... **10.00**
Skeleton .......................... **9.50**
Smurf, 1980s ....................... **2.00**
Speedy Gonzales, 1970–80 .......... **10.00**
Spiderman, NF ..................... **15.00**
Spike, Tom and Jerry, 1980s ......... **10.00**
Tinkerbell, 1960s .................. **75.00**
Tom and Jerry, Tom, 1980s .......... **10.00**

**Tom and Jerry, MGM, Hong Kong, 4¼″ h Tom, 4⅛″ h Jerry, price each $10.00.**

Truck, 4″ h, orange base, dark brown cab top, c1976 .................. **20.00**
Whistle, 4″ h, pink base, yellow and red whistle, 1974–76 ................ **20.00**
Wile E Coyote, 1970–80 ............ **5.00**
Witch, 1960s ...................... **1.00**
Wonder Woman, soft head, 1970s .... **35.00**

# PHOENIX BIRD CHINA

**Collecting Hints:** Phoenix Bird pattern has over 450 different shapes and sizes. The quality found in the execution of design, shades of blue, and shape of the ware itself also varies. All these factors must be considered in pricing. The maker's mark tends to add value; over 100 marks have been cataloged.

The more one studies Phoenix Bird china, the more one recognizes the variances. Collectors are urged to travel with a notebook in which is listed the shape, pattern, backstamp, dimensions, and conditions of the pieces owned. If the head of the phoenix is on a forward slant and its head feathers point upwards, also on somewhat of a slant, the rest of the motif will be well executed. If this is combined with a piece having an oversized border, the collector has found a "superior piece." Generally these superior pieces are marked with a flower with a "T" inside, but not always. The one rule about Phoenix Bird is that there always is an exception to the rule.

Don't buy Phoenix Bird unseen. Insist on a drawing of the piece, but most preferably a photograph. Photographs can be deceiving so ask for the dimensions as well. Xeroxing a plate is helpful for a buyer's identification of Phoenix Bird China or any of the similar Phoenix patterns.

**History:** The manufacture of Phoenix Bird pattern china began in the late 19th century. The ware was heavily imported into the United States during the 1920s to the 1940s. The Phoenix Bird pattern shows a bird facing back over its left wing, spots on its chest and wings that spread upward. The vast majority of the ware was of the transfer print variety. Blue and white was the dominant color scheme. Pieces also can be found in green (celadon), but are quite rare. Coveted are the few hand painted pieces in blue which are signed with six Japanese characters on the underside and which always have the heart border.

Some of the transfer pieces also have a heart like border and are referred to as HO–O for identification. Many of these early pieces are not marked. The majority of Phoenix Bird has the traditional border called the cloud and mountain (c/m) and sometimes has "Nippon" backstamped when of the 1891–1921 era.

Phoenix Bird pattern china primarily was sold through Woolworth's 5 & 10 Cent stores. It could also be ordered from the wholesale catalogs of Butler Brothers and the Charles William stores, the latter also retailing it at its New York city store. All the pieces offered were only the most basic shapes. Phoenix Bird also was carried by A. A. Vantine Co., NY, exported by Morimura Brothers, Japan.

A Phoenix Bird breakfast set could be acquired by selling a certain number of subscriptions to *Needlecraft* magazine. Ward's Grocery Catalog and A. J. Kasper Importers, Chicago, offered a Phoenix Bird cup and saucer as a premium for purchasing a particular brand of tea or coffee.

Once known as "Blue Howo Bird China," the Phoenix Bird pattern is the most sought after of several variations of the HO–O bird series. Other variations are:

Firebird—one of several less common patterns, flowing tail dragging downward; majority are hand painted, marked with six Oriental characters.

Flying Dragon—all over pattern comes in blue and white as well as green and white; always has six characters underneath; bird's wings are fatter and rounder; in place of flower there is a pinwheel like design.

Flying Turkey—blue and white with heart border, head always facing forward; no spots on chest; and left wing, as one faces design, only half showing; majority is transfer printed, a larger minority than Phoenix Bird is hand painted, mark is six Oriental characters.

Howo—in some cases the pattern's name is on the underside along with "Noritake," other times it is not; phoenix shows no feet, flower is more peony like.

Twin Phoenix—made by Noritake, but not always marked; pattern is only on outer edge, rest is white; two birds face one another in pairs.

During the 1920s and 1930s an overwhelming number of potteries put their trademarks on the pieces. A majority have "Made in Japan," an M/wreath (concave M), crossed stems with a convex "M," or a flower with a "T" inside and "Japan" underneath. The last mark shows up on some of the more uniquely shaped pieces and pieces of highest quality. Most Japanese potteries were destroyed during WWII, making it difficult to trace production records. The Phoenix Bird pattern was copied by an English firm, Myott & Son, in the mid–1930s. The English examples are earthenware and not porcelain as are the Japanese pieces.

**References:** Joan Collett Oates, *Phoenix Bird Chinaware, Book I* (1984), *Book II* (1985), *Book III* (1986), *Book 4* (1989), published by author.

**Collectors' Club:** Phoenix Bird Collectors of America, 685 S. Washington, Constantine, MI 49042.

**Museums:** Historic Cherry Hill, Albany, NY; Huntingdon County Historical Society, Huntingdon, PA; Charles A. Lindbergh Home, Little Falls, MN; Eleanor Roosevelt's Vall–Kill Cottage, Hyde Park, NY.

**Advisor:** Joan Collett Oates.

**REPRODUCTION ALERT.** Reproductions of later shapes, with the exception of cups and saucers, have been around since 1970. The reproductions are more modern in shape, have more precise designs, more brilliant blue, have a milk–white ground and rarely are backstamped, with the exception of a covered jam jar and a butter pat dish. The reproductions generally had paper stickers on them at one time. Diagonal lines within the various designs are prevalent. The all–over design is more sparse on the post 1970 pieces and does not always reach the bottom of an item as it does on earlier Phoenix Bird; the majority of pieces do not have a backstamp.

A new type of Phoenix is on the market in various forms and also is a dark blue design. It is called "T–Bird" for identification. At least one maker has been identified, Takahashi. Sometimes it is found with a group of Oriental markings within a blue square.

**Note:** The numbering system used to identify pieces is from the four volume set of *Phoenix Bird Chinaware* by Joan Collett Oates.

**Nut Tubs, handled, price each $25.00.**

Butter Tub .......... **47.00**
Butter Tub Drain .......... **18.00**
Cake Server/Plate .......... **65.00**
Cereal Dish, 6" d .......... **12.00**
Chocolate Cup, handle .......... **22.00**
Cup and Saucer .......... **8.00**
Eggcup
  Double .......... **18.00**
  Single .......... **12.00**
Fruit Dish, 5½" d .......... **8.00**
Gravy Boat and Underplate .......... **65.00**
Mayonnaise Dish, three ball feet .......... **35.00**
Mustard Pot, cov .......... **45.00**
Plate
  6" d, bread and butter .......... **7.00**
  7" d, dessert .......... **10.00**
  8½" d, luncheon .......... **18.00**
  9½" d, breakfast .......... **35.00**
  9¾" d, dinner .......... **48.00**
Platter
  8" l .......... **30.00**
  12" l .......... **50.00**
  17" l .......... **145.00**
Salt and Pepper Shakers, pr
  #2, round, fat .......... **35.00**
  #6, six sided .......... **25.00**
  #7, bell shape .......... **28.00**
Soup Dish, 7¼" d .......... **36.00**
Teapot, cov
  #7, medium, round .......... **45.00**
  #10 .......... **55.00**
Tile, round .......... **35.00**
Vegetable Dish, 7" oval .......... **35.00**
Vegetable Tureen, cov .......... **135.00**

# PHOTOGRAPHS

**Collecting Hints:** The first and most important thing to remember is that most personal photographs, no matter how old, are virtually worthless. This is especially true of unidentified family views.

Value rests in content and artistry. Photographs of towns, occupations, and other special interest categories do have value to collectors. Pictures of children sledding down a snow bank or standard soldiers in uniform usually do not.

Take a few minutes during your next visit to your local library and review the books dealing with twentieth century photographers. Memorize their names and work. Examples of their work do turn up in unexpected places. However, before paying a premium, double check to make certain that the example is not one from a mass produced folio. These usually have very limited value.

**History:** Next to the Bible, the most important book a family owned in the second half of the nineteenth and first half of the twentieth centuries was the nucleated family photo album. Filled primarily with individual head and shoulder photographs in the early period to numerous christening, graduation, wedding, and vacation photographs in the later period, it provided a visual chronicle of the family's history. Also accompanying the album are usually dozens of envelopes with pictures and negatives that were meant to be added "some day."

The chief problem is that most photographs are unidentified. The individuals who took or received the pictures knew who everyone was. Information was passed orally from generation to generation. Most information was lost by the third and fourth generations.

In late nineteenth and early twentieth century albums, principal photographs are cartes de visite and cabinet cards. It is also common to find memorial cards and mass–produced photographs of important military and historical figures. Pictures that show a person in a working environment, identifiable building or street scene, or a special holiday, e.g., Christmas, are eagerly sought. Most studio shots have little value.

Many of the albums were ornately decorated in velvet and applied ormolu. Some covers contained celluloid pictures, ranging in theme from a beautiful young woman to the battleship *Maine*. The Victorian decorating craze drew attention to these albums in the late 1980s. Prices have risen significantly over the last several years.

Cartes de visite, or calling card, photographs were patented in France in 1854, flourished from 1857 to 1910, and survived into the 1920s. The most common cartes de visite were 2¼ x 3¾" head and shoulder portraits printed on albumen paper and mounted on 2½ x 4" cards. Multi–lens cameras were used by the photographer to produce four to eight exposures on a single glass negative plate. A contact print was made from this which would yield four to eight identical photographs on one piece of photographic paper. The photographs would be cut apart and mounted on cards. These cards were put in albums or simply handed out when visiting, similar to today's business cards.

In 1866 the cabinet card was introduced in England and shortly thereafter in the United States. It was produced similarly to cartes de visite, but could have utilized several styles of photographic processes. A cabinet card measured 4 x 5" and was mounted on a 4½ x 6½" card. Portraits in cabinet size were more appealing because of the large facial detail and the fact that the images could be retouched. By the 1880s the cabinet card was as popular as the carte de visite and by the 1890s was produced almost exclusively. Cabinet cards flourished until shortly after the turn of the century.

George Eastman revolutionized the photography industry in 1888 when his simple box camera was introduced. It was small—3¼ x 3¾ x 6½". The camera had a film magazine and could take 100 pictures without being reloaded. The pictures were 2½" in diameter. Many later models built upon the success of Kodak No. 1. Kodak's first folding camera was Model No. 4; the Brownie arrived in 1900.

Americans loved photographs. Everyone took pictures. A family's photographic treasures grew exponentially. Professional "art" photographers arrived on the scene. Folios were mass produced and sold in quantities.

Two developments in the post–1945 era changed the impact level of photographs in everyday life. The 35mm slide diminished the importance of the print. Home movie cameras and later the video camera made amateur moving pictures possible. Many modern families no longer maintain a photograph album or family photograph archives. They simply do not have the desire or time.

**References:** Stuart Bennett, *How To Buy Photographs,* Salem House, 1987; William C. Darrah, *Cartes de Visite in Nineteenth Century Photography,* William C. Darrah, 1981; B. E. C. Howarth–Loomes, *Victorian Photography: An Introduction for Collectors and Connoisseurs,* St. Martin's Press, Inc., 1974; O. Henry Mace, *Collector's Guide to Early Photographs,* Wallace–Homestead, 1990; Norman E. Martinus and Harry L. Rinker, *Warman's Paper,* Wallace–Homestead, 1993; Lou W. McCullough, *Card Photographs, A Guide To Their History and Value,* Schiffer Publishing, Ltd., 1981; Floyd and Marion Rinhart, *American Miniature Case Art,* A. S. Barnes and Co., Inc., 1969; Susan Theran, *Leonard's Annual Price Index of Prints, Posters and Photographs, Volume I,* Auction Index, Inc., 1992; Susan Theran, *Prints, Posters and Photographs: Identification and Price Guide,* Avon Books, 1993; John Waldsmith, *Stereoviews, An Illustrated History and Price Guide,* Wallace–Homestead, 1991.

**Periodicals:** *The Photograph Collector,* 163 Amsterdam Ave. #201, New York, NY 10023; *The Photographic Historian,* Box B, Granby, MA 01033.

**Collectors' Clubs:** American Photographical Historical Society, 520 West 44th St, New York, NY 10036; Photographic Historical Society of New England, Inc., P. O. Box 189, West Newton Station, Boston, MA 02165; Western Photographic Collectors Association, P. O. Box 4294, Whittier, CA 90607.

**Museums:** International Museum of Photography, George Eastman House, Rochester, NY; Smithsonian Institution, Washington, D. C., University of Texas at Austin, Austin, TX.

**REPRODUCTION ALERT:** Excellent reproductions of Lincoln as well as other Civil War era figures on cartes de visite and cabinet cards have been made.

**Note:** Prices listed are for black and white photographs in excellent condition. Photographs with soiling, staining, tears, or copy photographs are worth less than half prices listed.

## CABINET CARDS

Blacks
- Black Boy, fancy dress, large bow .. **10.00**
- Woman, Alabama ................ **12.00**

Children, boy on tricycle, metal wheels, trimmed ........................ **10.00**

Military, general, soldiers, and older boys, c1880, 5 x 6" .............. **15.00**

Political, McKinley and Wife ........ **8.00**

**Cabinet Card, portrait, 1880s, 4⅛ x 6½", $2.00.**

## CARTES DE VISITE

Children
- Boy with American Flag ........... **12.00**

Circus, Mr & Mrs General Tom Thumb, wearing wedding costumes, pub by EHT Anthony from Brady negative, 1863 ........................ **10.00**

Famous People
- Colonel JJ Astor, New York, JH Bufford, Pub, Boston .............. **15.00**
- Minnie Ha–Ha, Upton photo ...... **18.00**

Foreign
- Egyptian Woman, water jug on head **12.00**
- English Military Officer ............ **6.00**

Fraternal, man wearing Masonic uniform ........................... **8.00**

Military, General Hancock, 1824–1886 **12.00**

Political, Abraham Lincoln .......... **15.00**

**Cartes de Visite, dog, $5.00.**

## PHOTOGRAPHS

Animals
- Dog in Buggy .................... **8.00**
- Girl with Puppy .................. **6.00**

Blacks
- Two Men, posed with liquor bottles, 1920s ........................ **8.00**
- Woman, well dressed, 1911 ....... **8.00**

Children
- Girls in Horse–Drawn Cart, 4¼ x 6½" **8.00**
- Girl with Doll, 5 x 7" ............. **10.00**
- Two Boys with Bicycles, in cornfield **6.00**
- Two Girls by Organ, 6 x 8" ........ **10.00**

Disasters, train wreck at bridge, PA Lines, 8 x 10" ................... **10.00**

Farm Machinery, thresher and wagons **6.00**

Holiday, Christmas tree, fully decorated, dolls and toys beneath, 10 x 12" ... **40.00**

Military
- Mexican Revolutionist, standing beside smiling woman ............ **8.00**
- Underwood Bi–Plane, German, wrecked, newspaper photo, WWI, 5 x 7½" ....................... **8.00**
- USA Aviation Corps, 1918, 5¼ x 6¾" **20.00**

Occupational
- Donut Shop, "Sip and Bite Donut Shop, ext., 7 x 9" .............. **25.00**

Grocery Store, int., 5 x 7" ......... **20.00**
Hotel Store Front, Merchants Hotel, EK Smith Paper Twines, New England, 4½ x 6½" ................ **15.00**
Office, int., 7 x 9" ................ **15.00**
Silver Shop, int., 6 x 8" ........... **25.00**
Store Front, AJ Metge, Dry Goods, Notions, Candy, 8 x 10" ......... **20.00**
Supermarket, int., 1950s, 8 x 10" .. **15.00**
Tailor Shop, ext., bicycle in front ... **10.00**

Parade, small bark house on wagon, decorated with flags, children looking out, 4½ x 8" ..................... **8.00**

Police
Mug Shot, black man, trapping on railroad property, 1926 .......... **10.00**
Policeman, late 1800s, 6 x 9" ...... **10.00**

Political, Calvin Coolidge, with owners of Lakeside Inn, FL, 7 x 11" ....... **15.00**

Scenic
Harbor of Vladivostok, Siberia, ships and ship building, Sept 8, 1902, 8 x 11½" ....................... **20.00**
Natural Bridge of Virginia, Burrows, hand tinted, framed, 18½ x 15" .. **45.00**

Transportation
Delivery Truck, J Batthof, Folcroft, PA, 1928, 3½ x 4½" ............ **8.00**
Man with Motorcycle, 1943 ....... **8.00**

# PIG COLLECTIBLES

**Collecting Hints:** Bisque and porcelain pig items from the late 19th century European potters are most widely sought by collectors. Souvenir items should have the decals in good shape; occasionally the gilding wears off from rubbing or washing.

**History:** Historically the pig has been an important food source in the rural economies of Europe and America. It was one of the first animals imported into the American colonies. A fatted sow was the standard gift to a rural preacher on his birthday or holiday.

As a decorative motif the pig gained prominence with the figurines and planters made in the late 19th century by English, German, and Austrian potters. These "pink" porcelain pigs with green decoration were popular souvenir or prize items at fairs or carnivals or could be purchased at five–and–dime stores.

Many pig figurines were banks. "Piggy Bank" became a standard term for the coin bank by the early 20th century. When tourist attractions began along America's sea coasts and in the mountain areas, many of the pig designs showed up as souvenir items with the name of the area applied in gilded decal form.

The pig motif appeared on the advertising items associated with farm products and life. The era of the movie cartoon introduced "Porky Pig" and Walt Disney's "Three Little Pigs."

In the late 1970s pig collectibles caught fire again. Specialty shops selling nothing but pig related items were found in the New England area. *Time* magazine devoted a page and one–half to the pig phenomena in one of its 1981 issues.

**Advisor:** Mary Hamburg.

**See:** Cartoon Characters and Disneyana

**REPRODUCTION ALERT:** Reproductions of three German–style, painted bisque figurines have been spotted in the market. They are pig by outhouse, pig playing piano, and pig poking out of large purse. The porcelain is much rougher and the green is a darker shade.

Ashtray
Artist, pig painting, pig sketch on tablet ............................ **85.00**
Bowling, one pig bowling, another watching, pink with green, 5" w . **90.00**
Photographer, two pigs looking into old fashioned camera, 4½" w .... **75.00**
Two pigs looking into old fashioned Victrola, 4½" w ................ **75.00**
Two pigs hugging, sitting in dish, bisque, stamped "Made in Germany" **80.00**

**Bank, plaster, hand painted floral dec and facial features, incised "copyright ABCO" on back, coin slot between ears, rubber stopper, 8⅝" h, $12.00.**

Bank
Carnival Glass, orange, Anchor Hocking ...................... **10.00**
Ceramic
Saving His Pennies To Make Pounds, pink pig alongside of bank, 3½" h ................. **95.00**
Souvenir of Danville, IL, front of pink pig sticking out of bank, back sticking out other side, yellow pouch, gold trim, 3½" h .. **50.00**

Basket, pink pig poking out of basket, orange seal ...................... **50.00**

Figurine
- Automobile, two pigs .......... **55.00**
- Barber Shop Scene, Little Bit Off The Top, incised "Made in Germany," 2¾" h .......... **80.00**
- Caboose, two pink pigs .......... **80.00**
- Canoe, pink pig .......... **75.00**
- Cart, pink pig wheeling cart with three piglets, titled "The More The Merrier" .......... **75.00**
- Champagne Cork, two pigs in front, Heidsieck Dry Champagne, 3" h . **85.00**
- Chef, pig standing by barrel, blue hat and jacket .......... **95.00**
- Cradle, pig sitting in center .......... **60.00**
- Dutch Shoe, pig sitting in opening .. **35.00**
- Gazebo, orange roof, two pink pigs sitting on bench, 5½" h .......... **100.00**
- Jar, orange seal, pig alongside, 2¾" h **60.00**
- Jumping over green fence, black, bisque .......... **65.00**
- Looking In Outhouse, titled "Engaged," 2½" w, 4" h .......... **80.00**
- Looking inside bassinet, 3½" h .......... **60.00**
- Mama pig holding piglet in blue blanket, looking at rabbit, titled "Was not happy until he got it" .......... **65.00**
- Money Bag, pink pig poking out of top, "$5,000,000" on front .......... **72.00**
- Mushrooms, three pigs sitting on trough, two orange mushrooms, 4¾" l .......... **88.00**
- Playing Organ, second pig playing banjo, titled "Home Sweet Home" **85.00**
- Table Tennis, two pink pigs playing, titled "Patience" .......... **90.00**
- Train Engine, pig engineer, 4¼" l ... **90.00**
- Washtub With Pig .......... **60.00**
- Windmill, sitting pink pig, orange roof .......... **80.00**

Gravy Boat, two light pink pigs swinging, porcelain, English, 4" w .......... **55.00**

Inkwell, pink pig sitting on top, 3" h .. **100.00**

Match Safe, pink pig poking head through fence, 4½" w .......... **65.00**

Planter, one riding in sled, another standing behind, German, 6" l .......... **200.00**

Salt and Pepper Shakers, pr, ceramic, white, hand painted, one wearing red kerchief, other wearing blue, marked "Japan" .......... **7.50**

Salt, open
- Three little pigs around water trough, 2½" h .......... **50.00**
- Two pigs alongside bucket, stamped "Made In Germany," 3½" h .......... **50.00**

Toothpick Holder
- Photographer, pink pig with camera **55.00**
- Pig leaning on fence, mug in hand, 3" h .......... **60.00**
- Three large pigs in front of water trough, 4" h .......... **60.00**
- Two little pigs in front of egg, 2¾" h **50.00**

Vase
- Red Devil, arm around pink pig, sitting on log, 7¼" l .......... **110.00**
- Shoe, two pigs looking out, German **60.00**

Watch Fob, bronze, "We Save 'Em," United Serum Co, Kansas City, KS, 1912 .......... **25.00**

# PINBALL MACHINES

**Collecting Hints:** Cosmetic condition is paramount. Graphics are complex and difficult to impossible to repair. Graphics are unique to a specific model, especially backglass and playfield plastics, making replacements scarce. Prices are given for cosmetically good, 95% or more of backglass decoration present, games in good working condition.

Some wear is expected in pinballs as a sign that the game was a good one, but bare wood detracts from overall condition. Watch for signs of loose ink on the rear of the glass. Unrestorable games with good cosmetics are valuable for restoration of other games. Discount 30 to 40% of the price for a non–working game.

Add 10% if the paper items such as score card, instruction card, and schematic are present and in good condition. It is fair to suggest that regardless of mechanical condition, a game in good cosmetic condition is worth roughly twice what the same game is worth in poor cosmetic condition.

Pinball collecting is a new hobby which is still developing. It can be started inexpensively, but requires space to maintain. The tremendous diversity of models made has prevented the market from becoming well developed. There are relatively few people restoring antique pinball machines for sale. Expect to buy games in non–working condition and learn to repair them yourself.

**History:** Pinball machines can trace their heritage back to the mid–1700s. However, it was not until 1931 when Gottlieb introduced "Baffle Ball" that pinball machines caught on and became a popular and commercial success. It was the Depression, and people were hungry for something novel and the opportunity to make money. Pinball machines had both. The first games were entirely mechanical, cost about twenty dollars and were produced in large numbers—25,000 to 50,000 were not uncommon.

Pinball developments include:

1932—addition of legs
1933—electric, at first using batteries
1936—addition of bumpers
1947—advent of flippers
1950—kicking rubbers

1953—score totalizers
1954—multiple players
1977—solid state electronics

The size also underwent change. The early countertops were 16 x 32 inches. Later models were free standing with the base 21 x 52 inches and the backbox 24 x 30 inches.

The total number of pinball models that have been manufactured has not yet been determined. Some suggest over 10,000 different models from 200 plus makers. After 1940 most models were produced in quantities of 500 to 2,000; occasionally games had production figures as high as 10,000. Pinball machines have always enjoyed a high attrition rate. New models made the most money and were introduced by several of the major manufacturers at the rate of one entirely new model every three weeks during the mid–1940s and 1950s. Today the rate of new model introduction has slowed to an average of four to six new games per year.

Most operators of pinballs used the older games for spare parts to repair newer models. Earning life was less than three years in most markets. Many games were warehoused or destroyed to keep them from becoming competition for the operator's newest games; they did not want older pinball machines winding up in the wrong hands. At the very least, the coin mechanisms were removed before the game was sold. Most machines that have survived have come from home basements or from operators' storage.

Most pinballs were made in Chicago. Major manufacturers were Gottlieb, Williams, and Bally. Pinballs by D. Gottlieb & Co. are the most sought after due to generally superior play and graphics, from the 1947 to mid–1970s period especially.

Pinball art is part of the popular culture and kinetic art. The strength of the pinball playfield design carried Gottlieb as the predominant maker through the 1950s and into the 1970s. During the 1960s Gottlieb's fame grew due to the animated backglasses, intended to both amuse and attract players, which featured movable units as part of the artwork. The combination of animation and availability make the 1960s machines a key target period for collectors.

The advent of solid state games in 1977, coupled with the video game boom, dramatically changed the pinball machine market. The late electromechanical games became obsolete from a commercial point of view. Initially Bally was the predominant maker, but Williams has since attained this position. Solid state game production was high as manufacturers attempted to replace all obsolete electromechanical games. A severe dent in pinball machine production was caused by the video games of the 1980s. Collectors, who are rediscovering the silver ball, are helping the pinball machine recover some of its popularity.

**References:** Richard Bueschel, *Pinball I: Illustrated Historical Guide To Pinball Machines, Volume 1,* Hoflin Publishing Ltd., 1988; Heirbert Eiden and Jurgen Lukas, *Pinball Machines,* Schiffer Publishing, Ltd., 1992; Gary Flower and Bill Kurtz, *Pinball: The Lure of the Silver Ball,* published by authors; Bill Kurtz, *Slot Machines and Coin–Op Games,* Chartwell Books, Inc, 1991; Donald Mueting and Robert Hawkins, *The Pinball Reference Guide,* Mead Co.

**Periodicals:** *Gameroom Magazine,* 1014 Mt. Tabor Rd, New Albany, IN 47150; *Pin Game,* 31937 Olde Franklin Dr, Farmington Hills, MI 48334; *Pinball Trader,* P. O. Box 1795, Campbell, CA 95009.

**Note:** Pinballs are listed by machine name and fall into various classifications: novelty with no awards, replay which awards free games, add–a–ball which awards extra balls instead of games, and bingo where players add additional coins to increase the odds of winning bingo cards played. Some payout games were made in the mid to late 1930s which paid out coins for achieving scoring objectives. After the first add–a–ball games in 1960, many game designs were issued as both replay and add–a–ball with different game names and slight play rules modifications but similar art work.

Bally
1933, Airway, first mechanical scoring .......... **325.00**
1947, Nudgy, electric shaker ...... **425.00**
1951, Coney Island, bingo ........ **350.00**
1963, Moon Shot, replay .......... **275.00**
1964, Mad World, captive ball ..... **250.00**
1968, Rock Makers, replay, unusual playfield .......... **250.00**
1968, Safari, replay .............. **275.00**
1973, Nip–It, ball grabber ......... **225.00**
1975, Bon Voyage, replay ......... **275.00**
1978, Lost World, electronic ....... **350.00**
1979, Harlem Globetrotters, electronic .......... **300.00**
1980, Xenon, electronic .......... **425.00**

Chicago Coin
1948, Spinball, spinner action ..... **175.00**
1974, Gin, replay ................ **175.00**

Exhibit
1941, Big Parade, patriotic theme, classic art .......... **450.00**
1947, Mam'selle, replay .......... **400.00**

Genco
1937, Cargo .................... **375.00**
1949, Black Gold, replay ......... **325.00**

Gottlieb
1934, Relay, relay balls ........... **275.00**
1936, Daily Races, one–ball ....... **375.00**
1948, Buccaneer, replay, mirrored graphics .......... **350.00**
1950, Just 21, turret shooter ....... **325.00**

**Gottlieb's Sinbad, D Gottlieb & Co., 25¢ play, electric, wood case, 1978, 22 x 52″ top surface, $325.00.**

1954, Mystical Marvel, replay, double award .......... **450.00**
1955, Duette, replay, first 2–player . **325.00**
1956, Auto Race, replay .......... **350.00**
1961, Big Casino, replay .......... **250.00**
1963, Gigi .......... **375.00**
1965, Cow Poke, animation classic . **475.00**
1966, Hurdy Gurdy, add–a–ball version of Central Park .......... **375.00**
1967, King of Dinosaurs, replay, roto **375.00**
1968, Royal Guard, replay, snap target .......... **300.00**
1969, Spin–A–Card, replay .......... **300.00**
1970, Aquarius, replay .......... **325.00**
1971, Roller Coaster, replay, multi–level .......... **325.00**
1975, Atlantis, replay .......... **350.00**
1977, Target Alpha, multi–player ... **350.00**
1978, Close Encounters, electronic . **300.00**
1981, Black Hole, electronic, multi–level .......... **475.00**

Mills Novelty Co, 1932, Official, push button ball lift .......... **350.00**

Pacific Amusement, 1934, Lite–A–Line, first light up backboard .......... **325.00**

Rock–Ola
1932, Juggle Ball, countertop, rod ball manipulator .......... **295.00**
1935, Flash, early free play .......... **315.00**

United, 1951, ABC, first bingo .......... **400.00**

Williams
1948, Yanks, .baseball theme, animated .......... **300.00**
1952, Four Corners, replay .......... **375.00**
1953, Army Navy, replay, reel scoring **300.00**
1956, Perky, replay .......... **325.00**
1958, Gusher, disappearing bumper **375.00**
1961, Metro, replay .......... **225.00**
1964, Palooka, add–a–ball .......... **275.00**
1967, Touchdown, animation .......... **250.00**
1972, Olympic Hockey, replay .......... **275.00**
1973, Travel Time, timed play .......... **225.00**
1975, Triple Strike, replay .......... **300.00**
1977, Grand Prix, replay .......... **350.00**
1980, Firepower, electronic .......... **450.00**

# PIN–UP ART

**Collecting Hints:** Try to collect calendars intact. There is a growing practice among dealers to separate calendar pages, cut off the date information, and sell the individual sheets in hopes of making more money. Buyers are urged not to succumb to supporting this practice.

Concentrate on the work of one artist. Little research has been done on the pin–up artists so it is a wide open field. The original works of art, whether in oils or pastels, on which calendar sheets and magazine covers are based, have begun to appear on the market. High prices are being asked, but the market is not yet stabilized—beware!

Pin–up material can be found in many other collectible categories. Usually the items are referred to as "girlies" on the list. Many secondary pin–up items are not signed, but a collector can easily identify an artist's style.

**History:** Charles Dana Gibson created the first true pin– up girl with his creation of the Gibson Girl in the early 1900s. Other artists followed such as Howard Chandler Christy, Coles Phillips and Charles Sheldon. The film magazines of the 1920s, such as *Film Fun* and *Real Screen Fun,* developed the concept further. Their front covers featured the minimally clad beauties designed to attract a male readership.

The 1930s featured the work of cover artists Charles Sheldon, Cardwell Higgins and George Petty. Sheldon did calendar art for Brown & Bigelow as well as covers. *Esquire* began in 1933; its first Petty gatefold appeared in 1939.

The golden age of pin–up art was 1935 to 1955. The 1940s brought Alberto Vargas (the "s" was dropped at *Esquire's* request), Gillete Elvgren, Billy DeVorss, Joyce Ballantyne and Earl Moran into the picture. Pin–up girl art appeared everywhere—magazine covers, blotters, souvenir items, posters, punchboards, etc. Many other artists adopted the style.

Photographic advertising and changing American tastes ended the pin–up reign by the early 1960s.

**References:** Denis C. Jackson, *The Price And Identification Guide To Alberto Vargas And George Petty, Second Edition,* published by author, 1987; Denis C. Jackson, *The Price And Identification Guide To Coles Philips,* published by author, 1986; Norman E. Martinus and Harry L. Rinker, *Warman's Paper,* Wallace–Homestead, 1993.

**Advisor:** Dick Bitterman.

Calendar
- 1942, Esquire, Varga Girl, 8½ x 12", plastic spiral binding, 12 pgs, horizontal format, verses by Phil Stack **65.00**
- 1945, Starlight, Earl Moran, full color blonde, nude, dark green drape, black ground .................. **35.00**
- 1947, Petty, 9 x 12", spiral bound, orig envelope, Fawcett Publications **45.00**
- 1948, *Esquire* Glamour Gallery, 8½ x 12" .......................... **40.00**
- 1954, Petty Girl, 8¼ x 11", 12 pgs, vertical format, verses ........... **55.00**
- 1956, Marilyn Monroe, 8 x 14", four full color pictures .............. **200.00**
- 1961, *Playboy* Playmate, 5½ x 6½", desk, MIB ..................... **45.00**

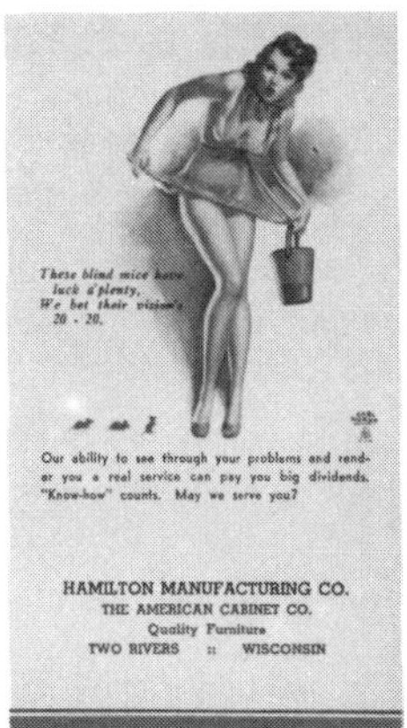


**Calendar, Earl Moran, ". . . Three Blind Mice," May, 1948, 3¼ x 6", $15.00.**

Card, 3½ x 5", c1940, set of 3
- Earl Moran, red ground ........... **18.00**
- Zoe Mozert, full color ............ **15.00**

Christmas Card, 5½ x 8", tan, red, black, and blue, MacPherson ...... **22.00**

Cigarette Lighter, 1⅞" h, black and white photos, green and red tints ... **27.00**

Date Book, *Esquire* 5 x 7", color cov, spiral binding, full color pin–up photos, copyright 1943, George Hurrell **29.00**

Folder
- Petty Girl Revue, from Dec 1941 *Esquire* issue, double sided, verses, different girl in each drawing, four 3¾ x 8½" drawings, six 5 x 7⅝" drawings, one 6½ x 5½" drawing **45.00**
- Sally of Hollywood & Vine, cardboard, sliding insert changes from dress to underwear to nude ...... **22.00**

Hair Pin, Petty, orig 4 x 5½" yellow, red, black, and white card, 1948, artist sgd ............................ **20.00**

Kit, *Esquire* Magazine, 1944 Varga girl calendar, 8½ x 12", Susan Hayward puzzle, 10 x 13", orig 10 x 14" envelope ......................... **65.00**

Label, punchboard, 3¾ x 8", Elvgren, unused ........................ **10.00**

Magazine
- *Marilyn Monroe Pin–Ups,* 1953, 8½ x 11", 32 pgs, black and white and full color photos ............... **70.00**
- *Movieland Pin–Ups,* Anita Ekberg, cov, 1955 .................... **16.00**

Match Book Cover
- Petty Girl, "Its In The Bag," Martins Tavern, Chicago, late 1940s ..... **3.00**
- Petty Girl, "Snug As A Bug," Martins Tavern, Chicago, late 1940s ..... **3.00**

Note Pad, 3 x 4½", pastel, 1944 calendar on back .................. **6.00**

Playing Cards
- Bob Elson's Petty Pipping, 52 cards, dressed as bride ................ **25.00**
- Vargas Girl Drawings, 53 cards, different illus, plastic coated, mfg by Creative Playing Card Co, St. Louis, green box .................... **150.00**

Poster
- 17 x 33", full color, woman in shorts walking wire hair terrier, c1951, Walt Otto .................... **50.00**
- 22 x 40", Martin Senour Paint, "If It's Worth Covering, It's Worth Martin Senour Synthol Enamel," woman removing robe to reveal sheer underwear ...................... **100.00**

# PLANTERS PEANUTS

**Collecting Hints:** Planters Peanuts memorabilia is easily identified by the famous Mr. Peanut trademark. Items from the 1906 to 1916 period have the "Planters Nut And Chocolate Company" logo.

Papier mache, diecut, and ceramic pieces must be in very good condition. Cast iron and tin pieces should be free of rust and dents and have good graphics and color.

**History:** Amedeo Obici and Mario Peruzzi organized the Planters Nut And Chocolate Company in Wilkes–Barre, Pennsylvania, in 1906. Obici had conducted a small peanut business for several years and was known locally as the "Peanut Specialist."

Early peanut sales were the Spanish salted red skins which sold for 10¢ per pound. Soon after Obici developed the whole, white, blanched peanut, his product became the consumer's favorite.

In 1916 a young Italian boy submitted a rough version of the now famous monocled and distinguished Mr. Peanut as an entry in a contest held by Planters to develop a trademark. A wide variety of premium and promotional items was issued shortly thereafter.

Planters eventually was purchased by Standard Brands, which itself later became a division of Nabisco.

**References:** Norman E. Martinus and Harry L. Rinker, *Warman's Paper,* Wallace–Homestead, 1993; Richard D. and Barbara Reddock, *Planters Peanuts Advertising And Collectibles,* Wallace–Homestead Book Company, 1978, out–of–print.

**Collectors' Club:** Peanut Pals, P. O. Box 4465, Huntsville, AL 35815.

**Advisor:** Leonard Calabrese.

**REPRODUCTION ALERT**

**Bookmark, diecut cardboard, souvenir 1939 New York World's Fair, yellow, black, and white, 6½" h, $20.00.**

Ashtray, metal, Mr Peanut standing in center .......... **25.00**
Beer Pitcher, 60 oz, Mr Peanut 75th Birthday .......... **75.00**
Clock, alarm, yellow face, red back .. **75.00**
Coasters, cork, Mr Peanut 75th Birthday, price for set of four .......... **6.00**
Coloring Book, Presidents to Kennedy . **15.00**
Display
  Bowl, plastic, multicolored decal ... **50.00**
Football, Mr Peanut .......... **22.00**
Jar, peanut lid
  Barrel, orig label .......... **375.00**
  Fishbowl, orig label .......... **175.00**
  Four corners .......... **350.00**
  Six sided, yellow .......... **110.00**
  Square .......... **110.00**
Jewelry, pin, Victory, 1940s .......... **75.00**
Key Chain, brass coin, Mr Peanut 75th Birthday .......... **75.00**
Letter Opener, Mr Peanut, brass ...... **110.00**
Megaphone, yellow, 7½" l, Mr Peanut 75th Birthday .......... **10.00**
Mug, Mr Peanut logo
  Ceramic, white, 1960s .......... **75.00**
  Glass, old yellow figure .......... **65.00**
Night Light, Mr Peanut .......... **15.00**
Parade Costume, Mr Peanut .......... **675.00**
Peanut Butter Maker, Mr Peanut, MIB . **12.00**
Peanut Butter Pail, Mr Peanut Circus, orig lid .......... **750.00**
Pen and Pencil Set, Cross, Mr Peanut 75th Birthday, MIB .......... **50.00**
Pencil, mechanical, Mr Peanut, in oil . **6.00**
Post Card .......... **10.00**
Punchboard, 8 x 4½", unused, 5¢, blue can of cocktail peanuts on left, Mr Peanut and various cocktails on right, 1930s .......... **95.00**
Shipping Box, cardboard, multicolored design on three sides and top ...... **40.00**
Shot Glass, Mr Peanut 75th Birthday .. **20.00**
Sign, radio show, blue printing in Italian, oil can, Planters Edible Oil Co, Suffolk, VA, USA, 9¾ x 14¾" ...... **25.00**
Wrist Watch, yellow and black, Mr Peanut on face, leather band .......... **50.00**

# PLASTICS

**Collecting Hints:** The key point to remember about plastic items is that they were mass–produced, often in numbers in the high hundreds of thousands or millions. The concept of rare does not apply. Because of these large production runs, it is wise to stress condition as a major value consideration. Period surface appearance is also important.

The price difference between pieces that are in the collecting market verses those in the process of surfacing, e.g., at garage sales, is often large. You can save considerable money if you are willing to devote time to the hunt. Likewise, shop and compare. Prices vary within the trade.

There are few collectors of celluloid per se. Most celluloid is sought because it relates to another collecting field. It was possible to place a printed message on a celluloid surface. For this reason celluloid was a popular medium for the advertising giveaways of the 1880 to 1900 period. Old celluloid is quite brittle and can be easily broken. It must be handled carefully. Collectors should be aware of celluloid's flammable tendencies.

Bakelite often is confused with acrylic and other types of plastic. There are three key questions to help identify Bakelite: 1) Is it thick and in a bright, primary color [black, green, red, or yellow]?; 2) Is the object from the 1920 to 1940 period?; and, 3) Is the object normally associated with a synthetic material?

**History:** Plastic is derived from the Greek word *plasticos* that translated as "able to be molded." A dictionary definition states "any of numerous organic synthetic or processed materials that are mostly thermoplastic or thermosetting polymers of high molecular weight and that can be molded, cast, extruded, drawn, or laminated into objects, films, or filaments."

Hundreds of different types of plastics—natural, semisynthetic, and synthetic—are known. With the exception of celluloid and Bakelite, it makes little difference to collectors the type of plastic from which the object is manufactured.

Celluloid is the trade name for a thin, tough, flammable material made of cellulose nitrate and camphor. It was invented just prior to 1870 and used mainly in making toilet articles. It also was an inexpensive material for jewelry, figurines, vases, etc. Celluloid frequently was made to simulate more expensive materials, e.g., amber, bone, ivory, and tortoise shell. Celluloid became a popular medium for the toy industry of the 1920s and 1930s. Character toys included Charlie Chaplin and Charlie McCarthy. The advent of Bakelite and acrylic plastic brought an end to celluloid items.

Bakelite, a substitute for hard rubber, celluloid, and similar materials, is a synthetic resinous material made from formaldehyde and phenol. It was invented by L. H. Baekeland in 1913. Bakelite was easily dyed and molded into many brightly colored objects during the Art Deco period. Bakelite has been used as the secondary element in many household and kitchen items (especially handles), as ornamentation on clothing, and in jewelry of the Art Deco and Modernism periods.

Acrylic, also known as Lucite (DuPont's tradename) or Plexiglas (Rohm and Haas Company tradename), was developed in 1927. This lightweight, petrochemical plastic is valued for its transparent and translucent qualities. It is highly versatile, having a surface that can range from dull to glossy and a body that can be cast, cut, drilled, extruded, faceted, molded, or shaped. Its major drawbacks are that it scratches easily, tends to yellow (older examples), and does not resist heat well.

**References:** Lillian Baker, *Twentieth Century Fashionable Plastic Jewelry,* Collector Books, 1992; Corinne Davidov and Ginny Redington Dawes, *The Bakelite Jewelry Book,* Abbeville Press, 1988; Jan Lindenberger, *Collecting Plastics: A Handbook and Price Guide,* Schiffer Publishing, Ltd., 1991; Lyndi Stewart McNulty, *Wallace–Homestead Price Guide To Plastic Collectibles,* Wallace–Homestead, 1987, 1992 value update.

## BAKELITE

Ashtray
- Advertising, Power's Coffee Shop, Fargo, ND .......... **40.00**
- Horse logo, Davies .......... **18.00**

Bar Utensil Set, green handles, five piece set .......... **40.00**
Clock, Telechron, black, octagon .......... **85.00**
Corn Cob Holders, orig box .......... **30.00**
Desk Light, stepped base, revolving tin globe, stem, pen and paper clip holders .......... **45.00**
Flashlight, swivel head .......... **18.00**
Inkwell, Skrip .......... **25.00**
Jewelry
- Beads, 27½" l, deep red, oval facet cut, graduated, 1920s .......... **65.00**
- Bracelet
  - Bangle
    - Carved, florals, butterscotch .......... **70.00**
    - Narrow .......... **8.00**
    - Wide, 3" w, orange, carved .......... **70.00**
  - Hinged, gray, rhinestones .......... **75.00**
  - Link, cherries, red .......... **135.00**
- Brooch
  - Cut Log, cherry .......... **100.00**
  - Life Preserver, red .......... **25.00**
- Clip, reverse carved, painted dec .......... **45.00**
- Earrings, pr, round, orange, rhinestones, sgd "Weiss" .......... **32.00**
- Necklace
  - Acorns .......... **275.00**
  - Cherries, red .......... **135.00**
  - Circles, multicolored, celluloid chain .......... **325.00**
  - Heart, yellow, celluloid chain .......... **225.00**
- Pin
  - Cherries, dangling .......... **225.00**
  - Cowboy Hat, longhorn .......... **70.00**
  - Feather, red .......... **18.00**
  - Horse head, boots and horseshoe hanging .......... **250.00**
  - Scottie, black .......... **65.00**
  - USA, linked letters .......... **145.00**
  - Vegetables, dangling .......... **235.00**
- Suite, white, hinged bracelet with rhinestones, 1½" d matching round earrings .......... **110.00**

Lighter, table, Dunhill, standing nude, 3 x 5" h .......... **125.00**
Pencil Sharpener
- Joe Carioca, figural .......... **55.00**
- Donald Duck, figural .......... **65.00**
- Mickey Mouse decal, green .......... **50.00**

Poker Chip Caddy, round, brown .......... **15.50**

Poker Set, 500 poker chips, six Bakelite trays with center copper ashtray, red, green, gold, bright green, light green, turquoise, orig fitted carrying case .. **220.00**
Radio/Lamp, Lumitone, rocket shape, 1940s .......................... **160.00**
Radio, RCA Victor, police band ...... **65.00**
Record Player, Decca, 45 rpm record player, RCA Redhead style radio, c1950 .......................... **85.00**

**Bakelite, record player, RCA Victor, Model 45-EY-2, dark brown, electric, 10⅝ x 8⅝ x 8¼″, $45.00.**

Shaving Brush, Klenzo, two part handle **8.50**
Television, brown, 8″ w screen, small hairline crack on top, working condition .......................... **175.00**
Tip Tray, green .......................... **8.00**
Toiletry Box, cov .......................... **20.00**

## CATALIN

Clock, GE, alarm, Catalin drapery, plastic case .......................... **55.00**
Radio, Crosley, brown .............. **30.00**
Trophy, auto racing, 20″ h, two colors **125.00**

## CELLULOID

Brush and Comb Set, pink, hp, flowers, orig box, 1920s .................. **40.00**
Calculator, 3″ d, mechanical disk, calculates cost of gasoline ranging from 34 to 44¢ per gallon, American Art Works, c1940 .................. **25.00**
Card Holder, black base, two Mickey Mouse figures, paper stick reads "Walt Disney Enterprises Ltd/Japan," 1930s .......................... **90.00**
Charm, pig in green overalls, pink cap, holding gray trowel, brass loop, Japan, early 1930s .................. **30.00**
Doll
 3¼″ h, bride and groom, Kewpie type, crepe paper clothes, price for pair .......................... **40.00**

**Celluloid, swan, cobalt blue, magenta, and teal feathers, red feet and beak, USA, 4″ l, 3½″ h, $10.00.**

 8½″ h, cloth body, turtle mark, tiny hole back of head and nose ..... **65.00**
Ink Blotter Pad, 3¼ x 7¾″, adv for India–Down Bedding, cardboard pad, celluloid cov, c1910 .............. **75.00**
Memo Book, Spirit of St Louis ....... **18.00**
Nail File, folding, figural, lady's leg, painted high heel and garter ....... **35.00**
Note Hook, Breakfast Cheer Coffee, inserted rigid wire, full color coffee can illus, green ground, early 1900s .... **65.00**
Rattle, turtle shape ................ **15.00**
Ruler, 7½″ l, diecut, Western Union, silver and blue logo, telegraph and cable rates on back, 1905 patent ..... **25.00**
Stamp Case, 1½ x 2½″, Aetna Life Insurance Co, Hartford, CT, red and white, 1907 calendar ............ **18.00**
Tape Measure, figural, pig, hp ....... **35.00**
Toy
 Airship, 1½ x 2¼ x 5½″, hollow, red and blue, wood wheels, pull string, US Star Co logo on tail fin, 1930s **100.00**
 Black Boy, 8″ h, jointed ........... **95.00**
 Felix The Cat, 2″ h, jointed ........ **85.00**
 Hawaiian Dancer, 8½″ h, windup .. **125.00**
 Rabbit pushing cart, windup, 1950s **100.00**
 Santa, windup, umbrella with Santa and reindeer .................. **120.00**
Vanity Compact, hanger, tassel ....... **85.00**

## PLASTIC

Bowl, gray, multicolored speckles, marked "Texas Ware" ........... **15.00**
Bread Box, red and white plastic ..... **20.00**
Cake Safe, Art Deco styling .......... **32.00**
Canister Set, red sq container, white name, white lid, price for set of four **15.00**
Jewelry, pin, Scottie in doghouse ..... **68.00**
Match Holder, wall type, red ........ **7.50**
Powder Shaker, Kewpie, 6½″ h, marked "Irwin Toys," price for pair ........ **37.00**
Sewing Box, round, pink, clear lid, divided int. ...................... **10.00**

Spice Shelf, pink, cut–out letters, repaired crack .......... **25.00**
Spoon Rest, chef holding two pans, white, black trim .......... **7.50**
Thimble, adv, NuMaid Margarine .... **2.50**
Tray, 13 x 7" .......... **15.00**

# PLAYING CARDS

**Collecting Hints:** Always purchase complete decks in very good condition. Do research to identify the exact number of cards needed. An American straight deck has 52 cards and usually a joker; pinochle requires 48 cards; tarot decks use 78. In addition to decks, uncut sheets and single cards, if very early, are sought by collectors.

Many collectors focus on topics. Examples are politics, trains, World's Fairs, animals, airlines, advertising, etc. Most collectors of travel–souvenir cards prefer a photographic scene on the face.

The most valuable playing card decks are unusual either in respect to publisher, size, shape, or subject. Prices for decks of late 19th and 20th century cards remain modest.

**History:** The first use of playing cards dates to 12th century China. By 1400 playing cards were in use throughout Europe. French cards were known specifically for their ornate designs. The first American cards were published by Jazaniah Ford, Milton, Massachusetts, in the late 1700s. United States innovations include upper corner indexes, classic joker, standard size, and slick finish for shuffling. Bicycle Brand was introduced in 1885 by the U.S. Playing Card Company of Cincinnati.

Card designs have been drawn or printed in every conceivable size and on a variety of surfaces. Miniature playing cards appealed to children. Novelty decks came in round, crooked, and diecut shapes. Numerous card games, besides the standard four suit deck, were created for adults and children.

**References:** Phil Bollhagen (comp.), *The Great Book of Railroad Playing Cards,* published by author, 1991; Everett Grist, *Advertising Playing Cards: An Identification and Value Guide,* Collector Books, 1992; Gene Hochman, *Encyclopedia of American Playing Cards,* published by author, 1976 to 1982, six parts, out–of–print; Sylvia Mann, *Collecting Playing Cards,* Crown, 1966; Norman E. Martinus and Harry L. Rinker, *Warman's Paper,* Wallace–Homestead, 1993; Roger Tilley, *Playing Cards,* Octopus, London, 1973.

**Collectors' Clubs:** Chicago Playing Card Collectors, Inc., 1559 West Platt Blvd., Chicago, IL 60626; Playing Card Collectors Assn., Inc., P. O. Box 554, Bristol, WI 53104.

**Note:** We have organized our list by both topic and country. Although concentrating heavily on cards by American manufacturers, some foreign makers are included.

## COUNTRY

Austria, La Provence, Piatnik, 1960, 53 cards .......... **22.00**
England, Prince of Wales National Relief Fund, WWI, De La Rue, 1914, MIB **32.00**
France, The Parlou Sibyl, Grimaud, 1968, 3 x 4½", 52 cards .......... **20.00**
Italy, Cucci, Maseghini, c1969, 2 x 3⅝", 40 cards complete, orig box ....... **20.00**
United States, New York, 1901 scenes **32.50**

## TOPIC

Advertising
- A–1 Tire Co, Buy War Bonds ...... **7.50**
- Beau Brummel Ties the Best, man wearing top hat and fancy tie .... **7.50**
- Benjamin, World Leader in Lighting, globe, red, black, and gold ...... **2.50**
- Best Grand Laundry, "We wash everything with Ivory Soap" .......... **5.00**
- Blue Bonnet, trademark character .. **10.00**
- Campbell's Chunky Soup, soup can, red, white, and silver .......... **3.50**
- Central Banknote Company, Chicago, New York, black and white, eagle **10.00**
- Clifford's Rexall Pharmacy, "The Drug Store That Cares," black and white touring car illus .......... **7.50**
- Conoco .......... **7.00**
- Eckerd Drug Stores, black and white **2.50**

**Advertising, Rust-Oleum, Brown & Bigelow, orig box, $7.50.**

Gerber Baby Formula, Modilac, formula can, black ground, white border . . . . . . . . . . . . . . . . . . . . . . . . . . **6.50**
Indiana National Bank of Indianapolis, red and gold . . . . . . . . . . . . . . . **6.50**
Kiddie Kookies with Arrowroot, sign post, red, white, and gold . . . . . . . **6.50**
Phoenix Title & Trust Co, Home Office Building illus . . . . . . . . . . . . . . **10.00**
Schoep's Ice Cream, "made from fresh Cream and eggs," flag, red, white, blue, and gold . . . . . . . . . . . **2.50**
Western Plowman, Moline, IL, c1888 **125.00**
Aviation
Boeing Stratoliner, 1940 . . . . . . . . . . . **15.00**
Delta Airlines, San Francisco, trolley **10.00**
Pan Am, logo, blue and white . . . . . **8.00**
Animals, Hunting Dogs, boxed . . . . . . . **6.00**
Brewery
Carling Stag Beer, beer can . . . . . . . . **10.00**
Coors, waterfall . . . . . . . . . . . . . . . . . . **17.50**
Joule's Stone Ales, A Trump Card From Stone Staffs, red and white . **7.50**
Primo Hawaiian Beer . . . . . . . . . . . . . **15.00**
Car Racing, Indianapolis Motor Speedway, 500 Mile Race, logo . . . . . . . . . **10.00**
Casinos
Caesar's Palace, Las Vegas, Nevada, black and gold logos . . . . . . . . . . . **5.00**
Desert Inn, poolside illus . . . . . . . . . . **10.00**
Golden Nugget, neon marquee . . . . **6.50**
Schiaparelli, white rose, red lace, black ground . . . . . . . . . . . . . . . . . **10.00**
Famous Illustrators
Maxfield Parrish, The Lamp Seller of Bagdad, Mazda lamps adv, cardboard slip case . . . . . . . . . . . . . . . . . **65.00**
Norman Rockwell, Seasons, boxed, unopened . . . . . . . . . . . . . . . . . . . . . **12.00**
Games and Fortune Telling
H–Bar–O, 32 cards, instructions . . . **15.00**
Nile Fortune Telling Cards, 1897–1904 . . . . . . . . . . . . . . . . . . . . . . . . **18.00**
Union Leaders, canasta deck . . . . . . **10.00**
Nautical
Anchorage Yacht Basin, Fort Lauderdale, FL, black anchor and lettering, red ground . . . . . . . . . . . . . . . . **7.50**
On the Mississippi at St Louis, MO, *Huck Finn* and *SS Admiral* . . . . . . **10.00**
United States Lines, *SS Leviathan*, United States Shipping Board . . . . **17.50**
Waterman Line, gold, navy blue, and white . . . . . . . . . . . . . . . . . . . . . . . . . **15.00**
Oil Companies
Gulf, logo, black and white checkerboard border . . . . . . . . . . . . . . . . . . **7.50**
Moco, monkey wearing cap, yellow ground . . . . . . . . . . . . . . . . . . . . . . . . **10.00**
Railroad
C & O RR, Chessie Cat . . . . . . . . . . . **25.00**
New York Central System, two sealed decks, "Morning Along The Hudson" and "Super–Van," faux suede box, 1960s . . . . . . . . . . . . . . . . . . . . **20.00**
Pennsylvania Railroad, double deck **70.00**
World's Fair and Exposition
1901 Buffalo, Pan American, color design, orig box . . . . . . . . . . . . . . . . **35.00**
1933, Chicago World's Fair, two jokers, orig box . . . . . . . . . . . . . . . . . . . **30.00**
Tobacco
Camel Cigarettes, silhouette camels, one black, 22 yellow, red ground **10.00**
Kent, two cigarette packs, chess set . **7.50**
Marlboro, cigarette pack . . . . . . . . . . **6.50**
Salem, cigarette pack . . . . . . . . . . . . . **3.50**

# POCKET KNIVES

**Collecting Hints:** The pocket knife collector has to compete with other collectors such as advertising, character collectors, and period collectors.

The pocket knife with a celluloid handle and advertising underneath dates back to the 1880s. Celluloid handled knives are considered much more desirable than the plastic handled models. Collectors also tend to shy from purely souvenir related knives.

**History:** Pocket knife collecting falls into two major categories. There are collectors who concentrate on the utilitarian and functional knives from firms such as Alcas, Case, Colonial, Ka–Bar, Queen, Remington, Schrade, and Winchester. The second group deals with advertising, character, and other knives, which, while meant to be used, were sold with a secondary function in mind. These knives were made by companies such as Aerial Cutlery Co., Canton Cutlery Co., Golden Rule Cutlery Co., Imperial Knife Company, and Novelty Cutlery Co.

The larger manufacturing firms also made advertising, character, and figural knives. Some knives were giveaways or sold for a small premium, but most were sold in general stores and souvenir shops.

**References:** Bernard Levine, *Levine's Guide To Knives And Their Values, Third Edition,* DBI Books, Inc., 1993; C. Houston Price, *The Official Price Guide To Collector Knives, Tenth Edition,* House of Collectibles, 1991; Jim Sargent, *Sargent American Premium Guide To Knives and Razors: Identification and Values, Third Edition* Books Americana, 1992; Roy Ritchie and Ron Stewart, *The Standard Knife Collector's Guide: Identification and Values, Second Edition,* Collector Books, 1993.

**Periodicals:** *Edges,* P. O. Box 22007, Chattanooga, TN 37422; *Knife World,* P. O. Box 3395, Knoxville, TN 37927.

**Collectors' Clubs:** American Blade Collectors, P. O. Box 22007, Chattanooga, TN 37422; National Knife Collectors Association, P. O. Box 21070, Chattanooga, TN 37421.

**Museum:** National Knife Museum, Chattanooga, TN.

**REPRODUCTION ALERT:** Advertising knives, especially Coca–Cola, have been heavily reproduced.

**Note:** See *Warman's Antiques And Their Prices* for a list of knife prices for major manufacturers.

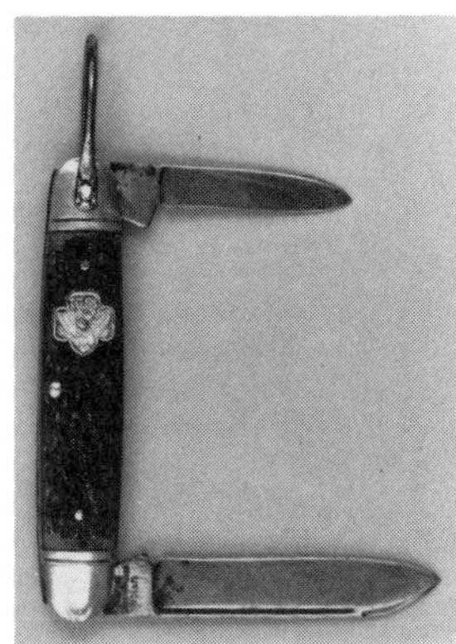

**Girl Scout, Utica, 3⅜″ black plastic handles, aluminum liners, 2 blades, GSA #11-312, $20.00.**

Advertising
- Chicago Livestock Exchange, Keen Cutter, EC dogleg jack, nickel and silver, 3¼″ l .......... **50.00**
- Say It With Flowers, florist adv, imitation ivory, marked on ivory, 4¼″ l .......... **90.00**
- St Pauli Girl Beer, nickel and silver, 4″ .......... **35.00**
- Sunshine Biscuits, 3¼″ l, two blades, brass lined, white, marked "Imperial, Providence, RI" .......... **35.00**

Case Bros, Hobo 6452, green bone, tested II, fork rusted, knife blade worn, 3¾″ l .......... **110.00**

Case XX Jr, skinning knife and sheath .......... **32.00**

Character
- Dick Tracy, blue and white illus, two blades, 3¼″ l .......... **35.00**
- Tom Mix and Tony, celluloid, black and white illus, c1930, 3″ l .......... **30.00**

Fritz, Ilgene, grafting .......... **25.00**

Kabar, dog's head, piece missing from bone handle on back .......... **275.00**

Keen Kutter
- Bartender, brown, three blades, 3¼″ l .......... **75.00**
- Military Knife, gutta–percha, can opener and marlin spike, marked "Oil The Joints," 4⅞″ l .......... **85.00**

Morley, W. H. & Sons, bone handles .......... **22.00**

Remington, blade and corkscrew, bottle opener handle, marked and encircled "Remington UMC," 3⅛″ l .......... **70.00**

Robeson
- #62652, two plates, brass lined, stag handle, 3¾″ l .......... **65.00**
- #922295, Shuredge .......... **30.00**
- Stockman's, aluminum handle .......... **65.00**

Schmidt & Ziegler, #4031 .......... **22.00**

# POLICE COLLECTIBLES

**Collecting Hints:** Police collectibles are primarily collected by people employed in law enforcement areas. Collectors often base their collection on badges or material from a specific locality. As a result, prices are regionalized, e.g., a California collector is more interested in California material than items from another state.

Condition is critical. Badges were worn everyday so a minimum of wear is expected.

The emphasis on police shows on television has attracted many non–law enforcement people to the field of police collectibles.

**History:** The first American colonists appointed someone from among their midst to maintain and enforce the laws of the land. The local sheriff was an important social and political position.

The mid–nineteenth century witnessed the development of two important trends: the growth of the professional police force in cities and the romanticizing of the western lawman. Arthur Conan Doyle's Sherlock Holmes novels popularized the modernization of police methods. Magazines, such as the *Police Gazette,* kept the public's attention focused on the sensationalism of police work.

The Gangster era of the 1920s and 30s and the arrival of the "G–Men," glamorized by Hollywood movies, kept police work in the limelight. Finally, television capitalized on the public enthusiasm for police drama through shows such as Dragnet, The Untouchables, Starsky and Hutch, and Hill Street Blues.

**References:** Monty McCord, *Police Cars: A Photographic History,* Krause Publications, 1991; George E. Virgines, *Badges of Law and Order,* Cochran Publishing Co., 1987.

**REPRODUCTION ALERT,** especially police badges.

Badge
- Colorado, El Paso County, Deputy Sheriff, worn nickel, eagle top shield, officer's name .......... **100.00**

Illinois, Chicago, Police, Detective Sergeant, six pointed star, German silver . . . . . . . . . . . . . . . . . . . . . . . . . **125.00**
Idaho, US Deputy Marshall, 1930s . **100.00**
Missouri, Township Deputy Constable . . . . . . . . . . . . . . . . . . . . . . . . . **40.00**
Nebraska, Omaha, US Secret Service **75.00**
Oregon, Multnomah County, Deputy Sheriff circle, shield cut out center, six ball tips around edge . . . . . . . . **125.00**
Texas
Dallas, County Constable . . . . . . . **45.00**
Marion County, Deputy Sheriff, five pointed star . . . . . . . . . . . . . . . . . **68.00**
Washington, Seattle, Police, sterling **40.00**
Belt Buckle, NYC, brass . . . . . . . . . . . . . **75.00**
Book, *Game Laws, State of Illinois,* 1909 **15.00**
Call Box, Chicago Police, cast aluminum, c1920 . . . . . . . . . . . . . . . . . . . . **100.00**

**Handcuffs, $50.00.**

Magazine Cover, Saturday Evening Post, Norman Rockwell illus, Nov, 1939 . **10.00**
Patch, Baltimore Police, cloth . . . . . . . . **3.50**
Photograph, police chief and fire chief posing in front of wagon, company storefront in background, 1900 . . . . . **125.00**
Post Card, Texas Ranger, horseback . . **5.00**
Receipt, Wells Fargo, money, 1885 . . . **28.00**
Shaving Mug, blue uniform, badge, nightstick . . . . . . . . . . . . . . . . . . . . . . **675.00**
Sheet Music, *Police Parade March,* 1917 . . . . . . . . . . . . . . . . . . . . . . . . . . **25.00**
Toy, patrol car, litho tin windup, red and yellow, Cragston, c1950 . . . . . . . . . . **25.00**
Uniform, Alabama Highway Patrol, jacket, hat, and holster, 1950s . . . . . **250.00**

# POLITICAL AND CAMPAIGN ITEMS

**Collecting Hints:** Items selling below $100 move frequently enough to establish firm prices. Items above that price fluctuate according to supply and demand. Many individuals now recognize the value of political items, acquiring them and holding them for future sale. As a result, modern material has a relatively low market value.

The pioneering work in the identification of political materials has been done by Theodore L. Hake, whose books are listed below. Two books have greatly assisted in the identification and cataloging of campaign materials, especially for the earlier period: Herbert R. Collins's *Threads of History* and Edmund B. Sullivan's *American Political Badges and Medalets 1789–1892.*

**History:** Since 1800 the American presidency always has been a contest between two or more candidates. Initially, souvenirs were issued to celebrate victories. Items issued during a campaign to show support for a candidate were actively distributed in the William Henry Harrison election of 1840.

Campaign items cover a wide variety of materials—buttons, bandannas, tokens, license plates, etc. The only limiting factor has been the promoter's imagination. The advent of television campaigning has reduced the emphasis on individual items. Modern campaigns do not seem to have the variety of materials which were issued earlier.

Modern collectors should be aware of Kennedy material. Much has been reproduced and many items were issued after his death. Knowledgeable collectors also keep in touch with Presidential libraries to find out what type of souvenir items they are offering for sale. The collector should concentrate on the items from the time of the actual campaigns.

**References:** Herbert R. Collins, *Threads of History,* Smithsonian Institute Press, 1979; Theodore L. Hake, *Hake's Guide to Presidential Campaign Collectibles,* Wallace-Homestead, 1992; Theodore L. Hake, *Encyclopedia of Political Buttons, United States, 1896–1972,* Americana & Collectibles Press, 1985; Theodore L. Hake, *Political Buttons, Book II, 1920–1976,* Americana & Collectibles Press, 1977; Theodore L. Hake, *Political Buttons, Book III, 1789–1916,* Americana & Collectibles Press, 1978; Theodore L. Hake, *1991 Revised Prices For The Encyclopedia Of Political Buttons,* Americana & Collectibles Press, 1991; Keith Melder, *Hail To The Candidate: Presidential Campaigns From Banners To Broadcasts,* Smithsonian Institution Press, 1992; Edmund B. Sullivan, *American Political Badges and Medalets, 1789–1892,* Quarterman Publications, Inc., 1981.

For information about the Americana & Collectibles Press, write to: Americana & Collectibles Press, P.O. Box 1444, York, PA 17405.

**Periodicals:** *The Political Bandwagon,* P.O. Box 348, Leola, PA 17540; *The Political Collector Newspaper,* P.O. Box 5171, York, PA 17405.

**Collectors' Club:** American Political Items Collectors, P. O. Box 340339, San Antonio, TX 78234.

**Museums:** Museum of American Political Life, Hartford, CT; Smithsonian Museum, Washington, DC.

**Advisor:** Ted Hake.

William McKinley, 1896 and 1900
- Glass, 4" h, portrait and slogan, 1896 **20.00**
- Lapel Stud, 7/8" l, "McKinley–Protection '96," brass, diecut, Napoleon's hat shape .................... **25.00**
- Plate, 8 x 10½", glass, oval, McKinley in center, inscribed "It Is God's Way/His Will Be Done/Born 1843–Died 1901" .................. **35.00**
- Ribbon
  - 2½ x 6", yellow, black "Sound Money Club/NPR Employees/ McKinley," brass hanger and pin **25.00**
  - 3 x 7", red, white, and blue, "McKinley and Hobart," gold stamped shield and flag, brass hanger and braid tassels ....... **30.00**
- Tray, aluminum, McKinley and Roosevelt sepia portraits, inscribed "Nominated Philadelphia June 1900," millinery adv on reverse .. **25.00**

**McKinley, pin, metal, McKinley Club member, emb image, Bastian Bros. Co., Rochester, NY, 4" h, 1¾" d medallion, $60.00.**

William Jennings Bryan, 1896, 1900, and 1908
- Jugate, 1¼", Bryan–Stevenson, black and white portraits surrounded by red, white, and blue flags, gold details ......................... **40.00**
- Mug, 3½" h, pressed glass, raised portrait, "The People's Money/Wm J Bryan," raised geometric pattern, flared edge, c1896 ............ **45.00**
- Pinback Button, 7/8", "Our Choice–Rosebery Cigar," black and white, silver ground ................. **90.00**
- Post Card, 3⅝ x 5½", colored, Bryan with shock of corn, "From Mr. Bryan's Fairview Farm," 1908 .... **15.00**
- Watch Fob, enamel, Bryan–Kern, eagles and flags center, strap ....... **30.00**

Theodore Roosevelt, 1904 and 1912
- Badge, Inaugural, 1905, gold letters, blue ground, celluloid bar, brass Capitol Building ................ **50.00**
- Bandanna, 21 x 24", red and white, Roosevelt sepia portrait center, "Progressive/Roosevelt/1912/Battle Flag" .......................... **85.00**
- Mirror, pocket, 2¼", flesh tone sepia bust portrait .................. **65.00**
- Plate, 10" d, "Theodore Roosevelt/ 26th President of the U.S.," blue and white, portrait with raised edge, scenes border, marked "The Rowland & Marsellus Co/Staffordshire/ England" ................ **40.00**
- Noisemaker, 4½" l, wood, black stenciled "Roosevelt–Fairbanks" at top, inscribed underneath "For A Rattling Good Auditor, Try Frank A. Sarstedt" ...................... **75.00**
- Ribbon, 2½ x 8", white fabric, blue portrait, inscription "Progressive Convention/Lincoln, Nebr/Sept 3, 1912" ...................... **40.00**
- Sheet Music, 7 x 11", blue on white, inscribed "Dedicated To The GOP/ A Victory Is Ours/A Rousing Republican Campaign Song," 1904 copyright ......................... **15.00**
- Watch Fob, 1¾ x 2", "Roosevelt and Fairbanks," brass ............... **20.00**

Alton B. Parker, 1904
- Jugate, 1¼", brass, Parker and Davis, flag shield on top ............. **35.00**
- Pinback Button, 1¼", black and white portrait surrounded by Capitol dome, outlined in gold, red, white, and blue star and stripe design ... **60.00**
- Stud, metal, bust of Parker in wreath **15.00**

William Howard Taft, 1908 and 1912
- Bottle Stopper, 2½ x 3 x 3½", painted composition Taft's head, bottom cork marked "Made In Germany," c1952 ....................... **75.00**
- Change Tray, 4½" d, litho tin, jugate portraits of Taft and Sherman, rim caption "Grand Old Party/1856 To 1908," black and gold border .... **125.00**
- Jugate, 7/8", Taft–Sherman portraits .. **20.00**
- Lapel Stud, ½", gold on dark blue ... **12.00**

**Taft, post card, $15.00.**

Mug, 5" h, figural, numbered and marked "Made In Germany," c1908 ........ 75.00
Pinback Button, 1¼", "Taft From Chicago to Washington," black, white, and red, Taft riding GOP elephant and carrying "Big Stick" ........ 300.00
Post Card, red, white, and blue, flag motif, inscribed "For President Of USA/Wm H Taft of Ohio," inked message reverse, 1908 cancellation 15.00
Poster, 11 x 14", sepia portrait, signature, bottom edge marked "Copyright 1908 Moffett Studio/ Chicago" ........ 25.00
Watch Fob, brass, diecut, black detailing ........ 20.00

Woodrow Wilson, 1912 and 1916
Jugate, "Wilson and Marshall," black and white ........ 40.00
Pennant, 7 x 17", felt, dark purple, crimped tin support bar on edge, two brown cords for hanging, gold lettering, inscribed "Mardi Gras/ 1913 Mobile, AL," diecut paper shield with black and white picture and inscribed "March 4 Inauguration/1913 Washingt'n DC" ...... 25.00
Pinback Button, "For President 1912 Woodrow Wilson," black and white ........ 15.00
Stickpin, 2¼", black and white photo, brass frame, dark blue edge ..... 25.00
Watch Fob, "Wilson/His Pen Mightier Than The Sword," metal, copper finish, portrait, scale with quill pen outweighing sword ........ 30.00

Charles Evans Hughes, 1916
Jugate, Hughes and Fairbanks, black and white photo ........ 50.00
Pinback Button, black and white picture surrounded by gold oval, red, white, and blue flag, green wreath with red berries ........ 35.00
Watch Fob, 1½" d, celluloid, sepia, bust portrait, name below ....... 60.00

Warren G. Harding, 1920
Bell, "Ring For Harding and Coolidge," copper finish ........ 20.00
Lapel Stud, metal, diecut, walking elephant, name on side ........ 12.00
Pinback Button, "For President Warren G. Harding," brown and white portrait, dark blue rim ........ 15.00
Purse, coin, leather, silvered brass clip, President Harding between two sets of flags ........ 35.00

James M. Cox, 1920
Pinback Button, 7⅟₁₆", "Gov Cox" and slogan, black and white ..... 30.00
Sheet Music, *The Tie That Binds or Jimmy Is The Man For Us* ....... 35.00
Stamp, "Governor James M. Cox, Put The Ax To Tax," black and white portrait, red border ........ 30.00

**Pinback Buttons, left: Harding and Coolidge,⅝" d, blue and white, $10.00; right: Coolidge and Dawes, red, white, and blue, ¾" d, $12.00.**

Calvin Coolidge, 1924
Bell, "Ring For Coolidge," brass .... 15.00
Jugate,⅞", "For President Coolidge/ Vice–President Dawes," black and white, ........ 30.00
Lapel Stud, metal diecut, elephant, name on side ........ 10.00
Mirror, 2⅛", celluloid, black and white, trigate, 1924, DE Senator and Governor ........ 200.00
Stickpin, brass, diecut, horseshoe design spells out name ........ 40.00
Thimble, "Coolidge & Dawes," aluminum, red, white, and blue band bottom edge ........ 15.00

John W. Davis, 1924
Dish, 4" d, glass, incised inscription "Compliments of Hazel/Atlas Glass Co/John W. Davis Day Aug 11–24, Clarksburg, WV" ........ 40.00
Pin, "Davis 1924," metal, diamond shape, comet in relief ........ 60.00
Poster, 22 x 16", sepia, formal portrait, 1924 ........ 50.00

Herbert Hoover, 1928 and 1932

- License Plate, 5 x 12", cast aluminum, diecut letters and Capitol dome, silver finish ..... **100.00**
- Pencil, 8" l, "Hoover For President 1928," yellow, composition head on top, silver lettering ..... **15.00**
- Pin, "Who Who Hoover," enamel, owl, ..... **30.00**
- Pinback Button, ¾", "Keep Hoover/Be Safe," brass, gold raised letters, dark blue background ..... **25.00**
- Portrait, 3½", black and white, dark blue rim, black background ..... **200.00**

Alfred E. Smith, 1928

- Jugate, 1¼", "Smith/Robinson," black and white portraits, dark blue background, gold red, white, and blue design ..... **500.00**
- Lapel Stud, brass, brown derby hat design ..... **10.00**
- License Plate, "Al Smith For President," 4½ x 12", tin, painted, raised red letters ..... **30.00**
- Pencil, "Smith For President 1928," green, composition head on top, silver lettering ..... **15.00**
- Pinback Button, 1", "Al Smith/A Winner For You," gray and white cello, orig back paper ..... **125.00**
- Token, 1", "Al Smith Lucky Pocket Piece/For Personal Liberty and National Prosperity 1928," brass, donkey, ..... **8.00**

Franklin D. Roosevelt, 1932, 1936, 1940, and 1944

- Ashtray, 4½ x 6½ x 1", metal, mounted 1½" bronze inaugural medal in center, handles with raised eagle design, stamped "Guildcraft" and dated "Jan 20, 1941" ..... **75.00**
- Banner, 9 x 11½", cloth, red, white, and blue, metal bar, brass loop for hanging, inscribed "God Bless America/Our Next President/Franklin D. Roosevelt" ..... **30.00**
- License Plate, 3½" d, metal, red reflective background, blue and white slogan, silver edge ..... **35.00**
- Pin, 1¼", metal, painted red, white, and blue, gold center, cut out initials ..... **20.00**
- Pinback Button, 1¼", "I Gotta Go And Vote For FDR," red lettering, white background ..... **10.00**
- Portrait, color, silvered brass rect frame ..... **15.00**
- Poster, 15 x 21", black and white photo, Roosevelt and Horner at dining table, c1936 ..... **30.00**
- Record, FDR Speeches, 78 rpm records, two volumes, set of twelve records ..... **75.00**
- Ring, campaign, slivered brass, black portrait, "Roosevelt/Garner," and dates "1932–1940" on each side of band ..... **20.00**
- Ticket, Inauguration, 2½ x 6", black and white FDR and Garner portraits, yellow sunburst, marked "It Is Suggested That The Larger Portion Of This Ticket Be Retained As A Souvenir Of The First Inaugural Ever To Be Held On Jan 20" ..... **25.00**

**FDR, cigar label, red, blue, and gold, 6¼ x 9", $10.00.**

Alfred Landon, 1936

- Jugate, ⅞", Landon/Knox, brown, white, and yellow, diecut brass sunflower petal backing ..... **25.00**
- License Plate, 4" d, 5½" h, metal, blue celluloid insert, blue and white inscription "Landon/Knox" . **45.00**
- Matchbook, red, white, blue, and yellow, lists candidates outside and inside, unused ..... **10.00**
- Pin, brass, red, white, and blue enamel, elephant in center ..... **15.00**
- Pinback Button, 1¾", yellow sunflower design with brown portrait center ..... **15.00**
- Poster, 14 x 21", "Landon and Knox For Us," red, white, and blue, 1936 **40.00**
- Tab, "Landon/Knox," litho, red, white, blue, and yellow ..... **10.00**
- Whistle, 1", "Landon & Knox Rep," aluminum, blue enamel band ..... **25.00**

Wendell L. Willkie, 1940

- Ashtray, 3½" d, glass, red name, blue slogan "Preparedness–Peace–Prosperity" ..... **15.00**
- Banner, 9 x 11½", fabric, red, white, and blue, metal support rod, brass hanging loop, inscribed "God Bless America/Our Next President/Wendell Willkie" ..... **30.00**
- Die Cup, 3" h, 2½" d, "Don't Gamble, Elect Willkie," leather, give

away from Rome Sporting Goods Mfg Co, Rome, NY ............ **10.00**
License Plate, 4 x 13½", orange, gold letters outlined in dark blue, blue edge .......................... **30.00**
Pinback Button
¾", "For President Will," blue and white, attached silvered brass key ......................... **15.00**
⅞", "I'm For Willkie and McNary" **50.00**
Plaque, 9½", celluloid, black and white portrait, dark blue background with white and red circles, orig pink cord ................ **100.00**
Sticker, 3½ x 6", diecut, foil, silver, blue, and red, inscribed "Willkie/The Hope Of America" ......... **15.00**

Thomas E. Dewey, 1944 and 1948
Jugate, ⅞", "Dewey–Warren," black and white, 1948 ............... **30.00**
Pennant, 4½ x 12", felt, white and maroon, four streamers ......... **15.00**
Tab, litho, red, white, and blue, red eagle center, Dewey in blue banner **5.00**

Harry S. Truman, 1948
Program, 8 x 11", Official Inaugural Program 1949, 72 pgs, orig mailing envelope ..................... **40.00**
Ribbon, 2 x 7½", fabric, white, inscribed in black "President Truman Committee," and "Stand" in red . **30.00**
Sticker, 1½ x 2¼", red, white, and blue, inscribed "1950/ The American Way/Register And Vote/President Truman," set of 6 .......... **10.00**
Ticket, Inauguration, 2½ x 4½", red, white, blue, and yellow, seating information front, reverse with black and white jugate picture of Truman and Barkley .................. **25.00**

Dwight D. Eisenhower, 1952 and 1956
Display Card, 13½ x 19", cardboard, black and white photo, easel back, c1956 ....................... **30.00**
Handkerchief, 25" sq ............ **60.00**
License Plate, 6 x 12", "I Like IKE," metal, white, raised black letter .. **20.00**
Nodder, 6" h, composition, late 1950s ....................... **40.00**
Panel, 7 x 22½", fabric, white and dark blue, inscription "Citizens For Eisenhower" .................. **25.00**
Pen, 5" l, brass, black and white plastic, portrait, slogan "For The Love Of Ike–Vote Republican" ........ **25.00**
Pennant, felt, dark blue
8½ x 24", "Your Best Bet In 52 For A Winning Team," yellow image **15.00**
11 x 30", white, gray, and pink inscription and image, inscribed "Second Inauguration Jan 20 1957" ..................... **25.00**
Pinback Button
1¼", "Dem–Ike–Crats For Eisenhower," blue picture, red, white, and blue background ......... **10.00**
2½" d, "Give Ike A Republican Congress" ....................... **10.00**
3½", "I Like Ike," blue and white, Bastian Brothers ............. **5.00**
Poster, 12 x 17", "Welcome Mr. President/We'll See You At The Civic Auditorium Wed, Oct 17, 6 PM," black and white ................ **25.00**
Socks, pr, gray, red "I Like Ike" motto, orig cardboard insert and orange and blue paper tag ............ **15.00**
Trivet, 4½ x 8", cast iron, painted black, ceramic insert, inscribed "General And Mrs. Dwight D. Eisenhower," back marked "Pilkington/England," c1956 ........... **12.00**

Adlai E. Stevenson, 1952 and 1956
Booklet, *A Man Named Stevenson,* Democratic National Committee, 1952, 16 pgs, 5 x 7", 16 pgs .... **10.00**
License Plate, 4 x 12", metal, white raised dark blue letters .......... **20.00**
Pinback Button
3", "Adlai–Estes," celluloid, red, white, and blue .............. **8.00**
4" d, "America Needs Stevenson," red, white, and blue .......... **10.00**
Record, 78 rpm, plastic, 7" sq cardboard with black and white portrait, Philadelphia AFL–CIO endorsement ..................... **20.00**
Tab, 1", litho, black and white, Stevenson in block letters .......... **1.50**

John F. Kennedy, 1960
Bank, 9" d, plastic, silver, JFK half dollar design with 1964 date, unused, 1960s .................. **15.00**
Cigarette Lighter, 1½" d, copper finish, coin shape, inscribed "John F Kennedy 1917–1963/35th President–USA," Statue of Liberty on back ......................... **10.00**
Hat, campaign, 11 x 13 x 3½", plastic, molded, white, red, white, and blue paper band brim, inscribed "Kennedy For President," oval black and white pictures left and right, black and white portrait on top ......................... **50.00**
Invitation, Inaugural, 8½ x 11", engraved, emb gold inaugural seal, 4 pgs ......................... **20.00**
Keychain, brass bust of JFK, metal plate joins ring inscribed and dates of birth and death, 1963–64 ..... **12.00**
Magazine, *Life,* Jan 27, 1961, "The Kennedy Inauguration," black and

white photos, 15 pgs of inauguration .......... **8.00**

Plate

6″ d, china, color portrait, Mrs. Kennedy seated in yellow chair, Kennedy standing behind, gold design, c1961 .......... **10.00**

7½″ d, china, glazed, full color portrait center President and Mrs. Kennedy, early 1960s .......... **15.00**

Playing Cards, Kennedy Kards, complete deck, boxed, 1963 copyright **35.00**

Record, JFK Memorial Album, speeches from Nov 22, 1963, WMCA Radio, 33 rpm .......... **30.00**

Salt and Pepper Shakers, pr, china, JFK in rocking chair, orig stopper, paper labels marked "Japan" .... **35.00**

Tapestry, 19 x 37″, woven, JFK and Capitol building, made in Belgium **15.00**



**Nixon, bumper sticker, red, white, and blue, 9½ x 4″, $8.00.**

Richard M. Nixon, 1960, 1968, and 1972

Bank, 3 x 7 x 4½″, mechanical, cast iron, elephant, white, red raised letters, inscribed "Vote Right/Nixon Agnew In '72/Better The Second Time Around" .......... **75.00**

Book, *Six Crises,* Doubleday, 1962, dj, 460 pgs, black pen signature "Richard Nixon" .......... **75.00**

Dart Board, 11½ x 11½″, fiberboard, silk screened design, Nixon giving "V" sign, pair of brass and yellow plastic darts, metal hanging tab .. **15.00**

Figure, 3 x 5 x 4″, vinyl, elephant with Nixon head, back with black and tan world and blue blanket with "R" and "Nixon," marked "GOP," c1972 .......... **15.00**

Hat, 4 x 11″, paper, blue and white, slogan "Experience Counts," 1960 **8.00**

Invitation, Inauguration, 8 x 11″, cardboard, emb gold inaugural seal, 1973 .......... **10.00**

License Plate, 6 x 12″, red and blue on silver reflective background ... **15.00**

Medal, 2¾″ d, Franklin Mint serial number 18151, edge marked "Solid Bronze," plastic holder ... **20.00**

Pinback Button

1¾″, "Dependability, Intergrity, Capability, Knowledge," red, white, and blue .......... **10.00**

3½″, "Keep Dick On The Job," black and white, red, white, and blue background .......... **15.00**

Plate, 9″ d, "Richard M. Nixon 37th President," china, full color portrait, gold rim band, c1968 ...... **15.00**

Lyndon B. Johnson, 1964

Figure, 5″, vinyl, wearing red, white, and blue campaign button, orig unopened cellophane package, Remco .......... **35.00**

Hat, campaign, "LBJ For The USA," orange felt, red on white fabric band .......... **10.00**

Jugate, black and white photo on white, white initials on dark blue, red section center with white National Maritime Union AFL–CIO/Pres Joseph Curran "Says All The Way" .......... **50.00**

Pinback Button, 6″, "Inauguration Lyndon Baines Johnson Jan 20, 1965 Washington DC," full color portrait, red, white, and blue rim . **10.00**

Wall Plaque, 9″ d, celluloid, black and white portraits of LBJ and HHH **12.00**

Barry M. Goldwater, 1964

Eye Glasses, "Go Goldwater," cardboard, black on white, penciled note used at San Francisco convention .......... **10.00**

License Plate, 4 x 12″, metal, yellow, raised blue letters, "Victory In '64" slogan .......... **10.00**

Pinback Button

3½″, "Save America/Goldwater–Miller," red, white, and blue, abstract flag design .......... **15.00**

6″, "Barry Goldwater 64," black and white portrait, blue background, red and white curved line, three star shape designs .. **10.00**

Poster, 14 x 21″, "A Choice . . . Not An Echo," red, white, and blue .. **15.00**

Hubert H. Humphrey, 1968

Pencil, mechanical, black plastic and brass, Vice President's seal ...... **4.00**

Pinback Button, 1¾″, "Hubie Baby," celluloid, orange letters, brown ground .......... **4.00**

Tab, 2″, "Labor For Humphrey," blue, green, red, white, and black ..... **4.00**

Tie Tack, brass, diecut, initials "HHH," 1968 .......... **2.00**

George McGovern, 1972

Comb, "McGovern–Shriver," plastic, blue, smiling face .......... **4.00**

Pinback Button, 3", "McGovern," brown shaded portrait .......... **12.00**
Shopping Bag, 15 x 17", "President McGovern '72," white and dark blue .......................... **5.00**
Tab, "McGovern/Shriver," blue and white ......................... **2.00**

Gerald R. Ford, 1974
Jugate, 1", "Ford/For/76/with Rocky," celluloid, red, white, and black .. **4.00**
Pinback Button, 2¼", "Win With Ford," multicolored ............. **4.00**
Tab, "President Ford '76," white ... **1.50**

James E. Carter, 1976
Christmas Card, 8½ x 11", watercolor and signature, adults and children look at Santa holding "Carter/Mondale/1980" sign, White House background .................. **10.00**
Jugate, 3", "Carter/Mondale," black and white, red, white, blue, yellow, and brown scrolls, flag and eagle ......................... **5.00**
Pinback Button
3", red, white, blue, and tan, Carter with peanut body ........... **5.00**
6", "Inauguration Day Jan 20, 1977," black and white portraits, green background, red, white, and blue designs ............ **5.00**
Poster, 14 x 22", green and white, inset with close up of Carter ..... **2.00**

Ronald Reagan, 1980 and 1984
Card
Anniversary, 5 x 8", paper, red and white border, emb gold Presidential Seal, "Congratulations On Your Anniversary" and four line inscription, unused White House envelope .................... **12.00**
Musical, 6 x 8", cellophane cov, gold "Reagan–Bush" on front, full color Reagan and Bush photo and quote inside, plays Star Spangled Banner and red lights glow when opened ........... **15.00**
Pinback Button, 2¾", red, heart shape "California Loves Reagan '76," white letters .................. **10.00**
Press ID, 3 x 4½", full color, laminated, metal neck chain, inscription "Jan 20, 1981/Reagan Inauguration/ ABC News/Press" ...... **15.00**

# POST CARDS

**Collecting Hints:** Concentrate on one subject area, publisher, or illustrator. Collect cards in mint condition, when possible.

The more common the holiday, the larger the city, the more popular the tourist attraction, the easier it will be to find post cards about these subjects because of the millions of cards that still remain in these categories. The smaller runs of "real" photo post cards are the most desirable of the scenic cards. Photographic cards of families and individuals, unless they show occupations, unusual toys, dolls, or teddy bears have little value.

Stamps and cancellation marks may affect the value of cards, but rarely. Consult a philatelic guide.

Post cards fall into two main categories: view cards and topics. View cards are easiest to sell in their local geographic region. European view cards, while very interesting, are difficult to sell in America.

It must be stressed that age alone does not determine price. A birthday post card from 1918 may sell for only ten cents, while a political campaign card from the 1950s may bring ten dollars. Every collectible is governed by supply and demand.

Although the most popular collecting period is 1898–1918, the increasing costs of post cards from this era have turned collectors' interest to post cards from the 1920s, 1930s, and 1940s. The main interest in the 1920–1930 period is cards with an Art Deco motif. The cards collected from the 1940s are "linens" which feature a textured "linen–like" paper surface.

Cards from the 1950–1970 period are called chromes because of their shiny surface paper. Advertising post cards from this chrome era are rapidly gaining popularity while still selling for under $3.00.

**History:** The golden age of post cards dates from 1898 to 1918. While there are cards printed earlier, they are collected for their postal history. Post cards prior to 1898 are called "pioneer" cards.

European publishers, especially in England and Germany, produced the vast majority of cards during the golden age. The major post card publishers are Raphael Tuck (England), Paul Finkenrath of Berlin (PFB–German), and Whitney, Detroit Publishing Co., and John Winsch (United States). However, many American publishers had their stock produced in Europe, hence, "Made in Bavaria" imprints. While some Tuck cards are high priced, many are still available in the "ten cent" boxes.

Styles changed rapidly, and manufacturers responded to every need. The linen post card which gained popularity in the 1940s was quickly replaced by the chrome cards of the post–1950 period.

**References:** Many of the best books are out–of–print. However, they are available through libraries. Ask your library to utilize the inter–library loan system.

*Postcard Collector Annual,* published annually by Jones Publishing; Diane Allmen, *The Official Price Guide to Postcards,* House of Collectibles, 1990; Janet A. Banneck, *The Antique Postcards of Rose O'Neill,* Greater Chicago Productions, 1922; John Margolies, *Palaces of Dreams: Movie Theater Postcards,* Bulfince Press, 1993; Norman E. Martinus and Harry L. Rinker, *Warman's Paper,* Wallace–Homestead, 1993; J. L. Mashburn, *The Postcard Price Guide: A Comprehensive Listing,* World Comm, 1992; Joseph Lee Mashburn, *The Super Rare Postcards of Harrison Fisher,* World Comm, 1992; Frederic and Mary Megson, *American Advertising Postcards—Set and Series: 1890–1920,* published by authors, 1985; Mary and Frederick Megson, *American Exposition Postcards, 1870–1920: A Catalog And Price Guide,* The Postcard Lovers, 1992; Susan Brown Nicholson, *Antique Postcard Sets and Series Price Guide,* Greater Chicago Productions, 1993; Cynthia Rubin and Morgan Williams, *Larger Than Life; The American Tall–Tale Postcard, 1905–1915,* Abbeville Press, 1990; Dorothy B. Ryan, *Picture Postcards In The United States, 1893–1918,* Clarkson N. Potter, 1982, paperback edition; Jack H. Smith, *Postcard Companion: The Collector's Reference,* Wallace–Homestead Book Company, 1989; Robert Ward, *Investment Guide To North American Real Photo Postcards,* Antique Paper Guild, 1991; Jane Wood, *The Collector's Guide To Post Cards,* L–W Promotions, 1984, 1993 value update.

**Periodicals:** *Barr's Postcard News,* 70 S. 6th Street, Lansing, IA 52151; *Postcard Collector,* Joe Jones Publishing, P. O. Box 337, Iola, WI 54945.

**Collectors' Clubs:** *Barr's Postcard News* and the *Postcard Collector* publish lists of over fifty regional clubs in the United States and Canada.

**Advisor:** Susan Brown Nicholson

**Note:** The following prices are for cards in excellent to mint condition—no sign of edgewear, no creases, not trimmed, no writing on the picture side of the card, no tears, and no dirt. Each defect would reduce the price given by 10%.

## ADVERTISING

Allentown postals .................. **30.00**
Bell Telephone .................. **15.00**
Bull Durham .................. **30.00**
Buster Brown .................. **12.00**
Campbell Soup adv
  Horizontal format .................. **35.00**
  Vertical format .................. **85.00**
Chief Sleepy Eye .................. **150.00**
Coca–Cola, Duster Girl .................. **450.00**
Cracker Jack Bears .................. **25.00**
DuPont Gun, dogs .................. **100.00**
Frog–in–the–Throat
  Oversized .................. **50.00**
  Small Size .................. **45.00**
Gold Dust Twins .................. **50.00**
Job Cigarettes
  Mucha .................. **300.00**
  Other artist .................. **100.00**
Kornelia Kinks .................. **10.00**
McDonald's .................. **6.00**
Quaddy .................. **20.00**
Studebaker Wagon .................. **65.00**
Swifts Pride .................. **15.00**
Tupperware .................. **3.00**
Vin Fiz .................. **100.00**
Zeno Gum .................. **6.00**

## ARTIST SIGNED

Atwell, Mabel Lucie
  Early by Tuck .................. **20.00**
  Regular, comic .................. **15.00**
Basch, Arpad, Art Nouveau .................. **150.00**
Bertiglia, children .................. **15.00**
Boileau, Philip
  By Reinthal Neuman .................. **20.00**
  Tuck Publishing .................. **150.00**
Bompard, art dec .................. **15.00**
Boulanger, Maurice, cats .................. **20.00**
Brill, Ginks .................. **10.00**
Browne, Tom
  American Baseball series .................. **15.00**
  English comic series .................. **3.50**
Brundage, Frances
  Children .................. **10.00**
  Early chromolithographic .................. **30.00**
Brunelleschi, Art Nouveau .................. **150.00**
Busi, Art Deco .................. **15.00**
Caldecott
  Early .................. **5.00**
  1974 reprints .................. **.25**
Carmichael, comic .................. **3.00**
Carr, Gene, comic .................. **8.00**
Chiostri, Art Deco .................. **40.00**
Christy, Howard Chandler .................. **10.00**
Clapsaddle, Ellen
  Children .................. **9.00**
  Floral, sleds, crosses .................. **3.00**
  Halloween, mechanical .................. **150.00**
  Suffrage .................. **55.00**
Corbella, Art Deco .................. **15.00**
Corbett, Bertha, sunbonnets .................. **12.00**
Curtis, E, children .................. **3.00**
Daniell, Eva, Art Nouveau .................. **100.00**
Drayton/Weiderseim, Grace, children . **30.00**
Dwig .................. **10.00**
Fidler, Alice Luella, women .................. **10.00**
Fisher, Harrison .................. **15.00**
Gassaway, K, children .................. **6.00**
Gibson, Charles Dana .................. **5.00**
Golay, Mary, flowers .................. **2.00**
Greiner, M
  Blacks .................. **8.00**

**Artist Signed, Drayton, $30.00.**

- Children **3.50**
- Molly and Her Teddy **15.00**

- Griggs, HB **9.00**
- Gunn, Archie **3.50**
- Gutmann, Bessie Pease **25.00**
- Humphrey, Maud, sgd **75.00**
- Innes, John **5.00**
- Johnson, J, children **6.00**
- Kirchner, Raphael
  - First period **125.00**
  - Second period **65.00**
  - Third period **45.00**
- Klein, Catherine
  - Alphabet **15.00**
  - Alphabet, letters X, Y, Z **25.00**
  - Floral **3.00**
- Koehler, Mela, early **100.00**
- Mauzan, Art Deco **15.00**
- May, Phil, British **6.00**
- McCay, Winsor, Little Nemo **30.00**
- Mucha, Alphonse
  - Art Nouveau, months of the year **125.00**
  - Art Nouveau, Slavic period **60.00**
  - Women, full card design **500.00**
- O'Neill, Rose
  - Pickings from Puck, Blacks **150.00**
  - Kewpies **40.00**
  - Suffrage **200.00**
- Opper, Frederick, comic **6.00**
- Outcault
  - Buster Brown calendars **12.00**
  - Yellow Kid calendars **75.00**
- Parkinson, Ethel, children **6.00**
- Patella, women **25.00**
- Payne, Harry **22.00**
- Phillips, Cole **30.00**
- Price, Mary Evans **5.00**
- Remington, Frederic **25.00**
- Robinson, Robert **25.00**
- Rockwell, Norman, after 1918 **35.00**
- Russell, Charles **9.00**
- Shinn, Cobb **4.00**
- Smith, Jessie Wilcox **15.00**
- Studdy, Bonzo Dog **10.00**
- Tam, Jean **15.00**
- Thiele, Arthur
  - Blacks
    - Large faces **35.00**
    - On bikes **35.00**
  - Cats
    - In action **30.00**
    - Large heads **30.00**
- Twelvetrees, Charles, comic, children **5.00**
- Underwood, Clarence **8.00**
- Upton, Florence, Golliwoggs, Tuck **35.00**
- Wain, Louis
  - Cat **45.00**
  - Dog **25.00**
  - Paper dolls **300.00**
- Wall, Bernhardt, sunbonnets **15.00**
- Wood, Lawson **6.00**

## EXPOSITION

- Alaska–Yukon–Pacific **6.00**
- California Midwinter **200.00**
- Cotton States Exposition **125.00**
- Hudson–Fulton **10.00**
- Jamestown Bears, mechanical, 144 designs on one card **500.00**
- Lewis and Clark **10.00**
- Pan American
  - Black and white **5.00**
  - Color **10.00**
- Panama–California **4.50**
- Panama–Pacific
  - General **8.00**
  - Mitchell Publishing **2.00**
- Portland Rose Festival **3.50**
- Portola Festival
  - Poster style **15.00**
  - Views **1.50**
- Priest of Pallas **10.00**
- St Louis, 1904
  - Eggshell paper **6.00**
  - Hold to light type
    - General **35.00**
    - Inside Inn scene **150.00**
  - Silver background **7.50**
- Trans–Mississippi
  - Advertising **100.00**
  - Officials **55.00**
- World Columbian, 1893
  - Officials **15.00**
  - Pre–Officials, without seals **100.00**

## GREETINGS

- April Fools
  - American comic **1.50**
  - French litho with fish **5.00**
- Birthday
  - Children **.50**
  - Floral **.10**

Christmas, no Santa .... **.25**
Christmas, Santa
- German, highly embossed .... **30.00**
- Installment, unused .... **150.00**
- Red Suits .... **8.00**
- Suits other than red .... **15.00**

Easter
- Animals, dressed .... **6.00**
- Chicks or rabbits .... **2.00**
- Children dressed as animals .... **4.50**
- Crosses .... **.50**

Fourth of July
- Children .... **6.00**
- Uncle Sam .... **6.00**
- Others .... **1.50**

**Greeting, comical, $7.00.**

Ground Hog Day
- Early large image .... **200.00**
- After 1930 .... **25.00**

Halloween
- Children .... **6.00**
- Children, extremely colorful or artist sgd .... **10.00**
- Plain .... **2.00**

Labor Day
- Lounsbury Publishing .... **200.00**
- Nash Publishing .... **85.00**

Leap Year .... **4.50**
Mother's Day, early .... **5.00**
New Year
- Bells .... **.50**
- Children or Father Time .... **2.50**

St Patrick's Day
- Children .... **4.50**
- No children .... **1.50**

Thanksgiving
- Children .... **3.50**
- No children .... **1.00**

Valentines
- Children, women .... **3.50**
- Hearts, comic .... **1.00**

## PATRIOTIC

Decoration Day .... **7.50**
Lincoln .... **4.50**
Patriotic Songs .... **3.00**
Uncle Sam .... **7.50**
Washington .... **3.50**
World War II, linen .... **1.00**

## PHOTOGRAPHIC

Children under Christmas trees .... **3.50**
Children with animals or toys .... **4.50**
Christmas trees .... **2.00**
Circus Performer, close–up .... **8.00**
Exaggerations
- Conrad Publishing, after 1935 .... **6.00**
- Martin Publishing .... **8.50**
- Martin Publishing, US Coin .... **75.00**

Family, unidentified .... **.50**
Main Streets
- Large cities .... **4.00**
- Small towns .... **9.00**
- Unidentified .... **.50**
- With trains or trolleys .... **20.00**

People on Paper Moons .... **3.00**
Railroad Depots, with trains, identified **20.00**
Shop Exteriors, identified .... **6.00**
Shop Interiors
- Clear images or products .... **15.00**
- Workers, barbers, blacksmiths, etc. .. **20.00**

## POLITICAL AND SOCIAL HISTORY

Billy Possum .... **15.00**
Blacks .... **12.00**
Campaign
- 1900 .... **75.00**
- 1904 .... **45.00**

Indians, named .... **8.00**
Jewish, comic .... **8.00**
McKinley's death .... **6.00**
Prohibition .... **6.00**
Roosevelt's African Tour .... **3.00**
Russo–Japanese War .... **25.00**
Suffrage
- Cargill publisher
  - Number 111 only .... **150.00**
- General .... **30.00**
- Parades .... **20.00**

Taft, cartoons .... **15.00**
Wilson .... **8.00**

## PUBLISHERS

Detroit
- Indians .... **10.00**
- Views .... **1.50**

Paul Finkenrath/Berlin (PFB)
- Children .... **8.00**
- Comic .... **6.00**

- Punch and Judy, mechanical ....... **100.00**
- Santas .......................... **30.00**

Paul Finkenrath/Berlin (PFB), greetings **1.50**

Tuck Publishing
- Children, unsigned ............... **4.50**
- Greetings ........................ **1.00**
- Views ............................ **1.00**

Whitney
- Children ......................... **4.50**
- Nibble Picks, Santas .............. **12.00**

Winsch Publishing
- Greetings ........................ **1.50**
- Halloween, SL Schmucker ......... **100.00**
- Santas .......................... **30.00**
- Valentines, SL Schmucker ......... **35.00**

## RARE AND UNUSUAL

Boileau, Tuck ...................... **150.00**
Coke Advertising, Hamilton King ..... **400.00**
DuPont Dirigible ................... **125.00**
Greenaway, Kate, sgd ............... **200.00**
Hold–To–Lights, other than buildings . **40.00**
Installment, Uncle Sam ............. **150.00**
Kewpies
- Gross Publishing Co .............. **125.00**
- Ice Cream advertising, spell "Victory" **200.00**

Mechanicals ........................ **85.00**
Paper Dolls, Tuck .................. **100.00**
Santa Claus
- Black Faced ..................... **150.00**
- Hold–To–Light ................... **200.00**

Silks
- Applied, Santas and state bells ..... **45.00**
- Woven .......................... **100.00**

Tuck Scouts, Harry Payne ........... **125.00**
Warner Corset, Mucha ............... **300.00**
Waverly Cycle, Mucha ............. **13,500.00**
Wiener Werkstatte, Kokoschka ...... **3,000.00**

# POSTERS

**Collecting Hints:** Posters are collected either for their subject and historical value, e.g. movie, railroad, minstrel, etc., or for the aesthetic appeal. Modern art historians have recognized the poster as one of the most creative art forms of our times.

Often a popular film would be re–released several times over a period of years. Most re–releases can be identified by looking at the lower right corner in the white border area. A re–release will usually be indicated with an "R" and a diagonal slash mark with the year of the newest release. Therefore, a "R/47" would indicate a 1947 issue.

**History:** The poster was an extremely effective and critical means of mass communication, especially in the period before 1920. Enormous quantities were produced, helped in part by the propaganda role played by posters in World War I.

Print runs of two million were not unknown. Posters were not meant to be saved. Once they served their purpose, they tended to be destroyed. The paradox of high production and low survival is one of the fascinating aspects of poster history.

The posters of the late 19th century and early 20th century represent the pinnacle of American lithography printing. The advertising posters of firms such as Strobridge or Courier are true classics. Philadelphia was one center for the poster industry.

Europe pioneered in posters with high artistic and aesthetic content. Many major artists of the 20th century designed posters. Poster art still plays a key role throughout Europe today.

**References:** John Barnicoat, *A Concise History of Posters,* Harry Abrams, Inc., 1976; Tony Fusco, *The Official Identification and Price Guide To Posters,* House of Collectibles, 1990; Norman E. Martinus and Harry L. Rinker, *Warman's Paper,* Wallace–Homestead, 1993; Walton Rawls, *Wake Up, America!: World War I And The American Poster,* Abbeville Press, 1988; Stephen Rebello and Richard Allen, *Reel Art: Great Posters From The Golden Age of the Silver Screen,* Abbeville Press, 1988; George Theofiles, *American Posters of World War I: A Price and Collector's Guide,* Dafram House Publishers, Inc.; Susan Theran, *Leonard's Annual Price Index of Prints, Posters and Photographs, Volume I,* Auction Index, inc., 1992; Susan Theran, *Prints, Posters, and Photographs: Identification and Price Guide,* Avon Books, 1993; Jon R. Warren, *Warren's Movie Poster Price Guide, 1993 Edition,* American Collector's Exchange, 1992.

**Advisor:** George Theofiles.

**REPRODUCTION ALERT:** Some of the posters by A. M. Cassandre have been reproduced in France.

## ADVERTISING

Avalon Cigarettes, 10 x 16", Union Made, full color, smiling girl, Anon, c1940 ........................ **45.00**
Bickmore Shave Cream, 30 x 21", man putting shave cream on brush, 1930 **25.00**
Camomille Liqueur, 32 x 51", yellow bottle illus, blue background, c1890 **225.00**
Ferry's Seeds, 20½ x 27½", blonde lady wearing military bib overalls, 1910 . **60.00**
Fireman's Fund Insurance Co, 14 x 18", litho decal transfer, fireman rescuing young girl, flaming background, W E Delappe, c1920 .................. **150.00**
Hilton–The Starched Collar For Fall–Toke Brothers, Ltd, 11 x 21", celluloid

collars, autumn leaves background, c1915 .......... **50.00**
Old Dutch Cleanser, 15 x 20", fabric, can illus, blue and white background, red border, 1930s .......... **75.00**
RCA New Records, 13 x 35", announced latest monthly releases, c1924, set of 4 .......... **150.00**
Savon Cadum, 47 x 62", smiling baby beside tub, soap dish, deep blue background, Anon, c1890 .......... **575.00**
Sony Sugar Cones, 18 x 8", child looking at ice cream cone, Anon, c1923 **75.00**
Tuttle's Horse Elixir, 30 x 46", black, yellow, and red .......... **150.00**
Welch's Wine Coolers, 11 x 21", "Wouldn't This Hit The Spot Right Now? Taste It...You'll Love It, Says Eddie Cantor," 1952 .......... **100.00**

**Movie, *Invitation to a Gunfighter,* Yul Brynner, Louis Rulew, United Artists, 1964, $20.00.**

STRENGTHEN
AMERICA
CHARACTER
COUNTS
BOY SCOUTS OF AMERICA
51st ANNIVERSARY 1961


**Boy Scouts, multicolored, 51st Anniversary, 1961, 13¼ x 19", $18.00.**

## MOVIES

African Queen, 22 x 31", Bogart and Hepburn, 1960s .......... **150.00**
Anatomy Of A Murder, 27 x 41, Saul Bass design, Columbia, 1959 .......... **125.00**
Assignment in Brittany, 27 x 41", Pieree Aumont, Susan Peters, MGM, 1943 **95.00**
Blonde Alibi, 27 x 41", Martha O'Driscoll, Universal, 1946 .......... **165.00**
Bonzo Goes To College, 27 x 41", Maureen O'Sullivan, Edmund Gwenn, Universal, 1952 .......... **125.00**
Camille, 27 x 41", Greta Garbo, Robert Taylor, MGM, 1936 .......... **425.00**
Close Call For Ellery Queen, 27 x 41", William Gargan, Margaret Lindsay, Columbia, 1941 .......... **100.00**
Dangerous When Wet, 27 x 41", Esther Williams and Fernando Lamas, MGM, 1953 .......... **75.00**
Frenzy, 27 x 41", Alfred Hitchcock, Universal, 1972 .......... **45.00**
Fuller Brush Girl, 14 x 36", Lucille Ball, Eddie Albert, Columbia, 1950 .......... **110.00**
Harvard Here I Come, 27 x 41", Leon Errol, Grace McDonald, Universal, 1941 .......... **150.00**
Hellcats of the Navy, 27 x 41", Ronald Reagan, Nancy Davis, Columbia, 1957 .......... **200.00**
I'll Be Seeing You, 27 x 41", Ginger Rogers, C–Joseph Cotton, Shirley Temple, United Artists, 1945 .......... **150.00**
Lone Wolf and His Lady, 27 x 41", Ron Randell, Columbia, 1949 .......... **125.00**
Miracles For Sale, 27 x 41", Robert Young, Florence Rice, MGM, 1939 . **150.00**
My Favorite Spy, 27 x 41", Bob Hope and Hedy Lamarr, Paramount, 1951 **100.00**
Rhapsody In Blue, 27 x 41", Robert Alda, Warner Bros, 1946 .......... **110.00**
She Went To The Races, 27 x 41", James Craig and Ava Gardner, MGM, 1945 **75.00**
Song of Nevada, 27 x 41", Roy Rogers and Dale Evans, Republic Pictures, 1949 .......... **110.00**
Sorority House, 27 x 41", Anne Shirley and James Ellison, RKO, 1939 .......... **100.00**
This Woman Is Dangerous, 27 x 41", Joan Crawford, Warner Bros, 1952 . **75.00**
Unholy Partners, 27 x 41", Edward G Robinson, MGM, 1941 .......... **150.00**
Wild Geese Calling, 27 x 41", Henry Fonda and Joan Bennett, Fox, 1941 . **175.00**
Young Widow, 27 x 41", Jane Russell, Louis Hayward, United Artists, 1946 **100.00**

## PUBLISHING

Clack Boo, April 1896, 19 x 12", full moon smiling down on rows of cats, Anon .......... **150.00**
Harper's July, 14 x 22", The German Struggle For Liberty, Edward Penfield, 1895 .......... **150.00**
Mucha Cover Illustration, 8 x 7", Literary Digest cov, Alphonse Mucha, 1907 .......... **50.00**
Philadelphia Enquirer's Boys and Girls Christmas Book, 19 x 24", Victorian ladies hold hands of young child, Wilson, 1901 .......... **125.00**
St Nicholas, New Years Number, 13 x 20", boy wearing snowshoes, George A Williams, 1898 .......... **125.00**
To Date, 11 x 13", colored lithos for Xmas and New Years Number magazines, Barnes, 1895 .......... **100.00**
Zezette, 49 x 54", novel, attendants feeding dismembered body to caged cats, 1890 .......... **200.00**

## SPORTS

Daily Express, Boxing, 20 x 30", full color litho of boxing glove, Anon, 1948 .......... **100.00**
Daily Mail, Football News, 20 x 30", soccer match image, Anon, c1950 . **75.00**
Golden Gloves Story, 27 x 41", full color boxing litho, Eagle Lion, 1950 ..... **175.00**
Muhammad Ali–The Greatest, 28 x 22", full color design of Ali, Columbia Pictures, 1977 .......... **95.00**
Play Safe–Wear A Pal, 15 x 23", full color golfer teeing off, diecut, Anon, 1935 .......... **75.00**
Restringing By Skilled Craftsmen, 17 x 21", diecut, Wilson Tennis Equipment, Anon, c1935 .......... **85.00**
Ski In Vail, 19 x 27", cartoon skier, jet black background, Hoffman, c1968 **39.00**
Wilson Badminton Equipment, 21 x 26", diecut, man running with racquet, green and black, Anon, c1935 ..... **75.00**

## THEATER

Carter Beats The Devil, 14 x 22", Otis Litho, 1920s .......... **75.00**
Dangers of A Great City, 21 x 28", color litho, men fighting in office, Anon, c1900 .......... **150.00**
Felix Ferry, 26 x 40", Art Deco style, cabaret singer, black, white, and blue, Anon, 1931 .......... **175.00**
Human Hearts–An Idyl of the Arkansas Hills, 21 x 28", young blonde haired child looking to sky, pink and red hearts, c1905 .......... **165.00**
Key Largo, 14 x 22", portrait center, black and red motif, Anon, c1930 .. **65.00**
New York State Theater–Lincoln Center, 30 x 45", Robert Indiana, 1964 .... **325.00**
Slaves of the Mine, 29 x 42", American melodrama, Enquirer Co, Cincinnati, c1890 .......... **225.00**
The Worried Husbands, 17 x 22", stone litho, blue, red, and black, c1900 .. **125.00**

## TRANSPORTATION

American Airlines, East Coast, 30 x 40", seaman carving sailing ship, McKnight Kauffer, 1948 .......... **250.00**
British Railways, The Night Ferry, 25 x 40", woodcut design, sleeping cars on ferry between London and Paris, A N Wolstenholme .......... **280.00**
Buick, Kansas City, 25 x 38", black and white, 1921–22 .......... **85.00**
Chesapeake Steamship Co, 31 x 40", litho, 1915 .......... **250.00**
Cunard Line–*RMS Caronia,* 18 x 22", litho of ship in exotic Mediterranean setting, Anon, 1948 .......... **150.00**
E.V.M. Bicycle, 19 x 27", workman and tools, Art Nouveau bicycle parts border, Tamagno, c1910 .......... **175.00**
Lufthansa Airlines, 25 x 39", waving stewardess on airliner stairs, Anon, 1955 .......... **95.00**
Mercedes Benz, 23 x 33", brown, blue, black, red, and yellow, white ground, futuristic race car against ghostly logo, 1955 .......... **975.00**
Scandinavian Airlines System, 29 x 18", map design, red, blue, and yellow, Otto Nielsen, c1955 .......... **80.00**
The Greyhound Lines, 20 x 20" streamlined bus, passing southern plantation, Walt Brownson, c1938 ....... **150.00**
The Pierce Arrow, 8 x 10", placard, color, J Sheridan .......... **80.00**

## TRAVEL

Acapulco, 26 x 33", color silk screen image, bathing beauty, Anon, 1960 . **95.00**
Britain In Winter, 19 x 29", horseman, hunters, and tourists, rustic inn, Terence Cuneo, 1948 .......... **125.00**
Come To Ulster, 50 x 40", sailboats and fishermen gliding in front of lighthouse, Norman Wilkinson, 1935 ... **450.00**
French Seaside Resorts, 25 x 39", red, white, and blue striped cabana and seashore scene, Jean Picart le Doux, 1947 .......... **300.00**

Guadalajara, 18 x 27″, caricature of Mexican band, nightscape background, Anon, c1955 .......... **95.00**
Isle of Wight, 50 x 40″, rural landscape, earth tones, c1935 .......... **375.00**
Lucerne, Festival of Music 1957, 25 x 40″, viola in blocks of red, orange, green, purple, and black, Piatti, 1957 **250.00**
Mexico, 18 x 27″, young Mexican boy with piggy bank, 1949 .......... **125.00**
Panama Pacific Liner, New York–California, 27 x 23″, white liner going through Panama Canal, orig frame, brass plaque, c1920 .......... **250.00**
See Tel–Aviv, 25 x 39″, full color, city design in bright colors, N Gutman, 1958 .......... **200.00**
The Queen of Bermuda Entering Hamilton Harbor, 30 x 39″, silkscreen, multicolored design, Adolph Treidler, 1947 .......... **275.00**
There's Plenty To See In Ontario, 17 x 23″, cartoon montage of sun, water, and tourists, Ontario Travel Commission, Anon, c1953 .......... **65.00**
Visit London, 25 x 40″, litho Mounted Household Cavalry parade, c1948 .. **275.00**

## WORLD WAR I

Be Patriotic–Sign Your Country's Pledge To Save Food, 20 x 30″, Columbia figure wrapped in stars and stripes, Paul Stahr, 1918 .......... **90.00**
Hold Up Your End, 20 x 30″, nurse holding stretcher, bursting shell, yellow background, W P King, 1918 ...... **125.00**
If You Want to Fight–Join The Marines, 30 x 41″, woman in front of panorama of charging marines, Howard Chandler Christy, 1943 .......... **575.00**
Joan Of Arc Saved France, Women Of America Save Your Country, 30 x 40″, lovely Joan of Arc image, Haskel Coffin, 1918 .......... **150.00**
I Shall Expect Every Man Who Is Not A Slacker, 29 x 43″, Columbia figure, H Paus, 1918 .......... **200.00**
Remember The Flag of Liberty Support It!, 20 x 30″, immigrant family on dock, steamer, and American flag, Anon, 1918 .......... **100.00**
US Marines–Soldiers Of The Sea, 29 x 40″, Marines signaling from beach, marine life and action vignettes, J C Leyendecker, c1915 .......... **175.00**

## WORLD WAR II

All Soldiers Can't Be In The Infantry, 17 x 25″, charging soldier with bayonet, battle ribbons, and globe, Steele Savage, 1944 .......... **125.00**
Army Air Forces Want You! WACS Keep 'Em Flying, 19 x 27″, "Go to your US Army recruiting station now," WAC inspecting propeller and motor, Anon **125.00**
Battle Stations! Keep 'Em Fighting, 31 x 41″, Naval bugler on gun deck, worker at lathe, Anon, 1942 ....... **125.00**
Buy War Bonds, 14 x 22″, Uncle Sam leading battle, N C Wyeth, 1942 ... **125.00**
Forest Fires–Another Enemy To Conquer, 19 x 26″, cartoon image, squirrels in nest, fire background, Anon, 1944 .......... **65.00**
I'm Counting On You! Don't Discuss Troop Movements, Ship Sailings, War Equipment, 20 x 28″, Uncle Sam with finger to lip, blue background, L Helguera, 1943 .......... **95.00**
Men Of Valor–They Fight For You, 25 x 36″, Menard charging with tommy gun in muted colors, Hubert Rogers, 1942 .......... **175.00**

**Together, British WWII, 20 x 30″, $150.00.**

Serve your Country In the Waves, 28 x 40″, girl admiringly looking at photo, John Falter, 1944 .......... **175.00**
Spars, 28 x 42″, blonde Spar salutes pioneer woman, covered wagon, J Valentin, 1943 .......... **200.00**
United For Victory, 22 x 28″, locomotive, red, white, and blue stars and stripes, Anon, c1944 .......... **100.00**
We're In The Army Now, 10 x 15″, orange and purple, Anon, c1943 ..... **75.00**
Woman's Place In War, 25 x 38″, WAC weather observer with instrument, Irving Cooper, 1944 .......... **125.00**

# ELVIS PRESLEY

**Collecting Hints:** Official Elvis Presley items are usually copyrighted and many are dated.

Learn to differentiate between items licensed during Elvis's lifetime and the wealth of "fantasy" items issued after his death. The latter are collectibles, but have nowhere near the value of the pre–1977 material.

Also accept the fact that much of the modern limited edition issues are purely speculative investments. It is best to buy them because you like them and plan to live with them for an extended period of time.

**History:** When Elvis Presley became a rock 'n' roll star, he became one of the first singers to have a promotion which was aimed at teenagers. The first Elvis merchandise appeared in 1956. During the following years new merchandise was added both in America and foreign countries. After his death in 1977, a vast number of new Elvis collectibles appeared.

**References:** Rosalind Cranor, *Elvis Collectibles,* Collector Books, 1983, out–of–print; Norman E. Martinus and Harry L. Rinker, *Warman's Paper,* Wallace–Homestead, 1993; Jerry Osborne, Perry Cox, and Joe Lindsay, *The Official Price Guide To Memorabilia of Elvis Presley and The Beatles,* House of Collectibles, 1988; Richard Peters, *Elvis, The Golden Anniversary Tribute,* Salem House, 1984.

**Museums:** Jimmy Velvet's Elvis Presley Museum, Franklin, TN; Graceland, Memphis, TN.

Belt, metal, gold colored, intricate mesh, two eagle head fasteners, "Russian Double Eagle" ............... **48.50**
Booklet
  Dial E!–I Love You, 1962 ......... **15.00**
  Elvis Presley–Man or Mouse, Chaw Mank, privately printed, 1960 ... **15.00**
  Elvis, Yesterday, Today & Always, Triton Press, 1980 ................ **5.00**
Calendar Card, pocket, Elvis photo, 1963 .......................... **8.00**
Christmas Card, You Took, The World Wide Elvis Presley Fan Club, 1958 . **20.00**
Concert Ticket, Asheville, NC, May 30, 1977, unused .................... **30.00**
Dog Tag, silver link chain, tag inscribed "Presley, Elvis,/53310761/Type O," engraved portrait and signature, orig display card, 1956 Elvis Presley Enterprises copyright ................ **50.00**
Drink Mixer, figural, guitar, 1950s .... **20.00**
Hat, paper, army style, GI Blues, 1960 **35.00**
Jewelry
  Charm Bracelet, 1956 ............ **50.00**
  Necklace, chain, heart, dated 1956 . **45.00**
Lobby Card
  *Fun In Acapulco,* 14 x 22" ......... **35.00**
  *Jailhouse Rock,* fight scene, 1957 ... **60.00**
Magazine
  *Country Music Record Time,* 1977–78 ........................... **10.00**
  *Elvis Monthly,* April, 1961 ......... **12.00**
  *Fan's Star Library Magazine,* Elvis in Army cov, 1959 ................ **15.00**
  *Photoplay,* November, 1974 ....... **5.00**
Music Box, Love Me Tender, limited edition ......................... **30.00**
Pennant, 29" l, felt, blue, yellow design and lettering, black and white photo, white "Love, Elvis" signature, c1960 **40.00**
Pinback Button
  I Like Elvis, 1¾" d, red and white, c1956 ....................... **12.00**
  Always Elvis and VIP, 2½" d, Sept 10, 1978 fan reunion, red inscriptions, black and white photo .......... **12.00**
  Memorial, 3½" d, four black and white photos, red and white inscriptions top, bottom purple and white, 1977 .................. **5.00**
Photo Card, moss color, Elvis in green jacket, late 1950s ................ **10.00**
Post Card, 3½ x 5½", Easter Greetings, Elvis wearing gray tux, red ground, unused ........................ **35.00**

**Post Card, color photo, brown border, 1987 Elvis Presley Ent. Inc., 4 x 6", $8.00.**

Poster
  *Easy Come, Easy Go,* store, 1967 ... **40.00**
  Elvis Presley–Las Vegas, 1976, GAMMA, orig tube and wrapper . **15.00**
  Give Elvis for Christmas, store, RCA, 1959 ......................... **40.00**
Purse, clutch, 1956 ................ **35.00**
Record
  Double Trouble, monogram, long play, photo included, RCA ...... **25.00**
  Elvis Is Back, long play, black label, RCA Victor .................... **100.00**

Heartbreak Hotel, extra play, RCA Victor ........................ **20.00**
Scarf, 8 x 38", pale blue, stitched border, printed "Sincerely Elvis Presley" signature, orig tag "100% Polyester/ Made In USA" .................. **75.00**
Sheet Music
*How Do You Think I Feel?*, 4 pgs, purple photo, 1954 copyright .... **25.00**
*Treat Me Nice*, 1957 ............ **10.00**
Wallet, vinyl, tan, blue, pink, white, and flesh tone illus front cov, blue and gold stars, back 1956 Elvis Presley Enterprises copyright ................ **150.00**

# PSYCHEDELIC COLLECTIBLES

**Collecting Hints:** Look for psychedelic material in a wide range of areas, e.g., books, magazines, and newspapers, clothing, jewelry, home decorations, music and music festivals, and television. Include as many three dimensional items as possible.

When displaying your collection, keep it concentrated in one location. The psychedelic era emphasized a wild intermingling of color and design.

An excellent collection can be built focusing solely on pieces associated with the social protest movement. Collect over a wide range. A collection of just anti-war material is too limited.

**History:** Psychedelic collectibles are defined by period, 1960s and 1970s, and by the highly innovative use of colors and design. The roots of psychedelic art and color are many, e.g., late nineteenth century graphics, paisley fabrics, quilts and coverlets, the color reversal techniques of Joseph Alberts, American Indian art, and dancer Loie Fuller's diaphanous material which produced a light show as she moved and swirled.

It was a period without limits on design. As a result, the period was marked by eclecticism, rather than unity. Among its features was the incorporation of new technological advances, e.g., vinyl, polyester, metallic fabrics, non–woven fabric (paper), into its products. Inflatable plastic furniture was made. Everywhere the look was "far out" and informal.

Peter Max was the leading designer of the period. Few items in the late 1960s escaped his art. Although mass produced, many items fall into the scarce category.

**References:** Paul D. Grushkin, *The Art of Rock: Posters from Presley to Punk*, Abbeville Press, 1987; Alison Fox, *Rock & Pop—Phillips Collector's Guide*, Dunestyle Publishing/Boxtree, 1988; Joel Lobenthal, *Radical Rags: Fashions of the Sixties*, Abbeville Press, 1990.

Ashtray, 10" d, pottery, Peter Max design, white, brown, black, orange pink, blue, and green, Iroquois China, Syracuse, NY .............. **50.00**
Belt, cloth, leather fringed ends, green, light green, orange, and gold design, c1968 ......................... **10.00**
Book
Cummings, G Walker, ed, *The Great Poster Trip–Eureka*, Coyne & Blanchard, 1968 .................. **20.00**
Farren, Mick, ed, *Get On Down*, Futura Publications and Dempsey & Squires, Great Britain, 1977 ..... **30.00**
Johannsen, Brad, *High Tide*, Harmony Books, Crown Publishers, 1972 ......................... **25.00**
Book Cover, Peter Max design, paper, multicolored design, orange background, 21 x 14", unused, 1969–70 **20.00**
Clothing
Dress, Flower Fantasy, paper, pink, yellow, green, and white, Hallmark, Kansas City, MO, c1969 ... **18.00**
Jacket, Granny Takes A Trip, black, pink and green sequins, c1970 ... **50.00**
Lounging Outfit, bold black and white floral design, c1968 ............ **30.00**
Mini Dress, cotton, blue, orange, pink, yellow, and green print, 1969–70 ..................... **35.00**
Shirt, dacron polyester and cotton, brown and white design, Majesty label, c1970 .................. **25.00**
Comic Book, The Forty Year Old Hippie, No 2, 1979, The Rip Off Press, Inc ............................ **5.00**
Concert Poster
Junior Wells/Sons of Champlin/Santana Blues Band, Bill Henry, artist, May 17–19, 1968, blue, pink, gold, brown, and white design, 13⅞ x 19⅞" .................. **35.00**
Miller Blues Band/Doors/Daily Flash, Victor Moscosco, artist, June 1–4, 1967, blue, pink, and green, 13⅞ x 19$^{15}/_{16}$" ..................... **50.00**
Moby Grape/The Charlatans, Victor Moscosco, artist, February 24–25, 1967, orange, blue, and bright pink, 14 x 20" ................. **40.00**
The Doors/Jim Kweskin Jug Band, Bonnie MacLean, artist, June 9–10, 1967, ocher, pink, and black, 14 x 23" .......................... **85.00**
Curtain Section, 60" l, plastic, beaded, red, white, and blue, c1969 ....... **40.00**
Greeting Card, 8 x 14½", Laughfin, 1969 .......................... **15.00**
Headband, cloth, elastic band, blue and white, peace signs and birds, c1970 **10.00**

Jewelry
Choker
Cloth, white, green, black, and yellow, metal peace charm ....... **8.00**
Metal, gold, continuous peace signs, 15½" l ................ **18.00**
Slave Bracelet, gold colored metal, amber glass stones, 1968–69 .... **25.00**
Lava Lamp, 15" h, red, ............. **50.00**
Magazine
*Avant Garde,* 1960s .............. **18.00**
*Freak Out USA,* February, 1967 .... **15.00**
Movie Poster
*Hair,* 10¾" l, Tarot Productions, Inc, Los Angeles, CA, multicolored, 1969 ......................... **35.00**
*The Trip,* 40 x 60", black, white, and yellow, American International Pictures, 1967 .................... **150.00**
Necktie
Emilio Pucci, bold brown, gray, and black design, 1968–70 .......... **25.00**
Peter Max, orange, yellow, and blue design ........................ **50.00**
Pillow, 16½ x 19", needlepoint, Peter Max design, black, orange, blue, red, white, purple, green, and yellow butterfly design, c1972 ............. **65.00**
Newspaper, *San Francisco Oracle* .... **40.00**
Pinback Button, 2½" d, Woodstock, blue, white, and orange, 1969 ..... **25.00**
Plate, 9⅜" d, glass, Peter Max design, white, blue, red, yellow, pink, and black, Houze Glass Co, c1967 ..... **45.00**
Poster
Black Light, El Condor, Star City Distributing Inc, Los Angeles, CA, black, white, blue, purple, pink, and orange, 40 x 26", 1970 ..... **35.00**
George Harrison, *Look* magazine, Richard Avedon, artist, green, orange, and white, 22⅜ x 31", 1967 **75.00**

**Poster, Allman Brothers, green, reprint, $20.00.**

Psychedelic Shop–Jook Savage Art Show, Rick Griffin, artist, white and black, 14 x 20" ................ **100.00**
Top Cat, Peter Max Poster Corp, New York, No 19, black and white with blue, green, yellow, and pink flourescent, 24 x 36", 1967 ......... **250.00**
Purse, vinyl, bold black and white design, c1969 ..................... **30.00**
Side Table, 16¼" h, fiberboard, black, purple, light blue, and dark blue silkscreen print, Joyce Miller, Manufactured by William Products, York, PA, 1967 .......................... **150.00**
Switchplate Cover, cardboard, black, white peace sign ................. **15.00**
Toy, Yellow Submarine, orig box, Corgi, 1968 .......................... **325.00**
Umbrella, 26½" h, vinyl, Peter Max design, yellow, purple, green, gray, black, and white, Made In USA, 1968–69 ........................ **350.00**
Watch Band, Vari–view plastic, multicolored design, c1969 ........ **12.00**
Window Curtain, pr, each panel 25 x 42", Peter Max design, orange, blue, yellow, white, green, and pink design, c1971 .................... **85.00**

# PUNCHBOARDS

**Collecting Hints:** Punchboards which are unpunched are collectible. A punched board has little value unless it is an extremely rare design. Like most advertising items, price is determined by graphics and subject matter.

The majority of punchboards sell in the $8.00 to $30.00 range. The high end of the range is represented by boards such as Golden Gate Bridge at $85.00 and Baseball Classic at $100.00.

**History:** Punchboards are self–contained games of chance made of pressed paper containing holes with coded tickets inside each hole. For an agreed amount the player uses a "punch" to extract the ticket of his or her choice. Prizes are awarded to the winning ticket. Punch prices can be 1¢, 2¢, 3¢, 5¢, 10¢, 20¢, 50¢, $1.00 or more.

Not all tickets were numbered. Fruit symbols were used extensively as well as animals. Some punchboards had no printing at all, just colored tickets. Other ticket themes included dice, cards, dominoes, words, etc. One early board had Mack Sennet bathing beauties.

Punchboards come in an endless variety of styles. Names reflected the themes of the boards. Barrel of Winners, Break the Bank, Baseball, More Smokes, Lucky Lulu and Take It Off were just a few.

At first punchboards were used to award cash. As legal attempts to outlaw gambling arose, prizes were switched to candy, cigars, cigarettes, jewelry, radios, clocks, cameras, sporting goods, toys, beer, chocolate, etc.

The golden age of punchboards was the 1920s to the 1950s. Attention was focused on the keyed punchboard in the film *The Flim Flam Man.* This negative publicity hurt the punchboard industry.

**Reference:** Norman E. Martinus and Harry L. Rinker, *Warman's Paper,* Wallace–Homestead, 1993.

**Museum:** Amusement Sales, 127 North Main, Midvale, UT 84047.

**Advisor:** Clark Phelps.

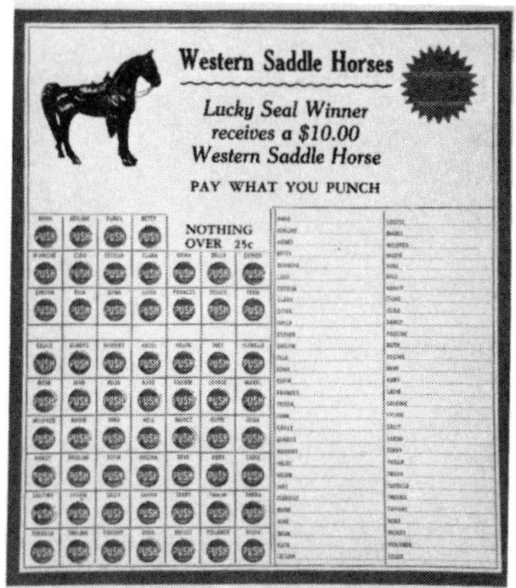


**Western Saddle Horses, 25¢ maximum punch, 6½ × 7¼", $8.00**

| | |
|---|---|
| Bag O Dough, 10 x 11" | 45.00 |
| Baseball Classic, 10 x 11" | 55.00 |
| Beat The Ten, 5 x 4" | 20.00 |
| Bell Pots, slot symbols, $1.00 punch | 30.00 |
| Big Bills, 25¢ punch | 18.00 |
| Big Game, fruit symbols | 16.00 |
| Block Buster, double jackpot, cash payout, 5¢ per punch | 18.00 |
| Canasta, 5¢ punch, removable score card | 50.00 |
| Charlie Ten Spots | 14.00 |
| Cross Country Winner, seals, cash pay | 20.00 |
| Delicious Cherries | 10.00 |
| Dime Joe, cash pay, 10¢ punch | 15.00 |
| E Z Jack, 5 x 11" | 30.00 |
| Full Of Tens, 25¢ punch, cash pay | 15.00 |
| Good As Gold, colorful, seals | 20.00 |
| High Bidder, 9 x 13" | 55.00 |
| Hi Yo Silver, 25¢ punch, cash pay with jackpot | 15.00 |
| Joe's Special Prize, 25¢ punch, cash board | 18.00 |
| Junior Kitty, kitten picture, cash pay | 30.00 |
| National Pastime, 4 x 5" | 50.00 |
| National Winner | 20.00 |
| Nickel Fins, 1,000 holes with seals | 15.00 |
| Pass–Hit & Crap, dice tickets, 50¢ punch | 40.00 |
| Pick A Cherry, cherry seals, cash pay | 20.00 |
| Planters Peanuts, 5¢ punch, peanut logo | 30.00 |
| Prize Pots, red head girl, 50¢ punch | 65.00 |
| Small Change, 9 x 11" | 35.00 |
| Sports Push Cards, baseball, football, basketball | 5.00 |
| Take It Easy, colorful, nude | 50.00 |
| Ten Big Sawbucks, 20¢ cash board | 20.00 |
| Worth Going For, 50¢ punch, girlie board | 20.00 |
| Yankee Trader | 20.00 |
| Your Pick, 10¢ punch, money seals | 30.00 |
| Yukon Gold, 9 x 12" | 40.00 |

# PURINTON POTTERY

**Collecting Hints:** The most popular patterns among collectors are Apple, Intaglio (brown), Normandy Plaid (red), Maywood, and Pennsylvania Dutch. Variations, e.g., a green ground Intaglio, are known for many of these patterns.

Purinton also made a number of kitchenware and specialty pieces. These should not be overlooked. Among the harder to find items are animal figurines, tea tiles, and a Tom and Jerry bowl and mug set.

**History:** Bernard Purinton founded Purinton Pottery in 1936 in Wellsville, Ohio. This pilot plant produced decorative dinnerware as well as some special order pieces. In 1940 Roy Underwood, president of Knox Glass Company, approached Purinton about moving his operation to Knox's community, Shippenville.

In 1941 the pottery relocated to a newly built plant in Shippenville, Pennsylvania. The company's first product at the new plant, a two cup premium teapot for McCormick Tea Company, rolled off the line on December 7, 1941.

Dorothy Purinton and William H. Blair, her brother, were the chief designers for the company. Maywood, Plaid, and several Pennsylvania German designs were among the patterns attributed to Dorothy Purinton. William Blair, a graduate of the Cleveland School of Art, designed the Apple and Intaglio patterns.

Initially slipware was cast. Later it was pressed using a Ram Press process. Clays came from Florida, Kentucky, North Carolina, and Tennessee.

Purinton Pottery did not use decals as did many of its competitors. Greenware was hand painted by locally trained decorators who then dipped the decorated pieces into glaze. This demanded a specially formulated body and a more expensive manufacturing process. Hand painting also allowed for some of the variations in technique and colors found on Purinton ware today.

Purinton made a complete dinnerware line for each pattern plus a host of accessory pieces ranging from candleholders to vases. Dinnerware patterns were open stock. Purinton's ware received national distribution. Select lines were exported.

The plant ceased operations in 1958, reopened briefly, and finally closed for good in 1959. Cheap foreign imports was cited as the cause of the company's decline.

**References:** Pat Dole, *Purinton Pottery,* published by author, 1984; Pat Dole, *Purinton Pottery: Book II,* Denton Publishing, 1990; Harvey Duke, *The Official Identification and Price Guide to Pottery and Porcelain, Seventh Edition*, House of Collectibles, 1989; Lois Lehner, *Lehner's Encyclopedia of U. S. Marks on Pottery, Porcelain & Clay,* Collector Books, 1988.

### APPLE

Canister Set, cov, four, sugar, coffee, and tea . . . . . . **90.00**
Casserole, cov, oval . . . . . . **24.00**
Coffeepot, cov . . . . . . **25.00**
Cookie Jar . . . . . . **38.00**
Creamer
  Double Spout, 1½" h . . . . . . **10.00**
  High Lip . . . . . . **9.00**
Cup and Saucer . . . . . . **12.00**
Drip Jar, cov . . . . . . **20.00**
Kent Jug, pt . . . . . . **15.00**
Plate
  8" d, salad . . . . . . **9.00**
  9" d, luncheon . . . . . . **14.00**
  12" d, grill . . . . . . **20.00**
Salt and Pepper Shakers, pr
  Range . . . . . . **25.00**
  Small, jug . . . . . . **15.00**
Sugar, cov . . . . . . **12.00**
Vegetable Bowl, oval . . . . . . **20.00**

### FRUIT

Creamer and Sugar, cov . . . . . . **15.00**
Pitcher, large . . . . . . **30.00**

**Apple, plate, 6⅞" w, $5.00.**

Plate, dinner, 9¾" d . . . . . . **12.00**
Relish dish, three part, handled . . . . . . **15.00**

### MAYWOOD

Kent Jug, 1 pt . . . . . . **20.00**
Marmalade, cov . . . . . . **30.00**
Pitcher, 2 pt . . . . . . **28.00**
Platter, oblong, 12" l . . . . . . **30.00**
Teapot, cov, 6 cup . . . . . . **32.00**
Vegetable, cov, oval, handled, 9" l . . . **45.00**

### PENNSYLVANIA DUTCH

Canister Set, cov, flour, coffee, sugar, tea . . . . . . **175.00**
Cereal Bowl . . . . . . **12.00**
Cookie Jar, cov . . . . . . **50.00**
Creamer and Sugar, cov . . . . . . **36.00**
Vinegar and Oil Jugs, pr . . . . . . **45.00**

### PLAID

Coffee Mug, 8 oz . . . . . . **15.00**
Dutch Jug, 2 pt . . . . . . **12.00**
Grease Jar, cov . . . . . . **20.00**
Plate, dinner, 9¾" d . . . . . . **12.00**
Roll Tray, oblong, 11" l . . . . . . **15.00**
Salt and Pepper Shakers, pr, jug . . . . . . **6.00**

# PUZZLES

**Collecting Hints:** Choose a rationale for collecting based on your interests. Some collectors choose puzzles for their visual appeal, some for the challenge of putting them together, and others for the patterns used in cutting the puzzles. Some collectors specialize according to subject matter, e.g., advertising, maps, transportation, or comic characters. Puzzles are easiest to find in the east, where historically they were most popular.

Puzzles are often difficult to date. Collectors should be aware that some puzzles, such as Milton Bradley's Smashed Up Locomotive, were produced for decades. The most popular prints were kept in inventory or reproduced as need arose, often by several different manufacturers. Thus, the date when a puzzle was made is often years later than the date or copyright on the print or box.

Collectors should avoid puzzles whose manufacturer can not be determined, unless the puzzle has specially attractive graphics or craftmanship.

Assembled puzzles can be displayed in frames, but should *never* be glued together. Exposure to light over long periods of time will cause fading. Dax or other plastic box frames are ideal for displays which can be changed periodically.

The market for puzzles is increasing because collectors of toys and character items usually want one or more puzzles in their collections too. Prices have especially soared for character puzzles and top quality nineteenth century children's puzzles.

The number of collectors is growing, so that prices have risen about 50 percent in the last five years. Puzzle collecting is most established in England. Prices for European children's puzzles were well defined in 1984 when Sotheby's auctioned the dazzling Hannas collection in London.

**History:** John Spilsbury, a London mapmaker, made the first jigsaw puzzles in the 1760s. Spilsbury "dissected" maps and sold them as educational toys. By 1850 children's jigsaw puzzles on all subjects were being made in the United States. Prominent manufacturers of the late nineteenth century include McLoughlin Brothers, Milton Bradley, and Selchow and Righter. Although the prints on very early puzzles were hand colored, color lithography was almost universal by 1870.

The early puzzles were made from solid wood or thick cardboard, with individual pieces "hand cut" one at a time with saws. Nineteenth century puzzles had few interlocking pieces, usually only on the edges. The widespread use of plywood and better saws after World War I led to more complex puzzle designs with all the pieces interlocking. Thinner cardboard puzzles, with all the pieces stamped out at once by steel dies, were introduced around 1890. Gradually these die–cut puzzles supplanted the hand–cut puzzles.

Puzzles for adults, more than 75 pieces, are a product of the twentieth century. Their introduction in 1908 unleashed a craze lasting several years. Puzzles were even more popular in the depression years of 1932–35 when many unemployed people had time to both cut up puzzles and put them back together. This period saw the emergence of many small–scale craftspeople who cut puzzles for local markets.

Some makers, such as Par (1932–1974), specialized in high quality custom designed wood puzzles for celebrities. Few makers of the more expensive hand–cut puzzles survived after World War II. Today there are only a handful of craftspeople still cutting puzzles in the United States. Among the post World War II die–cut puzzles, Springbok, now owned by Hallmark, is the premier domestic manufacturer.

**References:** Linda Hannas, *The English Jigsaw Puzzle*, 1760–1890, Wayland, 1972, out–of–print; Linda Hannas, *The Jigsaw Book*, Dial Press, 1981; Dana Gehman Morykan and Harry L. Rinker, *Warman's Country Antiques & Collectibles*, Wallace–Homestead, 1992; Norman E. Martinus and Harry L. Rinker, *Warman's Paper*, Wallace–Homestead, 1993; Harry L. Rinker, *Collector's Guide To Toys, Games, and Puzzles*, Wallace–Homestead, 1991; Francene and Louis Sabin, *The One, The Only, The Original Jigsaw Puzzle Book*, Henry Regnery Co., Chicago, 1977, out–of– print; Anne D. Williams, *Jigsaw Puzzles: An Illustrated History and Price Guide*, Wallace–Homestead Book Company, 1990.

**Collectors' Club:** American Game Collectors Association, 49 Brooks Ave., Lewiston, ME 04240.

**Museums:** Most toy and game museums include some jigsaw puzzles in their collections. The Dairy Barn (P. O. Box 747, Athens, OH 45701) mounts an exhibit of antique and collectible puzzles when it hosts the National Jigsaw Puzzle Championships which is held every other year.

**Advisor:** Harry L. Rinker.

**Price Notes:** Prices quoted refer to puzzles in very good condition, with the original box, and with *no* missing pieces. If pieces are missing, prices are generally 25 to 50 percent lower, although a very rare puzzle may still be well worth collecting even with missing pieces. A missing box should subtract about 25 percent from the price.

The only way to be sure of condition is to see the puzzle assembled. Unassembled puzzles should be priced cheaper, since graphics, condition and completeness can not be easily determined.

Twentieth century die–cut cardboard puzzles are quite inexpensive, usually in the 50¢ to $4.00 range. These puzzles are usually nondescript, e.g., autumn woods, storms at sea, etc.

Handcut wooden puzzles for adults are more costly, generally $5.00 to $65.00. Price depends on subject matter, number of pieces, and quality of cut. Nineteenth century children's puzzles command the highest prices, often $50.00 to $500.00. They are still less expensive than many contemporary children's games of the same period.

**Note:** Dimensions listed give width first, then height.

## CHILDREN/JUVENILE PUZZLES

### Pre–1915

Mrs. Alice J. Chamberlain, Temple of Knowledge, wood, 86 hand cut pcs, 11½ x 18¼", double–sided puzzle, temple on obverse, map of Palestine on reverse, c1890, 7½ x 9½" wood and cardboard box ............... **85.00**

George H. Chinnock, New York, Centennial Exhibition Puzzle Blocks, wood, set of five hand cut puzzles,

**Picture Puzzle, Steamship, McLoughlin Brothers, multicolor litho, wood box, 1896, 19¼ x 7¾", $325.00**

each puzzle approx 30 pcs, each puzzle 20¾" w, height varies from 4 to 6", four guide pictures, fifth on lid, buildings shown are Art Gallery, Machinery Hall, Horticultural Hall, Agricultural Hall, and Main Building, 1875, 22 x 11½" wood box ....... 500.00

Davis, Porter & Co., Philadelphia, Little Folks New Dissected Pictures, paper on wood, 17 hand colored and hand cut pieces, 11 x 17", double sided, "Pennsylvania Rail Road" on obverse, city scenes on reverse, 1865, 6¼ x 8" wood box ............... 600.00

Wallie Dorr, The B.B.B.B. Puzzle, 30 hand cut wooden blocks in frame tray, 17¾ x 5¾", Brooklyn Bridge and East River with a variety of boats, copyright 1889, 18 x 6" box ........... 1,650.00

McLoughlin Brothers

Old Woman & Pig Picture Puzzle, composition board, 20 x 12", pig, chased by group of character figures, jumps over fence, woman stands by fence with arms raised, copyright 1890, 9 x 13" box ..... 225.00

St. Nicholas Picture Puzzle, composition board, 19 x 12", Santa in sleigh pulled by reindeer racing through night sky over Victorian rural homestead, part of Young America Series, copyright 1890, 12 x 8" box .......................... 550.00

Peter G. Thomson, Cincinnati, OH, The Cut Up Punch & Judy Puzzle, sliced stiff board, 44 pcs, 12¼ x 16", guide picture, c1880s, 6½ x 5½" cardboard box ........................... 300.00

## 1915–1945

Consolidated Paper Box Co., Somerville, MA

Children's Puzzles, No. 200, two puzzle set ("Cleanliness" and "Kiddie Orchestra"), diecut cardboard, approx 50 pc per puzzle, each puzzle 10¾ x 8¾", c1930s, cardboard box with guide picture for "Kiddie Orchestra" .................... 15.00

2 Perfect Jig Saw Type Interlocking Children's Puzzles, two puzzle set, No. 41, "No. 5 THE SWING/SKATING," diecut cardboard, 50 pcs each puzzle, 7¼ x 9¼", early 1940s, box has United States Savings Bonds and Stamps stamp, cardboard box ................. 10.00

Harter Publishing Co., Cleveland, OH, H–110 Cinderella Puzzles, four puzzle set, diecut cardboard, 40 pcs each puzzle, 7½ x 9½", Fern Bisel Peat illustrator, 1931, cardboard box with guide picture for one of puzzles .... 40.00

Madmar Quality Co., Utica, NY

Granny Goose Picture Puzzle, Series 318A, three puzzle set, diecut cardboard, 12 pcs each puzzle, 7⅞ x 9⅞", all puzzles have a fairy tale theme, Mary LaFetra Russell illustrator, 1930s, cardboard box ..... 40.00

Princess Cut–Out Picture Puzzle, Series No. 420, double sided, saw cut 5–ply cardboard, "The Royal Outlaw" (tiger, R. Atkinson Fox illus.)/ untitled (three children walking down staircase in Victorian mansion, St. Bernard at bottom of steps), 36 pcs, 6⅝ x 8⅝", c1903s, cardboard box, guide picture of tiger on box lid ................. 25.00

**Little People's Picture Puzzle, Parker Bros., two puzzles, multicolor litho, sgd Alice Hirschberg, c1915, 12¾ x 9", $50.00.**

Louis Marx & Co., Double Set Jigsaw Puzzle, double sided, "Cottage of Dreams/Moon Mullins," wood, 145 pcs [box reads 150 pcs], 9½ x 6¾", cardboard box ................... 75.00

Parker Brothers

Fairy Land Picture Puzzle, No. 0756, untitled (young girl on footstool, mouse on bonnet of tall case clock), 35 pcs, 6 x 8", M. L. Kirk illustrator, c1910s, cardboard box with guide picture on lid ........ 30.00

Famous Art Picture Puzzles, two puzzle set, saw cut cardboard, both pictures untitled (Arabic horsemen in desert; group of Dutch children returning from harbor), 15 pcs each puzzle, 12½ x 8⅝", c1910s, box lid features picture of Doge's Palace in Venice .................... **20.00**

Saalfield Publishing Co., Akron, OH, No. 909, Bringing Up Father Picture Puzzles, four puzzle set, diecut cardboard, various die cut variations, 9½ x 7½", 1933, cardboard box with guide picture for Jigg's fall after stepping on banana .................. **50.00**

Wylder, St. Louis, MO, Combination Ocean Liner and World Map Puzzles, saw cut composition, 28 pcs, 12¼ x 9", double sided, *Berengaria* entering New York Harbor on obverse, map of work on obverse, c1930s, cardboard box with guide picture on lid ...... **30.00**

## Post–1945

American Publishing Corp.

No. 1242, Six Million Dollar Man, diecut cardboard, 204 pcs, 17¼ x 11", fight involving radio active material, 1975, 4⅛" d, 5½" h plastic/metal can .................... **8.00**

No. 1509, Suzanne Somers as Chrissy in Three's Company Jigsaw Puzzle, diecut cardboard, 204 pcs, 11¹⁄₁₆ x 17¼", swimsuit pose, late 1970s, cardboard box with guide picture **15.00**

Milton Bradley, No. 4501–5, Captain Kangaroo Puzzles, four puzzle set, diecut cardboard, 20 pcs each puzzle, approx 6½ x 10", cardboard box with guide picture for portion of two puzzles ........................ **20.00**

Built–Rite, Junior Picture Puzzle, Famous TV Stars, No. 1229, Set 101, Robin Hood, 100 pcs, 13⅝ x 10¾", Robin Hood's Merry Men, same picture used on Sta–N–Place frame tray, cardboard box with guide picture .. **17.50**

E. E. Fairchild Corp., Weird–Ohs Picture Puzzle, Freddy Flameout: The Way Out Jet Jockey, diecut cardboard, 108 pcs, approx 15 x 10½", Freddy in Jet, 1963, cardboard box with guide picture .................... **25.00**

Golden, trademark of Western Pub. Co., No. 4605–46, Masters of the Universe Jigsaw Puzzle, diecut cardboard, 100 pcs, approx 11½ x 15", fighting water monster, cardboard box **2.00**

H–G Toys, Long Beach, NY

Evil Knievel, Ring of Fire, No. 475–04, diecut cardboard, 150 pcs, 10 x 14", Knievel on Harley Davidson flys through fire ring, 1974, 3⅝" d, 6⅜" h cardboard/metal/plastic tube can, mkd "harcord/Jersey City, NJ" **12.50**

Laverne and Shirley, No. 425–01, diecut cardboard, 150 pcs, 10 x 14", four scenes, two of Laverne and Shirley at playground, cardboard box with guide picture .... **10.00**

Showgun Warriers, No. 455–04, "Great Mazinga," diecut cardboard, 150 pcs, 10 x 14", late 1970s, cardboard box with guide picture ........................ **3.00**

Jaymar Specialty Co., New York, NY

Beetle Bailey Picture Puzzle, "Potato Artist," diecut cardboard, 63 pcs, 13¹⁵⁄₁₆ x 9¾", cardboard box with guide picture .................. **5.00**

Playland Child's Picture Puzzle, Series No. 1, Organ Grinder, diecut cardboard, 67 pcs, 1946, cardboard box with guide picture .... **4.00**

No. 8672, The Beverly Hillbillies, Jed, Elly May, and Granny, diecut cardboard, 63 pcs, approx 10 x 14", leaning on stair railing, mid–1960s, cardboard box with guide picture ........................ **20.00**

Walt Disney's Interlocking Jig Saw Puzzle, Three Little Pigs, diecut cardboard, over 300 pcs, approx 22 x 14", box border with blue ground and white polka dots, late 1940s, cardboard box with guide picture ........................ **20.00**

Kenner, No. 40100, Star Wars, Artoo–Detoo/See–Three Pio, diecut cardboard, 140 pcs, approx 14 x 18", 1977, cardboard box with guide picture ........................... **7.50**

M. T. Matthews Publishing Co., 3D Picture Puzzle, two puzzles (mother and young zebra in cage and railroad ride at amusement park), stereo glasses, frame tray format, each puzzle 30 pcs, 8½ x 11¾", cardboard box .... **25.00**

Saalfield Company, Happy Friends Picture Puzzles, No. 7352, three puzzle set, diecut cardboard, 44 pcs each puzzle, 8¾ x 10¼", Lajos Segner illus, 1949, cardboard box with guide picture for one of puzzles ......... **17.50**

B. Shackman, NY, No. 3713, Dimensional Donkey Puzzle, wood, 14 pcs, 4 x 3¼ x 1½", Shackman paper label on bottom of puzzle, made in Japan, c1950s, cardboard box with paper label ............................ **5.00**

Waddington, English, Captain Scarlett and the Mysterons, No. 929, Colonel White Briefing Captains Scarlet, Blue, and Grey, diecut cardboard, 251 pcs, 13 x 10½", cardboard box with guide picture .......................... **50.00**

Whitman

No. 4404, Series No. 303, Authorized Jr. Jigsaw Puzzle, Gunsmoke, diecut cardboard, 63 pcs, Matt leaning against wall loading gun, cardboard box with guide picture **20.00**

No. 4429, Series No. 302, Jig Saw Puzzle, untitled (events associated with life of President Theodore Roosevelt), diecut cardboard, 63 pcs, approx 15" x 11½", cardboard box with guide picture .......... **4.00**

No. 4610, Doc Savage Jigsaw Puzzle, diecut cardboard, 100 pieces, 14 x 18", Doc Savage with clinched fists, cardboard box with guide picture .......................... **5.00**

No. 4657–3, A Big Little Book Jigsaw Puzzle, Tom and Jerry, diecut cardboard, 99 pcs, approx 10 x 13", 1967, cardboard box with guide picture ........................ **12.50**

## Frame Trays

Milton Bradley, No. 4435–X3, The Official New York World's Fair 1964–1965, Greyhound at the Fair, 28 pcs, 14¼ x 10¼" .................... **20.00**

Built–Rite, Sta–N–Place, No. 18, Rusty Riley, fine hidden animals and clown in sketch, 24 pcs, 12½ x 8¾", copyright 1949 ...................... **15.00**

Great Lakes Press, Rochester, NY, Your Congressman Frank Horton 36th Congressional District of New York, 35 pcs, 11 x 14", portion of orig cellophane wrap remains .............. **15.00**

Jaymar

No. 2389–3, Bugs Bunny Inlaid Puzzle, Bugs dressed as Indian confronts Indian brave holding Porky and Petunia Pig hostage, 30 pcs, 12¾ x 9¾" .................... **15.00**

No. 2576, Walt Disney's Pinocchio, whale attacking raft, 35 pcs, 14 x 11" .......................... **17.50**

Walt Disney's 101 Dalmatians, admiring birth of pup, 30 pcs, 12¾ x 9¾" .......................... **10.00**

Saalfield Artcraft, Angela Cartwright, America's Little Darling on Nationwide TV, The Danny Thomas Show, 27 pcs, 10½ x 14", copyright 1962 . **30.00**

A. M. Walzer, Dover, NJ, No. 75, untitled, young baby drinks milk from bottle assisted by terrier, 34 pcs, 10⅞ x 14", Charlotte Becker illus ....... **12.50**

Whitman Publishing

No. 4424, Santa Claus seated among toys and sack reading from "Good Boys and Girls" book to reindeer, 26 pcs, 11¼ x 14½" ............ **15.00**

No. 4427, Rifleman, cartoon drawing by Al Andersen of Lucas and Mark hiding behind rocks, Indians on horseback approaching in distance, 18 pcs, 11⅜ x 14½", copyright 1960, portion of orig cellophane wrap remains .................. **20.00**

No. 4427, Roy Rogers Picture Puzzle, Roy prepares to mount Trigger, 25 pcs, 11⅜ x 14½" ............... **25.00**

# ADULT PUZZLES

## Hand Cut

**Note**: Pieces counts are approximate for many of the hand cut puzzles.

A–1 Puzzle Club, untitled (Impressionist landscape by August Renoir), woman strolling along tree shaded road, wood, 600 pcs, 24 x 20", c1910, box missing ........................ **75.00**

Milton Bradley

Attributed to, untitled (Gaston Roulle picture of large boats sailing on Grand Canal of Venice in blustery wind), wood 482 pcs of which 62 are figural, some color line cutting, 23 x 16", box missing ........... **50.00**

Premier Jigsaw Puzzle, Tyrolean Waters, alpine scene of castle, lake, and mountains, wood, 300 pcs, 15 x 11", 1937, orig box ........... **40.00**

Damon (attributed to), Lunch–time, Norman Price print of boy sharing his lunch with puppy, wood, 178 pcs of which 32 are figurals, some color line cutting, 11 x 16", pre–1930, orig box with red ribbon tie, hand label with name Damon who is presumed to be cutter .......................... **35.00**

Glencraft/Glendex, Sailing Off Block Island, yawl under full sail off Block Island Lighthouse, Y. E. Goderberg illus, wood, 512 pcs, 19 x 14", 1960s, orig box ........................ **40.00**

Hanks Puzzle Shop, Conway, NH, Over Field and Fence, hunt scene with horses and hounds in pursuit, wood, 519 pcs, 16 x 20", box missing .... **37.50**

Kilborne Jig Saw Puzzle, Trenton, NJ, The Mill Pond Has Gone to Sleep, Will Thompson print of lakeside cottage at sunset, 200 pcs of which 13 are figural, some color line cutting, 10 x 12", est working time of 2 hours and 45 minutes, orig box .......... **25.00**

Kingsbridge (Sweden)

The Arrival (A Hunting Morn), hunters pausing in Tudor town, L. Cox illus, wood, 400 pcs, 15 x 11", 1960s, orig box . . . . . . . . . . . . . . . . . . . . . **30.00**

The Harbour, fishing and sailboats at village dock, 197 pcs, many pieces cut nearly identical shapes, 11 x 9", 1960s, orig tubular container with guide picture . . . . . . . . . . . . . . . . . **20.00**

Little Gem Jig–Saw Puzzle, The Evening Devotion, bedside scene of mother with child saying prayers, dog obliging, wood, 270 pcs, 10 x 12", 1930s, orig box . . . . . . . . . . . . . . . . . . . . . . . **35.00**

Miller's Pharmacy, Cumberland Mills, ME, Bowl of Roses, colorful still life, wood, 231 pcs, 12 x 10", orig box . **22.50**

Bessie J. Nowell, Bangor, ME, untitled (One of Us), J. H. Shard picture of Native American chieftans and white man in ceremonial dress inside tent, composition board, 434 pcs, 23 x 19", cutters name stamped on back of puzzle, box missing . . . . . . . . . . . . . **30.00**

Parker Brothers

Jig–a–Jig Picture Puzzle, The Stag, F. F. English print of stag at sunset, wood, 82 pcs, 6 x 8", 1905, orig box . . . . . . . . . . . . . . . . . . . . . . . . **20.00**

Pastime Picture Puzzle

A Pioneer Christmas, families returning to homestead with Christmas tree, wood, 104 pcs, 7 x 5", 1932, orig box . . . . . . . . . . . . . . **25.00**

Cottage By The Road, autumn sunset scene of early American homestead, wood, 400 pcs of which 48 are figural, some color line cutting, 16 x 20", 1933, orig box . . . . . . . . . . . . . . . . . . . . . . **45.00**

The Introduction, musician being introduced to Elizabethan lady in baronial hall, 202 pcs of which 35 are figural, 13 x 10", 1940s, orig box . . . . . . . . . . . . . . . . . . **30.00**

Untitled, American west scene of fertile valley with background of sandstone buttes and snow capped mountains, wood, 523 pcs of which 60 are figural, color line cutting throughout, 23 x 16", box missing . . . . . . . . . . . . . . . . **50.00**

Winter Sunset, country cottage by steam, village in background, M. Thompson illus, wood, 122 pcs of which 11 are figural, 10 x 7", 1931, orig box . . . . . . . . . . . . . . **20.00**

Homer F. Pike, Washington's Headquarters at Valley Forge, 1915 print by English (mfr Ketterlinus Litho Mfg), 266 pcs, 11" sq, orig "Old Homestead" chocolate box on bottom of which is written "Homer F. Pike, Mfr." . . . . . . . . . . . . . . . . . . . . . . . . . **30.00**

Bernard S. Rose (Rental Library), Darkness Before Dawn: Emancipation Day, fireside scene of Abraham Lincoln and Mary Todd Lincoln, wood, 318 pcs, 15 x 11", c1930s, orig box **30.00**

Charles W. Russell, Auburn, MA, Sunset in Normandy, canal barge passing old farmstead, 347 pcs of which 37 are figural, some color line cutting, 16 x 12", c1920s, orig box . . . . . . . . . . . . **37.50**

Joseph K. Straus

Calm of Night, Frederick D. Ogden print of moonlit scene of log cabin and mountain lake, 300 pcs, 12 x 16", 1940s, orig box . . . . . . . . . . . **15.00**

Welcome Home, C. Moss & Co. 1941 print of father and child in sleigh bringing home Christmas tree, wood, 488 pcs, 21 x 16", 1940s, orig box . . . . . . . . . . . . . . . . . . . . . **20.00**

White Clipper, three masted square rigger under full sail, D. Sherring illus, wood, 282 pcs, 16 x 12", orig box . . . . . . . . . . . . . . . . . . . . . . . . . **17.50**

Ullman's Society Picture Puzzles, Down by the Mill, Thomas B. Craig pastoral print of sheep returning to farmstead at sunset, 385 pcs, 20 x 16", 1930s, orig box, lid has picture of lady doing puzzle . . . . . . . . . . . . . . . . . . . . . . . . **45.00**

Victory Artistic Wood Jigsaw Puzzle

The Lobster Pot, fishing boats beached in old world harbor, 200 pcs of which 12 are crudely cut figurals, 13 x 10", orig gold box . . **20.00**

The Unexpected Party, V. De Beauvoir Ward print of gentlemen on horseback and servants outside Tudor inn, 500 pcs of which 27 are figural, 19 x 15", 1940s, orig gold box . . . . . . . . . . . . . . . . . . . . . . . . . **45.00**

Unidentified Cutters (titles created by sellers)

A Melody of Old Egypt, Henry Clive print of 1930s style glamour girl in evening gown posed before the great pyramids at night, 694 pcs, color line cutting, 16 x 20", orig box with #41 on label . . . . . . . . . . **55.00**

A Mother's Love, Herst's Boston American Sunday Supplement, print of mother tending child in cradle, copyright 1901, wood, 160 pcs, 11 x 17", box but may not be orig . . . . . . . . . . . . . . . . . . . . . . . . **25.00**

A Serious Case, Norman Rockwell comical print of village doctor examining girl's doll, wood, 294 pcs, 9 x 12", c1930s, orig box missing **25.00**

Fox & Ducks, *Field and Stream* type picture of red fox stalking mallards, wood, 415 pcs, 17 x 35", late 1930s or early 1940s, box but probably not orig .................. **35.00**
General Electric Company, Walter L. Greene Art Deco era picture of GE plant/industrial park, wood, 252 pieces of which two are figurals, 10 x 14", plain box mkd "Old Rustic Bridge" that does not match ..... **25.00**
House for Sale, real estate type picture of modern Colonial house, composition board, 211 pcs, 18 x 15", 1940s, 1942 Christmas card box ........................ **15.00**
Keeping the Faith, British family watches WWII planes returning at sunset, composition board, 537 pcs, 22 x 16", box missing ...... **20.00**
Whistling in the Dark, *Saturday Evening Post* type picture of young boy and dog sneaking away at night, 125 pcs of which two are figurals and 5 reverse swastikas, 7 x 9", early 1940s, orig box .......... **15.00**

## Diecut, cardboard, Jigsaw Puzzle Craze, 1932–33

American News Company and Branches, Jig of Jigs, No. 1, Queen's Page, Maxfield Parrish illus, drawing from *The Knave of Hearts*, over 250 pcs, 9½ x 12" .................. **100.00**
Dell Publishing Co., New York, NY, Movie Mix–Up!, Clark Gable, black and white head and shoulders photograph, 8½ x 12", paper envelope . **75.00**
Einson–Freeman Co., Long Island City, NY
"Every Week" Jig–Saw Puzzle
No. 12, Peter Pan, Peter Pan sitting on rock outcropping holding flute and look at nest of young birds, 10½ x 14½", Eggleston illus ........................ **12.50**
No. 22, First Lesson, dog teaching four pups how to hunt peasant, 10½ x 14½", Lynn Bogue Hunt illus ....................... **14.00**
No. 27, The Cradle Maker, mother with baby looks over shoulder of young boy making cradle from carton scraps, 165 pcs, 10½ x 14¼", Walter Beach Humphrey illus ....................... **17.50**
Radio Stars, Series No. 2, Kate Smith "Jig–Saw" Puzzle: The Song Bird of the South!, face is central focus, insert images in upper and lower right corners, 228 pcs, 10⅛ x 14½" **35.00**

Gelco Interlocking Puzzle Company, Chicago, IL, Weekly Interlocking Jigsaw, No. 2, The Old Fort, approx 150 pcs, 11¾ x 8¾" ................. **12.50**
Jig 'A Word Manufacturing Co., St. Paul, MN, Jig 'A Word Series, No. 1–A, over 300 pcs, 12" sq, jigsaw puzzle and clues presented on box lid, puzzle provides solution to cross word puzzle ......................... **15.00**
Kindel–Graham, San Francisco, CA, The Jigger Picture Puzzle Weekly, Series 104 – Mission Dolores, over 300 pcs, box cov design similar to that used by Viking Manufacturing Co.'s Picture Puzzle Weekly ........... **15.00**
Midwest Distributors, Minneapolis, Screen Books Magazine, Tarzan of the Apes Jig–Saw, Johnny Weissmuller astride elephant, 10¾ x 8½", paper envelope ................. **135.00**
Movie Cut–Ups, Peabody, MA
No. 6, Air Hostess, featuring Evalyn Knapp, A Columbia Picture, 320 pcs, 10 x 13½" ............... **35.00**
No. 14, Secrets, Mary Pickford and Leslie Howard, A United Artists Picture, 304 pcs, 10 x 13¼", wrapped in label from Pippins Cigars reading "IT'S A PIPPINS JIG" **50.00**
Novelty Distributing Company, Newark, NJ, "Famous Comics" Jig Saw Type Puzzle, No. 2, The Gumps, back of box contains three portions of cartoon strip, puzzle completes panel, over 250 pcs, 13 x 11¾", mfd by Stephens Kindred & Co., New York ......... **40.00**
R–M Sales Corporation, New York, NY, Duo Jig Puzzle, two to the set, B–4 Morocco and B–5 Masquerade, 154 pcs each puzzle, 7¼ x 9¼", puzzles in set have different color backs .... **15.00**
Santway Photo–Craft Company, Inc., Watertown, NY, The Muddle, The New Jig Puzzle, Fine Art Series B–2, The Fishing Fleet, 300 pcs, 15 x 11" **10.00**
Geo. P. Schlicher & Son, Allentown, PA, The Essell Picture Puzzle, No. 5, Street Scene, over 200 pcs, 14 5/16 x 8⅞", J. E. Berninger illus .......... **12.50**
University Distributing Company, Cambridge, MA, Jig of the Week
No. 4, The Prairie Fire, portion of Currier and Ives print, 300 pcs, 13⅜ x 10⅛" .................. **15.00**
No. 17, Milday of the Tavern, two cavaliers sit at tavern table as serving girl approaches with bowl of fruit, 300 pcs, 13⅛ x 10" ....... **8.00**
No. 25, So Near, Yet So Far, newspaper boy hold papers in one hand and money in another as he looks

in window of pet shop at Terrier pup and window label reading "FOR SALE/$25.00," 300 pcs, 10⅛ x 13¼", Hy Hintermeister illus ... **12.50**

Unknown manufacturer, souvenir puzzle of 1933 inaugural, faces of Roosevelt and Garner flank capitol, "TOGETHER WE PROSPER," 9⅝ x 7⅞", orig cellophane envelope .......... **35.00**

J. H. Van Patten, Los Angeles, CA, California Better Picture Puzzle, No. 85, English Gardens .................. **10.00**

Viking Manufacturing Company, Boston, MA, Picture Puzzle Weekly
- B–1, Battle of Bunker Hill, print of Trumbell painting, 13¾ x 10" .... **10.00**
- C–5, Static, dog howls as two hunters in cabin play radio, 10 x 13¾" ... **14.00**
- E–1, A Party At Murano, group embarking from Venetian gondola onto terrace where party is in progress, 14½ x 10½" ............. **20.00**

## Diecut, cardboard, post–1933

Milton Bradley, No. 4934, Mayfair Jig Picture Puzzle, Moonbeam's Princess, pin–up style picture of Indian Princess in moonlight, over 200 pcs, orig box ....................... **10.00**

Consolidated Paper Box Company
- Big 10, No. 10, Statue of Liberty, 280 pcs, 15⅛ x 10⅛", box with light blue and white checkerboard ground ....................... **7.50**
- Perfect Picture Puzzle
  - No. 16, Progress, amphibious plane flies over three masted sailing ship, 280 pcs, 10¼ x 15½", orig box .................. **10.00**
  - 1410, Port of Hope (Spanish Galleon), 266 pcs, 10⅜ x 13¾" ... **5.00**

Harter Publishing Co., Cleveland, OH, H–131 Series, over 200 pcs, approx 11 x 15"
- Series II, No. 5, Puppy Love, Annie Benson Muller illus ............. **4.00**
- Series II, No. 10, Red Demon of the Forest, Philip R. Goodwin illus ... **6.00**
- Series V, No. 3, Castle Rock ....... **2.50**

Knobby–Cut Picture Puzzle, The Limit of Wind and Sail, Spanish galleons on raging sea, 208 pcs, 11⅞ x 9¾", orig box ........................... **7.50**

Regent Specialties, Inc., Rochester, NY, DeLuxe Picture Puzzle, Shall We Go Sailing, 391 pcs, 19⅛ x 15½" ..... **7.50**

Tuco Manufacturing Corp.
- Religious Interlocking Picture Puzzle, Christ's Entrance Into Jerusalem, painting by Plockhorst, diecut cardboard, 300 to 500 pcs, approx 16 x 20", cardboard box with guide picture ........................ **4.00**
- Soap Opera Puzzles, No. 8857, General Hospital, Alan, Monica, and Susan, diecut cardboard, over 350 pcs, approx 15 x 11", head and shoulder portraits of stars, cardboard box with guide picture, unopened ....................... **4.00**

## ADVERTISING PUZZLES

American Bakers Association, "What Enriched Bread Does For Me," diecut cardboard, frame tray format, 10 pcs, 9⅛ x 5½", loaf of bread with each part containing formation about nutritional value, 1955 copyright, orig packaging missing ................ **6.00**

American Bank and Trust Co. of PA., BankAmericard, "Takes the puzzle out of your banking," diecut cardboard, 16 pcs, 4 x 5", symbols for bank and credit card superimposed over photograph of coins on wire mesh, orig packaging missing ...... **4.00**

Birds Eye, "Birds Eye Puts It All Together Jigsaw Puzzle," diecut cardboard, unopened, lid shows "Clarence Birdseye..the man who started an industry" standing in front of Birds Eye Frosted Foods freezer in old fashion country store, 9 x 6 x 2" box ...... **7.50**

Black Cat Hosiery Co., Kenosha, WI, diecut cardboard, 60 pcs, 5 x 7", shows young boy and girl stacking building blocks that spell Black Cat Hosiery, ca. 1908, paper envelope . **65.00**

Burlington Socks, "Guess whose show is selling Burlington Socks on T.V. this fall?," diecut cardboard, 21 pcs, 8 x 10⅜", black and white, shows pair of feet in Burlington socks, answer to question is Dean Martin, textile mailing sack with applied paper label ... **35.00**

Campfire or Angelus Marshmallows, "Spanish Galleon," No. 4 in series of 4, 48 pcs, 6⅝ x 9⅝", 1933, paper envelope ....................... **12.50**

Cocomalt, R. B. Davis Co., JS2, "The Flying Family," diecut cardboard, 65 pcs, 6½ x 9⅞", Col. Hutchinson and family superimposed on map of western part of U.S. showing route family traveled, [**NOTE**—in order for puzzle to be complete, it should be accompanied by a four page pamphlet about how to become a Flight Commander], 1933, paper envelope
- Puzzle and envelope ............ **15.00**
- Puzzle, pamphlet insert, and envelope .......................... **25.00**

**A Bully Time in Spain, Standard Oil Co. premium, two sided, 1933, $40.00.**

Essolube, "The Five Star Theatre Presents Foiled By Essolube: A Jig–Saw–Melodrama," 150 pcs, 17 x 11¼", features series of characters (Zero–Doccus; Karbo–Nockus; Moto–Muchus; Oilio–Gobelus; and, Moto–Raspus) in jungle setting, Dr. Seuss illustrator, 1933, paper envelope ... **80.00**

Fischer Baking Company, Fisher's Vitamin "D" Bread, No. 4 from series of 6, diecut cardboard, untitled—parade of children featuring young boy riding a St. Bernard in whose mouth is a basket with a loaf of Fischer's bread, 49 pcs, 9¼ x 7", 1933, paper envelope with guide picture on front and advertising and "How to Use This Puzzle" on back ................ **17.50**

Fritz Company, Lawrence, KS, "Home For The Yuletide," stock puzzle made by Thos. D. Murphy Co., Red Oak, IA, applied label for Fritz Company, a gasoline service station, 8⅛ x 6⅛ x¾" box ........................... **12.50**

Johnson Wax, Raid Picture Puzzle, diecut cardboard, 156 pcs, 11¾" sq, bugs interrupted in their feasting, illus by Don Pegler, 2⅞" d, 8" h cardboard/metal/plastic tube can ............. **20.00**

Kolynos Company, New Haven, CT, "Just Plain Bill," 150 pcs, 12 x 9", David, Bill, and Nancy in barbershop, 1933, paper envelope ....... **27.50**

Law. Lottier, "Chew Tobacco Puzzle," wood, 16 pcs, 10 x 10¼", Victorian parlor showing young male dressed in sailor's suit assembled example of puzzle, c1900–10, cardboard box with engraved sheet on lid, notation on lid reads "RICHMOND ENGRAVING CO," 10½ x 10⅜" lid ........ **250.00**

Maxwell, "BUILD A MAXWELL PIECE BY PIECE," diecut cardboard, 28 pcs, block format, 8 x 5", double sided, front shows family in car in oval with information in each of four corners, back features alphabet features for car, e.g., "A for ABLE That's Easy To See," envelope, 5½ x 3⅛", puzzle shows car for $595, back of envelope reads "New Prices Effective, January 1st, 1917: Roadster—$620; Touring Card—$635; F.O.B. Detroit" ...... **150.00**

Metropolitan Property and Liability Insurance Company, "MET WORKS," diecut cardboard, 36 pcs, 7" sq, features Peanuts gang (Linus, Lucy, Schroeder, and Snoopy) playing on top of children's block, 1988, orig shrink wrap .................... **15.00**

Psychodynamic Consultants, Inc., Clayton, MO, "WE HAVE MOVED FEB. 1ST. 1980 PARKWAY TOWER," diecut cardboard, 28 pcs, 10⅞ x 8½", map of Clayton, MO, showing office move from one location in the city to another, orig packaging missing .... **10.00**

Reynold Tobacco Company, Winston Puzzle, "Pajama Sunday," diecut cardboard, approx 20 x 12½", interlocking, 1972, 8 x 5 x 2¼" red cardboard mailing box ................ **10.00**

Scott & Bowne, "SCOTT'S EMULSION OF COD LIVER OIL," diecut cardboard, 60 pcs, 13¼ x 10⅝", shows the Scott fisherman standing in harbor at Balstad, Lofoten Islands, Norway, Site of Scott & Bowne's Cod Liver Oil Refinery, seven pieces spell out "SCOTT'S," 1933–35, orig packaging missing ......................... **75.00**

Trans World Airlines, "The airport waiting game and how to beat it," diecut cardboard, 35 pcs, 15¼ x 10¾", photograph of a game board with airplane, passengers, and TWA personnel, TWA personnel motif, 2⅞" d, 7½" h cardboard/metal tube can mkd "HARCORD/JERSEY CITY, NJ" ..... **20.00**

Wendy's International, "WHERE'S THE BEEF?", diecut cardboard, 9 pcs, 4 x 5½", features face of Clara Peller, 1984, orig packaging missing ...... **10.00**

WFSB, Eyewitness News, "We fit right into your day!/NEWS 5 o'clock/3," diecut cardboard, 15 pcs, 5 x 6¾", show white male and Black female news anchors, 2⅞" d, 2" h round can **7.50**

## MULTIPURPOSE PUZZLES

Book,Sam See, *Let's Play Together: The Second Eye–Cue Builder Book*, S. C. Platt, Series 200, 1945, four puzzle set, diecut frame tray format, games popular with children of many lands theme, 9½ x 11¾", plastic spiral bound ........................ **30.00**

Business Card/Puzzle, Monarch Coal, sold only by S. P. Morris, Baltic & Kentucky Aves., Atlantic City, NJ, diecut poster board, two deer in winter forest scene, duplicate picture top and bottom, top picture with business card information on back, bottom 14 pc punchout puzzle with frame remaining, 3½ x 3⅞" full size, at least three Monarch Coal examples, each with different scene, known ....... **10.00**

Game/Puzzle

Ideal Toy Corporation, No. 2017–2–100, Skooz–It Heckle and Jeckle Pick–A–Picture Game, pick pieces in an attempt to complete puzzles, 1963, 4¼" d, 8¼" h cardboard/metal tube container ............ **50.00**

Toddy, Two Game Puzzle (jigsaw puzzle that makes into a game board), "Calcutta Sweepstakes," No. 5 of 6 in Toddy Travel Series, diecut cardboard, 50 pcs, name "TODDY" spelled out in pcs, 13 x 9¾", spinner, punchout discs numbered 1 through 4 in corners, 1933, 10 x 13¼ x7⁄16" cardboard box ... **45.00**

Giveaway premiums, Squirrel Brand Co., Cambridge, MA, Squirrel Jig Puzzles, "ONE FREE with every Penny Purchase," cut out pieces from card and assemble into puzzle, four different cards (No. 1—Queer Fellow [clown face]; No. 2—Singing Sam from the Sunny South; No. 3—A Fine Old Ship; No. 4—Squirrel), individual card 3½ x 5⅜", c1930

Box of one hundred contains 25 of each view, 8⅛ x 6⅛ x 1" cardboard box

No. 2, Black theme .............. **5.00**

No. 1, 3, or 4 .................. **2.00**

Mystery, Pearl Publishing Company, Brooklyn, NY, Mystery Puzzle of the Month, No. 2, Case of the Duplicate Door, 208 pcs, 11½ x 13½", 16 page story booklet with solution to mystery **17.50**

Photograph on a puzzle, E. J. Curtis, Inc., Pittsfield, MA, JIG SAW PUZZLE ENLARGEMENT from your negative, wood, 7¾ x 9¾", 128 pcs, Mildred Carlson taken a Sulfield Academy in CT about 1931, 5⅜ x 6¾ x 1" cardboard box ....................... **25.00**

### JIGSAW PUZZLE EPHEMERA

Comic Book

*Jigsaw: Man of a Thousand Parts*, Vol. 1, No. 2, Dec 1966, Funday Funnies, Inc., Harvery Thriller, 12¢, fine cond ..................... **7.00**

*Ms. Tree, "Jigsaw,"*, No. 13, November 1984, Aardvark–Vanaheim, Inc., Max Collins and Terry Beatty artists, $1.70, jigsaw puzzle theme cover, excellent cond ........... **3.50**

Magazine, *Playboy*, Vol. 18, No. 9, Sept 1971, jigsaw puzzle theme cover, good cond ................ **6.00**

Paperback, Leslie Ford, *Siren in the Night*, Bantam Book, No. 303, very good cond ...................... **3.00**

# RACING COLLECTIBLES

**Collecting Hints:** This is a field of heroes and also fans. Collectors love the winners. A household name counts. Losers are important only when major races are involved. Pre–1945 material is especially desirable because few individuals were into collecting prior to that time.

The field does have problems with reproductions and copycats. Check every item carefully. Beware of paying premium prices for items made within the last twenty years.

Auto racing collectibles are one of the hot collectible markets of the 1990s. Although interest in Indy 500 collectibles remains strong, the market is dominated by NASCAR collectibles. In fact, the market is so strong that racing collectibles have their own separate show circuit and supporting literature.

Because racing collecting is in its infancy, price speculation is rampant. Market manipulators abound. In addition, copycat, fantasy, and contemporary limited edition items are being introduced into the market as fast as they can be absorbed. A shakeout appears years in the future. In the interim, check your engine and gear up for fast action.

There are so many horse racing collectibles that one needs to specialize from the beginning. Collector focuses include a particular horse racing type or a specific horse race, a breed or specific horse, or racing prints and images. Each year there are a number of specialized auctions devoted to horse racing, ranging from sporting prints sales at the major New York auction houses to benefit auctions for the Thoroughbred Retirement Foundation.

**History:** Man's quest for speed is as old as time. Although this category focuses primarily on automobile and horse racing, other types of racing memorabilia are included. If it moves, it will and can be raced.

Automobile racing dates to before the turn of the century. Many of the earliest races took place in Europe. By the first decade of the twentieth century, automobile racing was part of the American scene.

The Indianapolis 500 began in 1911 and was interrupted only by World War II. In addition to Formula 1 racing, the NASCAR circuit has achieved tremendous popularity with American racing fans. Cult heroes such as Richard Petty have become household names.

The history of horse racing dates back to the domestication of the horse itself. Prehistoric cave drawings show horse racing. The Greeks engaged in chariot racing as early as 600 B.C. As civilization spread, so did the racing of horses. Each ethnic group and culture added its own unique slant.

The British developed the concept of the Thoroughbreds, a group of horses that are descendants of three great Arabian stallions—Carley Arabian, Byerley Turk, and Goldolphin Arabian. Receiving royal sponsorship, horse racing became the Sport of Kings.

Horse racing reached America during the colonial period. By the 1800s four mile match races between regional champions were common. In 1863 Saratoga Race Track was built. The first Belmont Stakes was run at Jerome Park in 1867. As the nineteenth century ended over 300 race tracks operated a seasonal card. By 1908, society's strong reaction against gambling reduced the number of American race tracks to twenty-five.

Of course, the premier American horse race is the Kentucky Derby. Programs date from 1924 and glasses, a favorite with collectors, from the late 1930s.

**References:** Willis Ackerman, *Dan Patch: Mass Merchandiser*, published by author, 1981; William Boddy, *The History of Motor Racing*, G. P. Putnam's Sons, 1977.

**Periodicals:** *Collector's World*, NA–TEX Publishing, PO Box 562029, Charlotte, NC 28256; *Racing Collectibles Price Guide*, SportsStars Inc., PO Box 608114, Orlando, FL 32860.

**Collectors' Clubs:** National Indy 500 Collectors Club, 10505 N. Delaware Street, Indianapolis, IN 46280; Sport of Kings Society, 1406 Annen Lane, Madison, WI 53711.

**Museums:** Aiken Thoroughbred Racing Hall of Fame & Museum, Aiken, SC; Indianapolis Motor Speedway Hall of Fame Museum, Speedway, IN; International Motor Sports Hall of Fame, Talladega, AL; Harness Racing Hall of Fame, Goshen, NY; The Kentucky Derby Museum, Louisville, KY; National Museum of Racing & Hall of Fame, Saratoga Springs, NY.

500 MILE RACE WINNERS
4
1920 Gaston Chevrolet CAR NO. 4
MONROE • AVG. SPEED 88.62 MPH.


**Car, trade card, SW, Indianapolis 500, hand colored, wax coated, yearly winners from 1911 through 1952, 3¾ x 2½", price each card, $1.00.**

## AUTO RACING

Game

- Auto Race Game, four box spinners, four metal racing cars, instructions on back box cov, multicolored litho playing board, orig box, Milton Bradley, c1925 .......... **95.00**
- Champion Road Race, 18 x 12" playing board, cutout spinner, six cutout race cars, printed instructions, Champion Spark Plugs adv ...... **25.00**
- Flip It: Auto Race and Transcontinental Tour, two metal cars, gameboard, and die, instruction sheet, De Luxe Game Corp, c1920 ..... **40.00**

Goblet, 4½" h, clear, 1970 Indianapolis 500, inscribed "Mayor's Breakfast–1970," black and yellow racing symbols .......... **20.00**

Keychain Tag, Indianapolis Motor Speedway/Home Of The 500, 1¼", emb brass, entry gate on one side, racing car on reverse, 1960s ....... **12.00**

Magazine, *Racing Pictorial,* late 1963, 48 pgs, Indianapolis 500 racers, color photos of Richard Petty, A J Foyt, Fireball Roberts, Parnelli Jones, and others, 8½ x 11" .......... **10.00**

Pin, 1980 Indiana Lions, Speedway, 1½ x 1¾", enameled brass, state outline, Lions symbol, checkered flag, and racetrack .......... **15.00**

Pinback Button

- Auto Derby Speedway, Chicago, June 26, 1915, blue and white ....... **4.00**
- Cobe Cup Race, June 18–19, 1909, Crown Point, IN, red, early race car with two men .......... **35.00**
- George Vanderbilt Cup Race, multicolored .......... **12.00**

Indianapolis For Hoosier Hospitality, The Speedway City, multicolored, race car, 1930s . . . . . . . . . . . . . . . . **12.00**
Indianapolis The Speedway City, 2½" d, yellow, red, and black, 1930s . **75.00**
Merrimack Valley Automobile Race, September 6–10, 1909, Lowell, MA, early race car, red and white **20.00**
Roosevelt Raceway, 1¼" d, red, white, and blue, race car, 1930s . **30.00**
Souvenir of Midget Auto Races, red, white, and blue, 1930s . . . . . . . . . **5.00**
Poster, Indianapolis 500, 1967, 22 x 14" **35.00**
Program, Indianapolis 500, May, 1947 **90.00**
Whiskey Bottle
Famous Firsts, Indy Racer #11, 1971 **38.00**
Jim Beam
Beam on Wheels, Bobby Unser Olsonite Eagle, 1975 . . . . . . . . . . . . **45.00**
Sports Series, Indy 500, 1970 . . . . **8.00**

## HORSE RACING

Card Game, Derby Day, The Unique Race Game, 48 multicolored litho cards, instruction booklet, red and black numbered cardboard chips, c1900 . . . . . . . . . . . . . . . . . . . . . . . . . **35.00**
Display, The Great Match, New York Racing Association, 1975, buttons and two page horse race sheet under glass, 2 x 13 x 14" wood frame . . . . **100.00**
Game, The Derby Steeple Chase, four wood counters, 18 wood chips, and spinner, multicolored litho race track board, orig box, c1890 . . . . . . . . . . . **85.00**
Glass, 5¼" h
1964 Kentucky Derby/Churchill Downs, frosted, horse head illus, gold inscription, white lettering on back . . . . . . . . . . . . . . . . . . . . . . . . . **12.00**
1977 Kentucky Derby, case of 48 . . **100.00**
1979 Kentucky Derby, frosted sides, colorful Churchill Downs racing scene, list of Derby winners on back from 1875 to 1978 . . . . . . . . **18.00**
1986, Kentucky Derby, clear, frosted white panel, red roses and green leaf accents, red and green inscriptions . . . . . . . . . . . . . . . . . . . . . . . . . **10.00**

**Plate, Dan Patch, Champion Harness Horse of the World, porcelain, white, black and white photo center, gold trim, East Liverpool Potteries, 8⅜" d, $60.00.**

Magazine, *Sports Illustrated,* April 28, 1958, Silky Sullivan . . . . . . . . . . . . . . **10.00**
Nodder, 6½" h, composition, jockey, holding saddle and yellow and blue blanket, sq base painted red, stamped Japan 1962 . . . . . . . . . . . . . . . . . . . . . **60.00**
Paperweight, 2¼ x 2½", Churchill Downs, Louisville, KY, metal, horseshoe image, center shield, brass finish, early 1900s . . . . . . . . . . . . . . . . . **25.00**
Pennant, 18" l, Derby Day, felt, red, white lettering, red and white design with pink accents, 1939 . . . . . . . . . . . **15.00**
Pinback Button
Budweiser Million Horse Race, Arlington Park, August 28, 1983, 3" d, multicolored . . . . . . . . . . . . . . . . **5.00**
Derby Day, Sept 13, 1904, Topeka, KS, sepia photo . . . . . . . . . . . . . . . . **12.00**
Doyle Derby, 1¼", orange and black, jockey on galloping horse, 1930s . **10.00**
Meet Me at Columbus, Grand Circuit Races, Sept 16th to 27th, 1907, blue and white . . . . . . . . . . . . . . . . . **15.00**

Portrait
Bergen/Celebrated American Jockey, white racing outfit, "American Pepsin Gum Go" on back . . . . . . . . . . **20.00**
Osborne/Celebrated English Jockey, purple and white racing colors, inscribed . . . . . . . . . . . . . . . . . . . . . . **15.00**
Sam'l Doggett, Jockey, Oneck Stables Colors, purple and gold racing outfit, "High Admiral Cigarettes" on back . . . . . . . . . . . . . . . . . . . . . . . . . **25.00**
Print, 20½ x 16", The American Quarter Horse Racing, Randy Steffen, 1972 . **10.00**
Program
Arlington Park, Chicago, June 23, 1943, 4 x 8½" . . . . . . . . . . . . . . . . . **15.00**
Kentucky Derby, May 4, 1963, 4 x 9" **18.00**
Shaving Mug, occupational, jockey on horse, No. 2, "John M Rosefield," gold leaf trim, 3½" d, 3¾" h . . . . . . . **350.00**

Stickpin, ¾", jockey cap on entwined initials "CMC," brass, green and white enamel accents, dated 1906 . . **25.00**
Ticket, 2¼ x 3½", Kentucky Derby, Saturday, May 2, 1936 . . . . . . . . . . . . . **8.00**
Whiskey Bottle
Aesthetic Specialties, Inc, Kentucky Derby, 1979 . . . . . . . . . . . . . . . . . . . **45.00**
Jim Beam, Sports Series Kentucky Derby 95th, pink roses, 1969 . . . . **8.00**

## MISCELLANEOUS

Aviation
- Game, The New World To World Airship Race, The Chicago Game Co, orig box . . . . . . **95.00**
- Pinback Button 1⅜" d, National Air Races, Cleveland, 1932, silver litho, red, white, and blue . . . . . . **25.00**

Bicycle
- Game, Game of Bicycle Race, four wood counters, six colored wheel men, and spinner, instructions on box, wood box . . . . . . **200.00**
- Pinback Button, Novelty Cycle Race Meet, Labor Day, Sept 5th, 1898, red, white, blue, and black . . . . . . **15.00**

Boating
- Game
  - Speed Boat Race, bottom box playing board, Milton Bradley, 1930s **25.00**
  - The Outboard Motor Race, orig box, Milton Bradley . . . . . . **25.00**
  - Yacht Race, four round wood markers, spinner, instruction on box back cov, multicolored litho board, orig box, Milton Bradley, c1905 . . . . . . **30.00**

Motorcycle, medal, 1½" d, American Motorcycle Association National Competition, silvered brass, emb, relief illus of motorcycle race, applied enameled metal symbol, back engraved "Second Place/12 Mi. 21:35 Cu. In. Solo," maroon fabric ribbon **200.00**

Snowmobile, pinback button, 2¼" d, 1969 Grand Prix Snowmobile Races, annual Tip–Up winter sports, Houghton Lake, MI, orange, black, and white . . . . . . **12.00**

# RADIO CHARACTERS AND PERSONALITIES

**Collecting Hints:** Many items associated with radio characters and personalities were offered as premiums. This category focuses mostly on the non–premium items. Radio premiums have their own separate listing elsewhere in this book.

Don't overlook the vast amount of material related to the radio shows themselves. This can include scripts, props, and a wealth of publicity material. Collecting autographed photographs was popular, and many appear on the market. Books, especially Big Little Books and similar types, featured many radio related characters and stories.

Radio characters and personalities found their way into movies and television. Serious collectors do differentiate the products which spun off from these other two areas.

**History:** The radio show was a dominant force in American life from the 1920s to the early 1950s. Amos and Andy began in 1929, The Shadow in 1930, and Chandu the Magician in 1932. Although many of the characters were fictional, the individuals who portrayed them became public idols. A number of figures achieved fame on their own—Eddie Cantor, Don McNeill of The Breakfast Club, George Burns and Gracie Allen, Arthur Godfrey, and Jack Benny.

Sponsors and manufacturers were quick to capitalize on the fame of the radio characters and personalities. Premiums were offered as part of the shows themes. However, merchandising did not stop with premiums. Many non–premium materials such as bubble gum cards, figurines, games, publicity photographs, dolls, etc., were issued. Magazine advertisements often featured radio personalities.

**References:** Norman E. Martinus and Harry L. Rinker, *Warman's Paper,* Wallace–Homestead, 1993; Tom Tumbusch, *Tomart's Price Guide To Radio Premium and Cereal Box Collectibles,* Wallace–Homestead, 1991.

**See:** Big Little Books, Comic Books, Radio Premiums, Super Heroes.

**Booklet, *Popular Radio Stars,* Charles E. Donaldson, The Washington Service Bureau, biographical sketches, 30 pgs, 1942, 5⅜ x 8⅜", $8.00.**

Amos 'n Andy
- Ashtray, plaster, figures flanking barrel, "Ise Regusted," 1930s, 5 x 5 x 8" . . . . . . **90.00**
- Booklet, All About Amos 'n Andy, photos, scripts, 128 pgs, 1929 . . . **50.00**
- Figures, pr, bisque, painted, stamped "Pfeffer Porzellan, Gotha, Germany, "#6495 and #9496, 1920–30, 4" h . . . . . . **300.00**

Game, Card Party, M Davis Co, two score pads, eight tallies, orig box, 1938 .......... **70.00**
Greeting Card, get well, black and white photo, Hall Brothers, 1931, 4½ x 5½″ .......... **30.00**
Post Card, Atlantic City .......... **10.00**
Sheet Music, *Three Little Words,* 1930 **25.00**
Andrew Sisters, Rhythm Song Folio, 1940 .......... **3.00**
Charlie McCarthy
Bank, composition .......... **58.00**
Greeting Card, get well, talking .... **20.00**
Pencil Sharpener, diecut plastic, figural, color decal, 1930s .......... **70.00**
Radio, plastic, ivory colored, figural, electric, Majestic, c1940, 6″ h ... **800.00**
Record Album, *Lessons in Ventriloquism,* 33⅓ rpm, wrapped, mint . **25.00**
Soap, figural, Kerk Gild, 1930–40, 4″ h, orig box .......... **75.00**
Ventriloquist Dummy .......... **125.00**
Wrapper, Bergen's Better Bubble Gum .......... **6.00**
Dick Steel, Boy Police Reporter, photograph, cast boarding plane .......... **10.00**
Don Winslow, bank, Uncle Don's Earnest Saver Club, oval, paper label, photo and cartoon illus, Greenwich Savings Bank, New York City, 1930s, 2¼″ h .......... **35.00**
Eddie Cantor
Big Little Book, *Eddie Cantor In An Hour With You,* Whitman, #774, 1934 .......... **30.00**
Book, *Eddie Cantor in Laughland,* Goldsmith Publishing Co, 1934 .. **25.00**
Poster, paper, movie and radio show adv, New Pebeco Tooth Paste, 1935–36, 11½ x 19″ .......... **70.00**
Edgar Bergen, photograph, Bergen and Charlie McCarthy .......... **8.00**
Ethel Merman, sign, cardboard, Radio Star Magazine adv, 8½ x 12″ ...... **15.00**
Fibber McGee and Molly, record album, four 78 rpm records, live broadcasts, colorful Fibber design on cover, 1947, 10¼ x 12″ .......... **50.00**
Jack Armstrong, reel, magnetic tape, The All American Boy Radio Shows, 15 minute episodes, 1940–41, 7 pcs **70.00**
Jack Benny
Program, Jack Benny Show, black and white photos, Phil Harris signature, 12 pgs, late 1930s, 9 x 12″ ...... **24.00**
Record Set, four 78 rpm records, comedy sketches, Top Ten Records, orig cov, 1947 .......... **45.00**
Jimmie Allen
Drawstring Bag, cloth, white, red printing both sides, Cleo Cola logo, Bottle cap, and "Listen To The Air Adventures of Jimmie Allen Every Broadcast For Bulletins About Premiums," c1934, 4 x 6″ .......... **150.00**
Model, Thunderbolt, 1930s, 19″ l 24″ wingspan, 1930s, orig box ...... **100.00**

**Fibber McGee and Molly, game, Fibber McGee and the Wistful Vista Mystery, Milton Bradley, #4768, 1940, $15.00.**

Joe Penner, valentine, mechanical, diecut, Penner holding duck on shoulder, eyeballs and mouth move back and forth, "I'll Gladly Buy A Duck," 1930–40, 4½ x 7″ .......... **20.00**
John White, Death Valley Days, song folio, *Cowboy Songs in Death Valley,* 1934 .......... **8.00**
Kate Smith
Autograph, A & P Coffee Service, Office of Kate Smith stationery, bold signature, 1936, 7 x 10″ ........ **30.00**
Pinback Button, photo illus, black and red lettering "Kate Smith's Philadelphia A & P Party, Nov 4, 1935, Hello Everybody," white ground, 2¼″ d .......... **25.00**
Kitty Kelly, pinback button, black, white, and green, "Tune In Columbia Broadcast System, Pretty Kitty Kelly," 1¼″ d .......... **7.50**
Les Paul, song folio, 1951 .......... **3.00**
Little Orphan Annie
Big Little Book, *Little Orphan Annie and Sandy,* Whitman, #716, 1933 **35.00**
Book, *The Little Orphan Annie Book,* James Whitcomb Riley, color illus by Ethel Betts, 1908 .......... **25.00**
Glass, The Sunday Funnies, clear, continuous Annie, Sandy, Daddy Warbucks, Asp, and Punjab illus, 1976, 5½″ h .......... **12.50**
Mug, 50 Year Anniversary, plastic, white, red lid, 1932 and 1983 Annie and Sandy illus, Ovaltine premium, 1982, 5″ h .......... **15.00**
Salt Shaker, composition .......... **15.00**
Stove, child's, 1930s .......... **50.00**

Quiz Kids, game, electric, Rapaport Bros, orig box and instructions ..... **18.00**
Ralph Edwards, book, *Radio's Truth or Consequences Party Book,* 1940 ... **8.00**
Seckatary Hawkins, record brush, Decca, The Ink Spots adv ......... **15.00**
Sgt Preston
Coloring Book, Whitman, 32 pgs, unused, 1943, 8½ x 11½" ......... **20.00**
Coloring Set, orig box ............ **50.00**
Poster, Quaker Puffed Wheat and Puffed Rice cereal adv, Mounted Police Whistle offer, c1950, 16½ x 22" ........................... **200.00**
Skippy
Figurine, bisque, jointed arms, Japan, 1930s, 4 x 5 x 1" box ........... **60.00**
Playing Cards, 36 numbered cards, Poll Parrot shoe sticker on lid, mid 1930s, 4 x 5 x 1" box ........... **60.00**
The Shadow
Blotter, cardboard, orange, blue, and white, red silhouette, 1940s, 4 x 9" **20.00**
Board Game, The Shadow, Toy Creations, 20" sq board, one wood token, play money, colored discs, four wood black cap dice, dice shaker, 1940 .................. **250.00**
Book, *The Living Shadow,* Maxwell Grant, c1931 .................. **8.00**
Figure, china, glossy black cloak and hat, c1930, 7" ................. **250.00**
Matchbook, diecut Shadow image .. **35.00**
Sticker, "Shadow On The Air Every Sunday Afternoon," Blue Coal adv, 1¼ x 2½" ..................... **20.00**
Will Rogers, booklet, broadcast highlights, April–June, 1930 ........... **8.00**

# RADIO PREMIUMS

**Collecting Hints:** Most collections are centered around one or two specific personalities or radio programs.

**History:** Radio premiums are nostalgic reminders of childhood memories of radio shows. Sponsors of shows frequently used their products to promote the collection of premiums, such as saving box tops to exchange for gifts tied in with the program or personality.

**References:** Norman E. Martinus and Harry L. Rinker, *Warman's Paper,* Wallace–Homestead, 1993; Tom Tumbusch, *Tomart's Price Guide To Radio Premium and Cereal Box Collectibles,* Wallace–Homestead, 1991.

**REPRODUCTION ALERT**

**See:** Radio Characters and Personalities.

**Ed Wynn, Texaco Fire Chief, face mask, autographed and framed, 1933, $55.00. Photograph courtesy of James D. Julia, Inc.**

Amos & Andy, map of Weber City, Pepsodent, 1935, orig letter and mailer . **50.00**
Chandu the Magician
Chinese Coin Trick ............... **20.00**
Photograph, wearing costume ...... **30.00**
Charlie McCarthy
Radio Game, 1938 ............... **15.00**
Spoon .......................... **10.00**
Cisco Kid
Paper Cricket Gun ................ **18.00**
Radio Face Mask ................. **15.00**
Tip–Top Puzzle, illus envelope ..... **30.00**
Death Valley Days
Story of Death Valley, 1932 ........ **18.00**
Old Ranger's Seed Packets ........ **15.00**
Dick Tracy
Aviation Wings, 1938 ............. **35.00**
Belt Badge, Detective Club, leather pouch back .................. **45.00**
Paper Pop Gun, 1942 ............. **10.00**
Rubber Band Gun ................ **20.00**
Siren Plane, 1938 ................ **85.00**
Dizzy Dean Winners Club
Lucky Piece, 1930s ............... **40.00**
Ring, Win With Dizzy Dean, 1930s **95.00**
Don McNeill's Breakfast Club
Breakfast Club Yearbook, 1949 ..... **7.00**
Membership Card ................ **6.00**
Don Winslow of the Navy, ensign pin . **30.00**
Eddie Cantor, booklet, "How to Make A Quack–Quack," Chase & Sanborn, 1932 .......................... **20.00**
Fibber McGee and Molly, Molly spinner, 1936 ...................... **225.00**
Fred Allen, Donut Book ............. **5.00**
Jack Armstrong
Dragon Talisman Map, spinner and game pieces, 1936 ............. **125.00**
Explorer Telescope, 1938 ......... **15.00**
Shooting Propeller Plane Gun, Daisy, 1933 ........................ **40.00**
Jimmie Allen
Membership Card, Skelly .......... **10.00**
Whistle, brass ................... **45.00**
Joe Corntassel, photograph, Ovaltine and ROA, orig mailer, 1930 ....... **45.00**
Joe E Brown Club
Booklet, "You Said A Mouthful,"

Meier's Bread, 1944 ............ **20.00**
Membership Ring ................ **50.00**
Little Orphan Annie
Bandanna, 1934 ................. **35.00**
Mask, 1933 ..................... **50.00**
Mug, ceramic, 1932 .............. **45.00**
School Pin, 1938 ................. **25.00**
Song Sheet, Ovaltine and ROA, 1931 **15.00**
Talking Stationery Set, 1937 ....... **50.00**
Lone Ranger
Charm Bracelet, 1933 ............ **200.00**
Merita Mask, 1934–38 ............ **35.00**
Ring, National Defenders .......... **95.00**
Secret Portfolio, National Defenders, 1941 ......................... **75.00**

**Jack Armstrong, Pedometer, aluminum, enameled center, belt clip, 2⅝" d, $25.00.**

Lone Wolf Tribe, manual, Wrigley's 1932 ........................... **50.00**
Lum and Abner, Horlick malted maker **60.00**
One Man's Family, Barbour family scrapbook, 1946 ................. **10.00**
Seckatary Hawkins, fair and square spinner, 1932 .................... **20.00**
Sgt Preston, signal flashlight, 1949 .... **35.00**
Skippy
Bowl, Beetleware ................ **15.00**
Christmas Card .................. **15.00**
Sky King, stamping kit .............. **28.00**
The Shadow, ring, plastic, blue coal, glow–in–the–dark, 1941 .......... **325.00**
Thompson Malted Milk, Life Line Chart, 1930, orig mailer ................ **25.00**
Young Forty–Niners
Indian Village, punch–out ......... **100.00**
Map ............................ **50.00**

# RADIOS

**Collecting Hints:** Radio collectors divide into three groups: those who collect because of nostalgia and those interested in history and/or acquiring radios that represent periods prior to or after World War II, and collectors of personality and figural radios. Most collectors find broadcasting, and therefore broadcast receivers, their primary interest.

The significant divisions of broadcast receivers that are represented in a small collection are:

—Crystal sets and battery powered receivers of the early 1920s
—Rectangular electric table models of the late 1920s
—Cathedrals, tombstones, and consoles of the Thirties
—Midget plastic portables and wood cabinet table models built before and after World War II
—Shaped Bakelite and other plastic cased radios
—Personality and figural radios beginning in the 1930s and extending into the 1960s.

Because the emphasis for nostalgia seems to fall on the decade of the Thirties, the cathedral style, socket powered radios, e.g., the Philco series, have become sought after items. Recently the younger set has exhibited a very strong nostalgia interest in the plastic cabinet radios built between 1945 and 1960.

The underlying force that values a radio to a traditional collector, and consequently sets the price in the market, is rarity. Very rare radios usually go directly to major collectors, seldom appearing in the general market. Wireless equipment and radios used commercially before World War I are considered rare and are not listed here.

With the newer radio collector, the controlling force is novelty with the outside appearance the primary feature. The radio must play; but, shape, color, decoration, and condition of the case far outweigh the internal workings of the set in determining desirability and consequently the price. Enclosures that represent things or figures e.g., Mickey Mouse, command premium prices.

The prices of 1920s radio sets have been stabilized by collectors' demands. Typical prices are listed. The values of Thirties' radios fall into two ranges. Cathedrals bring an average of $100 to $150 with Philco and Atwater Kent on the high end, and names like Airline and Stewart Warner on the low end. Consoles bring substantially lower prices, seldom reaching $100 except for very ornate models, such as the Victrola Hyperion or Orchestrion and the Atwater Kent Model 812.

The squarish table models of the later Thirties and the midget sets of the late 1930s and 1940s recently have attracted the attention of nostalgia buffs and new collectors. Generally their demand in the face of supply keeps their price low, holding below $75. An exception to this rule is based on decoration. Columns, figurework, and dramatic changes in texture add interest and raise the potential prices. A radio with columns outlining the dial or the speaker opening can command $150. Another exception to this is the novelty radio. Treasure chest barrels, mirrored cases, and specialty items bring prices as high as $500.

The value of a radio is directly related to its condition. The critical factors are appearance and operability. The prices listed are for sets of average to good condition and based upon an electrically complete receiver that operates when powered.

Minor scratches are to be expected as is alligatoring of the surface finish. Gouges, cracks, and delaminated surfaces will cut the price by 50%. However, the penalty for a crack or broken place for plastic closures is severe. A Catalin radio with a blue case might bring $400–$600 in good condition, but with a visible crack the price drops to $30.

If parts, tubes, or components are missing or if major repairs must be made in order for the set to work, the price again must be reduced by as much as 50%. A particular radio that is unrestored, in excellent or mint condition, and playing satisfactorily can command an increase of 30 to 50% over the prices listed below.

In addition to radios, many collectors specialize in a facet of the general radio art such as loudspeakers, tubes, microphones, memorabilia, or brand names. As a result, auxiliary and related radio items are becoming collectibles along with radios themselves.

**History:** The art and science of radio as a communication medium is barely ninety years old. Marconi was the first to assemble and employ the transmission and reception instruments that permitted electric message–sending without the use of direct connections. The early name for radio was "Wireless," and the first application was in 1898 as a means of controlling ships. Early wireless equipment is not generally considered a collectible since its historic value makes it important for museum display.

Between 1905 and the end of World War I many technical advances, including the invention of the vacuum tube by DeForest, resulted in an extensive communication art and a very strong amateur interest in the strange new technology. The receiving equipment from that period is considered highly desirable by collectors and historians but is rarely available outside the main body of early radio and wireless collectors.

By 1920, radio technology offered the means to talk to large numbers of people simultaneously and bring music from concert halls directly into living rooms. The result was the development of a new art that changed the American way of life during the 1920s. The world became familiar in the average listener's home.

Radio receivers changed substantially in the decade of the Twenties, going from black boxes with many knobs and dials and powered from expensive and messy batteries, to styled furniture, simple to use, and operated from the house current that had become the standard source of energy for service in the home. During the Twenties radios grew more complicated and powerful as well as more ornate. Consoles appeared, loudspeakers were incorporated into them, and sound fidelity joined distance as criteria for quality.

In the early 1930s demand changed. The large expensive console gave way to small but effective table models. The era of the "cathedral" and the "tombstone" began. By the end of the Thirties, the midget radio had become popular. Quality of sound was replaced by reduction of price and most homes had more than one radio.

Shortly after World War II the miniature tubes developed for the military were applied to domestic radios. The result was further reduction in size with a substantial improvement in quality. The advent of FM also speeded the development. Plastic technology made possible the production of attractive cases in many styles and colors.

The other development that drastically changed the radio receiver was the invention of the transistor in 1927. A whole new family of radio sets that could be carried in the shirt pocket became popular. As they became less and less expensive, their popularity grew rapidly. Consequently, they were throwaways when they stopped working. Today they are not easy to find in good condition and are quite collectible.

**References:** Robert F. Breed, *Collecting Transistor Novelty Radios: A Value Guide,* L–W Books, 1990; Marty and Sue Bunis, *Collector's Guide To Antique Radios, Second Edition* Collector Books, 1992; Philip Collins, *Radio Redux: Listening In Style,* Chronicle Books, 1992; Philip Collins, *Radios: The Golden Age,* Chronicle Books, 1987; Alan Douglas, *Radio Manufacturers of the 1920's, Volume I* (1988) and *Volume 2* (1989), *Volume 3* (1991), The Vestal Press; Robert Grinder and George Fathauer, *Radio Collector's Directory and Price Guide,*, Ironwood Press, 1986; David Johnson, *Antique Radio Restoration Guide, Second Edition,* Wallace–Homestead, 1992; David and Betty Johnson, *Guide To Old Radios–Pointers, Pictures, and Prices,* Wallace–Homestead, 1989; Michael Lawlor, *Lawlor's Radio Values: Catalin, Character Mirrored, Novelty, Plastic,* Bare Bones Press, 1991; Harry Poster, *Poster's Radio and Television Price Guide, 1920–1990,* Wallace–Hometead, 1993; Harry Poster, *The Illustrated Price Guide To Vintage Televisions and Deco Radios,* published by author, 1991; John Sideli, *Classic Plastic Radios of the 1930s and 1940s: A Collector's Guide To Catalin Radios,* E. P. Dutton, 1990; Scott Wood (ed.), *Evolution Of The Radio,* L–W Book Sales, 1991, 1992 value update.

**Periodicals:** *Antique Radio Classified*, P. O. Box 802, Carlisle, MA 01746; *Radio Age*, 636 Cambridge Road, Augusta, GA 30909.

**Collectors' Clubs:** Antique Radio Club of America, 3445 Adaline Drive, Stow, OH 44224; Antique Wireless Association, 59 Main St, Bloomfield, NY 14469.

**Museums:** Antique Wireless Museum (AWA), Holcomb, NY; Caperton's Radio Museum, Louisville, KY; Muchow's Historical Radio Museum, Elgin, IL; Museum of Wonderful Wireless, Minneapolis, MN; New England Museum of Wireless and Steam, East Greenwich, RI; Voice of the Twenties, Orient, NY.

**Advisor:** Lewis S. Walters.

**Channel Master, Model 6511, table, green plastic case, AM, 12¼ x 5 x 6¼", $18.00.**

Admiral
- Model 33, 35, 37, battery, portable . **25.00**
- Plastic, portable, brown . . . . . . . . . . . **35.00**
- Tilt tuner console . . . . . . . . . . . . . . . **90.00**

Advertising
- Amoco Gas, pump shape, orig box . **30.00**
- Atlas Car Battery . . . . . . . . . . . . . . . . **40.00**
- Mobil Oil, MIB . . . . . . . . . . . . . . . . . **30.00**
- Pet Milk . . . . . . . . . . . . . . . . . . . . . . . **40.00**
- Schlitz Beer . . . . . . . . . . . . . . . . . . . . **25.00**
- Stroh's Beer . . . . . . . . . . . . . . . . . . . . **25.00**
- Tropicana Orange Juice . . . . . . . . . . **10.00**
- Winston Cigarettes . . . . . . . . . . . . . . **30.00**

Arvin
- Character, Hoppy, lariatenna
  - Black . . . . . . . . . . . . . . . . . . . . . . . . **310.00**
  - Red . . . . . . . . . . . . . . . . . . . . . . . . . . **425.00**
- Clock radio, 1954 . . . . . . . . . . . . . . . **30.00**
- Plastic, table model, brown . . . . . . . . **30.00**
- Rhythm series, table and console model . . . . . . . . . . . . . . . . . . . . . . . . **150.00**

Atwater Kent
- Model 10A, instruments on board, five tubes . . . . . . . . . . . . . . . . . . . . **325.00**
- Model 12, instruments on board, six tubes . . . . . . . . . . . . . . . . . . . . . . . . **350.00**
- Model 20, mahogany case, three dials **120.00**
- Model 30, mahogany case, single dial **125.00**
- Model 40, metal cabinet, electric . . **50.00**
- Model 46, table model, green metal case, 1929 . . . . . . . . . . . . . . . . . . . . **115.00**
- Model 55, electric, set in Kiel table . **150.00**
- Model 70, 80, 90 Series, console style **30.00**
- Model 80, 90 Series, table model . . **325.00**

Bulova, clock radio, #100 . . . . . . . . . . **40.00**

Catalin and other phenolic case radios
- A partial list of manufacturers includes Addison, Air–King, Bendix, Crosley, De Wald, Emerson, Fada, General Electric, Garod, Kadette, Motorola, RCA, Sentinel, Sonors, Sparton, Stewart–Warner, Zenith. The prices for these radios are almost independent of brand name but depend directly on the color.
  - Black . . . . . . . . . . . . . . . . . . . . . . . . . **30.00**
  - Blue . . . . . . . . . . . . . . . . . . . . . . . . . . **200.00**
  - Brown . . . . . . . . . . . . . . . . . . . . . . . . **25.00**
  - Green . . . . . . . . . . . . . . . . . . . . . . . . **175.00**
  - Red . . . . . . . . . . . . . . . . . . . . . . . . . . **95.00**
  - Yellow . . . . . . . . . . . . . . . . . . . . . . . . **100.00**

Crosley
- Bandbox, #601 . . . . . . . . . . . . . . . . . . **75.00**
- Cathedral 167 . . . . . . . . . . . . . . . . . . **195.00**
- Gemchest, #609, console, 1928 . . . **275.00**
- Harko or Ace V . . . . . . . . . . . . . . . . . **275.00**
- Litlfella, cathedral, 1932 . . . . . . . . . . **175.00**
- Pup . . . . . . . . . . . . . . . . . . . . . . . . . . . **120.00**
- Sheraton, cathedral, wood, 1933 . . . **260.00**
- Showbox, #706, table model, 1928 **100.00**
- Sky Rocket, portable, 1953 . . . . . . . . **25.00**
- Travette and Companion . . . . . . . . . . **85.00**
- 4–29 . . . . . . . . . . . . . . . . . . . . . . . . . . **125.00**
- IV . . . . . . . . . . . . . . . . . . . . . . . . . . . . **175.00**
- VI . . . . . . . . . . . . . . . . . . . . . . . . . . . . **200.00**
- X . . . . . . . . . . . . . . . . . . . . . . . . . . . . **200.00**
- 516, table model, tombstone . . . . . . **75.00**

DeForest
- D–10, coil . . . . . . . . . . . . . . . . . . . . . . **510.00**
- Everyman, crystal . . . . . . . . . . . . . . . . **375.00**

Dumont Tura 103, 1947 . . . . . . . . . . . . **150.00**

Emerson
- AU–190, tombstone, catalin, gold, three knobs, 1938 . . . . . . . . . . . . . .**1,000.00**
- AX–211, Little Miracle, table model, plastic midget, AC/DC . . . . . . . . . . **55.00**
- CL–256, Strad, table model, violin shape, louvers, AC/DC . . . . . . . . . . **390.00**
- #410, Mickey Mouse, table model, wood, black and silver, two knobs, AC . . . . . . . . . . . . . . . . . . . . . . . . .**1,150.00**
- #411, Mickey Mouse, table model, pressed wood . . . . . . . . . . . . . . . . .**1,300.00**
- #520, catalin . . . . . . . . . . . . . . . . . . . . **175.00**
- #570, Memento, table model, jewelry box style . . . . . . . . . . . . . . . . . . **110.00**

Fada
- L–56, Bell, catalin, wrap around louvers, AC, 1939 . . . . . . . . . . . . . . . .**1,000.00**
- #43, cathedral, wood, scalloped top **225.00**

#136, table model, catalin, louvers, flare base, 1941 .......... **1,000.00**
#252, table model, temple, catalin, horizontal grill, 1941 .......... **475.00**
#265, table model, plastic, Deco grill, 1936 .......... **70.00**
#740, 1947 .......... **75.00**

Federal
Crystal Set .......... **110.00**
58 DX, table model, DC .......... **500.00**
59, table model, DC .......... **850.00**
110, table model, DC .......... **550.00**

Freed Eiseman
Electric Set, #11 .......... **100.00**
NR5, 6, and 7, DC .......... **75.00**

Freshman Masterpiece .......... **150.00**

General Electric
Model 517, plastic, red .......... **40.00**
Model H530, tombstone, wood, 1939 .......... **75.00**
Model P715D, portable, transistor, metal, leatherette, 1958 .......... **25.00**
Model P750A, portable, leather case, lattice grill .......... **35.00**
Model S–22, tombstone, stand, brass handle .......... **225.00**

Grebe
CR Series, set .......... **400.00**
Electric, set .......... **85.00**
Syncrophase, two tone wood case .. **175.00**

Hallicrafters, Model S40B, not working **50.00**

Kadette, International Radio Corp
Junior .......... **50.00**
Pocket Size .......... **300.00**
36, 87 .......... **30.00**

Majestic, pre–WWII
Charlie McCarthy, 1938 .......... **1,000.00**
Console .......... **50.00**
Table model .......... **45.00**
Treasure Chest, redwood trim, 1933 **225.00**

Mohawk, battery operated .......... **75.00**

Montgomery Ward, Airline, AC–DC, table model, pre–WWII .......... **35.00**

Motorola
Jewel Box, portable, plastic .......... **70.00**
Plastic, portable, brown .......... **30.00**
Playboy, maroon, metal, chrome, 1941 .......... **35.00**
Playmate, Jr, metal, inner dial, 1948 **40.00**
Portable, #68L, plastic coated, cloth, 1948 .......... **60.00**
Ranger, #700, portable, 1957 .......... **35.00**
Table model .......... **30.00**
Table model with clock, 1956 .......... **20.00**

Neutrowound .......... **275.00**

Novelty, figural
Bowling Pin, MIB .......... **65.00**
Golf Club, Japan .......... **45.00**
Microphone, Tune To WGGH 1150 **65.00**
Snoopy's Doghouse .......... **55.00**

Paragon
RA 10, DA amplifier .......... **550.00**
RD5 .......... **575.00**

Phenolic cases (see Catalin)

Philco
Cathedrals, up to Model 90 .......... **85.00**
Clock radio .......... **35.00**
Console .......... **40.00**
Model 116 .......... **80.00**
Table models after 1932 .......... **20.00**
Transistor, pocket .......... **15.00**

Philmore, crystal set
Early .......... **40.00**
Modern .......... **10.00**

Poley, cabinet for Atwater Kent .......... **275.00**

Radiola
I .......... **500.00**
II .......... **300.00**
V or VI .......... **410.00**
X, Regenoflex, WD11 tube .......... **250.00**
17 and 18 .......... **90.00**
24 and 26 .......... **275.00**
25 and 28 .......... **185.00**
33, speaker .......... **110.00**
60 .......... **110.00**

RCA
H–125, Little Jewel, portable, plastic, metal trim .......... **60.00**
H–161, table model, rainbow dial .. **45.00**
H–188, table model, plastic, Oriental design .......... **70.00**
Portable, transistor, checkered grill . **30.00**
#120, cathedral, electric .......... **225.00**

Radicon, clock radio .......... **85.00**

Regency, TR–4, transistor .......... **35.00**

Tom Thumb, model TT–600 .......... **40.00**

Western Electric
4B .......... **450.00**
4D .......... **400.00**

Westinghouse
Aeriola Jr, table model .......... **250.00**
Little Jewel, #1251, handle missing **75.00**
RADA or RC .......... **90.00**

Wilcox–Gay, A–53, Thin Man, table model, plastic, horizontal bar .......... **50.00**

Zenith
Cathedral .......... **60.00**
Console .......... **45.00**
Midget, transistor .......... **15.00**
Model 5–G–401D, portable, gray, handle, 1949 .......... **35.00**
Trans Oceanic, T–600, table model **80.00**

# RAILROAD ITEMS

**Collecting Hints:** Most collectors concentrate on one railroad as opposed to one type of object. Railroad material always brings a higher price in the area from which it originated. Local collectors tend to concentrate on local railroads. Material from railroads which operated for only a short time realizes the highest prices. Nostalgia also influences the collector.

There are many local railroad clubs. Railroad buffs tend to have their own specialized swap meets and exhibitions. A large one is held in Gaithersburg, Maryland, in the fall each year.

**History:** It was a canal company, the Delaware and Hudson, which used the first steam locomotive in America. The Stourbridge Lion moved coal from the mines to the canal wharfs. Just as America was entering its great canal era in 1825, the railroad was gaining a foothold. William Strickland recommended to the Commonwealth of Pennsylvania that they not build canals, but concentrate on the railroad. His advice went unheeded.

By the 1840s the railroad was established. Numerous private companies, many in business for only a short time, were organized.

The Civil War demonstrated the effectiveness of the railroad. Immediately following the war the transcontinental railroad was completed, and entrepreneurs such as Gould and Vanderbilt constructed financial empires built on railroads. Mergers created huge systems. The golden age of the railroad extended from the 1880s to the 1940s.

After 1950 the railroads suffered from poor management, a bloated labor force, lack of maintenance, and competition from other forms of transportation. The 1970s saw the federal government enter the picture through Conrail and Amtrak. Thousands of miles of track were abandoned. Many railroads failed or were merged. Today the system still is fighting for survival.

**References:** Stanley L. Baker, *Railroad Collectibles: An Illustrated Value Guide, Fourth Edition,* Collector Books, 1990, 1993 value update; Phil Bollhagen, (comp.), *The Great Book Of Railroad Playing Cards,* published by author, 1991; Arthur Dominy and Rudolph A. Morgenfruh, *Silver At Your Service,* published by authors, 1987; Richard Luckin, *Dining On Rails: An Encyclopedia Of Railroad China,* RK Publishing, 1983, 1990 reprint, out–of–print; Everett L. Maffett, *Silver Banquet II,* Silver Press, 1990; Norman E. Martinus and Harry L. Rinker, *Warman's Paper,* Wallace–Homestead, 1993; Douglas McIntyre, *The Official Guide To Railroad Dining Car China,* Walsworth Press Co, Inc, 1990; Larry R. Paul, *Sparkling Crystal: A Collector's Guide To Railroad Glassware,* Railroadiana Collectors Assoc., Inc., 1990.

**Periodicals:** *Key, Lock and Lantern,* P.O. Box 65, Demarest, NJ 07627; *U. S. Rail News,* P. O. Box 7007, Huntingdon Woods, MI 48070.

**Collectors' Clubs:** Railroad Enthusiasts, 456 Main Street, West Townsend, MA 01474; Railroadiana Collectors Association, 795 Aspen Drive, Buffalo Grove, IL 60089; Railway and Locomotive Historical Society, P. O. Box 1418, Westford, MA 01886.

**Museums:** Baltimore and Ohio Railroad, Baltimore, MD; Museum of Transportation, Brookline, MA; New York Museum of Transportation, West Henrietta, NY; California State Railroad Museum, Sacramento, CA.

**Guide Book, Chicago Railroad Fair, 16 pgs, first edition, 1948, 8¼ x 10¾", $20.00.**

| Item | Price |
|---|---|
| Ashtray, Southern Railway | **14.00** |
| Bell, steam locomotive, brass | **700.00** |
| Blotter, Soo Line, 1920s, unused | **2.00** |
| Book | |
| *Lore of the Train,* Ellis | **15.00** |
| *Train Wrecks,* R Reed | **8.00** |
| *World Atlas of Railways,* 1978 | **15.00** |
| Brochure, Santa Fe RR, 78 pgs, 1936 | **14.00** |
| Button, clothing, Chicago St Paul, price for group of 46 | **45.00** |
| Calendar | |
| 1950, B & O | **24.00** |
| 1958, Union Pacific, wall | **24.00** |
| 1963, Frisco Railroad, wall | **24.00** |
| Catalog | |
| American Locomotive Sales Co, New York, NY, 1918, 181 pages, 6 x 9¼" | **100.00** |
| Newark Electric Co, Chicago, IL, c1933, 32 pages, 5½ x 8½" | **36.00** |
| Ralph H Hillhouse, Elliott, IA, 1917, 48 pages, 3 x 5¾", titled "Watchmaker & Jeweler, Hamilton Watch Agency, The Hamilton Time Book, For The Railroad Men of America" | **18.00** |
| Check, Old Colony, Newport Railroad, 1869 | **10.00** |
| China | |
| Bouillon Cup | |
| Wabash Banner | **65.00** |
| WP, Feather Friver, top logo, Shenango | **25.00** |

Butter Pat, Mimbreno, Syracuse China, full backstamp ........... **45.00**
Celery Dish, Union Pacific, 10", oval, blue and gold pattern, backstamped "Scannell China" ...... **35.00**
Coffee Cup, Illinois Central, Coral pattern ........................ **12.50**
Creamer
B & O ........................ **37.00**
SP, Prairie Mountain, Wildflower . **25.00**
Cup, Santa Fe, double handle, set of three ......................... **65.00**
Cup and Saucer
B & O, blue and white .......... **95.00**
NYC, Mercury, Syracuse, backstamped .................... **50.00**
Southern Pacific ................ **55.00**
Demitasse Cup, Southern Peach Blossom, backstamp "Sou Rwy, Buffalo China" ....................... **50.00**
Grapefruit Dish, PRR, Purple Laurel **25.00**
Hi Ball Glass
New York Central Mutual Assoc, 100 Years, 1869–1969, 5½" h, set of six, orig box ........... **65.00**
PA RR, price for set of four ...... **50.00**
Ice Cream, PRR, Purple Laurel ..... **45.00**
Mustard Jar, NYC, Mercury ........ **40.00**
Oatmeal Dish, PRR, Purple Laurel .. **45.00**
Plate
B & O, 10" d, divided, Cheat River **120.00**
Missouri Pacific, state flowers .... **250.00**
NYC, dinner, Mohawk, salmon–pink and black, top marked ... **36.00**
Union Pacific Streamliner, 10½" d **30.00**
Platter
Southern, Peach Blossom, top marked with logo and "Southern Serves The South," Buffalo China **100.00**
Union Pacific, 8", oval, Challenger pattern, top marked "The Challenger," backstamped Union Pacific RR ..................... **35.00**
Service Plate, B & O ............. **70.00**
Soup Plate
New York Central, marked "Syracuse China" ................. **24.00**
PRR, Purple Laurel, 6½" d, broad lip, Sterling China ............ **45.00**
Union Pacific, 9", rimmed, Harriman Blue pattern, backstamped UP Overland Route logo ...... **40.00**
Sugar, cov, B & O, Shenango ...... **62.00**
Crossing Sign, porcelain ............ **100.00**
Flashlight, PRR, 7½", domed glass .... **50.00**
Folder, Chicago Century of Progress, PA RR, 16 pgs, black and white photos of fair, RR travel info, 1934 ........ **12.00**
Hardware
Baggage Check, brass, Texas Central RR, local, 1⅝ x 2", strap, Poole Bros, Chicago ................. **35.00**
Box Car Seal, Wiscasset, Waterville & Farmington RR, bears identification WW & F RY Co, plus serial number **5.00**
Ticket Dater Dies, NYHH & HRR Bridgeport, fits Aurora machine .. **35.00**
Hat, agent
Boston & Maine, gold finish, curved top ......................... **38.00**
Burlington Route ................. **95.00**

**Pamphlet, Northern Pacific, scenic four part foldout, black and red Yellowstone Park line logo, black and white photos, 1920s, 8 x 11", $15.00.**

Lantern
B & LRR, brass top, bell bottom .... **500.00**
B & MRR, brass top, bell bottom, red cast barrel globe ............... **350.00**
Chesapeake & Ohio .............. **55.00**
CRR of NJ, bell bottom, star headlight **150.00**
D & H RR, Adlake Kero, red Fresnel globe ......................... **28.00**
DW & P, blue emb globe .......... **500.00**
LV RR, caboose, Lehigh Valley RR, orig chimney .................. **100.00**
Rock Island Lines, Dietz heavy iron body casting, inspector type ..... **120.00**
Southern, Armspear Manufacturing, clear cast 5⅜" globe ............ **75.00**
Union Pacific, Adams & Westlake, Adlake Reliable, 1913–P, clear 5⅜" globe ......................... **42.00**
Lantern Globe, Norfolk & Western, red, tall ............................ **27.50**
Lapel Button
Chicago North Western—Safety First, enameled brass ................ **12.00**
Lake Shore & Michigan Southern, mail sack shape ................ **42.00**
Linens
Blanket, Soo Line, wool, gray and tan squares, canted style logo in center **100.00**

Dish Towel, 18 x 16", cotton, tan, triple blue Burlington Route logos and safety slogans .............. **7.50**
Hand Towel, 16" sq, white
AT & SF RY, 1948, interwoven name on red stripe ........... **7.00**
UPRR, interwoven on white stripe **7.00**
Headrest Cover
PRR, 15 x 18", tan ground, brown logo, electric train ............ **10.00**
Seaboard Coast, 17 x 16", gold ground, interwoven green "Seaboard Coast Line Railroad" with train and palm trees .......... **6.00**
Napkin
Burlington Route, 20" sq, linen, white, woven logo ........... **7.00**
Illinois Central, 19" sq, linen, white, woven center logo ..... **12.50**
Rio Grande, linen, white, woven markings ................... **10.00**
Pillowcase
Burlington Northern, Pillow Rental 50¢ to Destination, 20" sq, white, ink stamp ............ **6.50**
Property of Pullman Co, 30 x 14", white, ink stamped logo ....... **6.50**
Tablecloth, 36 x 42"
California Zephyr, white, interwoven oval logo ............ **15.00**
Denver & Rio Grande, white, linen, woven "Rio Grande" double markings ................... **15.00**
Illinois Central, dining car, large woven center logo, peach ..... **20.00**
Lock, T & P, chain key, patent 1920 .. **40.00**
Magazine
*Baltimore & Ohio Railroad Magazine,* July 1959, 24 pages ........... **10.00**
*New York Central Lines Magazine,* 1930, price for ten issues ........ **95.00**
Map, 42 x 48", Railroad, Post Office, Township, County, NY State, 1901–2, lists 71 railroad lines, mileage, terminals, 71 steamship lines, New York, Jersey City and Hoboken, rolled up, colored ..................... **140.00**
Matchbook, Union Pacific, 1 x 2¼ x 4" box, eight 2 x 2¼" complete and unused orig adv matchbooks, full color, identified scenes, c1950 .......... **10.00**
Medal
Illinois Central, bronze, service, 1901 **45.00**
Southern Pacific, perfect station award, 1919, bars for 1920 and 1923 ......................... **75.00**
Menu
C & O ......................... **20.00**
Lehigh Valley, Black Diamond Express, dinner, 1927, chef and train on cov ........................ **35.00**
NYC, Thrift Grill, folder, 1955 ..... **3.50**
Santa Fe, Super Chief, luncheon menu, folder, 1971 ............. **4.00**
Union Pacific, City of Los Angeles, domeliner, breakfast, 1971 ...... **2.50**
Milk Bottle, half pint, Missouri Pacific **15.00**
Nail File, Cotton Belt RR ............ **7.50**
Pass, employee, West Jersey & Seashore Railroad, 2½ x 4", limitations text on back, 1905 ..................... **8.00**
Passenger Tag, L A Thompson Scenic Railway, 3" d cardboard string tag, full color illus of open air rail excursion car passing erupting volcano, reverse printed in green, "The L A Thompson Marine Scenic Railway, Dreamland Park," early 1900s ............... **12.00**
Photograph, 23 "Railroad Maintenance Employees," holding tools, 9 x 7" .. **25.00**
Playing Cards
Erie RR, 100th Anniversary, double deck ......................... **50.00**
Illinois Central, unopened ......... **25.00**
N & W, gold circular logo, double deck, orig box ................ **30.00**
Northern Pacific, logo on top, multicolored ................... **20.00**
Pocket Journal, 1967 ............... **6.00**
Poster
Chicago Aurora & Elgin RR, "Bad Order," 3½ x 8", printed on stiff card **2.00**
New York Central, poster/handbill, "State Fair, Syracuse, Sept 7 to Sept 12, 1931," includes fare chart from numerous stations on upstate branch lines, old NYC oval herald with speeding locomotive ....... **8.50**
Old Colony Line to Cottage City, Oak Bluffs, Martha's Vineyard & Nantucket, map of line and connections, c1880, 18 x 28" .......... **35.00**

**Sheet Music, *Wabash Cannon Ball,* Rex Griffin, Calumet Music Co., 1939, 9 x 12", $8.00.**

Record Book, Keystone Overalls ..... **8.00**
Silver Flatware and Hollowware
ACL, bouillon spoon, Zephyr, marked "ACL," and "Int'l" ............. **20.00**
GM & O, dinner fork, Broadway pattern, International .............. **15.00**
Lackawanna, sugar, cov, back marked "Lackawanna, International" .... **125.00**
New Haven RR
Creamer, individual size, 2 oz, marked "Reed & Barton" ...... **24.00**
Tray, 8", oval, deep, backstamped "New Haven RR, International, 1936" ...................... **25.00**
New York Central
Cocktail Fork, marked "International Silver" ................ **15.00**
Demitasse Spoon, marked "International Silver" .............. **10.00**
Ladle, small, marked "International Silver" ...................... **15.00**
Illinois Central
Dessert Spoon ................. **12.50**
Domed Serving Cov, 6", marked "I.C.R.R." ................... **30.00**
Knife ......................... **12.50**
Pencil Holder .................. **30.00**
PRR, dinner knife, Broadway pattern, marked "PPR" ................. **8.50**
Santa Fe, dinner knife, Albany pattern **8.00**
Southern Pacific, soup spoon ...... **18.00**

Switch Keys, see KEYS
Switch Lock
Adlake, Penn Central, brass ....... **20.00**
CCC & St Louis, steel ............. **12.50**
Time Book, Carhatt Mfg, 1907, AF of L platform, census, safety info ....... **6.00**
Timetable
Boston, Maine, 1938 ............. **15.00**
Canadian Pacific, 1922 ........... **15.00**
Lackawanna, 16 pgs, 1947 ........ **8.00**
Milwaukee Road, 1943 ........... **15.00**
Missouri Pacific, 1938 ............ **15.00**
New York City, 1942 ............. **12.00**
New York, New Haven, Hartford, 1942 ......................... **15.00**
Rock Island Railroad, paper, Victorian woman in fancy dining car, 1881 **165.00**
Santa Fe, 1937 .................. **17.00**
Seaboard RR, April, 1948 ......... **8.00**
So America via Lamport & Holt Line, 1916 ......................... **6.00**
Southern RR, 1948 ............... **8.00**
Union Pacific, 1938 .............. **15.00**

Torch, D L & W, 14" l ............. **65.00**
Travel Guide
MOPAC, 1939, color covers ....... **25.00**
Northern Pacific, Dude Ranch Vacations, 1930s ................... **20.00**
Voucher, Union Pacific, Denver & Gulf Railway, 1890s .................. **3.00**
Waybill
Boston & Worcester and Western Railroads, 4½ x 15", small woodcut of old locomotive pulling two cars, filled in, 1848 ................. **3.75**
Kennebec Central, large size, filled in **4.75**

# RAZORS

**Collecting Hints:** A major revolution has occurred in razor collecting in the 1980s. At the beginning of the decade almost all collectors focused on the straight razor. By the late–1980s the collecting of safety razors and their related material as well as electric shavers has achieved a popularity that should equal or exceed that of the straight razor collectors by the 1990s.

Many straight razor collectors focus on the products of a single manufacturer. Value is increased by certain names, e.g., H. Boker, Case, M. Price, Joseph Rogers, Simmons Hardware, Will & Finck, Winchester, and George Wostenholm. The ornateness of the handle and blade pattern also influences value. The fancier the handle or more intricately etched the blade, the higher the price. Rarest handle materials are pearl, stag, Sterling silver, pressed horn, and carved ivory. Rarest blades are those with scenes etched across the entire front.

Initially safety razor collectors are focusing on those razors that were packaged in elaborately lithographed tins during the 1890 to 1915 period. Since a safety razor involves several items, i.e., razor, blades, case or tin, instructions, etc., completeness is a critical factor. Support items such as blade banks, boxes, and sharpeners also attract collectors. Many safety razors from the early period already exceed $50. As a result, new collectors are seeking safety razors from the 1920s through the 1950s because a comprehensive collection can still be assembled at a modest price.

When buying an electric shaver, make certain that it is complete and in working order. Many were sold originally with cleaning kits, most of which have been lost.

**History:** Razors date back several thousand years. Early man used sharpened stones. The Egyptians, Greeks, and Romans had metal razors.

Straight razors made prior to 1800 generally were crudely stamped WARRENTED or CAST STEEL with the maker's mark on the tang. Until 1870 almost all razors for the American market were manufactured in Sheffield, England. Most blades were wedge shaped; many were etched with slogans or scenes. Handles were made of natural materials—various horns, tortoise shell, bone, ivory, stag, silver and pearl. All razors were handmade.

After 1870 most straight razors were machine made with hollow ground blades and synthetic handle materials. Razors of this period usually were manufactured in Germany (Solingen) or in American cutlery factories. Hundreds of molded celluloid handle patterns were produced, such as nude women, eagles, deer, boats, windmill scenes, etc.

By 1900 the safety razor was challenging the straight razor for popularity among the shaving community. A wealth of safety razor patents were issued in the first decade of the 20th century. World War I insured the dominance of the safety razor as American troops abroad made it their preferred shaving method.

By the 1930s the first electric shavers appeared. However, electric shavers did not achieve universal acceptance until the 1950s.

**References:** Robert A. Doyle, *Straight Razor Collecting,* Collector Books, 1980, out–of–print; Phillip L. Krumholz, *Value Guide For Barberiana & Shaving Collectibles,* Ad Libs Publishing Co., 1988; Jim Sargent, *Sargent American Premium Guide To Knives & Razors: Identification And Values, Third Edition,* Books Americana, 1992.

**Collectors' Club:** Safety Razor Collectors' Guild, P. O. Box 885, Crescent City, CA 95531.

Christy Safety Razor, black case, 4½ x 2 x 1" . . . . . . . . . . **15.00**
Curfit, The Woman's Razor, patent date 1945, gold plated, orig box, 2⅜ x 3½ x 1" . . . . . . . . . . **15.00**
Devine Caretaker, Chicago, ivory handle, double edge, blade guard, leather cov wood box, adv sharpener **75.00**
Enders Speed Razor Travel Set, gold plated razor, strop, orig Stropper & Williams Glider shaving cream, black fabric case, snap lid, 6⅞ x 5 x 2" . . **35.00**
Eversharp Schick Injector, 1940s, blades missing
 Aqua handle, gold plated, cardboard box, 2⅜ x 4⅝ x 1" . . . . . . . . . . **15.00**
 Black handle, gold plated, black and clear plastic case, 4½ x 2½ x 1⅛" **12.00**
 White and tan handle, gold plated, black and clear plastic case, 4½ x 2½ x 1⅛" . . . . . . . . . . **12.00**
 White handle, red plastic case, 4⅞ x 2½ x 1⅛" . . . . . . . . . . **6.00**
Gem Feather Weight Deluxe Model Gift Set, No 198, 6¾ x 5⅜ x 1½", MIB, price for set . . . . . . . . . . **30.00**
Gem Safety Razor, gold plated, white handle, plastic case, 1940s, 5⅛ x 2¼ x 1¼" . . . . . . . . . . **10.00**
Gillette Big Fellow, metal black box, wood dovetailed box, 1920s, 4½ x 2⅞ x 1⅜" . . . . . . . . . . **40.00**
Hoffritz, angle head razor, chrome metal case, two black boxes, 3½ x 2⅛ x 2" . . . . . . . . . . **25.00**
Keen Kutter, black case, 1920s, 4¼ x 1⅝ x⅞" . . . . . . . . . . **25.00**
Kewtie, lady's, 2⅝ x 3½ x 1", price for set . . . . . . . . . . **15.00**
Pacific Safety Razor, large hollow handle, 4¾ x 2½ x 1½", MIB . . . . . . . . . . **12.00**
Schermack, lady's, round shaving head, octagonal, tan marbleized celluloid case, 2¾ x 1⅛" . . . . . . . . . . **25.00**
Schick
 Repeating, gold plated, cardboard box, 6½ x 1¼ x 1" . . . . . . . . . . **35.00**
 Super Classic II, International Silver Co, lady's, raised flowered handle and lady's ring, pink leather cov box, 7½ x 2¾ x 1⅝", MIB . . . . . . **125.00**
Simplex Military Safety Razor, Stock No 29–R–1035, 1940s, 4⅛ x 2¼ x¾", MIB . . . . . . . . . . **15.00**
Stahley Line, windup, black pigskin case, orig box, 5⅜ x 3 x 1⅝" . . . . . . **35.00**

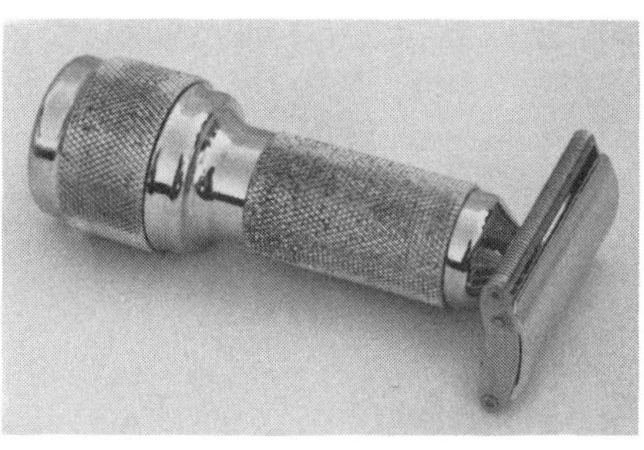

**Stahly Live Blade, vibrating, 3¾" l, $50.00.**

Star Safety Razor, government issue, 1940s, 4⅛ x 2¼ x¾", MIB . . . . . . . . **15.00**
The "4 S" Razor, transition type, c1920, 6 x 1⅜ x 1½", MIB . . . . . . . . . . **20.00**
Valot Auto Strop Safety Razor, Model C, adv "The Community Weekly of Character," 1920s, 4⅛ x 1⅞ x 1⅜", price for razor and strop set . . . . . . . **15.00**
Wilkinson Sword Company, plated, seven day set, razor fitted in holder over leather strop, day of week engraved on blades, blue velvet satin lined chrome case . . . . . . . . . . **50.00**

# REAMERS

**Collecting Hints:** Reamers seldom are found in mint condition. Cone and rim nicks are usually acceptable, but cracked pieces bring considerably less. Ceramic figurals and U. S. made glass are collected more than any other category.

Reamer collecting first became popular with the advent of the Depression Glass collector in the mid–1960s. Reamer collecting can be an endless hobby. It may be impossible to assemble one of every example made. One–of–a–kind samples do exist; they never were put into mass production.

**History:** Devices for getting the juice from citrus fruit have been around almost as long as the fruit itself. These devices range in materials from wood to glass and from nickel plated and Sterling silver to fine china.

Many different kinds of mechanical reamers were devised before the first glass one was pressed around 1885. Very few reamers have been designed since 1940 when frozen juice entered the market. Modern day ceramists are making clown and teapot shaped reamers.

**References:** Gene Florence, *Kitchen Glassware of the Depression Years, Fourth Edition,* Collector Books, 1990, 1992 value update; Mary Walker, *Reamers—200 Years,* Muski Publishers, 1980, separate price guide; Mary Walker, *The Second Book, More Reamers—200 Years,* Muski Publishers, 1983.

**Collectors' Club:** National Reamer Collectors Association, Rt. 3, Box 67, Frederick, WI 54837.

**REPRODUCTION ALERT.** Reproduced reamers include:

An old 5″ Imperial Glass Co. reamer, originally made in clear glass, was reproduced for Edna Barnes in dark amethyst. 1,500 were made. The reproduction is marked "IG" and "81."

Mrs. Barnes has reproduced several old 4½″ Jenkins Glass Co. reamers in limited editions. The reproductions are also made in a 2¼″ size. All Jenkins copies are marked with a "B" in a circle.

**Note:** The first book on reamers, now out–of–print, was written by Ken and Linda Ricketts in 1974. Their numbering system was continued by Mary Walker in *Reamers—200 Years*. The Ricketts–Walker numbers will be found in the china and metal sections. The numbers in parentheses in the glass section are from Gene Florence's *Kitchen Glassware of the Depression Years*

## CHINA AND CERAMIC

Austria, 2¾″ h, white, pink flowers, green trim (D–106) ............... **45.00**
Bavaria, 3½″ h, 2 pcs, white, red, yellow, and green flowers, gold trim (D–119) ........................... **50.00**
Czechoslovakia, 6″ h, 2 pcs, orange shape, white, green leaves, marked "Erphila" (L–37) ................. **35.00**

**China, orange shape, TT in linked diamonds, made in Japan, $45.00.**

England
3½″ h, white, orange and yellow flowers (D–107) ................ **45.00**
3¾″ h, 2 pcs, orange shape, orange body, green leaves (L–20) ....... **24.00**
France, 3¼″ d, white, red, purple, and yellow flowers, green leaves, gold trim (D–112) .................... **18.00**
Germany
3½″ h, scrolling flow blue dec, white ground (E–60) ................. **55.00**
5″ d, Goebel, yellow, (E–108) ...... **50.00**
Japan
3″ h, saucer type on pedestal, loop handle, fruit dec (D–59) ......... **40.00**
3¾″ h, 2 pcs, strawberry shape, red, green leaves and handle, marked "Occupied Japan" ............ **65.00**
4½″, baby's orange, blue on white (B–4) ........................ **28.00**
4¾″ h, lemon, yellow, white flowers, green leaves (L–40) ............. **40.00**
5″, orange, textured orange peel ext., yellow, green leaves, white int. (L–39) .......................... **48.00**
8½″, pitcher and tumbler, blue and white windmill dec (P–87) ....... **48.00**
Limoges, 5¼″ d, scalloped, orange and pearl luster, brown handle (E–79) ... **125.00**
Nippon, 3¼″ h, 2 pcs, hp, white, floral dec ............................ **75.00**
United States
Ade–O–Matic Genuine, 9″ h, green **95.00**
Jiffy Juicer, large bowl with cone center, elongated loop handle, ten colors known, Pat 1938 (A–5) ...... **60.00**
Red Wing, 6¼″ d, gray, red and blue design (A–16) .................. **300.00**
Universal, Cambridge, OH, 9″ h, 2 pcs, pitcher, cream, lavender lilies, green leaves, silver trim (P–104) .. **155.00**
Zippy, 3¼″ h, 6½″ d, hand crank cone, Wolverine Products, Detroit, MI, several colors (A–4) ......... **60.00**

**GLASS** (Measurements indicate width, not including spout and handle)

Anchor Hocking Glass Co, 6¼" d, lime green, pouring spout .............. **22.00**
Depression, 7½", green ............. **20.00**
Fenton, transparent green, pointed cone, tab handle (131–7–5) ....... **95.00**
Fry, 6⁵⁄₁₆" d, opal, pouring spout ..... **45.00**
Hazel Atlas
  Criss–cross, 2 pcs, orange size, pink **165.00**
  Pink, tab handle, large (138–4–4) .. **26.00**
Jeannette Glass Co
  Delphite, Jennyware .............. **75.00**
  Light Jadite, 2 pcs, two cup ........ **35.00**
Jenkins Glass Co, 5¼" d, green (N–212) **50.00**
McKee, 8", green glaze, 1948 ....... **18.00**
US Glass Co, light pink, two cup pitcher set (151–2–1) .................... **35.00**

## METAL

Aluminum Pat, 8" l, 161609 Mpls, Minn **2.00**
Bernard Rice & Sons Apollo EPNS, 3¾" h, 2 pcs (PM–70) ................. **90.00**
Dunlap's Improved, 9½" l, iron hinged (M–17) ........................ **32.00**
Gem Squeezer, 2 pcs, aluminum, crank handle, table model (M–100) ...... **10.00**
Hong Kong, 2½" h, 2 pcs, stainless steel, flat (M–205) ................ **8.50**
Kwicky Juicer, aluminum, pan style, Quam–Nichols Co (M–97) ........ **8.00**
Nasco–Royal, 6" l, scissor type (M–265) **8.00**
Presto Juicer, metal stand, porcelain juicer (m–112) .................... **60.00**
Wagner Ware, 6" d, cast aluminum, skillet shape, long rect seed dams beneath cone, hole in handle, two spouts (M–96) .................. **18.00**
Williams, 9¾" l, iron, hinged, glass insert (M–60) ...................... **32.00**
Yates, EPNS, 4¾" d, 2 pcs (PM–73) ... **130.00**

# RECORDS

**Collecting Hints:** Collectors tend to focus on one particular area of the music field, e.g., jazz, the big bands, or rock 'n' roll, or on one artist. Purchase records with original dust jackets and covers whenever possible.

Also check the records carefully for scratches. If the record cannot be played, it is worthless.

Proper storage of records is critical to maintaining their value. Keep stacks small. It is best to store them vertically. Place acid free paper between the albums to prevent bleeding of ink from one cover to the next.

**History:** The first records were cylinders produced by Thomas Edison in 1877 and played on a phonograph of his design. Edison received a patent in 1878, but soon dropped the project in order to perfect the light bulb.

Alexander Graham Bell, Edison's friend, was excited about the phonograph and developed the graphaphone, which was marketed successfully by 1889. Early phonographs and graphaphones had hand cranks which wound the mechanism and kept the cylinders moving.

About 1900 Emile Berliner developed a phonograph which used a flat disc, similar to today's records. The United States Gramophone Company marketed his design in 1901. The company eventually became RCA Victor. By 1910 discs were more popular than cylinders.

The record industry continued to develop as progress was made in the preservation of sound and the increased quality of sound. The initial size of 78 rpm records was replaced by 45 rpm, then 33⅓ rpm, and finally, compact discs.

**References:** Les R. Docks, *American Premium Record Guide, 1900–1965, Fourth Edition,* Books Americana, 1992; Steve Gelfand, *Television Theme Recordings: An Illustrated Discography, 1951–1991,* Popular Culture, 1993; Anthony J. Gribin and Matthew M. Schiff, *Doo–Wop: The Forgotten Third Of Rock 'n Roll,* Krause Publications, 1992; Vito R. Marino and Anthony C. Furfero, *The Official Price Guide To Frank Sinatra Collectibles, Records and CDs,* House of Collectibles, 1993; Bonni J. Miller (ed.), *Goldmine's 1993 Annual: The Standard Reference For Music Collectors,* Krause Publications, 1993; Jerry Osborne, *The Official Price Guide Movie/TV Soundtracks and Original Cast Albums,* House of Collectibles, 1991; Jerry Osborne, *The Official Price Guide To Records, Tenth Edition,* House of Collectibles, 1993; Neal Umphred, *Goldmine's Price Guide To Collectible Jazz Albums, 1949–1969,* Krause Publications, 1992; Neal Umphred, *Goldmine's Price Guide To Collectible Record Albums, Third Edition* Krause Publications, 1993; Neal Umphred, *Goldmine's Rock 'n Roll 45 RPM Record Price Guide, Second Edition,* Krause Publications, 1992.

**Periodicals:** *DISCoveries,* P. O. Box 255, Port Townsend, WA 98368; *Goldmine,* 700 E. State Street, Iola, WI 54990.

**Note:** Prices are for first pressings in original dust jackets or albums.

**Additional Listings:** Elvis Presley and Rock 'N' Roll.

Advertising
  Atlantic Keeps Your Car On The Go **5.00**
  Chevrolet, Ben Cartwright, Musical Message ...................... **12.00**
  Philco Ford, Voices From The Moon, MIP ......................... **15.00**
  Travelers Insurance Co, Triumph of Man, New York World's Fair ..... **8.00**

Aiken Country String Band, Carolina Stompdown, Okeh, 45143 ........ **8.00**
Allen Brothers, Glorious Night Blues, Victor, 23707 .................... **50.00**
Armstrong, Louis
  Basin Street Blues, Okeh, 8690, 1928 **25.00**
  I'm A Ding Dong Daddy, Okeh, 41442, 1930 .................. **15.00**
  Jazz Lips, Okeh, 8346, 1926 ...... **35.00**
Barth, Belle, If I Embarrass You Tell Your Friends, orig sleeve ............... **15.00**
Beatles, White Album ............... **20.00**
Beatles & Frank Ifeld, LP, Vee Jay 1085, 1964 orig issue, never played ...... **145.00**
Bennett, Boyd, Rockin' Up A Storm, King, 4985 ..................... **10.00**
Berry, Chuck
  Let It Rock, Chess, 1747 .......... **15.00**
  Reeling And Rocking, Chess, 1683 . **12.00**
Brown, Les
  Boogie Woogie, Bluebird, 7858, 1938 ......................... **5.00**
  Sunday, Columbia, 36724, 1942 ... **3.00**
Calloway, Cab
  Jitterbug, Victor, 24592, 1934 ..... **8.00**
  St Louis Blues, Brunswick, 4936, 1930 ......................... **5.00**
  The Levee Low Down, Banner, 32221, 1931 .................. **7.00**
Carson, Johnny, two record set, 25th anniversary poster, orig sleeve ....... **15.00**
Carter Family, On The Rock, Victor, 25313 .......................... **25.00**
Casinos, Then You Can Tell Me Goodbye, LP ....................... **20.00**
Chad & Jeremy
  Sing for You, mono, never played .. **25.00**
  Yesterday's Gone, LP, never played . **95.00**
Cole, Nat King
  Early Morning Blues, Decca, 8541, 1941 ........................ **4.00**
  Scotchin' with the Soda, Decca, 8556, 1941 ................... **4.00**
Cosby, Bill
  I Started Out As A Child, orig sleeve **15.00**
  Why Is There Air, orig sleeve ...... **15.00**
Count Basie
  Basie Boogie, Okeh, 6330, 1941 ... **4.00**
  Honeysuckle Rose, Decca, 1141, 1937 ........................ **7.00**
  Panassie Stomp, Decca, 2224, 1938 **5.00**
Disney Pictures, Mickey's Christmas Carol, picture disk, never played ... **50.00**
Domino, Fats
  Million Sellers by Fats, LP ......... **20.00**
  Reeling and Rocking, Imperial, 5180 **30.00**
Dorsey Brothers
  Have A Little Faith In Me, Banner, 0571, 1930 ................... **10.00**
  The Spell of the Blues, Okeh, 41181, 1929 ......................... **25.00**
Dorsey, Lee, Working in the Coal Mine, LP ............................. **20.00**
Dove, Ronnie
  Cry, LP ......................... **8.00**
  I'll Make All Your Dreams Come True, LP ........................... **8.00**
  Sings The Hits For You, LP ........ **8.00**
Ellington, Duke
  Jubilee Stomp, Okeh, 41013, 1938 . **15.00**
  New Orleans Low–Down, Vocalion, 1086, 1927 .................. **75.00**
Freddie & The Dreamers, LP, Mercury SR61017 ........................ **20.00**
Goodman, Benny
  Shirt Tail Stomp, Brunswick, 3975, 1928 ......................... **10.00**
  Wolverine Blues, Vocalion, 15656, 1928 ......................... **40.00**
Greene, Lorne, Ponderosa, album .... **12.00**
Hackberry Ramblers, Cajun Crawl, Bluebird, 2013 .................. **12.00**
Haley, Bill, Shake, Rattle And Roll, Decca, 5260 .................... **35.00**
Herman, Woody
  Amen, Decca, 18346, 1942 ....... **3.00**
  Blue Downstairs/Upstairs, Decca, 2508, 1939 .................. **3.00**
  Wintertime Dreams, Decca, 1056, 1936 ......................... **10.00**
Ink Spots, Ebb Tide, King, 1297 ...... **10.00**
Jackson 5
  14 Greatest Hits, picture disk, never played ....................... **50.00**
  16 Greatest Hits, cassette, with glove **15.00**
Lennon, John, 2 Virgins, LP ......... **65.00**
Let's Polka ....................... **12.00**
Lewis, Jerry Lee
  Great Balls Of Fire, Sun, 281 ...... **15.00**
  Whole Lot Of Shakin' Going On, Sun, 267 ......................... **5.00**
Miller, Glen
  A Blues Serenade, Columbia, 3051D, 1935 ........................ **30.00**
  I Got Rhythm, Brunswick, 7915, 1937 ........................ **8.00**
Monroe Brothers, My Last Moving Day, Bluebird, 7273 .................. **8.00**
Movie and TV Soundtrack
  The Addams Family, RCA Victor, 1964 ........................ **25.00**
  Bye Bye Birdie, Columbia, orig cast, 1960 ........................ **15.00**
  Damn Yankees, RCA Victor, orig cast, green cov, 1955 ............... **30.00**
  For Whom The Bell Tolls, Decca, 1950 ........................ **40.00**
  King Kong, United Artists, 1976 .... **8.00**
  Kiss Me Kate, MGM .............. **65.00**
  Madame X, Decca, 1966 .......... **15.00**
  New York, New York, United Artists, 1977 ........................ **5.00**
  Oklahoma, Decca, orig cast, 1953 . **40.00**

Rose Marie, MGM ............... **65.00**
The Robe, Decca, 1953 ........... **20.00**
Sayonara, RCA Victor, 1957 ....... **50.00**
To Kill A Mockingbird, Ava, 1963 .. **15.00**
Wagon Train, Mercury, 1959 ...... **25.00**
Nazi, Germany, Marches, Songs, & Speeches, LP .................... **40.00**
Ono, Yoko, Fly, LP ................. **20.00**
Orbison, Roy, Lonely and Blue, Monument, 4002, 14002 ............... **25.00**
Presley, Elvis
Collector's Edition, LP, five record set **60.00**
Commemorative Album, LP, two record set ...................... **10.00**
Elvis In Person At The International Hotel, Las Vegas, NV, c1970 .... **35.00**
How A Legend Was Born, LP, Italian **20.00**
Let's Be Friends, LP ............... **20.00**
25th Anniversary, Limited Edition, four cassette set ................ **45.00**
Worldwide 50 Gold Award Hits, Vol 1, double 8 track set ............ **15.00**

**Record Album, *Elvis' Christmas Album*, RCA Victor, LPM-1951, $25.00.**

Smokey The Bear, book and record set **25.00**
Sonny and Cher, Live In Las Vegas, Vol 2, Sahara Hotel, c1973 ........... **30.00**
Surfaris, Wipe–Out, DFS, 11/12 ...... **15.00**
Teardrops, The Stars Are Out Tonight, Josie, 766 ...................... **30.00**
The Coasters
Keep Rockin' With The Coasters, Atco, 4502 .................... **12.00**
One By One, Atco, 123 ........... **25.00**
The Everly Brothers, Bye Bye Love, Cadence, 1315 ..................... **15.00**
The Palisades, Chapel Bells, Debra, 1003 .......................... **8.00**
Thunder, Johnny, Loop De Loop, LP .. **20.00**
Under Hawaiian Skies with Johnny Pineapple and Orchestra, three records, picture on cov ............. **20.00**
Vogue Picture Record, Basin Street Blues, New Orleans street scene with Blacks ......................... **45.00**
Willis, Bob & His Texas Playboys
I Ain't Got Nobody, Vocalion, 03206 **10.00**
Mexicali Rose, Vocalion, 03086 .... **12.00**

# RED WING POTTERY

**Collecting Hints:** Red Wing Pottery can be found with various marks and paper labels. Some of the marks include a red wing which is stamped on, a raised "Red Wing U.S.A. #___", and an impressed "Red Wing U.S.A. #___". Paper labels were used as early as 1930. Pieces with paper labels easily lost their only mark.

Many manufacturers used the same mold patterns. Study the references to become familiar with the Red Wing forms.

**History:** The category of Red Wing Pottery covers several potteries which started in Red Wing, Minnesota. The first pottery, named Red Wing Stoneware Company, was started in 1868 by David Hallem. The primary product of this company was stoneware. The mark used by this company was a red wing stamped under the glaze. The Minnesota Stoneware Company was started in 1883. The North Star Stoneware Company opened a factory in the same area in 1892 and went out of business in 1896. The mark used by this company included a raised star and the words Red Wing.

The Red Wing Stoneware Company and the Minnesota Stoneware Company merged in 1892. The new company was called the Red Wing Union Stoneware Company. The new company made stoneware until 1920 when it introduced a line of pottery.

In 1936 the name of the company was changed to Red Wing Potteries Incorporated. They continued to make pottery until the 1940s. During the 1930s they introduced several lines of dinnerware. These patterns were all hand painted, very popular, and sold through department stores, Sears, and gift stamp centers. The production of dinnerware declined in the 1950s. The company began producing hotel and restaurant china in the early 1960s. The plant was closed in 1967.

**References:** Dan and Gail DePasquale and Larry Peterson, *Red Wing Collectibles,* Collector Books, 1983, 1992 value update; Gary and Bonnie Tefft, *Red Wing Potters and Their Wares, Second Edition* Locust Enterprises, 1987; Lyndon C. Viel, *The Clay Giants: The Stoneware of Red Wing, Goodhue County, Minnesota, Book 2* (1980), *Book 3* (1987), Wallace–Homestead, out–of–print.

**Collectors' Club:** Red Wing Collectors Society, Route 3, Box 146, Monticello, MN 55362.

**Compote, mauve, scalloped rim, 6¼″ h, 8⅛″ d, "M-5008," $18.00.**

**BOB WHITE.** Casual shape, 1956–1967.

| | |
|---|---|
| Butter Dish | **65.00** |
| Casserole, 2 qt | **25.00** |
| Cookie Jar, no lid | **30.00** |
| Cup and Saucer | **17.50** |
| Hors d'oeuvre Bird | **45.00** |
| Pitcher | **35.00** |
| Plate, 6″ d | **3.75** |
| Platter, 13″ l | **15.00** |
| Vegetable Bowl, divided | **20.00** |

**COUNTRY GARDEN.** Anniversary shape, 1953.

| | |
|---|---|
| Gravy | **22.00** |
| Nappy | **16.00** |
| Plate | |
| 8″ d, salad | **10.00** |
| 10½″ d, dinner | **15.00** |
| Sauce Dish | **10.00** |
| Vegetable, divided | **20.00** |

**IRIS.** Concord shape, 1947.

| | |
|---|---|
| Bowl, 5½″ d | **8.00** |
| Casserole, cov, skillet shape | **25.00** |
| Creamer | **5.00** |
| Relish, three part, 12″ l | **14.00** |

**LUTE SONG.** Casual shape, True China, 1960.

| | |
|---|---|
| Beverage Server | **45.00** |
| Bowl, 8″ d | **15.00** |
| Bread Tray, 19″ l | **20.00** |
| Butter Dish | **20.00** |
| Casserole | **25.00** |
| Celery, 16″ l | **15.00** |
| Creamer | **10.00** |
| Platter, 13″ l | **15.00** |
| Vegetable Bowl, divided | **20.00** |

**MAGNOLIA.** Concord shape, 1947.

| | |
|---|---|
| Bowl, 5″ d | **5.00** |
| Cup | **4.50** |
| Cup and Saucer | **6.00** |
| Plate | |
| 6″ d, bread and butter | **3.50** |
| 7″ d, salad | **4.00** |
| 10″ d, dinner | **8.00** |
| Chop | **15.00** |
| Saucer | **1.50** |

**MERRILEAF.** True China, 1960, floral decoration.

| | |
|---|---|
| Bread Tray, 23″ l | **50.00** |
| Celery, 15″ l | **30.00** |

**ROUND UP.** Casual shape, 1958.

| | |
|---|---|
| Cup | **40.00** |
| Saucer | **12.00** |
| Server, center handle, 6″ d | **38.00** |

**SMART SET.** Casual shape, 1955.

| | |
|---|---|
| Casserole, cov, 2 qt, wire base | **95.00** |
| Cruet | **50.00** |
| Gravy, cov, stand | **35.00** |
| Relish | **30.00** |
| Salt and Pepper Shakers, pr, tall | **65.00** |
| Sugar, cov | **30.00** |
| Teapot | **275.00** |
| Vegetable Bowl, 9″ d | **32.00** |

**TAMPICO.** Futura shape, 1955.

| | |
|---|---|
| Bowl | |
| 5½″ d | **8.00** |
| 6½″ d | **10.00** |
| 8″ d | **25.00** |
| 9″ d | **25.00** |
| 12″ d | **40.00** |
| Creamer and Sugar, cov | **30.00** |
| Cup and Saucer | **12.00** |
| Gravy, underplate | **25.00** |
| Pitcher, water | **25.00** |
| Plate | |
| Bread and Butter | **5.00** |
| Dinner | **10.00** |
| Salad | **7.50** |
| Platter, 13″ l | **25.00** |
| Relish, divided | **25.00** |
| Salt and Pepper Shakers, pr | **25.00** |
| Tidbit Tray, 2 tiers | **25.00** |

**MISCELLANEOUS**

| | |
|---|---|
| Console Set, crackle glaze, royal blue, black candlesticks, Oriental woman carrying bamboo baskets on shoulders, #1365, price for three piece set | **165.00** |

Figure, reclining draped female lute player with doe, deep high gloss maroon, #2507 .................... **195.00**
Vase, #1378, pink and gray, c1950 .. **25.00**

# ROBOTS

**Collecting Hints:** The name for robots comes from markings on the robot or box and from the trade. Hence, some robots have more than one name. Do research to know exactly what robot you have. A leading auctioneer of robots is Lloyd Ralston Toys, Fairfield, Connecticut.

Condition is critical. Damaged lithographed tin is almost impossible to repair and repaint. Toys in mint condition in the original box are the most desirable. The price difference between a mint robot and one in very good condition may be as high as 200%.

Working condition is important, but not critical. Many robots never worked well, and larger robots stripped their gearing quickly. The rarer the robot, the less important is the question of working condition.

Finally, if you play with your robot, do not leave the batteries in the toy. If they leak or rust, the damage may destroy the value of the toy.

**History:** Atomic Robot Man, made in Japan between 1948 and 1949, is the grandfather of all robot toys. He is an all metal wind-up toy, less than 5" high and rather crudely made. Japanese robots of the early 1950s tended to be the friction or wind-up variety, patterned in brightly lithographed tin and made from recycled materials.

By the late 1950s robots had entered the battery-powered age. Limited quantities of early models were produced; parts from one model were used in later models with slight or no variations. The robot craze was enhanced by Hollywood's production of movies such as "Destination Moon" (1950) and "Forbidden Planet" (1956). Roby the Robot came from this latter movie.

Many Japanese manufacturers were small and lasted only a few years. Leading firms include Horikawa Toys, Nomura Toys, and Yonezawa Toys. Cragstan was an American importer who sold Japanese-made toys under its own label. Marx and Ideal entered the picture in the 1970s. Modern robots are being imported from China and Taiwan.

The TV program "Lost in Space" (1965–68) inspired copies of its robot character. However, the quality of the late 1960s toys began to suffer as more and more plastic was added; robots were redesigned to reduce sharp edges as required by the United States government.

Modern robots include R2D2 and C3PO from the Star Wars epics, Twiki from NBC's "Buck Rodgers," and V.I.N.C.E.N.T. from Disney's "The Black Hole." Robots are firmly established in American science fiction and among collectors.

**References:** Teruhisa Kitahara, *Tin Toy Dreams: Robots,* Chronicle Books, 1985; Teruhisa Kitahara, *Yesterday's Toys, & Robots, Spaceships, and Monsters,* Chronicle Books, 1988; Robert Maline, *The Robot Book,* Push Pin Press/Harcourt Brace, 1978; Crystal and Leland Payton, *Space Toys,* Collectors Compass, 1982; Stephen J. Sansweet, *Science Fiction Toys and Models,* Vol. 1, Starlog Press, 1980.

**Note:** The following abbreviations are used:
SH = Horikawa Toys
TM = K. K. Masutoku Toy Factory
TN = Nomura Toys
Y = Yonezawa Toys

Attacking Martian Robot, tin, brown, red feet, walks with swinging arms, battery operated, orig box, S–H Company, 1950s .................... **350.00**
Big Max Robot, plastic, remote control, Remco, 1958 .................... **280.00**
Blazer Superhero Robot, tin, red, yellow, blue, and black, plastic arms, windup, orig box, Bullmark, 1960s . **175.00**
Captain Future Superhero Robot, tin litho, vinyl cape, walks with swinging arms, windup, Japan, 1960s ....... **125.00**
Dalek Robot, 6½" h, orig box, Marx, 1965 .......................... **225.00**
Ding–A–Lings, 5½" h, fireman, plastic, Topper Corp, 1970s .............. **50.00**
Dynamic Fighter Robot, Junior Toy Company, 1960s ................. **120.00**
Excavator Robot, S–H Company, 1960s **150.00**
Gear Robot, tin, gray, red feet, gray plastic arms, Y Company, 1960s ....... **450.00**
Golden Roto Robot, tin litho and plastic, battery operated, S–H Company, 1960s ......................... **250.00**
Hysterical Robot, walks forward, shakes head, S–H Company, 1960s ....... **275.00**
Japanese Robot Warrior, plastic, walks forward, ST, 1960s ............... **75.00**
Lost In Space Robot, 22" h, battery operated, Masuyada, 1985 .......... **120.00**
Mars Explorer Robot, S–H Company, 1950s ......................... **425.00**
Martian Robot, SJM Company, 1970s . **120.00**
Mighty Robot, tin, windup, sparkling chest, walks ..................... **95.00**
Monster Robot, space helmet reveals growling lighted dragon, walks ..... **95.00**
New Astronaut Robot, plastic, brown, orange guns, rotating body, blinking lights, battery operated, S–H Co, 1970s ......................... **140.00**
Piston Robot, orig box, S–H Company, 1960s ......................... **225.00**

**Battery Operated, litho tin, red chest, blue arms, legs, and head, walks, chest opens, gun shoots, rotates 360 degrees, marked "Made in Japan," 11¼" h, $160.00.**

Planet Robot, light blue, metal claws, battery operated, KO, 1960s ....... **140.00**
Radar Robot, S–H Company, 1970s ... **135.00**
Robby The Robot, 4" h, windup, Masudaya, 1985 .................... **20.00**
Robot 2500, lighted eye, flashing chest, Durham Ind, 1970s ............... **110.00**
Rom, 13" h, plastic, three attachments and instruction sheet, Parker Brothers, 1979 .......................... **50.00**
Rotate O Matic Super Astronaut, tin litho, battery operated, S–H Company, 1960s ..................... **75.00**
Rusher Robot, plastic, gray, black rubber wheels, S–H Company, 1960s .. **225.00**
SH, tin, five actions, Japanese, 1950s, orig box ........................ **200.00**
Shogun Warrior, tin litho, plastic head, windup, Tamara, 1960s ........... **140.00**
Space Patrol Robot, tin, gray and red, battery operated, S–H Co, 1950s ... **225.00**
Star Strider Robot, red, Horikawa ..... **200.00**
Super Hero Robot, tin litho, vinyl head, ST, 1960s ....................... **125.00**
Video Robot, tin, space scenes, S–H Company, 1960s ................. **145.00**
V.I.N.C.E.N.T., 3½" h, plastic, gray, windup, Marx, 1980 .............. **15.00**
Wizard of Oz Tin Man Robot, plastic, silver and blue, Remco, 1969 ...... **175.00**
Yakkity Yob, plastic, turquoise and red, manually operated, Eldon, 1960s ... **300.00**
Zerak The Blue Destroyer, display case, Ideal, 1968 ...................... **125.00**

# ROCK 'N' ROLL

**Collecting Hints:** Many rock 'n' roll collections are centered around one artist. Flea markets and thrift shops are good places to look for rock 'n' roll items. Prices range according to the singer or group. The stars who have died usually command a higher price.

Glossy 8 x 10's of singers, unautographed, are generally worth $1.00.

**History:** Rock music can be traced back to early rhythm and blues music. It progressed and reached its golden age in the 1950s. The current nostalgia craze of the 1950s has produced some modern rock 'n' roll which is well received. Rock 'n' roll memorabilia exists in large quantities, each singer or group having many promotional pieces made.

**References:** Les R. Docks, *American Premium Record Guide, 1900–1965, Fourth Edition,* Books Americana, 1992; Alison Fox, *Rock & Pop,* Boxtree Ltd. (London), 1988; Anthony J. Gribin and Matthew M. Schiff, *Doo-Wop: The Forgotten Third Of Rock 'n Roll,* Krause Publications, 1992; Paul Grushkin, *The Art of Rock—Posters From Presley To Punk,* Abbeville Press, 1986; David K. Henkel, *The Official Price Guide To Rock And Roll,* House of Collectibles, 1992. Hilary Kay, *Rock and Roll Collectables,* Sotheby's; Karen and John Lesniweski, *Kiss Collectibles: Identification And Value Guide,* Avon Books, 1993; Norman E. Martinus and Harry L. Rinker, *Warman's Paper,* Wallace–Homestead, 1993; Neal Umphred, *Goldmine's Rock 'n Roll 45 RPM Record Price Guide, Second Edition,* Krause Publications, 1992.

**See:** Beatles and Presley, Elvis.

Anka, Paul
 Handkerchief ..................... **12.00**
 Record, *Diana,* long play, ABC Paramount ........................ **12.00**
Avalon, Frankie, pinback button, Frankie Avalon–Venus, 3½", black and white portrait, bright pink rim ...... **20.00**
Beatles, stockings, pr, orig pkg ....... **95.00**
Bee Gees
 Scrapbook, 9 x 12", 34 pgs ........ **15.00**
 Thermos, plastic, yellow .......... **15.00**
Berry, Chuck, record, *Johnny B Goode,* 78 rpm, Chess ................... **10.00**
Charles, Ray, autograph, photo, 8 x 10", black and white glossy ............ **40.00**
Chicago, poster, album insert, 22 x 33", sepia photos, group name in shades of blue, Columbia Records, c1970 . **12.00**
Chubby Checker
 Autograph, photo, 8 x 10", black and white glossy, sgd "It Ain't Over Till It's Over, Keep It Up, Love Chubby Checker 86" .................... **30.00**
 Record, *The Class,* 78 rpm, Parkway **45.00**
Clark, Dick
 Pennant, American Bandstand, paper, 7½ x 12", adv ................. **5.00**

Pinback Button, 3" d, litho tin, black and white photo, dark green ground ........ **10.00**
Record Case, 5 x 8 x 8", cardboard, full color photo and signature, blue, white plastic handle, brass closure, holds 45 rpm records ... **40.00**
Tie Clip, 1¾" h, Dick Clark American Bandstand, gold colored metal ... **10.00**
Watch Fob, The Band–Standers, jitter bugging couple, music notes, marked "Ajax Belt" ........ **25.00**

Dave Clark Five
Figure, 3" h, three from set of 5, plastic, two with name tag, mid 1960s **50.00**
Program, Dave Clark Five Show, Arthur Kimbrell Presents, 1964, English ........ **45.00**

Dean, James, book, *I, James Dean,* T T Thomas, Popular Library, 1957, soft cover, 4 x 7", 128 pgs ........ **20.00**
Duran Duran, game, Duran Duran Into The Arena, Milton Bradley, 1985 copyright ........ **15.00**
Dylan, Bob, sheet music, 9 x 12", 4 pgs, *It Ain't Me, Babe,* black and white photo front cover, 1964 copyright .. **15.00**
Eddy, Duane, record, *Ring Of Fire* and *Bobbie,* 7 x 7" paper slip cover, Jamie label, 1961 ........ **12.00**
Everly Brothers, sheet music, 9 x 12", 4 pgs, *So It Always Will Be,* pink tone photo on front cover, 1963 copyright **10.00**

**Sheet Music, *Blue Suede Shoes,* Carl Perkins, $15.00.**

Fats Domino, photo, 10 x 8", color, seated at piano ........ **30.00**
Fleetwood Mac, poster, 33 x 46", Jan 1970 concert, Deutsches Museum, Munich, West Germany ........ **30.00**
Grateful Dead, poster, 14 x 20", Grateful Dead Fan Club, black and white photo, gold and blue background, marked "The Golden Road To Unlimited Devotion," late 1960s ........ **50.00**
Haley, Bill and His Comets, Lobby Card, 11 x 14", *Don't Knock The Rock,* Columbia, 1957 ........ **25.00**
Herman's Hermits, record, *The End Of The World* and *I'm Henry VIII, I Am,* MGM label, 1965 ........ **15.00**
Holly, Buddy, record, "Words of Love," 45 rpm, Coral ........ **18.00**
Joplin, Janis, book cover, 13 x 20", paper, full color picture of Cheap Thrills album, 1969 ........ **10.00**

Kiss
Belt Buckle, 3¾", oval, brass, Kiss inscription, red, amber, and silver, blue background, 1977 copyright **15.00**
Colorforms, MIB ........ **25.00**
Costume, Gene Simmons, molded and diecut plastic mask, vinyl and fabric costume, boxed, Collegeville Costumes, 1978 copyright ....... **25.00**
Game, Kiss on Tour, MIB ........ **55.00**
Mirror, printed black portrait design, silver background, wood frame, late 1970s ........ **30.00**
Puzzle, jigsaw, MIB ........ **45.00**

Lauper, Cyndi, photo, 11 x 14", black and white glossy ........ **85.00**
Lewis, Jerry Lee, record, *Whole Lot of Shakin' Going On* and *It'll Be Me,* 45 rpm, Sun label, 1956 ........ **20.00**

Monkees
Bracelet, orig card ........ **35.00**
Game, 17" sq board, four unpunched figures, 7½" plastic guitar with rubber band strings, unpunched spinner, boxed, Transogram, 1967 ... **75.00**
Guitar, 20" h, plastic, full color diecut paper label, Mattel, 1966 copyright **75.00**
Magazine, *16 Magazine,* Vol 8, #9, February 1967, features Monkees and various other performers, 68 pgs ........ **12.00**
Playing Cards, 52 card deck, black and white photos, boxed, Ed–U–Cards, 1966 ........ **25.00**
Puppet, 5" h, Mickey Dolenz, plastic torso, movable arms, molded vinyl head, brown curly hair, 1970 copyright ........ **15.00**
Sunglasses, Monkees Shades ....... **35.00**
Thermos ........ **55.00**
Viewmaster Reel, set of 3, Last Wheelbarrow to Pokeyville ...... **10.00**

Moody Blues, poster, 18½ x 25½", April 1, 1970 concert, Terrace Ballroom, Salt Lake City, UT ........ **50.00**

Nelson, Ricky
Earrings, clip on, black and white photo, card marked "Broadway

Creation/American Styles Jewelry (sic)" .......... **7.50**
Photograph, autographs of family, matted, framed .......... **150.00**

Orbison, Roy, sheet music, 9 x 12", 4 pgs, *Leah,* black and white photo front cover, Acuff–Rose Publications, Nashville, 1962 copyright .......... **12.00**

Osmonds, lunch box, 7 x 8 x 4", litho metal, thermos, unused, 1973 copyright .......... **20.00**

Rolling Stones
Book, *Rolling Stones Pixerama Foldbook,* 12 glossy photos, 1964 .......... **25.00**
Magazine, *Life,* July 14, 1972, Rolling Stones cover article, 78 pgs .......... **10.00**
Program, Rolling Stones Show Concert, John Smith Production, August 23–30, 1964 .......... **100.00**

Simon & Garfunkel, poster, album insert, 22 x 33", black and white head photo, outline body with full color bridge and sunset scene, 1968 Columbia Records copyright .......... **15.00**

The Doors, poster, 24 x 36", white logo, green border on bottom, Doors Production Corp, 1968 copyright .......... **20.00**

**Jigsaw Puzzle, The Doors, black and white photo image, 10 x 8", $15.00.**

Van Halen, Eddie, photo, 8 x 10", color **50.00**

Woodstock
Book, *Woodstock 69,* Scholastic Book Services, Joseph J Sia, 1970 copyright, 124 pgs .......... **25.00**
Pin, 1½", Woodstock 69, enameled brass, white dove on blue guitar central design, red background .......... **30.00**

# NORMAN ROCKWELL

**Collecting Hints:** Learn all you can about Norman Rockwell if you plan to collect his many artworks. His original artworks and illustrations have been transferred onto various types of objects by clubs and manufacturers.

**History:** Norman Rockwell, the famous American artist, was born on February 3, 1894. His first professional illustrations were for a children's book, *Tell Me Why Stories,* at age 18. Next he worked for *Boy's Life* magazine. Then he illustrated for the Boy Scouts and other magazines. By his death in November 1978, he had painted over 2,000 paintings.

Many of his paintings were done in oil and reproduced as magazine covers, advertisements, illustrations, calendars, and book sketches. Over 320 of these paintings became covers for the *Saturday Evening Post.*

Norman Rockwell painted everyday people in everyday situations with a little humor mixed in with the sentiment. His paintings and illustrations are well loved because of this sensitive nature. He painted people he knew and places with which he was familiar. New England landscapes are found in many of his illustrations.

Because his works are so well liked, they have been reproduced on many objects. These new collectibles should not be confused with the original artwork and illustrations. The new collectibles, however, offer Norman Rockwell illustrations to the average pocketbook and serve to keep his work alive.

**References:** Denis C. Jackson, *The Norman Rockwell Identification and Value Guide,* published by author, 1985; Mary Moline, *Norman Rockwell Collectibles Value Guide, Sixth Edition,* Green Valley World, 1988.

**Collectors' Club:** Rockwell Society of America, 597 Saw Mill River Road, Ardsley, NY 10502.

**Museums:** The Norman Rockwell Museum at the Old Corner House, Stockbridge, MA; Norman Rockwell Museum, Northbrook, IL.

Bell
Gorham
1975, Santa's Helper .......... **45.00**
1982, Lovers .......... **30.00**
1983, Christmas Medley .......... **30.00**
Grossman, Dave
1975, Christmas, first edition .......... **30.00**
1976, Ben Franklin Bicentennial . **28.00**
1979, Leapfrog .......... **50.00**

Figurine
Gorham
1976, Saying Grace .......... **150.00**
1980, Four Seasons, A Helping Hand, price for set of 4 .......... **450.00**
1982, Jolly Coachman .......... **50.00**
1983, Christmas Dancers .......... **75.00**
Dave Grossman Designs, Inc.
1973, No Swimming .......... **45.00**
1978, At The Doctors .......... **125.00**
1980, Exasperated Nanny .......... **125.00**

1982, Doctor and the Doll ...... **125.00**
1983, The Graduate ............ **32.00**
Lynell Studios
1979, Snow Queen ............. **85.00**
1980, Cradle of Love ........... **85.00**
1981, A Daily Prayer ........... **30.00**
Rockwell Museum
1978, Bedtime ................. **50.00**
1979, Bride & Groom .......... **90.00**
1980, Wrapping Christmas Presents **120.00**
1981, Music Maker ............. **90.00**
1982, Giving Thanks ........... **160.00**
1983, Painter .................. **90.00**
Ingot
Franklin Mint
1972, Spirit of Scouting, price for set of 12 .................... **275.00**
1974, Tribute to Robert Frost, price for set of 12 ................ **285.00**
Hamilton Mint
1975, Saturday Evening Post Covers, price for set of 12 ........ **210.00**
1977, Charles Dickens .......... **50.00**
Magazine
*American Artist,* July, 1976, Self Portrait and article ................ **15.00**
*Country Gentleman,* 1979, memorial issue ........................ **20.00**
*Saturday Evening Post,* August, 1977, 250th Edition, Rockwell cov, illus, and portfolio .................. **25.00**
Magazine Cover
*American Boy*
1916, Dec .................... **30.00**
1920, April .................... **27.50**
*American Legion,* 1978, July ....... **5.00**
*Boys Life*
1915, Aug .................... **50.00**
1947, Feb ..................... **45.00**
1957, June .................... **42.50**
*Colliers,* 1919
March 1 ...................... **25.00**
April 19 ...................... **20.00**
*Country Gentleman*
1918, Feb 9 ................... **50.00**
1920, May 8 .................. **48.50**
1922, March 18 ............... **45.00**
*Family Circle,* 1967, Dec, Santa Claus **10.00**
*Fisk Club News,* 1917, May ....... **18.00**
*Jack and Jill,* 1974, Dec ........... **5.00**
*Literary Digest*
1918, Dec 14 ................. **30.00**
1920, Sept 4 .................. **25.00**
1922, April 15 ................. **18.00**
*Look,* 1964, July 14 .............. **10.00**
*McCall's,* 1964, Dec .............. **12.00**
*Parents*
1939, Jan ..................... **10.00**
1951, May .................... **9.00**
*Red Cross,* April, 1918 ............ **25.00**
*Saturday Evening Post*
1916, Oct 14 .................. **100.00**

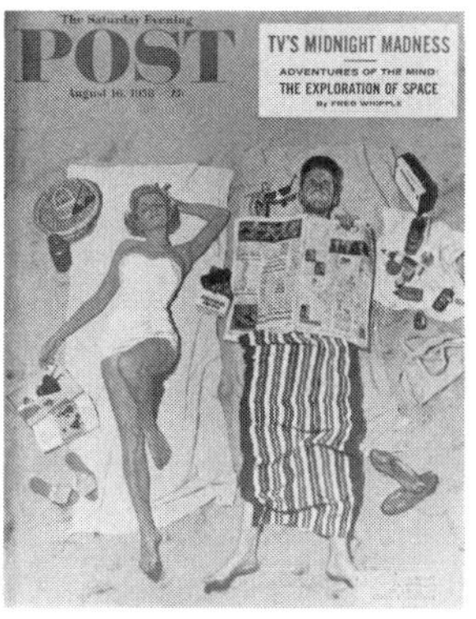


**Magazine, *Saturday Evening Post,* August 16, 1958, $20.00.**

1918, Jan 26 .................. **90.00**
1920, June 19 ................. **65.00**
1922, Feb 18 .................. **85.00**
1945, March 21 ............... **70.00**
1946, Nov 16 ................. **25.00**
1950, April 29 ................. **80.00**
1952, Aug 30 .................. **40.00**
1955, March 12 ............... **20.00**
1957, Sept 7 .................. **21.50**
1960, Feb 13 .................. **60.00**
1962, Jan 13 .................. **12.00**
1963, Sept 12, John F Kennedy .. **12.00**
*Scouting*
1934, Feb ..................... **10.00**
1944, Dec .................... **12.00**
1953, Oct ..................... **8.50**
*TV Guide,* 1970, May 16 .......... **5.00**
*Yankee,* 1972, Aug .............. **9.50**
Paperweight, River Shore ............ **100.00**
Plate
Franklin Mint
1970, Bringing Home The Tree .. **330.00**
1971, Under The Mistletoe ...... **175.00**
1972, The Carolers ............. **165.00**
1973, Trimming The Tree ....... **165.00**
1974, Hanging The Wreath ...... **180.00**
1975, Home For Christmas ...... **190.00**
Gorham
Boy Scout, 1975, Our Heritage .. **60.00**
Christmas Series
1974, Tiny Tim .............. **65.00**
1975, Good Deeds ........... **64.00**
1976, Christmas Trio ......... **60.00**
1977, Yuletide Reckoning ..... **45.00**
1978, Planning Christmas Visits **25.00**
1979, Santa's Helpers ......... **20.00**
1980, Letter to Santa ......... **25.00**
1981, Santa Plans His Visit .... **30.00**
1982, The Jolly Coachman .... **30.00**
1983, Christmas Dancers ...... **30.00**
1984, Christmas Medley ...... **30.00**
Four Seasons, price for set of 4
1971, A Boy & His Dog ....... **400.00**

1972, Young Love ............ **200.00**
1973, Ages of Love ........... **300.00**
1974, Grandpa & Me ......... **175.00**
1975, Me & My Pal .......... **200.00**
1976, Grand Pals ............ **200.00**
1978, The Tender Years ....... **115.00**
1979, A Helping Hand ........ **100.00**
1980, Dad's Boy ............. **130.00**
1981, Old Timers ............ **100.00**
1982, Life With Father ........ **100.00**
1983, Old Buddies ........... **115.00**
1984, Traveling Salesman ..... **115.00**

Grossman Designs, Dave
Annual Series, bas–relief
1979, Leapfrog ............. **50.00**
1980, Lovers ............... **60.00**
1981, Dreams of Long Ago .... **60.00**
1982, Doctor And The Doll ... **65.00**
Christmas Series, bas–relief
1980, Christmas Trio, FE ...... **80.00**
1981, Santa's Good Boys ...... **75.00**
1982, Faces of Christmas ...... **75.00**
Huckleberry Finn Series
1979, The Secret ............ **49.00**
1980, Listening ............. **40.00**
1981, No Kings Nor Dukes .... **40.00**
Tom Sawyer Series
1976, Whitewashing Fence .... **75.00**
1977, Take Your Medicine .... **50.00**
1978, Lost In Cave .......... **50.00**

Lynell Studios
Christmas
1979, Snow Queen .......... **30.00**
1980, Surprises For All ........ **30.00**
Mother's Day
1980, Cradle of Love ......... **40.00**
1981, Mother's Blessing ....... **30.00**
1983, Dear Mother .......... **26.00**

River Shore
1979, Spring Flowers .......... **120.00**
1980, Looking Out To Sea ...... **110.00**
1982, Jennie & Tina ........... **40.00**

Rockwell Museum
American Family Series
1978, Baby's First Step ........ **80.00**
1979, First Prom ............ **30.00**
American Family II Series
1980, New Arrival .......... **40.00**
1981, At The Circus .......... **96.00**

Rockwell Society
Christmas Series
1974, Scotty Gets His Tree .... **160.00**
1975, Angel With Black Eye ... **100.00**
1976, Golden Christmas ...... **55.00**
1977, Toy Shop Window ...... **50.00**
1978, Christmas Dream ....... **50.00**
1979, Somebody's Up There ... **30.00**
1980, Scotty Plays Santa ...... **32.00**
1981, Wrapped Up In Christmas **30.00**
1982, Christmas Courtship .... **30.00**
1983, Santa on the Subway .... **30.00**
1984, Santa in his Workshop .. **25.00**

**Limited Edition Plate, Edwin M. Knowles, Rockwell Society, Rediscovered Women Series, Dreaming in the Attic, 8½" d, $25.00.**

Heritage Series
1977, Toy Maker ............. **260.00**
1978, The Cobbler ........... **155.00**
1979, Lighthouse Keeper's Daughter .................. **80.00**
1980, Ship Builder ........... **60.00**
1981, Music Maker ........... **30.00**
1982, The Tycoon ............ **20.00**
1983, Painter ............... **25.00**
1984, Story Teller ............ **25.00**
Mother's Day Series
1976, A Mother's Love ........ **120.00**
1977, Faith ................. **75.00**
1978, Bedtime ............... **100.00**
1979, Reflections ............ **38.00**
1980, A Mother's Pride ....... **30.00**
1981, After The Party ......... **25.00**
1982, Cooking Lesson ........ **25.00**
1983, Add Two Cups ......... **24.00**
1984, Grandma's Courting Dress **25.00**

Royal Devon
Christmas Series
1975, Downhill Daring ....... **50.00**
1976, The Christmas Gift ...... **90.00**
1977, The Big Moment ....... **80.00**
1978, Puppets For Christmas ... **45.00**
1979, One Present Too Many .. **35.00**
1980, Gramps Meets Gramps .. **35.00**
Mother's Day Series
1975, Doctor And The Doll ... **85.00**
1976, Puppy Love ............ **80.00**
1977, The Family ............ **90.00**
1978, Mother's Day Off ....... **72.00**
1979, Mother's Evening Out ... **35.00**
1980, Mother's Treat ......... **35.00**

Playing Cards, Four Seasons, unopened, orig box ....................... **12.00**

Stein
Gorham, Pensive Pals ............. **37.50**
Rockwell Museum
Braving The Storm ............. **75.00**
Fishin' Pals .................. **75.00**
For A Good Boy .............. **95.00**
Looking Out To Sea ............ **125.00**
The Music Lesson ............. **90.00**

# ROSEVILLE POTTERY

**Collecting Hints:** Because of the availability of pieces in Roseville's later commercial ware, the prices for this type of ware are stable and unlikely to rise rapidly.

For the popular middle period patterns, which were made during the Depression and had limited production and sale, the prices are strong. Among the most popular patterns from this middle period are Blackberry, Cherry Blossom, Falline, Ferella, Jonquil, Morning Glory, Sunflower, and Windsor. The Art Deco craze has focused on Futura, especially the more angular shaped pieces.

Pinecone in blue or brown glaze continues to have a strong following as do the earlier lines of Juvenile and Donatello.

Desirable shapes include baskets, bookends, cookie jars, ewers, tea sets, and wall pockets.

Most pieces are marked. However, during the middle period paper stickers were used. These often were removed, leaving the piece unmarked.

Roseville made over one hundred and fifty different lines or patterns. Novice collectors would benefit from reading one of the several books about Roseville and viewing the offerings of dealers who specialize in art pottery. Collections generally are organized around a specific pattern or shape.

**History:** In the late 1880s a group of investors purchased the J. B. Owens Pottery in Roseville, Ohio, and made utilitarian stoneware items. In 1892 the firm was incorporated and joined by George F. Young who became general manager. Four generations of Youngs controlled Roseville until the early 1950s.

A series of acquisitions began: Midland Pottery of Roseville in 1898, Clark Stoneware Plant in Zanesville (formerly used by Peters and Reed), and Muskingum Stoneware (Mosaic Tile Company) in Zanesville. 1898 also saw offices move from Roseville to Zanesville.

In 1900 Roseville developed its art pottery line—Rozane. Ross Purdy designed a line to compete with Weller's Louwelsa. Rozane became a trade name to cover a large series of lines by designers such as Christian Neilson, John J. Herold, and Gazo Fudji. The art lines of hand decorated underglaze pottery were made in limited quantities after 1919.

The success of Roseville depended on its commercial lines, first developed by John J. Herald and Frederick Rhead in the first decade of the 1900s. Decorating techniques included transfers, pouncing (a method producing a pattern on the ware which could be followed), and air brush or sponging following embossed motifs. Among the lines from this early period are Dutch, Juvenile, Cameo, and Holland.

George Young retired in 1918. Frank Ferrell replaced Harry Rhead, who had replaced Frederick Rhead, as art director. Ferrell developed over 80 lines, the first being Sylvan. The economic depression of the 1930s caused Roseville to look for new product lines. Pine Cone was introduced in 1935, made for 15 years, and issued in over 75 shapes.

In the 1940s a series of high gloss glazes were tried to revive certain lines. Other changes were made to respond to the fluctuating contemporary markets. Mayfair and Wincraft date from this period. In 1952 Raymor dinnerware was produced. None of these changes brought economic success back to Roseville. In November, 1954, Roseville was bought by the Mosaic Tile Company.

**References:** John W. Humphries, *A Price Guide To Roseville Pottery By The Numbers,* published by author, 1993; Sharon and Bob Huxford, *Roseville Pottery: Price Guide No. 9,* Collector Books, 1993; Sharon and Bob Huxford, (eds.), *The Collectors Encyclopedia of Roseville Pottery, First Series,* Collector Books, 1976, 1993 value update; Sharon and Bob Huxford, *The Collectors Encyclopedia of Roseville Pottery, Second Series,* Collector Books, 1980, 1993 value update; Dana Gehman Morykan and Harry L. Rinker, *Warman's Country Antiques & Collectibles,* Wallace–Homestead, 1992.

**Collectors' Club:** American Art Pottery Association, 9825 Upton Circle, Bloomington, MN 55431.

**Note:** For pieces in the middle and upper price range see *Warman's Antiques And Their Prices.*

Basket
- Columbine, blue, 376–10, 1/123 ... **175.00**
- Florane, 10″ d ... **135.00**
- Peony, pink, 378–10, 1/119 ... **135.00**
- Snowberry, blue, 1BK–10, 1/133 ... **145.00**
- White Rose, pink, 363–10, 1/112 .. **115.00**

Bookends, pr, Pine Cone, brown ... **185.00**

Bowl
- Carnelian I, pedestal, blue ... **55.00**
- Clematis, blue, 12″ d ... **145.00**
- Fuchsia, green, 847–8 ... **95.00**
- Pine Cone, blue, 179–9 ... **150.00**

Candle Holders, pr
- Fuchsia, green, 1133–5 ... **165.00**
- Rosecraft, blue, 8″ h ... **80.00**
- Zephyr Lily, green, 1163–4½ ... **75.00**

Candlestick, Donatello, no handle, 1915, 8″ h ... **225.00**

Cereal Bowl, sitting puppy ... **45.00**

Child's Feeding Dish, sitting rabbit ... **120.00**

Console Bowl
- Fuchsia, green, 353–14 ... **150.00**
- Teasel, beige, 345–12 ... **55.00**

White Rose, blue, 393–12, 2/133 .. **95.00**
Zephyr Lily, green, 476–10 ........ **85.00**
Console Set, Thorn Apple, brown, 13" w bowl, pair of 5½" h double bud vases .......................... **185.00**
Cornucopia
Columbine, 7" h ................ **65.00**
Foxglove, blue, 166–6, 2/135 ...... **45.00**
Snowberry, 6" h ................. **45.00**
White Rose, blue, double, 145–8, 1/113 ......................... **85.00**
Creamer, child's, sitting puppy ....... **95.00**
Ewer
Bleeding Heart, blue, 972–10, 1/109 **175.00**
Foxglove, blue, 5–10, 1/123 ....... **155.00**
Gardenia, tan, 618, 15" h ......... **225.00**
Magnolia, brown, 15–15, 1/121 ... **245.00**
Flowerpot and Saucer, Bushberry, 5" h **160.00**
Hanging Basket
Apple Blossom, green ............ **135.00**
Bushberry, pink ................. **150.00**
Fuchsia, brown ................. **195.00**
Ixia, yellow .................... **185.00**
White Rose, blue ................ **145.00**
Zephyr Lily, green ............... **125.00**
Jardiniere
Columbine, blue, 655–4 .......... **65.00**
Fuchsia, brown, 645–4 ........... **85.00**
Lamp, Carnelian II, green, 12" h ..... **375.00**
Pitcher
Bushberry, blue, ice lip ........... **225.00**
Cow, c1916 .................... **275.00**
Creamware Medallion, 4" h ....... **55.00**
Planter, Magnolia, green, 183–6, 2/137 **48.00**
Plate, Jack Horner, rolled edge, 8" d .. **95.00**
Urn, Cherry Blossom, brown
6" h, 1/95/3/5 .................... **145.00**
7" h, 1/95/1/2 .................... **185.00**

**Vase, Laurel 8, yellow, triangular foil label, 8" h, $125.00.**

Vase
Apple Blossom .................. **95.00**
Baneda, green, 2/123/3/1, 7" h ..... **235.00**
Bushberry, brown, 156–8, 2/147 ... **90.00**
Cherry Blossom, pink, 1/95/3/2, 7" h **225.00**
Clematis, brown, 128–8, 1/127 .... **50.00**
Cosmos, tan, 135–8 .............. **120.00**
Foxglove, green and pink, 53–14 ... **275.00**
Fuchsia, brown, 900–9 ........... **185.00**
Futura, green, 289–9, 1/160 ....... **190.00**
Ixia
Green, 856–8, 2/119 ........... **75.00**
Yellow, 854–7 ................. **65.00**
Laurel, yellow
6" h, 1/99/2/4 .................. **90.00**
9" h, 1/99/2/2 .................. **175.00**
Magnolia, green, 98–15 ........... **225.00**
Mayfair, 10" h ................... **65.00**
Monticello, brown, 1/91/1/1, 4" h .. **130.00**
Pine Cone, blue, 711–10 .......... **425.00**
Savona, green, 12" h ............. **150.00**
Teasel, beige, 888–12, 2/124 ...... **55.00**
Tourmaline ...................... **45.00**
Tuscany, gray
7" h, 6" w ..................... **65.00**
8" h, 1/79/2/2 .................. **85.00**
White Rose, blue
147–8, 1/113 .................. **75.00**
979–6 ........................ **55.00**
987–9 ........................ **95.00**
Wincraft, green, 287–12 .......... **90.00**
Wall Pocket
Bushberry, brown ................ **145.00**
Clematis, brown ................. **100.00**
Lotus, red ...................... **340.00**
Sunflower, 1/85/1/2, 8" h .......... **485.00**
Zephyr Lily, brown ............... **125.00**
Window Box, Gardenia, green, 669–19 **115.00**

# ROYAL CHINA

**Collecting Hints:** Collectors tend to concentrate on specific patterns. Among the most favored are Bluebell (1940s), Currier and Ives (1949–50), Colonial Homestead (ca. 1951–52), Old Curiosity Shop (early 1950s), Regal (1937), Royalty (1936), blue and pink willow ware (1940s), and Windsor.

Royal China patterns were widely distributed. Colonial Homestead was sold by Sears through the 1960s. The result is that pieces are relatively common and prices moderate.

Because of easy accessibility, only purchase pieces in fine to excellent condition. Do not buy pieces whose surface is marked or marred in any way.

**History:** The Royal China Company, located in Sebring, Ohio, utilized remodeled facilities that originally housed the Oliver China Company and later the E. H. Sebring Company. Royal China began operations in 1934.

The company produced an enormous number of dinnerware patterns. The backs of pieces usually contain the names of the shape, line, and decoration. In addition to many variations of company backstamps, Royal China also produced objects with private backstamps. All records of these markings were lost in a fire in 1970.

The company's Currier and Ives pattern, designed by Gordon Parker, was introduced in 1949–50. Early marks were date coded. Other early 1950s patterns include Colonial Homestead and Old Curiosity Shop.

In 1964 Royal China purchased the French–Saxon China Company, Sebring, which it operated as a wholly owned subsidiary. On December 31, 1969, Royal China was acquired by the Jeannette Corporation. When fire struck the Royal China Sebring plant in 1970, Royal moved its operations to the French–Saxon plant.

The company changed hands several times, being owned briefly by the Coca–Cola Company, the J. Corporation from Boston, and Nordic Capitol of New York, New York. Production continued until August 1986 when operations ceased.

**References:** Jo Cunningham, *The Collector's Encyclopedia of American Dinnerware*, Collector Books, 1982, 1992 value update; Harvey Duke, *The Official Identification And Price Guide To Pottery And Porcelain, Seventh Edition*, House of Collectibles, 1989; and Lois Lehner, *Lehner's Encyclopedia of U. S. Marks on Pottery, Porcelain & Clay*, Collector Books, 1988.

**COLONIAL HOMESTEAD.** Heritage Series, introduced 1950–1952. Sold by Sears.

Bowl
- 5½" d, fruit ........ **3.00**
- 6¼" d, cereal ........ **5.00**

Cake Plate, 10" d, tab handles ........ **12.00**
Casserole, cov ........ **30.00**
Creamer and Sugar, cov ........ **12.00**
Cup and Saucer ........ **4.00**
Gravy, underplate ........ **18.00**
Plate
- 6" d, bread and butter ........ **1.50**
- 7" d, salad ........ **2.50**
- 10" d, dinner ........ **3.50**
- 12" d, chop ........ **12.00**

Salt and Pepper Shakers, pr ........ **10.00**
Teapot, cov ........ **35.00**

**CURRIER & IVES.** Blue and White scenic design, Cavalier Ironstone, introduced 1949–1950. Part of the Heritage Series.

Ashtray ........ **7.50**
Bowl
- 5½" d, fruit ........ **3.00**
- 6" d, cereal ........ **9.00**

Cake Plate, 10" d, tab handles ........ **12.00**
Casserole, covered ........ **50.00**
Creamer and Sugar, covered ........ **10.00**
Cup and Saucer ........ **3.50**
Gravy Boat ........ **10.00**
Mug ........ **10.00**
Pie Baker ........ **12.00**
Plate
- 6" d, bread and butter ........ **2.00**
- 10¼" d, dinner ........ **4.00**
- 12" d, chop ........ **15.00**

Platter, oval ........ **15.00**
Salt and Pepper Shakers, pr ........ **12.00**
Soup, flat ........ **6.00**
Vegetable, open
- 9" d ........ **10.00**
- 10" d ........ **18.00**

**Currier & Ives, fruit bowl, 5½" d, $3.00.**

**MEMORY LANE.** Pink and white.

Berry Bowl ........ **4.00**
Creamer ........ **5.00**
Cup and Saucer ........ **3.00**
Plate
- 6" d, bread and butter ........ **4.00**
- 10" d, dinner ........ **5.00**

Soup, flat ........ **4.50**
Sugar, open ........ **5.00**

**OLD CURIOSITY SHOP.** Cavalier shape, 1950s.

Ashtray ........ **5.00**
Bowl
- 5½" d ........ **3.50**
- 9" d ........ **12.00**
- 10" d ........ **16.50**

Cake Plate, 10" d, handles ........ **15.00**
Casserole, cov ........ **45.00**
Creamer and Sugar, cov ........ **10.00**
Cup and Saucer ........ **4.00**
Gravy ........ **10.00**
Plate
- 6" d, bread and butter ........ **2.00**
- 10" d, dinner ........ **4.00**

Salt and Pepper Shakers, pr ........ **10.00**
Soup, flat, 8½" d ........ **6.00**
Teapot ........ **50.00**

# SALOON COLLECTIBLES

**Collecting Hints:** Collectors concentrate on materials from the pre–prohibition (1918) era, with many recreating the decor of an old time saloon in one room of their house. The favorite motif is the western saloon, copied after the generic saloons of "B" movie westerns and the television cowboy programs of the 1950s and 1960s.

A few pioneering collectors are recreating the small urban neighborhood bars of the 1920s through the 1950s. "Cheers" imitations are common.

Saloon collectors are subject to heavy competition for their material from advertising, breweriana, coin operated, western, and whiskey memorabilia collectors. In addition, many modern bars like to decorate with older saloon items.

The current western decorating craze is creating a renewal of interest in saloon memorabilia. Prices that have been stable for almost a decade are showing signs of modest increase.

**History:** The American saloon always has been a refuge and playground for off duty males throughout history. Women and children often were forbidden to enter this masculine turf. Gambling, cursing, drinking, smoking, and fighting were the primary forms of entertainment at the saloon. The illusion exists that life was much more exciting in a yesteryear saloon than a modern bar.

The saloon consisted of many units–the back bar, the front bar, and the room itself. All types of materials existed to fill needs, from bottles to spittoons. In addition, most saloons featured a wealth of advertising from broadsides to mirrors. Its popularity as a meeting place assured advertisers that their messages would be read.

**References:** Roger Baker, *Old West Antiques & Collectibles Illustrated Price Guide*; George J. Baley, *Back Bar Breweriana: A Guide To Advertising, Beer Statues, and Beer Shelf Signs*, L–W Book Sales, 1992.

Advertising, figure, Teachers Scotch Whiskey ........ **35.00**

Back Bar, carved wood
- 94" l, mahogany, leaded windows and mirrors ........ **8,000.00**
- 190" l, stained glass columns, marble top, dated 1910 ........ **9,000.00**

Bottle
- Cylinder
  - Burke's Union Club, 8" h, clear .. **35.00**
  - Westminster Rye, 11" h, cut letters emb in gold ........ **100.00**
- Decanter
  - Belle of Kentucky, clear, ribbed, gold cut letters, stopper ....... **100.00**
  - Maryland Club, 8½" h, cut, fluted neck, cut stopper ........ **45.00**
  - Old Canterbury Whiskey, 10" h, three rows of oval cuts around neck, two rows around body, gold cut letters ........ **125.00**
  - Right and Ready Whiskey, Cortwright Co, New York, fluted neck and base, gold letters ......... **120.00**

Cash Register, National, brass, wood base, two drawers ........ **1,000.00**

Counter Display, 11½" h, 12" l, Cognac Brandy, Hennessy dog with bag, Schieffeinc Co, NY ........ **85.00**

Ice Chopper, cast steel, wood handle, Gilchrist ........ **25.00**

Match Dispenser, 3¾ x 2½ x 12", metal and cast iron, dark blue, black base, "1¢ Match Dispenser" ........ **125.00**

Photograph, interior scene with mustached bar keeper, fixtures, bar, 8 x 6", c1900 ........ **115.00**

Player Piano, coin–operated, rebuilt case, stained glass section lights up, includes rolls ........ **4,000.00**

Salt and Pepper Shakers, Cuckenheimer Whiskey, glass bottles ........ **15.00**

Shot Glass, etched, "Ruby Saloon" ... **20.00**

Sign
- Coles Peruvian Bark & Cherry Bitters, porcelain ........ **475.00**
- Ginger Cordial, Clayton and Russel, reverse painting on glass, 15 x 8" . **380.00**
- Old Overholt Pennsylvania Rye, gold, silver leaf, reverse painting on glass, orig ornate wood frame .... **400.00**
- Schmidt City Club, tin litho, 9" d ... **60.00**
- Sherwood Pure Rye, leaf lettering outlined in red and green, reverse painting on glass, orig ornate wood frame ........ **375.00**

Spittoon
- 6" d, 4" h, redware, small bottom, large mouth ........ **50.00**
- 7½" d, 4" h, pottery, brown, glazed, ribbed flared bowl, beaded rim, white mouth ........ **75.00**
- 8½" d, 5½" h, cast iron, white porcelain int., c1850 ........ **45.00**
- 24" d, 5½" h, porcelain, green, white int. ........ **35.00**

Tobacco Dispenser, "The Good Judge Recommends Right–Out Chewing Tobacco" ........ **150.00**

Token, brass, Deer Lodge, Montana .. **12.00**

Tray, 12" d, Straus, Gunst & Co, Full Dress Maryland Rye, tip, 1907 ..... **100.00**

Whiskey Dispenser, 15½" h, glass, etched, "Ask for Sanderson's Whiskey" ........ **475.00**

# SALT AND PEPPER SHAKERS

**Collecting Hints:** Collect only sets in very good condition. Make certain the set has the proper two pieces, and base if applicable. China shakers should show no signs of cracking. Original paint and decoration should be intact on all china and metal figures. All parts should be present, including the closure if important.

A collector will have to compete with collectors in other areas, e.g., advertising, animal groups, Blacks, and holiday collectibles. Many shakers will have souvenir labels which may have been added later to stock items. The form, not the label, is the important element.

Black figural shakers are rising in price. The same is true for advertising sets and comic and cartoon characters.

**History:** The Victorian era saw the advent of the elaborate glass and fine china salt and pepper shaker. The pioneering research work by Arthur Goodwin Peterson in books such as *Glass Salt Shakers: 1,000 Patterns* attracted collectors to this area. Figural and souvenir shakers, most dating from the mid–20th century and later, were looked down upon by this group.

This attitude is slowly changing. More and more people are collecting the figural and souvenir shakers, especially since prices are lower. Many of these patterns were made by Japanese firms and imported heavily after World War II.

Production of a form might continue for decades; hence, it is difficult to tell an early example from a modern one. This is one factor in keeping prices low.

**References:** Gideon Bosker, *Great Shakes: Salt and Pepper For All Tastes,* Abbeville Press, 1986; Gideon Bosker, *Salt and Pepper Shakers: Identification And Price Guide,* Avon Books, 1993; Melva Davern, *Collectors' Encyclopedia of Figural and Novelty Salt & Pepper Shakers, First Series* 1985, 1991 value update, *Second Series* 1990, 1993 value update; Collector Books, 1985; Helene Guarnaccia, *Salt & Pepper Shakers: Identification and Values, Book I* 1985, 1993 value update, *Book II* 1989, 1993 value update, *Book III,* 1991, *Book IV,* 1993, Collector Books; Mildred and Ralph Lechner, *The World Of Salt Shakers, Second Edition,* Collector Books, 1992; Arthur G. Peterson, *Glass Salt Shakers,* Wallace–Homestead, 1970, out–of–print; Mike Schneider, *The Complete Salt And Pepper Book,* Schiffer Publishing, Ltd., 1993.

**Collectors' Clubs:** Antique and Art Glass Salt Shaker Collectors Society, 2832 Rapidan Trail, Maitland, FL 32751; Novelty Salt and Pepper Shakers Club, 581 Joy Road, Battle Creek, MI 49017; Westmoreland Glass Society, 2712 Glenwood, Independence, MO 64052.

Advertising
- Blue Label, amber, beer bottles, tin tops . . . . **12.00**
- Falstaff, amber, beer bottles, tin tops **12.00**
- Fort Pitt Beer . . . . **12.00**
- Ken–L–Ration, dog and cat, plastic, 1950s . . . . **20.00**
- Mixmaster, plastic, 1950s . . . . **20.00**
- Nipper, phonograph, plastic, 1950s . **20.00**
- Pachmayr Gun Works, LA, shotgun shells, red, orig box . . . . **45.00**
- Ruppert, amber, beer bottles, tin tops **12.00**
- Schlitz, amber, beer bottles, tin tops **12.00**
- Seagrams Gin, glass . . . . **6.00**
- Texaco, gas pumps, plastic, decal dec **18.00**
- Westinghouse, washer and dryer, plastic, 1950s . . . . **20.00**

Ceramic
- Bananas, yellow and tan . . . . **6.50**
- Bell, pink flower, Rosemeade . . . . **35.00**
- Bloodhound Dog Heads, Rosemeade **35.00**
- Cactus, Rosemeade . . . . **12.00**
- Calico Cat, black . . . . **15.00**
- Chickens, Rosemeade . . . . **25.00**
- Christmas Trees . . . . **20.00**

**Fish, ceramic, one green, one brown, red trim, Japan, 2½" h, $3.00.**

- Conestoga Wagons, 3½", brown and black, white tops . . . . **8.50**
- Dutch Twins, Van Tellingen . . . . **21.00**
- Eggs in Basket, 2¾", white salt egg, brown pepper egg, brown and beige basket . . . . **7.50**
- Flamingos, Rosemeade . . . . **50.00**
- Humpty Dumpty, seated on wall . . . **24.00**
- Mickey Mouse, white glaze, c1940 . **45.00**
- Prairie Dogs, Rosemeade . . . . **40.00**
- Schmoos, Red Wing . . . . **110.00**
- Smokey The Bear . . . . **15.00**
- Turkeys, multicolored . . . . **15.00**

Chalkware, Mammy and Chef, white, black, and red . . . . **20.00**

Depression Glass
- American Sweetheart, monax, single **100.00**
- Banded Rings, dec . . . . **40.00**
- Diana, amber . . . . **65.00**
- English Hobnail, pink . . . . **70.00**
- Florentine No. 2, crystal . . . . **35.00**
- Hazel Atlas, cobalt blue . . . . **24.00**

Starlight, crystal . . . . . . . . . . . . . . . . . . **18.00**
Waterford, crystal . . . . . . . . . . . . . . . . **5.00**
Hand Painted
Amish Couple, 3½″ h, bearded man, black hat and boots, woman with white bonnet and apron . . . . . . . . . **10.00**
Doorway Garden, house door with salt and pepper as flowers, green lawn base . . . . . . . . . . . . . . . . . . . . . **15.00**
Mammy and Chef, marked "Japan" . **165.00**
Mermaids, 3″ h, reclining, blue–green bodies, long blonde hair . . . . . . . . **8.50**
Metal
Amish Couple, 3″ h, cast iron, hp, bright colors . . . . . . . . . . . . . . . . . . . **8.50**
Dogs, sitting, painted cast metal, green, applied glass eyes . . . . . . . . **85.00**
Grapes on branch, 3″ h, silvered cast metal, glass grapes . . . . . . . . . . . . . **10.00**
Pistol, 4″ l . . . . . . . . . . . . . . . . . . . . . . . **15.00**
Plastic
Barbeque Grill, 1950s . . . . . . . . . . . . **20.00**
Couple, in car, 1950s . . . . . . . . . . . . . **20.00**
Lawnmower, 1950s . . . . . . . . . . . . . . . **20.00**
Television, 1950s . . . . . . . . . . . . . . . . **20.00**
Willi and Millie, penguins, 1950s . . **20.00**

# SANTA CLAUS

**Collecting Hints:** The number of Santa Claus related items is endless. Collectors are advised to concentrate on one form (postcards, toys, etc.) or a brief time period. New collectors will find the hard plasic 1950s Santas easily accessible and generally at a reasonable price.

**History:** The idea for Santa Claus developed from stories about St. Nicholas, who lived about 300 A.D. By the 1500s, "Father Christmas" in England, "Pere Noel" in France, and "Weihnachtsmann" in Germany were well established.

Until the 1800s Santa Claus was pictured as a tall, thin, stately man wearing bishop's robes and riding a white horse. Washington Irving in *Knickerbocker's History of New York,* 1809, made him as a stout, jolly man who wore a broad brimmed hat and huge breeches and smoked a long pipe. The traditional Santa Claus image came from Clement C. Moore's poem "An Account of a Visit from St. Nicholas" (*Troy Sentinal,* NY, 1823) and the cartoon characterizations by Thomas Nast which appeared in *Harper's Weekly* between 1863 and 1886.

**References:** Ann Bahar, *Santa Dolls: Historical To Contemporary,* Hobby House Press, 1992; E. Willis Jones, *The Santa Claus Book,* Walker, 1976; Polly and Pam Judd, *Santa Dolls and Figurines Price Guide: Antique To Contemporary,* Hobby House Press, 1992; Maggie Rogers and Peter R. Hallinan, *The Santa Claus Picture Book: An Appraisal Guide,* E. P. Dutton, Inc., 1984.

**Additional Listings:** Christmas Items.

Advertising
Ornament, cardboard
Santa holding slate, inviting people to join Robesonia State Bank Christmas Club, 1932 . . . . . . . . . **5.00**
Santa with toys, Dundee Smart Clothes, Allentown, PA, 1941 . . **5.00**
Pinback Button, 1¼″, Orr's Dept Store, Santa, light green background, black letters, 1940–50 . . . **15.00**
Sign
Angelus Marshmallows, 9½ x 12″, cardboard, diecut, full color Santa, toys, and product, 1930s . . . . . . . . **200.00**
Greetings from Coca–Cola, 7 x 13″, cardboard, diecut, full color, easel back, 1948 . . . . . . . . . . . . . . . . . . . . **75.00**
Trade Card, Swoolson Spice Co, Santa and reindeer . . . . . . . . . . . . . **12.00**
Automata, battery operated, 9″, pulling toys from pack, Japan . . . . . . . . . . . . . **55.00**
Bank
5″ h, pewter, brass trim, relief Father Christmas . . . . . . . . . . . . . . . . . . . . . **295.00**
6½″ h, metal, Santa sleeping in chair, advertising figural type for many banks . . . . . . . . . . . . . . . . . . . . . . . . . **30.00**
11″ h, chalkware, Santa in chimney, pack of toys on back, 1950s . . . . . **25.00**
Book, *How Santa Filled the Christmas Stockings,* Stecher Litho Co, Rochester, NY, 1916 . . . . . . . . . . . . . . . . . . . . **12.00**
Candelabrum, brass, figural, Father Christmas, English . . . . . . . . . . . . . . . . **85.00**
Candy Box, cardboard, rect
Santa face on all sides, background color varies, string handle, 1950s **6.50**
Santa's head in corner, dark red background, 1930s . . . . . . . . . . . . . . . . . **10.00**
Candy Container
Cardboard, 8″ h, round, red flocked coat, opens at belt line, nodding

**Paper Dolls, Drayton, 16 x 11½″, $18.00.**

head on metal spring, West Germany, 1950s .................. **30.00**
Composition, 5″ h, composition face, rabbit fur beard, red felt body, Santa sitting on pile of wood logs, Germany, 1920s .................. **110.00**
Glass
5″ h, Father Christmas, standing, dark green, painted white beard, metal screw on lid/base, USA .. **100.00**
5½″ h, Father Christmas, red, foot in chimney, metal base, marked "Victory Candy Co, USA" ..... **75.00**
6″ h, Santa, standing, painted red, white, and black, plastic head, screw on lid, 1950s, USA ..... **65.00**
Papier Mache
4″ h, Santa, rotund, standing, red coat, gold trim, opening in base **35.00**
4½″ h, red coat, huge belly, white beard, jolly face, USA ........ **38.00**
6″ h, white coat with red trim, open pack, USA .................. **38.00**
9″ h, Santa standing in chimney, white coat with red and green trim, opening in base, 1920s .. **85.00**
Plaster, 8″ h, Father Christmas, molded, white mica covered long coat, black boots, white hood with chenille trim, long white beard, detailed painted face, opening in base, Germany, 1900–20s ....... **550.00**
Plastic
4″ h, soft plastic, white with black and red trim, head removes, 1960s ..................... **5.00**
5″ h, rotund, Santa holding white tennis racket, red coat, standing, USA, 1950s ................ **15.00**
Candy Mold, tin, Santa and sleigh .... **30.00**
Children's Books
Johnson, Annie Fellow, *Miss Santa Claus of the Pullman,* The Century Co, NY, 1913 ................. **6.50**
Moore, Clement, *The Night Before Christmas*
Cupples and Leon Co, publisher, NY, 1913 .................. **15.00**
John C Winston, publisher, Philadelphia, 1942, Everett Shin, illustrator .................... **12.00**
Page, Thomas Nelson, *A Captured Santa Claus,* Charles Scribner's & Sons, NY, 1905 ............... **6.50**
Figure
Bisque
2½″ h, red, white, and green, standing, marked "Japan," 1930s **18.00**
3½″ h, red and white, USA, 1950s **20.00**
Cardboard
3″ h, flat, inserted in slot in cardboard sleigh, USA, 1950s ..... **10.00**
4″ h, rolled red flocked coat, black legs, paper face, holding green tree, marked "Japan," 1930s ... **22.00**
6″ h, rolled red flocked coat, black legs, white celluloid face, holding white bell, marked "Japan," 1930s ..................... **30.00**

Celluloid
¾″ h, Santa in sleigh, one deer, marked "Japan," 1930s ....... **25.00**
3½″ l, red and cream Santa in shell sleigh, one deer ............. **28.00**
4″ h, Santa standing on three books, USA ........................ **22.00**
5″ h, Father Christmas, red and green, Japan ................. **35.00**
6½″ h, Santa, one hand to beard, other hand holding doll behind back, Japan ................. **38.00**
7″ l, Santa in sleigh, red, white, and green, one white deer, marked "Irwin, USA" ............... **40.00**
12″ l, red Santa, cardboard sleigh, four brown celluloid deer, Japan **48.00**

Chalk, 5″ h, standing, red and white, pack on back, USA, 1950s ...... **12.00**

Chenille, Japan
3″ h, green, bisque face ......... **18.00**
4″ h, white, paper face .......... **18.00**
5″ h, blue, bisque face .......... **22.00**
Composition
3½″ h, Father Christmas, long red coat, Germany ............... **30.00**
6″ l, Santa, rabbit fur beard, moss cart, pulled by composition deer, Germany .................... **200.00**
12″ l, Santa, rabbit fur beard, purple felt coat, wooden sleigh, Germany ....................... **350.00**

Cotton Batting
3″ h, red, black legs and arms, composition face, cardboard airplane, Japan ................. **75.00**
4″ h, red, black legs and arms, composition face, Japan ....... **40.00**
8″ h, white, black legs, white hands, composition face, Japan **90.00**

Home Made
11″ h, standing, pressed cardboard face, cloth stuffed body, mica cov base .................... **75.00**
14″ h, stuffed cloth body, red coat, blue pants, stitched face, white spun glass trim ............... **50.00**

Papier Mache
7″ h, red coat with black trim, hand raised, standing on white base . **32.00**
10″ h, red coat with white trim, blue eyes, standing, hands on pockets .................... **55.00**

Plastic
4½″ h, red and white, standing in green cart, red wheels ........ **7.50**
9″ h, red and white, waving with interior light, 1950s .......... **20.00**
12″ h, wall hung, face with interior light, 1950s ................ **25.00**
24″ h, red and white, interior light, 1950s ...................... **25.00**
Greeting Card, Merry Christmas, 8″ h, fold out, Santa on front, int. with pictures to trace, 1930s .............. **3.00**
Lantern, battery operated, metal base, Japan, 1950s
Santa Face ...................... **25.00**
Standing Santa .................. **25.00**
Light Bulb
2½″ h, milk glass, two sided face, Japan ........................ **15.00**
3″ h, lacquered clear glass, Father Christmas, Germany ............ **60.00**

**Light Bulb, painted milk glass, Japan, 3″ h, $28.00.**

Ornament
Blown Glass, 5¼″ h, gold and red suit, frosted beard .............. **150.00**
Celluloid, 3″ h, Santa in chimney, red and white ..................... **60.00**
Mercury Glass, Germany
3″ h, white coat ................ **38.00**
4″ h, face ..................... **85.00**
Perfume Bottle, 3″ h, pale green blown glass ........................... **48.00**
Post Card
"A Merry Christmas To You," Santa in red coat, seated in snowy forest, basket of toys on his back, an angel whispering in his ear, Germany, 1909 ......................... **10.00**
"A Very Merry Christmas," Santa in red coat and brown pants, climbing in chimney, 1920 .............. **3.50**
"Christmas Greetings," Santa with short beard, red stocking cap, red coat with brown fur trim, Germany, 1922 ......................... **6.00**
"Dear Little Santa," sketch of Santa in workshop, Buffalo and Toronto .. **3.50**
"Merry Xmas," Father Christmas, head only, holding gold cane, Germany ......................... **7.00**

**Post Card, emb, color litho, red suit, Germany, 1900s, $5.00.**

Roly Poly
Celluloid, Santa standing on white ball .......................... **28.00**
Molded Cardboard, 7″ h, brightly painted, 1920s ................ **450.00**
Telegram, Western Union, Holiday Greetings, Santa on top of form with Christmas trees, dated Dec 24, 1946 **10.00**
Toy
Friction, 4″ h, plastic, wheels in base, marked "Fun World, Inc, USA" .. **5.00**
Stuffed, cloth
4″ h, red and white plush material, plastic face, orig chimney box, USA ........................ **45.00**
6″, terry cloth, 1950s ........... **8.00**
Windup
Celluloid, 7″ h, Santa in middle of carousel, white deer around outside, red and green ........... **45.00**
Tin, Santa in sleigh, Japan ....... **40.00**

# SCOUTING

**Collecting Hints:** Nostalgia is one of the principal reasons for collecting scouting memorabilia; individuals often focus on the period when they were in the scouting movement. Other collectors select themes, e.g., handbooks, jamborees, writings by scout movement leaders, Eagle Scout material, etc. Jamboree ephemera is especially desirable.

Scouting scholars have produced a wealth of well researched material on the scouting movement. Many of these pamphlets are privately printed and can be located by contacting dealers specializing in scouting items.

Scout material enjoys popularity among collectors. The greatest price fluctuation occurs in modern material and as collectors define new specialized collecting areas.

Girl Scout material is about five to ten years behind Boy Scout material in respect to collecting interest. A collection can still be assembled for a modest investment. While Boy Scout uniforms have remained constant in design throughout time, the Girl Scout uniform changed almost every decade. This increases the number of desirable collectibles.

**History:** The Boy Scout movement began in America under the direction of William D. Boyce, inspired by a helping hand he received from one of Baden–Powell's English scouts when he was lost in a London fog in 1910. Other American boy organizations, such as the one organized by Dan Beard, were quickly brought into the Boy Scout movement. In 1916 the Boy Scouts received a charter from the United States Congress. Key leaders in the movement were Ernest Thompson–Seton, Dan Beard, W. D. Boyce, and James West.

A young illustrator, Norman Rockwell, received his first job as editor of *Boys' Life* in 1913, which began a lifelong association with the Boy Scouts.

The first international jamboree was held in England in 1920. America's first jamboree was held in 1937 in Washington, D.C. Manufacturers, quick to recognize the potential for profits, issued a wealth of Boy Scout material. Local councils and Order of the Arrow lodges have added significantly to this base, especially in the area of patches.

The Girl Scout movement began on March 12, 1912, under the direction of Juliette Gordon Low of Savannah, Georgia. The movement grew rapidly and in 1928 the Girl Scout manual suggested selling cookies as a way of raising funds. The Girl Scout movement also received wide recognition for its activities during World War II, selling over $3 million of bonds in the fourth Liberty Loan drive.

**References:** Mary Degenhardt and Judy Kirsch, *Girl Scout Collector's Guide,* Wallace–Homestead, 1987; William Hillcourt, *Norman Rockwell's World of Scouting,* Harry Abrams, 1977; Alburtus Hoogeveen, *Arapaho I, Council Shoulder Patches, Red & Whites, Council Patches, Jamboree Patches, Council Histories,* privately printed; Alburtus Hoogeveen, Arapaho II, *Order of the Arrow, Complete Guide To Order Of Arrow Insignia,* privately printed; Norman E. Martinus and Harry L. Rinker, *Warman's Paper,* Wallace–Homestead, 1993; J. Bryan Putman, ed., *Official Price Guide To Scouting Collectibles,* House of Collectibles, 1982; R. J. Sayers, *Identification & Value Guide To Scouting Collectibles,* Books Americana, 1984; Harry D. Thorsen, *Scouts On Stamps Of The World,* privately printed.

**Collectors' Club:** Scouts On Stamps Society International, 7406 Park Dr., Tampa, FL 33610.

**Periodical:** *Scout Memorabilia Magazine,* c/o The Lawrence L. Lee Scouting Museum, P. O. Box 1121, Manchester, NH 03105.

**Museums:** Murray State University National Museum of the Boy Scouts Of America, Murray, KY; Girl Scout National Headquarters, New York, NY; The Lawrence L. Lee Scouting Museum and Max J. Silber Scouting Library, Manchester, NH; Juliette Gordon Low Girl Scout National Center, 142 Bull Street, Savannah, GA; Western Scout Museum, Los Angeles; Zitelman Scout Museum, Rockford, IL.

**REPRODUCTION ALERT,** especially Boy Scout jamboree patches and rare Order of the Arrow patches.

CUB SCOUT GRADUATION CERTIFICATE

THIS IS TO CERTIFY THAT

CUB SCOUT

a member of Pack

has achieved the rank, and is therefore, after satisfactory review by the Scoutmaster, eligible to become a Tenderfoot Scout.

THIS GRADUATION CERTIFICATE

is awarded with the best wishes of every member of his Cub Scout pack and a hearty welcome from members of Troop

This day of

**Cub Scouts, graduation certificate, printed color, 1955, 8½ x 5½", $12.00.**

## BOY SCOUTS

| | |
|---|---|
| Achievement Pin, ½" sq, Cub Scout, Wolf | **4.00** |
| Book, *Golden Anniversary Book of Scouting,* 1959, 1st ed, dj, Norman Rockwell | **22.00** |
| Calendar, 7½ x 14", 1954, "A Scout is Reverent," Norman Rockwell | **12.00** |
| Canteen, 1930s | **15.00** |
| First Aid Kit, Boy Scouts of America Official First Aid Kit, 4 x 6 x 2" litho tin box, dark olive green khaki, green and red design on lid, Johnson & Johnson, 1930s | **25.00** |
| Flashlight, Official Cub Scout Flashlight, 5½" l, metal, emb Cub Scout insignia on cap, orig box, Boy Scouts of America/National Supply Service, 1940–50 | **20.00** |

**Boy Scouts, handbook, 1927, $35.00.**

Handbook
*Handbook for Boys*
1st printing, 5th edition ......... **6.00**
9th printing, 1914, Tanner ...... **90.00**
18th printing ................. **50.00**
*Handbook for Patrol Leaders,* 10th printing ....................... **10.00**
*Handbook for Scoutmasters*
1st edition, 1913–14 .......... **65.00**
2nd edition, 9th printing, 1926, sgd "Bunner Berg" .............. **30.00**
Jack Knife, Imperial, Fairmount ...... **14.00**
Jamborees, National
1937, patch ................... **95.00**
1950, silk neckerchief ........... **35.00**
1957, pocket patch ............... **18.00**
1960, picture book ............... **12.50**
1969, lapel pin ................. **10.00**
1977, arm band, felt ............. **85.00**
Magazine, *Boy's Life,* 1st issue reprint, March 1, 1911 .................. **10.00**
Matchbox, 3¾" h, Marbles, metal, cylindrical, orig box ................ **35.00**
Membership Card, 7 x 3¾" open, tri–fold, cardboard, #A6614408, dated 1945, orig envelope .............. **10.00**
Mess Kit, Boy Scout's Litt'l Vitt'l Kit, Imperial, BSA #1374 ............... **5.00**
Neckerchief, Philmont, silk screened, red, gold border ................ **5.00**
Newsletter, June, 1922, National Council, Boy Scouts of America, 8 pages **15.00**
Patch
America's Bicentennial 1975–77, 3 x 4½", woven fabric, woven gold Boy Scout emblem ............ **6.00**
Greater NY Council Camporee, 1953, 3" d, woven fabric ............. **4.00**
Patrol Flag, cloth, printed, Dan Beard . **7.50**
Pin
Collar, National Staff, vertical, lock clasp ......................... **40.00**
Hat, JASM, light green enamel, screw back .......................... **40.00**
Lapel, Sea Scout Quartermaster, sterling ........................ **45.00**
Pocket Knife
Boy Scout, sheath, 8½" l, marked "Official Boy Scout" ........... **48.00**
Cub Scout, blue handles, three blades, raised shield, orig box, Camillus, BSA #1885 ........... **15.00**
Sharpening Stone, #1314, 2 x 4¼" yellow box ......................... **7.00**
Utensils, Boy Scout Chow Kit, spoon and folding knife and fork, brown leather case with stamped emblem on front ........................... **25.00**
Whistle, BSA, brass cylindrical ....... **20.00**
Yearbook
1926, The Boy Scouts Year Book ... **18.00**
1938, The Boy Scouts Year Book of Fun in Fiction .................. **12.00**
1942, The Boy Scouts Year Book of Hobbies for Fathers & Sons ...... **10.00**

## GIRL SCOUTS

Catalog, Girl Scouts, Inc, New York, NY, National Equipment Service
Girls Edition official uniforms for Scouts and Brownies, 1940, 40 pages, 8½ x 11½" .............. **23.00**
Leaders Edition, 1941, 40 pages, 8½ x 11" ........................ **23.00**
Handbook
*Brownie Scout Handbook,* 8th printing .......................... **4.00**
*Girl Scout Handbook*
1st printing, new edition ........ **10.00**
16th printing .................. **3.00**
*Scouting For Girls,* 2nd edition, 6th printing, 1925 ................ **6.00**
Pocket Knife
Brownie, brown plastic handles, one blade, Utica .................. **15.00**
Girl Scout
Kutmaster, 3⅝" l clear plastic over green handles, four blades, GSA #11–310 ................... **20.00**
Utica, 3⅜" green plastic handles with stamped shield, four blades **75.00**
Ring, sterling, six sided green enamel with emblem .................... **20.00**
Utensil, Girl Scout Chow Kit, spoon and folding knife and fork, dark green leather case with stamped emblem . **25.00**

# SEWING ITEMS

**Collecting Hints:** Collectors tend to favor Sterling silver items. However, don't overlook the material in metals, ivory, celluloid, plastic, and wood. Some metals were plated; the plating should be in very good condition before you buy a piece.

Advertising and souvenir items are part of sewing history. Focusing on one of these aspects will develop a fascinating collection. Another focus is on a certain instrument, with tape measures among the most common. Finally, figural items have a high value because of their strong popularity.

Most collectors concentrate on material from the Victorian era. A novice collector might look to the 20th century, especially the Art Deco and Art Nouveau periods, to build a collection.

**History:** Sewing was considered an essential skill of a young woman of the 19th century. The wealth of early American samplers attests to the talents of many of these young seamstresses.

During the Victorian era a vast assortment of practical as well as whimsical sewing devices appeared on the market. Among the forms were tape measures, pincushions, stilettos for punchwork, and crochet hooks. The sewing birds attached to table tops were a standard fixture in the parlor.

Many early sewing tools, e.g., needleholders, emery holders and sewing boxes, were made of wood. However, the Sterling silver tool was considered the height of elegance. Thimbles were the most popular. Sterling silver–handled items included darning eggs, stilettos, and thread holders.

In the 20th century needlecases and sewing kits were an important advertising giveaway. Plastic sewing materials are available, but they have not attracted much collector interest.

**References:** Pamela Clabburn, *The Needlework Dictionary,* William Morrow & Co., 1976; Joyce Clement, *The Official Price Guide To Sewing Collectibles,* House of Collectibles, 1987, out–of–print; Gay Ann Rogers, *American Silver Thimbles,* Haggerston Press, 1989; Gay Ann Rogers, *An Illustrated History Of Needlework Tools,* Needlework Unlimited, 1983, 1989 price guide; Gay Ann Rogers, *Price Guide Keyed To American Silver Thimbles,* Needlework Unlimited, 1989; James W. Slaten, *Antique American Sewing Machines: A Value Guide,* Singer Dealer Museum, 1992; Estelle Zalkin, *Zalkin's Handbook of Thimbles and Sewing Implements,* Warman Publishing Co., Inc., 1988.

**Museums:** Fabric Hall, Historic Deerfield, Deerfield, MA; Museum of American History, Smithsonian Institution, Washington, DC; Shelburne Museum, Shelburne, VT.

**See:** Thimbles.

Bobbin, ivory, Chinese, Victorian, carved flowers, pr ....... **140.00**
Bodkin Case, Tartanware, marked "Buchanan" ....... **95.00**
Book, *Barbours Lace Making & Needlework,* 1896, 97 pgs ....... **30.00**
Button Hook
  Bone Handle, 2½" l ....... **13.00**
  Mother–of–Pearl Handle, natural curvature, 6" l ....... **38.00**
Catalog, Domestic Sewing Machines, New York, NY, illus of Family Model series, c1882, 10 pgs, 5¾ x 10¼", folded ....... **30.00**
Crochet Thread Holder, figural, apple, thread through stem, 4 x 3½" ....... **23.00**
Darner, amber glass ....... **50.00**
Embroidery Scissors, black steel German scissors, sweet grass holder ....... **25.00**
Guide, Stimpson Eyelet Selector, paper, 5½" d, round, center rotates to select size of grommet, illus, c1950 ....... **15.00**
Manual, "Directions for Using Wilcox & Gibbs Automatic Noiseless Sewing Machine," New York, NY, 1921, 38 pgs, 5 x 8" ....... **15.00**
Mending Kit, bakelite, red and ivory, bakelite thimble cap, 3¾" h ....... **20.00**
Mirror, The World's B B Pin Mirror, Germany, metal and leatherette ....... **35.00**
Needle Book
  Army and Navy ....... **18.50**
  Bromo Seltzer ....... **15.00**

**Needle Book, adv, ACME Super Markets, 4 x 6", $4.00.**

Needle Case
  Bakelite, doll shape ....... **25.00**
  Silver, ribbed, 2½" h ....... **15.00**
  Silverplate ....... **12.00**
  Wood, Russian type doll ....... **7.50**
Needle Tin, RCA Victor, The Grammophone Co, Nipper, orig needles ....... **35.00**
Pattern, Standard Fashions, lady's and children's, 1900 ....... **15.00**
Pincushion
  Figural
    Doll, arms at head, 2½" ....... **10.00**
    Slipper, beaded leather, 5", 1920s **45.00**
  Indian beadwork, bead, 10 x 9" ....... **125.00**
Pin Holder
  Advertising, Keystone Boots, Col-

chester Rubbers, Philadelphia, 1¾", celluloid, silvered tin frame, black and white, knee boot illus, c1880 .......... **40.00**
Shoe, patterned metal .......... **5.00**
Sewing Bird, brass, emb, orig clamp, pin cushion missing .......... **100.00**
Sewing Box, Wheeler & Wheeler, carved lid, logo, 1920s, unused .... **65.00**
Sewing Clamp, oak, pincushion, 9" h . **95.00**
Sewing Kit
Advertising, Lydia Pinkham, metal tube .......... **10.00**
Celluloid case, scissors, thimble, thread .......... **10.00**
Chrome case, round, cushion top, thread, thimble, and thread ...... **16.50**
Silk Winder, mother–of–pearl, petal shape .......... **65.00**
Tape Measure
Advertising
Colgate's Fab, 1½", celluloid, full color detergent soap box on front, text on back, c1930 ..... **30.00**
Kodak Finishing, 1¾", celluloid, blue inscription, red rim design, Minnesota photo shop illus, c1930 .......... **25.00**
Lackawanna Coal, 1½", bright orange and black, celluloid, c1930 **18.00**
Parisian Novelty Co, 1½", blue and white, celluloid, adv text, c1920 **28.00**
Portland Cement .......... **25.00**
Quality Drugs, 1¾", blue and white, celluloid, brass case, inscribed name of pharmacist .... **35.00**
Stromberg Carburetor .......... **25.00**
White King Washing Machine Soap, 1½", blue and white celluloid, trademark picture on both sides, c1920 .......... **35.00**
Figural
Egg, enameled, figural housefly as tape end .......... **30.00**
Pig, wearing hat, early plastic .... **37.00**
Ship .......... **30.00**
Thimble, 14 K gold, Lucie .......... **60.00**
Thimble Holder, sweet grass, lid and loop .......... **22.00**
Thread Box
Coats, wood .......... **20.00**
Hemingway, cardboard, litho of child, orig thread .......... **20.00**
Watch Fob, 1½" d, "Broom Sewing Machine," silvered metal, raised elaborate sewing machine dec, "The Baltimore Automatic Broom Sewing Machine" on back, Hamilton, Cassard, early 1900s .......... **40.00**
Yarn Basket, 7½" d, sweet grass, handled, lid .......... **45.00**

# SHAWNEE POTTERY

**Collecting Hints:** Many Shawnee pieces came in several color variations. Some pieces also contained both painted and decal decorations. The available literature will indicate some, but not all of the variations.

Not a great deal of interest is being shown in the Shawnee art and dinnerware lines. Among the lines are Cameo, Cheria (Petit Point), Diora, and Touche (Liana). New collectors may wish to concentrate in these areas.

**History:** The Shawnee Pottery Co. was founded in 1937 in Zanesville, Ohio. The company acquired a 650,000 square foot plant that formerly housed the American Encaustic Tiling Company. There it produced as many as 100,000 pieces of pottery per day. In 1961 the plant closed.

Shawnee limited its chief production to kitchenware, decorative art pottery, and dinnerware. Distribution was primarily through jobbers and chain stores.

Shawnee can be marked "Shawnee," "Shawnee U.S.A.," "USA #—," "Kenwood," or with character names, e.g., "Pat. Smiley," "Pat. Winnie," etc.

**References:** Mark Supnick, *Collecting Shawnee Pottery,* L–W Books, 1989, 1992 value update; Duane and Janice Vanderbilt, *The Collector's Guide To Shawnee Pottery,* Collector Books, 1992.

Ashtray, set of four .......... **28.00**
Bank, Smiley Pig, dark chocolate base **355.00**
Bowl
Corn King
#5 .......... **25.00**
#6, 6½" d .......... **30.00**
#92, 6" d .......... **25.00**
Corn Queen, #5 .......... **25.00**
Casserole, cov
Corn King, #74, large .......... **50.00**
Lobster, French style, 2 qt .......... **30.00**
Coffeepot, #54, large emb flower .... **98.00**
Cookie Jar
Basket of Fruit .......... **85.00**
Clown, seal .......... **225.00**
Dutch Boy, gold trim, minor wear to gold .......... **255.00**
Owl, gold trim .......... **275.00**
Puss N' Boots .......... **130.00**
Sailor Boy, blue stars, black collar and tie, slight paint wear .......... **115.00**
Smiley Pig
Chrysanthemums .......... **225.00**
Shamrocks .......... **175.00**
Tulips .......... **185.00**
Corn Dish, Corn King, oval .......... **25.00**
Creamer
Corn King .......... **20.00**
Tulips .......... **30.00**

Ewer, Rum Rill, cream and brown, #448, 10″ h .......... 35.00
Figure
  Dog, gold trim .......... 75.00
  Rabbit .......... 30.00
  Squirrel .......... 30.00
Mug, Corn Queen .......... 30.00
Pitcher
  Bo Peep, blue bonnet .......... 75.00
  Corn King
    #70 .......... 5.00
    #71 .......... 50.00
  Elephant .......... 25.00
  Grist Mill, #35 .......... 10.00
  Little Boy Blue, #46 .......... 50.00
Planter
  Butterfly .......... 15.00
  Covered Wagon, green, 6 x 9½″ .......... 20.00
  Donkey and Cart .......... 12.00
  Elf Shoe, green .......... 16.00
  Fawn, yellow, #624 .......... 24.00
  Girl, #534 .......... 18.00
  Grist Mill, #169 .......... 16.00
  Polynesian Lady .......... 30.00
  Wishing Well, brown .......... 24.00
Plate
  Corn King, dinner, #68 .......... 15.00
  Corn Queen, #69 .......... 15.00
Platter, Corn King, #96 .......... 40.00
Relish Tray, Corn King, #79 .......... 22.00
Salt and Pepper Shakers, pr
  Bear, ivory and gold, 3¼″ h .......... 55.00
  Corn King
    Range .......... 20.00
    Small, 3½″ h .......... 12.00
  Dutch Boy and Girl
    Range .......... 65.00
    Small .......... 25.00
  Fruit, small .......... 25.00
  Owl, green eyes, orig paper label .......... 30.00
  Pig, range .......... 90.00
  Roosters
    Range .......... 45.00
    Small, 3¼″ h .......... 40.00
  Sailor, small .......... 18.00
  Watering Pail, 3¼″ h .......... 45.00
  White Corn, range .......... 30.00
  Winnie Pig, blue collars .......... 60.00
Shoe, high hell .......... 11.00
Spoon Rest, flower, green and yellow .......... 18.00
String Holder, green and yellow .......... 18.00
Sugar Jar, cov
  Fruit Basket .......... 24.00
  White Corn .......... 30.00
Sugar Shaker, White Corn .......... 60.00
Teapot
  Corn King, individual, #65 .......... 100.00
  Flower
    Blue, gold trim .......... 30.00
    Red .......... 22.00
  Granny Anne .......... 60.00
  White Corn .......... 60.00

**Teapot, Tom The Piper's Son, #44, $48.00.**

Vase
  Dove, gold trim .......... 24.00
  Leaf .......... 24.00
  Swan, bud, gold trim .......... 12.00
Vegetable Bowl, Corn King, #95 .......... 40.00
Wall Pocket, birdhouse, bluebirds .......... 15.00

# SHEET MUSIC

**Collecting Hints:** Center your collection around a theme—show tunes, songs of World War I, Sousa marches, Black material, songs of a certain lyricist or composer—the list is endless.

Be careful about stacking your sheets on top of one another. The ink on the covers tends to bleed. The most ideal solution is to place acid free paper between each cover and sheet.

Unfortunately, people used tape to repair tears in old sheet music. This discolors and detracts from value. Seek professional help in removing tape from rarer sheets.

During the late 1980s, mid–nineteenth century sheet music has risen rapidly in value. World War I and covers featuring Blacks currently enjoy great popularity among collectors.

**History:** Sheet music, especially piano scores, dates to the early 19th century. The early music contains some of the finest examples of lithography. Much of this music was bound in volumes and accompanied a young lady when she was married.

Sheet music covers chronicle the social, political, and trends of any historical period. The golden age of the hand illustrated cover dates from 1885. Leading artists such as James Montgomery Flagg used their talents in the sheet music area. Cover art work was critical to helping the song sell.

Once radio and talking pictures became popular, covers featured the stars. A song sheet might be issued in dozens of different cover versions depending on who was featured. By the 1950s piano playing was no longer as popular and song sheets failed to maintain their high quality of design.

**References:** Debbie Dillon, *Collectors Guide To Sheet Music*, L–W Promotions, 1988, 1993 value update; Anna Marie Guiheen and Marie–Reine A. Pafik, *The Sheet Music Reference and Price Guide*, Collector Books, 1992; Norman E. Martinus and Harry L. Rinker, *Warman's Paper*, Wallace–Homestead, 1993; Daniel B. Priest, *American Sheet Music With Prices*, Wallace–Homestead, 1978.

**Collectors' Clubs:** National Sheet Music Society, 1597 Fair Park, Los Angeles, CA 90041; New York Sheet Music Society, P. O. Box 1214, Great Neck, NY 11023; Remember That Song, 5821 North 67th Ave., Suite 103–306, Glendale, AZ 85301; The Sheet Music Exchange, P. O. Box 69, Quicksburg, VA 22847.

***Wait Till You Get Them Up In the Air Boys,* Broadway Music Corp, $8\frac{7}{8}$ x $11\frac{7}{8}$", $10.00.**

*After The First Of July,* Allen, 1919 . . . **4.00**

*America, Here's My Boy,* WWI patriotic pictorial . . . **7.50**

*A Song to Remember,* Paul Muni and Merle Oberon, 1945 . . . **7.00**

*Beautiful Isle of Somewhere,* Fearis, 1901 . . . **5.00**

*Bell Bottom Trousers* . . . **12.00**

*Born To Lose,* Eddy Arnold, 1943 . . . **9.00**

*Brazil,* Walt Disney, Saludos Amigos, 1942 . . . **15.00**

*Bus Stop,* Marilyn Monroe . . . **40.00**

*Buttons & Bows,* Bob Hope and Jane Russell, 1948 . . . **12.00**

*Cat–Tails,* Grace Drayton cov, 1927 . . . **35.00**

*Chattanooga Choo Choo,* 1941 . . . **3.00**

*Columbia Victorious,* 1917 . . . **3.00**

*Cool Water,* Tex Williams, 1936 . . . **9.00**

*Cryin' For The Moon,* Conley, 1926 . . . **2.00**

*Der Feuhrer's Face,* 1942 . . . **12.00**

*Evacuation Day March, 1883,* Gen George Washington cover . . . **5.00**

*Everybody Loves A College Girl,* Kerry Mills, 1911 . . . **5.00**

*For Freedom & Humanity,* 1917 . . . **3.00**

*GI Jive,* 1943 . . . **12.00**

*Give A Little Credit To The Navy,* WWI patriotic pictorial . . . **5.00**

*Glow Worm,* Paul Lincke, 1902 . . . **5.00**

*God Be With Our Boys To–Night,* 1917 **3.00**

*Gone With The Wind,* Irving Berlin, 1937, 9 x 12" . . . **25.00**

*Happy Trails,* Roy Rogers . . . **25.00**

*Heigh–Ho,* 1937 . . . **20.00**

*Hello Montreal,* Irving Berlin . . . **10.00**

*Hush A Bye Ma Baby,* 1914 . . . **4.00**

*I Ain't Got Weary Yet,* WWI patriotic pictorial . . . **5.00**

*I Don't Want To Get Well,* WWI patriotic pictorial . . . **5.00**

*I Found A New Way To Go To Town,* Mae West cov, 1933 . . . **8.00**

*I'll Get By,* 1943 . . . **3.00**

*I'll Never Change Dear,* Stoney and Wilma Lee Cooper, 1944 . . . **6.00**

*I'm Gonna Getcha, I Betcha,* Red River Dave, 1947 . . . **10.00**

*I'm in the Market for You,* Janet Gaynor and Charles Ferrell, 1930 . . . **7.00**

*I Wish I Knew,* 1945 . . . **3.00**

*Jungle Fever,* Marion Davies, 1934 . . . **7.00**

*Listen To The Mocking Bird,* Drumheller, 1908 . . . **7.50**

*Love Letters,* Jennifer Jones, 1945 . . . **3.00**

*Meet Me In St Louis, Louis,* 1904 . . . **5.00**

*Moonbeams and Dreams of You,* 1907 **4.00**

*Mrs Casey Jones,* Newton, 1915 . . . **30.00**

*Normandy Chimes,* Powell, 1913 . . . **4.00**

***Pepper Sauce a Hot-Rag,* Vandersloot Music Pub. Co., brown and black covers, sgd M. J. Dittmar cov illus, 1910, $10\frac{1}{2}$ x $13\frac{1}{2}$", $50.00.**

*O Dem Golden Slippers,* 1935 ....... **10.00**
*Oh Come My Love,* Tex Atchison, 1946 **10.00**
*Oh Susanna,* Foster, 1935 ........... **4.00**
*Our Flag & Freedom,* 1917 .......... **3.00**
*Over The Rainbow,* whole cast pictured on cov ........................ **30.00**
*Peace & Liberty,* 1917 ............... **3.00**
*Pinocchio,* 1940 .................. **30.00**
*Red River Valley,* Gene Autry cov, 1935 **10.00**
*Rose Petals,* Wm T Pierson, 1910 .... **4.50**
*San Fernando Valley,* Bing Crosby .... **12.00**
*Silver Sleighbells,* E T Paull, 1906 .... **12.00**
*Sleepy Head,* Davies and Cooper, 1934 **7.00**
*Snow White,* 1937 ................ **20.00**
*So Long Mother,* Al Jolson, World War I soldier, Jerome Remick ............ **22.00**
*Some Day,* 1937 .................. **20.00**
*Stowaway,* Shirley Temple ........... **20.00**
*Stuff Like That There,* 1945 .......... **3.00**
*Sweetheart Waltz,* George Burns and Gracie Allen .................... **12.00**
*That International Rag,* Irving Berlin, Uncle Sam cov ................. **10.00**
*That Silver Haired Daddy of Mine,* 1932 **10.00**
*That Sinatra Swing,* Frank Sinatra, 1944 **10.00**
*The Flying Fortress,* Gene Autry, 1944 . **10.00**
*The Rose of No Man's Land,* WWI patriotic pictorial .................. **5.00**
*This Is The Army,* 1942 ............ **12.00**
*Those Draftin' Blues,* WWI patriotic pictorial .......................... **5.00**
*Turtle Dove Polka,* Franz Behr, 1900 .. **3.50**
*Walking the Floor Over You,* American Music, 1941 .................... **9.00**
*When I Dream About the Wabash,* Roy Rogers, 1945 .................. **10.00**
*When The Boys Come Home,* WWI patriotic pictorial .................. **5.00**
*Whistle While You Work,* 1937 ....... **20.00**
*You Belong To My Heart,* Walt Disney **12.00**
*You Don't Learn That In School,* Nat King Cole, 1947 ................ **4.00**
*You're As Pretty as a Picture,* Deanna Durbin, 1938 .................. **7.00**

# SILVER FLATWARE

**Collecting Hints:** Focus on one pattern by one maker. Several makers used the same pattern name and a similar pattern design. Always check the backmarks carefully; several thousand patterns were manufactured. Popularity of pattern, not necessarily age, is the key to pricing.

A monogram on a piece will reduce its value substantially, at least by 50%. On Sterling, monograms occasionally can be removed. This, however, is not the case with silver plate. A worn piece of silver plate virtually has no market value.

Silver flatware sold in sets often brings less than pieces sold individually. The reason is that many buyers are looking to replace pieces or add place settings to a pattern they already own. Sterling silver sets certainly retain their value better than silver plate sets. A number of dealers specializing in replacement services have evolved in past years. Many advertise in the issues of *The Antique Trader Weekly.*

Flatware marked as Alaska Silver, German Silver, Lashar Silver, and Nickel Silver is not silver plated. These materials are alloys designed to imitate silver plate.

Doris Snell's *American Silverplated Flatware Patterns* contains a section on the care and cleaning of flatware. Individuals must keep in mind that plated wares have only a very thin surface over the base metal. Once removed, it cannot be easily replaced.

Finally, there is one form of silver flatware that has value with a monogram. It is the flatware used by American railroads, for which there exists a strong market among railroad buffs.

**History:** The silver table service became a hallmark of elegance during the Victorian era. The homes of the wealthy had Sterling silver services made by Gorham, Kirk, Tiffany, and Towle. Silver place settings became part of a young girl's hope chest and a staple wedding gift. Sterling silver consists of 925 parts silver and 75 parts copper per 1,000 parts sterling.

When electroplating became popular, silver plated flatware gave the common man a chance to imitate the wealthy. Silver plated flatware has a thin layer of silver plated by a chemical process, known as electrolysis, onto a base metal, usually britannia (an alloy of tin, antimony and copper) or white metal (an alloy of tin, copper and lead or bismuth). Leading silver plate manufacturers are Alvin, Gorham, International Silver Co. (a modern company which merged many older companies such as Holmes & Edwards, Rogers, etc.), Oneida, Reed & Barton, Wm. Rogers, and Wallace.

**References:** Fredna Harris Davis and Kenneth K. Deibel, *Silver Plated Flatware Patterns,* Bluebonnet Press, 1981; Maryanne Dolan, *1830's–1990's American Sterling Silver Flatware: A Collector's Identification And Value Guide,* Books Americana, 1993; Tere Hagan, *Silverplated Flatware: An Identification & Value Guide, Revised Fourth Edition,* Collector Books, 1990; *Jewelers' Circular Keystone Sterling Flatware Pattern Index, Second Edition,* Wallace–Homestead, 1989; Joel Langford, *Silver: A Practical Guide To Collecting Silverware And Identifying Hallmarks,* Chartwell Books, Inc., 1991; Everett L. Maffet, *Silver Banquet II: A Compendium On Railroad Dining Car Silver Serving Pieces,* Silver Press, 1990; Benton Seymour Rabinovitch, *Antique Silver Servers For The Dining Table,* Joslin Hall, 1991; Dorothy T. and H. Ivan Rainwater, *American Silverplate,* Schiffer Publishing, Ltd., 1988; Jeri Schwartz, *The Official Identification and Price Guide To*

*Silver and Silverplate, Sixth Edition* House of Collectibles, 1989.

**Periodical:** *Silver,* P. O. Box 1243, Whitter, CA 90609.

Acanthus, George Jensen, coffee spoon .... **36.00**
Antique, Rogers
- Bouillon Spoon .... **11.00**
- Butter Knife .... **9.00**
- Fork .... **15.00**
- Gravy Ladle .... **36.00**
- Pickle Fork .... **11.00**
- Salad Fork .... **16.00**
- Tablespoon .... **30.00**

Ben Franklin, Towle
- Fruit Knife, hollow handle .... **22.00**
- Strawberry Fork .... **20.00**

Bridal Bouquet, Alvin
- Butter Pick .... **55.00**
- Luncheon Fork, monogram .... **25.00**
- Luncheon Knife, monogram .... **25.00**
- Teaspoon .... **20.00**

Burgandy, Reed & Barton
- Luncheon Fork .... **24.00**
- Luncheon Knife .... **24.00**
- Salad Fork .... **25.00**
- Teaspoon .... **20.00**

Candlelight, Towle
- Demitasse Spoon .... **14.00**
- Gravy Ladle .... **40.00**

Canterbury, Towle
- Bonbon Scoop, monogram .... **75.00**
- Bonbon Spoon, monogram .... **28.00**
- Butter Spreader, filled handle .... **20.00**
- Demitasse Spoon, monogram .... **14.00**
- Gravy Ladle .... **50.00**
- Salad Fork, monogram .... **55.00**
- Youth Fork, monogram .... **15.00**

Chantilly, Gorham
- Butter Spreader, filled handle, monogram .... **12.50**
- Salad Fork, monogram .... **22.50**
- Sugar Shell, monogram .... **27.50**

Chippendale, Towle
- Berry Spoon .... **56.00**
- Cold Meat Fork .... **47.00**
- Cream Soup .... **23.00**
- Fork .... **18.00**
- Gravy Ladle .... **50.00**
- Salad Fork .... **25.00**
- Strawberry Fork .... **20.00**
- Sugar Spoon .... **20.00**
- Tablespoon .... **48.00**
- Teaspoon .... **11.00**

Craftsman, Towle, pickle fork .... **12.00**
Eglantine, Gorham, butter spreader, master, etched blade .... **75.00**
El Grandee, Towle
- Cocktail Fork .... **18.00**
- Tablespoon, pierced .... **60.00**

Esplanade, Towle
- Cocktail Fork .... **12.00**
- Cold Meat Fork .... **58.00**
- Demitasse Spoon .... **10.00**
- Dinner Fork .... **24.00**
- Iced Tea Fork .... **20.00**
- Sauce Ladle .... **30.00**
- Tablespoon, pierced .... **58.00**

Fontana, Towle
- Cheese Server .... **14.00**
- Cold Meat Fork .... **45.00**
- Fork .... **18.00**
- Gravy Ladle .... **44.00**
- Olive Fork .... **14.00**
- Pie Server .... **27.00**
- Salad Fork .... **23.00**
- Sugar Spoon .... **17.00**
- Tablespoon .... **40.00**

French Provincial
- Butter Spreader, hollow handle .... **14.00**
- Cream Soup .... **22.00**
- Teaspoon .... **10.00**

George and Martha, Westmoreland
- Gravy Ladle .... **38.00**
- Tomato Server .... **55.00**

Georgian, Towle
- Coffee Spoon, 4¾" l .... **20.00**
- Pickle Fork, monogram .... **95.00**
- Steak Knife .... **30.00**
- Teaspoon, 5⅝" l .... **14.00**

Golden Aegean Weave
- Cold Meat Fork .... **72.00**
- Dinner Fork .... **36.00**
- Iced Tea Spoon .... **28.00**
- Olive Fork .... **22.00**
- Pie Server .... **40.00**
- Salad Fork .... **35.00**
- Sugar Spoon .... **33.00**
- Tablespoon, pierced .... **70.00**
- Teaspoon .... **18.00**

Grand Duchess, Towle, salad set .... **196.00**
Grande Baroque, Wallace
- Cream Soup .... **28.00**
- Dinner Fork .... **40.00**
- Luncheon Fork .... **28.00**
- Luncheon Knife .... **24.00**
- Place Setting, dinner .... **100.00**

Hannah Hull, Tuttle
- Demitasse Spoon .... **16.00**
- Dessert Spoon .... **35.00**
- Gravy Ladle .... **75.00**
- Iced Tea Spoon .... **28.00**
- Luncheon Fork .... **30.00**
- Luncheon Knife .... **30.00**
- Salad Set .... **25.00**
- Sugar Spoon .... **32.00**
- Tablespoon .... **60.00**

Hunt Club, Gorham
- Butter Fork, monogram .... **7.00**
- Citrus Spoon, monogram .... **16.00**
- Cold Meat Fork, monogram .... **23.00**
- Demitasse Spoon, monogram .... **7.00**

Dinner Fork, monogram ........... **11.00**
Dinner Knife, monogram .......... **9.00**
Ice Cream Fork, monogram ........ **16.00**
Iced Tea Spoon, monogram ....... **9.00**
Napkin Clip .................... **10.00**
Serving Spoon, monogram ......... **21.00**
Teaspoon ....................... **14.00**

Inaugural, State House
Butter Fork, master ............... **9.00**
Cream Soup ..................... **12.00**
English Server .................. **20.00**
Grapefruit Knife ................. **13.00**
Grill Fork, 7⅝″ l ................ **9.50**
Grill Knife, 8⅜″ l ................ **11.00**
Place Setting, grill ................ **43.00**

Intermezzo, National
Butter Fork ...................... **8.00**
Citrus Spoon ..................... **12.00**
Cream Soup ..................... **10.00**
English Server ................... **18.00**
Fork, 7⅛″ l ...................... **10.00**
Grill Fork ....................... **12.00**
Knife, 8⅞″ l ..................... **16.00**
Napkin Clip ..................... **13.00**
Place Setting, luncheon ........... **39.00**
Salad Fork ...................... **13.00**
Sugar Spoon ..................... **9.00**

**Cuban, American International Silver Co., oyster spoon, oyster bowl, c1911, $35.00.**

Jefferson, Lunt
Cocktail Fork, monogram ......... **10.00**
Knife, 9⅝″ l .................... **14.00**
Serving Spoon .................. **25.00**

Joan of Arc, International
Citrus Spoon, monogram .......... **14.00**
Fork, 7¼″ l ..................... **19.00**

King Albert, Whiting
Baked Potato Serving Fork ......... **25.00**
Butter Fork ...................... **9.00**
Citrus Spoon ..................... **19.00**
Demitasse Spoon ................ **8.00**
English Server ................... **20.00**
Fork, 7¼″ l ..................... **13.00**
Ice Cream Fork .................. **18.00**
Knife, 8⅞″ l ..................... **9.00**
Place Setting, luncheon ........... **46.00**
Soup Spoon, monogram ........... **9.00**
Sugar Spoon ..................... **12.00**

King Richard, Towle
Bonbon Spoon ................... **40.00**
Butter Spreader, hollow handle
Individual ..................... **20.00**
Master ........................ **28.00**
Cake Server, hollow handle ........ **40.00**
Cheese Server .................. **30.00**
Citrus Spoon .................... **25.00**
Cocktail ........................ **20.00**
Cold Meat Fork .................. **75.00**
Cream Soup Spoon ............... **30.00**
Fork .......................... **30.00**
Gravy Ladle .................... **58.00**
Iced Tea Spoon .................. **28.00**
Jam Spoon ...................... **30.00**
Knife, monogram ................ **25.00**
Lunch Fork ...................... **28.00**
Luncheon Knife .................. **24.00**
Place Setting, dinner .............. **80.00**
Roast Meat Holder ............... **60.00**
Salad Fork ...................... **28.00**
Soup Spoon, oval ................ **28.00**
Steak Knife ..................... **28.00**
Strawberry Fork .................. **20.00**
Sugar Spoon ..................... **29.00**
Tablespoon ..................... **55.00**
Teaspoon ....................... **15.00**
Tomato Server .................. **125.00**

Lady Baltimore, Whiting
Knife, 8⅝″ l .................... **9.00**
Serving Spoon, pierced, monogram . **11.00**
Soup Spoon, monogram ........... **9.00**

Lady Diana, Towle
Baked Potato Serving Fork, monogram ........................ **22.00**
Bread Knife ..................... **18.00**
Citrus Spoon .................... **18.00**
Cocktail Fork ................... **12.00**
Cold Meat Fork .................. **24.00**
Cream Soup, monogram .......... **8.00**
Demitasse Spoon ................ **8.00**
Dessert Spoon, monogram ......... **9.00**
English Server, monogram ......... **16.00**
Fork, 7¼″ l ..................... **12.00**
Gravy Ladle .................... **20.00**
Grapefruit Knife ................. **11.00**
Gumbo Spoon, monogram ........ **10.00**
Ice Cream Fork .................. **18.00**
Iced Tea Spoon .................. **14.00**
Knife, 9½″ l, monogram .......... **9.00**
Napkin Clips .................... **11.00**
Olive Fork, monogram ............ **8.00**
Serving Spoon .................. **20.00**

Lafayette, Towle
Bouillon Spoon .................. **12.00**
Butter Fork, monogram ........... **7.00**
Butter Spreader, hollow handle, monogram ....................... **7.00**
Demitasse Spoon ................. **8.00**
Olive Spoon ..................... **22.00**

Serving Fork, 8⅜" l ... **48.00**
Serving Spoon, pierced ... **43.00**
Teaspoon, 5⅜" l, monogram ... **4.00**

Lancaster, Gorham
Baked Potato Serving Fork, monogram ... **21.00**
Beef Fork, large ... **35.00**
Cake Saw ... **225.00**
Citrus Spoon ... **40.00**
Cocktail Fork ... **10.00**
Dessert Spoon, monogram ... **14.00**
Dinner Fork, monogram ... **10.00**
Dinner Knife ... **15.00**
English Server, monogram ... **18.00**
Lettuce Fork, monogram ... **55.00**
Oyster Ladle ... **250.00**
Pie Server ... **125.00**
Sardine Fork, monogram ... **60.00**
Serving Spoon, monogram ... **18.00**
Sugar Spoon, monogram ... **9.00**
Teaspoon, 5⅞" l ... **7.00**
Tomato Server, monogram ... **125.00**

Legato, Towle
Bonbon Spoon ... **25.00**
Jelly Server ... **18.00**

Lenox, Weidlich
Butter Fork ... **9.00**
Place Setting, luncheon ... **46.00**
Teaspoon ... **9.00**

Les Cinq Fleurs, Reed & Barton
English Server, monogram ... **25.00**
Fork, 7" l ... **41.00**
Knife, 9" l ... **28.00**
Soup Spoon, monogram ... **28.00**
Sugar Tongs ... **40.00**
Teaspoon, 5¼" l, monogram ... **14.00**

Lily
Watson, teaspoon ... **20.00**
Whiting, butter spreaders, filled handle ... **15.00**

Lorna Doone, Alvin
Baked Potato Serving Fork ... **26.00**
Berry Spoon, 9" l, monogram ... **34.00**
Butter Fork ... **10.00**
Citrus Spoon ... **18.00**
Demitasse Spoon ... **8.00**
English Server ... **18.00**
Fork, 7" l ... **12.00**
Salad Fork ... **17.00**

Louis XIV, Towle
Butter Spreader, filled handle ... **10.00**
Coffee Spoon ... **8.00**

Louis XV, Whiting
Butter Spreader, filled handle ... **10.00**
Sardine Fork ... **40.00**

Lucerne, Wallace, gravy ladle ... **60.00**

Marguerite, Gorham
Cocktail Fork ... **12.50**
Gravy Ladle, monogram ... **50.00**

Mary Chilton
Cold Meat Fork, 7⅛" l ... **40.00**
Cucumber Server, monogram ... **50.00**

**Louvain, Rogers Bros., teaspoon, c1918, $4.00.**

Demitasse Spoon ... **15.00**
Sauce Ladle ... **22.00**
Tomato Server ... **75.00**

Old Colonial, Towle
Bonbon Spoon ... **55.00**
Butter Spreader, master, flat, monogram ... **50.00**
Chocolate Spoon, 4¾" l ... **45.00**
Cold Meat Fork, 7⅝" l ... **95.00**
Gumbo Spoon ... **32.00**
Ice Cream Fork ... **30.00**
Luncheon Fork ... **25.00**
Luncheon Knife ... **25.00**
Olive Fork ... **35.00**
Soup Spoon, oval ... **40.00**
Steak Knife ... **32.00**
Strawberry Fork ... **20.00**
Tomato Server ... **85.00**

Old English, Towle
Chocolate Spoon, monogram, price for set of eight ... **235.00**
Egg Spoon, monogram, price for set of six ... **175.00**

Old Master, Towle
Butter Spreader, filled handle ... **18.00**
Cake Server, hollow handle ... **28.00**
Cheese Server ... **16.00**
Cream Soup ... **25.00**
Iced Tea Spoon ... **25.00**
Jelly Server ... **27.00**
Letter Opener, hollow handle ... **22.00**
Luncheon Fork ... **22.00**
Luncheon Knife ... **24.00**
Pickle Fork ... **22.00**
Pie Server ... **30.00**
Place Setting, Luncheon ... **75.00**
Salad Fork ... **25.00**
Sugar Spoon ... **25.00**
Tablespoon, pierced ... **55.00**
Teaspoon ... **13.00**

Old Newbury, Towle
Citrus Spoon, monogram ... **15.00**
Gravy Ladle ... **50.00**
Strawberry Fork ... **20.00**
Sugar Spoon ... **20.00**
Teaspoon ... **10.00**

Onslow, Tuttle
Butter Knife, hollow handle ... **30.00**
Luncheon Fork ... **30.00**
Luncheon Knife ... **30.00**
Place Setting
Dinner ... **140.00**
Luncheon ... **120.00**

Teaspoon . . . . . . . . . . . . . . . . . . . . . . . **40.00**
Paul Revere, Towle
Gravy Ladle . . . . . . . . . . . . . . . . . . . . . **48.00**
Ice Cream Fork . . . . . . . . . . . . . . . . . . **25.00**
Pie Server, hollow handle . . . . . . . . . **28.00**
Strawberry Fork . . . . . . . . . . . . . . . . . . **20.00**
Rose, Stieff
Butter Knife, flat . . . . . . . . . . . . . . . . **12.00**
Teaspoon . . . . . . . . . . . . . . . . . . . . . . . **15.00**
Rose Point, Wallace
Butter Knife . . . . . . . . . . . . . . . . . . . . . **14.00**
Fork . . . . . . . . . . . . . . . . . . . . . . . . . . . **19.00**
Knife . . . . . . . . . . . . . . . . . . . . . . . . . . **17.00**
Pie Server . . . . . . . . . . . . . . . . . . . . . . . **30.00**
Salad Fork . . . . . . . . . . . . . . . . . . . . . . . **23.00**
Tablespoon . . . . . . . . . . . . . . . . . . . . . . **42.00**
Silver Plumes, Towle
Cocktail Fork . . . . . . . . . . . . . . . . . . . . **14.00**
Cold Meat Fork . . . . . . . . . . . . . . . . . . **45.00**
Cream Soup Spoon . . . . . . . . . . . . . . . **23.00**
Fork . . . . . . . . . . . . . . . . . . . . . . . . . . . **23.00**
Iced Tea Spoon . . . . . . . . . . . . . . . . . . **22.00**
Jam Spoon . . . . . . . . . . . . . . . . . . . . . . **19.00**
Nut Spoon . . . . . . . . . . . . . . . . . . . . . . **25.00**
Pie Server . . . . . . . . . . . . . . . . . . . . . . . **30.00**
Salad Fork . . . . . . . . . . . . . . . . . . . . . . . **21.00**
Tablespoon . . . . . . . . . . . . . . . . . . . . . . **38.00**
Tomato Server . . . . . . . . . . . . . . . . . . . **77.00**
Strasbourg, Gorham, salad set, 9" l, monogram . . . . . . . . . . . . . . . . . . . . . **165.00**
Thistle, Blackinton, cold meat fork, monogram . . . . . . . . . . . . . . . . . . . . . **65.00**
Undine, Wood & Hughes
Dinner Fork, monogram . . . . . . . . . . . **15.00**
Luncheon Fork . . . . . . . . . . . . . . . . . . . **18.00**
Luncheon Knife . . . . . . . . . . . . . . . . . . **18.00**
Violet, Wallace
Aspic Slice, monogram . . . . . . . . . . . **110.00**
Berry Serving Spoon, monogram . . . **85.00**
Bonbon, monogram . . . . . . . . . . . . . . **65.00**
Cake Saw, monogram . . . . . . . . . . . . . **100.00**
Cocktail Fork, monogram . . . . . . . . . **15.00**
Cold Meat Fork, monogram . . . . . . . **70.00**
Demitasse Spoon, monogram . . . . . . **20.00**
Dinner Fork . . . . . . . . . . . . . . . . . . . . . **30.00**
Dinner Knife . . . . . . . . . . . . . . . . . . . . . **30.00**
Gumbo Spoon . . . . . . . . . . . . . . . . . . . **25.00**
Luncheon Fork . . . . . . . . . . . . . . . . . . . **24.00**
Luncheon Knife . . . . . . . . . . . . . . . . . . **24.00**
Salad Fork, monogram . . . . . . . . . . . . **30.00**
Sauce Ladle, monogram . . . . . . . . . . . **37.50**
Sugar Shell, monogram . . . . . . . . . . . **25.00**
Sugar Tongs, monogram . . . . . . . . . . **45.00**
Teaspoon, monogram . . . . . . . . . . . . . **15.00**

# SLOT MACHINES

**Collecting Hints:** Check the laws in your state. Some states permit the collecting of slot machines manufactured prior to 1941, while others permit the collecting of all machines 25 years old or older provided that they are not used for gambling. A few states prohibit the ownership of any gambling machine.

A complete slot machine is one that is in working order, has no wood missing on the case, and no cracked castings. All that is needed to restore the machine is some work on appearance. Restoration costs range from $100 to over a thousand dollars. The average restoration includes plating of all castings, refinishing the cabinet, repainting the castings to the original colors, rebuilding the mechanism, tuning up the operation of the mechanism, new reel strips, and a new award card. A quality restoration will add between $400 to $800 to the value of a machine. If buying a restored machine from a dealer, a guarantee usually is given.

Most collectors stay away from foreign machines; foreign coins are hard to find. If the machine has been converted to accept American coins, it frequently may jam or not pay off the proper amount on a winner.

Condition, rarity, and desirability are all very important in determining the value of a machine. Try to find one that is in as close to new condition as possible, as "mint original" machines are bringing the same or more money than restored machines.

**History:** The first three–reel slot machine was invented in 1905 by Charles Fey in San Francisco. The machine was called the Liberty Bell. One of the three known survivors can be seen at the Liberty Bell Saloon, his grandson's restaurant, in Reno, Nevada.

In 1910 the classic fruit symbols were copyrighted by Mills Novelty Company. They were immediately copied by other manufacturers. The first symbols still are popular on contemporary casino machines. The wood cabinet was replaced by cast iron in 1916. By 1922 aluminum fronts were the norm for most machines. In 1928 the jackpot was added.

The 1930s innovations included more reliable and improved mechanisms with more sophisticated coin entry and advance and slug detection systems. In the 1940s drill–proof and cheat–resistant devices were added. The 1950s brought electronic lighting and electronics.

Although the goosenecks of the 1920s and 1930s often are more intricate and rarer than the models of the 1930s and 1940s, the gimmick and more beautiful machines of this later period, such as Rolatop, Treasury, Kitty or Triplex, bring more money.

**References:** Jerry Ayliffe, *American Premium Guide To Jukeboxes and Slot Machines, Third Edition,* Books Americana, 1991; Richard Bueschel, *Illustrated Guide To 100 Collectible Slot Machines, Volume 1,* Hoflin Publishing Co., 1978, 1989 value update; Marshall Fey, *Slot Machines: A Pictorial History of the First 100 Years,* published by author, 1983; Bill Kurtz, *Slot Machines And Coin–Op Games: A Collector's Guide To One Armed Bandits And Amusement Machines,* Chartwell Books, 1991; Daniel R. Mead, *Loose Change Blue Book Slot Machine Price Guide, 1986–87 Edition,* published by author, 1987.

**Periodicals:** *Chicago Land Slot Machine & Jukebox Gazette,* and *Coin–Op Newsletter* are published by Ken Durham, 909 26th St., N.W., Washington, DC 20037; *Classical Amusements,* 12644 Chapel Road, P. O. Box 315, Clifton, VA 22024; *The Coin Slot,* 4401 Zephyr St., Wheatridge, CO 80033; *Loose Change,,* 1515 South Commerce Street, Las Vegas, NV 89102.

**Note:** All machines listed are priced as if they were in "good" condition, meaning the machine is complete and working. An incomplete or non–working machine is worth only 30% to 70% of the listed price.

Machines listed are for 5¢ and 10¢. Quarter and 50¢ machines can run several hundred dollars higher. A silver dollar machine, if you are lucky enough to find one, can add $400 to $800 to the price.

Buckley
- Bones, countertop, spinning disks roll dice for craps, similar to Bally's Reliance . . . . . . . . . . . . . . . . . . **3,500–5,000.00**
- Criss Cross, revamp of Mills machine, escalator coin entry, fancy casting around escalator and jackpot, usually has guaranteed jackpot **800–1,000.00**

Caille
- Cadet, circular jackpot, escalator moves from bottom up . . . **800–1,200.00**
- Detroit Floor Wheel, upright one reeler, six way play action, bettors pick color wheel will land on . **7,000–9,500.00**
- Playboy, three reel, jackpot, c1936 . . . . . . . . . . . . . . . . **800–1,600.00**
- Superior, nude woman on front, scroll–work lower casting, coin entry in center above award card . . . . . . . . . . . . . . . . . . . **1,400–1,800.00**
- Victory Mint, center pull handle, ladies pictured on both sides of handle . . . . . . . . . . . . . . . . . . . . **3,500–5,000.00**

Groetchen, Columbia, ⅔ the size of normal slot machine, club handle, small reels, coins go around in circle behind coin head . . . . . . . . . . . **300–500.00**

Jennings
- Challenger Console, 4′ h, vertical glass and horizontal glass with silkscreen design, reels seen from top of lower glass, plays two coin denominations, usually 5¢ and 25¢ . . . . . . . . . . . . . . . . . . . **1,400–1,800.00**
- Duchess, three reel, front vendor with mints or candy displayed behind windows flanking jackpot, orig decal, c1934 . . . . . . . . . . . . . . **1,600–2,500.00**
- Export Chief, chrome finish, brass tiered triangle above jackpot . . . . . . . . . . . . . . . . . . . . **800–1,100.00**
- Four Star Chief, Indian carrying deer on front, large Indian chief above jackpot, four stars on top . **850–1,150.00**
- Governor, tic tac toe theme, Indian head above jackpot . . . . . . **750–1,000.00**
- Little Duke, large coin headcasting on top of machine, classic Art Deco design, reels spin concentrically . . . . . . . . . . . . . . . . . . . **950–1,350.00**
- Silver Moon, moon above jackpot, stars on side of jackpot . . . **750–950.00**
- Sportsman, golf ball vendor, pay card placed at angle . . . . . . . . . . **1,400–2,000.00**
- Standard Chief, chrome finish, teardrop design on both sides of jackpot, flat Indian above jackpot . . . . . . . . . . . . . . . . . . . . **800–1,100.00**
- Victoria, three reel, two jackpots, fortune strips, c1932 . . . . . . . **1,500–2,500.00**
- Victory Chief, wood front, eagle above jackpot, minutemen soldiers to right and left of eagle . . **750–950.00**

**Firebird, Mills, 5¢, side vendor, $1,500.00.**

Mills
- Black Cherry, escalator, painted silver with black case, four applied cherries, bib award card front . **850–1,000.00**
- Criss Cross, high top, orig condition, working . . . . . . . . . . . . . . . . . . . . . . **700.00**
- Diamond Front, escalator, ten raised diamonds around large "bib" award card . . . . . . . . . . . . . **850–1,200.00**
- Futurity Bell, three reel, 5¢, 1936 . . . . . . . . . . . . . . . . . . **1,900–2,800.00**
- Lion Front, gooseneck coin entry, large lion with mouth open around

jackpot, three rows of six circles below reels . . . . . . . . . . . . . **1,150–1,450.00**
Melon Bell, three reel, high top, melon on front, 1948 . . . . **1,200–1,800.00**
Mint Vendor, Future Play feature . . **1,200.00**
Mystery Front, three reels, 26" h, c1932 . . . . . . . . . . . . . . . . . **1,500–2,500.00**
Operator Bell, 23½", 5¢, three reel . . . . . . . . . . . . . . . . . . . . **500–800.00**
Poinsettia, gooseneck coin entry, flowers on lower casting, Liberty bell under coin entry . . . . . **800–1,100.00**
Silent Golden, three reel, Roman's head on front, 1932 . . . . . **1,900–2,800.00**
Twentieth Century, 5' 5", 5¢, oak case, nickel plated mounts, cast paw feet . . . . . . . . . . . . . . . **3,000–5,000.00**
Vest Pocket, three reel, box shape, plain design, 1938 . . . . . . . **350–550.00**

Pace
All Star Comet, rotary escalator, stars and vertical pointed stripes on front . . . . . . . . . . . . . . . . . . . **850–1,150.00**
Bantam, three reel, jackpot vendor front, appealing design . . . **1,200–1,800.00**
Star, three reel, circular coin escalator, 25¢, c1948 . . . . . . . . . **850–1,300.00**

Watling
Blue Seal, gooseneck, twin jackpot, fancy front . . . . . . . . . . . . . . **900–1,100.00**
Exchange, one wheel, countertop model, five way coin head, oak case, c1910 . . . . . . . . . . . . **2,000–3,000.00**
Gumball Vendor, gooseneck, ornate casting around reels, gumball vendors on each side of twin jackpot, 1¢ only . . . . . . . . . . . . . . . . **1,000–1,200.00**
Rol-a-top, rotary escalator, twin jackpot with eagle above, checkerboard . . . . . . . . . . . . . . . . . . **1,300–1,700.00**

# L. E. SMITH GLASS COMPANY

**Collecting Hints:** L.E. Smith glass is hand made and usually unmarked. Some older pieces bear a "C" in a circle with a tiny "S." Current glass has a paper label. The collector of older items should especially study black and Depression pieces. The Moon and Star pattern has been reproduced for many years. Smith glass of recent manufacture is found in house sales, flea markets, and gift and antique shops.

**History:** L. E. Smith Glass Company was founded in 1907 in Mount Pleasant, Pennsylvania, by Lewis E. Smith. Although Smith left the company shortly after establishment, it still bears his name. Early products were cooking articles and utilitarian objects such as glass percolator tops, fruit jars, sanitary sugar bowls, and reamers.

In the 20s, green, amber, canary, amethyst, and blue colors were introduced along with an extensive line of soda fountain wares. The company also made milk glass, console and dresser sets, and the always popular fish–shaped aquariums. During the 1930s, Smith became the largest producer of black glass. Popular dinner set lines were Homestead, Melba, Do–Si–Do, By Cracky, Romanesque, and Mount Pleasant.

L. E. Smith presently manufactures colored reproduction glass and interesting decorative objects. A factory outlet is available as well as factory tours. Contact the factory for specific times.

**References:** Lee Garmon and Dick Spencer, *Glass Animals Of The Depression Era,* Collector Books, 1993; Ellen Tischbein Schroy, *Warman's Glass,* Wallace–Homestead, 1992; Hazel Marie Weatherman, *Colored Glassware of the Depression Era 2,* Glassbooks, Inc., 1982.

Animal
Cat, black, c1930 . . . . . . . . . . . . . . . . **20.00**
Cow, black, c1930 . . . . . . . . . . . . . . . **18.00**
Dog, Scottie, black, c1930 . . . . . . . . **20.00**
Goose, black, c1930 . . . . . . . . . . . . . **18.00**
Horse, rearing
Green . . . . . . . . . . . . . . . . . . . . . . . . **35.00**
Red . . . . . . . . . . . . . . . . . . . . . . . . . . **35.00**
Rooster, black, c1930 . . . . . . . . . . . . . **15.00**
Swan, small, white opaque . . . . . . . . **15.00**
Aquarium, 10" h, 15" l, green, King–Fish, c1920 . . . . . . . . . . . . . . . . . . . . . **250.00**
Ashtray, elephant, black . . . . . . . . . . . . **30.00**
Bookends, pr
Horse Head, clear . . . . . . . . . . . . . . . . **45.00**
Rearing Horse, clear . . . . . . . . . . . . . . **45.00**
Bowl
#77, amethyst . . . . . . . . . . . . . . . . . . . **8.00**
#515, 7" d, ftd, black . . . . . . . . . . . . **18.00**
Cake Plate, Do–Si–Do, handles . . . . . . **12.00**
Candlesticks, pr
By Cracky, green . . . . . . . . . . . . . . . . **12.00**
Mt Pleasant, black . . . . . . . . . . . . . . . . **15.00**
Romanesque, pink . . . . . . . . . . . . . . . **10.00**
Casserole, Melba, 9½" l, oval . . . . . . . . **15.00**
Cologne Bottle, Colonial, black . . . . . . **30.00**
Compote, cov, Moon n' Star, amberina **35.00**
Cookie Jar, cov, black amethyst, floral dec . . . . . . . . . . . . . . . . . . . . . . . . . . . **45.00**
Cordial Tray, #381, black . . . . . . . . . . . **9.50**
Creamer
Do–Si–Do . . . . . . . . . . . . . . . . . . . . . . . **3.00**
Homestead, pink . . . . . . . . . . . . . . . . . **5.00**
Moon n' Star, amberina . . . . . . . . . . . **10.00**
Cruet, Moon n' Star, ruby . . . . . . . . . . . **30.00**
Cup and Saucer
Do–Si–Do, pink, gold trim . . . . . . . . **6.50**
Melba, pink . . . . . . . . . . . . . . . . . . . . . **4.50**
Fairy Lamp, Moon n' Star, ruby . . . . . . **30.00**
Fern Dish, 3 ftd, 1930s
Greek Key
Black . . . . . . . . . . . . . . . . . . . . . . . . . **18.00**

White, opaque ........ 8.00
Kent ........ 8.50
Flower Block, By Cracky, 3″ h ........ 3.75
Flower Pot, 4″ h, black, silver floral dec 8.00
Goblet, water, Moon 'n Star, amberina 15.00
Mayonnaise, Kent ........ 6.00
Mug, crystal, 12 oz ........ 5.00
Parfait
Homestead ........ 5.00
Soda Shop ........ 5.00
Planter, black amethyst, nude dancers on sides, marked "L. E. Smith" .... 45.00

**Creamer and Sugar, miniature, orange to red-orange, 2″ h, $8.50.**

Plate
6″ d, Melba, amethyst ........ 4.50
8″ d
Homestead, pink ........ 4.50
Mt Pleasant, pink, scalloped edge 6.00
9″ d, Homestead, grill ........ 5.00
Rose Bowl, Mt Pleasant, cobalt blue, rolled edges ........ 18.00
Salt and Pepper Shakers, pr
Dresden, white ........ 18.00
Mt Pleasant, cobalt blue ........ 24.00
Sherbet, Romanesque, black ........ 10.00
Slipper, 2½″ h, Daisy and Button, amber 4.00
Soda Glass
Jumbo, crystal, ribbed ........ 6.50
Soda Shop ........ 6.00
Sugar, cov
Homestead ........ 5.50
Kent ........ 6.50
Melba ........ 6.00
Moon n' Star, amberina ........ 12.00
Tray, 15 x 6″, crystal, oval ........ 10.00
Urn, 8½″ h, black, emb, two handles, ftd ........ 40.00
Vase
6″ h, #49, black ........ 11.00
6½″ h, #102–4, black ........ 10.00
7″ h, #433, dancing girls, black ... 18.00
7¼″ h, #1900, black ........ 18.00
7½″ h, Romanesque, fan shape, black 12.00
Violet Bowl, Hobnail, white opaque .. 7.50
Window Box, F W Woolworth ........ 25.00
Wine
Moon 'n Star, amberina ........ 12.00
Ruby bowl, crystal stem ........ 5.00

# SNOWDOMES

**Collecting Hints:** Snowdomes are water filled paperweights with figurines and/or panels inside a globe or dome, which are magnified by the water. The water contains loose particles (white snow, metallic or colored flecks, etc.) which swirl when the globe is turned upside down.

There are two distinctly different types of snowdomes. The first have round, leaded glass balls set on a base of ceramic, Bakelite, or other plastic, wood or "marble." These are older and generally 3–4″ high. The second have plastic objects, in dozens of shapes ranging from simple designs such as drums, cubes, and bottles, to elaborate figurals. Production of this second type, which average 2½″ high, started in the 1950s.

Within both categories, especially the plastic, there are many sub–groups and themes which appeal to collectors, e.g., Christmas (probably the most familiar), tourist souvenirs, Biblical scenes, Disney and other cartoon characters, commercial advertisements, fairy tales, scenic railroads, famous buildings, sailing ships, geographic regions, or one from each state.

There is great variety not only in the subject of the inner image of snowdomes, but in the outer shapes as well. Collectors find it challenging to find as many of the dozens of shapes as possible.

Figurals are divided into two categories: first, the entire object is a figural, such as a house, apple, a bear, or seated cartoon character with the water ball incorporated into the design at different places, and second, a plastic figurine is placed on top of the dome. Christmas figurals alone constitute a large category. At least six different figurines of a standing Santa are known, to say nothing of the dozens of elaborate designs. Other novelty features include battery powered flashing lights which illuminate the inner scene; salt and pepper snowdomes, perpetual calendars and banks designed in the base; and water/ring toss games.

Many snowdomes have parts that move: a seesaw, bobbing objects attached to strings, and small objects that move back and forth on a groove in the bottom of the dome. Objects range from a ferry or bus to Elvis Presley.

The value of a particular snowdome depends on several factors, starting with the physical condition of the object itself. In dealing with glass domes it is important that the water is clear enough to see the object or is at a level which does not distort the image. Although it is possible to open and refill many of the older glass and ceramic or Bakelite base styles, it is a risky procedure. Examine, also, whether the ceramic base is cracked, the condition of the label (if there is one), the condition of the figurine, and whether the paint has chipped or the colors seem faded.

The water level is not a factor in any plastic snowdome that has a plug either on the bottom of the base, or at the top of the dome. Bottle on its side shapes cannot be refilled, and the domes designed by the Marx Company in the 1960s have safety plugs that cannot be removed. Safety caps on the plugs of snowdomes made for "Walt Disney Production" can be pried off with a knife point. Murky water can be drained and replaced. Clumped, dirty snow can be caught in a handkerchief, washed, and put back. While distilled water is preferred, tap water will stay clear for a year.

Of great importance is whether the front of the dome is free of streaking that obscures the scene inside. Any cracks or holes would prevent refilling with water.

While long-time collectors recognize common snowdomes, even new collectors can make an educated guess at scarcity by remembering a few key points. Snowdomes with a glass, ceramic, or Bakelite base, single figurine, and no specific label on the base were the most common. The same figurine with a decal on the base saying "Souvenir of. . . . ." is more valuable as a smaller number were sold of that figurine with that particular decal. The same figurine was used for innumerable places, hence there is often no connection between the object and the place. An incongruous match–up may have value to a particular collector, but would not necessarily affect its market value. Of greater value are those snowdomes which were obviously made for a specific place or event, where the object and the decal match, e. g., the ceramic base snowdome with a bisque Trylon and Perisphere in globe, with a decal "1939 Worlds Fair."

Plastic snowdomes are also subject to the same principle of logic. "Generic" ones, without a name plaque, had the widest possible distribution.

Souvenirs of states and popular tourist attractions had a wide distribution. Since many more were made and sold their prices are lower than commemoratives or souvenirs of smaller places. SCARCITY, which can be determined by the size or popularity of a city or tourist attraction, is very important in pricing snowdomes and is a factor in the desirability of particular domes.

While mismatched figurines and decals of the glass/ceramic style should not be priced higher than logical match–ups, there are many examples of obvious mistakes in the plastic variety which are worth more than a perfect one, e. g., a dome with "Milano" printed upside down or a souvenir of a religious shrine with a "Kings Island" plaque.

The age of a plastic snowdome affects its value and can usually be determined by examining stylistic differences. It is often the style associated with a certain era that bears on its value, rather than the actual age itself. Generally, early snowdomes (50s and 60s) have greater detail and more sophisticated colors. Later snowdomes are less rich in detail and have a harsh, mass produced appearance. Many early mass produced snowdomes look as if they were hand painted. Characters often have a "folk" quality to them. Most important, earlier snowdomes have much more specific detail. 1950s and 1960s state souvenirs have many panels inside, depicting noted tourist attractions, famous citizens, and the state slogan. Later versions use only one feature. The newest mass produced state souvenirs consist of a rainbow with a pot of gold and a glittery outline of the state's shape on a clear panel. There is no individuality.

The effects of time on snowdomes vary. A dome's physical deterioration, i. e., fading, chipping paint, even "bleaching" of the words on the plaque must be constantly evaluated by the collector. The plastic snowdomes that were introduced in the 50s were fragile objects, easily broken, and often discarded. It is indeed a challenge to find unusual "survivors."

**History:** Snowdomes originated in mid–19th century Europe, particularly in France, where they evolved from the round, solid glass paperweights. By 1878 there were seven French manufacturers of snowdomes. They also were produced in what is now Germany, Austria, Poland, and Czechoslovakia, often in "cottage industries."

Snowdomes were widely popular during the Victorian era as paperweights, souvenirs, and toys. Early domes featured religious scenes and saints, tourist sites, and children and animals associated with winter or water. A variety of materials was used to create the "snow," ranging from ground porcelain and bone to rice. The figurines inside was made of carved bone, wax, porcelain, china, metal, or stone. The bases were made in a variety of shapes in many materials, including marble, wood, glass, and metal.

German companies exported their snowdomes to North American in the 1920s. The bases were blue cobalt glass and were occasionally etched with the name of a town or tourist attraction.

The first American patent was granted in 1927 to a design of a fish floating on a string among seaweed. The Novelty Pond Company of Pittsburgh was the manufacturer. Japanese companies soon copied the idea. Novelty and other American manufacturers used a black plastic base, either smooth or tiered; Japanese companies used a glazed brown cermaic base.

In addition to an enormous number of figurine designs, either painted or unpainted bisque, domes also featured Art Deco buildings, saints, and snow babies. Another design form consisted of a flat, rubberized insert showing a photograph of a tourist attraction, such as Niagara Falls or the Skyline Drive.

The Atlas Crystal Works was founded in the early 1940s to fill the void created by the unavailability of the popular glazed style which had been made in Japan. Atlas became the giant in the snowdome field, creating hundreds of different designs. Popular series included U.S. servicemen, servicewomen, and generals. Decals were added by towns and tourist attractions, creating some unusual matches, e.g., a skier from "Atlantic City."

Snowdomes also were manufactured in Italy in the late 1940s using a distinctive scalloped–shaped base covered with seashells and pebbles. The glass globe contains a flat rubberized panel with the name of the tourist attraction or Saint shown inside written on a shell on the base.

In the 1950s, the Driss Company, Chicago, Illinois, made four designs of popular characters—"Frosty the Snowman," "Rudolph the Red Nosed Reindeer in the Snow," "Davy Crockett," and "The Lone Ranger: The Last Round Up" with the decals on the base. The Davy Crockett and Lone Ranger domes used identical figurines, in identical poses, with different clothes and accessories. The Lone Ranger domes also was a ring toss game, you looped his lasso over the calf's head. The Driss Company made many other "novelty" designs, such as an American flag with red, white, and blue "snow."

Progressive Products, of Union, New Jersey, created a variation of the classic snowdome in the 1940s and 1950s. They filled their glass ball with an oily liquid, either clear or yellow, and used a glittery "snow." They squared the base and widened it at the bottom, giving it a more angular, Art Deco look. In addition to their "generic" snowdomes with a single object inside, they made souvenirs with the name of a place written on the front of the base.

Their specialties, however, were awards and commercial advertisements. Many of the awards used a royal blue or red base with white trim around the bottom. One image could be adapted to many uses: a golden crown suspended in the liquid was used for a Winter Sports King, an ad for "Crown Termite Control," and a Baltimore newspaper. The same was true for a specific backdrop panel. There were three basic designs—an Art Deco city skyline, country landscape, and a Southwest Indian scene. A wide range of objects and images were placed inside the ball: trucks, ships, a Masonic symbol, faucet, a fishing boat used for seafood restaurants, and even a two sided photo of a publishing house owner.

In the early 1950s three West German companies, using plastic, created small cubed or domed snowdomes. Koziol and Walter & Prediger, two of these companies, remain in business manufacturing hand painted domes with blizzards of white snow. Herr Koziol claims it was the "domed" view of a winter snow scene as seen through the rear window of a VW that inspired the shape. As a result of court action, Walter & Prediger gained the right to the dome shape and Koziol was restricted to the round ball shape.

The Erwin Perzy Company of Vienna, Austria, founded in 1900, creates glass snowdomes with traditional themes such as Christmas and other holidays, snowmen, skiers, mountain chalets, clowns, bears, and sailboats. These have smooth black (or white) plastic bases and a red sticker that reads "Made in Austria."

The majority of plastic and glass snowdomes in the 1990s are made in the Orient. A few are produced in France and Italy. There are no American manufacturers, but rather dozens of large gift companies who design and import an array of styles, shapes, and themes. Enesco Corporation, Elk Grove Village, Illinois, is one of the largest.

**Reference:** Nancy McMichael, *Snowdomes*, Abbeville Press, 1990.

**Collectors' Club:** Snow Biz, P.O. Box 53262, Washington, D.C. 20009.

**Advisor:** Nancy McMichael.

**Atlas Crystal Works, man and dog, glass ball, ceramic base, 4¼" h, $40.00.**

Advertising

Coca–Cola, plastic dome, girl ice skater sitting on log, trees, 1970s, 2⅝ x 2⅛" ..... **15.00**

Crown Termite Control, glass ball, oily liquid, brown Bakelite base, 3" w, 4" h, 1950s ..... **60.00**

Jello, plastic dome, 1970s, 3¼" l, 2¾" w, 2½" h ..... **30.00**

Newsweek, "No one covers the world like Newsweek" printed on red plastic base, large dome, globe inside with floating plastic bars printed with Newsweek, 3½" l, 2½" w, 2¾" h ..... **35.00**

Nikon, camera company logo, small plastic dome ..... **20.00**

Sears Kenmore, America's Largest Selling Washers and Dryers, rect, one piece salt and pepper shaker, woman standing next to appliances, 1970s, 3½ x 2½ x 1" ..... **35.00**
Tuohy Trucking Corp, glass ball, oily liquid, brown Bakelite base, 1950s **60.00**

Amusement Park
Cedar Point, Sandusky, OH, plastic, two dolphins on see–saw, gold printed letters on plaque on waved base, 1970s .................. **12.00**
Coney Island, bathing beauty, scalloped base with sea shells, 1940s, 2" d glass ball ................. **20.00**
Wildworld, water slide, early 1980s, 2¾" plastic ball, 2⅞" red base ... **8.00**

Ashtray, Yellowstone Park, black Bakelite, bisque figure, off white tiered base, early 1940s, 2¾" d glass ball . **60.00**

Award, glass ball, oily liquid, sq red Bakelite base, bowling ball and three pins in globe, Bowler City, High Score Award, 1950s .................... **55.00**

Bank, plastic, Mt Vernon, VA printed on front, house scene, red base, 1960s, 2¾" d ball ...................... **10.00**

Black
Just A Little Mammy Down In Dixie, leaded glass ball, black ceramic base, gold decal, red trim, black mammy figure, Atlas Crystal Works, Covington, TN .......... **100.00**
Watermelon Boy Down In New Orleans, gold decal on front of black ceramic base, heavy glass globe, painted figure of black boy eating watermelon, marked "Atlas Crystal Works, Covington, Tenn," 1940s . **100.00**

Bottle
Flatside
Caverns of Luray, cavern scene, early 1970s, 5" l ............. **8.00**
New Orleans, LA, neck plaque, Bourbon Street, St Louis Cathedral, Trade Mark, Brulatour Courtyard plaques, 1960s, 6" l . **12.00**
USS Yorktown–CVIO, Patriots Point, Charleston, SC, plastic, carrier, relief 3–D helicopter and plane, 1970s, 5" l ............ **15.00**
Round, sits on stand
Blue Nose, sailing boat, 1970s, 4½" l, 1½" d ................ **8.00**
Texas, The Lone Star State, bull moves on slide, oil wells, gold cap, early 1970s, 5¼" l ....... **10.00**
Two sailboats, silver flecks, gold cap, gold stand, 5⅜ x 1½" .... **4.00**
Upright, Mennonite male and female figures, silver snow, red cap, 1970s, 4½ x 1½", price for pair .. **12.00**

Boxed Set, Winter Snow Scenes, Assorted by Marx, set of six small plastic domes, c1960, winter scenes
Sold individually ................. **10.00**
Sold as set ...................... **100.00**

Calendar, plastic, red base with four openings where date shows, San Francisco, CA, bridge and city scene, cable car moves on slide, 1970s, 2¾" d ball ......................... **6.00**

Cartoon Character
Dogpatch USA, TV shape, plastic, brown, shows Mammy and Pappy Yokum, 1960s, 2⅝ x 2½ x¾" .... **12.00**
Pink Panther, plastic dome, Panther skating around Inspector Clouseau, 1980s ....................... **10.00**
Popeye, figural, seated, plastic, holds water ball between hands, Olive Oyl, Sweetpea, and Wimpy in row boat that moves, King Features Syndicate, 1950s .................. **60.00**

Character
Elvis, singing into microphone, rect shape, figure moves back and forth in front of Graceland mansion panel, Graceland plaque, 1970s . **15.00**
Little Orphan Annie, plastic dome, Annie and Sandy, 1970s, 3⅝ x 2⅞ x 2¾" ....................... **15.00**
Lone Ranger, round glass ball, Bakelite base, green, yellow, and red, Lone Ranger: The Last Round–Up decal, 1950s .................. **60.00**

Christmas
Bell, clear, red church and pine trees, 1970s ....................... **8.00**
Boot, clear, five pine trees, red house, waving snowman, and children, holly trim, 1970s ............... **8.00**
Chimney, red brick design, Santa's head and arms raise, Santa on sled in cube shaped dome, marked "Curt S. Adler Inc, Reg Appl 961 554," 1970s .................. **15.00**
Elf, figural, red suit, green jester collar, ball in tummy, snowman, trees, and house scene, 1960s ......... **20.00**
Fireplace, child sleeping in pajamas on hearth, Santa in sled on see–saw in dome, marked "CSA Inc, Curt S. Adler, Inc., NY, NY 10010," 1970s, 3½ x 3¼ x 2¼" ............... **20.00**
Frosty the Snowman
Figural, standing, black boots and top hat, removable broomstick, angel and deer in ball, 1960s, 5½" h ...................... **12.00**
Round, decal, yellow plastic base, marked "Frosty the Snowman, A & RS, Inc," 1950s ............ **40.00**
Mountain, frosted, textured plastic,

red houses perched on ledges, three wise men leading camels to Bethlehem in dome, 1960s, 4¾ x 4¾ x 3" . . . . . . . . . . 20.00

Rocking Horse, white horse, red runner, red fabric mane, 2¾" dome with Santa in sleigh on see–saw, marked "Curt S. Adler, Inc., NY, NY 10010," 1970s . . . . . . . . . . 20.00

Rudolph the Red Nosed Reindeer, green plastic base, "Rudolph the Red Nosed Reindeer in the Snow, copyright RLM" on decal, 1950s . 40.00

Santa

- Figural, driving sleigh, two reindeer, rect dome with elf sitting under a mushroom, 1960s, 5¾ x 3½ x 1" . . . . . . . . . . 25.00
- Walking, plastic, bag of toys over shoulder, round dome, 1970s . . 5.00
- Workshop, figural, red brick design, Mr. and Mrs. Claus work at workbench, rocking horse, marked "SANTA'S WORKSHOP" on top . . . . . . . . . . 20.00

Tree, green, painted Christmas balls, Santa riding on reindeer, 1960s, 2¾" dome, 5¾ x 4½" . . . . . . . . . . 15.00

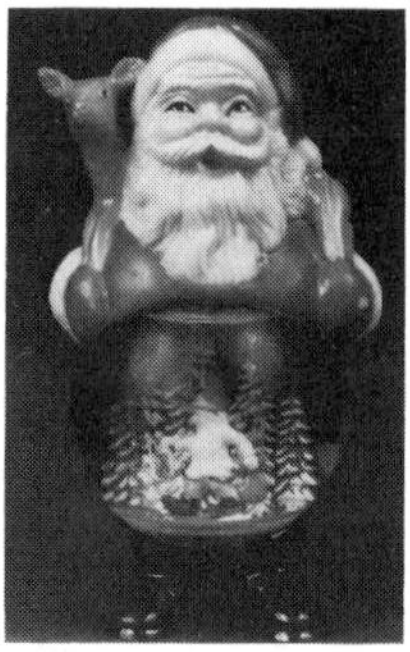

**Santa Claus, plastic, #8824, Hong Kong, 5½" h, $12.00.**

Disney

- Mickey Mouse, figural, plastic, castle scene, 1960s, holds 2" d ball in lap, 5" h . . . . . . . . . . 50.00
- The Wonderful World of Disney, plastic dome, Mickey and Minnie in front of castle, multicolored snow, early 1970s, 3⅝ x 2⅞ x 2¾" . . . . 15.00

Fairy Tales

- Gingerbread House, figural, candies, sweets, and logs on all sides, partially open on three sides, fourth side is open at window, Hansel, Gretel, and witch inside, 1970s, 2¾ x 1½ x 4¼" . . . . . . . . . . 20.00
- Sleeping Beauty and Prince Charming, castle, rounded dome, green ground and base, "Made in West Germany," 1970s . . . . . . . . . . 6.00

Figural

- Apple, red, green leaves, round white base, New York City plaque, 1980s 15.00
- Bear, walking, plastic, two bears on see–saw and "Great Smokey Mts," 1970s . . . . . . . . . . 15.00
- Captain, dressed in uniform with right arm raised, sailing ship, "Bar Harbor, ME," 1970s, 2½" d ball in tummy, 5¾" h . . . . . . . . . . 20.00
- Church, steeple, plastic, altar, bride, and groom, marked "W Germany" on bottom, 1980s, 2¼ x 2¾ x 2½" 15.00
- Drum, red top, blue bottom, gold braiding criss–crossing drum, "Let Freedom Ring" printed on top with flag, "1776–1976" on plaque, Freedom Bell swings from hook, 3¼ x 2¼" . . . . . . . . . . 8.00
- Frog, plastic, green, sitting upright, frogs and grass scene, "Puerto Rico" on plaque, 1980s, 2½" d ball in middle, 5" h . . . . . . . . . . 12.00
- Swordfish, arches over dome, "Florida," early 1970s, 4½" l . . . . . . . . . 20.00
- Tiger, two tigers in dome, "Southwick's Wild Animal Farm, Mendon, MA," 1970s, 3½" h . . . . . . . . 18.00
- Treasure Chest, gold colored plastic frame, clear sides, Nassau on plaque, red lobster, fish, and seaweed, 1970s, 2½ x 3½ x 1¾" . . . 6.00

Flag, American, glass globe, plastic white base, red, white, and blue snow, marked "The Driss Company, Chicago, IL, Made in USA," 1950s . 40.00

Fraternal, Masonic symbol, glass ball, oily liquid

- George Washington Masonic National Memorial, sq brown Bakelite base, gold letters, 1950s . . . . . . . . 50.00
- Mizpah Lodge, No. 245, F. & A.M. Harry J. Freedman W. M. 1958 printed blue Bakelite base . . . . . . . 55.00

Game, ring toss

- Giraffe, plastic dome, two giraffes, hoops go over necks, decal "The Pacifier," 1970s . . . . . . . . . . 10.00
- Lobster, plastic dome, plastic hoops, marked "Louisiana," early 1980s, 3 x 2 x 1" . . . . . . . . . . 8.00

Halloween

- Cat, figural, black, 2¾" d orange plastic ball, witch riding broomstick, 6½" h . . . . . . . . . . 40.00
- Jack 'O Lantern, black cat, 3¾" d clear glass ball, wood base . . . . . . 10.00
- Owl, figural, brown, orange ground, outstretched wing, scarecrow in 2¼" ball, 5½" h . . . . . . . . . . 40.00

Moving Parts
- Balloons on string, monkey swings on hook, four animals in cage, "Philadelphia Zoo," 1970s, 3½ x 2¾ x 3" 12.00
- Champagne, shot, and martini glass on strings, naked lady, "The Bar is Open" bar scene painted backdrop, "This one is on me" plaque, "Las Vegas" on outside, 1960s, 3¾ x 2¾ x 2¼" 16.00
- Dice, red, float in water, blue ground, main strip in Vegas scene, 1970s, 2⅝ x 2 x 2¼" 8.00
- Fish on string, green seaweed, three fish, "Ocean City, MD," 1970s 6.00
- Rocking Horse on glider, toy soldier on his back, arched dome, black base, 1970s, 3⅛ x 1¼ x 2⅝" 8.00
- Train, steam locomotive, moves in front of train image background, small dome, 1980s 5.00
- Trolley, Golden Gate Bridge, San Francisco, Chinatown background, small dome, 1970s 6.00
- Wagon, horse–drawn, bottle shape, moves in and out of covered barn, large dome, New Hampshire, 1970s 8.00

Museum
- Ripley's Museum, St Augustine, FL, Cabin of Pennies, "tow(sic) Headed Calf," plastic bottle, flat sides, three plaques, three scenes, and background panel, 1960s, 6" l 12.00
- Salem Witch Museum, 1692, small plastic dome, house and witch on broomstick, 1970s, 2¾ x 2¼ x 2" 9.00
- The American Museum of Natural History, Hayden Planetarium, NY, plastic dome, printing on back, camera and city skyline scene, 1980s, 2¾ x 2¼ x 2" 8.00

Ocean Liner
- *Queen Mary,* Long Beach, CA, plastic dome, cutout of ship on ocean, printed and town panels, 1970s 12.00
- *SS United States,* oily liquid, ship in front of Art Deco skyline, blue base with red trim and white printing, 1950s, 2¾" glass globe 55.00

Pencil Sharpener, large dome, Niagara Falls, Maid of the Mist, 1970s 8.00

Religious
- Crucifixion, plastic dome, Jesus on cross, battery operated, 1960s, 3⅝ x 2⅞ x 2¾" 20.00
- Moses Crossing Red Sea, plastic dome, Moses with raised staff parting the sea, 1970s, 2¾ x 2¼ x 2" 15.00
- Nativity Scene, small plastic dome, 1980s 4.00
- The Last Supper, plastic dome, Disciples at table, 1970s, 2¾ x 2¼ x 2" 12.00

Roly Poly, snowman figural top, Santa in sled, marked "CSA Inc. 4482 Curt S. Adler Inc, NY, NY 10010, UK Design Reg No 969 255," 1970s, 2¾" dome 15.00

Salt and Pepper Shakers, pr
- Civil War, plastic, pink "P" with American flag, blue "S" with Rebel flag, soldiers and cannon scene, back compartments, 1960s, 3¼ x 1¼ x 2" 20.00
- Florida's Silver Springs, TV shape, plastic, blue "P," pink "S," boat on see–saw, side compartments, 1970s, 3 x 2¼ x 1" 18.00
- Sydney Harbor Bridge, plastic, rect, mustard yellow, ship moves on slide and bridge scene, 1970s 15.00

Soap Dish, shell shape, plastic, blue, dome sits on back of dish, bridge and river scene, 1000 Islands, NY, 1970s, 4 x 4¼" 20.00

Souvenir
- Atlantic City, four tiers, painted figure of girl on angled sled, brown ceramic base, 1930s, 4 x 2½ x 2¾" 40.00
- Chateau Frontenac, Quebec, Canada, color drawing, glass top, black Bakelite base, marked "Metropolitan Supplies Ltd., Canada Reg. 1948 Patent" 45.00
- Denmark, plastic dome, Viking ship, 1960s, 2¾ x 2¼ x 2" 10.00
- Dewey Beach, plastic dome, seagull and sea shells, 1960s, 2¾ x 2¼ x 2" 8.00
- Durban, South Africa, plastic dome, costumed man pulling carriage, 1970s 15.00
- Empire State Building, New York City,

**Souvenir of Skyline Drive, decal label, cottage and two trees, glass ball, ceramic base, 4" h, $45.00.**

gold letters, inverted glass cone, black Bakelite base, 1950s, 4¾" h . . . **12.00**
Grand Canyon National Park, plaque, round dome, burro standing in front of dark mountain scene, 1960s . . . **8.00**
Mammoth Cave, KY, plastic dome, cavern scene, 1960s . . . **9.00**
Ocean City, MD, rect plastic dome with goldfish on string, 1980s, 2¾ x 1¾" . . . **4.00**
Ontario, Canada, gold decal, painted, bisque lighthouse, glass top, blue glass base, marked "Germany," 1920s . . . **35.00**
Philadelphia, PA, plastic dome, yellow background, Liberty Bell and two flags, early 1980s . . . **6.00**
Pilgrim Memorial Monument, Provincetown, MA, four tiers, gold decal, bisque building, glass top, brown ceramic base, 1930s . . . **50.00**
Ricardo di Roma, Vatican scene, white marble tiered base, 1930s, 2½" d glass ball . . . **40.00**
Roy Rogers and Dale Evans Museum, Victorville, CA, plastic dome, barn scene and Trigger moves on slide, 1960s . . . **15.00**
Scotland, drum shape, plastic, Bagpiper figure, red top, blue bottom, gold braid criss–crosses, 1980s, 3¼ x 2¼" . . . **10.00**
St Paul's Cathedral, London, plastic dome, cathedral and double decker bus move on slide, early 1980s, 3⅝ x 2⅞ x 2¾" . . . **8.00**
Souvenir of Mardi Gras, New Orleans, painted King Rex figure, black ceramic base with gold decal, early 1930s, 2½" d ball . . . **60.00**
Terminal Tower Building, Cleveland, OH, plaque, 1970s . . . **8.00**

States
Arizona, plastic, white base, road runner and cactus, 1970s, 3 x 2½ x 1¼" . . . **8.00**
Georgia, The Peach State, bottle, flat sides, plastic, two alligators on see–saw, tree, and mountain, 1960s, 5" l . . . **10.00**
Indiana, The Hoosier State, plastic dome, Indy 500 scene, 1970s . . . **9.00**
Montana, figural, black bear, plastic, two deer on see–saw, state name on chest, marked "UVC–Inc 1972" on bottom, 2½" d ball, 5" h . . . **20.00**
Virginia, small dome, state outline and bird on branch, late 1970s . . . **6.00**

World's Fair
1939 New York World's Fair, Trylon and Perisphere bisque figurine, brown ceramic base
With decal . . . **90.00**
Without decal . . . **70.00**
New York World's Fair 1964–65
Unisphere, plastic, round ball, red sq base, perpetual calendar, "Unisphere presented by USS United States Steel, 1964 NYWF" . . . **16.00**
Vatican Pavilion, plastic dome, two Swiss guards scene, pavilion background, "New York World's Fair" plaque . . . **20.00**
Expo 67, Montreal Canada, plaque, fireworks background . . . **15.00**
1982 Worlds Fair, tall dome, Sunsphere, 3½ x 2 x 1¼" . . . **12.00**
1984 World's Fair, plastic dome, fair archway, ferry moves back and forth on groove, plaque . . . **10.00**

World War II
Douglas MacArthur, America's Hero, glass ball, black ceramic base, bisque bust . . . **45.00**
General Eisenhower, glass ball, black ceramic base, bisque bust, "General Dwight D. Eisenhower, Commander in Chief, Allied Invasion Forces" decal, marked "Atlas Crystal Works, Covington, TN, US Patents 231423/4/5," 1940s . . . **60.00**
Plane, painted bisque figurine, red star on wings, tail and nose markings, glass ball, black ceramic base, marked "Atlas Crystal Works, Trenton, NJ, Patents Pending, Made in USA," 1940s . . . **40.00**
Sailor, glass globe, saluting figure in sailor suit, black ceramic base, 1940s . . . **35.00**

# SODA BOTTLES

**History:** Soda bottles were made to contain soda water and soft drinks. A beverage manufacturer usually made his own bottles and sold them within a limited area. Coddball stoppers and a stopper perfected by Hutchinson were popular with early manufacturers before the advent of metal or screw top caps.

**References:** Paul & Karen Bates, *Commemorative Soda Bottles,* Soda Mart, 1988; Paul & Karen Bates, *Embossed Soda Bottles,* Soda Mart, 1988; Paul & Karen Bates, *Painted Label Soda Bottles,* Soda Mart, 1988; Ralph & Terry Kovel, *The Kovels' Bottle Price List, Ninth Edition,* Crown Publishers, Inc., 1992; Jim Megura, *The Official Identification and Price Guide To Bottles, Eleventh Edition,* House of Collectibles, 1991; Tom Morrison, *Root Beer: Advertising and Collectibles,* Schiffer Publishing, Ltd., 1992; Carlo & Dot

Sellari, *The Standard Old Bottle Price Guide,* Collector Books, 1989.

**Note:** The books by Paul and Karen Bates are continually updated through a subscription service.

**Periodical:** *Antique Bottle And Glass Collector,* P. O. Box 187, East Greenville, PA 18041.

**See:** Coca–Cola, Moxie, Pepsi and Soft Drink Collectibles.

**James Wise, Allentown, PA, blue, emb lettering, 6⅞" h, $5.00.**

Abilena National Cathartic Water, amber, 10" h . . . . . . **6.00**
Alter & Wilson Manuf, light green, applied top, 7" h . . . . . . **17.50**
Bacon's Soda Works, light green, blob top, 7" h . . . . . . **8.00**
Bryant's Root Beer, This Bottle Makes Five Gallons, amber, applied top, 4½" h . . . . . . **4.00**
Cape Arco Soda Works, Marshfield, OR, round, light green applied top, 7" h . **8.00**
Coke, 24" h . . . . . . **25.00**
Deadwood, SD, blob top . . . . . . **125.00**
Deamer Grass Valley, aqua, blob top, 7¼" h . . . . . . **5.00**
Dr Pepper, Colorado . . . . . . **17.50**
English Soda, light green, applied top, 8" h . . . . . . **4.00**
Fizz, Southern State Siphon Bottling Co, golden amber, 11" h . . . . . . **15.00**
Golden West Soda Works, light green, 7" h . . . . . . **10.00**
Hawaiian Soda Works, aqua, emb, 7½" h . . . . . . **8.00**
Hippo Size Soda Water, clear, crown top, 10" h . . . . . . **5.00**
Jackson's Napa Soda, crown cap, 7¼" h . . . . . . **5.00**
Kolshorn, Chas & Bros, Savannah, GA, aqua, blob top, 8" h . . . . . . **15.00**
Los Angeles Soda Works, aqua, 8" h . . **5.00**
Mendocin Bottling Works, A L Reynolds, light green, 7" h . . . . . . **7.00**
Mission Dry Sparkling, black, 9¾" h . . **3.00**
Nevada City Soda Works, ETR Powell, aqua, applied top, 7" h . . . . . . **8.00**
Orange Crush Co, Pat'd July 20, 1926, light green, 9" h . . . . . . **3.50**
Perrier, clear, bowling pin shape, paper label, 8½" h . . . . . . **2.00**
Phenis Nerve Beverage Co, Boston, clear, crown cap, 9½" h . . . . . . **4.00**
Rapid City Bottling Works, light green, crown cap, 8" h . . . . . . **5.00**
Ross's Royal Belfast Ginger Ale, green, diamond shape paper label, 10" h . . **5.00**
Sandahl Beverages, clear, 8" h . . . . . . **4.00**
Scott & Gilbert Co, San Francisco, brown, crown top, 10" h . . . . . . **5.00**
Sequoia Soda Works, aqua, 7½" h . . . . **5.00**
Solano Soda Works, aqua, 8" h . . . . . . **5.00**
Tahoe Soda Springs Natural Mineral Water, light green, 7½" h . . . . . . **9.00**
Union Glass Works, dark blue, blob top, 7 1/23" h . . . . . . **20.00**
Williams Bros, San Jose, CA . . . . . . **7.00**
XLCR Soda Works, light green, 7¼" . . **5.00**

# SODA FOUNTAIN COLLECTIBLES

**Collecting Hints:** The first decision collectors need to make is the chronological period upon which they will focus. More and more collectors are focusing on the 1920–1960 period because the material is more readily available.

Smart collectors seek out as many photograph images as they can find before collecting in earnest. Three excellent sources are the post card, magazine (advertising tear sheets and articles), and photographic markets. Soda fountain pictures also appear in ice cream history books.

Specialize immediately. If you are going to recreate the back–bar of a soda fountain, you should have a buying budget in excess of $10,000. Back–bar material, from the bar itself to soda dispensers, is expensive. Decorator interest helps keep the prices high.

Almost every soda fountain item crosses over into another collecting category. Again, this helps keep prices high. Collectors find that they do better working with established dealers than competing at auction. However, this having been said, the number of advertising auctions that include soda fountain material is increasing.

**History:** From the late 1880s through the end of the 1960s the local soda fountain was the social center of small town America, especially for teenagers. The soda fountain provided a center for conversation and gossip, a haven to satisfy the mid–afternoon munchies, and a source for the most current popular magazines.

In the period prior to World War I independent soda fountains were common. Many supplemented fountain income by selling periodicals, personal necessities, and household supplies. Eventually many added cards and gifts as a revenue enhancer.

Most soda fountains sold ice cream. However, do not confuse a soda fountain with an ice cream parlor. The latter sold ice cream exclusively. The soda fountain's fare was much broader.

As the twentieth century progressed, the independent soda fountain faded from the scene. It survived in thousands of drugstores and small general merchandise stores scattered across America.

The soda fountain became passe in the 1960s as specialized merchandising and franchises gained in popularity. Ben and Jerry's and Hägen Daz are simply not the same.

**References:** Douglas Congdon–Martin, *Drugstore and Soda Fountain Antiques*, Schiffer Publishing, 1991; Paul Dickson, *The Great American Ice Cream Book*, Galahad Books, 1972; Ralph Pomeroy, *The Ice Cream Connection*, Paddington Press, 1975.

**Collectors' Club:** The Ice Screamer, PO Box 5387, Lancaster, PA 17601.

**Museums:** Greenfield Village, Dearborn, MI; Museum of Science and Industry, Finigan's Ice Cream Parlor, Chicago, IL; Smithsonian Institution, Washington, D.C.

**REPRODUCTION ALERT.**

Ashtray, Richland Snack Bar, tin ...... **4.00**
Bin, counter, Quaker Brand Salted Peanuts, 9 x 13¾ x 4¼" .............. **40.00**
Blackboard, Squirt, 15 x 30" ......... **18.00**
Can, Abbott's Ice Cream, ½ gal, Amish girl, c1940 ...................... **15.00**
Catalog
  Bastian–Blessing Co, Chicago, IL, Cat No. 73, Soda Fountain Parts & Carbonators, 1955, 65 pages, 8½ x 11" **28.00**
  Liquid Carbonic Corp, Chicago, IL, Red Diamond and Simplex Soda Fountains, c1943, 20 pages, four pages of color illus, 8½ x 11" .... **30.00**
  Stanley Knight Corp, Chicago, IL, Soda Fountains, Instructions & Specifications, c1944, 52 pages, 7 x 10" ........................ **30.00**
Clock, Seven–Up, "You Like It, It Likes You," wood frame ................ **75.00**
Display Case, countertop, Popcorn, wood and glass, hinged lid, 11 x 11" **45.00**
Display Rack
  Beech–Nut Chewing Gum, 1920s .. **300.00**
  Lance Candy, four shelves ......... **15.00**
Door Pull, Drink Hire's, tin .......... **50.00**
Fan
  Goold's Orangeade, cardboard, wooden handle ................ **15.00**

**Alka-Seltzer Dispenser, cast iron, chrome plated, blue paint, 13½" h, $70.00**

  Hoffman Willis Ice Cream Co, girl eating ice cream ............... **15.00**
Hot Plate, commercial, Nestle's Hot Chocolate, 8" x 12" standing metal sign, red and white snowman graphics, late 1940s–early 1950s ........ **95.00**
Ice Chipper, Gilchrist, #50 .......... **8.00**
Ice Cream Cone Holder, Vortex, patented 1916 ...................... **6.50**
Ice Cream Dish
  Amber, banana split .............. **12.50**
  Depression Glass, American Sweetheart pattern clear glass insert, chrome metal base ............. **15.00**
Ice Cream Scoop
  Dover, brass ..................... **68.50**
  Erie, round, size 8, aluminum ..... **180.00**
  Gilchrist, #30, size 8, polished .... **65.00**
  No–Pak 31, size 5 ............... **75.00**
  Scoop Rite ...................... **15.00**
Jar, Borden's Malted Milk, glass label . **175.00**
Magazine Cover, *Saturday Evening Post*, young soda jerk talking to girls at counter, Norman Rockwell, Aug 22, 1953 .......................... **12.00**
Malt Machine
  Arnold #15 ..................... **135.00**
  Hamilton–Beach, #18, porcelain ... **125.00**
Milk Shake Mixer, Hamilton–Beach
  Single Head, green enamel finish, two speed settings ................. **135.00**
  Triple Head, cream enamel finish, highly polished chrome nameplate, three speed settings ............. **265.00**
Mirror, Horlicks Malted Milk, maid with cow ........................... **30.00**
Paper Cone Dispenser, 11" l, glass tube, metal holder, "Soda Fountain Drinks & Ice Cream Served in Vortex," gold label, wall mount ................ **40.00**
Pinback Button
  Hi–Hat Ice Cream Soda 10¢, 2¼" d, McCrory's, c1940 .............. **15.00**
  Sanderson's Drug Store, 1" d, blue and white, soda fountain glass illus,

"Ice Cream Soda/Choice Cigars/ Fine Candies," 1901–12 . . . . . . . . **24.00**
Post Card, Gunther's Soda Fountain, Chicago . . . . . . . . . . . . . . . . . . . . . . . . **12.00**
Pretzel Jar, Seyfert's Original Butter Pretzels, glass, orig lid, 10½" h . . . . **60.00**
Sign
Bowey's Hot Chocolate, black logo . **150.00**
Coca–Cola, fountain service, porcelain, diecut, shield shape . . . . . . . . **425.00**
Golden Rod Ice Cream, diecut, girl with ice cream . . . . . . . . . . . . . . . . . **85.00**
Nehi, diecut, woman at marble soda fountain, sitting on wire stool, sipping through two straws, giant bottle on floor, Columbus, GA, 1920 **1,250.00**
Orange County Fountain, 24 x 18", porcelain on steel, yellow oval center, blue and white lettering, dark blue ground . . . . . . . . . . . . . . . . . . . **100.00**
Soda Holder, metal, blue, . . . . . . . . . . . **5.00**
Straw Jar, glass
Frosted Panel . . . . . . . . . . . . . . . . . . . . **225.00**
Green Panel . . . . . . . . . . . . . . . . . . . . . **410.00**
Pattern Glass, Illinois pattern, lid . . . **450.00**
Red, metal lid, 1950s . . . . . . . . . . . . . **175.00**
Syrup Dispenser Pump, Hires . . . . . . . . **135.00**
Thermometer, Hire's Root Beer, tin, bottle shape, 28½" . . . . . . . . . . . . . . . . . . **65.00**
Tin, Schraffts's Marshmallow Topping, 25 lbs . . . . . . . . . . . . . . . . . . . . . . . . . . **35.00**
Tray
Chero–Cola . . . . . . . . . . . . . . . . . . . . . **65.00**
Furnace Ice Cream, girl holding serving tray, 1920s . . . . . . . . . . . . . . . . . **150.00**
Hoefler Ice Cream, oval, woman eating ice cream . . . . . . . . . . . . . . . . . . **200.00**
Schuller's Ice Cream, 13 x 11", ice cream sodas and cones . . . . . . . . . **200.00**

# SOFT DRINK COLLECTIBLES

**Collecting Hints:** Coca–Cola items have dominated the field. Only recently have collectors begun concentrating on other soft drink manufacturing companies. Soft drink collectors must compete with collectors of advertising, bottles and premiums for the same material.

National brands such as Canada Dry, Dr. Pepper, and Pepsi–Cola are best known. However, regional soft drink bottling plants do exist, and their products are fertile ground for the novice collector.

**History:** Sarsaparilla, a name associated with soft drinks, began as a medicinal product. When carbonated water was added, it became a soft drink and was consumed for pleasure rather than medical purposes. However, sarsaparilla was only one type of ingredient added to carbonated water to produce soft drinks.

Each company had its special formula. Although Coca–Cola has a large market share, other companies provided challenges in different historical periods. Moxie was followed by Hire's which in turn gave way to Pepsi–Cola and 7–Up.

The 1950s brought soft drinks to the forefront of everyday life. Large advertising campaigns and promotional products produced a wealth of material. Regional bottling plants were strong and produced local specialties such as "Birch Beer" in eastern Pennsylvania. By 1970 most of these local plants had closed.

Many large companies had operations outside of the United States, which also produced a wealth of advertising and promotional materials. Today, the diet soda is a response to the American lifestyle of the 1980s.

**References:** Norman E. Martinus and Harry L. Rinker, *Warman's Paper,* Wallace–Homestead, 1993; Tom Morrison, *Root Beer: Advertising and Collectibles,* Schiffer Publishing, Ltd., 1992.

**Collectors' Clubs:** Dr. Pepper 10–2–4 Collectors Club, 1529 John Smith, Irving, TX 75061; National Pop Can Collectors, 1124 Tyler St., Fairfield, CA 94533.

**See:** Coca–Cola, Moxie, Pepsi, Soda Bottles, and Soda Fountain Collectibles.

**Catalog, NEHI premiums, red, black, and white cov, 6 pgs, 1920s, 5⅜ x 8¼", $25.00.**

Ashtray, Dr Pepper . . . . . . . . . . . . . . . . . **7.00**
Bank
Vess Cola . . . . . . . . . . . . . . . . . . . . . . . **6.00**
Whistle Cola . . . . . . . . . . . . . . . . . . . . **6.00**
Banner, Lime Cola, canvas . . . . . . . . . . **40.00**
Beanie, Dr Pepper, with charms . . . . . . **15.00**
Blotter, Nehi Soda, 1930s . . . . . . . . . . . **3.00**

Bottle Carrier
- Kist Soda, cardboard .............. **4.00**
- RC Cola, aluminum .............. **12.00**

Bottle Display, 7–Up, 1949 .......... **4.50**
Bottle Opener, 7–Up, wall type ...... **30.00**
Calendar
- Dr Pepper, 1937, Earl Moran Art, framed ........................ **140.00**
- Nu–Grape, 1941 ................. **35.00**
- RC Cola, 1967 .................. **150.00**
- Suncrest Orange, 1960 ............ **38.00**

Can, Dr Pepper, cone top ........... **20.00**
Clock
- Dr Pepper ....................... **120.00**
- Hires Root Beer, wall, plastic ...... **25.00**
- 7–Up ........................... **30.00**
- Whistle Orange ................. **37.50**

Cooler, Squirt, round, colorful ....... **95.00**
Door Pull, 7–Up .................. **24.00**
Fan
- Dr Pepper, cardboard ............. **38.00**
- Nu–Icy Soda, cardboard .......... **30.00**

Label, Dr Pepper, paper ............. **10.00**
Menu Board
- Orange Crush ................... **55.00**
- Squirt, tin, emb bottle ........... **85.00**

Mug
- Dad's Root Beer ................ **10.00**
- Hires Root Beer, glass, 1940s ...... **10.00**
- Twin Kiss Root Beer, 3" .......... **10.00**

**Mug, Hires Rootbeer, Villeroy and Block, #2327, $185.00.**

Pencil, Orange Crush, mechanical .... **20.00**
Pencil Clip, 7/8" celluloid
- Orange–Crush, black and white inscription, orange ground, c1930 . **8.00**
- 7–Up, black, white, and red logo .. **5.00**

Pinback Button
- 1¼", Cherry Smash, George Washington portrait, dark red ground shaded to olive green, black inscription, c1911 ............... **28.00**
- 1¾", Dad's Root Beer, litho, bottle cap, yellow, red, blue, white, and black, c1940 .................. **15.00**

Pitcher, Orange Crush, chrome lid .... **110.00**
Playing Cards, Nu–Grape, single deck, slide out box .................... **22.00**
Sign
- B–1 Lemon Soda, 12 x 14 x 6", light up .......................... **20.00**
- Canada Dry, porcelain ............ **35.00**
- Cliquot Club Soda, 14 x 20", stand–up, cardboard, Eskimos pulling sled **24.00**
- Dixie Springs Soda, 18 x 24", stand–up, cardboard, 1940s ........... **20.00**
- Dr Pepper
  - Cardboard, early ............... **120.00**
  - Plastic, metal frame ............ **35.00**
- Grapette, 12 x 24", tin, emb, 1940s **35.00**
- Hires
  - Drink Hires, cardboard ......... **30.00**
  - R–J, round .................... **65.00**
- John Collins Soda, 24 x 18", 1940s . **65.00**
- Mason's Root Beer ............... **38.00**
- Mission Orange of California, 25" h, tin, 1950s ..................... **90.00**
- Mountain Dew, hillbilly, 35" h, tin . **245.00**
- Nesbitt's Orange, 48 x 16", tin, 1938 **165.00**
- Norka Ginger Ale, tin, bottle, 1940s **35.00**
- Nu–Grape Soda, tin, yellow and blue, dated March 9, 1920 ...... **125.00**
- Orange, Lemon, Lime Crush, emb tin **350.00**
- 7–Up
  - Neon, figural, fountain glass, straw, fizz bubbles, three colors ...... **650.00**
  - Tin .......................... **35.00**
- Squirt, 8", cardboard, double sided, c1949 ....................... **24.00**
- Sun Drop, tin, bottle cap shape, 36" **275.00**
- Sunrise Orange, tin, bottled by Coca–Cola .......................... **90.00**

Thermometer
- Dr Pepper ...................... **55.00**
- Frostie Root Beer ............... **35.00**
- Mason's Root Beer .............. **65.00**
- Nu–Grape, 16" l ................ **135.00**
- Orange Crush ................... **100.00**
- RC Cola ....................... **65.00**
- Suncrest Orange ................ **65.00**

Tip Tray, Royal Crown Cola ......... **38.00**
Toy, Howel's Root Beer, 8" h, wood, mechanical, trapeze, 5½" jointed wood figural elf, multicolored litho trim, c1920 ..................... **40.00**
Tray
- Hires Root Beer, 1935 ............ **85.00**
- Zipp's Cherrio 5¢, never used ..... **1,500.00**

Uniform Patch
- Dr Pepper
  - 7" .......................... **12.00**
  - 10", marked "Good for Life" .... **22.00**

Watch Fob
- Drink Chero–Cola 5 cents ......... **55.00**
- Hires Root Beer, 1½", octagonal, brass, raised "Drink Hires" and boy, early 1900s ............... **65.00**

Window Card, Diet–Way Cola ....... **40.00**

# SOLDIERS, DIMESTORE

**Collecting Hints:** Soldier figures are preferred over civilian figures. The most valuable figures are the ones which had short production runs, usually because they were less popular with the youthful collectors of the period.

O'Brien and Pielin use numbering systems to identify figures in their books. Newcomers should study these books, taking note of the numerous variations in style and color.

Condition, desirability and scarcity establish the price of a figure. Repainting or rust severely reduces the value.

Auction prices often mislead the beginning collector. While some rare figures have sold in the $150 to $300 range, most sell between $10 and $25.

**History:** Three dimensional lead, iron, and rubber soldier and civilian figures were produced in the United States by the millions before and after World War II. These figures were called "Dimestore Soldiers" because they were sold in "Five and Dime" stores of the era, the figures usually costing a nickel or dime. Although American toy soldiers can be traced back to the early 20th century, the golden age of the Dimestore Soldier was 1935 until 1942.

Four companies—Barclay, Manoil, Grey Iron and Auburn Rubber—mass produced the three–inch figures. Barclay and Manoil dominated the market, probably because their lead castings lent themselves to more realistic and imaginative poses than iron and rubber.

Barclay's early pre–war figures are identifiable by their separate glued–on and later clipped–on tin hats. When these are lost, the hole in the top of the head always identifies a Barclay.

The Manoil Company first produced soldiers, sailors, cowboys, and Indians. However, the younger buyers of the period strongly preferred military figures, perhaps emulating the newspaper headlines as World War II approached. Manoil's civilian figures were made in response to pacifist pressure and boycotts mounted before the war began.

Figures also were produced by such companies as All–Nu, American Alloy, American Soldier Co., Beton, Ideal, Jones, Lincoln Log, Miller, Playwood Plastics, Soljertoys, Tommy Toy, Tootsietoy, and Warren. Because of the short lived nature of these companies, numerous limited production figures command high prices, especially those of All–Nu, Jones, Tommy Toy, and Warren.

From 1942 through 1945 the wartime "scrap drives" devoured tons of the dimestore figures and the molds that produced them.

In late 1945 Barclay and Manoil introduced modernized military figures, but they never enjoyed their pre–war popularity. "Military operations" generally were phased out by the early 1950s. Similarly, the civilian figures could not compete with escalating labor costs and the competition of plastic.

**References:** Norman Joplin, *The Great Book Of Hollow–Cast Figures,* New Cavendish Books, 1992; Richard O'Brien, *Collecting Toy Soldiers: An Identification and Value Guide, Sixth Edition* Books Americana, 1993; Richard O'Brien, *Collecting Toy Soldiers: An Identification and Value Guide, No. 2,* Books Americana, 1992; Don Pielin, *American Dimestore Soldier Book,* privately printed, 1983.

**Periodicals:** *Old Toy Soldier Newsletter,* 209 N. Lombard, Oak Park, IL 60302; *Toy Soldier Review,* 127 74th Street, North Bergen, NJ 07047.

**Advisor:** Fred Wilhelm.

**REPRODUCTION ALERT.** Some manufacturers identify the newer products; many do not.

**Notes:** Prices listed are for figures in original condition with at least 95% of the paint remaining. Unless otherwise noted, uniform colors are brown.

## CIVILIAN FIGURE

Auburn Rubber
- Baseball ........ **28.00**
- Football ........ **28.00**

**Barclay, mailman, B189, $9.00**

Barclay
- Boy Scout, lighting fire ........ **38.00**
- Civilian Figures
  - Fireman with axe ........ **18.00**
  - Girl Skater ........ **8.00**
  - Mailman ........ **9.00**
  - Newsboy ........ **10.00**
  - Pirate ........ **8.00**
  - Policeman with raised arm ........ **8.00**
  - Redcap with bag ........ **15.00**

Santa Claus on skis . . . . . . . . . . . . . **55.00**
Woman Passenger with dog . . . . . **9.00**
Cowboys
Cowboy
Mounted, firing pistol . . . . . . . . . **12.00**
With lasso . . . . . . . . . . . . . . . . . . **15.00**
Indian
Standing, bow and arrow . . . . . . **8.00**
Tomahawk and shield . . . . . . . . **9.00**
Grey Iron
American Family Series, 2¼" h . . **5.00–25.00**
Western
Bandit, hands up . . . . . . . . . . . . . . . **4.00**
Cowboy
Hold–up man . . . . . . . . . . . . . . . **15.00**
Standing . . . . . . . . . . . . . . . . . . . **9.00**
Manoil
Happy Farm Series
Blacksmith
Making horseshoes . . . . . . . . . . . **20.00**
With wheel . . . . . . . . . . . . . . . . . **20.00**
Farmer, sowing grain . . . . . . . . . . . **18.00**
Lady
Sweeping . . . . . . . . . . . . . . . . . . **20.00**
With pie . . . . . . . . . . . . . . . . . . . **25.00**
Man
Chopping wood . . . . . . . . . . . . . **18.00**
Juggling barrel . . . . . . . . . . . . . . **30.00**
Man and woman on bench . . . . . . **18.00**
Watchman blowing out lantern . . . **25.00**
Western
Cowboy
Arm raised . . . . . . . . . . . . . . . . . **17.00**
One gun raised, flat base . . . . . . **14.00**
Cowgirl riding horse . . . . . . . . . . . **25.00**
Indian with knives . . . . . . . . . . . . . **18.00**

## MILITARY FIGURE

Auburn Rubber
Bugler . . . . . . . . . . . . . . . . . . . . . . . . **10.00**
Charging with Tommy gun . . . . . . . . **8.00**
Grenade Thrower . . . . . . . . . . . . . . . **15.00**
Machine Gunner, kneeling . . . . . . . . **11.00**
Marching with rifle . . . . . . . . . . . . . . **7.00**
Motorcycle with sidecar . . . . . . . . . . **55.00**
Motorcyclist . . . . . . . . . . . . . . . . . . . **30.00**
Soldier
Kneeling with binoculars . . . . . . . . **12.00**
Searchlight . . . . . . . . . . . . . . . . . . . **28.00**
Barclay, pod foot series
Post War, pot helmet
AA Gunner, standing . . . . . . . . . . . **16.00**
Flag Bearer . . . . . . . . . . . . . . . . . . . **15.00**
Machine Gunner, prone . . . . . . . . . **15.00**
Officer with sword . . . . . . . . . . . . . **15.00**
Rifleman, standing . . . . . . . . . . . . . **15.00**
Pre World War II
Ammo Carrier, tin hat . . . . . . . . . . . **16.00**
Anti–Aircraft Gunner, standing . . . **15.00**
Bugler, tin helmet . . . . . . . . . . . . . **15.00**
Cameraman, kneeling, tin hat . . . . **20.00**
Cook in white, holding roast . . . . . **12.00**
Dispatcher with dog . . . . . . . . . . . . **35.00**
Doctor, white coat, carrying bag . **12.00**
Flag Bearer, tin helmet . . . . . . . . . . **18.00**
Machine Gunner, kneeling, tin hat **10.00**
Marching with rifle, tin hat . . . . . . **12.00**
Marine Officer, marching, sword, blue uniform, tin hat . . . . . . . . . . **22.00**
Nurse, kneeling with cup, white . **15.00**
Parachutist, landing . . . . . . . . . . . . **25.00**
Pilot, standing . . . . . . . . . . . . . . . . . **18.00**
Sailor
Carrying flag, white . . . . . . . . . . **20.00**
Marching, white . . . . . . . . . . . . . **20.00**
Signal flags, white . . . . . . . . . . . . **20.00**
Sharpshooter
Prone . . . . . . . . . . . . . . . . . . . . . . . **15.00**
Standing . . . . . . . . . . . . . . . . . . . . **11.00**
Signalman with flags . . . . . . . . . . . . **20.00**
Soldier
Charging with rifle, gas mask . . **20.00**
Crawling, tin hat . . . . . . . . . . . . . **18.00**
Lying wounded, tin hat . . . . . . . **12.00**
Peeling potatoes . . . . . . . . . . . . . **20.00**
Prone with binoculars . . . . . . . . . **15.00**
Releasing pigeons, tin hat . . . . . **18.00**
Running with rifle . . . . . . . . . . . . **18.00**
Searchlight . . . . . . . . . . . . . . . . . . **20.00**
Standing at attention, tin hat . . . **14.00**
Stretcher Bearer . . . . . . . . . . . . . . . **15.00**
Telephone Operator, tin hat . . . . . **15.00**
Two man rocket team . . . . . . . . . . . **20.00**
Wireless Operator, antenna, tin hat **28.00**
Wounded
On crutches . . . . . . . . . . . . . . . . . **15.00**
Sitting, arm in sling . . . . . . . . . . . **15.00**
Podfoot Series, 2¾" h
Bomb Thrower . . . . . . . . . . . . . . . . **8.00**
Bugler . . . . . . . . . . . . . . . . . . . . . . . **7.00**
Flag Bearer . . . . . . . . . . . . . . . . . . . **10.00**
Machine Gunner
Charging . . . . . . . . . . . . . . . . . . . **6.00**
Prone . . . . . . . . . . . . . . . . . . . . . . . **8.00**
Nurse, white . . . . . . . . . . . . . . . . . . **18.00**
Officer . . . . . . . . . . . . . . . . . . . . . . . **6.00**
Pilot, standing . . . . . . . . . . . . . . . . . **9.00**
Sailor, blue . . . . . . . . . . . . . . . . . . . **8.00**
Soldier
Charging . . . . . . . . . . . . . . . . . . . **6.00**
Marching with rifle . . . . . . . . . . . **7.00**
With bazooka . . . . . . . . . . . . . . . **8.00**
Grey Iron
Cadet Officer . . . . . . . . . . . . . . . . . . **14.00**
Cavalryman . . . . . . . . . . . . . . . . . . . **25.00**
Colonial Soldier . . . . . . . . . . . . . . . . **15.00**
Doctor, white, bag . . . . . . . . . . . . . **12.00**
Doughboy
Crawling . . . . . . . . . . . . . . . . . . . . . **15.00**
Marching . . . . . . . . . . . . . . . . . . . . **10.00**
Rifle, kneeling . . . . . . . . . . . . . . . . **15.00**
Sentry . . . . . . . . . . . . . . . . . . . . . . . **10.00**
Signaling . . . . . . . . . . . . . . . . . . . . . **20.00**

Drum Major .......... 17.00
Drummer .......... 15.00
Ethiopian
  Charging .......... 35.00
  Marching .......... 28.00
Flag Bearer .......... 15.00
Machine Gunner
  Kneeling .......... 10.00
  Prone .......... 15.00
Nurse, white and blue .......... 12.00
Radio Operator .......... 45.00
Sailor
  Marching
    Blue .......... 12.00
    White .......... 14.00
  Wounded, crutches .......... 24.00
Manoil
Post War
  Flag Bearer .......... 25.00
  Marching with rifle .......... 16.00
  Soldier
    Bazooka .......... 20.00
    Mine Detector .......... 30.00
  Tommy Gunner, standing .......... 22.00
Post War, 2½" size, marked "USA"
  Aircraft Spotter .......... 25.00
  Aviator, holding bomb .......... 24.00
  Flag Bearer .......... 26.00
  Grenade Thrower .......... 24.00
  Machine Gunner, seated .......... 20.00
  Observer with binoculars .......... 27.00
  Soldier with bazooka .......... 18.00
Pre World War II
  Aviator .......... 15.00
  Bicycle Rider .......... 30.00
  Bomb Thrower, three grenades .......... 14.00
  Boxer .......... 65.00
  Cameraman, flash overhead .......... 35.00
  Cannon Loader .......... 14.00
  Cooks helper with ladle .......... 24.00
  Deep Sea Diver, silver .......... 15.00
  Doctor, white .......... 12.00
  Flag Bearer .......... 18.00
  Firefighter, "Hot Papa," gray .......... 65.00
  Hostess, green .......... 45.00
  Machine Gunner, prone .......... 15.00
  Marching .......... 16.00
  Navy Gunner, white, firing deck gun .......... 32.00
  Nurse, white, red dish .......... 16.00
  Observer with periscope .......... 20.00
  Radio Operator, standing .......... 33.00
  Rifleman, standing .......... 15.00
  Sailor, white .......... 18.00
  Sharpshooter, camouflage, prone .......... 20.00
  Signalman, white, two flags .......... 24.00
  Soldier
    At searchlight .......... 18.00
    Charging with bayonet .......... 28.00
    Gas mask and flare gun .......... 18.00
    Running with cannon .......... 28.00
    Sitting, eating .......... 26.00
    Wounded .......... 15.00
    Writing letter .......... 50.00
  Stretcher carrier, medical kit .......... 17.00
  Two man machine gun team .......... 20.00

# SOLDIERS, TOY

**Collecting Hints:** Consider three key factors: condition of the figures and the box, the age of the figures and the box, and the completeness of the set.

Toy soldiers were meant as playthings. However, collectors consider them an art form and pay premium prices only for excellent to mint examples. They want figures with complete paint, all moving parts, and additional parts.

The box is very important, controlling 10 to 20% of the price of a set. The style of the box is a clue to the date of the set. The same set may have been made for several decades. The older the manufacture date, the more valuable the set.

Sets have a specific number of pieces or parts. They must all be present to have full value. The number of pieces in each set, when known, is indicated in the listings below.

Beware of repainted older examples and modern reproductions. Toy soldiers still are being manufactured, both by large companies and private individuals. A contemporary collection may prove a worthwhile long–term investment, at least for the next generation.

**History:** The manufacture of toy soldiers began in the late 18th century by individuals such as the Hilperts of Nuremberg, Germany. The early figures were tin, pewter or composition. By the late 19th century companies in Britain (Britain, Courtenay), France (Blondel, Gerbeau and Mignot), and Switzerland (Gottschalk, Wehrli) were firmly established. Britain and Mignot dominated the market into the 20th century.

Mignot established its French stronghold by purchasing Cuperly, Blondel and Gerbeau, who had united to take over Lucotte. By 1950 Mignot had 20,000 models representing soldiers from around the world.

Britain developed the hollow cast soldiers in 1893. Movable arms also were another landmark. Eventually bases were made of plastic, followed finally by the whole figure in plastic. Production ceased within the last decade.

The English toy soldier was challenged in America in the 1930 to 1950 period by the dimestore soldiers of Barclay, Manoil, and others. Nevertheless, the Britains retained a share of the market because of their high quality. The collecting of toy soldiers remains very strong in the United States.

**References:** Cynthia Gaskill, (ed.), *Elastolin: More Miniature Figures And Groups From The Hausser Firm Of Germany, Including Select Fig-*

*ures From The Houses of Lineol, Tipple–topple, Durso, and Chailu, Volume 2,* Theriault's, 1991; Peter Johnson, *Toy Armies,* Forbes Museum, 1984; Norman Joplin, *The Great Book Of Hollow–Cast Figures,* New Cavendish Books, 1992; Henry I. Kurtz & Burtt R. Ehrlich, *The Art Of The Toy Soldier,* Abbeville Press, 1987; Richard O'Brien, *Collecting Toy Soldiers: An Identification and Value Guide, Sixth Edition* Books Americana, 1993; Richard O'Brien, *Collecting Toy Soldiers: An Identification and Value Guide, No. 2,* Books Americana, 1992; James Opie, *Collecting Toy Soldiers,* Pincushion Press, 1992; Art Presslaff, *Hitler's Army of Toy Soldiers Featuring Elastolin, Lineol, & Tipco, 1928–40: A Price Guide,* published by author, 1987; James Opie, *Britain's Toy Soldiers, 1893–1932,* Harper & Row, 1986; John Ruddle, *Collectors Guide To Britains Model Soldiers,* Argus Books Ltd, 1980; Theriault's (comp.), *Elastolin, Miniature Figures And Groups From The Hausser Firm Of Germany, 1900–1950,* Theriault's, 1990.

**Periodicals:** *Old Toy Soldier Newsletter,* 209 North Lombard, Oak Park, IL 60302; *Toy Soldier Review,* 127 74th Street, North Bergen, NJ 07047.

**Collectors' Clubs:** American Model Soldier Society, 1528 El Camino Real, San Carlos, CA 94070; Toy Soldier Collectors Of America, 6924 Stone's Throw Circle, #8203, St. Petersburg, FL 33710.

**REPRODUCTION ALERT**

Authenticast, Russian Infantry advancing with rifles at the ready, two officers carrying pistols and swords, no box, 14 . . . . . . . . **65.00**

Blenheim

B2, Coldstream Guards Colors, 1812, two color bearers, escort of four privates, orig box, 6, mint, box excellent . . . . . . . . **115.00**

B17, Royal Marines, 1923, marching at the slope, officer, sword at carry, orig box, 6, mint, box excellent . . **75.00**

B63, Royal Company of Archers Colors, two color bearers, escort of four privates, orig box, 6, mint, box excellent . . . . . . . . **90.00**

C13, 17th Lancers, 1879, foreign service order, officer, bugler, and trooper with lance, orig box, 3, mint, box excellent . . . . . . . . **150.00**

U. S. Naval Academy Color Guard, four standard bearers, escort of two midshipmen, orig box, 6, mint, box excellent . . . . . . . . **100.00**

Britain, sets only

7, British Soldiers, The Royal Fusiliers, City of London Regiment . . . **135.00**

**Britain, Soldiers of the British Empire, W. Britain #459993, $125.00.**

24, 9th Queen's Royal Lancers, mounted on the trot, slug lances and officer, no box, 6, excellent . **130.00**

27, Band of Line, full instrumentation and drum major, late pre–WW II set, retied in orig "Types of the World's Armies" box, 12, excellent, box good . . . . . . . . **200.00**

31, King's Dragons, pre war . . . . . . . **100.00**

48, Egyptian Camel Corps, mounted on camels, detachable riders, tied in orig box, 5, mint, box excellent **80.00**

55, Royal Marines . . . . . . . . **100.00**

100, Empress of India's Twenty–first lancers, 1903, box excellent . . . . . **225.00**

101, Band of the Life Guard, mounted in state dress, kettle drummer and bandmaster with baton, retied in orig box, 12, excellent to mint, box excellent . . . . . . . . **450.00**

147, Zulus of Africa, charging with spears and knobkerries, tied in orig box, 5, mint, box excellent . . . . . . **135.00**

177, Austro–Hungarian Infantry of the Line, marching slope arms, orange and red kepi and trousers, 6, excellent condition . . . . . . . . **150.00**

195, British Infantry, battle dress and steel helmets, marching at the trail, officer carrying swagger stick, orig box, 8, excellent, box excellent . . **125.00**

201, General Staff Officers, mounted, field marshal, general officer and two aides–de–camp, tied in orig box, 4, mint . . . . . . . . **200.00**

229, U. S. Cavalry Service Dress, olive uniform, bare handed swords at saddle, three brown, two black horses, 5, very good condition . . . **75.00**

1426, St John Ambulance, stretcher bearers and casualty, excellent . . . **115.00**

1470, Her Majesty's Stage Coach, 8 Windsor Greys, Queen Elizabeth II and Prince Philip, 10, excellent, orig Historical Series box, excellent **250.00**

1519, Waterloo Highlanders, standing at attention with muskets, 9, very good condition . . . . . . . . **175.00**

2017, British Army Ski Troops, white uniforms, no box, 4, excellent . . . **350.00**

2032, Red Army Infantry, summer uniform, May Day Parade pose, rifle with fixed bayonet, both arms move, 10, very good condition .. **85.00**
2039, The Life Guards, mounted and foot sentries, tied in orig box, 6, mint, box excellent ............ **90.00**
2092, Seaforth Highlanders, pipers, 1953, tied, box excellent ........ **200.00**
2094, State Open Landau, drawn by 6 Windsor grays, Queen Elizabeth II and Prince Philip, tied in orig box, 13, mint .................. **220.00**
2099, Venezuelan Military School Cadets, marching at the slope, officers and standard bearer, no box, 15, very good condition ......... **165.00**
9144, Royal Welsh Fusiliers, marching at the slope, officer and goat mascot, orig box, 7, excellent, box good ........................ **100.00**
9216, 9th Queens Royal Lancers, black uniform, standing horses, slung lance, excellent condition .. **125.00**
9301, Royal Company of Archers, Queen's Bodyguard of Scotland, long skirted coats, cap with feather, 14 .......................... **250.00**
9307, Sovereigns Standard of The Life Guards and Escort, trumpeter in state dress, farriers and corporals of The Royal Horse Guards, orig box, 8, mint, box good ............. **175.00**
9406, Mounted Band of the Lifeguards, state dress, musicians on horseback, gold and maroon jackets, matched, boxed set, excellent condition ..................... **550.00**
9482, U. S. Marines Color Party, two flagbearers, escort at shoulder arms, dress blues, excellent condition, box excellent ............. **235.00**

Elastolin/Lineol

Flak Gunner, blue and gray uniform, kneeling with shell, very good condition ......................... **40.00**
Medic, walking, helmet, big pack with red cross ................. **35.00**
Nurse, attending wounded, kneeling, holds foot of soldier sitting on keg, excellent condition ............. **40.00**
Staff Officer, pointing, field glasses, aristocratic pose ................ **35.00**

Heyde

Chicago Police, 1890s, on foot with billy clubs, including policeman with dog, standard bearer and mounted policeman, 11, very good **220.00**
French Ambulance Unit, horse drawn ambulance, two horse team, rider with whip, stretcher bearers, stretchers and casualties, mounted and foot medical officers and medical orderly, orig box, 14, very good, box fair ................. **280.00**
Hessian Infantry, 1777, marching at the slope, officers, standard bearer, four mounted dragoons, movable reins on horses, no box, 19, good **375.00**
German Infantry, WW I, attacking with fixed bayonets, officer with extended sword, no box, 11, very good ........................ **90.00**
U. S. Army World War I Pontoon Train, four horse drawn pontoon wagons, pontoon boats, engineer detail on foot with mounted officer, orig display box, 24, very good, box poor ..................... **470.00**

Mignot

Band of the 3rd Regiment of Dutch Grenadiers, 1812, body guard to King Louis Napoleon Bonaparte of Holland, full instrumentation, bandmaster, tied in orig box, 12, mint, box excellent ............. **350.00**
French Ambulance, set 1512, drawn by four horse team, horse handler, driver with whip, orig box, excellent, box excellent ............. **220.00**
French Cuirassiers, 1914, marching dismounted carrying swords, officer, bugler and standard bearer, orig box, 12, excellent .......... **75.00**
French Line Infantry, 1914, marching at the slope, trumpeter, standard bearer and officer, orig box, 12, excellent, box excellent ........... **80.00**
French Sailors, 1914, marching at the slope, blue uniforms, officer bugler and standard bearer, orig box, 12, mint to excellent, box excellent .. **175.00**
Julius Caesar's Chariot, drawn by four galloping horses, mounted on base, scenic backdrop, orig box, 6, mint, box excellent .................. **225.00**
Prussian Grenadier, 1800, assaulting, drummer, standard bearer and officer, c1955, no box, 12, very good **130.00**
602, Circus Display Set, four seated musicians, standing conductor with baton, clowns, show horses, trainer with whip and others, tied in orig box, 12, mint, box excellent ..... **200.00**
8th Bavarian Regiment, 1812, marching at the slope, blue uniforms, plumed helmets, officer, drummer, and standard bearer, tied in orig box, 12, mint, box excellent ..... **150.00**

Militia Models

Gatling Gun Team of 3rd London Rifles, Gatling gun and gunner, two ammunition carriers, officer hold-

ing binoculars, orig box, 5, mint, box excellent .................. **90.00**
The Pipes and Drums of 1st Battalion Royal Irish Rangers, limited edition, pipe major and four pipers, two snare and two tenor drummers, drum major, orig box, 11, mint, box excellent .................. **125.00**

Nostalgia
1st Gurkha Light Infantry, 1800, red and blue uniforms, marching with slung rifles, officer with sword at the carry, orig box, 8, excellent, box excellent .................. **80.00**
Kaffrarian Rifles, 1910, gray uniforms, plumed pith helmets, marching at the trail, officer with sword at the carry, orig box, 8, mint, box excellent .......................... **125.00**
New South Wales Irish Rifles, 1900, marching at the trail, officer holding sword at the carry, orig box, 8, mint, box excellent ............. **95.00**
New South Wales Lancers, 1900, marching carrying lances on the shoulder, khaki uniforms, trimmed in red and plumed campaign hats, officer holding swagger stick, orig box, 8, mint, box excellent ...... **85.00**

S. A. E.
1358, Royal Horse Guards, 1945, mounted at the halt with officer, orig box, 6, mint, box excellent .. **50.00**
1761, French Cuirassiers, mounted at the walk, orig box, 6, mint, box excellent ...................... **85.00**
3310, 1st Bengal Lancers, at the halt, orig box, 6, mint, box excellent .. **115.00**

# SOUVENIR AND COMMEMORATIVE ITEMS

**Collecting Hints:** Most collectors of souvenir and commemorative china and glass collect items from a region that is particularly interesting to them—a hometown, birthplace or place of special interest such as a President's home. This results in regional price variations. Local collectors do pay premium prices.

When collecting souvenir spoons be alert to several things: condition, material, subject, and any markings, dates, etc. Damaged spoons should be avoided unless they are scarce and needed to complete a collection. Some spoons have enamel crests and other decoration. This enameling should be in mint condition.

**History:** Souvenir and commemorative china and glass date to the early fairs and carnivals when a small trinket was purchased to take back home as a gift or remembrance of the event. Other types of commemorative glass include pattern and milk glass made to celebrate a particular event. Many types of souvenir glass and china originated at the world's fairs and expositions.

The peak of souvenir spoon collecting was reached in the late 1800s. During that time two important patents were issued. The first was issued on December 4, 1884, to Michael Gibney, a silversmith from New York who patented a design for flatware. The other important patent was the first spoon designed to commemorate a place. In 1881 Myron H. Kinsley received a patent for a spoon of Niagara Falls. The spoon showed the suspension bridge and was the first of many spoons to be made showing Niagara Falls.

Spoons depicting famous people soon followed with the issue in May, 1889, of a spoon showing George Washington. That was followed by the issuance of a Martha Washington spoon in October of 1889. These spoons, made by M. W. Galt of Washington, D.C., were not patented, but trademarked in 1890.

During the 1900s it became popular to have souvenir plates made for churches and local events such as centennials, homecomings, etc. These plates were well received because of their local interest. Collectors search for them today because they were made in a limited number. Many show how the area changed architecturally and culturally.

**References:** Bessie M. Lindsey, *American Historical Glass,* Charles E. Tuttle, 1967; Norman E. Martinus and Harry L. Rinker, *Warman's Paper,* Wallace–Homestead, 1993; Dorothy T. Rainwater and Donna H. Felger, *American Spoons, Souvenir and Historical,* Everybodys Press, Inc., 1977; Dorothy T. Rainwater and Donna H. Felger, *Spoons From Around The World,* Schiffer Publishing, Ltd., 1992; Frank Stefano, Jr., *Wedgwood Old Blue Historical Plates and Other Views of the United States Produced for Jones, McDuffe & Stratton Co., Boston, Importer, A Check–List With Illustrations,* published by author, 1975; *Sterling Silver, Silverplate, and Souvenir Spoons With Prices,* L–W Books, 1988, 1992 value update.

**Periodical:** *Spoony Scoop Newsletter,* 84 Oak Avenue, Shelton, CT 06484.

**Collectors' Clubs:** American Spoon Collectors, 4922 State Line, Westwood Hills, KS 66205; Antique Souvenir Collectors News, Box 562, Great Barrington, MA 01230.

**Note:** Spoons listed below are sterling silver teaspoons unless otherwise noted.

Ashtray
Florida, brass, shaped like state, emb attractions ...................... **12.00**

Memphis, TN, black boy, dog and dice .......................... **95.00**
Bandanna, *USS America*, silk ........ **6.00**
Book, *History Account of Silver Springs, FL*, 1938 ........................ **2.50**
Bookmark, Washington, DC, Capitol Building, brass, pinned ........... **26.50**
Bottle Opener, Brown Palace Hotel ... **22.00**
Bowl, Washington, DC, US Capitol, bas relief, oval, Syroco Wood ......... **12.00**
Box, Coney Island, laminated wood, 1950s Cyclone Roller Coaster scene **65.00**

**Key to the City, Key West, FL, gold plated, pinback, 2½″ l, $10.00.**

Compact, Hawaii, Elgin ............. **30.00**
Creamer
Mid Winter Fair, 1894, Swirl pattern, scalloped .................... **50.00**
Kentucky, figural, cow, mustard gold ground, marked "Souvenir of Kentucky" ....................... **8.00**
Dish, china, Atlantic City, muzzled puppy dec, marked "Germany" .... **50.00**
Figure, dog, marked "Souvenir 1897 F M King Co 1897," Galesburg Pottery **425.00**
Goblet
Minocqua, WI, Inverted Thumbprint, ruby stained .................. **35.00**
US Naval Supply Depot Comm Officer Mess, Mechanicsburg, PA, Depression glass, Bubble pattern, green ........................ **15.00**
Hair Receiver, Hershey, PA, round, lacy trim, gold lettering .............. **45.00**
Memo Pad, Aberdeen, SD, 1909, aluminum ......................... **16.00**
Mug
Elkport, IA, Punty Band pattern, green milk glass .................... **20.00**
Jackson Court House, Kansas City, MO, china ................... **10.00**
Joliet High School, Joliet, IL, china . **16.00**
Reedsburg, WI, clambroth ......... **25.00**
Two Harbors, MN, custard glass, Heisey ........................ **60.00**
Woodland Beach, ruby stained ..... **22.00**
Napkin Ring, *Battleship Maine*, silverplate ......................... **22.00**
Pin, enamel dec
New York City .................. **20.00**
Rockefeller Center ................ **20.00**

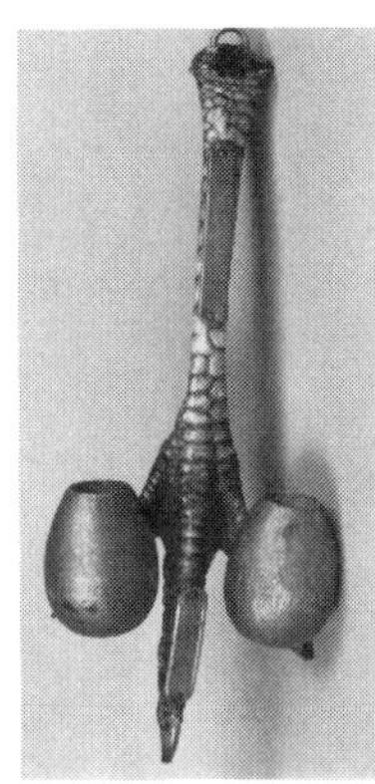

**Match Holder, Atlantic City, turkey leg, two wood cups, brass striker and tag, hanging ring, 10¼″ h, $25.00.**

Pinback Button, 1¼″ d
Asbury Park, NJ, black and gray, beach with bathers ............. **15.00**
Atlantic City, 1911, woman in red bathing suit, splashing male swimmer, Atlantic City skyline background ....................... **50.00**
Powder Jar, cov, New York, NY, sq, lacy trim, gold lettering and edge ....... **35.00**
Plate
Chickasha, OK, Carnegie Library, 7″ d, china ...................... **12.00**
Hamilton, OH, Court House, 6″ d, china ......................... **12.00**
Salt and Pepper Shakers, pr
Florida
Flamingos, 3″ h, hp, pink, marked "Souvenir of Florida" ......... **6.50**
Oranges, 3″ h, orange, green leaves, marked "Souvenir of Florida" ..................... **5.00**
Mexico, man and woman, marked "Souvenir of Mexico," nodders .. **30.00**
New York, Empire State Building, Statue of Liberty, silvered cast metal, marked "Souvenir of NY" . **8.00**
Texas, Mineral Wells, Baker Hotel .. **20.00**
Washington, DC, Washington Monument and White House, silvered cast metal, marked "Souvenir of Washington, DC" .............. **5.00**
Scrapbook, 1930 trip to Asheville, NC **20.00**
Spoon
Arlington, AZ, Arlington Hotel, grinning black boy handle, sterling ... **150.00**
Buffalo, NY, monument bowl, buffalo handle, demitasse .............. **15.00**
Chief Seattle Indian, Mt Rainier bowl, sterling ...................... **30.00**
Fairmont, MN, Opera House, sterling **45.00**
Flint, MI, Public Library ........... **20.00**

Greenfield, MO, All Souls Church, sterling ........ **38.00**
Hot Springs, AR, horse, people, sterling ........ **45.00**
Lake Merritt, Oakland, Indian ........ **40.00**
Little Rock, AR, state house bowl, shield handle, demitasse ........ **15.00**
Los Angeles, CA, Mt Lowe Incline Railroad bowl, rose handle ........ **30.00**
Marion, IA, High School, 1915 ........ **20.00**
Mexico, bull fight bowl, full figured matador handle, sterling ........ **85.00**
Minneapolis, MN, Compliments of Minneapolis Times, 1894, brass ........ **38.00**
Needles, CA, Rec Hall bowl, emb lily of the valley handle ........ **30.00**
Nome, AK, silver and gold mountains, seal, ocean, sterling ........ **75.00**
Owatonna, MN, Pillsbury Academy, sterling ........ **45.00**
Poughkeepsie, NY, Vassar College, 1901, sterling ........ **65.00**
Salt Lake City, UT, Saltaire, sterling ........ **38.00**
St Peter, MN, Gustavus Adolphus College, sterling ........ **45.00**
Ticonderoga, NY, sterling ........ **48.00**
Waddington, NY, sailboat, Indian, corn handle, sterling ........ **48.00**

**Spoon, Bermuda, sterling silver, flag, seal, and fish, hallmarked, $40.00.**

Spooner, Teddi, Masonic Temple, 1492–1893, Ruby Thumbprint pattern ........ **65.00**
Teapot, Lighthouse, Atlantic City, NJ, china, cobalt blue ground ........ **27.50**
Textile, luncheon cloth, map of Florida **9.00**
Thermometer, Hayward, WI, 6" l metal anchor, button type Indian bust under celluloid ........ **12.50**
Tin, Bunker Hill Monument, color litho **35.00**
Tray, Coney Island, illus of Luna Park, Steeplecase, other rides ........ **25.00**
Tumbler, Wright–Patterson Air Force Base Museum, 5½" h, clear glass, weighted bottom, gold and black illus, light blue illus of Wright Bros 1909 plane, Air Force insignia, jet aircraft on reverse, late 1950s ........ **10.00**
View Book, *Photostint Views of Picturesque Detroit, The Convention City,* sixteen color plates, 9 x 6" ........ **8.00**
Wine, Coney Island, 1905, ruby stained **30.00**

# SPACE ADVENTURERS AND EXPLORATION

**Collecting Hints:** There are four distinct eras of fictional space adventurers—Buck Rogers, Flash Gordon, the radio and television characters of the late 1940s and 1950s, and the Star Trek and Star Wars phenomenon. Condition is not as major a factor in Buck Rogers material, because of its rarity, as it is in the other three groups. Beware of dealers who break apart items and sell parts separately, especially game items.

In the early 1950s a wealth of tin, battery operated, friction, and wind–up toys, not associated with a specific Space Adventurer, were marketed in the shape of robots, space ships, and space guns. They are rapidly gaining in popularity.

The "Trekies" began holding conventions in the early 1970s. They issued many fantasy items, which must not be confused with items issued during the duration of the TV show. The fantasy items are numerous and have little value beyond the initial selling price.

The American and Russian space programs produced a wealth of souvenir and related material. Beware of astronaut signed material that may contain printed or autopen signatures.

**History:** In January, 1929, "Buck Rogers 2429 A.D." began its comic strip run. Buck, Wilma Deering, Dr. Huer, and Killer Kane, a villain, were the creation of Phillip Francis Nowlan and John F. Dille. The heyday of Buck Rogers material was 1933 to 1937 when products such as Cream of Wheat and Cocomalt issued Buck Rogers items as premiums.

Flash Gordon followed in the mid–1930s. Buster Crabbe gave life to the character in movie serials. Books, comics, premiums, and other merchandise enhanced the image during the 1940s.

The use of rockets at the end of World War II and the beginnings of the space research program gave reality to future space travel. Television quickly capitalized on this in the early 1950s with programs such as *Captain Video* and *Space Patrol*. Many other space heroes, such as Rocky Jones, had short–lived popularity.

*Star Trek* enjoyed a brief television run and became a cult fad in the early 1970s. *Star Trek: The Next Generation* has an established corp of watchers. *Star Wars* (Parts IV, V, and VI) and *ET* produced a wealth of merchandise which already is collectible.

In the 1950s, real life space pioneers and explorers replaced the fictional characters as the center of the public's attention. The entire world watched on July 12, 1969, as man first walked on the moon. Although space exploration has suffered occasional setbacks, the public remains fascinated with its findings and potential.

**References:** Sue Cornwell and Mike Kott, *The Official Price Guide To Star Trek and Star Wars Collectibles, Third Edition,* House of Collectibles, 1991; Christine Gentry and Sally Gibson–Downs, *Greenberg's Guide To Star Trek Collectibles, Volumes I–III,* Greenberg Publishing, Co., 1992; Don and Maggie Thompson, *The Official Price Guide To Science Fiction and Fantasy Collectibles, Third Edition,* House of Collectibles, 1989; Norman E. Martinus and Harry L. Rinker, *Warman's Paper,* Wallace–Homestead, 1993; Stephen J. Sansweet, *Star Wars: From Concept To Screen To Collectible,* Chronicle Books, 1992; T. N. Tumbusch, *Space Adventure Collectibles,* Wallace–Homestead, 1990.

**Periodical:** *Galaxy Patrol Newsletter,* 22 Colton St., Worcester, MA 01610.

**See:** Robots and Space Toys.

## CHARACTERS

Battlestar Galactica, board game, Milton Bradley, 1976, unused ......... **20.00**
Bruce Force, game, Lost in Outer Space, Ideal, 1963, orig 17 x 12" heavy cardboard envelope .................. **70.00**
Buck Rogers
 Atomic Pistol, metal, red celluloid window inserts, Daisy, 1930s, 10" l ............................ **225.00**
 Badge, Chief Explorer, Cream of Wheat premium, 1933–35 ...... **150.00**
 Big Little Book, Whitman
  *Buck Rogers and the Doom Comet,* #1178, 1935 ................ **75.00**
  *Buck Rogers 25th Century A.D.,* #742, 1932 ................. **100.00**
 Board Game
  John Dille, c1934, 3 Board Games, three 16 x 16" bi–fold litho game boards, orig instructions and box **240.00**
  Transogram, 1965 .............. **100.00**
 Booklet, Chicago World's Fair giveaway, *Buck Rogers Twenty–Fifth Century Presents A Century Of Progress,* stiff paper, folder holds pencil and tablet with Automatic Soap Flakes adv cov, 4½ x 6" .... **125.00**
 Cut–Out Adventure Book, Cocomalt premium, 1933–35, uncut ...... **1,600.00**
 Disintegrator Pistol, Cream of Wheat premium ...................... **150.00**
 Handerkerchief, Wilma, Cream of Wheat premium, 1933–35 ...... **300.00**
 Helmet and Rocket Pistol, cardboard set, 10" l snap gun, full color Buck Roger headdress, Einson Freeman, 1934, orig 11 x 11" litho envelope with store decal, instructions, and space graphics, unused ......... **800.00**
 Paint Book, Whitman, 96 pages, 11 x 14" .......................... **75.00**
 Pencil Box, red .................. **50.00**
 Playsuit, helmet with visor, shirt, vest, trousers, belt, leather holster, Daisy 9½" metal pistol, and three patches, Sackman Bros/Dille, 1934, orig box ................. **950.00**
 Rocket Police Patrol, windup, litho tin, rocket, Buck pilot, sparking action, Marx, 12½" l ............. **400.00**
 Solar Map, Cocomalt premium, 1933–35 ...................... **275.00**
 Sonic Ray, signal flashlight, plastic, black, yellow, and red, Norton–Honer, 1952, 7½" l, orig box .... **80.00**
 Space Ranger Kit, Sylvania premium, punchout sheets with helmet, rocket, pistol, spaceship, etc., c1952, orig 15 x 11" envelope, unused .......................... **95.00**
 Spaceship, Morton Salt premium, 1942 ......................... **60.00**
 Super Sonic Ray Gun, signal flashlight, plastic, yellow and green, Norton–Honer, 1955, 8" l, orig box **65.00**
Captain Video
 Board Game, Milton Bradley, 1950s **140.00**
 Goggles ......................... **95.00**
 Membership Card ................ **30.00**
 Mysto–Coder .................... **125.00**
 Ring
  Flying Saucer, two saucers ....... **350.00**
  Photo ......................... **100.00**
  Secret Sial ..................... **125.00**
 Rite–O–Lite, code gun, plastic, 4" l, with space map and secret message book, Power House Candy premium, 1950s .................. **45.00**
 Space Men, plastic, 12 different, price each ......................... **8.00**
Flash Gordon
 Autograph, 8 x 10" glossy color photo, Crabbe in swimming pool, blue "To Patty As You See I'm All Wet–As Usual, Sincerely, Buster Crabbe," late 1960s–early 1970s . **50.00**
 Bank, rocket, metal ............... **25.00**
 Big Little Book, *Flash Gordon In The Water World Of Mongo,* 424 pages, 1937 ......................... **40.00**
 Coloring Book, Whitman, 1952, unused ......................... **40.00**
 Dixie Lid, sepia photo titled "Buster Crabbe Starring in the Universal Chapter Play Flash Gordon," c1936, 2¼" d .................. **20.00**
 Home Foundry, metal character casting set, Home Foundry Mfg, KFS, 1934, orig 9 x 5 x 16" box ...... **850.00**

Jet Propelled Kite, paper, Flash illus, Aero Kite, 1950s, orig 24" l box .. **65.00**
Kite, plastic, multicolored image, transparent ground, Roalex Co, c1950, orig pkg ... **20.00**
Magazine Article, *Look*, #6, March 15, 1938, three page article and captioned scenes for movie *Trip To Mars* ... **25.00**
Pinback Button, black, white, and red, "Flash Gordon Club, Chicago, Herald and Examiner," 1⅛" d .... **60.00**
Puzzles, set of three, Milton Bradley, 1951, each puzzle 9 x 12", orig box **315.00**
Sparkling Rocket Fighter Ship, windup, litho tin, Marx/KFS, 1939, 12" l, orig box ... **500.00**
Wallet, vinyl, tan, color illus, zipper edge, 1949, unused ... **40.00**
Water Pistol, 1950s, MIB ... **145.00**

Lost In Space
Costume, Ben Cooper, 1965, unused **200.00**
Model Kit, robot, Aurora, 1968, unassembled ... **800.00**
Writing Tablet, cov with June Lockhart as Maureen Robinson wearing silver flight uniform, 1965, 8 x 10", unused ... **24.00**

Matt Mason
Firebolt Space Cannon, Mattel, flashing lights, 1968, orig box ... **80.00**
Unitred Space Vehicle, tows one–man space bubble, Mattel, 1968, orig box ... **30.00**

Rocky Jones
Pinback Button, portrait, "Rocky Jones, Space Ranger, Silvercup Bread," c1953 ... **20.00**
Space Ranger Wings, emb metal, gold and silver, planet center, 1953, 4 x 3" card ... **70.00**

Space 1999
Activity Book, cutout and color, Saalfield, 1975, unused ... **10.00**
Board Game, Milton Bradley, 1975 . **24.00**
Gum Card Wrapper, 1975, unopened **10.00**
Moon Car, MIP ... **70.00**
Playset, Moon Alpha Control Center, Mattel, 1975 ... **60.00**
View–Master Pack, 1975 ... **8.00**

Space Patrol
Badge, plastic ... **150.00**
Barrette, diecut plastic space pistol, orig card with litho rocket, Ben–Hur ... **75.00**
Binoculars, black ... **80.00**
Comic Book, #2, 1952 ... **75.00**
Cosmic Smoke Gun
Green, long barrel ... **175.00**
Red, short barrel ... **150.00**
Decoder Buckle, belt ... **150.00**
Drink Mixer, plastic rocket shaped container with straw, United Plastic Corp, c1952, 9" h, orig litho box with space motif ... **50.00**
Handbook ... **85.00**
Hydrogen Ray Gun Ring, adjustable brass band with star, rocketship, and missile dec, plastic space gun top with glow in the dark cap, 1950s ... **90.00**
Microscope, orig slides ... **175.00**
Periscope ... **125.00**
Record Album, Cadet Happy Joins Commander Corry, #2, Decca, c1950 ... **35.00**
Rocket Gun, black plastic, fires darts, US Plastics, 1950s, 9½" l, orig box **295.00**
Walkie–Talkie Space–A–Phones, plastic, red and white, 1952, orig mailing box ... **95.00**
Top Secret Diplomatic Pouch, Toys of Tomorrow, 25 stamps, stationery, stamp and coin albums, Space Patrol coins and money, 12 x 11" pouch, early 1950s, orig box .... **450.00**

Star Trek
Action Figure, Captain Kirk, 8" h, MIP **40.00**
Board Game, Ideal, 1967 ... **180.00**
Coloring Book
Saalfield, 1975, unused ... **10.00**
Whitman, 1968, unused ... **32.00**
Doll, Mr Spock, Knickerbocker, stuffed cloth, 12" h ... **75.00**
Klingon Battle Cruiser, Dinky, 10" l . **85.00**
Model Kit, K–7 Space Station, plastic, AMT, 1976, unassembled ... **24.00**
Oil Painting Set, Hasbro, 1967, 28 x 20", unused ... **290.00**
Record Set, *Star Trek: The Motion Picture*, book and record ... **3.00**
Tracer Gun, shoots jet discs, Rayline, 1967, MOC ... **40.00**
*USS Enterprise*, Dinky, 10" l, MIB .. **85.00**
View–Master Pack, 1968 ... **20.00**
Writing Tablet, cov with William Shatner as Captain Kirk, posed with

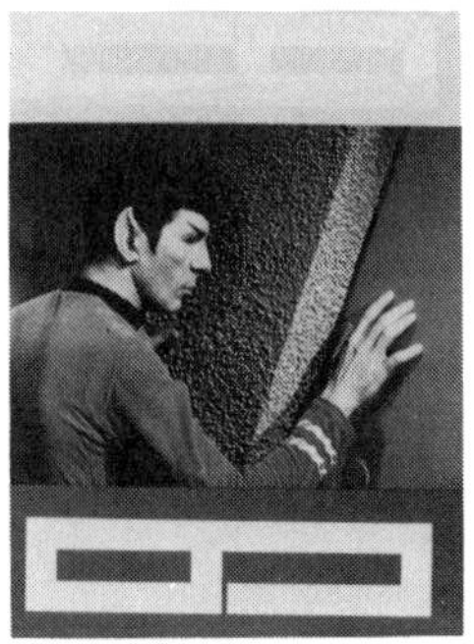

**Greeting Card, Mr. Spock, Random House Greetings, 1976, 5¾ x 7¾", $3.00.**

phaser rifle, planet and orbiting *USS Enterprise* in background, 1967, 8 x 10" .......... **25.00**

Star Wars

Action Figure, 12" h, MIB

C–3PO .......... **95.00**

Chewbacca .......... **95.00**

Darth Vader .......... **100.00**

Bank, Emperor's Royal Guard Figure, *Return of the Jedi,* Irwin, 1983, 10" h, orig box .......... **42.00**

Gum Card Wrapper, Topps, 1977, Darth Vader .......... **8.00**

Landspeeder Vehicle, MIB .......... **35.00**

Lunch Box, thermos, *Empire Strikes Back* .......... **65.00**

Mug, Princess Leia head, marked "Sigma" .......... **20.00**

Playsuit, Ben Cooper, 1977, orig box

C–3PO .......... **30.00**

Darth Vader .......... **24.00**

R2D2, radio controlled, MIB .......... **100.00**

Stuffed Toy, Chewbacca, plush, 15" h **30.00**

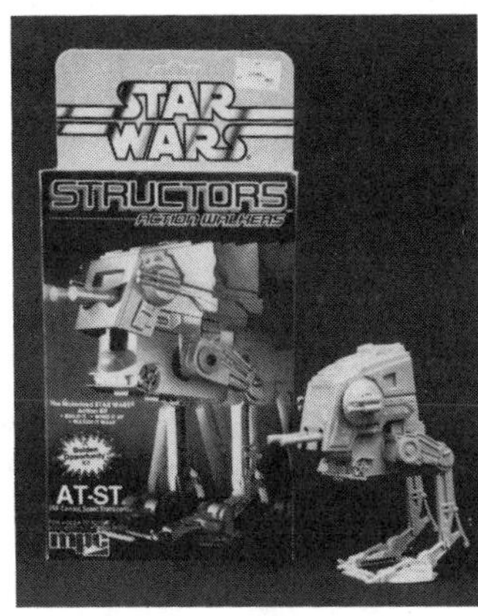


**Structors Action Walkers, All Terrain Scout Transport, windup, gray plastic, MPC, 1984, 4½" h, orig box, $15.00.**

Tom Corbett

Book, *A Trip to the Moon,* Wonder Books, color illus, 1953 .......... **20.00**

Book Bag, plastic, Ton on center flap, rocket designs on the side, red plastic handle, 11 x 14½" .......... **25.00**

Coloring Book .......... **40.00**

Decoder, cardboard, black, white, and red, membership card on back, 2½ x 4" .......... **30.00**

Lunch Box, litho metal, space scene, 1954 Rockhill Radio copyright, 7 x 8 x 4" .......... **75.00**

Model Kit, Space Cadet, customized **60.00**

Patch, Space Cadet, cloth, red, yellow, and blue, Kellogg's premium **25.00**

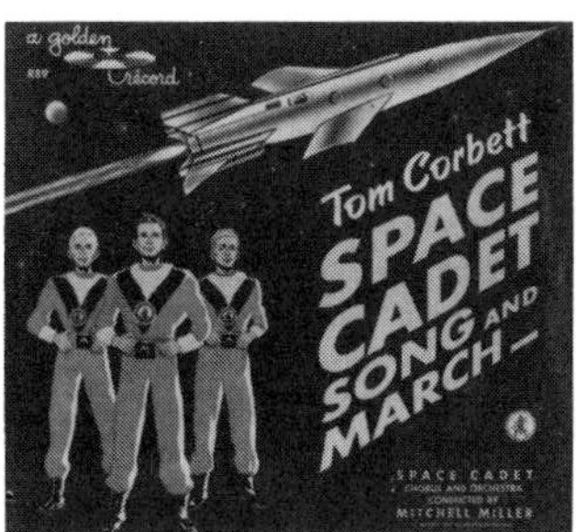


**Record Album, *Tom Corbett Space Cadet Song and March,* Golden Record, R89, 1951 Rockhill Productions, $20.00.**

Space Academy Set, playset, #7010, litho tin bukldings, plastic figures, Marx .......... **400.00**

Space Patrol Signal Siren Flashlight, c1952, 7" l, orig box .......... **50.00**

Space Pistol, litho tin, Marx, c1939, 10" l, orig box .......... **320.00**

Space Rifle, plastic .......... **150.00**

## EXPLORATION

Apollo Moon Exploring Set, two 1" figures, one space vehicle, one 4 x 2½" control computer with radar dishes and staircase to upper deck, Imperial, 1970, MIB .......... **15.00**

Bank, Freedom 7, plastic, silver, text on bottom, 4½" h .......... **40.00**

Book, *Into Space With The Astronauts,* Wonder Books, soft cov, early space flights, official National Aeronautics and Space Administration photos and drawings, 1965, 48 pages, 8 x 11" . **8.00**

Clock, Apollo 11, windup, animated, ivory case, red, white, and blue diecut metallic blue dial, Lux Clock Mfg Co, 4 x 4½ x 2" .......... **230.00**

Commemorative Medal, sterling silver, astronaut descending from landing module onto moon, "One Small Step" inscription, reverse with moon plaque, 1½" d, acrylic case .......... **35.00**

First Day Cover, Moon Landing, July 20, 1969, black, white, and silver, full color commemorative US postage stame, Washington DC postmark, 4¼ x 9½" .......... **20.00**

Gyroscope, Gemini, plastic, mid 1960s, MOC .......... **25.00**

Jigsaw Puzzle

Astronauts, Apollo 11 .......... **20.00**

Moon Map, Selchow & Righter, Rand McNally map of moon's surface, 1970, 10 x 14", orig box .......... **30.00**

Key Chain, brass, plastic insert on tag with Apollo 11 emblem, reverse with Lunar Module, orig box ........... **25.00**
Pennant, First Man On Moon, felt, red and white, blue trim, 29" l ........ **15.00**
Pinback Button
- Apollo 11, Moon Landing, black and white astronaut photo, red, white, and blue rim, 3½" d ............ **20.00**
- Challenger 7, black and white photo, purple ground, 3" d ............ **8.00**
- Gemini 6–7, Frank Borman and James Lovell, Dec, 1965, red, white, and blue, 3½" d .................. **25.00**

Plate, commemorative
- Apollo 14, glass, shaded blue lunar landscape, NASA symbol, c1971, 7½" d ........................ **25.00**
- John Glenn, china, white, black and white illus, gold trim, Feb 20, 1962 flight, 9¼" d .................. **20.00**

Record, *America's First Man In Orbit,* 33⅓ rpm, features John Glenn, orig sleeve and mailing envelope ....... **25.00**
Rug, woven, multicolored moon landing, red, white, and blue stars and stripes border, Italy label, 19½ x 37½" **50.00**
Spoon, Apollo 8, engraved astronauts' names and flight date, detailed design on handle, Kleps Arts, Holland, 4½" l .......................... **8.00**
View–Master Set
- Man in Space, Glenn's first flight, 1960s, sealed .................. **15.00**
- NASA's Manned Space Center, 1960s, sealed ........................ **12.00**

Whiskey Bottle
- Apollo, ceramic, beige, brown highlights, cork stopper, Thomas W Sims Distillery, Stanley, Ken/Dec 1969 ......................... **30.00**
- Apollo 14, commemorative, iridescent glass, blue, emb portraits one side, emblem other side, Wheaton Ltd Edition, Great American Series, 1971, 8½" h .................. **25.00**

## SPACE RELATED

Board Game
- Blast–Off, Waddington, 1969 ...... **80.00**
- Count–Down, Lowell, 1966 ....... **50.00**
- Orbit, Parker Brothers, 1959 ....... **52.00**

Book, *The Coming Exploration of the Universe,* Golden, hard cov, illus, 54 pages, 1959, 7 x 9" ............. **30.00**
Candy Tin, Variety Toffee, Riley Bros, England, boy astronauts point to stars and planets, 1950s, 6 x 1½" d ..... **60.00**
Card Game, Space Race, Ed–U–Card, 1969 ........................... **25.00**
Costume, Uranus Rocket Ship Leader, Charnas, 1970, orig box .......... **32.00**
Crayon Box, spaceship, stiff litho cardboard, enameled wood nose cone, diecut openings reveal multiplication tables .......................... **20.00**
Flashlight, Junior Astronaut Flashlite, plastic, key chain, 3" l, c1960, orig 4 x 8½" card, unopened ............ **18.00**
Game of Skill, Blast Off!, Aldon Industries, illustrated base card holds three space stations covered by 5" clear plastic dome, roll steel marble up each space station to center, 1955, 6½ x 8½" base, unused ........... **30.00**
Lunch Box, litho metal
- Astronauts' Moon Landing, thermos, 1969, unused .................. **98.00**
- Spaceship and Spacemen, dome top, 1960 ........................ **190.00**

Pen Knife, space motif, 1950s, 3½" l . **30.00**
Puzzle, frame tray, Space Scouts, 1953 **32.00**
Record, *Little Space Girl,* sleeve with three–eyed alien space girl floating in outer space, 1950s, unused ........ **12.00**
Stamp Book, Wonders of Space, 1954 **20.00**
Sweatshirt, child's size, spaceships and flying saucers motif, c1960 ........ **15.00**
Yo–Yo, Orbit Yo–Yo, plastic, satellite and planet Earth, colored string, CL Land, 1969, MOC ................ **10.00**

# SPACE TOYS

**Collecting Hints:** The original box is an important element in pricing, perhaps controlling 15% to 20% of the price. The artwork on the box may differ slightly from the toy inside; this is to be expected. The box also may provide the only clue to the correct name of the toy.

The early lithographed tin toys are more valuable than the later toys made of plastic. There is a great deal of speculation in modern toys, e.g., Star Wars material. Hence, the market shows great price fluctuation. Lloyd Ralston Toys, Fairfield, Connecticut, is a good barometer of the auction market.

Collect toys in very good to mint condition. Damaged and rusted lithographed tin is hard to repair. Check the battery box for damage. Don't ever leave batteries in a toy after you have played with it.

**History:** The Hollywood movies of the early 1950s drew attention to space travel. The launching of Sputnik and American satellites in the late 1950s and early 1960s enhanced this fascination. The advent of man in space culminating with the landing on the moon made the decade of the 1960s the golden age of space toys.

The toy industries of Japan and America responded to this interest. Lithographed tin and plastic models of astronauts, flying saucers, spacecraft and space vehicles followed quickly. Some were copies of original counterparts; most were the figments of the toy designer's imagination.

The 1970s saw a shift in emphasis from the space program and a decline in the production of science fiction–related toys. The earlier Japanese and American made products gave way to cheaper models from China and Taiwan.

**References:** Teruhisa Kitahara, *Yesterday's Toys, Robots, Spaceships, and Monsters,* Chronicle Books, 1988; Crystal and Leland Payton, *Space Toys,* Collectors Compass, 1982; Stephen J. Sansweet, *Science Fiction Toys and Models,* Vol. 1, Starlog Press, 1980; Leslie Singer, *Zap! Ray Gun Classics,* Chronicle Books, 1991.

**Note:** Any rocket related toy, whether military or space, is included in this category. The following abbreviations are used:

SH = Horikawa Toys
TM = K. K. Masutoko Toy Factory
TN = Nomura Toys
Y = Yonezawa Toys

**See:** Robots and Space Adventurers and Explorations.

**REPRODUCTION ALERT**

Astronauts and Spacemen
American Astronaut, model kit, #409–100, Aurora, 1967, sealed orig box .................... **60.00**
Astronaut
Cragstan, battery operated, litho tin, walks, raises and fires gun with rat–a–tat noise and flashing lights, plastic helmet, red version, Daiya, Japan, orig box .. **2,000.00**
NASA, windup, litho tin, sparking mechanism in red plastic chest insert, marked "NASA" on arm, N, Japan, 5½" h, orig window box ...................... **125.00**
Rosko Toy, battery operated, litho tin, walks, holds walkie–talkie with lights and beeping noise, flashing light in plastic helmet, TN, Japan, 13" h, orig box .... **3,200.00**
Attacking Martian, battery operated, litho tin and plastic robot, stop–and–go action, blinking pop–out guns in chest, shooting noise, SH, Japan, 9¼" h, orig box .......... **150.00**
Earth Man, astronaut, battery operated, litho tin, clear plastic visor on helmet, carries space rifle with flashing lights, two oxygen tanks and antenna on back, TN, Japan, 9½" h, orig box .............. **1,050.00**
Flying Kamen Rider with Spark, plastic, movable arms and legs, tin base, sparking mouth, Yonezawa, Japan, 11" l, orig box ........... **180.00**
Flying Mirrorman with Spark, plastic, movable arms and legs, tin base, sparking mouth, Yonezawa, Japan, 11" l, orig box ................ **180.00**
Man From Mars Astronaut, plastic, yellow, orange, and silver, red lightning bolts on spacesuit, carries double oxygen tanks, clear plastic domed helmet with rubber antenna, fires cosmic ray pistols, Irwin, 1950s, 11" h, orig box ..... **115.00**
Mat Astronaut, vinyl, movable arms, body, and leg, removable helmet, Yonezawa, Japan, orig box ...... **200.00**
Moon Creature, windup, litho tin, rubber ears, large plastic covered eyes, arms move, mouth opens, clicking sounds, Marx, 1960s, 5½" h, orig box ................... **200.00**
Planet Robot, windup, tin, plastic claw hands, sparking, KO, Japan, 9" h, orig box ................. **340.00**
Rotate–O–Matic Super Astronaut, battery operated, litho tin, astronaut face behind visor, chest doors open, blinking and shooting gun, rotating body, stop–and–go action, SH, Japan, 12" h, orig box ...... **165.00**
Space Man
Battery Operated, litho tin, astronaut, clear plastic visor on lighted helmet, carries space rifle one hand, working flashlight other hand, moving arms and legs, remote control battery box with litho missile, satellite, and stars on lid, TN, Japan, 9" h, orig box ...................... **1,250.00**
Walker, hard plastic, movable arms, walking leg action, walks on inclined plane, holding ray gun, wearing helmet and jet pack, 1950s, 6" h ........... **95.00**
Television Spaceman, battery operated, litho tin robot, metal antenna on/off switch, arms swing, eyes spin, TV screen in chest shows moving space scenes, screeching noise, Alps, Japan, 11" h, orig box **650.00**
Walking Moon Doctor, X–25, windup, litho tin and vinyl, robot–man wearing oversized glasses, swings arms, Daiya, Japan, orig box ......................... **925.00**
Flying Saucer
Flying Saucer Z–106, friction, litho

tin, red, blue, and yellow, three litho astronauts in windows, protruding tailfins, sparking, MT, Japan, 1950s . . . . . . . . . . . . . . . . . . . **290.00**

Martian Flying Saucer With Sparks, Z–10, litho tin, plastic canopy, full figured astronaut moves around cockpit in circular motion, sparking, underside marked "The Red Man From Space," TN, Japan, 1950s, 7″ d, orig box . . . . . . . . . . . **415.00**

Spacecraft Jupiter, flying saucer, windup, litho tin, tin astronaut, plastic bubble, sparks, engine noise, K, Japan, 5″ d, orig box . . . **95.00**

X–7 Space Explorer Ship, battery operated, litho tin, plastic base, bump–and–go action, beeping noise, flashing lights around saucer, full bodied astronaut, MT, Japan, 9″ d, orig box . . . . . . . . . . . . . . . . . . . **140.00**

**Flying Saucer, 5053, Item No. 758, battery operated, litho tin top, plastic base, bubble, rockets, and prop, bump-and-go action, Y, Japan, 8″ d, 6″ h, orig box, $125.00.**

Gun

Flashy–Ray Gun, battery operated, tin, TN, Japan, 18″ l, orig box . . . **95.00**

Jack Dan Space Gun, cap pistol, metal, CEFA, Spain, 1950s, 8″ l, orig box . . . . . . . . . . . . . . . . . . . . . **250.00**

Rex Mars Planet Patrol Sparkling Pistol, windup, plastic, red, Marx, 7″ l, orig box . . . . . . . . . . . . . . . . . . . . **170.00**

Space Super Jet Gun, litho tin, retracting plastic barrel, firing sound, KO, Japan, 9½″ l, orig box . . . . . . . . . . **255.00**

Miscellaneous

Astro Dog, battery operated, remote control, plastic and plush, Snoopy type dog wearing bubble helmet and spacesuit, carries NASA briefcase and American flag, barks, wags tail, walks, Yonezawa, Japan, 10″ h, orig box . . . . . . . . . . . . . . . . **75.00**

Jet Roller Coaster, No. 28A, windup, litho tin, futuristic bus travels on ramps, Wolverine, 12″ l, orig box **225.00**

Lunar Expedition, track toy, vacuform plastic planet surface base with built–up USA–NASA tower, windup litho tin and plastic lunar vehicle, Technofix, W Germany, 1950s, 10 x 15″ base, orig box . . . **250.00**

Moon Walker, cardboard model of US space capsule, child can stand inside, lift sides, and walk around, cut–away windows, four landing legs, Perry, 1966, 38″ h, orig box **100.00**

Rocket Express, #286, windup, litho tin, two space vehicles orbit around spinning Earth on oval racetrack, Technofix, W Germany, 1950s, orig box . . . . . . . . . . . . . . . . . . . . . **545.00**

Space Bulldog, friction, tin, marble eyes roll, mouth opens and closes, Japan, 6″ l . . . . . . . . . . . . . . . . . . . . **285.00**

Space Helmet, plastic

Banner, silver, radar goggles, spaceship mounted on top, 1952, orig box . . . . . . . . . . . . . . . **450.00**

Ideal, Colonel McCauley, *Men Into Space* TV show, visor, 1960, orig box . . . . . . . . . . . . . . . . . . . . . . **90.00**

Spaceship Journey to Jupiter, board game, folding board, cosmic spinner, four markers, 12 Space–O–Gram cards, instructions, litho box with Rocket King IV spaceship illus, All Fair . . . . . . . . . . . . . . . . . . . . . . **285.00**

Swinging Baby Robot, windup, litho tin, robot on swing, space illus frame, M, Japan, 3½″ h robot, orig box . . . . . . . . . . . . . . . . . . . . . . . . . **800.00**

Wristcompass, gold and silver colored molded rockets surround compass face, spaceman's head on top enclosed by clear plastic dome space helmet, space graphics on wristband, 1953 . . . . . . . . . . . . . . . **70.00**

Spacecraft, Rockets, and Capsules

Capsule Mercury, friction, litho tin, "United States," beep–beep noised, full figure astronaut in cockpit, detailed litho int., plastic windshields, SH, Japan, 9″ l, orig box . . . . . . . . . . . . . . . . . . . . . . . . . **325.00**

Electronic Count Down, battery operated, plastic, control board with windup launching mechanism, rockets, rotating antenna, instructions, Ideal, 1950s, 21 x 10″, orig box . . . . . . . . . . . . . . . . . . . . . . . . . **85.00**

Fire Rocket X–0077, friction, litho tin, plastic astronaut on saucer shaped seat ejects when rocket hits obstruction, foldup rear wings, siren noise, sparking, Y, Japan, 14" l, orig box .......... **520.00**

Florida Air Boat, battery operated, astronauts with bubble helmets at controls, emb rockets at rear, marked "Regulus" on sides, ATC, Japan, 8½" l, orig box .......... **175.00**

Flying Jeep, friction, litho tin, "Navy," pilot and gunner, clear plastic windscreen, spinning satellite disc, Indian Head Logo, Japan, 6½" l, orig box .......... **285.00**

Mystery Space Ship, gyroscope powered, plastic, astronauts and alien creatures, base, Marx, 1950s, 9" d ship, orig box .......... **160.00**

New Space Capsule, battery operated, litho tin, marked "United States" and "NASA," tinted plastic dome, litho tin astronaut with TV camera pops out of open hatch door, SH, Japan, 8½" l, orig box . **135.00**

Rocket Racer, friction, litho tin, #7, pilot in cockpit, Saturn image on tailfin, engine noise, MT, Japan, 7" l .......... **95.00**

Rocket Space Ship, friction, litho tin, red, green, and yellow, litho astronauts with bubble helmets, K, Japan, 3½" l .......... **140.00**

Rocket X–6 Racer, rocket, friction, litho tin, blue, red, and yellow, Saturn style planets at front, litho pilot in cockpit, MT, Japan, 1950s, 3½" l .......... **105.00**

Space Ship, SS–18, litho tin, astronaut under clear plastic dome, detailed dashboard instruments, "Space Ship" on hood, S & E, Japan, 9" l, orig box .......... **95.00**

Space Station, battery operated, litho tin, bump–and–go action, flashing lights, noise, astronaut pilot, TN, Japan, 9" d .......... **165.00**

Sparkling Space Ranger, friction, litho tin, blue, red, and yellow, Elvin, Japan, 7" l, orig box .......... **135.00**

Strange Explorer, battery operated, turnover tank, litho tin, soldier in cockpit, King Kong type gorilla turnover mechanism, shooting and engine noises, DSK, Japan, 8" l, orig box .......... **280.00**

Two Stage Rocket Launching Pad, battery operated, litho tin launching pad base, plastic "Jupiter" rocket, Linemar, 1950s, orig box . **385.00**

Tanks and Vehicles

Captain Robo Space Transporter, plastic, astronaut driver under dome, removable battery operated robot in cargo area, Y, Japan, 11" l, orig box .......... **85.00**

Exploration Train, battery operated, litho tin, rocket shaped locomotive with lights, transmitter car, radar car, and missile carrier, 12 track sections, K, Japan, 21" l, orig box **850.00**

Flash Strat–O–Wagon, litho tin, red, white, and blue, wood wheels, adjustable front wheels, Wyandotte, 1930s, 6" l, orig box .......... **150.00**

Future Car, "Sea Hawk," battery operated, space car with astronaut pilot, bump–and–go action, flashing lights, roof opens, engine noise, Y, Japan, 12" l, MIB .......... **665.00**

Jupiter Rocket Truck, friction, litho tin, "Guided Missile USA Unit 10" on sides, litho soldiers in window, carries spring loaded rubber missile, Marx, 1950s, 14" l, orig box **185.00**

Mobile Satellite Tracking Station, battery operated, litho tin, Cape Canaveral on sides, satellite monitor with TV screen mounted on top, rotating roof antenna, Yonezawa, Japan, 1950s, 8" l, orig box ..... **275.00**

Moon Explorer

M–27, battery operated, litho tin, astronaut driver, clear plastic dome, revolving rear lights, motor noise, rotating antenna, suction cup legs, second astronaut with camera at hatch door, plastic missile shaped remote control, Yonezawa, Japan, 9" l, 7" h, orig box .......... **700.00**

X–1, #4801, battery operated, plastic, red, yellow, white, and blue, trailer with crank operated missile launcher, three missiles, audio and visual telegraph key transmits messages, electric geiger counter, Ideal, 25" l, orig box .......... **175.00**

Radar Tank, battery operated, litho tin, bump–and–go action, spinning antenna, flashing lights, MT, Japan, 8" l, orig box .......... **290.00**

Robo–Tank TR–2, battery operated, litho tin and plastic, bump–and–go action, shoots lighted gun, TN, Japan, 5" h, orig box .......... **175.00**

Robotank–Z, battery operated, litho tin, plastic arms and head dome, shoots gun with flashing light, arms swing, motor noise, speaks Japanese, TN, Japan, 6" l, 11" h, orig box .......... **395.00**

SP–1 Space Car, friction, litho tin, tinted windows, Linemar, Japan, 7" l .......... **100.00**

Space Patrol Tank, friction, litho tin, tin astronaut driver, plastic canopy, engine noise, Japan, 4½" l ...... **85.00**

Space Robot Car, battery operated, litho tin, robot driver, air expelled from radar–like mechanism in bed keeps styrofoam balls suspended in air, flashing lights, Y, Japan, 9" l .. **425.00**

Space Tank, friction, litho tin, "Super Robot" driver, adjustable turret, gun noise, SH, Japan, 9" l, orig box **700.00**

Space Tank V–2, battery operated, litho tin, Robbie Robot driver, TV screen with rocket and planet pictures mounted on back, bump–and–go action, KO, Japan, 6" l, orig box ......................... **1,350.00**

Super Sonic Race Car No. 36, friction, litho tin, streamlined futuristic design, engine and popping noise, MT, Japan, 9" l, orig box ........ **125.00**

# SPORTS COLLECTIBLES

**Collecting Hints:** The amount of material is unlimited. Pick a favorite sport and concentrate on it. Within the sport, narrow collecting emphasis to items associated with one league, team, or individual, equipment, or chronological era. Include as much three dimensional material as possible.

Each sport has a "hall of fame." Make a point to visit it and get to know its staff—an excellent source of leads for material that the museum does not want. Induction ceremonies provide an excellent opportunity to make contact with heroes of the sport as well as with other collectors.

**History:** Individuals have been saving sports–related equipment since the inception of sports. Some was passed down from generation to generation for reuse. The balance occupied dark spaces in closets, attics, and basements.

In the 1980s two key trends brought collectors' attention to sports collectibles. First, decorators began using old sports items, especially in restaurant decor. Second, card collectors began to discover the thrill of owing the "real" thing. Although the principal thrust was on baseball memorabilia, by the beginning of the 1990s all sport categories were collectible, with automobile racing, boxing, football, and horse racing especially strong.

**References:** Ted Hake and Roger Steckler, *An Illustrated Price Guide to Non–Paper Sports Collectibles*, Hake's Americana & Collectibles Press, 1986; Roderick A. Malloy, *Malloy's Sports Collectibles Value Guide*, Wallace–Homestead, 1993; Norman E. Martinus and Harry L. Rinker, *Warman's Paper*, Wallace–Homestead, 1993.

**Periodicals:** *Sports Collectors Digest*, 700 East State Street, Iola, WI 54990; *The Olympic Collectors Newsletter*, P. O. Box 41630, Tucson, AZ 85717.

**See:** Baseball Collectibles and Golf Collectibles.

## Basketball

Figure, Starting Lineup, Kenner

Individual

Charles Barkley, 1992 ........... **30.00**

Larry Bird, 1988 ............... **24.00**

Magic Johnson, 1992 ........... **25.00**

Mark Price, 1988 .............. **60.00**

Legends Collection, Wilt Chamberlain, 1989 ..................... **30.00**

Slam Dunk Superstars, Michael Jordan, 1989 ..................... **100.00**

Nodder, 7" h, Seattle Supersonics, composition, figure holding basketball, gold round base, late 1970s ....... **25.00**

Pinback Button, Basketball Golden Jubilee, Dr J A Naismith, Springfield, MA, 1891–1941, orange, black lettering and illus .................. **22.00**

Program, Harlem Globetrotters, 1948–49, 16 pgs, 8½ x 11" ............. **25.00**

Record, Harlem Globetrotters–Sweet Georgia Brown, 45 rpm, illus sleeve **15.00**

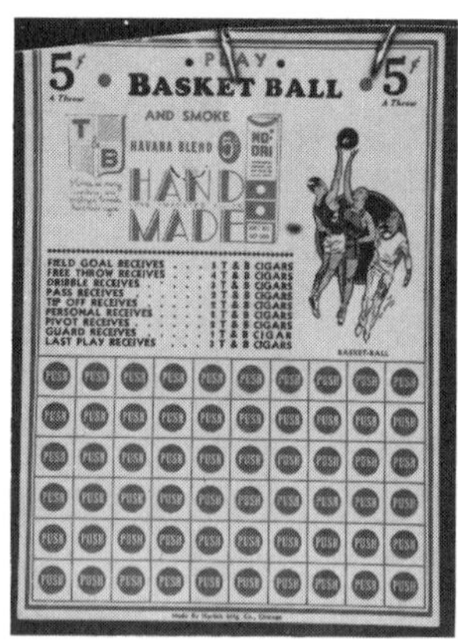


**Punchboard, Play Basket Ball, Havana Blend Cigar adv, red, blue, and white, 5¢, 1930s, 7¼ x 10", $17.50.**

## Boating

Catalog

Thompson Bros Outboard Motor Boats, Canoes, Motor Boats, 1929, 32 pages, 8 x 10¾" ............ **20.00**

Waterman Porto, Early Outboard Motors, 1915, 18 pages ............ **75.00**

Magazine, *Sports Illustrated,* September 6, 1954, sailing .................. **15.00**

Pinback Button

Devil's Lake Regatta, 1¼" d, blue and white, speedboat races, July, 1934 **12.00**

Outboard Regatta, 2⅛" d, tan, cello, black lettering, 1930s ........... **12.00**

## Body Building

Badge, patron, World's Weightlifting Championships, Sept 26–27, 1947, brass, yellow fabric ribbon ........ **15.00**

Exerciser, Jiffy–Gym, black rubber stretch belt, molded rubber hand grips, instruction sheet, orig box, Moosehead–Whitely Co, NY, 1950s **22.00**

Magazine, *Sports Illustrated,* April 14, 1975, Vasili Alexeyev ............. **4.50**

Poster, 14 x 22", York Streamlined Barbell and Body Building System, red and blue, 1950s ................. **15.00**

Ribbon, 1950 Weightlifting/Mr America, brass hanger bar, attached blue and white ribbon, gold lettering .... **15.00**

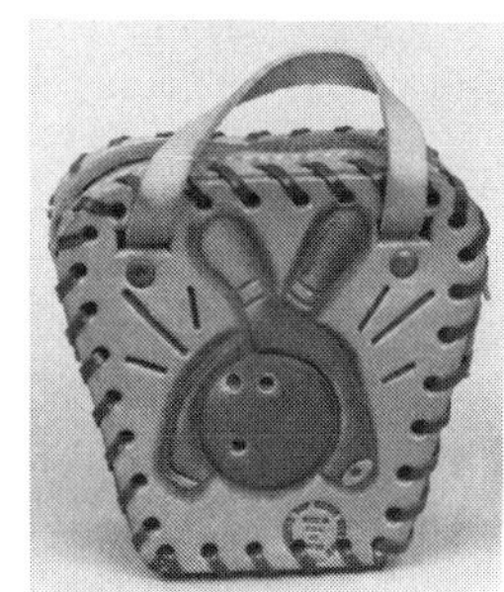

**Change Purse, leather, miniature bowling ball bag, Mafco, 8¼" w, 3⅛" h, $2.00.**

## Bowling

Game, Bowling, A Board Game, orig box, Parker Bros, 1896 ........... **50.00**

Magazine, *Sports Illustrated,* March 28, 1955, Steve Nagy ................ **8.00**

Nodder, 6" h, "You're Right Down My Alley," composition, man holding bowling ball, mounted on wood block base ...................... **45.00**

Pinback Button

American Bowling Congress, 32nd Annual Tournament, red, white, and blue, 1930s ............... **8.00**

Dallas Turnverein Bowling Club, There's No Use Crying Baby Houston! You Can't Have This Cup, blue, white, and black, 1901–10 . **20.00**

**Arcade Card, John Gonsalves, green tone real photo, 1940s, 3⅜ x 5⅜", $7.50.**

## Boxing

Book, *Jack Dempsey/The Idol of Histiana,* 1936 revised edition, Nat Fleischer, 158 pgs, inked autograph "To Bob/Best Wishes/Nat Fleischer" **25.00**

Boxing Gloves, Rocky Graziano, orig box ........................... **135.00**

Bust, John Sullivan, Red Top Beer .... **240.00**

Charm, miniature, plastic, printed boxer's name

Ike Williams, red, lightweight champion, 1945–51 ................. **8.00**

Mickey Walker, white, welterweight champion, 1922–26 ............ **10.00**

Flask, John Sullivan ................. **225.00**

Game, Muhammad Ali's Boxing Ring, mechanical, Mego Corp, 1976 copyright Herbert Muhammad Enterprise Inc, orig box .................... **50.00**

Magazine

*Sports Illustrated,* June 18, 1973, George Foreman on cover ....... **15.00**

*Time,* Cassius Clay cover .......... **12.00**

Pinback Button

Jack Johnson, Heavyweight Champion, black and white, 1911–20 . **50.00**

Sonny Liston, black and white, 1960s **8.00**

Poster, 20 x 30", chromolithograph of two boxers, Samson Kina, Goffart, Brussels, c1910 .................. **275.00**

Record, The Champ Sings, Cassius Clay, Stand By Me and I Am The Greatest, 45 rpm, black and white photo on sleeve ......................... **25.00**

Ring, Gene Tunney, plastic, yellow, insert illus, issued by Kellogg's cereals, 1950s ......................... **12.50**

Statue, Louis Golden, Hollywood Studios, 1947 ..................... **350.00**

## Football

Bank, 6" h, Pittsburgh Steelers, plastic, helmet shape, 1970s . . . . . . . . . . . . . . **23.00**
Cigarette Lighter, San Francisco 49ers Super Bowl XVI Champs, silvered metal and plastic . . . . . . . . . . . . . . . . . **22.00**
Cushion, stadium, 11 x 16", vinyl, stuffed, red, NFL team names and mascot illus, orig tag, unused, 1950s **18.00**
Game, Vince Lombardi's Game, orig box, Research Games, Inc, 1970 copyright . . . . . . . . . . . . . . . . . . . . . . . **25.00**
Magazine
  *Sports Illustrated,* August 17, 1970, Joe Namath . . . . . . . . . . . . . . . . . . **8.00**
  *TV Guide,* January 20, 1979, Super Bowl XIII cover . . . . . . . . . . . . . . . . **4.00**
Nodder
  Atlanta Falcons, gold round base . . . **25.00**
  Cleveland Browns, wood brown square base . . . . . . . . . . . . . . . . . . **65.00**
Patch, Super Bowl V, 1970, Baltimore and Dallas . . . . . . . . . . . . . . . . . . . . . **60.00**
Pencil Case, 5 x 8½", National Football League, vinyl, pale blue . . . . . . . . . . . **25.00**
Pinback Button
  Rockne of Notre Dame, black and white photo, 1930s . . . . . . . . . . . . . **15.00**
  St Louis Cardinals, black, red, and white, football and cardinal, 1960s **5.00**
  The Sugar Bowl Fordham, New Orleans, LA, purple, 1942 . . . . . . . . . **5.00**

**Pinback Button, football shape, black and white photo of 1933 Bloomfield football team, 3" l, $8.00.**

Press Pin, Super Bowl XV, 1980, Oakland and Philadelphia . . . . . . . . . . . . . **175.00**
Program
  American Football Conference Division, Miami and Kansas City, 1971 **30.00**
  Illinois–Notre Dame Football Game, October 9, 1937, 20 pgs, black and white photos and roster, 8 x 11" . . **25.00**
  National Football Conference Championship, Minnesota and LA Rams, 1974 . . . . . . . . . . . . . . . . . . . . . . . . . **18.00**
  National Football Conference Division, San Francisco and Detroit, 1983 . . . . . . . . . . . . . . . . . . . . . . . . . **13.00**
  National Football League Conference, Dallas and Cleveland, 1967 . . . . . **75.00**
  Super Bowl XVII, 1982, Washington and Miami . . . . . . . . . . . . . . . . . . . **22.00**
Ticket Stub
  American Football League Championship, 1967, Oakland and Houston . . . . . . . . . . . . . . . . . . . . . . . . . . **22.00**
  NFC Division, 1977, Minnesota and LA Rams . . . . . . . . . . . . . . . . . . . . . **10.00**
  Super Bowl I, 1966, Green Bay and Kansas City . . . . . . . . . . . . . . . . . . . **125.00**
  Super Bowl VIII, 1973, Miami and Minnesota . . . . . . . . . . . . . . . . . . . . **75.00**
Yearbook, Green Bay Packers 1974 Yearbook, autographed by coaches and players . . . . . . . . . . . . . . . . . . . . . . **18.00**

## Hockey

Bubble Gum Card
  Brian Bellows, O–Pee–Chee, #167, 1983–84 . . . . . . . . . . . . . . . . . . . . . **14.00**
  Glenn Anderson, O–Pee–Chee, #108, 1981–82 . . . . . . . . . . . . . . . . **9.00**
  Jimmy Carson, Topps, #92, 1987–88 **5.25**
  Pavel Bure, Upper Deck, #526, 1990–91 **18.00**
  Wayne Gretzky, Topps, #250, 1980–81 . . . . . . . . . . . . . . . . . . . . . . . . . . **135.00**
Figure, Bobby Hull, hand signed, Gartlan USA . . . . . . . . . . . . . . . . . . . . . . . **250.00**
Hockey Stick, autographed
  Bobby Hull . . . . . . . . . . . . . . . . . . . . . . **135.00**
  Wayne Gretzky . . . . . . . . . . . . . . . . . . **165.00**
Magazine, *Sports Illustrated,* December 11, 1967, Bobby Orr on cover . . . . . **12.00**
Nodder
  Canadiens, sq base, 1961–62 . . . . . . **60.00**
  Flyers, gold oval base, 1966–69 . . . . **200.00**
  Rangers, sq base, 1961–62 . . . . . . . . **75.00**

## Miscellaneous

Catalog, Elmira Arms Sporting Goods, 1931, 180 pages . . . . . . . . . . . . . . . . . **30.00**
Chart, Field & Court Dimensions–Compliments of Lowe & Campbell Athletic Goods, 1942, various sporting illus, 22½ x 17½" . . . . . . . . . . . . . . . . . . . . . **18.00**
Handbook, Spalding, 1930s . . . . . . . . . **15.00**
Nodder, majorette . . . . . . . . . . . . . . . . . . **25.00**
Pinback Button
  All–American Soap Box Derby, red, white, and blue, 1954 . . . . . . . . . . **8.00**
  Sweitzer Non–Partisan Billiard Fan Club, red, white, and blue, 1920s **12.00**

Poster, Fidass Sporting Goods, 29 x 52", F Romoli, Italian soccer player, 1946 **300.00**
Record Book, rugby, Scottish, 1937 ... **15.00**
Track, AAU Championship, two mile run, 1913 ... **35.00**

## Olympics

Cigarette Lighter, 2¾" l, 1984 Winter Olympics, red plastic, silvered metal, Olympic ring symbol, insignia, and "Sarajevo, Yugoslavia" in black on one side, black cartoon snowman illus other side ... **10.00**
Cushion, stadium, 11 x 13½", 1956 Summer, red vinyl, yellow, white, and blue Olympics logo ... **45.00**
Fan, Tenth Olympic Games/1932/Los Angeles, folding, paper, hp, balsa sticks, chapel building illus, Olympic symbol, Japan ... **34.00**
Figure, Starting Lineup, Kenner, USA Olympic Team, 1992 ... **75.00**
Flask, 5½" h, white china, issued by Lufthansa Airlines, Olympic logo, "XVII Olympiade Rom 1960" inscription ... **15.00**
Glass, 5½" h, 1932 Olympics, clear, frosted white picture ... **50.00**
Magazine, *Sports Illustrated,* September 5, 1960, Rome Olympics Ceremonies **6.00**
Pinback button
American Olympic Fund Contributor, oval, red, white, and blue, 1928 . **8.00**
New York State, Olympic Winter Games Commission, red and white, 1930s ... **10.00**
Plate, 7" d, 1968, gold leaf, Mexico and torch dec ... **60.00**
Post Card, 1912 Stockholm Olympics, black and white photo, 3½ x 5½" .. **25.00**
Tray, 11 x 15", 1976 Olympics, Montreal, litho metal, Coca–Cola adv ... **35.00**
Wristwatch, 1980 Olympics, Timex, battery operated, orig plastic display case ... **110.00**

## Swimming

Autograph, Gertrude Ederly, 6½ x 8" sheet, printed black and white drawing, blue ink inscription "Hold Strongly To 'Faith' in All You Do!/Best Always/Swimmingly Yours/Gertrude Trudy Ederly/New York/Successful Channel Swim/August 6, 1926/35 miles In 40½ Hrs/Cape Gris Nez to Kingdown," inked 1969 date ... **22.00**
Magazine, *Sports Illustrated,* January 29, 1962, Chet Jastremski ... **5.00**
Poster, Aquatics Swimming Is A Life–Saver for Yourself & Others–Learn to Be at Home in the Water, 11926 ... **10.00**

## Tennis

Magazine, *Sports Illustrated,* July 15, 1974, Jimmy Connors and Chris Evert **7.50**
Pinback Button, US Open Tennis Championship, 2⅛", cello, 1975 championships ... **10.00**
Poster, Play Helps Study, colorful tennis motif, 1924 ... **20.00**
Tennis Racket, 27" l, Maureen Connolly, full color portrait on handle, Wilson Sporting Goods Co, 1950s ... **15.00**

# STANGL POTTERY

**Collecting Hints:** Stangl Pottery produced several lines of highly collectible dinnerware and decorative accessories, including the famed Stangl birds. The red bodied dinnerware was produced in distinctive shapes and patterns. Shapes were designated by numbers. Pattern names include: Country Garden, Fruit, Tulip, Thistle, and Wild Rose. Special Christmas, advertising, and commemorative wares also were produced.

Bright colors and bold simplistic patterns make Stangl pottery a favorite with Country collectors. Stangl's factory sold seconds from its factory store long before outlet malls became popular. Large sets of Stangl dinnerware currently command high prices at auctions, flea markets, and even antiques shops.

Stangl's ceramic birds were produced from 1940 until 1972. The birds were produced in Stangl's Trenton plant, then shipped to the Flemington plant for hand painting. During World War II the demand for these birds and Stangl pottery was so great that 40 to 60 decorators could not keep up with the demand. Orders were contracted out to private homes. These pieces were then returned for firing and finishing. Colors used to decorate these birds varied according to the artist. Several birds were reissued between 1972 and 1977. These reissues are dated on the bottom and worth approximately one half the value of the older birds.

As many as ten different trademarks were used. Dinnerware was marked and often signed by the decorator. Most birds are numbered; many are artist signed. However, signatures are useful for dating purposes only and add little to values.

**History:** The origins of Fulper Pottery, the predecessor to Stangl, are clouded. The company claimed a date of 1805. Paul Evans, a major American art pottery researcher, suggests an 1814 date. Regardless of which date is right, by the middle of the nineteenth century an active pottery was located in Flemington, New Jersey.

When Samuel Hill, the pottery's founder, died in 1858, the pottery was acquired by Abraham Fulper, a nephew. Abraham died in 1881, and the business continued under the direction of Edward, George W., and William, Fulper's sons.

In 1910 Johann Martin Stangl began working at Fulper as a chemist and plant superintendent. He left Fulper in 1914 to work briefly for Haeger Potteries. By 1920 Stangl was serving as general manager at Fulper. In 1926 Fulper acquired the Anchor Pottery in Trenton, New Jersey, where a line of solid color dinnerware in the California patio style was produced.

William Fulper died in 1928, at which time Stangl became president of the firm. In 1920 Johann Martin Stangl purchased Fulper and Stangl Pottery was born. During the 1920s production emphasis shifted from art pottery to dinner and utilitarian wares.

In 1929 fire destroyed the Flemington pottery. Rather than rebuild, a former ice cream factory was converted to a showroom and production facility. By the end of the 1930s production was concentrated in Trenton with the Flemington kiln used primarily for demonstration purposes.

On August 25, 1965, fire struck the Trenton plant. The damaged portion of the plant was rebuilt by May 1966. On February 13, 1972, Johann Martin Stangl died. Frank Wheaton, Jr., of Wheaton Industries, Millville, N.J., purchased the plant in June 1972 and continued Stangl production. In 1978 the Pfaltzgraff Company purchased the company's assets from Wheaton. Production ceased. The Flemington factory became a Pfaltzgraff factory outlet. One of the original kilns remains intact to exemplify the hard work and high temperatures involved in the production of pottery.

**References:** Harvey Duke, *Stangl Pottery,* Wallace–Homestead, 1993; Joan Dworkin and Martha Horman, *A Guide To Stangl Pottery Birds,* Willow Pond Books, Inc., 1973, out–of–print; Norma Rehl, *The Collectors Handbook of Stangl Pottery,* Democrat Press, 1982.

## BIRDS

#3276D, Bluebirds .......... **175.00**
#3400, Lovebirds .......... **50.00**
#3404, Lovebirds .......... **135.00**
#3405D, Cockatoos, 9½" h .......... **65.00**
#3443, Duck .......... **275.00**
#3449, Parrot .......... **125.00**
#3581, Chickadees .......... **175.00**
#3596, Cardinal, gray .......... **62.00**
#3598, Kentucky Warbler .......... **40.00**
#3628, Fieffers Hummingbird .......... **115.00**
#3635, Goldfinches .......... **175.00**
#3716, Blue Jay with leaf .......... **450.00**
#3814, Black Throated Warbler .......... **85.00**
#3848, Gold Crowned Kinglet .......... **110.00**
#34020, Orioles, small chip on beak . **80.00**
#34025, Oriole .......... **55.00**
#34060D, Double Kingfishers .......... **150.00**
#37510, Red Headed Woodpecker ... **300.00**

## DINNERWARE

Apple Delight, #5161, 1965
Cake Stand .......... **20.00**
Casserole, 6" d .......... **15.00**
Cereal Bowl .......... **12.00**
Gravy, liner .......... **35.00**
Plate
8" d, salad .......... **10.00**
10" d, dinner .......... **15.00**
Relish Tray .......... **22.00**
Salad Bowl, 10" d .......... **35.00**

Bella Rosa, 1960
Butter Dish, ¼ lb .......... **35.00**
Casserole, individual, stick handle .. **15.00**
Cup and Saucer .......... **12.50**
Fruit Dish, 5½" d .......... **10.00**
Pitcher, ½ pt .......... **20.00**
Plate, 6" d, bread and butter .......... **5.00**
Server, center handle .......... **8.00**

Colonial, #1388
Ball Jug, ice lip, Silver Green .......... **35.00**
Bean Pot, individual, Persian Yellow **18.00**
Chop Plate, 12½" d colonial Blue .. **20.00**
Casserole, 8" d, Silver Green .......... **35.00**
Eggcup, Colonial Blue .......... **8.00**
Plate, 10" d, dinner, Colonial Blue . **12.00**
Relish, two sections, 7" l, Persian Yellow .......... **20.00**
Teapot, individual, Tangerine .......... **30.00**
Vegetable Bowl, oval, 10" l, Tangerine .......... **16.00**

Country Garden
Coaster .......... **10.00**
Creamer and Sugar .......... **25.00**
Cup and Saucer .......... **15.00**
Gravy Boat and Stand .......... **32.00**
Pickle Dish .......... **20.00**
Pitcher, 2 qt .......... **45.00**
Soup Bowl, lug handle .......... **15.00**

Dahlia
Cereal Bowl .......... **15.00**
Plate
6" d, bread and butter .......... **4.50**
8" d, salad .......... **8.00**
Platter, oval, 14¾" l .......... **35.00**
Server, center handle .......... **10.00**
Tile, 6" sq .......... **20.00**

Fruit, #3697, 1942
Bean Pot, two handled .......... **60.00**
Chop Plate, 14½" d .......... **40.00**
Coffeepot, 4 cup .......... **60.00**
Mixing Bowl, 7" d .......... **25.00**
Plate
7" d .......... **10.00**
10" d .......... **18.00**
Relish Dish .......... **25.00**

Salad Bowl, 12″ d ................ **50.00**
Sherbet .......................... **24.00**
Garden Flower
Casserole, Balloon Flower, 6″ d .... **22.00**
Chop Plate, Tiger Lily, 12½″ d ..... **40.00**
Creamer, individual, Rose ......... **12.00**
Cup and Saucer, Rose cup, Leaves saucer ........................ **15.00**
Furit Bowl, Calendula, 5½″ d ...... **12.00**
Pitcher, 2 qt, Sunflower ........... **40.00**

**Garden Flower, dinner plate, 11½″ d, $10.00.**

Plate
8″ d, Bleeding Heart ............ **12.00**
9″ d, Tiger Lily ................. **12.00**
Teapot, Sunflower ................ **45.00**
Golden Harvest, #3887, 1953
Coffee Mug, 2 cup ............... **25.00**
Cup and Saucer .................. **10.00**
Plate
8″ d ........................ **12.00**
11″ d ....................... **20.00**
Salt and Pepper Shakers, pr ........ **24.00**
Vegetable Bowl, divided .......... **35.00**
Magnolia, #3870, 1952
Butter Dish ...................... **35.00**
Condiment Tray .................. **22.00**
Creamer and Sugar ............... **20.00**
Cup and Saucer .................. **10.00**
Pitcher, 1 qt ..................... **30.00**
Salt and Pepper Shakers, pr ........ **16.00**
Orchard Song, #5110, 1962
Coaster ......................... **7.50**
Fruit Bowl, 5½″ d ................ **10.00**
Platter, 13¾″ l ................... **35.00**
Server, two tiers ................. **20.00**
Thistle, #3847, 1951
Coaster ......................... **10.00**
Mixing Bowl, 5½″ d .............. **20.00**
Plate, 9″ d ...................... **10.00**
Sauce Boat ...................... **18.00**
Vegetable Bowl, divided .......... **32.00**

## GIFTWARE

Ashtray
Oval, Sportsmen, #3926, 10⅝″ l
Pheasant ...................... **35.00**
Quail ......................... **48.00**
Wood duck .................... **45.00**
Round, 5″ d
Apple Tree, #3845 ............. **15.00**
Flower, #3801 ................. **12.00**
Basket, Terra Rose, #3251, 11 x 9″ ... **75.00**
Bowl, Antique Gold, #4061, 8″ d .... **25.00**
Cigarette Box, cov, rect, 7¼ x 3⅜″
Heart, #3638 .................... **35.00**
Hummingbird, #3842 ............ **40.00**
Pitcher, Antique Gold, #4052, 14½″ h **35.00**
Planter, Platina, swan, #5033, 6¾″ h . **20.00**
Vase
Terra Rose, #3442, 6″ h .......... **20.00**
Tropical Ware, #2027, 8″ h ....... **100.00**
Wall Pocket, Cosmos, green matte, #2091, 1937 .................... **40.00**

# STEREOGRAPHS

**Collecting Hints:** Value is determined by condition, subject, photographer (if famous), rarity, and age—prior to 1870 or after 1935. A revenue stamp on the back indicates an age of 1864–66, when a federal war tax was imposed. Litho printed cards have very little value.

Collect images that are of good grade or above, except for extremely rare images. Very good condition means some wear on the mount and a little dirt on the photo. Folds, marks on the photo, or badly worn mounts reduce values by at least 50%. Faded or light photos also reduce value.

Don't try to clean cards or straighten them. Cards were made curved to heighten the stereo effect, an improvement made in 1880.

With common cards it pays to shop around to get the best price. With rarer cards it pays to buy them when you see them since values are increasing annually. Dealers who are members of the National Stereoscopic Association are very protective of their reputation and offer a good starting point for the novice collector.

Use your public library to study thoroughly the subject matter you are collecting; it is a key element to assembling a meaningful collection.

**History:** Stereographs, also known as stereo views, stereo view cards, or stereoscope cards, were first issued in the United States on glass and paper in 1854. From the late 1850s through the 1930s, the stereograph was an important visual record of every major event, famous person, comic situation, and natural scene. It was the popular news and entertainment medium until replaced by movies, picture magazines, and radio.

The major early publishers were Anthony (1859–1873), Kilburn (1865–1907), Langeheim (1854–1861), and Weller (1861–1875). By the 1880–1910 period the market was controlled by large firms among which were Davis (Kilburn), Griffith & Griffith, International View Company, Keystone, Stereo Travel, Underwood & Underwood, Universal Photo Art, and H.C. White.

**References:** William C. Darrah, *Stereo Views, A History Of Stereographs in America And Their Collection,* published by author, 1964, out–of–print; William C. Darrah, *The World of Stereographs,* published by author, 1977, out–of–print; Norman E. Martinus and Harry L. Rinker, *Warman's Paper,* Wallace–Homestead, 1993; John S. Waldsmith, *Stereo Views: An Illustrated History and Price Guide,* Wallace–Homestead, 1991.

**Collectors' Club:** National Stereoscopic Association, Box 14801, Columbus, OH 43214.

**Advisor:** John S. Waldsmith.

**Note:** Prices given are for very good condition, i.e., some wear and slight soiling. For excellent condition add 25%, and for mint perfect image and mount, double the price. Reverse the process for fair, i.e., moderate soiling, some damage to mount, minor glue marks, some foxing (brown spots) and poor folded mount, very dirty and damage to tone or both images. Where applicable, a price range is given.

Animal
Birds, Hurst's 2nd series, #7, birds in tree . . . . . . . . . . . . . . . . . . . . . . . . . . . **4.00**
Cat
Keystone #2314, average cat view . **5–6.00**
Keystone #9651, man and cat . . . . . **4.00**
Soule, The Pickwickian Ride, highly collectible . . . . . . . . . . . . . . . . . . . . **20.00**
Dog
Kilburn #1644, "Home Protection," dog close up . . . . . . . . . . . . . . . . . **6.00**
U & U, the puppies singing school . **4.00**
Universal #3231, average dog view **4–5.00**
Farm Yard, Kilburn #739, sheep and cows, 1870s . . . . . . . . . . . . . . . . . . . . **4.00**
Horses, Schreiber & Sons, Jarvis and sulky, early . . . . . . . . . . . . . . . . . . . . . **18.00**
Walrus, Keystone #V21232, Bronx Zoo **3.00**
Zoo, London Stereo Company, animals in London Zoo, each . . . . . . . . . . . . . **8–10.00**

Astronomy
Comet, Keystone #16645, Morehouse's . . . . . . . . . . . . . . . . . . . . . . . . **9.50**
Mars, Keystone #16767T, the planet . . **6.00**
Moon
Beer Bros. 1866, photo by Rutherford **15.00**
Kilburn #2630, full moon . . . . . . . . . **6.00**
Soule #602, last quarter . . . . . . . . . . **8.00**
Planetarium, Keystone #32688, Adler's Chicago . . . . . . . . . . . . . . . . . . . . . . . . **10.00**

Aviation
Air Mail Plane
Keystone #29446, at Cleveland **30.00**
Keystone #32372, Inaugural, Ford Tri-motor, air-rail service NY to LA, 7/2/29 . . . . . . . . . . . . . . . . . . . . . . . . **20.00**
Aviators, Keystone #26408t, 6 men who first circled earth . . . . . . . . . . . . . **25.00**
Balloon, Anthony #4114, Prof. Lowe's flight from 6th Ave. in NYC . . . . . . . . **100.00**
Dirigibles and Zeppelins, Keystone
#17397, Los Angeles at Lakehurst **45–50.00**
#17398, The Los Angeles . . . . . . . . . **45.00**
#18000, flying over German town . **6.00**
#32277, Graf Zeppelin in hanger at Lakehurst, NJ . . . . . . . . . . . . . . . . . **35.00**
#32740, framework of ZRS-4, Akron . . . . . . . . . . . . . . . . . . . . . . **55–65.00**
#V19216, 1918, R-34 at Mineola, from WWI set, common view . . . . **15.00**
Doolittle, Keystone #28031, Major Doolittle, 1931 . . . . . . . . . . . . . . . . . . **65.00**
General View, Keystone #32785, five biplanes fly over Chicago's field museum . . . . . . . . . . . . . . . . . . . . . . . . . . **20.00**
Lindbergh, Keystone
#28029, in plane with wife . . . . . . . **55.00**
#30262T, next to Spirit of St. Louis **30.00**
Plane, Keystone
#18920, Michelin bomber . . . . . . . . **20.00**
#19049, Nieuport . . . . . . . . . . . . . . . . **10.00**
#V18921, twin seat fighter . . . . . . . . **9.00**
Wright Bros., Keystone #V96103, in flight at Ft. Meyers . . . . . . . . . . . . . . . **85.00**

Black
Keystone #9506, "we done all dis a' morning," picking cotton . . . . . . . . . . **6.00**
Kilburn #14317, boy and mule, typical, common . . . . . . . . . . . . . . . . . . . . . . . **3.00**
Singley
#10209, "one never came up," swimmers . . . . . . . . . . . . . . . . . . . . . . . . . . **12.00**
#10217, "one got an upper cut," fighting . . . . . . . . . . . . . . . . . . . . . . . . . . . . **10.00**
U & U, "Cotton is King," picking . . . . **5.00**
U & U, "Keystone, Kilburn," Whiting, etc., cheating at cards, stealing millions, infidelity, etc . . . . . . . . . . . . . **10–15.00**
Whiting
#960, "there's a watermelon smiling on the vine" . . . . . . . . . . . . . . . . . . **10.00**
#961, "Happiest Coon" . . . . . . . . . . **8.00**
Cave
Keystone
#9586, man in front of Great Oregon Caves . . . . . . . . . . . . . . . . . . . . . . . . **6.00**
#33516, int. of Crystal Springs Cave, Carlsbad . . . . . . . . . . . . . . . . . . . . . **4.50**
U & U, Luray Caverns, typical . . . . . . . **8.00**
Waldack, 1866, Mammoth Cave, typical early magnesium light view . . . . **15.00**

**Children, Playing Soldier, Keystone View Co., P193, $3.00.**

Christmas
Brownies & Santa, Universal #4679, Graves, sleigh in foreground ....... **20.00**
Children with Tree
Griffith #16833, children's Christmas dinner ........................ **18.00**
Keystone, 1895, #987, Santa in front of fireplace .................... **15.00**
Santa coming down chimney, Keystone #11434, Santa with toys .......... **25.00**
Santa with Toys, Keystone 1898, #9445, Santa loaded with toys ..... **14.00**

Comics
Bicycle Bum, Graves #4551–58, "Weary Willie," 4 card set ........ **20.00**
Drinking
Kilburn 1892, #7348, "Brown just in from the club" ................. **3.00**
R. Y. Young 1901, Woman drinking, two cards, unusual subject ...... **16.00**
U & U, 1897, man sneaks in after drinking, 2 card set ............. **7.50**
English, boy carves roast, "The Attack," ivory mount, hand tinted .......... **4.00**
Humor
Keystone #2346-7, before (cuddling) and after (reading) marriage ...... **7.00**
U & U, 1904, "Four queens and a jack," 4 girls and a jackass ...... **6.00**
Infidelity
Foolin–around, 1910, husband fools around with his secretary, 12 cards **48.00**
Keystone #12312–22, The French Cook–Communist version ....... **50.00**
U & U
Sneaking–in, 1897, caught by wife after nite on the town ......... **8.00**
The French Cook, 10 card set .... **50.00**
Romance
U & U, "Going with Stream," hugging couple ....................... **6.00**
Weller #353, "Unexpected," necking **4.00**
Rumors, H. C. White, 5576-5578, quickest way to spread news: "Tell a graph, tell a phone, tell a woman," 3 card set ........................ **20.00**
Sentimental, American Stereo, #2001-2012, He goes to war; wounded; returns; reunited, etc., 12 card set ... **60.00**

Wedding Set, White #5510–19, getting ready, wedding, reception, alone in bedroom ....................... **40.00**

Disaster
Boston Fire, 1872, Soule, ruins ...... **8.00**
Chicago Fire, 1871, Lovejoy & Foster, ruins .......................... **9.00**
Galveston Flood, 1900, Graves, ruins . **10.00**
Johnstown Flood, ruins
Barker .......................... **9.00**
U & U .......................... **7.00**
Mill Creek Flood, 1874, popular series, house .......................... **4.00**
Portland Fire, 1866, Soule #469, ruins **8.00**
St. Pierre Eruption, Kilburn #14941, ruins .......................... **3.00**
San Francisco Earthquake Scenes
Keystone #13264, Market St ....... **9.00**
U & U #8180, California St ....... **16.00**
White #8713, wrecked houses ..... **20.00**
Train Wreck, Dole ................. **50.00**
Worcester, MA, Flood, 1876, Lawrence, damage ......................... **5.00**

**Disasters, Underwood & Underwood, #8204, Great destruction wrought by earthquake and fire—showing Temple Emanuel—San Francisco, Cal., $9.00.**

Doll
Graves #4362, Sunday School Class .. **20.00**
Kilburn
#15, tired of play ................ **15.00**
When will Santa come? ........... **12.00**
U & U
#6922, playing doctor ............ **15.00**
#6952, girl asleep with cat and doll **9.00**
Webster & Albee #160, doll's maypole **20.00**

Entertainer
Actress, J. Gurney & Son, 1870s, Mrs. Scott or Mrs. Roland, etc. ......... **10.00**
Dancers, Keystone #33959, Bali, Dutch Indies .......................... **2.00**
Natives, Keystone #16423, Java, good costumes ........................ **3.00**
Singer
J. Gurney & Son, Annie Cary ...... **15.00**
James Cremer, opera, studio pose in costume ...................... **12.00**

Exposition
NY Sanitary Fair, Anthony #1689-2864, fair view of fountain (for better view, double value) .... 15.00
1872, World Peace Jubilee, Boston Pollock, interior view .... 8.00
1876, U.S. Close Up Centennial, Centennial Photo Co.
  Common view of grounds and buildings .... 5.00–10.00
  Corliss Engine .... 12.00
  Monorail .... 65.00
  Statue of Liberty Hand .... 85.00
1894
  California Mid-Winter, Kilburn #9474-2894, urns, etc. (for better subject, double value) .... 12.00
  Columbian Chicago, Kilburn
    Most views .... 4–7.00
    Ferris Wheel .... 7–10.00
1901, Pan American Buffalo, Kilburn
  Most views .... 4–6.00
  President McKinley .... 7–9.00
1904, Louisiana Purchase Exposition, St. Louis
  Graves for Universal Photo or U & U, most views .... 4–8.00
  White #8491, Education & Manufacturing buildings .... 8.00
  Whiting #620, Missouri Fruit Exhibit 12.00
1905, Lewis & Clark Centennial, Portland, Watson Fine Art #34, building 9.00
1907, Jamestown Exposition, Keystone #14219, life saving demonstration . 7.00
1908, West Michigan State Fair, Keystone #21507 .... 12.00
1933, Century of Progress, Chicago, Keystone #32993, Lief Ericksen Dr. .... 12–20.00

Hunting & Fishing
Bass, Ingersoll #3159, string of bass .. 7.00
Deer, Keystone #26396, hunters and kill, typical .... 5.00
Halibut, Keystone #22520, commercial fishing .... 5.00
Moose, Keystone #9452, 1899, typical big game kill .... 6.00
Trout, Kilburn, #115, 1870, a day's catch .... 5.00
Wildcat, Keystone #12264, man shoots sleeping wildcat .... 6.00

Indian
Burge, J. C., Apaches bathing .... 75–125.00
Continental Stereo Co., Pueblo eating bread .... 50–65.00
Griffith #11873, Esquimau at St. Louis Fair .... 8.00
Hayes, F. J.
  #865, Crow burial ground .... 18–25.00
  #1742, Sioux .... 20–30.00

**Indians, Keystone View Co., #T164, Chief Two-Guns-White-Calf and companions in Medicine Lodge Ceremony, Glacier National Park, Montana, history on back, $20.00.**

Ingersoll #496, lithograph of Gray Eagle, typical printed Indian .... 2.00
Jackson, Wm. H., #202, Otoe, with bow, rare .... 80–100.00
Keystone
  #23095, Chief Black Hawk .... 10.00
  #23118, Indian girl, common view . 4–5.00
  #V23181, Blackfeet .... 8.00
Montgomery Ward, squaws .... 6.00
Soule #1312, Piute squaw .... 40–60.00
U & U
  Hopi .... 9.00
  Wolpi .... 8.00
White #12279, pueblo .... 12.00

Mining
Alaska Gold Rush
  Keystone
    #9191, men with supplies getting ready to climb the "golden stairs" at Chilkoot Pass .... 9.00
    #9195, preparing to climb the "golden stairs," common .... 9.00
    #21100, panning for gold .... 12.00
  U & U #10655, looking into glory hole .... 15.00
  Universal, Graves, 1902, man working a sluice, scarce card by scarce publisher .... 40.00
Easter, Anthony #474, working a gold chute .... 45.00
Gold Hill, Houseworth #743, city overview .... 65–95.00
Hydraulic, Houseworth #799, typical water spraying .... 60–80.00
Virginia City
  Houseworth #713, street view .... 65–95.00
  Watkins
    Opera House .... 75–95.00
    Panorama, new series .... 85–125.00

Miscellaneous
Auto
  Keystone #22143, employees leaving Ford .... 8.00
  U & U, early auto in Los Angeles, 1903 .... 17–20.00

Beach scenes, H.C. White, #476, bathers, Atlantic City .......... **5.00**
Bicycles
Kilburn #11924, women and bike .. **6.00**
Thorne, big two wheeler, early 1870s .......... **35–50.00**
Circus
U & U, Chicago .......... **20.00**
Windsor & Whipple, Olean, NY, people with elephant .......... **35–40.00**
Crystal Palace, yellow mount, outside, general view .......... **25.00**
Firefighting
Early 1870s, unknown maker, close view of pumpers .......... **40.00**
Keystone #11684, action view of pumpers .......... **25.00**
Glass Stereos
Foreign Scenes, e.g., Fifth, etc. ... **60–80.00**
United States Scenes, e.g., Niagara Falls .......... **50–100.00**
Groups, various, Rogers statuaries such as "Taking the Oath," or "Courtship in Sleepy Hollow" .......... **7-9.00**
Gypsies, unknown maker, in front of tent .......... **15–20.00**
Hawaii, Keystone
#10156, hula girls .......... **9.00**
#10162, Waikiki Beach .......... **9.50**
Lighthouses
Keystone #29207, common view .. **4.00**
Williams, Minot Ledge Light ...... **15–17.00**
New York City, Anthony #3938, typical street view .......... **15–25.00**
Opium Dens
X82, 1900 .......... **25.00**
Unknown Maker, two tier bed, pipe for smoking opium .......... **60.00**
Prisons, Pach, view of cabinets of rifles **15.00**
Tinted Views
Foreign .......... **4–6.00**
United States .......... **5–10.00**
Tunnel, ward #808 Hoosac Tunnel, just completed .......... **15.00**
Toy train, Keystone P-21329, boy playing with Lionel trains .......... **25.00**

National Park
Death Valley, Keystone #32666, pool . **9.00**
Garden of the Gods, Rodeo McKenney, Pike's Peak .......... **5.00**
Grand Teton, Wm. H. Jackson, #503, average for this prized photographer **20.00**
Yellowstone
Jackson, Wm. H., #422, average for this prized photographer .......... **15.00**
Universal, nice, average peak view . **4.00**
Yosemite
Keystone #4001, Nevada Falls ..... **4.00**
Kilburn #9284, Bridal Veil Falls .... **4.00**
Reilly, tourists at Yosemite Falls .... **8.00**
U & U, Glacier Point .......... **5.00**

Niagara Falls
Anthony #3731, falls .......... **4.00**
Barker, ice bridge .......... **2.00**
U & U
Tourists, common .......... **2.00**
Whirlpool rapids .......... **1.00**
White #7, tourists, 1903 .......... **5.00**

Occupational
Blacksmith, Keystone #18206, many tools in picture .......... **5.00**
Cowboys, Keystone
#12465, Kansas .......... **7.00**
#13641, Yellowstone, Montana .... **7.50**
Farming, Kilburn #1796, hay, 1870s .. **7.00**
Fireman
G. K. Proctor, Mid-distance hookladder, horse drawn .......... **35.00**
1870s, good view of steam pumper . **45.00**
Milkman, Keystone #P-26392, horsedrawn wagon .......... **10.00**
Mill, U & U, linen factory, typical industrial view .......... **2–3.00**
Store, Keystone #18209, grocery store int. .......... **15.00**

Oil
Pennsylvania
Detlor & Waddell, #76, burning tanks **15.00**
Robbins #32, Triumph Hill ........ **13.00**
Keystone #20352T, shooting a well **5.00**
Robbins, #88, gas well .......... **8.00**
Wilt Brothers, Allegheny area ...... **8.00**
Texas, Keystone #34864, tanks near Kilgore, common .......... **6.00**

Person, Famous
Barton, Clara, Keystone #28002, founder of American Red Cross ....... **50–60.00**
Buffalo Bill, American Scenery #1399, on horseback in New York City, most common view .......... **50.00**
Buntline, Ned, J. Gurney, portrait .... **150.00**
Burbank, Luther, Keystone #16746, with a cactus .......... **8.00**
Bryan, W. J., Keystone #15539, on way to hotel in NYC .......... **30.00**
Coolidge, President, Keystone
#26303, President and Cabinet, scarce view .......... **50.00**
#26303 .......... **30.00**
#28004, at desk, typical .......... **12.00**
Custar, General
Lovejoy & Foster, with bear he killed .......... **300–450.00**
Taylor #2438, with his dog in camp .......... **500–600.00**
Czar of Russia, U & U, with President of France .......... **10.00**
Edison, Thomas
Keystone, #V28007, in lab ........ **100.00**
U & U, in lab .......... **100–150.00**

Edison, Ford and Firestone, Keystone
#18551 ...................... **75–125.00**
#45612 ...................... **75-125.00**
Eisenhower, President, Keystone, at table with microphones, about 1954, rare ...................... **150–250.00**
Faraqutt, Admiral, Anthony, from Prominent Portrait Series ............... **40.00**
Ford, Henry, Keystone #28023 ...... **60.00**
Gandhi, Mahatma, Keystone #33852, portrait ...................... **25–35.00**
Gehrig, Lou, Keystone #32597, baseball player ................... **150–200.00**
Grant, President, Bierstadt Bros., on Mount Washington ............... **75.00**
Hayes, B., president, party at Hastings ...................... **75–100.00**
Harding, W., president, addressing boy scouts ...................... **15–20.00**
Hoover, President, Keystone #28012, close portrait .................... **35.00**
Kettering, C. F., Keystone, inventor of auto self starter .................. **60.00**
Kingman, Seth, no maker, famous California Trapper ................. **95–120.00**
Lincoln, Abraham, Anthony
Funeral, #4596 ................. **50–65.00**
President, #2969, scarce, highly prized view ............... **800–1,200.00**
Marconi, Keystone #V11969, radio inventor ...................... **45.00**
McKinley, President, Keystone, Kilburn, U & U, most views ............... **5–15.00**
Morse, Samuel, J. Gurney ........ **175–225.00**
Queen Victoria, U & U 1897, having breakfast with Princesses .......... **35.00**
Rockefeller, J.D., Keystone #V11961, world's richest man ............... **25.00**
Rogers, Will, Keystone #32796, at 1932 Chicago Democratic Convention ...................... **75.00**
Roosevelt, Franklin D., president, Keystone #33535, at his desk ......... **75.00**
Roosevelt, Theodore, president
Keystone, Kilburn, U & U, most views [at Panama Canal, Glacier Pt., Yosemite, etc.] ................. **8–30.00**
U & U, on horseback, typical view ...................... **12–20.00**
Ruth, Babe, Keystone #32590, baseball player ...................... **200–250.00**
Sarazen, Gene, Keystone #32436, golfer ...................... **35.00**
Schmeling, Max, Keystone #28028, boxer ...................... **75.00**
Shaw, Dr. Anna, Keystone #V26151, suffrage leader ................... **25.00**
Shaw, George Bernard, Keystone #34505, on a ship .............. **50–60.00**
Strauss, Johann, Gurney, typical of a Gurney well-known person such as Bret Harte, Horace Greeley, etc .... **90.00**
Taft, President, U & U #10062, at desk **20.00**
Thomas, Lowell, Keystone #32812, world travel expert and newsman .. **50.00**
Twain, Mark
Evans & Soule ................... **350.00**
U & U #8010 or White #13055, in bed writing .................... **250.00**
Washington, Booker T., Keystone #V11960, with Andrew Carnegie . **50–70.00**
Wirewalkers, Barker
Belleni on wire .................. **10.00**
Blondin on rope ................. **15.00**
Young, Brigham, C. W. Carter, bust portrait ...................... **20.00**

Photographer, Famous
Brady, Anthony
1863, Tom Thumb Wedding, famous ...................... **100–125.00**
#428, Captain Custer with Confederate prisoner ............... **900.00**
#3376, Jeff Davis Mansion ........ **50.00**
Houseworth, San Francisco, e.g.,
#150, show photo studio ...... **100–150.00**
#429, Golden Gate ............. **35–45.00**
Langenheim, 1856, Trenton Falls, typical view, but scarce, on glass ...... **135.00**
Muybridge
#318, The Golden Gate .......... **80.00**
#880, Geyer Springs ............ **35–45.00**
#1623, Indian scouts ............. **250.00**
O'Sullivan, T.H., Anthony #826, Men's Quarters ...................... **60.00**
Pond, C. L., #786, Mirror Lake ...... **30.00**
Watkins, C. E.
Panoramic, #1338, from Telegraph Hill ...................... **45–55.00**
San Francisco street scene, e.g., #767, panorama from Russian Hill **55.00**
Trains, any .................. **75–150.00**
Virginia City, NV, Panorama, new series ...................... **90.00**
Yosemite series, #1066, Yosemite Falls ...................... **25–30.00**

Photographica
Camera, Houseworth #1107, wet plate camera in Yosemite ............... **75.00**
Comic, Keystone #423, many viewers and cards in this comic "mouse" routine ...................... **15.00**
Gallery, American scenery, street with gallery sign visible ................ **50.00**
Photo Wagon, Weitfle's Photograph Van, close view with sign on wagon **75–150.00**
Photography with stereo camera above street, Keystone #8283, classic collectible ...................... **65.00**
Viewing, Keystone #11917, looking through viewer .................. **10.00**

Railroad
American stereo, view in Penn Station **15.00**

Centennial, 1876 Monorail, World's Fair, scarce ...................... **65.00**
Keystone
#2367, loop at Georgetown, common ......................... **5.00**
#7090, interior of Baldwin Works .. **8.00**
#37509, The Chief, 1930s ........ **75.00**
Kilburn
#135, pushing car up Jacob's Ladder .......................... **7.00**
#432, large side view of locomotive **35.00**
#779, train with engineer posed, 1870 ......................... **55.00**
#2941, silver ore train ........... **5.00**
U & U
#52, train going through Pillars of Hercules, common ............ **7.00**
#6218, Royal Gorge, common .... **5.00**
Universal Photo Art #2876, Columbian Express ......................... **20.00**
Unknown Maker, dramatic close-up of a 1870 locomotive ............... **75.00**

Religious
Bates, open *Bible* , St. Luke ......... **3.00**
Keystone, Billy Sunday, evangelist .... **20.00**
Keystone, Kilburn, U & U, Holy Land, Palestine, etc .................... **1–2.00**
Pope, any ........................ **4–7.50**
Life of Christ, unmarked, usually set of photos of drawings or lithographed set, per set of 10-12 ............. **7.00**
Shakers, Irving, view of people ...... **50–75.00**

Risque
1820's, unmarked, typical "peek-a-boo" .......................... **10–20.00**
Griffith #2427, two girls, arms around each other, lightly clad ........... **20.00**
Keystone, #9489, school girls retiring, in nightgowns .................. **7.00**
Nude, early, bare breast ............ **45.00**
Nude, 1920s or 1930s .............. **40.00**

Sets
Boxer Rebellion, U & U 1901, 72 cards, rare .......................... **200.00**
Bullfight, U & U, set of 15 .......... **100.00**
China, Stereo Travel, set of 100, unusual subject ................... **400.00**
Egypt, U & U set of 100, better subject, typical ......................... **310.00**
France
Stereo Travel, set of 30, typical for this publisher, popular country ....... **70.00**
U & U, set of 100 ............... **250.00**
Glacier Park, Forsyth, set of 30 ...**125–150.00**
India, U & U, set of 100 ............ **250.00**
Italy, U & U, set of 100 ............ **200.00**
Jerusalem, U & U, set of 30, poor subject ........................... **30–40.00**
Switzerland, U & U, set of 100, guidebook and maps .................. **200.00**
United States, U & U, set of 100, good U. S. tour ...................... **350.00**
Wild Flowers, Keystone, 100, hand tinted .......................... **400.00**
World Tour, Keystone
Set of 200, trip from U.S. around world and back ................ **350.00**
Set of 400 .....................**500–700.00**
Set of 600, trip from U.S. around world and back, oak cabinet **900–1,000.00**
Yellowstone, U & U, set of 30 .....**90–100.00**
Yosemite, U & U, set of 30 .......**100–125.00**

Ship
Battleships
Griffith #2535, 1902, USS *Brooklyn* **8.00**
Universal Photo Art, USS *Raleigh*, common ..................... **7-9.00**
Cruiser, White #7422, 1901, USS *New York* ........................... **10.00**
Deck View, American Stereo, 1899, USS *Iowa* ...................... **8.00**
Foreign, Keystone #16090, HMS *Albemarie* .......................... **6.00**

**Ship, James M. Davis, #12614, *The Iowa* U.S.N., 1897, $6.00.**

Riverboat, Anthony #7567, sternwheeler at Cincinnati .................. **25.00**
Sailboat, Anthony #22 or #5179, early view ..........................**15–20.00**
Steamers
*Pettit*
Wilson, 1880 ................**15–20.00**
*Yukon*
Keystone #24704, sternwheeler being loaded in Alaska ......................**33–35.00**
Steamships
Anthony #8691, *Bristol* , good average early view ................ **15.00**
London Stereo, *Great Eastern* , early view ......................... **75.00**
Submarine, Keystone #16667, at San Diego ........................ **8.00**

Survey
Amundsen, Keystone #13327, at Antoretie Glacier, 1911 .............. **7.00**

Gerlache, Keystone #13328, hunting seals at South Pole . . . . . . . . . . . . . . . **6.00**
Hayden, Jackson #796, people view, typical . . . . . . . . . . . . . . . . . . . . . . . .**22–25.00**
Lloyd, Grand Canyon, U & U, at work on mountain, 1903 . . . . . . . . . . . . . . . **25.00**
Perry, Greenland, Keystone #13325, ships . . . . . . . . . . . . . . . . . . . . . . . . . . **6.00**
Powell, #13, the wall, typical . . . . . . **10–20.00**
Wheeler, William Bell
#14, Canon de Chelle, wall, 1873 . **40.00**
#15, Canon de Chelle, wall, 1872 . **25.00**

Tissue, French
Ballon, close view . . . . . . . . . . . . . . . . .**60–70.00**
Diablo, 1870s, devils, skeletons, etc., good shape with lots of "evil" . . . . . **30.00**
Interior scene, 1870s, minor damage, viewable . . . . . . . . . . . . . . . . . . . . . . **7.50**
Interior scene, 1870s, nice stereo, pin-pricked, no tears . . . . . . . . . . . . . . . . **20.00**
Wedding, Young #7, typical US, wedding vows . . . . . . . . . . . . . . . . . . . . . . **10.00**

War
Boer, U & U, artillery firing, typical view . . . . . . . . . . . . . . . . . . . . . . . . . **7.00**
Boxer Rebellion, U & U, 1901, typical view . . . . . . . . . . . . . . . . . . . . . . **4–7.00**
Civil War
Anthony
#3031, Dunlop Home . . . . . . . . **20.00**
#3365, Brady, Libby Prison, yellow mount . . . . . . . . . . . . . . . **25.00**
#3406, chair in which Lincoln was shot . . . . . . . . . . . . . . . . . **60.00**
Gardner #237, home of Rebel sharpshooter . . . . . . . . . . . . . . . .**45–50.00**
Taylor & Huntington
#458, Conferdate fortifications . **25.00**
#2557, pontoon boats . . . . . . . . **25.00**
#6705, powder magazine . . . . . **35.00**
Russo-Japanese, U & U #4380, general view of Port Arthur, typical view . . . . . . . . . . . . . . . . . . . . . . . . . **5.00**
Spanish American, U & U, typical view . . . . . . . . . . . . . . . . . . . . . . . . . .**5–12.00**
World War I
Set of 100 . . . . . . . . . . . . . . . . . . . . . **175.00**
Set of 200 . . . . . . . . . . . . . . . . . . . . . **300.00**
Set of 300 . . . . . . . . . . . . . . . . . . . . . **400.00**

Whaling
Freeman, beached whales . . . . . . . . . . . **50.00**
Keystone
#14768T, floating whale station, common . . . . . . . . . . . . . . . . . . . . . **10.00**
#V27198T, whalers cruising, common . . . . . . . . . . . . . . . . . . . . . . . . . **8.00**
Nickerson, beached whales, rare . . . . . **70.00**
Unknown maker, beached whale . . . .**18–30.00**

# STEREO VIEWERS

**Collecting Hints:** Condition is the key in determining price. Undamaged wooden hood models are scarce and demand a premium price if made of bird's–eye maple. All original parts increases the value. Lots of engraving adds 20% to 30%.

Longer lenses are better than small. Lenses held in place by metal are better than shimmed in by wood.

Because "aluminum" was the same price as silver in the late 19th century, aluminum viewers often are the more collectible.

**History:** There are many different types of stereo viewers. The familiar table viewer with an aluminum or wooden hood was the joint invention in 1860 of Oliver Wendell Holmes and Joseph Bates, a Boston photographer. This type of viewer also was made in a much scarcer pedestal model.

In hand viewers, three companies—Keystone, Griffith & Griffith, and Underwood & Underwood—produced viewers between 1899 and 1905 in the hundreds of thousands.

In the mid–1850s a combination stereo viewer and picture magnifier was developed in France and eventually made in England and the United States. The instrument was called a Graphascope. It usually consisted of three pieces and folded for storage. When set up, it had two round lenses for stereo viewing, a large round magnifying lens to view cabinet photographs and a slide, often with opaque glass, for viewing stereo glass slides. The height was adjustable.

A rotary or cabinet viewer was made from the late 1850s to about 1870. Becker is the best known maker. The standing floor models hold several hundred slides, the table models hold 50 to 100.

From the late 1860s to 1880s there were hundreds of different viewer designs. Models had folding wires, collapsible cases (Cortascope), pivoting lens to view postcards (Sears' Graphascope) and telescoping card holders. The cases also became ornate with silver, nickel and pearl trimmed in velvets and rosewood.

**Reference:** John Waldsmith, *Stereo Views, An Illustrated History and Price Guide,* Wallace–Homestead, 1991.

**Advisor:** John S. Waldsmith.

Binocular Style, Telebinocular, black crinkle metal finish, excellent optics, came with "book" box . . . . . . . . . . . **45.00**
Counter Top Style, Sculptoscope, Whiting, penny operated . . . . . . . . . . . . . **600.00**
Hand, wood
Folding handle, focusing slide, wire prong holder folds inward, c1890 **90.00**
Keystone, wide dark brown metal hood, metal clip handle . . . . . . . . . **75.00**

**Viewer, Keystone Monarch, wood frame, aluminum hood, $75.00.**

Rectangular hood, tongue and groove edges, fancy edge trim, screw–on handle . . . . . . . . . . . . . . . . . . . . . . . . **100.00**
Scissor device to focus, groove and wire device to hold card . . . . . . . . **125.00**
Pedestal, French or English, nickel plated with velvet hood . . . . . . . . . . . **450.00**
Stand, Bates–Holmes, paper or wood hood . . . . . . . . . . . . . . . . . . . . . . . . . . **175.00**
Stereographascope, Sears Best, rotating lens for photos or post cards . . . . . . . **100.00**

# STOCK AND BOND CERTIFICATES

**Collecting Hints:** Some of the factors that affect price are (1) date [with pre–1900 more popular and pre–1850 most desirable], (2) autographs of important persons [Vanderbilt, Rockefeller, J. P. Morgan, Wells and Fargo, etc.], (3) number issued [most bonds have number issued in text], and (4) attractiveness of the vignette.

Stocks and bonds are collected for a variety of reasons, among which are the graphic illustrations and the history of romantic times in America, including gold and silver mining, railroad history, and early automobile pioneers.

**History:** The use of stock to raise capital and spread the risk in a business venture dates back to England. Several American colonies were founded as joint venture stock companies. The New York Stock Exchange on Wall Street in New York City traces its roots to the late eighteenth century.

Stock certificates with attractive vignettes date to the beginning of the nineteenth century. As engraving and printing techniques developed, so did the elaborateness of the stock and bond certificates. Important engraving houses emerged among which were the American Bank Note Company and Rawdon, Wright & Hatch.

**References:** Norman E. Martinus and Harry L. Rinker, *Warman's Paper,* Wallace–Homestead, 1993; Bill Yatchman, *The Stock & Bond Collectors Price Guide,* published by author, 1985.

**Periodical:** *Bank Note Reporter,* 700 East State Street, Iola, WI 54990.

**Collectors' Club:** Bond and Share Society, 26 Broadway, New York, NY 10004.

Automobile, stock
Cole Motor Car, 1909–25, man with woman feeding flame vignette
Green, not sgd and sealed . . . . . . . **25.00**
Orange, sgd, corporate seal . . . . . **35.00**
Kelly–Springfield Motor Truck Co, issued and canceled, 1910–20 seated woman, anvil, and gears vignette, green or purple, American Bank Note Company . . . . . . . . . . . **35.00**
Willys Corporation, issued, 1921, brown . . . . . . . . . . . . . . . . . . . . . . . . **15.00**
Business, stock
American Express Co, issued and canceled, 1860s, bulldog vignette, sgd "Henry Wells" and "William Fargo" . . . . . . . . . . . . . . . . . . . . . . . **750.00**
Broadway Joe's, issued and canceled, green or blue border, sports figure's restaurant . . . . . . . . . . . . . . . . . . . . . **10.00**
General Foods, issued and canceled, green, brown, or orange, engraved, vignette scene on right . . . . . . . . . . **2.50**
International Business Machines Corp, issued, brown . . . . . . . . . . . . **5.00**
International Immigration & Colonization Assn, Hawaii, 1911, issued, not canceled, map vignette . . . . . . **100.00**
Uncas National Bank of Norwich, 1900, green, gray and white, Indian, blacksmith, and sailing ship vignette . . . . . . . . . . . . . . . . . . . . . . **15.00**
Wells Fargo Bank & Union Trust, 1940s, issued and canceled, green pony express rider vignette . . . . . . **25.00**
Woolworth, F W Co, eagle over two hemispheres vignette, brown . . . . . **4.00**
Canal, bond, Pennsylvania Canal Company, issued and canceled, 1870, canal and surrounding area vignette, two revenue stamps . . . . . . . . . . . . . **125.00**
Industrial, stock
Colorado Milling & Elevator Co, issued and canceled, gold border, company buildings vignette, 1890s **25.00**
Edison Portland Cement Co, issued and canceled, engraved, rust or green, Thomas Edison vignette, 1900s . . . . . . . . . . . . . . . . . . . . . . . . **25.00**
Gray Manufacturing Co, issued and canceled, orange, dial pay telephone vignette . . . . . . . . . . . . . . . . . **15.00**
Jantzen Knitting Mills, 1930s, issued

and canceled, engraved, swimmer vignette, orange or green . . . . . . . . **20.00**

Sentinel Radio Corp, issued and canceled, green or brown, goddess and two radio towers vignette . . . . . . . . **5.00**

Waikea Mill Co, unissued, 1889, black and white sugar mill . . . . . . **45.00**

Mining

Bond, Sovereign Gold Mining, issued and canceled, $5,000, Canadian, 1903, peach borders, coupon . . . . **10.00**

Stock

Industry Gold & Silver Mining, 1870s, unissued, fancy design, mining vignette . . . . . . . . . . . . . . **20.00**

Isabella Gold Mining Co, Colorado, 1890s, issued and canceled, engraved, eagle vignette **8.00**

Sheba Gold & Silver Mining, Humboldt County, Nevada, issued, not canceled, three mining vignettes, gold seal . . . . . . . . . . . . . **20.00**

Sun–Hope Mining Co, Colorado, unissued, three mining vignettes **2.50**

Syndicate Mines, Inc, Nevada, unissued, brown, mining vignette, "V" cut cancel . . . . . . . . . . . . . . **3.50**

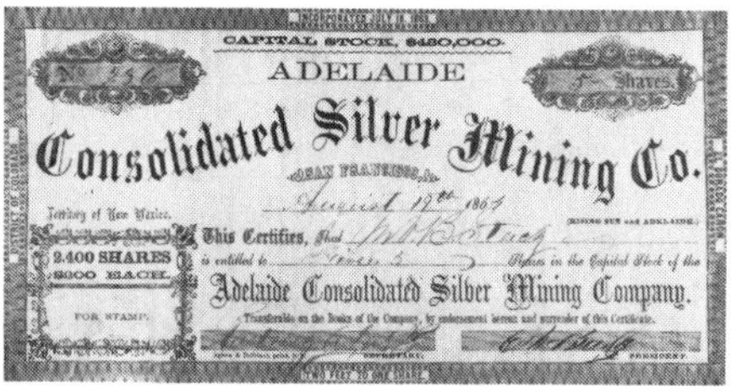

**Stock Certificate, Adelaide Consolidated Silver Mining Company, New Mexico, 1864, 2,400 shares, $330.00.**

Railroad

Bond

Cairo & Norfolk RR Co, Kentucky, 1908, issued, not canceled, orange, speeding train vignette, coupons . . . . . . . . . . . . . . . . . . . . **45.00**

New York, New Haven & Hartford, 1920, $10,000, issued and canceled, engraved, electric train vignette . . . . . . . . . . . . . . . . . . . . . **48.00**

Sacramento & Woodland RR, California, 1911, issued, not canceled, rust–brown, logo around capitol building vignette, coupons . . . . . . . . . . . . . . . . . . . . . . . **165.00**

Union Pacific RR, 1946, $1,000, issued and canceled, two engraved angles and company logo **15.00**

Stock

Cambridge Railroad Co, MA, 1880s, unissued, black and white . . . . . . . . . . . . . . . . . . . . . . **8.00**

Gulf, Mobile & Ohio, issued and canceled, engraved, blue or brown, two women and diesel train vignette . . . . . . . . . . . . . . . **3.50**

Illinois Central, issued and canceled, engraved, orange or brown, diesel train vignette . . . . **3.50**

Nashville & Decatur, 1880s, issued and canceled, green border, train vignette . . . . . . . . . . . . . . . . . . . . **25.00**

Raleigh & Gaston, 1870s, issued and canceled, two vignettes . . . **65.00**

Railways (Trolley)

Bond

Chicago & Wisconsin Valley Street Railways Co, 1912, $1,000, issued and canceled, first mortgage gold, black and white . . . . **25.00**

New Paltz & Highland Electric RR, 1893, $500, issued and canceled, trolley car vignettes, gold seal, two pages of coupons . . . . **95.00**

Southern Indiana, 1908, $1,000, issued and canceled, green . . . . **28.00**

Stock

California Street Cable RR Co, San Francisco, CA, 1884, unissued, cable car vignette . . . . . . . . . . . **35.00**

Omaha & Council Bluffs Street Railway, 1906, issued and canceled, blue, green, or pink . . . . . . . . . **20.00**

Rochelle & Southern, Illinois, 1900, unissued, black and white **12.00**

Rock Island & Eastern, Illinois, 1900, black and white, curved company name . . . . . . . . . . . . . **15.00**

Real Estate, stock, The Real Estate Association, Petaluma, CA, 1890s, issued, black and white . . . . . . . . . . . **25.00**

Utility

Bond

Columbus & Southern Ohio Electric Co, issued and canceled, blue, engraved . . . . . . . . . . . . . . . . . . . . **7.50**

Consolidated Edison Co, New York, $1,000, issued and canceled, engraved, blue or purple **8.00**

Long Island Lighting Co, issued and canceled, orange, engraved, woman, child, generator, and light vignette . . . . . . . . . . . . . . . . **7.50**

Stock

Communications Satellite Corp, 1960s, issued and canceled, green or blue, space vignette . . **4.00**

International Telephone & Telegraph, 1930s, blue, engraved, goddess and globe vignette . . . . **8.00**

Maryland Telecommunications, issued and canceled, green, drawn 1957 TV and TV camera vignette **8.00**
Philippine Long Distance Telephone Co, 1950s, issued and canceled, blue, engraved, woman on two globes vignette . **5.00**

# STUFFED TOYS

**Collecting Hints:** The collector tends to focus on one type of animal and collects material spanning a long time period. The company with the strongest collector following is Steiff.

Collectors stress very good to mint condition. Often stuffed toys had ribbons or clothing. All accessories must be intact to command full value.

**History:** The stuffed toy may have originated in Germany. Margarete Steiff GmbH of Germany began making stuffed toys for export beginning in 1880. By 1903 the teddy bear had joined Steiff's line and quickly worked its way to America. The first American teddy bears were made by the Ideal Toy Corporation. Not much is known about earlier manufacturers since companies were short lived and many toys have lost their labels.

The stuffed toy has enjoyed a favorite position in the American market. Some have music boxes inserted to enhance their appeal. Carnivals used stuffed toys as prizes. Since the 1960s America has been subjected to a wealth of stuffed toys imported from Japan, Taiwan, and China. These animals often are poorly made and are not popular among serious collectors.

**References:** Dottie Ayers and Donna Harrison, *Advertising Art of Steiff: Teddy Bears and Playthings,* Hobby House Press, 1990; Peggy and Alan Bialosky, *The Teddy Bear Catalog,* Workman Publishing, Revised Edition, 1984; Kim Brewer and Carol–Lynn Rössel Waugh, *The Official Price Guide To Antique & Modern Teddy Bears,* House of Collectibles, 1990; Pam Hebbs, *Collecting Teddy Bears,* Pincushion Press, 1992; Dee Hockenberry, *Collectible German Animals Value Guide: 1948–1968,* Hobby House Press, 1988; Margaret Fox Mandel, *Teddy Bears And Steiff Animals, First Series* 1984, 1991 value update; *Second Series* 1987, 1992 value update; and *Third Series* 1990, Collector Books; Terry and Doris Michaud, *Contemporary Teddy Bear Price Guide: Artists To Manufacturers,* Hobby House Press, 1992; Linda Mullins, *Teddy Bear And Friends Price Guide, Fourth Edition,* Hobby House Press, 1993; Linda Mullins, *Teddy Bears Past and Present, Volume II,* Hobby House Press, 1992; Christel and Rolf Pistorius, *Steiff: Sensational Teddy Bears, Animals, and Dolls,* Hobby House Press, 1991; Jean Wilson, *Steiff Toys Revised,* Wallace–Homestead, 1989.

**Periodical:** *Teddy Bear and Friends,* Hobby House Press, Inc., 900 Frederick St., Cumberland, MD 21502.

**Collectors' Clubs:** Good Bears Of The World, P. O. Box 13097, Toledo, OH 43613; Steiff Collectors Club, P. O. Box 798, Holland, OH 43528.

Alligator, 9½" l, vinyl, green and brown, glass eyes, c1950 . . . . . . . . . . . . . . . . **35.00**
Beaver, mohair, brown, Steiff . . . . . . . . **45.00**
Boa Constrictor, plush, multicolored, felt eyes and tongue, c1958 . . . . . . . **15.00**
Camel, 8" h, plush, tan, single hump, glass eyes, c1950 . . . . . . . . . . . . . . . . **70.00**
Cat
- 4" h, Tabby, orig bell, Steiff . . . . . . . . **65.00**
- 5¼" h, mohair, green plastic eyes, movable head and legs, Steiff, c1950 . . . . . . . . . . . . . . . . . . . . . . . **50.00**
- 10" h, long hair, black and white, orig brush and gold tag . . . . . . . . . . . . . **35.00**
- 11" h, Diva, long white fur, sitting, orig Steiff tag and button . . . . . . . . **115.00**

Character
- Curious George, 36" h, plush, knit yellow sweater, red cap, c1975 . . **50.00**
- Huckleberry Hound, 16" h . . . . . . . . **15.00**
- Jerry, orig tag . . . . . . . . . . . . . . . . . . . . **12.00**
- Mother Goose, 22" h, muslin, white, yellow, felt feet, white cotton bonnet, blue floral apron, c1962 . . . . **35.00**
- Sylvester Cat . . . . . . . . . . . . . . . . . . . . . **12.00**
- Teddy Ruxpin, worm friend, three tapes, extra outfit, mint . . . . . . . . . **80.00**
- Tony The Esso Tiger, orange and black, felt trim . . . . . . . . . . . . . . . . . **45.00**
- Winnie The Pooh . . . . . . . . . . . . . . . . **10.00**
- Yogi Bear . . . . . . . . . . . . . . . . . . . . . . . **7.00**

Chimp, unicycle, Steiff, MIB . . . . . . . . . **75.00**
Cow, 5½" l, felt, brown and white, glass eyes, wooden wheels . . . . . . . . . . . . . **65.00**
Deer, 15" h, Bambi, plush, Gund, c1953 . . . . . . . . . . . . . . . . . . . . . . . . . **60.00**
Dog
- Beagle, 9" h, plush, glass eyes . . . . . **25.00**
- Cocker, 8" h, standing, orig box . . . . **55.00**
- Poodle, 12" h, curly, gray, plaid coat, hat, and boots, c1925 . . . . . . . . . . **50.00**
- Schnauzer, 4" h, orig box . . . . . . . . . **40.00**
- Terrier, 11" h, white plush, black spots, swivel head, white muzzle, yellow glass eyes, embroidered features, red ribbon, c1925 . . . . . . . . **50.00**
- Victorian, canvas, saw dust filled, shoe button eyes . . . . . . . . . . . . . . . **40.00**

Duck, 4" h, calico, blue, yellow, and pink, embroidered wing and eye, hand made, c1950 . . . . . . . . . . . . . . . **5.00**

Elephant, 4″ h
Steiff, 1955 ... **100.00**
Unknown maker, orig plain box ... **50.00**
Frog, 9″ h, green velvet back, white satin underside, c1960 ... **12.00**
Giraffe, 42″ h, plush, yellow, brown spots, brown button eyes, brown yard tail, c1957 ... **20.00**
Goat, 6½″ h, standing, white, brown felt horns, Steiff ... **50.00**
Hen, 7″ h, gold and black spotted feathers, yellow plush head, felt tail, black button eyes, Steiff, c1949 ... **75.00**
Hippo, 13″ l, Mockie, mohair, Steiff, orig tags, 1950s ... **125.00**
Horse
15″ h, amber hopsacking, straw stuffing, reinforced stitching, pale yellow underbelly, amber glass eyes, stitched smiling mouth, applied ears, black fur mane, horsehair tail, velvet and leather saddle and harness, c1890 ... **95.00**
25″ h, burlap, brown, platform rocker, German ... **325.00**
Kangaroo, Knickerbocker, Roo, baby in pouch ... **40.00**
Lamb, 9″ h, white, fluffy, glass eyes, embroidered features, bell, flowers, and ribbon at neck, paper label ... **90.00**
Leopard, 16″ l, mohair, Steiff ear button and throat tag ... **200.00**

**Lion, Steiff, growler in back, ear button, 62″ l, 36″ h, $525.00. Photograph courtesy of James D. Julia, Inc.**

Lion
Reclining, straw stuffed body, glass eyes ... **285.00**
Vinyl face, My Toy Co ... **25.00**
Monkey, 9″ h, Hermann, brown mohair, fully jointed, Steiff ... **40.00**
Owl, 10″ h, Steiff ... **70.00**
Panda Bear, 10″ h, straw head, glass eyes, Dralon, orig box ... **225.00**
Parrot, 9″ h, Lora, glass eyes, Steiff ... **75.00**
Pig, 6″ h, plush, pink, pink felt cork screw tail, black and white felt eyes **25.00**
Polar Bear, Steiff, jointed legs ... **550.00**
Rabbit
12″ h, Steiff, Manni ... **175.00**
15″ h, Lenci, felt, eating carrot ... **30.00**
Raccoon, 6″ h, Raccy, plush, glass eyes, Steiff ... **50.00**
Seal, circus type, ball, Steiff, MIB ... **75.00**
Teddy Bear
5″ h, plush, standing, swivel head, orig "Character" label ... **45.00**
6″ h, plush, jointed, fully dressed, orig clothes, Berg label ... **65.00**
12″ h, brown, fully tagged, Steiff, c1972 ... **175.00**
14″ h, mohair, fully jointed, straw filled, shoe button eyes, hump, American, c1915–20 ... **325.00**
15″ h, yellow mohair, felt pads, glass eyes, growls, wear to pads, Clemmons ... **350.00**
16″ h, Molly Koala Bear, gray and tan, Steiff ... **135.00**
17″ h, plush, brown, tan paws, molded muzzle, Ideal Toy tag ... **50.00**
18″ h
Cotton, yellow, glass eyes, red felt laughing mouth, German ... **155.00**
Mohair, brown, glass eyes, cloth pads, growls ... **175.00**
19″ h, mohair, cloth pads, glass eyes, growls, German
Blue ... **215.00**
Yellow ... **200.00**
22″ h, cotton, yellow, glass eyes, cloth pads ... **165.00**
Tiger, 6″ l, plush, Steiff ... **65.00**
Turtle, 5½″ l, plush, felt trim, Steiff ... **45.00**
Zebra, 7″ h, black and white, button in ear, Steiff ... **75.00**

# SUPER HEROES

**Collecting Hints:** Concentrate on a single super hero. Because Superman, Batman, and Wonder Woman are the most popular, new collectors are advised to focus on other characters or one of the modern super heroes. Nostalgia is a principal motivation for many collectors; hence, they pay prices based on sentiment rather than true market value for some items.

Comics are a fine collectible but require careful handling and storage. An attractive display requires a three dimensional object. Novice collectors are advised to concentrate on these first before acquiring too many of the flat paper material.

**History:** The Super Hero and comic books go hand in hand. Superman made his debut in 1939 in the first issue of *Action Comics*, six years after Jerry Siegel and Joe Shuster conceived the idea of a man who flew. A newspaper strip, radio show, and movies followed. The Superman era produced a wealth of super heroes, among them Batman, Captain Marvel, Captain Midnight, The Green Hornet, The Green Lantern, The Shadow, and Wonder Woman.

These early heroes had extraordinary strength and/or cunning and lived normal lives as private citizens. A wealth of merchandising products surround these early super heroes. Their careers were enchanced further when television chose them as heroes for Saturday morning viewing as well as in prime time.

The Fantastic Four—Mr. Fantastic, The Human Torch, The Invisible Girl, and The Thing—introduced a new type of super hero, the mutant. Among the most famous of this later period are Captain America, Spiderman and The Hulk. Although these characters appear in comic form, the number of secondary items generated is small. Television has helped to promote a few of the characters, but the list of mutant super heroes is close to a hundred.

**References:** Steven H. Kimball, *Greenberg's Guide To Super Hero Toys, Volume I,* Greenberg Publishing Co., 1988; Jeff Rovin, *The Encyclopedia of Super Heroes,* Facts on File Publications, 1985.

**See:** Comic Books, Radio Characters, and Personalities.

Aquaman
- Character Glass, 1973 ............ **15.00**
- Costume, Ben Cooper, 1967 ....... **200.00**
- Jigsaw Puzzle, action scene, Whitman, 1967 .................... **40.00**
- Tattoo, 1967, mint in wrapper ..... **50.00**

Batman and Robin
- Banner, The Joker vs Batman, linen, wood rod and hanging cord, 1966 National Periodical Publications Inc copyright, 16½ x 29" ........ **50.00**

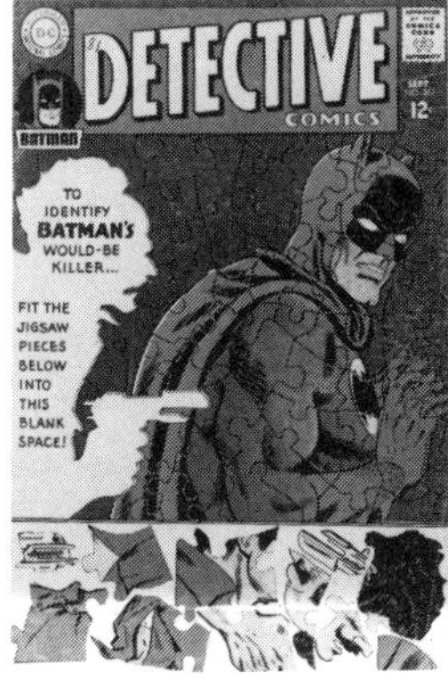


**Batman, comic book, Detective Comics, No. 367, September, $8.00.**

- Bat Man Car, friction, litho tin car, vinyl Batman with movable arms, radar screen with Robin fighting crooks on hood, Yanoman, Japan, 6" l, orig box ................. **1,450.00**
- Batman Shooting Range, Marx, 1966 National Periodical Publications Inc copyright .................. **75.00**
- Batmobile
  - Tin, battery operated, Batman and Robin passengers, bump–and–go action, flashing lights, jet noise, Taiwan, 10" l, orig box ....... **185.00**
  - Vinyl, inflatable, two–tone blue, clear windshield, tail fins, 3–D Batman with cape driver, 12½" l, NPPI, Japan, dated 1966 ...... **385.00**
- Costume, Batman, vinyl cape, mask, cuffs, and badge, black outfit with blue and yellow accents, orig display bag, 1966 National Periodical Publications copyright .......... **150.00**
- Gun, Batman Bat–Ray, 8" l, plastic, battery operated, orig box, 1977 DC Comics Inc copyright ........ **50.00**
- Ice Cream Carton, 5 x 7 x 3½", waxed cardboard, "Batman Slam Bang Vanilla Marshmallow Ice Cream," unused, 1966 National Periodical Publications copyright .......... **20.00**
- Lamp, 11" h, figural, vinyl, kneeling on one knee, blue fabric cape, c1966 ........................ **100.00**
- Model Kit, Batmobile, Aurora, #486–98, 1966, MIB ................ **300.00**
- Sneakers, white canvas, "Batman" label on heels, Randy, NPPI, c1966, orig box ..................... **125.00**
- Wristwatch, 7½" l, Batman illus on dial with diecut "Zap" and "Pow," red plastic bands, orig card, Marx, 1975 National Periodical Publications Inc copyright ............ **25.00**

Captain America
- Badge, Sentinel of Liberty, copper, 1941–43 ..................... **300.00**
- Board Game, Captain America Game, Milton bradley, 1966 ..... **60.00**
- Coloring Book, Whitman, 1966, 80 pages, 8 x 11", unused .......... **25.00**
- Costume, Ben Cooper, 1966, orig box **70.00**
- Membership Card, Sentinels of Liberty Club, 1941–43 ............. **100.00**
- Model Kit, Aurora, 1966, unassembled ......................... **400.00**
- Paperback Book, *The Great Gold Steal,* Bantam, 1968, 180 pages .. **15.00**
- Pinback Button, 3" d, Button World, 1966, mint in orig pkg .......... **24.00**

Captain Marvel
- Balloon Whistle, red and yellow, 1941, 4½" l ................... **40.00**

Beanie, felt, 1944–47 .......... **135.00**
Comic Book, 5 x 5", issue #11, Mighty Midgets Comics series, 1942 Fawcett Publications Inc copyright .......... **25.00**
Envelope, 4 x 9½", white, Captain Marvel Club headquarters address and color illus, 1940s .......... **15.00**
Key Chain, 1944–47 .......... **72.00**
Membership Button, litho tin, 1941 . **25.00**
Necktie, 1941 .......... **60.00**
Pencil Clip, 1944–47 .......... **35.00**
Pennant, felt, blue, 1944–47 ...... **85.00**
Puzzle, No. 1, unused, orig package, 1940s .......... **27.00**
Standup Figure, Rocket Raider, cardboard, Reed, 1940, unpunched, orig envelope .......... **100.00**

**Captain Marvel, jigsaw puzzle, Captain Marvel Rides the Engine of Doom, $25.00.**

Green Hornet
Coloring Book, used .......... **10.00**
Comic Book, issue #2, May, 1967, K K Publications Inc .......... **25.00**
Fork .......... **50.00**
Gum Card Wrapper, 1966 .......... **40.00**
Life Raft, inflatable, green, yellow, and black, Hornet logo, pistols on sides, control panel, Ideal, c1967, 20 x 32" flattened size .......... **945.00**
Lobby Card, *Bullets and Ballots* serial, Universal, 1939 .......... **50.00**
Membership Card, 2 x 3", The Green Hornet G–J–M Club, 1938 Golden Jersy Milk copyright .......... **75.00**
Pez Candy Container, 1966 .......... **300.00**
Post Card, 3½ x 5½", color glossy photo, unused, 1966 Greenway Productions Inc copyright .......... **15.00**
Print Putty, 16 page illus booklet, unused, orig pkg, 1966 .......... **50.00**
Ring, plastic Hornet center, 1966 ... **5.00**
Spoon, emb Hornet figure on handle, 1966 .......... **15.00**
T–Shirt, Hornet logo, 1966 .......... **40.00**

Iron Man
Flyer, styrofoam, Topps, 1966 ..... **45.00**
View–Master Pack, 1974 .......... **10.00**

Phantom
Board Game, Transogram, 1965, MIB **240.00**
Coloring Book, Ottenheimer, 1965, unused .......... **40.00**
Model Kit, Revell, 1965, unassembled, MIB .......... **190.00**
Oil Paint Set, Hasbro, 1965, 12 x 10", orig box .......... **130.00**
Transfer Set, Hasbro, 1965, orig 10 x 12" box .......... **60.00**

Spiderman
Collector Coin, bronze, "Your Friendly Neighborhood Spider–man," 1½" d, Marvel Comics, 1973 **30.00**
Costume, Ben Cooper, 1972 ....... **18.00**
Mobile Crime Lab, van, plastic, red and yellow, orig stickers, Empire copyright 1978 Marvel Comics, 7 x 18½" .......... **50.00**
Night Light, 3" h, plastic, black, white, and red, Cable Electric Products copyright 1977 Marvel Comics Group, orig display card .......... **15.00**
Party Mask, Reed, 1978, set of four, orig pkg .......... **12.00**

Supergirl
Costume, Ben Cooper, 1973, orig box **15.00**
Doll, superhero and alter ego clothing sets, Ideal, 1967, 12" h, window box .......... **950.00**

Superman
Autograph, Alyn, 8 x 10" photo .... **15.00**
Birthday Card, 4½ x 5½", color illus, 1941 Superman Inc copyright .... **50.00**
Book, *The Adventures of Superman,* overseas Armed Forces edition, 128 pgs .......... **400.00**
Board Game
Calling Superman, Transogram, board, cardboard figures, spinner, instructions, and obstacle cards, 1954, 9 x 17" box ...... **110.00**
Superman Match II, plastic game board, 64 plastic tiles, orig box, Ideal, DC Comics Inc 1979 copyright .......... **25.00**
Bubble Gum Wrapper, 2½ x 5½", red, white, and blue illus, yellow background, NCP copyright, 1940s **200.00**
Cake Set, dented box .......... **28.00**
Crusaders Ring, silvered brass, relief Superman image, slogan on bands, premium, 1930s .......... **150.00**
Doll .......... **20.00**
Glass, 4¼" h, clear, titled "Fighting The Dragon," orange illus and title, 1964 National Periodical Publications Inc copyright .......... **35.00**

Gym Bag, vinyl, DC Comics, 1971, 12 x 9 x 6" .................... **50.00**
Hand Puppet, vinyl head, plastic body, Ideal, 1966, 12" h, orig pkg **60.00**
Krypto–Raygun, Daisy, metal, emb flying Superman, c1940, 7" l, five film strips, orig box ............. **800.00**
Krypton Rocket, rocket missile, reserve fuel tank, Krypton Generating Pump, plastic, Park Plastics, 1956, 9 x 9" display box .............. **225.00**
Magazine, *Coronet,* Vol 20, #3, July, 1946, four page article .......... **25.00**
Playsuit, child's, Herman Iskin & Co, Telford, PA, late 1940s .......... **1,000.00**
Puzzle, slide tile, Roalex, 1966, unused, orig pkg ................. **70.00**
Slipper Socks, 1973 .............. **18.00**
Wristwatch, 7½" l, red plastic bands, dial with diecut planet illus and lightning bolt, orig blister card marked "Actually Keeps Time," Marx, 1975 National Periodical Publications Inc copyright ....... **45.00**
Yo–Yo, 2¼" d, plastic, blue, clear plastic dome over illus on each side, Duncan, 1978 DC Comics Inc copyright ..................... **15.00**

The Flash
Action Figure, 8" h, World's Greatest Super Heroes series, Mego copyright Marvel Comics Group 1974 . **100.00**
Board Game, Justice League of America, Hasbro, 1967 .............. **300.00**
Character Glass, Pepsi premium, 1973 ........................ **30.00**
Jigsaw Puzzle, battle scene, Whitman, 1967 .................... **60.00**
Model Kit, Aurora, 1963 .......... **98.00**
Ring, two–way flasher, 1960s ...... **20.00**

Thor
Pez Candy Container, 1960s ....... **90.00**
Walking Figure, mechanical, plastic, Marx, 1966, 5" h, orig box ...... **70.00**

Wonder Woman
Annual, hard cov, Egmont Publishing Ltd, 1980 DC Comics Inc copyright, 8 x 10½" ................ **20.00**
Book and Record Set 33⅓ rpm, Peter Pan, 16 page comic story, 1977, 12 x 12" cardboard sleeve .......... **15.00**
Doll, Mego, 1976, 12" h .......... **80.00**
Planter, ceramic, 1978 ............ **15.00**

# SWANKYSWIGS

**Collecting Hints:** Ideally select glasses whose pattern is clear and brightly colored. Rarer patterns include Carnival, Checkerboard, and Texas Centennial. Look–alike patterns from other manufacturers include the Rooster's Head, Cherry, Diamond over Triangle, and Circus pattern. The look–alike patterns date from the 1930s to the 1950s–60s.

**History:** Swankyswigs are decorated glass containers that were filled with Kraft Cheese Spreads. The first Swankyswigs date from the early 1930s. Production was discontinued during the last days of World War II because the paints were needed for the war effort. Production was resumed after the war ended. Several new patterns were introduced including Posy or Cornflower No. 2 (1947), Forget–Me–Not (1948), and Tulip No. 3 (1950). The last colored pattern was Bi–Centennial Tulip (1975).

In the mid–1970s, several copycat patterns emerged including: Wildlife Series (1975) and Sportsman Series (1976), most likely Canadian varieties; Rooster's Head; Cherry; Diamond over Triangle; and Circus. Kraft Cheese Spread is still available today, but in crystal–type glass.

Swankyswigs were very popular with economy minded ladies of the Depression era and were used as tumblers and juice containers. They served as perfect companions to Depression glass table services and also helped to chase away the Depression blues.

The first designs were hand applied. When the popularity of Swankyswigs increased, new and more intricate machine–made patterns were introduced. Designs were test marketed. As a result of limited distribution, designs that failed are hard to identify and find.

The lack of adequate records about Swankyswigs makes it very difficult to completely identify all patterns. Since 1979, quite a few look–alikes have appeared. Although these glasses were similar, only Kraft glasses are considered Swankyswigs.

**References:** Gene Florence, *Collectible Glassware From The 40's, 50's, 60's: An Illustrated Value Guide,* Collector Books, 1992; M. D. Fountain, *Swankyswigs, Price Guide,* privately printed, 1979; Ian Warner, *Swankyswigs, A Pattern Guide Checklist,* Depression Glass Daze, 1982.

**Advisor:** M. D. Fountain.

**Pricing Note:** If a Swankyswig retains its original label, add $4.00 to the value of the glass. Glasses with labels or original lids are scarcer than the checkerboards.

Antique (Early American antiques)
Black, coffeepot and trivets ........ **4.25**
Brown, coal bucket and clock ..... **4.00**
Orange, crib and butter churn ..... **2.25**
Bands, black and red .............. **3.00**
Bi–Centennial
Green, Coin Dot design, 1975 ..... **10.00**
Red, 1938 type tulip .............. **10.00**

Yellow, Coin Dot design, 1975 ..... **10.00**
Bustlin' Betsy ..................... **2.25**
Carnival, fired on Fiesta colors, dark blue, orange, yellow, or light yellow **8.00**
Checkerboard, green, red, and dark blue ........................... **25.00**
Daisies, red daisies on top row, white in middle, green leaves ........... **3.00**
Dots & Circles, black, blue, green, or red ............................ **4.50**
Kiddie Cup (or Animal)
Black, pony and duck ............ **2.25**
Blue, pig and bear ............... **2.00**
Brown, deer and squirrel .......... **2.00**
Dark Blue, pig and bear ........... **2.25**
Green, kitten and bunny .......... **2.00**
Orange, puppy and rooster ........ **2.00**
Red, bird and elephant ............ **2.00**

**Forget-Me-Not, dark blue flowers, green leaves, 1948, $3.00.**

Modern Flowers, dark and light blue; red or yellow
Cornflower ...................... **3.00**
Forget–me–not ................... **3.00**
Jonquil, yellow, green leaves ...... **3.00**
Posy ........................... **3.00**
Tulip, dark and light blue; red or yellow flowers, green leaves
No. 1, white leaves, 1937 ......... **6.00**
No. 2, six mold bands around top, 1938 ........................ **20.00**
No. 3, four molded bands around top **3.00**
Violets, blue flowers, green leaves .... **2.00**
Sailboat, red, green, or dark blue
Racing ......................... **20.00**
Sailing ......................... **20.00**
Star
Black .......................... **4.00**
Dark Blue ...................... **4.00**
Green .......................... **5.00**
Red ........................... **5.50**
Texas Centennial, cowboy riding bucking horse on one side, Texas state seal on other
Black .......................... **8.00**
Dark Blue ...................... **9.00**
Green .......................... **10.00**
Red ........................... **10.00**

# TAYLOR, SMITH, AND TAYLOR

**Collecting Hints:** Collector interest focuses primarily on the LuRay line, introduced in 1938 and named after Virginia's Luray Caverns. The line actually utilized forms from the Empire and Laurel lines. Pieces from the Coral–Craft line are very similar in appearance to pink LuRay. Do not confuse the two.

Vistosa, introduced in 1938, is another example of the California patio dinnerware movement that featured bright, solid color pieces. Unfortunately, the number of forms was restricted. As a result, many collectors shy away from it.

Pebbleford, a plain colored ware with sand–like specks, was the company's third most popular line. It is found in gray, dark blue green, light blue green, light tan, and yellow. The pattern is only moderately popular among collectors.

A dating system was used on some dinnerware lines. The three number code included month, year, and crew number. It was discontinued in the 1950s.

**History:** W. L. Smith, John N. Taylor, W. L. Taylor, Homer J. Taylor, and Joseph G. Lee founded Taylor, Smith, and Taylor in Chester, West Virginia, in 1899. In 1903 the firm reorganized and the Taylors bought Lee's interest. In 1906 Smith bought out the Taylors. The firm remained in the family's control until it was purchased by Anchor Hocking in 1973. The tableware division closed in 1981.

Taylor, Smith, and Taylor started production with a nine–kiln pottery. Local clays were used initially. Later only southern clays were used. Both earthenware and fine china bodies were produced. Several underglaze print patterns, e.g., Dogwood and Spring Bouquet, were made. These prints, made from the copper engravings of ceramic artist J. Palin Thorley, were designed exclusively for the company.

Taylor, Smith, and Taylor also made LuRay, produced from the 1930s through the early 1950s. Available in Windsor Blue, Persian Cream, Sharon Pink, Surf Green, and Chatham Gray, their coordinating colors encourage collectors to mix and match sets.

Competition for a portion of the dinnerware market of the 1930s through the 1950s was intense. LuRay was designed to compete with Russel Wright's American Modern. Vistosa was Taylor, Smith, and Taylor's answer to Homer Laughlin's Fiesta.

Taylor, Smith, and Taylor used several different backstamps and marks. Many contain the company name as well as the pattern and shape names.

**References:** Jo Cunningham, *The Collector's Encyclopedia of American Dinnerware,* Collector

Books, 1982, 1992 value update; Harvey Duke, *The Official Identification and Price Guide to Pottery and Porcelain, Seventh Edition*, House of Collectibles, 1989; Lois Lehner, *Lehner's Encyclopedia of U. S. Marks On Pottery, Porcelain and Clay*, Collector Books, 1988.

**Dandelion pattern, Delphian shape, platter, emb floral border, oval, gold trim, 13½" l, $12.00.**

**LU-RAY.** Produced from the late 1930s until the early 1950s. Available in five pastel colors: Chatham Gray, Persian Cream, Sharon Pink, Surf Green, and Windsor Blue.

Berry Bowl, Chatham Gray .......... **12.00**
Bowl, 36's
  Surf Green .......... **25.00**
  Windsor Blue .......... **25.00**
Cup, Chatham Gray .......... **15.00**
Cup and Saucer, Chatham Gray .......... **20.00**
Demitasse Cup, Persian Cream .......... **16.50**
Demitasse Cup and Saucer
  Sharon Pink .......... **20.00**
  Windsor Blue .......... **20.00**
Demitasse Sugar, cov, Windsor Blue .. **20.00**
Eggcup
  Persian Cream .......... **14.00**
  Sharon Pink .......... **18.00**
  Windsor Blue .......... **18.00**
Gravy, Persian Cream .......... **18.00**
Mixing Bowl, 8¾" d, Surf Green .......... **70.00**
Pitcher, ftd
  Sharon Pink .......... **60.00**
  Windsor Blue .......... **50.00**
Plate
  6½" d, Sharon Pink .......... **4.00**
  8" d
    Chatham Gray .......... **20.00**
    Sharon Pink .......... **14.00**
    Surf Green .......... **15.00**
    Windsor Blue .......... **12.00**
  9" d
    Chatham Gray .......... **15.00**
    Sharon Pink .......... **7.00**
  10" d, dinner
    Persian Cream .......... **12.00**
    Windsor Blue .......... **12.00**
  14" d, chop
    Persian Cream .......... **28.00**
    Surf Green .......... **20.00**
    Windsor Blue .......... **28.00**
Platter
  12" l, Surf Green .......... **10.00**
  13" l, Chatham Gray .......... **30.00**
Relish, four part
  Persian Cream .......... **80.00**
  Surf Green .......... **85.00**
Salad Bowl
  Persian Cream .......... **40.00**
  Surf Green .......... **40.00**
  Windsor Blue .......... **55.00**
Salt and Pepper Shakers, pr, Michigan decal .......... **12.00**
Sauce Boat, Windsor Blue .......... **12.00**
Soup
  Flat
    Chatham Gray .......... **30.00**
    Persian Cream .......... **15.00**
    Surf Green .......... **15.00**
    Windsor Blue .......... **12.00**
  Tab Handles
    Sharon Pink .......... **18.00**
    Surf Green .......... **18.00**
    Windsor Blue .......... **18.00**
Starter Set, Surf Green, 29 pcs .......... **55.00**
Teapot
  Persian Cream, curved .......... **60.00**
  Sharon Pink .......... **50.00**
Tray, center handle, Chatham Gray ... **80.00**
Tumbler
  Juice
    Persian Cream .......... **37.00**
    Sharon Pink .......... **35.00**
    Windsor Blue .......... **32.00**
  Water, Chatham Gray .......... **45.00**
Vase, bud, Surf Green .......... **150.00**
Vegetable Dish, oval, 10" l
  Chatham Gray .......... **30.00**
  Persian Cream .......... **10.00**
  Windsor Blue .......... **12.00**

**PETIT POINT BOUQUET.** Delphian shape dinnerware, late 1920s.

Cake Plate, 11" d, tab handled .......... **10.00**
Mixing Bowl, 9" d .......... **15.00**
Plate, dinner .......... **6.00**
Platter, 12½" d, tab handled .......... **12.00**

**VISTOSA.** Solid colored dinnerware similar to Homer Laughlin's Fiesta, Vistosa pieces have piecrust edges. Produced from 1938 until the early 1940s. Available in four colors: Cobalt Blue, Deep Yellow, Light Green, and Mango Red.

Bowl, 8″ d
  Cobalt Blue .................... **65.00**
  Mango Red .................... **65.00**
Creamer, Light Green .............. **10.00**
Gravy Boat, Cobalt Blue ........... **150.00**
Jug, Mango Red .................... **50.00**
Plate, 11″ d, chop, Mango Red ...... **15.00**
Salt and Pepper Shakers, pr, Cobalt Blue **20.00**
Soup, flat
  Deep Yellow .................. **20.00**
  Mango Red .................... **20.00**
Sugar, Light Green ................ **20.00**
Teacup, Cobalt Blue ............... **8.00**

# TEAPOTS

**Collecting Hints:** Most collectors focus on ceramic examples. Do not overlook teapots made in other materials ranging from silver and silver plate to wood.

The approach to collecting teapots is almost as unlimited as the number of teapot forms and designs. Some common approaches are country, color, design motif, and manufacturing material. One approach, albeit expensive, is to collect teapots designed by famous industrial designers.

**History:** The origin of the teapot has been traced back to the Chinese village of Vi–Hsing in the late sixteenth century. The teapots, similar to ones still being produced today, were no bigger than the tiny cups previously used for drinking tea.

By the seventeenth century, the drinking of tea spread throughout the world. Every pottery and porcelain manufacturer from the Orient to Europe to the Americas produced teapots. The number and variety is unlimited. Form ranges from functional to ornately decorative and whimsical. The vast majority of teapots available in today's market date from 1870 to the present.

**References:** Philip Miller and Michael Berthud, *An Anthology of British Teapots* (Available from: John Ives Bookseller, 5 Normanhurst Drive, Twickenham, Middlesex, TW1 1NA, England); Garth Clark, *The Eccentric Teapot: 400 Years of Invention*, Abbeville Press, 1989.

**Periodicals:** *Tea Talk*, 419 North Larchmont Blvd., #225, Los Angeles, CA 90004; *Tea Times Newsletter*, P. O. Box 841, Langley, WA 98260.

**Museums:** Greater Gibson County Area Chamber of Commerce, P. O. Box 464, Trenton, TN 38382, sponsors an annual Teapot Festival.

**Advisor:** Tina M. Carter.

**Reproduction Alert:** Watch out for figural teapots mimicking older ones, e.g., Granny Anne, Cottage Ware, small beckoning cat, and a blue and white duck. There are several modern Blue Willow patterns.

**China, Harker, Cameo pattern, white lily of the valley, peach ground, 5¼″ h, $12.00.**

Bone China, blue, white, and gold, Wedgwood, c1905 ............... **110.00**
China, 5″ h, floral, Victoria Carlsbad, Austria .......................... **30.00**
Clock, plastic, Sessions ............. **22.00**
Cottage Ware, house, lid is roof, marked "Price Kensington, Made in England, Ye Olde Cottage" ................ **28.00**
Dragonware, 6 cup, raised dragon and coralene dec, gold trim, marked "Made in Occupied Japan" ........ **30.00**
Earthenware
  Brown, "Simple Yet Perfect", c1905 **95.00**
  Double spout, slip dec, c1890 ..... **80.00**
Figural
  Bluebird, 6 cup, bright blue, Lefton China, Japan .................. **30.00**
  Cat, 6 cup, beckoning pose, black and white, green eyes and ribbon, paper label, Cortendorf, Germany **48.00**
  Scottie Man, spout is nose, lid is cap, brown, yellow or green, Wade, England ....................... **40.00**
  Snow White, 6″ h, lid is Snow White, body is her dress, dwarfs in relief, musical, marked "Walt Disney Productions" ..................... **50.00**
  Whimsical man, spout is nose, pastel pink, blue, and yellow, marked "Japan," c1930 ................... **25.00**
Ironstone, 2 cup, floral, Ellgreave, Wood & Sons, England ........... **35.00**
Jasperware, 2 cup, blue and white, Wedgwood, c1784 ............... **210.00**
Miniature
  Tea Set, teapot, creamer and sugar, cov casserole, salt and pepper, six plates, cups and saucers, Moss Rose, Japan ................... **85.00**
  White Glass, gold trim, rough seams, Made in Japan
    Teapot ........................ **7.00**
    Tea Set, teapot, creamer, and sugar **12.00**
Musical, 6 cup, oval, Japan ......... **10.00**

Pearl Luster, 6 cup, oval, gold trim, Poland . . . . . . . . . . . . . . . . . . . . . . . . . . . . **45.00**
Pottery, brown glaze, hp flowers, imp "Royal Canadian Art Pottery, Royal Dripless, Hamilton Canada" . . . . . . . **30.00**
Silver Lustre, 6 cup, hexagonal, Sutherland, England . . . . . . . . . . . . . . . . . . **60.00**
Souvenir
 2" h, tea set, teapot, cup and saucer, hp, California Redwoods, Chandelier Drive–Thru Tree, Victoria Ceramics, Japan, c1940 . . . . . . . . . . . **18.00**
 3¼" h, cobalt, scene, Lewis & Clark, Portland, OR, no mark, 1905 . . . . **15.00**
 4½" h, sq, gold trim, scene, US Capitol, Washington DC, Germany . . **20.00**
 5⅞" h, tepee shape, spout is Indian, handle is totem pole, "Greetings from Canada," made by Clarice Cliff, Britain, c1950 . . . . . . . . . . . . **150.00**

# TV PERSONALITIES & MEMORABILIA

**Collecting Hints:** Collectors of television memorabilia fall into two categories. One is those who specialize in acquiring items from a single television series. Among these, Star Trek, Hopalong Cassidy, Howdy Doody, Roy Rogers, and Leave It To Beaver are the most popular series. The other category specializes in television memorabilia of one type such as television guides, model kits, films, and cards.

There have been over 3,750 series on television since 1948. Therefore, the number of artifacts and memorabilia relating to television is large. Especially rich in television collectibles are the early space shows and cowboy adventure series. The premiums from these types are beginning to show up at auctions and commanding high prices; they are eagerly sought by the pop culture collectors.

Systematic scheduling of television programs developed a new type of publication called a "television guide". The early guides are sought avidly. The first schedules were regional such as *TV Today* in Philadelphia, *TV Press* in Louisville, *Radio–Television Life* in Los Angeles. The first national *TV Guide* was published on April 3, 1953. Collectors enjoy these older magazines because they are often good sources for early stories about stars and their lives.

**History:** The late 1940s and early 1950s was the golden age of television. The first programming began in 1948. Experimentation with programming, vast expansion, and rapid growth marked the period. Prime time live drama series were very successful. Many popular stars of today first appeared on these live dramas, such as Paul Newman, Steve McQueen, Rod Steiger, Jack Lemmon, and Grace Kelly. The stars signed autographs and photographs to promote the dramas. These items, plus scripts and other types of articles have become very collectible.

After the period of live drama came to an end, the Western assault began. In 1959 there were 26 Western series. Many of them were movie and radio heroes adapted to life on television. The Western era continued until the early 1960s when it was replaced by the space adventure series and science fiction.

The 1970s brought the era of situation comedies, including All In The Family and M*A*S*H*. The collectibles resulting from these series are numerous. Only time can tell what values they will have.

**References:** Jefferson Graham, *Come On Down!!!—The TV Game Show Book,* Abbeville Press, 1988; Ted Hake, *Hake's Guide To TV Collectibles,* Wallace–Homestead, 1990; David Inman, *The TV Encyclopedia,* Perigee Book, 1991; Norman E. Martinus and Harry L. Rinker, *Warman's Paper,* Wallace–Homestead, 1993; Brian Paquette and Paul Howley, *The Toys From U.N.C.L.E.: Memorabilia And Collectors Guide,* Entertainment Publishing, 1990; Neil Summers, *The Official TV Western Book, Volume 4,* The Old West Shop Publishing, 1992; Vincent Terrace, *Encyclopedia Of Television–Series, Pilots, And Specials, 1937–1973,* 3 volumes, New York, Zoetrope, 1986.

**Periodicals:** *Filmfax,* P. O. Box 1900, Evanston, IL 60204; *The TV Collector,* P. O. Box 1088, Easton, MA 02334.

**Museum:** Smithsonian Institution, Washington, DC.

Addams Family
 Card Game, Addams Family Card Game, MIB . . . . . . . . . . . . . . . . . . . . **55.00**
 Figure, 5" h, Morticia, plastic, marked "Morticia" and "Addams Family" on back, 1964 Filmways copyright **150.00**
 Record, 33⅓ rpm, six TV music themes, 12¼ x 12¼" cardboard slip case, RCA Victor label, 1965 copyright . . . . . . . . . . . . . . . . . . . . . . . . . **25.00**
All In The Family
 Game, Milton Bradley, 1972 . . . . . . . **18.00**
 Painting, watercolor, primitive style, little girl, dog under tree, sgd "Sally Struthers," mint in orig mailing tube **280.00**
A–Team, jigsaw puzzle . . . . . . . . . . . . . **5.00**
Ben Casey
 Pinback Button, 3½", white, blue lettering . . . . . . . . . . . . . . . . . . . . . . . . **15.00**
 Puzzle, 13½ x 24", Milton Bradley, 1962 copyright . . . . . . . . . . . . . . . . **25.00**
Beverly Hillbillies
 Coloring Book, 8 x 11", Whitman, 1963 . . . . . . . . . . . . . . . . . . . . . . . . **15.00**

**Beverly Hillbillies, book, *The Saga of Wildcat Creek,* Doris Schroeder, Whitman Publishing, Al Andersen and Arnie Kohn illus, hard cov, 212 pgs, 1963, 5¾ x 7¾", $15.00.**

Game, 18 x 18", unused, Standard Toykraft, 1963 . . . . . . . . . . . . . . . . **40.00**
Thermos, 6½" h, litho metal, red plastic cap, full color scene, Aladdin, 1962–64 . . . . . . . . . . . . . . . . . . . . . **25.00**
Bewitched
Activity Book, 8 x 11", 64 pgs, Treasure Books, 1965 . . . . . . . . . . . . . . **15.00**
Card Game, Stymie, 42 cards, 20 x 22" vinyl playing sheet with full color photos, boxed, Milton Bradley, 1965 . . . . . . . . . . . . . . . . . . . . . . . . **25.00**
Bonanza
Game, Rummy, table top, orig box, unused . . . . . . . . . . . . . . . . . . . . . . **95.00**
Gun and Holster Set . . . . . . . . . . . . . . **150.00**
Car 54, coloring book, 8 x 11", Whitman, 1962, 128 pgs, unused . . . . . . **30.00**
Charlie's Angels
Doll, Farrah Fawcett, 1977, orig box **35.00**
Jigsaw Puzzle . . . . . . . . . . . . . . . . . . . . **8.00**
CHIPS, wallet, orig display card, MGM **15.00**
Combat, card game, complete deck, 6 x 7½ x 1¼" box, Milton Bradley, 1964 copyright . . . . . . . . . . . . . . . . . . **20.00**
Dallas, jigsaw puzzle . . . . . . . . . . . . . . . **10.00**
Dark Shadows
Game, Dark Shadows, MIB . . . . . . . . **75.00**
Paperback Book . . . . . . . . . . . . . . . . . . **1.00**
Dennis the Menace, mug, 3½", plastic, molded, painted, early 1950s . . . . . . **12.00**
Dragnet, whistle . . . . . . . . . . . . . . . . . . **12.00**
Dr Kildare
Coloring Book, 8½ x 11", unused, Saalfield #9531, 1963 . . . . . . . . . . **15.00**
Pinback Button, 3½", blue lettering, pink background, early 1960s . . . . **12.00**
Stethoscope, MIB . . . . . . . . . . . . . . . . **20.00**
Flintstones
Game, The Flintstone's Cockamamies, Hanna Barbera Production, 1961 . . . . . . . . . . . . . . . . . . . . . . . . . **5.00**
Night Light, Barney and Fred . . . . . . **25.00**
Puzzle, four, complete in orig box . . **12.00**
General Hospital, game . . . . . . . . . . . . . **15.00**
Get Smart, poster, 21 x 24", paper, full color scene, issued by NBC–TV . . . . **40.00**
Gilligan's Island
Autographed, photo, 8 x 10" glossy, black and white, sgd by cast members . . . . . . . . . . . . . . . . . . . . . . . . . **150.00**
Coloring Book, 8 x 11", full color illus, unused, Whitman #1135, 1965 . . . . . . . . . . . . . . . . . . . . . . . . . **30.00**
Godfrey, Arthur
Souvenir Bag, 14 x 16", paper, brown, Godfrey with CBS microphone and adv products illus, Union Bag & Paper Corp, 1940–50 **20.00**
Ukulele, 21½" h, marbled brown plastic, ivory white front and tuning head, includes 16 page instruction and song book and automatic tuning attachment, 1950 copyright . . **75.00**
Gumby and Pokey, hand puppet, 1964, price for pair . . . . . . . . . . . . . . . . . . . **40.00**
Herman, Pee–Wee, doll, talking . . . . . **25.00**
Hogan's Heroes, lunch box and thermos **250.00**
Howdy Doody
Bottle, Flub–A–Dub, Grapette . . . . . **10.00**
Clock, Time Teacher, 10 x 18" . . . . . **25.00**
Marionette, Princess Summerfall–Winterspring . . . . . . . . . . . . . . . . . . **65.00**
Pennant . . . . . . . . . . . . . . . . . . . . . . . . **85.00**
Puppet, plastic, marked "Tee–Vee Toys"
Dilly Dally . . . . . . . . . . . . . . . . . . . . **35.00**
Howdy Doody . . . . . . . . . . . . . . . . . **35.00**
Mr Bluster . . . . . . . . . . . . . . . . . . . . **35.00**
Princess, broken feather . . . . . . . . . **20.00**
Ring, flashlight . . . . . . . . . . . . . . . . . . **140.00**

**Howdy Doody, 8mm film, Howdy Doody's Christmas, No. 824, Castle Films, orig 3" sq box, $25.00.**

I Love Lucy
Magazine, *Song Hits,* February, 1944, Lucille Ball cov . . . . . . . . . . . . . . . . **9.00**

I Love Lucy
- Coloring Book, 8½ x 11″, unused, Golden Press, 1963 ............ **30.00**
- Puppet, Little Ricky, c1950, MIB ... **60.00**

Julia, lunch box, 7 x 8½ x 4″, litho metal, full color illus, lime green trim, 6½″ h thermos with lime green plastic cap, unused, King–Seeley, 1969 copyright ........................ **50.00**

Knight Rider
- Coloring and Activity Book ........ **5.00**
- Wallet .......................... **6.00**

Kojak, game, The Stake Out, unused, Milton Bradley, 1975 ............ **25.00**

Laugh In, waste can, 13″ h, oval, litho metal, color photos on one side, other with "Sock It to Me" slogan, 1968 copyright ....................... **40.00**

Laverne and Shirley, jigsaw puzzle ... **15.00**

Lawerence Welk, book, *You're Never Too Young,* autographed .......... **10.00**

Leave It To Beaver
- Coloring Book, 8 x 11″, full color cover illus, Whitman, 1958 ...... **30.00**
- Game, Leave It To Beaver (Money Maker), 16¼ x 16¼″, board, black and white photo of Jerry Mathers on box lid, Hasbro, 1959 ....... **50.00**

Man from U.N.C.L.E., card game, orig box ........................... **22.00**

Maverick, costume, child's, western vest and jacket .................. **55.00**

M.A.S.H.
- Game ........................... **20.00**
- Wallet .......................... **8.00**

Mod Squad
- Book, *Assignment: The Arranger,* Whitman, 5¼ x 8″, 210 pgs, 1969 copyright ..................... **8.00**
- Puzzle, 14 x 20″, photo scene of cast characters, boxed, Milton Bradley, 1969 copyright ................ **12.00**

Mr Ed, puppet, hand, talking, 1962 ... **95.00**

Munsters
- Comic Book, Gold Key #3, July 1965 **15.00**
- Doll, 8½″ h, Herman, vinyl plastic, movable head, arms, and legs, orig tag, Ideal Toy, 1965 ............ **40.00**
- Figure, 6″ h, Herman, plastic, painted, 1964 copyright ......... **40.00**

My Favorite Martian, coloring book, 8½ x 11″, one colored page, Golden Press, 1964 ..................... **25.00**

Pinky Lee, game, Pinky Lee and The Runaway Frankfurters, Lisbeth Whiting Co, 1954 copyright ........... **50.00**

Popeye, Eraso board and magic screen set, MIB ....................... **75.00**

Rifleman, rifle ..................... **65.00**

Six Million Dollar Man
- Game ........................... **20.00**
- Record Album, 1978 ............. **15.00**
- Secret Code Puzzle ............... **4.00**

Skelton, Red, Halloween mask, 1950s
- Hobo ........................... **15.00**
- Pirate .......................... **15.00**

Soupy Sales
- Notebook, 3 ring, 10 x 11½″, vinyl cov, black, white, and fleshtone photo on front, 1966 copyright ... **40.00**
- Pinback Button, ⅞″ d, "Charter Member/Soupy Sales Society," 1960s .. **15.00**

Tarzan
- Better Little Book, *Tarzan and the Jewels of Opar,* #1495, Whitman, 1940 Edgar Rice Burroughs Inc copyright ...................... **75.00**
- Comic Book, Vol 1, No 26, Lex Barker photo, Dell Publishing Co .... **25.00**
- View Master Reel, set of 3, titles "Tarzan Finds A Son," "Tarzan Rescues Numa," and "Tarzan Saves The Jungle Explorer," orig envelope and booklet, 1955 copyright ......... **40.00**

Untouchables, TV Guide, Elliott Ness cov ............................ **15.00**

Voyage to the Bottom of the Sea, card game, boxed, Milton Bradley, 1964 . **40.00**

**Wagon Train, coloring book, Whitman Publishing, #1122, 1959, unused, 8½ x 11″, $25.00.**

Wagon Train, double gun and holster set, orig box .................... **165.00**

Welcome Back Kotter, jigsaw puzzle .. **10.00**

# TELEVISIONS

**Collecting Hints:** There are two distinct types of early television sets: mechanical and electronic. Mechanical televisions, the earliest, look nothing like their modern counterparts. Mechanical sets from the 1920s typically have a motorized 12″ diameter metal disc with a "glow tube" in back and a magnifier in front. Starting in 1938 sets used picture tubes as they do today. Generally the earlier the set, the smaller the screen. The easiest way to gauge the age of a television set is by the numbers found on the channel selector. Pre–1946 television sets will tune a maximum of five stations, usually channels 1–5. In 1946 channels 7–13 were added, thus sets made between 1946 and 1948 will show channels 1–13 on the station selector.

In 1949, channel 1 was dropped, leaving all 1949 and newer sets with V.H.F. channels 2–13, as we have them today. The U.H.F. band was added in 1953, thus any set with U.H.F. capability is less than 40 years old.

Brand and model number are essential to determining a set's worth. However, physical condition of the cabinet is much more important than the operating condition of the set.

**History:** There are three distinct eras of early television. The first, the "mechanical" era, was from 1925–32. Sets often were known as "radiovisors," since they were visual attachments to radios. Many mechanical television sets did not have cabinets and resembled an electric fan with a round metal disk in place of the blades. These units were most prevalent in the New York City and Chicago areas.

Any complete mechanical set is valued in the several thousand dollar range. Manufacturers included Jenkins, Baird, Western Television, Insuline Corp. of America, Short–Wave and Television Corp., Daven, See–All, Rawls, Pioneer, Travler Radio & Television Corp., and others.

The second era was the pre–World War II era, which spanned 1938–1941. These were the first all–electronic sets and usually were combined with a multi–band radio in fancy cabinets. A favorite design of the era was the use of a "mirror in the lid" arrangement, whereby a mirror in the underside of a lift–lid reflected the picture tube, which was pointed straight up. No more than 2,000 sets were produced during the three years. They were concentrated in those areas with prewar television stations: New York City, Albany/Schenectady/Troy, Philadelphia, Chicago, and Los Angeles. Depending on model and condition, these sets usually start at $1,000 and can range to $5,000 or more.

The final era of television started in 1946 with the resumption of post–war television production. Production rose rapidly. Few sets after 1949 have collectible value. There are some notable exceptions, e.g., the first "color wheel" sets [1951], the giant Dumont 30" screen sets [1953], and limited production or "oddball" sets.

**References:** Morgan E. McMahon, *A Flick of The Switch,* Vintage Radio, 1975; Harry Poster, *Poster's Radio And Televion Price Guide, 1920–1990,* Wallace–Homestead, 1993; Harry Poster and John Sakas, *1990 Price Guide To Vintage TV's and Collectible Radios,* Sight, Sound, Style, 1990; Scott Wood (ed.), *Classic TVs With Price Guide: Pre–War thru 1950s,* L–W Book Sales, 1992.

**Collectors' Club:** Antique Wireless Association, 59 Main St., Bloomfield, NY 14469.

**Caution:** Do not plug in a set that has been in storage for more than 30 years without an inspection by a serviceman. Components can go bad and short–circuit, causing a fire. Many early sets had no fuses for protection.

**Olympic, TV-104, table model, wood case, Bakelite knobs, 10" screen, 1948, $125.00.**

Admiral
- 19A11, table top, dark brown Bakelite, 7" screen, 1948 .......... **125.00**
- 19A15, table top, wood, 7" screen . **175.00**
- 20X122, console, Bakelite, 10" screen, 1950 .......... **350.00**
- 24A12, console, Bakelite, 12" screen, 1948 .......... **350.00**

Airline
- 84GSE–3011A, portable, leatherette, 7" screen, 1949 .......... **150.00**
- 94GSE–3015, portable, Telephoto Control button, 7" screen, 1948 .. **175.00**

Andrea, 1–F–5, console, wood, 5" screen, 1939 .......... **4,000.00**

Arvin, 4080T, table top, metal, limed oak front, 8" screen, 1950 .......... **150.00**

CBS–Columbia, RX90, console, color, wood, 15" screen .......... **500.00**

Coronado, FA 43–8965, table top, wood, 7" screen, 1949 .......... **200.00**

Crosley, 9–419, table top, wood, DuMont Chassis, 12" screen, 1949 . **100.00**

Delco, TV 71A, table top, wood, 7" screen, 1948 .......... **125.00**

DuMont, RA 103D, table top, 12" screen, 1949 .......... **100.00**

Emerson, 639, table top, 7" screen, 1949 .......... **150.00**

Fada, 799, table top, wood, 10" screen with magnifier, 1947 .......... **150.00**

General Electric
- 800, portable, Bakelite, 10" screen, 1948 .......... **200.00**

901, console, wood, combination projection TV, radio, and phonograph, 18 x 24", 1946 .......... **300.00**
17T027, portable, green metal case, 17" screen, 1956 .............. **75.00**
Hallicrafters, T505, table top, blonde wood, 7" screen, 1947 ............ **150.00**
ITI Guest Television, table top, metal, plexiglass front, four channels, 7" screen ......................... **600.00**
Motorola
9T1, table top, Bakelite, 8" screen .. **150.00**
17T32BZ, portable, metal, 17" screen, 1958 ................. **75.00**
TS 902, console, wood, color, 15" screen, color ................. **1,000.00**
V773, portable, leatherette, 7" screen, 1949 ................. **150.00**
XB–702, table top, wood, 7" screen, 1949 ......................... **175.00**
National, TV–7W, table top, mahogany, 7" screen, 1949 ................. **200.00**
Philco
48–1001, table top, walnut, 10" screen, 1948 ................. **125.00**
48–2500, console, projection, wood, 1948 ......................... **150.00**
49–702, table top, mahogany, 7" screen, 1949 ................. **225.00**
10L60, console, Predicta series, wood, 21" screen, 1960 ......... **100.00**
Pilot, TV–37, table top, magnifier attachment, 3" screen, 1949 ......... **250.00**
RCA
621 TS, table top, blonde wood, 7" screen, 1946 ................. **750.00**
721 TS, table top, wood, 10" screen, 1947 ......................... **125.00**
2T51, table top, metal, 12" screen, 1950 ......................... **100.00**
Raytheon/Belmont, 22A21, table top, wood, 7" screen, 1947 ............ **400.00**
Sentinel, 400TV, portable, leatherette, 7" screen, 1948 ................. **200.00**
Silvertone, 9115, portable, leatherette, 8" screen ...................... **150.00**
Stromberg Carlson, TC 10H, Manhattan Porthole, table top, wood, 10" d screen, 1958 ................... **125.00**
Zenith, 24H21, console, wood, 19" d screen, 1950 ................... **175.00**

# SHIRLEY TEMPLE

**Collecting Hints:** Dolls are made out of many materials—composition, cloth, chalk, papier mache, rubber, and vinyl. Composition dolls are the earliest. Shirley Temple's popularity received a renewed boost through television, resulting in a new series of Shirley Temple products being issued in the 1950s.

**History:** Shirley Jane Temple was born April 23, 1928, in Santa Monica, California. A movie scout discovered her at a dancing school. "Pie Covered Wagon" in 1932 was her screen test. During the 1930s she made twenty movies, earning as much as $75,000 per film.

Her mother supervised the licensing of over fifteen firms to make Shirley Temple products. These included dolls, glassware, china, jewelry, and soap. The first Shirley Temple dolls were made in 1934 by The Ideal Toy Company. They varied in height from 11 to 27 inches and were composition (pressed wood). Ideal made the first vinyl dolls in 1957.

**References:** John Axe, *The Encyclopedia of Celebrity Dolls*, Hobby House Press, Inc., 1983; Norman E. Martinus and Harry L. Rinker, *Warman's Paper,* Wallace–Homestead, 1993; Edward R. Pardella, *Shirley Temple Dolls And Fashion: A Collector's Guide To The World's Darling,* Schiffer Publishing, Ltd., 1992; Patricia R. Smith, *Shirley Temple Dolls And Collectibles, Series 1*, 1977, 1992 value update, and *Series 2* 1979, 1992 value update. Collector Books.

**REPRODUCTION ALERT**

Bank, 2" sq, celluloid, white, picture mounted on top, c1936 ........... **75.00**
Book
*Poor Little Rich Girl,*, soft cover, 32 pgs, 1936 Saalfield ............. **30.00**
*The Shirley Temple Treasury,* Random House, 1959, hard cover ........ **48.00**
*Through The Day,* No 1716 ........ **35.00**
Bowl, cereal ....................... **40.00**
Box, slipper, child's, 6 x 10½ x 3¼", gray and blue design, marked "Restful," mid 1930s ................ **75.00**
Candy Mold ....................... **25.00**
Coat, cashmere, label, Bambury orig, c1937 ......................... **285.00**
Doll
12" h, 1957 ..................... **65.00**
16" h, 1972, boxed ............... **125.00**

**Creamer, cobalt blue, 1938, 4½" h, $25.00.**

20″ h, with pin, Ideal . . . . . . . . . . . . . **400.00**
25″ h, orig clothing, pin . . . . . . . . . . . **850.00**
Dress, child's, satin, pink, ruffled, blue and white tag . . . . . . . . . . . . . . . . . . . . **50.00**
Embroidery Set, tablecloth, four napkins, hoop, needle, threads, plastic thimble, unused, Gabriel, 1960s . . . **50.00**
Fan, *I'll Be Seeing You,* teen–age Shirley holding RC Cola . . . . . . . . . . . . . . . . . **24.00**
Figure, 8½″ h, rubber, black Scottie dog under one arm, marked "Made in Czechoslovakia," mid 1930 . . . . . . . **90.00**
Game, The Little Colonel, orig box with Shirley's photo, Selchow & Righter, 1935 . . . . . . . . . . . . . . . . . . . . . . . . . . **70.00**
Mirror, pocket, 1¾″ d, celluloid, brown photo, pale pink background . . . . . . **45.00**
Movie Still, 8 x 10″, *Little Miss Marker,* Shirley on horse with Adolphe Menjou, Paramount Film, 1934 . . . . . . . . **20.00**
Mug . . . . . . . . . . . . . . . . . . . . . . . . . . . . **55.00**
Necklace, 14″ l, brass, ⅝″ cut out head disk, 1930s . . . . . . . . . . . . . . . . . . . . . . **100.00**
Paperdoll, Saalfield #1765, life size, 1936 . . . . . . . . . . . . . . . . . . . . . . . . . . **90.00**
Pinback Button, 1″ d, enamel on brass, "Sunday Referee/Shirley Temple League," 1930s, English newspaper issue . . . . . . . . . . . . . . . . . . . . . . . . . . **110.00**
Pitcher, 4½″ h, glass, blue, white portrait image, Wheaties offer, c1938 . . **40.00**
Post Card, 3½ x 5½″, glossy sepia picture, "Captain January" scene, unused, 1936 . . . . . . . . . . . . . . . . . . . . . . **15.00**
Ring, celluloid, red, black and white diecut head of Shirley, marked "Made in Japan" . . . . . . . . . . . . . . . . . . . . . . . **25.00**
Sewing Cards, six black and white cards, yarn, 5 x 7″ box, marked "Made by Saalfield 1936" . . . . . . . . . **45.00**
Sheet Music
*Good Night My Love,* 1936 . . . . . . . . **18.50**
*Pigskin Parade,* Shirley on back . . . . **10.00**
Song Album, 9 x 12″, 36 pgs, words and music, pink tinted film scenes . . . . . . **35.00**
Souvenir Book, 9 x 12″, Tournament of Roses Parade, Shirley as Grand Marshall, 32 pgs, 1939 . . . . . . . . . . . . . . . **22.00**
Toy, stage, 10 x 24 x 36″, cardboard, litho red cardboard curtains, yellow cords, early 1970s . . . . . . . . . . . . . . . . **50.00**

# THIMBLES

**Collecting Hints:** There are many ways to approach thimble collecting. You can collect by material (metal or porcelain), by design (cupids or commemorative), by types (advertising or political), or limited editions (modern collectibles). However, in reality, there is only one philosophy that should determine what you collect. Collect what you like.

There are thousands of thimbles. The wise collector narrows her approach. This saves money and enables her to assemble a meaningful collection.

The wonderful thing about thimble collecting is that there is something for everybody's budget. Collectors with unlimited funds can focus on gold thimbles. The person on a limited budget might look at advertising or modern collectible thimbles.

**History:** Silver thimbles were imported from England during the Colonial period, and only the wealthy could afford to buy them. By the late 18th century advertisements appeared in the *New York Weekly Post,* the *New York Gazette,* and the *Philadelphia Directory,* offering American made thimbles. These were gold, silver, or pinchbeck thimbles, some with steel caps.

The Industrial Revolution during the 19th century brought the "Golden Age" of thimble production. Machinery was created that could produce fine working thimbles. By the end of the 19th century, world production of thimbles was about eighty million per year.

Long before the sewing machine became a permanent member of the household, all sewing and mending was done by hand.

Needlework can be divided into two kinds: plain and fancy. Plain sewing required a utilitarian thimble made of steel, brass, or celluloid. A process for making celluloid thimbles was patented by William Halsey in 1880. Eugene Villiers patented a thimble molding process in the same year. Aluminum was a costly metal during the 19th century. Aluminum thimbles did not appear on the market until the 20th century, when it became cheaper and practical to make thimbles.

The frontier homemaker guarded her thimble. If it was lost, it was difficult to replace. Her source was in a general store, often miles away, or she had to wait until a traveling peddler came along. City ladies had no problem replacing a lost thimble. A selection was always available at the local dry good stores. The name "dry goods" assured a lady that no "wet goods," or alcoholic beverages, were sold in that store, and it was perfectly proper for her to shop there.

Fancy sewing was considered a parlor or social activity. Ornate thimbles made of precious metals were saved for this purpose. Many gold and silver thimbles were received as gifts. In years past proper etiquette did not permit a young man to give his lady any gift that was personal, such as jewelry or clothing. Flowers, books, or sweets were considered proper gifts. The thimble somehow bridged this rule of etiquette. A fancy gold or silver thimble was a welcomed gift. Many of these do not show signs of wear from constant use. This may result from the poor fit of the thimble or from it simply being too elegant for mundane work.

Advertising thimbles cover an extensive area of goods and services. These little advertising ploys helped a salesman to open a door. Tradesmen knew that these tokens would constantly remind the customer of their product. Many collectors specialize in collecting only advertising thimbles because they are easy to find and inexpensive to buy. Advertising thimbles made of celluloid or metal are older than the modern plastic examples. There was no standard method of distributing advertising thimbles. Most were handed to a potential customer by a salesman. Others were packaged with a product, such as flour or bread. Most were used for sewing, but others were not. In either case, advertising thimbles found a home in the family sewing basket.

The history of political campaign advertising thimbles began with the amendment giving the vote to women, ratified on August 20, 1920, just in time for the 1920 political campaign. The first Presidential candidate to use the advertising thimble was Warren Harding. Political thimbles are priced higher than other advertising thimbles. Thimble collectors find they have to compete with political memorabilia collectors for these.

**References:** Edwin Holmes, *A History of Thimbles,* Cornwall Books, 1985; Eleanor Johnson, *Thimbles,* Shires Publications, Aylesbuyr, Bucks, England, 1982; Myrtle Lundquist, *The Book of a Thousand Thimbles,* Wallace Homestead, 1970, out–of–print; Myrtle Lundquist, *Thimble Treasury,* Wallace Homestead, 1975, out–of–print; Myrtle Lundquist, *Thimbles Americana,* Wallace Homestead, 1981, out–of–print; Averil Mathis, *Antique and Collectible Thimbles,* Collector Books, 1986, 1989 value update, out–of–print; Bridget McConnell, *A Collector's Guide To Thimbles,* Wellfleet Books, 1990; Gay Ann Rogers, *American Silver Thimbles,* John Murray, 1989; Gay Ann Rogers, *Price Guided Keyed To American Silver Thimbles,* Needlework Unlimited, 1989; John von Holle, *Thimble Collectors Encyclopedia,* Wallace Homestead, 1986, out–of–print; Estelle Zalkin, *Zalkin's Handbook of Thimbles and Sewing Implements,* Wallace Homestead, 1988.

**Periodical:** *Thimbletter,* 93 Walnut Hill Rd, Newtown Highlands, MA 02161.

**Collectors' Club:** Thimble Collectors International, 6411 Montego Bay Drive, Louisville, KY 40228.

**Advisor:** Estelle Zalkin

**REPRODUCTION ALERT:** As soon as thimble collecting became a popular collectible, recast reproductions appeared in the market. The cast reproduction of a pre–revolution Russian enamel surfaced in antiques shows and shops across the country. The "84" Russian silver mark is clear, but the maker's mark is deliberately smeared. The rim of the reproduction is thick and inside the thimble is rough.

American thimbles have been reproduced. An artisan is casting many of the popular patterns, including the cottage scene, harbor scene with lighthouse, anchors, and chains, cupid and garlands, the teddy bear, two birds on a branch and other popular collectible thimbles. No maker's mark appear inside the cap and the "Sterling" mark is stamped on the band. This is the first clue that these are recast reproductions. It is illegal to use the word "Sterling" on any silver piece without the manufacturer's name or trademark. These cast thimbles are thick and rough inside. The cast thimbles are much heavier than the genuine machine drawn antique thimbles. The casting process does not duplicate the fine engraved designs that the originals have.

**Souvenir, Statue of Liberty, left: French, $50.00; right: Simons, $15.00.**

Gold, 1900–1940
- Plain band ....... **75.00**
- Scenic band ....... **100.00**
- Semi precious stones on band ....... **250.00**

Ivory
- Modern scrimshaw ....... **20.00**
- Vegetable ivory ....... **60.00**

Metal, common
- Brass
  - Ornate band ....... **15.00**
  - Plain band ....... **3.00**
- Cast pot metal, "For a Good Girl" ....... **2.00**
- Cloisonne on brass, Chinese ....... **10.00**
- Diragold, Scandinavian gold ....... **75.00**
- Toledo, Spain, damascene ....... **20.00**

Porcelain
- Meissen, German, modern, hand painted ....... **125.00**
- Modern collectible, transfer print design ....... **15.00**
- Royal Worcester, England, hand painted
  - Signed ....... **50.00**
  - Signed by Powell, birds ....... **300.00**

Silver, 1900–1940
- Applied wire work, Mexican ....... **10.00**
- Cupid in high relief ............... **125.00**
- Flowers in high relief ............. **50.00**
- Paneled band ..................... **35.00**
- Scenic band ...................... **35.00**

Souvenir and Commemorative, silver
- Columbian Exposition, 1892
  - Buildings in relief .............. **500.00**
  - Words only ..................... **400.00**
- Liberty Bell, 1976 issue ........... **75.00**
- St Louis Fair, 1904 ............... **600.00**
- Statue of Liberty, French ........... **50.00**

Thimble Holder and Gadget Holder
- Glass slipper ................... **100.00**
- Silver, round, filigree ........... **150.00**
- "M. T.," (Magic Thimble,) thread cutter and needle threader ......... **25.00**
- Thread Cutter, lip on band ........ **15.00**

# TINSEL ART

**Collecting Hints:** Look for those pieces which are elaborate in design and contain different colored foil. Signed pictures often are viewed as folk art and may be priced higher.

Nineteenth century material is preferred over the nondescript 20th century examples. However, Art Deco and Art Nouveau designs of quality are sought by collectors from these fields.

**History:** Tinsel pictures (or paintings) were both a "cottage art" and a commercial product which enjoyed popularity from the late 19th century through the 20th century. The "painting" took two forms. The first was similar to a reverse painting on glass. A design was placed on the glass and colored foil was placed behind to accent the piece. The second form consisted of a silhouette or cutting, separate from the glass, placed over a layer of crumpled foil.

The reverse painting type was highly personalized; a mother and her children could work on tinsel pictures as a family project. This handiwork often contained presentation remarks and was artist signed and dated. The silhouette type appears to be related to the Art Deco and Art Nouveau periods and may have been a form of souvenir at carnival games and the seashore. The sameness of many designs, e.g., flamingos in a swamp–like setting, denotes its commercial production.

**Reference:** Shirley Mace, *Encyclopedia Of Silhouette Collectibles On Glass,* Shadow Enterprises, 1992.

Basket of Flowers, multicolored, black ground, 17¾ x 13½" ............ **165.00**

Birds, drinking from stylized fountain, trees in background, 19th C, 23 x 27" **225.00**

**Birds and Flowers, multicolored, 8¾ x 10¾", $85.00.**

Flamingos, pink flamingos, palm tree, reeds, yellow sun, black ground, 10¾ x 8¾" .......................... **90.00**

Flower Arrangement, bowl, brightly colored ............................ **40.00**

Fountain, surrounded by garland of flowers, multicolored, 15¾ x 15½" . **120.00**

Lilacs, black ground, gilt frame, 10½ x 7½", 19th C ..................... **165.00**

Motto, Home Sweet Home, houses and trees, reverse painted, 12¼ x 18" ... **75.00**

Peacock, silver peacock, gold marbleized fence, black ground, authentic peacock feather tail, mounted as tray, 19 x 13" .................... **65.00**

Silhouettes, girl and boy, facing pr, framed .......................... **50.00**

Statue of Liberty, multicolored, reverse painting on glass highlights, ornate oval wooden frame ............... **90.00**

# TOOTHPICK HOLDERS

**Collecting Hints:** Toothpick holders have been confused with many forms—from match holders, shot glasses, miniature spoon holders to toy table settings, mustard pots without lids, rose or violet bowls, individual open sugars, and vases. Use toothpicks to test what you have. The toothpicks should rest well in the holder with an ample extension to allow an individual toothpick to be selected easily. Match holders often are figural in nature and have a striking surface on them.

The biggest danger to the collector is a salt shaker with a ground top or a wine glass with the stem removed. Knowing the forms of salt shakers and wine glasses will avoid any confusion.

Among the forms, perhaps the silverplated figural toothpicks are least appreciated. They offer the beginner a reasonable area upon which to build an inexpensive collection.

**History:** Toothpick holders are small containers used to hold toothpicks. They were an important table accessory during the Victorian period.

Toothpick holders were made in a wide range of material—Art glass, colored pattern glass, colored glass novelties, milk glass, china, bisque and porcelain, crystal pressed glass, cut glass, and silverplated figurals. Makers include both American and European firms.

Toothpick holders were used as souvenir items by applying decals or transfers. The same blank may contain several different location labels.

**References:** William Heacock, *Encyclopedia of Victorian Colored Pattern Glass, Book I, Toothpick Holders from A to Z, Second Edition*, Antique Publications, 1976, 1992 value update; William Heacock, *1000 Toothpick Holders: A Collector's Guide*, Antique Publications, 1977; William Heacock, *Rare & Unlisted Toothpick Holders,* Antique Publications, Inc., 1984; National Toothpick Holder Collectors Society, *Toothpick Holders: Glass, China, and Metal,* Antique Publications, 1993.

**Collectors' Club:** National Toothpick Holder Collectors Society, P. O. Box 246, Sawyer, MI 49125.

**Additional Listings:** See *Warman's Antiques And Their Prices.*

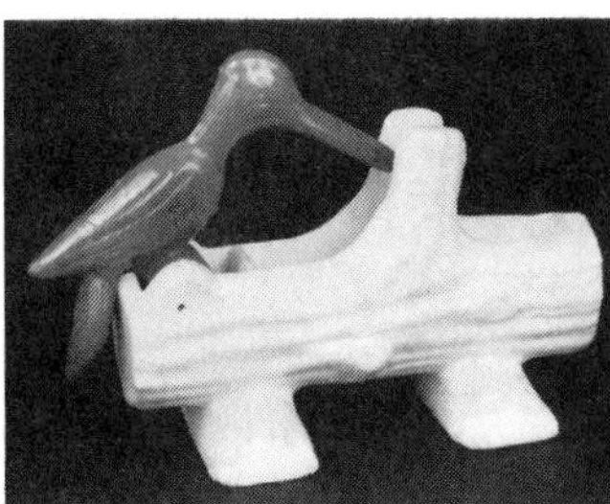

**Dispenser, molded plastic, white log, red bird with pronged beak, 4½" l, 2½" h, $10.00.**

Art Glass
- Amber, figural, picture frame, Greentown Glass . . . . **245.00**
- Cranberry, enamel dec . . . . **125.00**
- Custard
  - Chrysanthemum Sprig, blue, gold dec . . . . **300.00**
  - Souvenir, Belvedere, IL . . . . **35.00**
- Guttate, cranberry . . . . **175.00**
- Leaf Mold, cased cranberry spatter . **145.00**
- Purple Slag, figural, boot . . . . **50.00**
- Smith Bros, ribbed, opaque white, blue dot rim, pastel floral dec . . . . **125.00**

Brass
- Clown, marked "Jenning Bros" . . . . **30.00**
- Top Hat, umbrella . . . . **20.00**

China, bisque, and porcelain
- Bisque, figural
  - Cat, coachman outfit, barrel . . . . **55.00**
  - Dwarf, 4½" . . . . **25.00**
- Geisha Girl, 2½", blue rim . . . . **15.00**
- Majolica, figural, mouse with ear of corn . . . . **135.00**
- Nippon, hp owl sitting on a tree branch, blue night sky ground, small black beads on rim and base **110.00**
- Occupied Japan, donkey pulling cart **7.50**
- Schlegelmilch, RS Prussia, basket, roses dec . . . . **130.00**
- Top Hat, sunset hunting dog scene, green and cream ground, cobalt blue band . . . . **40.00**

Milk Glass
- Barrel, metal hoops . . . . **25.00**
- Basketweave, Bellaire . . . . **25.00**
- Horseshoe and Clover . . . . **22.00**
- Pansy, three handles, Kemple . . . . **35.00**
- Scrolled Shell, goofus dec . . . . **12.00**

Opalescent Glass
- Beatty Rib, blue . . . . **48.00**
- Diamond Spearpoint, blue . . . . **125.00**
- Melon . . . . **48.00**
- Overall Hobnail, blue . . . . **28.00**
- Stripe, white . . . . **30.00**
- Windows, cranberry . . . . **45.00**

Pattern Glass
- Bull's Eye and Fan . . . . **12.00**
- Button Arches, ruby stained, souvenir, "Mother, 1947" . . . . **20.00**
- California, green . . . . **50.00**
- Colonial, Cambridge, cobalt . . . . **25.00**
- Continental, Heisey . . . . **42.00**
- Delaware, green, gold trim . . . . **90.00**
- Ester, clear . . . . **45.00**
- Feather, clear . . . . **65.00**
- Galloway, clear . . . . **18.00**
- Heart, pink opaque . . . . **60.00**
- Hobb's Hobnail, vaseline . . . . **20.00**
- Illinois, adv . . . . **27.50**
- Iowa, clear . . . . **22.50**
- King's Crown, ruby stained . . . . **38.00**
- Michigan . . . . **30.00**
- Minnesota . . . . **45.00**
- Paddlewheel and Star, clear . . . . **25.00**
- Pretty Maid . . . . **60.00**
- Rising Sun . . . . **35.00**
- Royal Oak, frosted rubina . . . . **125.00**
- Swinger, clear and ruby . . . . **22.00**
- Three Dolphins, amber . . . . **45.00**
- Tulip with Sawtooth . . . . **40.00**
- Zipper Slash . . . . **25.00**

Silver Plate
- Cat and bucket . . . . **65.00**
- Child, holding umbrella, on turtle, marked "Pairpoint" . . . . **175.00**

Colonial Lady .................... **65.00**
Egg, chick emerging, feet on branch, sq base, marked "Hartford" ..... **70.00**
Rooster, 2" h, engraved "Picks" .... **48.00**
Wood, beaver, painted features, broad tail, hollowed out trunk ........... **5.00**

# TOYS

**Collecting Hints:** Condition is a very critical factor. Most collectors like to have examples in very fine to mint condition. The original box and any instructional sheets add to the value.

Sophisticated collectors concentrate on the tin and cast iron toys of the late 19th and early 20th centuries. However, more and more collectors are concentrating on the 1940 to 1970 period, including products from firms such as Fisher Price.

Many toys were characterizations of cartoon, radio, and television figures. A large number of collectible fields have some form of toy spinoff. The result is that the toy collector constantly is competing with the specialized collector.

**History:** In America the first cast iron toys began to appear shortly after the Civil War. Leading 19th century manufacturers included Hubley, Dent, Kenton, and Schoenhut. In the first decades of the 20th century Arcade, Buddy L, Marx, and Tootsietoy joined the earlier firms. The picture became complete with the addition of firms such as Built Rite, Ideal, and Fisher Price.

In Europe, Nuremberg, Germany, was the center for the toy industry from the late 18th through the mid–20th century. In England the Britain and Lesney companies challenged the German supremacy. Lesney originated the famous Matchbox toys. German manufacturers were especially skilled in the areas of toy trains and stuffed toys.

**References:** Linda Baker, *Modern Toys, American Toys, 1930–1980,* Collector Books, 1985, 1993 value update; Bill Bruegman, *Toys Of The Sixties: A Pictorial Guide,* Cap'n Penny Productions, Inc., 1991; Robert Carter and Eddy Rubinstein, *Yesterday's Yesteryears: Lesney "Matchbox" Models,* Haynes Publishing Group (London), 1986; Jurgen and Marianne Cieslik, *Lehmann Toys,* New Cavendish Books, 1982; Don Cranmer, *Collectors Encyclopedia, Toys–Banks,* L–W Books, 1986, 1993 value update; Edward Force, *Classic Miniature Vehicles: Made In Italy,* Schiffer Publishing Ltd., 1992; Edward Force, *Corgi Toys,* Schiffer Publishing Ltd., 1984, 1991 value update; Edward Force, *Dinky Toys,* Schiffer Publishing Ltd., 1988, 1992 value update; Edward Force, *Matchbox and Lledo Toys,* Schiffer Publishing Ltd., 1988; Edward Force, *Miniature Emergency Vehicles,* Schiffer Publishing Ltd., 1985; Richard Friz, *The Official Price Guide to Collectible Toys, 5th Edition,* House of Collectibles, 1990; Gordon Gardiner and Alistar Morris, *Illustrated Encyclopedia of Metal Toys,* Harmony House, 1984; Lillian Gottschalk, *American Toy Cars & Trucks,* Abbeville Press, 1985; Jeffrey C. Gurski, *Greenberg's Guide To Cadillac Models And Toys,* Greenberg Publishing Co., 1992; Jay Horowitz, *Marx Western Playsets: The Authorized Guide,* Greenberg Publishing Co., 1992; Joe Johnson and Dana McGuinn, *Toys That Talk: Over 300 Pullstring Dolls & Toys–1960s To Today,* Firefly Publishing, 1992; Dale Kelley, *Collecting The Tin Toy Car, 1950–1970,* Schiffer Publishing, Ltd, 1984; Constance King, *Metal Toy & Automata,* Chartwell Books, 1989; Samuel H. Logan and Charles H. Best, *Cast Iron Toy Guns And Capshooters,* published by authors, 1990; Ernest & Ida Long, *Dictionary Of Toys Sold In America,* published by author, two volumes; David Longest, *Character Toys and Collectibles, First Series* 1984, 1992 value update, and *Second Series* 1987, Collector Books; David Longest, *Toys: Antique & Collectible,* Collector Books, 1990, 1992 value update; L–W Book Sales, *Riding Toys,* L–W Book Sales, 1992; Charlie Mack, *Lesney's Matchbox Toys: Regular Wheel Years, 1947–1969,* Schiffer Publishing Ltd., 1992; Charlie Mack, *Lesney's Matchbox Toys: The Superfast Years, 1969–1982,* Schiffer Publishing Ltd., 1993; Albert W. McCollough, *The New Book Of Buddy L Toys, Volume I,* 1991, and *Volume II,* 1991, Greenberg Publishing Co.; Brian Moran, *Battery Toys: The Modern Automata,* Schiffer Publishing, Ltd, 1984; John J. Murray & Bruce Fox, *A Historical, Rarity, Value Guide: Fisher–Price, 1931–1963, Second Edition* Books Americana, 1991; Nigel Mynheer, *Tin Toys,* Boxtree (London), 1988; Richard O'Brien, *Collecting Toys: A Collectors Identification and Value Guide, Sixth Edition,* Books Americana, 1993; Bob Parker, *Hot Wheels: A Collector's Guide,* Schiffer Publishing, Ltd., 1993; Maxine A. Pinsky, *Greenberg's Guide To Marx Toys, Volume I* (1988) and *Volume II* (1990), Greenberg Publishing Co.; David Richter, *Collectors Guide to Tootsietoys,* Collector Books, 1990; Harry L. Rinker, *Collector's Guide To Toys, Games, and Puzzles,* Wallace–Homestead, 1991; Nancy Schiffer, *Matchbox Toys,* Schiffer Publishing Ltd., 1983; Robin Langley Sommer, *I Had One Of Those: Toys Of Our Generation,* Crescent Books, 1992; Jack Tempest, *Post–War Tin Toys: A Collector's Guide,* Wallace–Homestead, 1991; Tom Tumbusch, *Tomart's Price Guide To Hot Wheels,* Tomart Publications, 1993; Toy Shop Magazine, *Toy Shop 1993 Annual,* Krause Publications, 1993; Carol Turpen, *Baby Boomer Toys And Collectibles,* Schiffer Publishing, Ltd., 1993; Peter Viemeister, *Micro Cars,* Hamilton's, 1982; Gerhard C. Walter, *Metal Toys From Nuremberg: The Unique Mechanical Toys Of The Firm Of Georg Kellerman & Co. Of Nuremberg 1910–1979,* Schiffer Publishing, Ltd. 1992; James Weiland and Dr. Edward Force, *Tootsie Toys, World's First Die Cast Models,* Motorbooks International, 1980; Blair Whitton, *The Knopf Collector's Guide To American Toys,* Alfred A.Knopf, 1984.

**Periodicals:** *Antique Toy World,* P. O. Box 34509, Chicago, IL 60634; *Collectible Toys and Values,* Attic Books, Inc., 15 Danbury Road, Ridgefield, CT 06877; *Collecting Toys,* 21027 Crossroads Circle, Waukesha, WI 53187; *Model and Toy Collector,* 137 Casterton Ave., Akron, OH, 44303; *Plastic Figure & Playset Collector,* Box 1355, La Crosse, WI 54602; *Toybox, 8393 E. Holly Rd., Holly, MI 48442; Toy Collector and Price Guide,* 700 E. State St., Iola, WI 54990; *Toy Shop,* 700 East State St., Iola, WI 54990; *Wheel Goods Trader,* P. O. Box 435, Fraser, MI 48026; *U.S. Toy Collector Magazine,* P.O. Box 4244, Missoula, MT 59806; *YesterDaze Toys,* P. O. Box 57, 275 State Rd., Otisville, MI 48463.

**Collectors' Clubs:** Antique Toy Collectors of America, Two Wall Street, 15th Floor, New York, NY 10005; Matchbox Collectors Club, P. O. Box 119, Wood Ridge, NJ 07075; New Moon Matchbox and Label Club, 425 East 51st St., New York, NY 10022; Schoenhut Collectors Club, 45 Louis Ave., West Seneca, NY 14224.

**Museums:** American Museum of Automobile Miniatures, Andover, MA; Museum of the City of New York, New York, NY; Smithsonian Institution, Washington, DC; Margaret Woodbury Strong Museum, Rochester, NY; Toy Museum of Atlanta, Atlanta, GA.

**See:** Battery Operated, Cartoon Characters, Disneyana, Dolls, Games, Paper Dolls, Radio Characters, Dimestore Soldiers, Toy Soldiers, Toy Trains and many other categories.

## ALPS

Alps Shoji Ltd., located in Tokyo, Japan, was founded in 1948. The company manufactured windup and battery powered toys made from tin and plastic. Toys are marked "ALPS."

Baby in Walker, cloth and vinyl baby, metal walker shakes litho tin rattle, 10" h, orig box .................. **70.00**
Bar–X Cowboy, windup, litho tin, full figure cowboy on horse, twirls metal lariat, horse with leather tail and ears, 1950s, 6½" l, orig box ............ **130.00**
Bozo the Clown, windup, litho tin, plays drums, 8" h ................ **495.00**
Circus Trio, windup, litho tin, cloth over tin, composition, head, 7" h, orig box **95.00**
Lester the Jester, windup, litho tin, fabric clothing, 9" h, orig box ........... **385.00**
Sea Wolf, windup, litho tin, peg legged pirate with spy glass, 7" h, orig box . **275.00**
Smiling Sam the Carnival Man, windup, litho tin, and cloth, 9" h, orig box .. **385.00**
Strutting Parade, windup, litho tin, cowboy duck, twirls lariat, quacks, 8" h, orig box ........................ **100.00**

## ARCADE

The Arcade Manufacturing Company first produced toys in 1893. In 1919, the firm began to make the yellow cabs for the Yellow Cab Company of Chicago. The exclusive advertising rights were sold to the cab company with Arcade holding the right to make toy replicas of the cabs. This idea was popular and soon was used with Buick, Ford, etc., and McCormack and International Harvester farm equipment. The company continued until 1946 when it was sold to Rockwell Manufacturing Company of Pittsburgh.

Bus ................................ **100.00**
Fageol Bus ........................ **925.00**
Ford
Model A, sedan .................. **400.00**
Model T ........................ **475.00**
Horse and Sulky ................... **85.00**
Pickup Truck, cast iron, 5" l ......... **225.00**
Showboat ......................... **975.00**
Tractor, cast iron, 1930s ............ **100.00**
Weeden #49, steam engine ......... **525.00**

## BANDAI, Japan

Bandai Co., one of the many toy manufacturers which began production in Japan after World War II, started with tin toys and later changed to plastic and steel. Bandai Toys are found with friction action and battery operated. They are often marked "Bandai Toys, Japan." Bandai still produces toys and is a major Japanese exporter to the US and other foreign countries.

Aircraft Carrier and Helicopter, friction, litho tin, T15 Bay Carrier, helicopter props spin, 7" l, orig box .......... **150.00**
Cadillac 1959 Convertible, friction, litho tin, 11" l
Black .......................... **420.00**
Blue ........................... **335.00**
Lotus Elan, GT Car Series, friction, tin body, plastic wheels, roof, and steering wheel, 8" l, orig window box ... **68.00**
MG Racer, friction, litho tin, tin steering wheel, scalloped plastic windshield, "Winner 1956 Overland Race" on trunk, tin spare, chrome detail, engine noise, 8" l, orig box .......... **340.00**
Rambler Rebel Station Wagon, friction, litho tin, plastic steering wheel and windshields, late 1950s, 11" l, orig box ........................... **365.00**
Silver Pidgeon Motor Scooter, friction, litho tin, 9" l ..................... **425.00**

Vespa Motor Scooter, friction, litho tin, turning handlebars, 9″ l ........... **330.00**

## CHEIN

The Chein Company was in business from the 1930s through the 1950s. Most of these lithographed tin toys were sold in dimestores. Chein toys are clearly marked.

Army Cannon Truck, momentum, tin, Mack style, adjustable cannon, c1930, 9″ l ...................... **260.00**
Barnacle Bill, windup, litho tin, wearing barrel, 1930s, 7″ h ............... **275.00**
Broadway Trolley, momentum, litho tin, red and green, boom, c1930, 8″ l .. **310.00**
Checker Cab, momentum, litho tin, 1924, 8″ l ....................... **520.00**
Clown With Parasol, windup, litho tin, c1930, 7″ h ..................... **195.00**
Dan–Dee Skid Truck, windup, litho tin, pull down ramps, balloon tires, early mark, 9½″ l, orig box ............. **725.00**
Dump Truck, momentum, Mack style, lever dumping action, 9″ l .......... **75.00**
Hercules Ferris Wheel, windup, litho tin, 17″ h, orig box ............... **375.00**
Locomotive and Passenger Car, momentum, litho tin, marked "New York Central Lines," and "NYC & HR," car marked "Saratoga," c1930, 19″ l ... **480.00**
Mechanical Turtle, #145, windup, litho tin, native riding on back, 7″ l, orig box ........................... **320.00**
Pianola, player piano, six rolls ....... **300.00**
Roller Coaster, windup, litho tin, two cars, carnival midway scenes around base, 1960s, 19″ l, orig box ....... **365.00**
Skin Diver, windup, litho tin, plastic flippers, 11″ l, orig box ........... **140.00**
Waddling Duck, windup, litho tin, c1935, 4″ h ..................... **65.00**
Waddling Pig, windup, litho tin, c1935, 5″ h ........................... **75.00**

## CORGI

Playcraft Toys introduced Corgi miniature vehicles in 1956. This popular line soon became Corgi Toys. The first cars were made on a 1:45 to 1:48 scale. Corgi cars were the first miniature cars to have clear plastic windows. Other design features included opening doors and interiors. In 1972, the scale of 1:36 was introduced. This scale was more durable for play but less desirable to collectors. Finally, the company added other types of cars and trucks, including character representations.

BMC Mini–Countryman Wagon, #485, diecast, opening doors, plated roof rack with two plastic surf boards, plastic figure, 3½″ l, orig box ...... **80.00**
Citreon Safari, #475, diecast, plastic roof rack with attached skis, "Corgi Ski Club" hood decal, opening rear door, plastic figure, 4½″ l, orig box . **70.00**
Customized Chevrolet Corvette Sting Ray, #337, diecast, customized finish, plated air intake and exhaust system, complete decals, 4″ l, orig box **70.00**
Ford Mustang Fastback 2+2, #325, diecast, opening doors, plated bumpers, reclining seats, spring suspension, complete decals, 4″ l, orig box **45.00**
Ghia L.6.4 with Chrysler Engine, #241, diecast, sedan, opening doors, folding seats, opening bonnet and boot, driving mirror, Corgi dog at rear window, 4½″ l, orig box ............. **50.00**
Heinkel–I Economy Car, #233, diecast, spring suspension, steering wheel, 2½″ l, orig box .................. **65.00**
Hillan IMP, #328, diecast, opening rear window, auto folding seat, "1966–1967 Rallye Monte Carlo" decals, 3½″ l, orig box .................. **65.00**
Lancia Fulvia Sport Zagato, #322, diecast, opening doors and bonnet, detailed engine, molded int., plated trim, spring suspension, 4″ l, orig box **40.00**
Land Rover, #438, diecast, spring suspension, detachable hood, 4″ l, orig box ........................... **43.00**
Lincoln Continental, diecast, Executive Limousine, opening doors, bonnet, and trunk, 6″ l, orig box and insert . **40.00**
Mars Candy Truck, 1985, MIB ....... **12.00**
Volkswagen Breakdown Truck, #490, diecast, operating winch with tow hook, hinged tool, plastic box lid with plated tools, 4″ l, orig box ......... **65.00**

## COURTLAND

Courtland Manufacturing Company was founded by Walter Reach in 1944. Originally located in Camden, New Jersey, the company later moved to Philadelphia, Pennsylvania. The company closed in 1951.

Checker Cab, #4000, litho tin, green and yellow, 7″ l, orig box ......... **150.00**
Circus Truck, litho tin, truck pulls revolving cylinder with litho lion, bear, tiger, and elephant, 9″ l ........... **112.00**
City Meat Truck, #4000, litho tin, panel body, red and black, 7″ l, orig box . **135.00**
Coal Truck, windup, litho tin, coal chute, crank activated scissor dumping action, 1950s, 11″ l, orig box .. **130.00**
Fire Dept Truck, windup, litho tin, ladder raises, 9″ l, orig box ........... **212.00**

Mechanical Tractor, windup, litho tin, black rubber tires, 6″ l, orig box .... **115.00**
Modern Bakery Truck, #4000, windup, litho tin, panel body, red and yellow, 7″ l, orig box .... **135.00**

## DINKY

Dinky Toys, made by the Meccano Toy Company of England, were first created by Frank Hornby in 1933. The Dinky series of diecast cars and trucks continued until World War II precluded the use of metal for toys. In 1945, production of diecast metal toys began with the introduction of a military line, as well as new cars and trucks. Production continued in factories in England and France until competition from Corgi, Tootsietoy, and Matchbox caused a decline in sales. The Dinky line was discontinued in 1979.

Euclid Dump Truck, #965 .... **40.00**
Horse Box, #581 .... **40.00**
Muir Hill Dumper, #562 .... **35.00**
Panhard Esso, #32C .... **75.00**
Plymouth Station Wagon, #344 .... **30.00**
Tractor, Aveling–Barford, red and green, 1950s .... **36.00**

## ERTL

Fred Ertl, Senior, founded Ertl in 1945. Blueprints obtained from companies such as John Deere and International Harvester were used as patterns, thus insuring a high level of similarity when comparing the toy with the original. Ertl produces a full line of wheeled vehicles and is recognized as the world's largest manufacturer of toy farm equipment.

Bell Truck, Bell Telephone Pioneer, NY **15.00**
Campbell Soup Truck .... **25.00**
Coke Truck, #1 .... **95.00**
Majorette Mercedes 500L Roadster, MIB **22.00**
Pickup, Bell System .... **14.00**
Smurf Car .... **10.00**
Texaco Truck
#3 .... **325.00**
#4 .... **50.00**
Tractor, trailer .... **45.00**

## FISHER–PRICE

Fisher Price Toys was founded in East Aurora, NY, in 1930. The original company consisted of Irving L. Price, retired from F. W. Woolworth Co., Herman G. Fisher, who was associated with the Alderman–Fairchild Toy Co. in Churchville, NY, and Helen M. Schelle, a former toy store owner. Margaret Evans Price, wife of the company president, was the company's first artist and designer. She was formerly a writer and illustrator of children's books. The company began with sixteen designs. Herman Fisher resigned as president in 1966. In 1969 the company was acquired by the Quaker Oats Company.

Black and white rectangular logos appeared on all toys prior to 1962. The first plastic part was used after 1949.

**Fisher Price, Squeaky the Clown, #777, paper litho on wood, green plastic collar, 1958–60, 6½″ l, 9″ h, $150.00.**

Bucky Burro, #166 .... **200.00**
Bunny Cart, #10, 1940, 9″ l .... **45.00**
Chatter Monk, #798 .... **42.00**
Clock, #759 .... **26.00**
Doctor Kit, 1977 .... **15.00**
Donald Duck, #400 .... **75.00**
Donald Duck Cart, #500, 1951, 10″ l **200.00**
Duck Cart, #410 .... **55.00**
Katy Kackler, #140 .... **85.00**
Mickey Mouse Safety Patrol, #733 .... **150.00**
Peter Pig .... **48.00**
Pluto Pop–Up, #440 .... **125.00**
Pop–Up Kritter, patent Oct 5, 1926, stamped mark .... **175.00**
Radio, #759, wood .... **23.00**
Snoopy
#181 .... **48.00**
#693, pull toy .... **30.00**
Space Blazer, #750 .... **195.00**
Tailspin Tabby, #400 .... **85.00**
Teddy Zilo, #752, early .... **120.00**

## HUBLEY

The Hubley Manufacturing Company was founded in 1894 in Lancaster, Pennsylvania, by John Hubley. The first toys were cast iron. In 1940 cast iron was phased out and replaced with lesser metals and plastic. The production of cap pistols were increased as this time. By 1952, Hubley made more cap pistols than toys. Gabriel Industries bought Hubley in 1965.

Baby Speedboat, cast iron, emb "Baby" on side, 4½″ l .... **75.00**
Buick Convertible, diecast, black rubber tires, nickel plated windshield, 7″ l, 1940s, orig box .... **100.00**

Crash Car . . . . . . . . . . . . . . . . . . . . . . . . **60.00**
Fire Patrol, two horses, missing figures **350.00**
Folding Wing Jet, metal, wings fold up, retractable wheels, plastic canopy, 7″ l . . . . . . . . . . . . . . . . . . . . . . . . . . . . **330.00**
Ice Wagon . . . . . . . . . . . . . . . . . . . . . . . . **150.00**
Pickup, diecast, 11″ l . . . . . . . . . . . . . . . **40.00**
Racer . . . . . . . . . . . . . . . . . . . . . . . . . . . . **160.00**

## JAPANESE, POST WAR

Following World War II, a huge variety of tin toys produced in Osaka and the Koto District of Japan flooded the American market. The vast majority of these toys are marked only with the country of origin and a trademark, usually consisting of a two or three letter monogram. It is virtually impossible to trace these trademarks to a specific manufacturer. Also, many toys were assembled from parts made by several different factories. To make matters even more confusing, names found on boxes are often those of the agent or distributor, rather than the manufacturer.

The following toys are listed by their trademarks. When possible, the toy's manufacturer and/or distributor are also identified. Also see specific listings for other Japanese toy companies.

**Japanese, post war, Kanto Toys, F-10 Fighter, battery operated, litho tin and plastic, marked "KO", 11″ l, orig box, $150.00.**

Acorn
Pan American Airlines, four engine plane, friction, litho tin, metal propellers, 1950s, 11″ wingspan, orig box . . . . . . . . . . . . . . . . . . . . . . . . . **175.00**
United DC7, friction, litho tin, metal propellers activated by spinning wheels, 11″ wingspan . . . . . . . . . . . **170.00**
ATC, Asahi Toy Company
Cadillac, 1960s style, friction, litho tin, plastic steering wheel and windshields, detailed int., "Cadillac" hubcaps and license plates, 17″ l . . . . . . . . . . . . . . . . . . . . . . . . . **1,000.00**
Mary Open Television Car, friction, litho tin, 1953, 7″ l . . . . . . . . . . . . **85.00**
Mercedes Benz 230 SL, friction, tin, detailed litho tin int., black rubber tires . . . . . . . . . . . . . . . . . . . . . . . . . **140.00**
Subaru Sedan, friction, tin, detailed litho tin int., emb "Subaru" under front grill, 1950s, 6″ l . . . . . . . . . . . **285.00**
CK, John The Naughty, windup, celluloid, little boy with bulldog biting seat of his pants, prewar, 6″ h, orig box . **425.00**
Cragston
Dragon Fly, windup, litho tin, four plastic wings, 7″ l, orig box . . . . . . **150.00**
Harbor Patrol, windup, orig box . . . **130.00**
Daiya, Coin Taxi, battery operated, tin, bump–and–go action, coin activated, 6½″ l, orig box . . . . . . . . . . . . . . . . . **135.00**
H
Gasoline Tank Truck, Mobil Gas, friction, tin, Flying Horse logo, engine noise, 9″ l, orig box . . . . . . . . . . . **85.00**
Milk Tank Truck, friction, litho tin, green and white, red lettering, 1950s, 9″ l . . . . . . . . . . . . . . . . . . . **45.00**
HAJI, Mansei Toy Company
1966 Buick Riviera, friction, litho tin, hardtop convertible, doors open, retractable plastic windows open and close, adjustable bucket seats, 11″ l . . . . . . . . . . . . . . . . . . . . . . . . . **510.00**
Galloping Horse, windup, litho tin, cowboy rider holds pistol, 8″ l . . . **85.00**
I, Aerial Tightrope Clown, windup, tin and cloth, 8″ h, orig box . . . . . . . . . . **365.00**
JOY, 007 Unmarked Secret Agents Car, battery operated, 1960s Chevy sedan, bump–and–go action, retractable antenna, siren noise, flashing red light, 14″ l, orig box . . . . . . . . . . . . . . . . . **325.00**
K
1958 Ford Skyliner, friction, litho tin, hardtop convertible, Ford hubcaps, 10″ l, orig box . . . . . . . . . . . . . . . . **325.00**
Circus Clown, windup, litho tin, celluloid head, fabric costume, clown with spinning cylinder balance on nose, 7″ h, orig box with clown misspelled . . . . . . . . . . . . . . . . . . . . . **72.00**
Cycling Quacky, windup, litho tin, duck riding tricycle, quacks, 7″ l, orig box . . . . . . . . . . . . . . . . . . . . . **140.00**
M–35 Tank, battery operated, litho tin, rotating turret, gun noise, tin soldier in turret, 9″ l, orig box . . . **130.00**
Walking Circus Elephant, windup, plush, celluloid native sitting on trunk, 7″ l, orig box . . . . . . . . . . . . **215.00**
KA, US Army Air Fighter, friction, litho tin, plastic propellers, 8″ l, orig box **110.00**

KO, Kanto Toys
Ack Ack Jeep, friction, tin, full figure soldier driver, black rubber tire spare, gas can on back, firing guns, 7″ l, orig box .................. **60.00**
Musical Open Car Cadillac, battery operated, tin, driver wearing cowboy hat, plays music, 1950s style, 9″ l, orig box .................. **400.00**
Mego/SY, Japan, The Mego Man, windup, 7½″ h, orig box .......... **975.00**
Mikuni
Dog Chasing Puppy, windup, litho tin, dog with rubber tail chases puppy with flapping ears, 7″ l, orig box .......................... **112.00**
Wild Roaring Bull and Boy, windup, litho tin, bull drags boy holding onto his tail, 9″ l, orig box ...... **100.00**
MM
Boxing Monkey, plush over tin, hits punching bag, 6″ h, orig box .... **100.00**
Drummer Clown, windup, tin and cloth, 10″ h .................. **245.00**
Expander Elephant, windup, plush and litho tin, exercises, 6″ h, orig box .......................... **85.00**
MS, Highway Patrol Car, friction, litho tin, litho Broderick Crawford image and policeman hold guns out windows, Highway Patrol TV series, 5½″ l .......................... **85.00**
MSK, Buick, friction, litho tin, searchlight on hood, working windshield wipers, 7″ l, orig box ............ **125.00**
NGT, Fox the Magician, windup, tin and cloth, disappearing rabbit, 6″ h, orig box .......................... **375.00**
Rock Valley, 1953 Mercury, battery operated, tin, adjustable front wheels, tin steering wheel, 9½″ l, orig box .. **300.00**
SAN, Marusan Toys
Bus, School Line, friction, litho tin, early 1950s, 7½″ l, orig box ..... **310.00**
Panoramic Overland Bus, friction, litho tin, double decker, passengers at windows, driver and stewardess at front windshield, black passenger in rear seat, "World" destination plate, "8–1956" rear plate, 12½″ l, orig box .............. **550.00**
Sanyo, Continental III, automobile, friction, tin, plastic steering wheel and front windshield, 1950s, 9″ l, orig box **150.00**
S & E
Curtiss Jenny Trainer, bi–plane, friction, litho tin, spinning propeller, 11″ l, 10″ wingspan, unassembled, orig box ..................... **215.00**
Snapping Alligator, windup, litho tin, 12″ l, orig box ................ **150.00**
Showa, The Great Swanee River Boat, friction, litho tin, indented windows with litho passengers, plastic pistons, indented spoke wheels, 1950s, 11″ l, MIB ............................ **280.00**
SK, Tumbling Clown, windup, celluloid and cloth, 8″ h, orig box .......... **225.00**
SSS, Yellow Taxi, friction, litho tin, engine noise, 7″ l, orig box .......... **160.00**
SY, Traveling Sam the Peace Corps Man, windup, litho tin, 7″ h ............ **165.00**
Taiyo
Pepsi–Cola Ford Sedan, friction, litho tin, black rubber tires, "Ford" license plates, allover Pepsi graffiti, red, white, blue, and yellow, 10½″ l, orig window box ............. **440.00**
Rusher Z28 Camaro, battery operated, litho tin, bump–and–go and non–fall action, lights, 10″ l, orig box .......................... **70.00**
TET, Jungle Monkey, windup, litho tin and celluloid, two monkeys and palm trees, 13″ h, orig box ............ **135.00**
Tomiyama, Flying Circus, battery operated, litho tin, bear trapeze artists, two bears suspended from swings, third bear transfers back and forth, magnetic action, 17″ h, orig box and instructions ..................... **1,350.00**
TT, U–Turn Circus Cycle, windup, tin, 6″ l, orig box .................... **250.00**
YONE, Yoneya Toy Company
Champion Rider, windup, litho tin, motorcycle and rider, 5″ l, orig box **100.00**
Happy Grand'pa, windup, litho tin, grandpa on tree stump reading book and farm house on round base, revolving parasol, 5″ h, orig box .......................... **65.00**
Monkey Carousel, windup, litho tin, four revolving monkeys spin and tumble, 7″ h, orig box .......... **175.00**
Turn Over Circus Plane, windup, litho tin, clown pilot, 4″ wingspan, orig box ...................... **165.00**

## LEHMANN

The Ernst Paul Lehmann Company was located in Brandenburg, Germany. The company began in 1881 and continues to the present. Lehmann toys are known for attractive lithography and patina. The use of clockwork and mechanical friction action was prevalent. Export to the United States was sporadic after 1933. Most Lehmann toys were sold in America through jobbers, such as Butler Bros, George Broadway Rouss, and Montgomery Ward. Many popular toys, such as the Balky Mule, were offered for over 25 years. Lehmann toys are marked "E.P.L." and/or "Lehmann."

Africa, string wind drive, litho tin, ostrich pulling cart, c1900, 7" l, orig box . . . . . . . . . . . . . . . . . . . . . . . . . . **2,300.00**

New Century Cycle, windup, litho tin, black rider holds spinning umbrella over driver, 1907, 5" h . . . . . . . . . . . . **715.00**

Quack Quack, windup, litho tin, mallard duck pulling basket with three ducklings, 1903, 7½" l . . . . . . . . . . . . **350.00**

Sedan and Garage, litho tin, #765 windup sedan with steering wheel and spoked wheels, 6" l, #771 garage, 6 x 3", 1910s . . . . . . . . . . . . . . . **655.00**

## LINEMAR

Linemar is a subsidiary of Marx. Linemar toys are manufactured in Japan.

**Linemar, Service Station with Car, #J1199, battery operated, litho tin, orig box, 10¼" l, $225.00.**

Banjo Cowboy, windup, litho tin, 5½" h . . . . . . . . . . . . . . . . . . . . . . . . . **160.00**

Cabin Cruiser with Outboard Motor, battery operated, tin, metal engine, plastic windshields, cloth covered seats, 12" l, orig box . . . . . . . . . . . . . . **215.00**

Dick Tracy Police Car, battery operated, remote control, tin, "Dick Tracy" shield on doors, policeman driver, Chevy hubcaps, flashing roof light, siren noise, 1949, 9" l, orig box . . . . . **395.00**

Donald Duck With His 3 Nephews, windup, litho tin, Donald pulling Huey, Duey, and Louie, each holds rubber rifle, 11" l, orig box . . . . . . . **1,610.00**

Flintstones Hauler and Trailer, friction, litho tin, 1961, 12" l, orig box . . . . **3,200.00**

Huckleberry Aeroplane, friction, litho tin, vinyl head Yogi Bear pilot, litho Hanna Barbera cartoon characters on sides and wings, 1961, 9" l, orig box **1,900.00**

Pluto the Drum Major, windup, tin, 6" l, orig box . . . . . . . . . . . . . . . . . . . . . . **600.00**

Popeye Turnover Tank, windup, litho tin, 4" l . . . . . . . . . . . . . . . . . . . . . . . . **415.00**

Pretty Butterfly, windup, Geisha girl with tin fan and paper parasol, 9" h, orig box . . . . . . . . . . . . . . . . . . . . . . . **200.00**

RCA Service Truck, friction, litho tin, 3" l . . . . . . . . . . . . . . . . . . . . . . . . . . . . **75.00**

Skating Popeye, windup, litho tin, holds plate and spinach can, 7" . . . . . . . . . **725.00**

Sneezing Bear, battery operated, plush, eyes light, 10" h . . . . . . . . . . . . . . . . . **180.00**

Touchdown Pete, windup, tin, holding football, 1950s, 6" h, orig box . . . . . **440.00**

Trombone Player, windup, litho tin, 5½" h, orig box . . . . . . . . . . . . . . . . . . . . . **300.00**

Violin Player, windup, litho tin, red, white, and blue tuxedo, 5½" h . . . . . **190.00**

Walt Disney Delivery Wagon, friction, celluloid and litho tin, 6" l, orig box **850.00**

Walt Disney's Babes in Toyland Cart, friction, litho tin, soldier driver with vinyl head, WDP, 1961, 6" l . . . . . . . **240.00**

Wilma Flintstone on Tricycle, windup, celluloid Wilma, tin tricycle, rings bell, 1962, 4" l . . . . . . . . . . . . . . . . . . **415.00**

## MARX

Louis Marx founded the Marx Toy Company in 1921, stressing quality at the lowest possible price. His popular line of toys included every type of toy except dolls. The company was sold to Quaker Oats Company, who sold it in 1976 to the European company of Dunbee–Combex–Marx.

**Louis Marx & Co., Joe Penner and His Duck Goo Goo, windup, litho tin, c1930, 8" h, $425.00.**

Army Engineers Truck, friction, tin, canvas, bed cover, winch and boom assembly, 1950s, 22" l, MIB . . . . . . . . . **320.00**

Army Set, twenty flat soldiers, windup tin tank, tin cannon, wood bullets . . **200.00**

Automatic Fire House, litho tin, fire chief car and garage, 8″ l friction car, crashes through station doors, orig box .......... **470.00**
Balky Mule .......... **90.00**
BO Plenty .......... **275.00**
Bulldozer Climbing Tractor, windup, litho tin, marked "Caterpillar," engine noise, piston spring action plow, c1940, 10″ l, orig box .......... **170.00**
Charlie McCarthy Benzine Buggy, windup, litho tin, red wheels and steering wheel, 1938, 7″ l, orig box **1,225.00**
Cherokee Indian, orig accessories .... **10.00**
Crawler, Lumar Contractor, 1950, near mint .......... **125.00**
Dare Devil Flyer, #700, windup, litho tin, 6″ l, monoplane and zeppelin circle 10½″ h Empire State Building, c1935, orig box .......... **2,200.00**
Dick Tracy Police Station, litho tin, 7″ l friction squad car crashes through station doors, orig box .......... **695.00**
Dick Tracy Siren Squad Car, windup, battery operated roof light, litho tin, siren noise, 11″ l, orig instructions, key, and box .......... **485.00**
Disneyland Express Train, 1950, MIB . **195.00**
Doll House, tin, Mickey and Friends .. **135.00**
Driver Training Car, windup, litho tin, plastic roof, non–fall action, 1950s, 6½″ l, orig roof .......... **150.00**
Farm Set, mechanical tractor and mower, 1940s, orig 6⅜ x 8½ x 2¾″ red, yellow, and black box ........ **250.00**
Flintstone Pals on Dino, windup, litho tin, Fred with vinyl head, 8″ l, orig box .......... **685.00**
Give–A–Show Projector, 23 reels, MIB **25.00**
G–Man Gun, windup, litho tin, G–Man decal, sparking action, c1925, 4″ l, orig box .......... **185.00**
Gravel Dump Truck, 10″ l .......... **85.00**
Hometown Meat Market, litho tin, 1930s style meat market, three butchers, meats displayed in showcase, freezer, stool, and chair, 1930s, 5 x 2″, orig box .......... **285.00**
Hometown Movie Theatre, litho tin, orchestra in front, lobby and ticket booth on sides, paper litho movie on winding rods, c1930, 5 x 2″, orig box **400.00**
Hometown Police Station, litho tin, 1930s style police station with jail cells, elevated desk sergeant, motorcycle cop, two policeman, two crook figures, c1930, 5 x 2″, orig box .... **650.00**
Jumpin Jeep, windup, litho tin, four soldiers, 1930s, 6″ l, orig box ........ **325.00**
Lone Ranger, rider, rotating lasso ..... **350.00**
Machinery Moving Truck, tin, hoist winch, platform, engine, barrel, lumber, 21″ l, MIB .......... **600.00**
Mickey The Musician, windup, plastic and tin, plays xylophone, c1955, 12″ h, orig box .......... **965.00**
Midget Tractor, windup, litho tin, black rubber treads, tin farmer driver, c1925, 5″ l .......... **110.00**
Mortimer Snerd Tricky Auto, windup, litho tin, 1930s, orig box ......... **1,200.00**
Musical Circus, momentum, litho tin, horse pulls musical cylinder, 11″ l .. **110.00**
Newlyweds Dining Room, litho tin, 1920s style, accessories include china cabinet, grandfather clock, table, floor radio, and two chairs, c1925, 5 x 2½″, orig box .......... **165.00**
Parrot, battery operated, plush, tin perch, swings tail, flaps wings, eyes light, repeats spoken words, 14″ h .. **365.00**
Plane, US Army, #712, windup, sparking guns .......... **250.00**
Play Range, streamline, utensils, 8 x 7⅝ x 5″ orig box .......... **150.00**
Police Motorcycle, windup, litho tin, siren noise, c1930, 8½″ l, orig box .. **765.00**
Princess Wildflower, MIB .......... **95.00**
Range Rider, windup, litho tin, cowboy on horseback, twirls lasso, rocking metal base, 1950s, 11″ l .......... **270.00**
Road Hauler, Lumar, two piece, 1950, near mint .......... **125.00**
Roll Over Cat, windup, litho tin, wood ball between paws, 5″ l, orig box .. **125.00**
Royal Bus Line Bus, windup, tin, c1930, 11″ l .......... **960.00**
Roy Rogers Stage Coach Wagon Train, windup, tin and plastic, 14″ l, orig box .......... **330.00**
Sparkling Tank, windup, litho tin, c1935, 4″ l, orig box .......... **135.00**
Sparky Barky, rolls, head turns, horn, Ken–L Ration .......... **65.00**
Steam Shovel, Lumar Contractor, 1950, near mint .......... **125.00**
Streamline Siren Sparkling Pistol, Flash Gordon style, steel, "Celebration Pistol" decal on one side, "Spirit of 76" on other side, c1926, 7″ l, orig box . **450.00**
Tank, WWII, windup, litho tin, soldier pops up, 10″ l .......... **125.00**
Toto The Acrobat, orig box .......... **300.00**
Turn Over Tank, #5, windup, litho tin, c1935, 4″ l, orig box .......... **160.00**
Upsidown, tumble toy, tin, three clowns tumble down chute, invert toy to repeat action, c1925, 10″ h, orig box .......... **1,260.00**
USS Washington, battleship, windup, litho tin, sparking action, 15″ l ..... **165.00**
Warship, spinning, orig box ......... **300.00**
Wingshot, pinball game .......... **22.00**

## MATCHBOX

Matchbox cars were first manufactured by Lesney Products, an English company founded in 1947 by Leslie Smith and Rodney Smith. Their first diecast cars were made in 1953 on a scale of 1:75. The trademark "Matchbox" was registered in 1953. In 1979, Lesney Products Corp made over 5.5 million toys a week. The company was sold to Universal International in 1982.

Bullnose, Morris Crowley .......... **50.00**
Bus, Greyhound .......... **30.00**
Commando, MIB .......... **5.00**
Commer Ice Cream Canteen, #47, blue, oval roof decal, plain side decal, black plastic wheels, 1963 .... **28.00**
Crane, Favin .......... **22.00**
DUKW, #55 .......... **25.00**
Euclid Dump Truck, #6, yellow, 1964 **10.00**
Evening News Van, #42, yellow, metal wheels, decals, 1957 .......... **40.00**
Foden Cement Mixer, #26, orange, plastic drum, 1961 .......... **35.00**
Ford
  Station Wagon, #31 .......... **30.00**
  Wrecker .......... **30.00**
Horse–Drawn Cart, #7 .......... **50.00**
Karrier, Bantam 2 Ton, #37, Coca–Cola truck, yellow, gray plastic wheels, 1960 .......... **50.00**
Land–Rover Series II, jeep, #12, olive green, black plastic wheels, 1959 .. **20.00**
London Trolleybus, #56, double decker, red, decals, black plastic wheels, 1958 .......... **80.00**
Lotus, #19, race car, green, black plastic wheels, decals, 1966 .......... **18.00**
Merryweather Marquis Series III, fire engine, #9, red, silver ladder, 1959 .. **20.00**
Motorcycle, sidecar .......... **60.00**
Pickup, commercial, #50 .......... **20.00**
Rolls Royce, Phantom V, #44, silver–gray, trunk opens, 1964 .......... **30.00**

## MASUTOKU TOYS

The Masutoku Toy Company (a.k.a. Masuya Toys) was located in Tokyo, Japan. Founded following World War II, the company made tinplate novelty toys with the trademark "MT."

Bubble Lion, battery operated, litho tin, rubber tail, blows bubbles, 7" l, orig box .......... **145.00**
Fancy Dan the Juggling Man, windup, celluloid, 6" h .......... **275.00**
Hook and Ladder Truck, battery operated, litho tin, plastic fireman on back, extension ladder, light, siren, 13" l, orig box .......... **150.00**
Pirate Ship, battery operated, litho tin, heavy paper sails, three pirate figures on deck, light up jewels in treasure chest, plastic pirate flag, 13" l, orig box .......... **425.00**
Police Cycle with Sidecar, friction, tin, black rubber tires, early 1950s, 7" l . **500.00**
Tom & Jerry Formula Racing Car, battery operated, plastic and tin, vinyl head Tom driver, engine noise, late 1960s, 11" l, orig box .......... **180.00**
Tom & Jerry Hand Car, battery operated, litho tin, plastic head Jerry driver, bump–and–go action, 9" h, orig box **220.00**
US Air Force X–15, friction, tin, 9½" l, orig box .......... **170.00**
Walking Lovely Bear, windup, plush over tin, white, 5" l, orig box ...... **50.00**

**M, Japan, jeep, friction, litho tin, swiveling gunner, 6" l, 3" h, $20.00.**

## MISCELLANEOUS COMPANIES

American Flyer, race car set .......... **75.00**
AMSCO, Hatboro, PA
  Doll–E Delecto Scales, 14 x 14¼ x 6" orig box, 1955 .......... **250.00**
  Kidd–E Simoniz Polish Kit, 14¼ x 14 x 1¾" orig box showing kids polishing car, wagon, and tricycle, near mint .......... **350.00**
Automatic Toy
  Jungle Pete the Mechanical Alligator, windup, litho tin, snapping jaws, 15" l, orig box .......... **150.00**
  Walt Disney Character TV Set, windup, plastic, int. rotating cylinder shows scenes from *Peter Pan*, c1949, 5 x 5 x 4", MIB .......... **190.00**
Baldwin, Bowling Alley, King Pin, tin, mechanical bowler, ten wooden pins, MIB .......... **175.00**
Banner, American Express Toys Truck, steel, tin balloon tires, litho box, 12" l .......... **150.00**
Bissel, carpet sweeper, Little Queen .. **40.00**
Buddy L

Dump Truck, large, red cab, yellow box, 1950s .................... **125.00**
Tool Chest, wood, large, tools missing .......................... **45.00**
Converse, farm, wood, litho, animals, barn with removable roof, hay loft and feed pens, 1890 .............. **350.00**
Daisy, Missile Tank, battery operated, remote control, litho tin, fires darts at litho cardboard targets, 9″ l, orig box **150.00**
Fischer, Germany, limousine, penny toy, litho tin, oval rear window, chauffeur driven, 3½″ l .................... **160.00**
Gebrüder Einfalt, US Zone, Germany, Technofix trademark
Clown Bicyclist, windup, tin, 6″ h .. **775.00**
Racing Cyclist, #15, friction, litho tin, tin balloon tire front, 7″ l .... **180.00**
Gescha, Germany, Fighter Squadron, windup, litho tin, three 4″ l fighter planes attached by rod, adjustable formations, orig box .............. **300.00**
Gibbs, horse–drawn mail cart, #27, pull toy, litho paper on wood horse, jointed legs, tin mail wagon with spoke wheels, 1910, 12″ l ......... **200.00**
Gilbert, Chemistry Set
#7½, metal box ................. **80.00**
#10021, cardboard tube .......... **40.00**
#10032, cardboard tube .......... **45.00**
Girard, Airways Express, tri–motor air mail airplane, tin frame, celluloid propellers, litho tin wings, c1930, 13″ l ........................... **300.00**
Gong Bell Manufacturing Company, CT, Pay Phone, steel, 6¼ x 8½ x 2¾″, orig box, 1950 .................. **100.00**
Greppert & Kelch, Germany, racer, windup, litho tin, boat tail race car with tin driver and tires, c1925, 7″ l **550.00**
Grey Iron Casting Company, Mount Joy, PA, tools, set of five, cast metal, 7 x 10″ orig card, 1940 ............... **20.00**
Hot Wheels, Good Humor Truck ..... **12.00**
Ideal, Hickory Dickory Clock, talking, red, yellow, blue, and black, 1950s, MIB ........................... **50.00**
Irwin
Nina Mother's Helper, windup, plastic, five cleaning accessories, 1951, 6½″ h, MIB .................. **150.00**
Walt Disney's Dancing Cinderella, windup, plastic, waltzing Cinderella and Prince, 1950s, 5″ h, orig box .......................... **220.00**
Jouets en Paris, France, Air France Jet, windup, tin, black rubber tires, stop/go switch, 14″ wingspan, marked "JEP," orig box .................. **200.00**
Joustra, France, convertible, friction, litho tin, red and yellow, plastic driver and poodle, 13″ l ................ **180.00**
Kellermann & Co, Germany
Cabrio 359, windup, tin, hardtop convertible, driver wearing racing suit, tin balloon tires, marked "CKO," US Zone, 6″ l, orig box .. **415.00**
Double Rider Motorcycle, windup, litho tin, drives in figure "8" pattern, tin balloon tires, 6″ l ....... **460.00**
Train Set, penny toy, tin, locomotive, coal tender, and six 2″ l passenger cars, orig box .................. **480.00**
Kenton
Coffee Grinder, dealer sample ..... **75.00**
Horse–Drawn
Bakery Truck .................. **175.00**
Cart .......................... **100.00**
Racing Sulky, figure .............. **175.00**
Keystone
Steam Roller, pressed steel, 1930s, large ........................ **250.00**
Stove, windup, litho tin ........... **35.00**
Kiddie's Metal Toys, sand pail, litho tin, "Sea Side," sitting boy, girl on swing, and eagle perched on ball around sides, wire bail handle, wood and tin shovel, red and gold, c1900, 6″ h .. **70.00**
Kienberger, Nuremberg, Germany, The Great Billiard Champion, windup, litho tin, pool player and billiards table, wood base, 1911, 6″ l, orig box **620.00**
Lagco, Bobbin Express, pull toy, wood cart carries four celluloid children, heads rotate and bob, rattle sound, 1950s, 7½″ l, orig box ........... **80.00**
Lindstrom
Boat, windup, litho tin, adjustable rudder, spinning propeller, 1930s, 7″ l ......................... **95.00**
Dancing Mammy, windup, litho tin, 1930s, 8″ h .................. **365.00**
Sweeping Betty, windup, litho tin, holding broom, 1930s, 8″ h ..... **200.00**
Lionel, Mickey Mouse Circus Train, litho tin, 7″ l windup engine with key, Mickey stoker car, circus dining car, Mickey band car, cage car, track sections, 1930s .................. **3,600.00**
Martin, Admiral Perry of the North, #217, commemorates North Pole discovery, 8½″ l windup litho tin dog sled with Peary driver, tin hand painted North Pole replica with American flag erected at center, 1909 .. **1,250.00**
Mattel
Clown, windup, litho tin .......... **40.00**
Fanner Shootin' Shell, toy pistol, cowhide holster .................. **150.00**
Musical Circus Merry–Go–Round, #440, crank lever, litho tin, alternating plastic animals and children with instruments, animals spin, plays music, 1951, 7½″ h, orig box **160.00**

**Mattel, Jack in the Music Box, Jolly-Tune the Clown, cardboard box, tin lid, hard plastic head, fabric covered spring body, 5⅜ x 5⅜ x 5⅞", $12.00.**

Musical Man on the Flying Trapeze, turn crank, plastic clown, litho tin trapeze base, plays title tune, 1953, orig box .......... **95.00**
Mohawk, Toyland Pie Bakery Truck, momentum, litho tin, 1919, 6" l .... **145.00**
Nylint
Dirt Mover .......... **55.00**
Overhauler, heavy wheels .......... **55.00**
Printcraft, rubber stamp set, TST ...... **18.00**
Remco, tank, Bulldog, MIB .......... **65.00**
Rico, Spain, Campsa Gas Truck, windup, litho tin, red and yellow, spoked tin wheels, 1930s, 7" l ..... **165.00**
Schuco, West Germany
Disneyland Alweg–Monorail, #6333, blue and gray plastic train, track, 1950s, orig box .......... **580.00**
Motodrill 1006 Motorcycle, windup, litho tin, full figure rider, 1950s, 5" l, orig box .......... **585.00**
Telesteering Car 3000, windup, tin, variable speed controls and direction, 12 pylons, orig key, and steering wheel, 4¼" l, orig box with insert .......... **275.00**
Scott Manufacturing Company, Toto the Mechanical Walking Clown, windup, hard plastic, yellow, red, and white, hand painted features, c1950, 11" h, orig box .......... **85.00**
Sears, Japan, Boeing 747 Jet Plane, battery operated, plastic, exposed fuselage, jet noise, stewardesses walk up and down aisle, 15" l, orig box .... **85.00**
Smith–Miller, truck, semi, PIE, GMC .. **395.00**
Steelcraft, Chrysler Airflow, 1937, restored .......... **3,900.00**
Strauss
Dizzie Lizzie, windup, litho tin, 9" l, orig box .......... **600.00**
Red Cap Porter, windup, litho tin, black porter pushing dolly loaded with trunk, pop–up bulldog, c1920, 7" l .......... **600.00**
Tip Top The Walking Porter, windup, litho tin, black porter pushes baggage cart, c1920, 6" l, orig box . **1,315.00**
Structo
Dump Truck, construction co, 21" l, 1940s, orig box .......... **245.00**
Road Grader, 17" l .......... **85.00**
Rug Loom, large wood frame, orig box and partially made rug, c1920 **145.00**
Speed Boat, 12" l, wood, convertible top, outboard motor .......... **125.00**
Suburban Toy Company, PA, Golf Caddy, Fairway, metal shaft golf clubs, golf balls, and tees, red and black plaid, 1950s, 5 x 7¼ x 31" orig box, MIB .......... **75.00**
Sutcliffe, England, Sea Wolf Atomic Submarine, windup, tin, spinning propeller, 10" l, orig box .......... **120.00**
Texaco
Fire Truck .......... **75.00**
Tanker .......... **65.00**

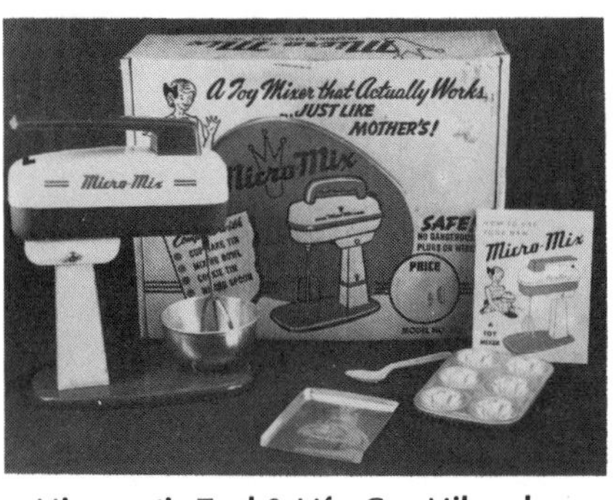


**Micromatic Tool & Mfg. Co., Milwaukee, WI, Micro-Mix Mixer, battery operated, tin, red and white, aluminum accessories, orig box, $150.00.**

Tinkertoys, 1915, orig tube .......... **32.00**
Tom Thumb
Cash Register .......... **18.00**
Typewriter, green .......... **45.00**
Weeden, Steam Engine Boiler, horizontal, cast base .......... **85.00**
Wells, England, Rolls Royce, litho tin, windup, 14" l .......... **700.00**
Winchester, roller skates, #10, MIB .. **120.00**
Withington, W Minot, ME, Take Down Bow & Arrow Set, 20 x 1½ x 4" orig box with illus of boy shooting arrow, red, yellow, and navy .......... **20.00**

## NOMURA TOYS

Nomura Toys, located in Tokyo, was one of the many Japanese suppliers of post war tin toys. Identified by the trademark "TN", the firm produced a large assortment of novelty toys ranging

**Sun Rubber Co., truck, #14, streamlined, red and yellow, 4¾" l, $50.00.**

from friction police cars to windup animals to the battery operated Charlie Weaver Bartender.

Calypso Joe, windup, litho tin, native drummer, 6" h .... **235.00**
Circus Boy, windup, tin, 6" h, orig box **310.00**
Dozo the Steaming Clown, battery operated, 14" h, orig box .... **300.00**
F–11 Jet Fighter, friction, litho tin, engine noise, 11" l .... **150.00**
Farm Truck, battery operated, litho tin, farmer John driver, exposed engine with lighted cylinders, bump–and–go action, bouncing basket of chicks in truck bed, 9" l, orig box .... **350.00**
Harley Davidson Cycle, friction, litho tin, tree working pistons, 1959, 9" l **320.00**
Ko–Ko the Sandwich Man, windup, tin, vinyl, and cloth, 8" h, orig box .... **165.00**
Lited Piston Action Plane, battery operated, litho tin, spinning propeller, 8 cylinder engine with flashing lights, tin pilot and co–pilot under canopy, engine noise, 14" l, orig box **395.00**
Merry–Go–Round Truck, friction, flat bed truck carrying carousel, three children riders, 1957, 8" l .... **145.00**
Musical Clown
  Battery Operated, cloth over tin, vinyl head, plays "London Bridge" on litho tin xylophone, 9" l, orig box **750.00**
  Windup, cloth over tin, vinyl face, plays drum, 7" h, orig box .... **100.00**
Percy Penguin, friction, litho tin, racing penguin on skis, wings flap, mouth opens, squeaking noises, 5" h, orig box .... **155.00**
Police Car, friction, litho tin, swiveling gun mounted on hood, engine noise, 7" l, orig box .... **120.00**
Police Patrol Auto–Tricycle, battery operated, tin, 10" l, orig box .... **515.00**
Sniffy Puppy, windup, litho tin, wiggles nose and tail, non–fall action, 6" l, orig box .... **70.00**
Yellow Cab, friction, litho tin, battery operated lighted sign on roof, engine noise, 8" l, orig box .... **360.00**

## OHIO ART

The Ohio Art Company was started in 1908 by Henry S. Winzeler, in Archbold, OH. The company produced metal picture frames. Toy production began in 1912. The 1969, Ohio Art purchased Emenee Industries. Ohio Art is noted for colorful lithographed tin toys.

Coney Island Roller Coaster, windup, litho vacuform plastic, 15 x 21" base with roller coaster above carnival scenes and "Coney Island" station, two 3" l litho tin cars, orig box .... **190.00**
Ferris Wheel .... **250.00**
Injun Chief, windup, litho tin, crawling Indian holds tomahawk, 8" l, orig box **325.00**
Magnasticks, orig box .... **25.00**
Mickey Mouse Sand Pail, litho tin, Mickey, Minnie, Donald, and Pluto in rowboat illus, 1930s, 5½" h .... **315.00**
Sand Set, four piece set, mint on orig card .... **48.00**

## TONKA

In 1946 Mound Metal Crafts Inc., Mound, Minnesota, manufactured the first Tonka Toys. *Tonka* was derived from the firm's proximity to the banks of Lake Minnetonka. The company introduced a full line of trucks in 1949. In 1956 it changed its name to Tonka Toys.

Big A Semi .... **35.00**
Car Carrier, c1960 .... **55.00**
Corvette, tin .... **50.00**
Dump Truck, red and green, 1950s .... **85.00**
Farm Truck .... **65.00**
Fire Pumper, 1964 .... **65.00**
Jeep .... **30.00**
Jeepster .... **45.00**
Road Grader .... **65.00**
Trailer House Hauler, roof missing .... **95.00**
Winnebago .... **49.00**
Wrecker, c1960 .... **70.00**

## TOOTSIETOY

The first Tootsietoys were made in 1911, although the name was not registered until 1924, and it was not until after 1930 that the name appeared on the toys. Tootsie was an early manufacturer of prizes for Cracker Jack. Tootsie produced copies of real vehicles beginning in 1914 and continued until World War II. After the war, cars were made as toys rather than models.

M G Roadster, 6" l .... **25.00**
Midgets Set #0510, cars, trucks, buses, and airplane, eight vehicles total, 1930s, orig box and insert .... **235.00**
Porsche .... **25.00**

Service Station Set #5710, eight 3″ l vehicles, gas station island, four traffic signs, car lift, orig box with fitted insert ............................ **440.00**

## TOPLAY, LTD.

Identified by the "TPS" trademark, this Japanese company was founded in 1956 and is well known for its litho tin windup toys.

Busy Choo Choo, windup, litho tin, 6 x 9″ base with litho track, 3″ l train, orig box ............................ **100.00**
Candy Loving Canine, windup, litho tin, flips candy ball from cup to mouth, 6″ h, orig box .................... **235.00**
Circus Parade, windup, litho tin, elephant pulling procession of three performing clowns, 11″ l, orig box .... **335.00**
Climbo the Climbing Clown, litho tin, climbs string, 6″ h, orig box ....... **285.00**
Giraffe, windup, litho tin, bounces beach ball, 9″ h .................. **130.00**
Girl Feeding Chickens, windup, litho tin, 5½″ h ....................... **275.00**
Girl Skipping Rope, windup, litho tin, boy and girl spin rope, smaller girl jumps, girls with vinyl faces, 12″ l, 6″ h, orig box ...................... **300.00**
Juggler, windup, litho tin, clown bounces ball behind back, 6″ h .... **365.00**
Monkey Basketball Player, windup, litho tin, shoots underhanded foul shots, 8″ l, orig box .............. **340.00**
Monkey Golfer, windup, litho tin, monkey hits ball across bridge into net, 7″ l, orig box ....................... **300.00**
Mounted Cavalryman with Cannon, windup, litho tin, soldier on horse, dragging cannon, 6″ l, orig box .... **500.00**
Mustang Stunt Car, battery operated, litho tin, detailed litho engine, 10″ l **115.00**
Mustang Swinger, battery operated, litho tin, 10″ l, orig box ........... **78.00**
Wagon Fantasyland, windup, litho tin, beetle pulling leaf with monkey driver and two spinning squirrel passengers, 12″ l, orig box ................... **325.00**

## UNIQUE ART COMPANY

Little is known of the exact origins of the Unique Art Manufacturing Company. Located in Newark, New Jersey, the firm was in business as early as 1916, the period in which it introduced its Merry Juggler and Charlie Chaplin toys. Unique was still operating as late as 1952.

Artie, windup, litho tin, clown driving car, 7″ l ......................... **350.00**
Bombo The Acrobat Monkey ........ **145.00**
Capitol Hill Racer, windup, tin, orig box **150.00**
Finnegan, windup, litho tin, porter and baggage cart loaded with suitcases, trunks, and crates, bump–and–go action, 13″ l ....................... **300.00**
Gertie Goose, windup, litho tin, 9″ l .. **150.00**
GI Joe and His Jouncing Jeep, windup, litho tin, orig box ................ **460.00**
GI Joe and K–9 Pups ............... **285.00**
Li'l Abner and his Dogpatch Band, windup, litho tin, Abner, Daisy, and Mammy and Pappy Yokum, 9″ l, orig box ...........................**1,400.00**
Lincoln Tunnel, windup, litho tin, cars and buses travel on expressway, Lincoln Tunnel one end, New York other end, policeman in middle, 24″ l, orig box ........................... **525.00**
Rodeo Joe, windup, litho tin, 1940s .. **250.00**
Sky Ranger, revolving plane and zeppelin, orig box .................. **450.00**

## UNKNOWN MAKERS

England, Hi–Wing Monoplane, windup, tin, balloon tires, metal propeller, 1930s, 17″ wingspan ....... **310.00**
France, motorcycle, sidecar, driver, detailed litho tin, momentum, balloon tires, luggage rack, glossy, marked "SFA France," 1930s, 6½″ l ....... **310.00**
Germany
- Bimbo, clown in car, windup, litho tin, US Zone, 4½″ l, orig box .... **135.00**
- Child in Stroller, penny toy, girl wearing blue dress with pinafore, 3″ h **360.00**
- Clown Rope Walker, windup, cloth, composition head, travels hand over hand on string, 7½″ h, orig box ......................... **235.00**
- Fishing Clown, windup, litho tin, fisherman circles as hooked fish ravels and unravels around posts, US Zone, 6″ h ................... **225.00**
- Happy Clown, windup, litho tin, US Zone, 6″ h, orig box ............ **280.00**
- Honeymoon Express, windup, litho tin, locomotive pulls coal car and two passenger cars around circular base with mountain tunnel and railroad bridge and station, 1930s, 10″ d ........................ **175.00**
- Horse–Drawn Cart, penny toy, tin, farmer driving cart, pull down rear gate, 4½″ l .................... **325.00**
- Ocean Liner, penny toy, windup, litho tin, metal masts, c1925, 4″ l ..... **615.00**
- Slugger Champions, windup, tin, black and white boxers in square ring, US Zone, 3½″ sq, orig box . **300.00**
- The Famous Juggler, windup, com-

position head, cloth body, plastic hands, 10″ h, orig box .......... **400.00**

Japan

American Circus Truck, friction, litho tin, pulls large cage with four full bodied tin wild cats, turn crank to remove animals, 11″ l .......... **225.00**

Animal See–Saw, windup, litho tin, elephant and zebra on see–saw playing drum, 7″ l .............. **585.00**

Auto Carrier, friction, litho tin, four 5″ l tin friction Cadillac cars, turn crank to unload cars, plastic windows, 18″ l .................... **260.00**

Barbecue Rotisserie, battery operated, tin, grill lights and smokes, door opens, chicken, utensils, and towel accessories, 7½″ h, orig box ..... **120.00**

Cat and Mouse, litho tin, pull string attaches mouse to cat, 6″ l, orig box **75.00**

Circus Clown on Unicycle, arms move up and down, legs pedal, 6½″ h ........................ **285.00**

Drive Car, friction, litho tin, full figure driver, c1955, 8½″ l, orig box ... **200.00**

Elephant, friction, litho tin, rubber tusks, vinyl trunk, litho tiara and blanket, ears flap, eyes roll, mouth opens, 8″ l .................... **185.00**

G–Men Motorcycle, friction, tin, black rubber front tire, early 1950s, 10″ l .......................... **485.00**

Good Time Charlie, windup, composition head, cloth body, tin feet, blows noisemaker, 11″ h, MIB ... **965.00**

Monkey Baseball Catcher, windup, litho tin, 1950s, 7″ h ........... **200.00**

Motorcycle #36, friction, litho tin, early 1950s, 5″ l ............... **125.00**

Ol' McDonald's Farm Truck, litho tin, VW pickup truck with animal cages in bed, celluloid cow head above tailgate, crowing rooster sounds, 6½″ l, orig box ................ **110.00**

Station Wagon, Rambler, tin, 1960s . **160.00**

Toto the Beloved Clown, windup, trapeze toy, wire frame, 6″ h celluloid clown, prewar, orig box ......... **130.00**

Tricycle Clown, battery operated, remote control, tin, cloth jacket, 7″ h **225.00**

VW Beetle, battery operated, litho tin, bump–and–go action, light engine with spinning fan, see–through trunk panel, plastic windshields and driver, 1950s, 10″ l ......... **185.00**

West Germany

Monkey Juggler, windup, plush, tin feet, twirls plastic dishes with balls attached, 1950s, 9½″ h, orig box . **55.00**

Puss N Boots, windup, tin, carrying tin pocketbook and cane, 5″ h, orig box ........................ **140.00**

## WOLVERINE

The Wolverine Supply & Mfg Co. was founded in 1903 and incorporated by Benjamin F. Bain in 1906. The first type of toys they produced were lithographed tin sand toys. They began to make girls' housekeeping toys and auction games by the 1920s. Production of toys continued and expanded in 1959 to include children's appliances, known as "Rite–Hite." The name was changed to Wolverine Toy Company in 1962. The company was originally located in Pittsburgh, PA, but relocated to Booneville, AK in 1970 after being acquired by Spang and Company.

Diving Submarine, windup, 13″ l ..... **185.00**

Icebox, tin ........................ **40.00**

Iron, Sunny Suzy, flat, electric ....... **18.00**

Kitchen Cabinet, No. 280, 1949, toy groceries, orig box ............... **150.00**

Merry Go Round, musical, four planes, four flags, 1930s ................. **595.00**

Refrigerator, No. 186, Frigidaire, pink, toy groceries, orig box ............ **150.00**

Sand Loader, litho tin, 8½ x 10¾ x 3½″, MIB ........................... **150.00**

Sandy Andy Merry Miller, litho tin, sand toy, 1930s, 13″ h, orig box and unopened can of sand ................ **340.00**

Sink, No. 198, metal, running water type, orig box .................. **150.00**

Submarine, orig box ................ **135.00**

Sunny Andy Street Car, pull toy, litho tin, c1935, 13″ l, orig box ......... **200.00**

The Corner Grocer, tin, foldout grocery store, six shelves, ten adv product boxes, store sign, scale, paper dispenser, meat and deli counter display, 12 x 32″ ....................... **225.00**

## WYANDOTTE

All Metal Products Company, located in Wyandotte, Michigan, has been in operation since the early 1920s. The company, better known as Wyandotte Toys, originally produced wood and steel toy weapons. In 1935 it introduced an innovative line of streamlined wheeled vehicles. The firm ceased operations in 1956.

Acrobatic Monkeys, windup, litho tin, 10″ d base with litho circus scenes, clown rides motorcycle around base, two monkeys spin on rods, orig box **1,275.00**

Circus Truck and Cage, pressed steel and tin, 11″ l truck, both with litho rear door panel with clown holding sign "Greatest Show on Earth," five animals, 1930s ................. **1,050.00**

Drum Truck, pressed steel ........... **125.00**

Hoky and Poky Hand–Car Clown, windup, tin, 6″ l, orig box ......... **245.00**
Livestock Truck, pressed steel, good graphics ........................ **105.00**
Miniature Town .................... **175.00**
Pop Gun, metal, wood stock, 1930s, 22″ l, orig box
Double Barrel .................. **90.00**
Single Barrel, pump action ........ **65.00**
Stake Truck
7″ l, pressed steel ................ **45.00**
20″ l, 1950s, near mint ........... **200.00**
Woody Car, retractable truck, replaced wheels ......................... **75.00**
Wrecker .......................... **75.00**

**Wyandotte, acrobat, windup, litho tin, 1930s, 9″ h, $150.00.**

## YONEZAWA COMPANY

Yonezawa toys are identified by their "Y" in a flower trademark. This is another of the many Japanese companies that flourished after World War II.

B–50 Boeing Superfortress, friction, litho tin, metal propellers, 19″ wingspan ........................... **412.00**
Boxing Dog, windup, plush and litho tin, sign around neck reads "Next 4th Round," 6″ h, orig box ............ **90.00**
F–100 Super Sabre Jet, friction, tin, sparking engine, engine noise, 1950s, 7″ l, orig box .................... **150.00**
Old Timer, battery operated, litho tin, man driving jalopy, bump–and–go action, 9″ l, orig box ............. **180.00**
Sight Seeing Bus, battery operated, tin, lift–up windows, cutout individual seats, tin driver, bump–and–go action, early 1950s, 9″ l, orig box .... **215.00**
USS United States, ocean liner, litho tin, working lights, 14″ l .............. **200.00**

# TRAINS, TOY

**Collecting Hints:** Prices do fluctuate. Prices from mail order houses and stores generally are higher than those found at train swap meets. A large train swap meet is held in York, Pennsylvania each year. Condition is critical. Items in fair condition (scratched, chipped, dented, rusted or warped) and below generally have little value to the collector.

Restoration is accepted, provided it is done accurately. It does enhance the price one or two grades. Spare parts are actively traded and sold among collectors to assist in restoration efforts.

Exterior condition often is more important than operating condition. If you require a piece to operate, you should test it before you buy it.

Toy trains is a very specialized field. Collectors tend to have their own meets. A wealth of literature is available, but only from specialized book, railroad or toy train dealers. Novice collectors should read extensively before beginning to buy.

**History:** Railroading was an important part of many boys' childhoods, largely because of the romance associated with the railroad and the emphasis on toy trains. Almost everyone had a train layout; basements, back rooms, or attics allowed the layout to remain up year–round.

The first toy trains were cast iron and tin; the wind–up motor added movement. The golden age of toy trains was 1920–1955 when electric powered units were available, and Ives, American Flyer and Lionel were household names. Construction of the rolling stock was of high quality. The advent of plastic in the late 1950s lessened this quality considerably.

Toy trains are designated by a model scale or gauge. The most popular are HO, N, O, and S. Narrow gauge was a response to the modern capacity to miniaturize. Its popularity has lessened in the last few years.

**References:** Paul V. Ambrose, *Greenberg's Guide to Lionel Trains, 1945–1969, Volume III, Sets*, Greenberg Publishing, 1990; Susan and Al Bagdade, *Collector's Guide To American Toy Trains,* Wallace–Homestead, 1990; John O. Bradshaw, *Greenberg's Guide To Kusan Trains,* Greenberg Publishing Co., 1987; Joe Deger (ed.), *Greenberg's Guide To American Flyer S Gauge, Fourth Edition, Volume I* Greenberg Publishing Co., 1991; Joe Deger (ed.), *Greenberg's Guide To American Flyer S Gauge, Volume II,* Greenberg Publishing Co., 1992; Joe Deger (ed.), *Greenberg's Guide To American Flyer S Gauge, Fourth Edition, Volume II* Greenberg Publishing Co., 1991; Joe Deger (ed.), *Greenberg's Guide To American Flyer S Gauge, Fourth Edition, Volume III* Greenberg Publishing Co., 1992; Richard Friz, *The Official Identification and Price Guide To Toy Trains,* House of Collectibles,

1990; Bruce C. Greenberg, *Greenberg's Guide To Ives Trains, 1901–1932, Volume II,* Greenberg Publishing Co., 1992; Bruce Greenberg (edited by Frank Reichenbach), *Greenberg's Guide To Ives Trains, 1901–1932, Volume I* 1991, *Volume II,* 1992, Greenberg Publishing; Bruce Greenberg, (edited by Christian F. Rohlfing), *Greenberg's Guide To Lionel Trains: 1901–1942, Volume 1* 1988, *Volume 2* 1988, Greenberg Publishing Co.; Bruce Greenberg (edited by Paul V. Ambrose), *Greenberg's Guide To Lionel Trains:1945–1969, Volume 1* 1993, *Volume 2* 1993, Greenberg Publishing Co.; Greenberg Publishing Co., Inc., *Greenberg's Lionel Catalogues, Volume V: 1955–1960,* Greenberg Publishing Company, Inc., 1992; Greenberg Publishing Company, Inc., *Greenberg's Marx Train Catalogues: 1938–1975,* Greenberg Publishing Company, Inc., 1992; John Hubbard, *The Story of Williams Electric Trains,* Greenberg Publishing Co., 1987; Steven H. Kimball, *Greenberg's Guide To American Flyer Prewar O Gauge,* Greenberg Publishing Co., 1987; Roland La Voie, *Greenberg's Guide To Lionel Trains, 1970–1991, Volume I,* 1991, *Volume II,* 1992, Greenberg Publishing Co., 1989; Roland E. La Voie, Michael A. Solly, and Louis A. Bohn, *Greenberg's Guide To Lionel Trains, 1970–1991, Volume II,* Greenberg Publishing Co., Inc., 1992; Lionel Book Committee Train Collectors Association, *Lionel Trains: Standard of the World, 1900–1943,* Train Collectors Association, 1989; Dallas J. Mallerich III, *Greenberg's American Toy Trains From 1900 with Current Prices,* Greenberg Publishing, 1990; Dallas J. Mallerich, III, *Greenberg's Guide to Athearn Trains,* Greenberg Publishing Co., 1987; Eric J. Matzke, *Greenberg's Guide To Marx Trains, Volume I,* 1989, *Volume II,* 1990, Greenberg Publishing Co.; Robert P. Monaghan, *Greenberg's Guide to Marklin OO/HO,* Greenberg Publishing Co., 1989; Richard O'Brien, *Collecting Toy Trains: An Identification and Value Guide, No. 3,* Books Americana, 1991; John R. Ottley, *Greenberg's Guide To LGB Trains,* Greenberg Publishing Co., 1989; Vincent Rosa and George J. Horan, *Greenberg Guide To HO Trains,* Greenberg Publishing Co., 1986; Alan R. Schuweiler, *Greenberg's Guide to American Flyer, Wide Gauge,* Greenberg Publishing Co., 1989; John David Spanagel, *Greenberg's Guide To Varney Trains,* Greenberg Publishing Co., Inc., 1991; Robert C. Whitacre, *Greenberg's Guide To Marx Trains Sets, Volume III,* Greenberg Publishing Co., Inc., 1992.

**Note:** Greenberg Publishing Company, Inc., (7543 Main Street, Sykesville, MD 21784) is the leading publisher of toy train literature. Anyone interested in the subject should write for their catalog and ask to be put on their mailing list.

**Periodical:** *Classic Toy Trains,* P. O. Box 1612, Waukesha, WI 53187.

**Collectors' Clubs:** Lionel Collector's Club of America, P.O. Box 479, La Salle, IL 61301; The National Model Railroad Association, 4121 Cromwell Road, Chattanooga, TN 37421; The Toy Train Operating Society, Inc., 25 West Walnut Street, Suite 308, Pasadena, CA 91103; The Train Collector's Association, P.O. Box 248, Strasburg, PA 17579.

**Note:** All prices given are for items in very good condition, meaning that the piece shows some signs of use but all parts are present and damage from use is minor.

## AMERICAN FLYER, S GAUGE

Accessories
- Bell Danger Signal, 584, 1946–47 .. **17.50**
- Billboard, 566, whistling, 1951–55 . **18.00**
- Eureka Diner, 275, 1952–53 ....... **40.00**
- Truss Bridge, 571, 1955–56 ....... **5.00**

Engines, Diesel, Electric, and Steam

Diesel and Electric
- 405, Silver Streak, 1952, Alco PA **80.00**
- 499, New Haven, 1956–57, GE Electric .................... **150.00**
- 21551, Northern Pacific, 1958, Alco PA .................... **100.00**

Motorized Unit
- 740, Handcar ................. **25.00**
- 743, Track Maintenance Car ..... **24.00**

Steam Locomotive
- 303, 4–4–2, Atlantic, 1954–56 .. **20.00**
- 316, 4–6–2, K–5, Pennsylvania, 1946 ...................... **45.00**
- 345, 4–6–2, Pacific, 1954 ....... **50.00**
- 21084, 4–6–2, 1957 ........... **40.00**

Rolling Stock

Box Car
- 623, Illinois Central, 1953 ....... **10.00**
- 734, Missouri Pacific, 1954 ..... **12.00**

Caboose
- 607 ......................... **8.50**
- 907 ......................... **17.50**
- 24526, 1957 .................. **12.00**

**American Flyer, S gauge, caboose, #630, 3/16" scale, red, 6" l, orig box, $15.00.**

Flat Car
609, American Flyer Lines, 1953 . **10.00**
915, Auto Unloading Car, 1953–56 **20.00**
24516, New Haven, 1957–59 ... **10.00**
Gondola
941, Frisco Lines, 1953–56 ...... **7.50**
C2009, Texas & Pacific ......... **9.00**
Hopper and Dump Car
719, C B & Q, 1950–54 ........ **30.00**
940, Wabash, 1953–56 ......... **12.00**
24225, Santa Fe, 1960–65 ...... **10.00**
Passenger Car
653, Pullman, 1946–53 ......... **25.00**
662, Vista Dome, 1950–52 ...... **24.00**
961, Jefferson, 1953–58 ......... **30.00**
24773, Columbus, 1957–58 ..... **45.00**
Tank Car
24313, Gulf, 1957–60 .......... **20.00**
24328, Shell, 1962–66 ......... **8.00**
24330, Baker's Chocolate, 1961–72 ......... **25.00**

## IVES

Accessories
Bridge, 91, O gauge, 1912–30 ..... **20.00**
Platform, cov, 119, 1905–14 ...... **100.00**
Locomotive
17, 0–4–0, 1908 ................ **300.00**
1118, 0–4–0, 1913–14 ........... **265.00**
1661, 2–4–0, steam, 1932 ........ **125.00**
3218, 0–4–0, 1917 .............. **125.00**
Passenger Car
52, Passenger Car, 1915–25 ....... **42.00**
130, Buffet, 1930 ............... **75.00**
136, Observation, 1926–30 ....... **35.00**
1813, Baggage, 1931–32 .......... **20.00**
Rolling Stock
Caboose, 121, 1929 .............. **75.00**
Gravel Car, 198, 1930 ........... **200.00**
Lumber, 57, O gauge, 1915–30 .... **35.00**

## LIONEL, O GAUGE

Accessories
Flag Pole, 89 .................... **20.00**
Lighting Set, 27, 1911–23 ......... **18.00**
Semaphore, 64 .................. **30.00**
Telegraph Pole, 85 ............... **12.00**
Tunnel, 120 .................... **35.00**
Engines, Diesel, Electric and Steam
Diesel and Electric
60, Lionelville, trolley type, aluminized paper reflector, 1955–58 ......... **175.00**
212, U. S. Marine Corps, Alco A, 1958–59 ................... **48.00**
614, Alaska, NW–2 Switcher, 1959–60 ................... **100.00**
706, 0–4–0, Electric, 1913–1916 **240.00**
3927, Lionel Lines, 1956–60 .... **60.00**
Steam Locomotives
203, 0–6–0, 1940–42 .......... **325.00**

**Lionel, No. 390-E steam engine and tender, 2-4-2, Blue Comet, steel boiler, diecast frame, Bild-A-Loco motor, two tone blue, brass domes and smokestack, copper trim, orig box, 1929–33, $990.00. Photograph courtesy of Bider's Antiques, Inc.**

233, 0–6–0, 1940–42 .......... **800.00**
665, 4l–6–4, 1954–59 .......... **75.00**
1062, 2–4–2, 1963–64 ......... **18.00**
Rolling Stock
Boxcar
638–2361, Van Camp's Pork & Beans, 1962 ................. **15.00**
714, 1940–42 ................. **335.00**
1514, Baby Ruth ............... **30.00**
2954, 1940–42 ............... **145.00**
3356, Santa Fe Railway Express, 1956–60 ................... **35.00**
3494–275, State of Maine, 1956–58 ........................ **55.00**
6050, Lionel Savings Bank, 1961, coin slot ................... **18.00**
6464–735, New Haven, 1969 ... **15.00**
6480, Explosives ............... **4.00**
Caboose
0017, NYC, 1939–42 ........... **50.00**
801, 1915–26 ................ **15.00**
1007, Lionel Lines, SP Die 3, 1948–52 ................... **1.50**
2457, Pennsylvania, semi–gloss red painted body, 1945–47 .... **25.00**
2357, silver and blue ........... **18.00**
6017, Lionel Lines, SP Dies, 1951–61 ........................ **15.00**
6119–50, D L & W, brown and white, 1957–59 ............. **20.00**
6417–50, Lehigh Valley, N5C, gray, 1954 ................. **32.00**
Flatcar
1887, Flat, fence and horses, 1959 **120.00**
3330, Flat, operating submarine kit, 1960–61 ............... **50.00**
3461, Log, dump, 1949–55 ..... **25.00**
3540, Operating Radar Car, 1959–60 ....................... **60.00**
6111, Flat, pipes, 1957 ......... **2.00**
6461, Transformer Car, 1949–50 . **25.00**
6650, IRBM Launcher, 1959–63 . **30.00**
6819, Flat, helicopter, 1959–60 .. **25.00**
Gondola
1717, 1933–40 ................ **24.00**
2452, Pennsylvania, 1945 ....... **4.50**

3444, Erie, 1957–59 ............ **30.00**
4452, Pennsylvania, 1946–48 ... **48.00**
6462, NYC, red ................ **4.50**
Hopper and Dump Car
0016, South Pacific, 1938–42 ... **60.00**
2816, 1935–42 ................ **48.00**
6446–1, N&W, marked "546446," 1954–55 .................... **25.00**
Passenger Car
530, Observation, 1926–32 ..... **16.00**
600, Pullman, 1933–42 ......... **75.00**
604, Observation, 1920–25 ..... **20.00**
605, Pullman, 1925–32 ......... **65.00**
637, Coach, 1936–39 .......... **55.00**
1673, Coach 1936–37 .......... **18.00**
1687, Observation ............. **145.00**
1866, West & Atlantic, Baggage, 1959–62 .................... **24.00**
2400, Maplewood, green and gray **25.00**
2401, Hillside, Pullman, 1948–49 **24.00**
2442, brown, gray trim ......... **35.00**
2522, President Harrison, 1962–66 **60.00**
2631, Observation, 1938–42 .... **25.00**
Tank Car
0045, Shell, 1939–42 ........... **50.00**
1515, 1933–37 ................ **25.00**
2465, Sunoco, 1946 ............ **8.00**
2955, 1940–42 ................ **165.00**
6025, Gulf, 1956–57 ........... **8.00**
6465, Lionel Lines, 1958–59 .... **5.00**

## N GAUGE

Atlas
Locomotive, EMD E8, diesel, Santa Fe **20.00**
Rolling Stock
Box Car, 2204, Great Northern .. **5.00**
Reefer, 2224, Blatz Beer ........ **2.00**
Pullman, 2601, Santa Fe ........ **7.50**
Lone Star
Locomotive
EL–65, F–7, Kansas City ........ **15.00**
EL–68, F–7, Canadian National .. **25.00**
Rolling Stock
Caboose, EL–141, Canadian Pacific ........................ **5.00**
Coach, EL–70, British Main Line . **3.50**
Rivarossi
Locomotive, 5001A, Santa Fe, diesel **35.00**
Rolling Stock
Diner, 5211D, Milwaukee Road .. **10.00**
Freight, 6001D, Conrail ......... **2.50**
Observation, 5231H, Southern ... **8.50**

# TYPEWRITERS

**Collecting Hints:** Patent dates marked on frames are not accurate indicators of age, as these only indicate the date of the mechanical innovation's patent. A machine with an 1890s patent date may have been made as long as twenty–five or more years later. The serial number is a far more useful tool in dating a machine. However, there are many different manufacturers' numbering systems that are unknown, extremely confusing, or illogical.

In quite a number of cases, the only way to date a particular machine is through the use of old advertisements and catalogs. These references can also reveal particular models, colors, and unusual features produced.

Most manual typewriters produced after 1920 have little value, albeit some later models with unusual features have attracted collector interest. Some Electro–mechanical (or electric) typewriters manufactured before 1933 are scarce and hence, valuable.

Domestic typewriter collectors are a small but steadily growing group. There is a well established and active international typewriter collecting community, especially in Europe where mechanical objects and typewriters are eagerly sought. American collectors have generally swapped and traded among themselves, thus keeping prices reduced. This is changing as a result of increased attention and interest in American machines by international collectors.

**History:** The first commercially produced American typewriter was the Sholes & Glidden Typewriter, manufactured by E. Remington & Sons in 1874. This typewriter produced a row of tiny, uneven capital letters. In 1876 Remington exhibited an example of the Sholes & Glidden at the Philadelphia United States Centennial Exhibition. For twenty–five cents people watched souvenir messages being typed, letters that are highly collectible today. Mark Twain was one of the first to purchase a Sholes & Glidden. Although his review of it was rather mixed, his *Life on the Mississippi* is thought to be the first typewritten manuscript.

In 1878 Remington produced the Perfected Type Writer #2, later named the "Standard Remington Typewriter #2." This machine was far more reliable and useful than its predecessor. Both of these typewriters typed on paper wound on a platen suspended over a circular typebasket. To view the typing performed, the carriage had to be lifted away from the basket. This was known as a blind typewriter and was the most common machine style for the next thirty years.

Like so many other manufacturers of the time, five major typewriter companies joined together in 1893 to form the Union Typewriter Company, in essence a trust formed to limit competition and fix prices. Members of the trust produced thick, squat, blind writing office machines exclusively, with little impetus for innovation. Two companies formed in competition to the Union Typewriter trust. Underwood Typewriter Company (1895) and L. C. Smith & Brothers Typewriter Company (1903) manufactured machines with a visible writing surface. These companies became the powerhouses of the typewriter industry for the next thirty years.

The first American made electric machines appeared and quickly disappeared just after the turn of the century. The famous Blickenderfer Electric and little–known Cahill Electric are two of the earliest examples. The first successful electric typewriter was the IBM Model 01, introduced in the early 1930s.

Early typewriters generally have a glossy black finish, sometimes decorated with colored pinstripes or, less frequently, high detailed painted designs and inlays. This was the general trend until the 1920s when various bright colors were used, generally on portable machines. Many examples had a wood grain finish. Black typewriters with a two–tone finish of glass and crackle panels were exclusively produced during the 1930s. Starting in the 1940s, typewriters and other office equipment was manufactured in "designer" colors to match office interiors.

The electronic typewriter, the newest advance in typewriting technology, is light, has few moving parts, and many additional features. The growth in personal computers and related printers is fast making the typewriter obsolete.

**References:** Michael H. Adler, *The Writing Machine,* George Allen & Unwin Ltd, 1973; Wilfred A. Beeching, *Century of the Typewriters,* William Heinemann, 1974; Richard N. Current, *The Typewriter and the Men Who Made It,* University of Illinois Press, 1954; Darryl Matter, *Simplex Typewriters from the Early Twentieth Century,* Green Gate Books, 1984; Dan R. Post, *Collector's Guide to Antique Typewriters,* Post–Era Books, 1981.

**Periodicals:** *The Typewriter Exchange,* 2125 Mt. Vernon Street, Philadelphia, PA 19130; *Typewriter Times,* 1216 Garden Street, Hoboken, NJ 07030.

**Collectors' Clubs:** Internationales Forum Historische Burowelt, Postfach 50 11 68, D–5000 Koln–50, Germany; Early Typewriter Collectors Association, 2591 Military Ave., Los Angeles, CA 90064.

**Museums:** Henry Ford Museum, Dearborn, MI; Milwaukee Public Museum, Milwaukee, WI; Onandaga Historical Society, Syracuse, NY; Smithsonian Institution, National Museum of American History, Washington, DC.

**Advisor:** Todd Holmes.

## TYPEWRITERS

Bennett Portable, last patent date 1908, 10¾ x 4¾ x 2½" case ............ **45.00**
Blickensderfer
  No. 5, orig oak case ............ **150.00**
  No. 7, cylinder type, Stanford, CT, oak case ............ **100.00**
Corona, fold up model, three row keyboard, black, orig case ............ **35.00**
Fox, metal case, early 1900s ............ **85.00**
Hammond
  Multiplex, orig wood case ............ **100.00**
  Swinging sector mechanism, three row straight keyboard, inking by ribbon, oak base, bentwood cov, c1890 ............ **185.00**
IBM, Selectric, electric, interchangable ball type face ............ **20.00**
Keystone ............ **75.00**
Merritt, linear index mechanism, plunger type selector, double shift, inking by roller, wooden base, orig oak case, c1900, 12½" l ............ **165.00**
O'Dell, No. 4, Chicago, 1885 ............ **80.00**
Oliver
  No. 4, c1900 ............ **35.00**
  No. 5, ivory colored keys, oak baseboard, stenciled tin cov ............ **100.00**
Remington
  No. 6, orig tin cov ............ **65.00**
  Portable, 1929 ............ **25.00**
Shole & Glidden ............ **275.00**
Simplex, Model I, index type, red, white, and blue, orig box ............ **45.00**
Underwood, #25, orig wood case, 1929 ............ **75.00**

## TYPEWRITER RIBBON TINS

Allied ............ **7.00**
Cavilier ............ **7.00**
Codo Super Fiber ............ **7.00**
Elk
  Round ............ **5.00**
  Square ............ **5.00**
Five O'Clock ............ **7.00**
Hallmark ............ **5.00**
Herald Square ............ **6.00**
High Grade ............ **5.00**
Ivory ............ **5.00**
Keelox ............ **5.00**
Kleanwrite ............ **7.00**
Madame Butterfly ............ **8.00**
M and M ............ **6.00**
Marvello ............ **7.00**
McGregor ............ **8.00**
Midnight ............ **5.00**
Miller Line
  Round ............ **5.00**
  Square ............ **5.00**
Old Town ............ **5.00**
Osborn ............ **5.00**
Panama ............ **8.00**
Park Avenue ............ **6.00**
Plenty Copy ............ **5.00**
Preferred ............ **7.00**
Remtico ............ **8.00**
Secretaral ............ **5.00**
Silkeelox ............ **5.00**

Silver .......... **5.00**
Standard .......... **7.00**
Star .......... **6.00**
Super Nylon .......... **6.00**
Sun Strand .......... **5.00**
Tagger .......... **5.00**
Thorobred .......... **5.00**
Type Bar
  Round .......... **5.00**
  Square .......... **5.00**
Twins .......... **8.00**
Value .......... **7.00**
Vertex .......... **6.00**
Vogue .......... **6.00**

# UNIVERSAL POTTERY

**Collecting Hints:** Not all Universal pottery carried the Universal name as part of the backstamp. Wares marked "Harmony House," "Sweet William/Sears Roebuck and Co.," and "Wheelock, Peoria" are part of the Universal production. Wheelock was a department store in Peoria, Illinois, that controlled the Cattail pattern on the Old Holland shape.

Like many pottery companies Universal had many shapes or styles of blanks, the most popular being Camwood, Old Holland, and Laurella. The same decal might be found on several different shapes.

The Cattail pattern had many accessory pieces. The 1940 and 1941 Sears catalogs listed an oval wastebasket, breakfast set, kitchen scale, linens, and bread box. Calico Fruits is another pattern with accessory pieces.

The Calico Fruits decal has not held up well over time. Collectors may have to settle for less than perfect pieces.

**History:** Universal Potteries of Cambridge, Ohio, was organized in 1934 by The Oxford Pottery Company. It purchased the Atlas–Globe plant properties. The Atlas–Globe operation was a merger of the Atlas China Company (formerly Crescent China Co. in 1921, Tritt in 1912 and Bradshaw in 1902) and the Globe China Company.

Even after the purchase, Universal retained the Oxford ware, made in Oxford, Ohio, as part of their dinnerware line. Another Oxford plant was used to manufacture tiles. The plant at Niles, Ohio, was dismantled.

The most popular lines of Universal were "Ballerina" and "Ballerina Mist." The company developed a detergent–resistant decal known as permacel, a key element in keeping a pattern bright. Production continued until 1960, when all plants were closed.

**References:** Jo Cunningham, *The Collector's Encyclopedia of American Dinnerware,* Collector Books, 1982, 1992 value update; Harvey Duke, *The Official Identification and Price Guide To Pottery and Porcelain, Seventh Edition,* House of Collectibles, 1989.

**Periodical:** *The Daze,* P.O. Box 57, 10271 State Rd., Otisville, MI 48463.

## BITTERSWEET

Drip Jar, cov .......... **20.00**
Mixing Bowl .......... **30.00**
Platter .......... **30.00**
Salad Bowl .......... **32.00**
Stack Set .......... **35.00**

## CALICO FRUIT

Custard Cup, 5 oz .......... **4.00**
Milk Jug, 3 qt .......... **22.00**
Plate, 6" d .......... **4.00**
Refrigerator Set, three jars, 4", 5", and 6" d .......... **45.00**
Salt and Pepper Shakers, pr, utility .......... **16.00**
Soup Bowl, tab handle .......... **6.00**
Utility Pitcher, cov .......... **38.00**
Utility Plate, 11½" d .......... **18.00**

**Cattail, butter dish, cov, $25.00.**

## CATTAILS

Bread Box, double compartment .......... **25.00**
Butter Dish, cov, 1 lb .......... **40.00**
Canteen Jug .......... **30.00**
Casserole, cov, 8¼" d .......... **15.00**
Cookie Jar, cov .......... **45.00**
Gravy Boat .......... **20.00**
Jug, side handle, cork stopper .......... **32.00**
Milk Pitcher, 1 qt .......... **20.00**
Pie Server .......... **20.00**
Platter, oval .......... **20.00**
Range Set, 5 pcs .......... **35.00**
Tea Set, 4 pcs .......... **25.00**

## LARGO

Bowl, small .......... **3.50**
Creamer .......... **5.00**
Pie Baker .......... **10.00**
Plate
  Dessert, 6" d .......... **3.00**
  Luncheon, square .......... **4.00**

Salt and Pepper Shakers, pr .......... **6.00**
Utility Bowl, cov .................. **6.00**

## RAMBLER ROSE

Gravy Boat ........................ **8.00**
Milk Pitcher ....................... **18.00**
Plate, 9″ d ........................ **6.00**
Salt Shaker, utility ................ **5.00**
Soup, flat ......................... **4.50**

## WOODVINE

Creamer and Sugar, cov ............. **18.00**
Cup and Saucer .................... **7.50**
Gravy Boat ........................ **10.00**
Plate, 9″ d ........................ **4.00**
Utility Jar, cov .................... **20.00**
Vegetable Bowl, oval ............... **8.00**

# VALENTINES

**Collecting Hints:** Valentine collectors tend to focus on cards made before 1930, with special emphasis on the nineteenth century. Cards made before 1800 are known, but most are in the hands of museums.

At present collectors tend to specialize in one type of card, e.g., transportation theme cards, lacey, honeycomb, etc. Comic sheets, Art Nouveau, and Art Deco cards are gaining in popularity. Valentine collectors now face heavy competition from other theme collectors who want valentines as supplements to their collections.

Condition of the card is more important than age in most cases. Collectors like clean cards in very good repair.

Early German mechanical cards open and close from the middle; later examples and reproductions pull down. Early mechanicals used more delicate pastel shades. Bright red is found on later cards.

Keep cards out of the light to prevent fading and brittleness. Store cards in layers in a drawer with acid free paper between them.

**History:** Early cards were handmade, often containing both handwritten verses and hand drawn pictures. Many cards also were hand colored and contained cutwork.

Mass production of machine made cards featuring chromolithography began after 1840. In 1847 Esther Howland of Worcester, Massachusetts, established a company to make valentines which were hand decorated with paper lace and other materials imported from England. They had a small "H" stamped in red in the top left corner. Howland's company eventually became the New England Valentine Company [N.E.V. Co.].

George C. Whitney and his brother founded a company after the Civil War which dominated the market from the 1870s through the first decades of the twentieth century. They bought out several competitors, one of which was the New England Valentine Company.

Lace paper was invented in 1834. The 1835 to 1860 period is known as the "golden age" of lacey cards.

Embossed paper was used in England after 1800. Embossed lithographs and woodcuts developed between 1825–40, with early examples being hand colored.

**References:** Ruth Webb Lee, *A History of Valentines, Fifth Edition,* Lee Publications, 1952; Norman E. Martinus and Harry L. Rinker, *Warman's Paper,* Wallace–Homestead, 1993; National Valentine Collectors Association, *Bulletins;* Frank Staff, *The Valentine And Its Origins,* out of print.

**Collectors' Club:** National Valentine Collectors Association, Box 1404, Santa Ana, CA 92702.

**Advisor:** Evalene Pulati.

**To Teacher, bi-fold, Cordially Yours, 4⅜ x 5⅜″, 1960s, $2.50.**

Cutout
Easel Back
Art Deco, folder, 1920s
  Heart shape, 3 x 3″ .............. **1.50**
  Lace, fancy, 5 x 7″ .............. **5.00**
  McLoughlin, layered lace dec, 6 x 9″ **9.00**
  Whitney, oblong, 3 x 5″ ........... **2.00**
Art Nouveau, folder, 1900s
  McLoughlin, layered lace dec, 6 x 9″ **12.50**
  Whitney, oblong, 3 x 5″ ........... **7.50**
Children's, mechancial
  Ferris Wheel, large ............... **37.50**
  Jumping Jack, large ............... **25.00**
  Kaleidoscope ..................... **25.00**
  Standup, children, 6 x 9″ .......... **15.00**
  Teeter Totter, 5 x 10″ ............ **18.50**
Comic
  Animated, 6 x 9″, early ........... **45.00**
  McLoughlin, 4 x 6″, c1898 ........ **6.50**

Occupational, early ............ **27.50**
Satirical, English, early ............ **25.00**
Easel Back, diecut, cardboard, c1900
Children ............ **15.00**
Hearts and cupids, 4 x 4" ............ **7.50**
Two part ............ **18.50**
Handmade
Cutwork
Pennsylvania Dutch, 5 x 7" ............ **250.00**
Watercolor work ............ **350.00**
Folder, small ............ **10.00**
Fraktur, love knot ............ **450.00**
Handdrawn, love knot, 9 x 9" ............ **300.00**
Pen and Ink Work, heart shape ............ **175.00**
Pinpricking, scene dec, 8 x 10" ............ **175.00**
Puzzle Purse, 12 x 12" ............ **300.00**
Honeycomb, pulldown, German
Beistle
Dark red, 7" ............ **7.50**
Toad Stool, 1920s ............ **7.50**
Wheel of Fortune ............ **15.00**
Binoculars, large ............ **45.00**
Children's
Garden scene ............ **12.50**
Tea party ............ **18.50**
Scale, white, large ............ **65.00**
Tunnel of Love, 1930s ............ **18.50**
Umbrella, pink, fancy ............ **45.00**
World Globe, large ............ **75.00**
Lacy, 1840–60
Folder
Double Layered, 8 x 10" ............ **125.00**
Small, sgd "H" ............ **35.00**
Mansell, satin center, 8 x 10" ............ **95.00**
Meek, written verse, 5 x 7" ............ **25.00**
Whitney, folder, fancy, 7 x 9" ............ **18.50**
Lithographed, 1830–60
American
Civil War soldier ............ **95.00**
Couple in garden ............ **45.00**
Girl with doll, 5 x 7" ............ **35.00**
Documentary, marriage license ............ **65.00**
English
Aquatint, marked "Unrqtd love" . **95.00**
Maiden in garden ............ **35.00**
Seaman, folder ............ **45.00**
Poem, lettersheet, illuminated ............ **45.00**
Mechanical, pull down, German
Automobile, large, 1910 ............ **85.00**
Children, simple design, small ............ **5.00**
Sailboat, small ............ **35.00**
Ship, large ............ **85.00**
Three layers, children, small ............ **13.50**
Novelty, 1885–1915
Double sided, silk fringe ............ **18.50**
Easel back, layered, parchment ............ **25.00**
Padded sachet envelope ............ **35.00**
Post Card
Hearts, flowers, and cherubs ............ **3.00**
Mechanical ............ **10.00**
Padded silk heart, photo of girl ............ **15.00**

# VENDING MACHINES

**Collecting Hints:** Since individual manufacturers offered such a wide range of models, some collectors choose to specialize in a particular brand of machine. Variations are important. Certain accessories, porcelain finish, colors or special mechanical features on an otherwise common machine can add much to its value.

Original paint adds value. But numerous machines, especially peanut vendors with salt damaged paint, have been repainted. Most vendors were in service for ten to twenty years or more. Repainting normally was done by the operator as part of the repair and maintenance of his route. Repaints, recent or otherwise, if nicely done, do not necessarily lessen the value of a desirable machine. Original paint should be retained if at all possible.

Decals add much to the appearance of a vendor and often are the only means of identifying it. Original decals, again, are the most desirable. Reproductions of many popular styles have been made and are a viable alternative if originals are not available.

Some reproduction parts also are available. In some cases, entire machines have been reproduced using new glass and castings. Using one or two new parts as a means of restoring an otherwise incomplete machine is generally accepted by collectors.

Collecting vending machines is a relatively new hobby. It has increased in popularity with other advertising collectibles. New machines constantly are being discovered, thus maintaining the fascination for the collector.

**History:** Most of us still remember the penny gumball or peanut machine of our childhood. Many still survive on location after thirty years or more of service, due in part to the strength and simplicity of their construction.

The years 1910 to 1940 were the heyday of the most collectible style of vendor, the globe type peanut or gumball machine. Machine manufacturers invested a great deal of money throughout this period in the form of advertising and research. Many new designs were patented.

The simple rugged designs proved the most popular with the operator who had an established route of vendors as a means of making a living. Many operators made their fortunes "a penny at a time," especially during the Depression when dollars were hard to come by. Fifty years later, the same vendor that originally cost four to fifteen dollars commands a much higher price.

In addition to the globe–style variety of vendor is the cabinet–style machine. These usually incorporate a clockwork mechanism and occasionally mechanical figurines to deliver the merchandise. The earliest examples of these were produced in the 1890s.

**References:** Nic Costa, *Automatic Pleasures: The History of the Coin Machine,* Kevin Frances Publishing, Ltd., 1988; Bill Enes, *Silent Salesmen: An Encyclopedia of Collectible Gum, Candy & Nut Machines,* published by author, 1987; Roger Pribbenow and Jimm Lehmann, *Gumball Guide,* privately printed.

**Periodicals:** *Coin Machine Trader,* 569 Kansas SE, P. O. Box 602, Huron, SD 57350; *Coin–Op Newsletter,* 909 26th St., NW, Washington, DC, 20037.

Aspirin, Reed's Aspirin Vendor, 10¢, graphics, orig aspirin packets ...... **395.00**
Cigarettes, Lucky Strike, 1¢, Wilson Mfg, dispenses single cigarettes, decal, c1931 ...................... **795.00**
Collar Button, Price Collar Button Vendor, 1901 ....................... **575.00**
Gum
- Adams' Tutti–Fruitti, oak case, c1900 **650.00**
- Bluebird Bowler, gumballs are played across miniature bowling alley, player can aim gumball and manually reset pins ................ **650.00**
- Columbus Model A, 1¢, replacement globe and padlock, restored, 1920s **265.00**
- Mansfield Automatic Clerk, etched front, clock wound mechanism, 1901 ......................... **325.00**
- Masters Gum Machine, 1¢ ........ **165.00**
- Penny King, marked, 1930s ....... **90.00**
- Rex, cast iron, cylinder globe, cross shape knob .................... **450.00**
- Scoopy Gum Vendor, Gaylord Manufacturing, figural baker opens oven door and scoops gumball into shoot, c1920 .................. **350.00**
- Silver Comet, 1¢, gum sticks ....... **165.00**
- Yu Chu, "Jar Top," refills sold complete with new jar globe, 1930s .. **150.00**

Match
- Advance Match Vendor ........... **395.00**
- Diamond, 1¢, book matches, c1920 **300.00**
- International Vending Match Machine, glass dome, c1910 ....... **800.00**

Multiple Products
- Four–In–One, dispenses four different products, Art Deco style, swivel base, four handles and coin entries, 1930s ........................ **400.00**
- National Self Service, 5¢, mint and gum, decal .................... **135.00**
- Premier Baseball Card and Gumball dispenser ...................... **265.00**
- Superior, peanut and gumball, round base and globe, 1920–30 ....... **175.00**

Peanut
- Abbey Peanut, 5¢ ................ **95.00**

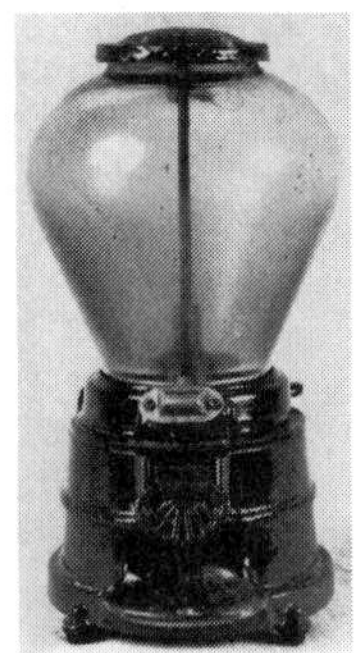

**Peanut Vendor, Hanse, 1¢, glass globe, cast-iron base, 8" w, 14" h, $358.00. Photograph courtesy of James D. Julia, Inc.**

- Advance No 11, steel construction, chrome plated front ............ **90.00**
- Chicago, nickel plated, cylinder globe, fancy and ornate, early 1900s ...................... **2,000.00**
- Griswold, 1¢, cast iron, painted, six legged base, early 1910s ........ **600.00**
- Hance, 1¢, painted or plated finishes, early 1900s .................... **500.00**
- Northwestern 33, porcelain finish, octagonal geometric base, cylinder globe, door marked "Northwestern," 1933 .................... **100.00**
- Regal Hot Nut Vendor, glass globe, light bulb, 1930s ............... **100.00**

Pencil, Parker, 5¢, cast metal ........ **345.00**
Stamp, Blue Anderson, 5¢ ........... **795.00**

# VERNON KILNS

**Collecting Hints:** Vernon Kilns used 48 different marks during its period of operation. Collect examples which are in very good condition and concentrate on the specialty items rather than dinnerware.

**History:** During the Depression, many small potteries flourished in southern California. One of these, Poxon China, was founded in Vernon, California, in 1912. This pottery was sold to Faye G. Bennison in 1931. It was renamed Vernon Kilns and also was known as Vernon Potteries, Ltd. Under Bennison's direction, the company became a leader in the pottery industry.

The high quality and versatility of its wares made it very popular. Besides a varied dinnerware line, Vernon Kilns also produced Walt Disney figurines, advertising, political, and fraternal items. One popular line was historical and commemorative plates, which included several plate series, featuring scenes from England, California missions, and the West.

Vernon Kilns survived the Depression, fires, earthquakes, and wars. However, it could not compete with the influx of imports. In January, 1958, the factory was closed. Metlox Potteries of Manhattan Beach, California, bought the trade name and molds along with the remaining stock.

**Reference:** Maxine Nelson, *Versatile Vernon Kilns, An Illustrated Value Guide, Book II,* Collector Books, 1983, out–of–print.

**Newsletter:** Vernon View, P. O. Box 945, Scottsdale, AZ 85252.

**BROWN-EYED SUSAN.** Montecito shape. Yellow daisies and green leaves on ivory ground, 1946–1958.

Creamer .......... **4.00**
Mug .......... **28.00**
Pitcher, 2 qt, ice lip .......... **40.00**
Plate, 6″ d .......... **3.00**
Platter, 12″ d, round .......... **12.00**
Salt and Pepper Shakers, pr .......... **18.00**
Teapot .......... **48.00**
Tumbler, 4 oz .......... **18.00**

**EARLY CALIFORNIA.** Montecito shape. Solid colors. Available in blue, brown, dark blue, green, ivory, maroon, peach, pink, orange, turquoise, and yellow, 1935–1947.

Demitasse Creamer, orange .......... **20.00**
Demitasse Cup and Saucer, dark blue . **25.00**
Eggcup, ivory .......... **9.50**

**GINGHAM.** Montecito shape. Green and yellow plaid with green border, 1949–1958.

Carafe .......... **28.00**
Casserole, handled .......... **25.00**
Cup .......... **5.00**
Pitcher, ice lip, 11½″ h .......... **45.00**
Plate, 10½″ d, dinner .......... **5.00**
Salt and Pepper Shakers, pr, large .... **35.00**
Serving Bowl, 9″ d .......... **16.00**

**Gingham, salt and pepper shakers, pr, green, yellow, and white plaid, $10.00.**

Soup Bowl, 8½″ d .......... **12.00**
Syrup Pitcher .......... **55.00**
Teapot, small nick on lid .......... **15.00**

**HAWAIIAN FLOWERS.** Ultra Shape. Designed by Don Blanding. Lotus flower transfer in pink, blue, maroon, or mustard, 1938.

Coffeepot, blue .......... **125.00**
Creamer and Sugar, blue .......... **45.00**
Cup, maroon .......... **20.00**
Dinner Service, maroon, 91 pcs ...... **850.00**
Plate
 6″ d, bread and butter, maroon .... **7.50**
 8″ d, luncheon, maroon .......... **18.00**
 9″ d, dinner, blue .......... **30.00**
 14″ d, chop, blue .......... **35.00**
Salt Shaker, maroon .......... **12.00**
Saucer, maroon .......... **9.00**
Sugar, cov, maroon .......... **22.00**

**HOMESPUN.** Montecito shape. Green, rust, and yellow plaid with rust border, 1949–1958.

Bowl, 5½″ d .......... **4.00**
Butter Dish .......... **35.00**
Creamer .......... **4.50**
Cup and Saucer .......... **5.00**
Gravy .......... **10.00**
Mixing Bowl, 8″ d .......... **16.00**
Plate
 7″ d, salad .......... **3.50**
 10″ d, dinner .......... **9.00**
Salt and Pepper Shakers, pr .......... **8.00**
Sauce Boat, 6½″ l .......... **8.00**
Sugar, cov .......... **8.00**
Tumbler .......... **25.00**
Vegetable Bowl, divided .......... **12.00**

**MOBY DICK.** Ultra shape. Transfer whaling scenes in blue, brown, maroon, and orange, 1939.

Bowl, tab handle, brown .......... **15.00**
Creamer, brown .......... **15.00**
Cup and Saucer, brown .......... **18.00**
Fruit Bowl, 5½″ d, brown .......... **10.00**
Plate, 7″ d, brown .......... **2.00**
Salt and Pepper Shakers, pr, brown ... **40.00**
Sauce Boat, brown .......... **24.00**
Soup Bowl, brown .......... **18.00**
Sugar, cov, brown .......... **28.00**

**MODERN CALIFORNIA.** Montecito shape. Available in solid colors of azure blue, ivory, gray, orchid, pistachio green, sand, and straw yellow, 1937–1947.

Bowl
 5½″ d, straw .......... **8.00**
 6″ d, straw, handled .......... **12.00**
 9″ d, pistachio .......... **35.00**

Cup, straw . . . . . . . . . . . . . . . . . . . . . . . . **10.00**
Cup and Saucer, azure . . . . . . . . . . . . . . **15.00**
Mug, pistachio, no handle . . . . . . . . . . . **28.00**
Plate
6¼" d , orchid . . . . . . . . . . . . . . . . . . . **6.00**
9¾" d, dinner, pistachio . . . . . . . . . . . **12.00**
Platter, 12½" l, pistachio . . . . . . . . . . . . **18.00**
Saucer, pistachio . . . . . . . . . . . . . . . . . . . **3.00**
Vegetable Bowl, oval, 9½" l, azure . . . **20.00**

**ORGANDIE.** Montecito shape. Brown and yellow plaid, 1940–1958.

Bowl
7¼" d . . . . . . . . . . . . . . . . . . . . . . . . . . **5.00**
9" d . . . . . . . . . . . . . . . . . . . . . . . . . . . **6.00**
Butter Dish . . . . . . . . . . . . . . . . . . . . . . . . **35.00**
Creamer . . . . . . . . . . . . . . . . . . . . . . . . . . **4.00**
Cup and Saucer . . . . . . . . . . . . . . . . . . . . **7.00**
Eggcup . . . . . . . . . . . . . . . . . . . . . . . . . . . **24.00**
Mixing Bowls, set of 5 . . . . . . . . . . . . . . **125.00**
Mug, 9 oz . . . . . . . . . . . . . . . . . . . . . . . . . **15.00**
Plate
6½" d, bread and butter . . . . . . . . . . . **2.00**
10½" d, dinner . . . . . . . . . . . . . . . . . . **10.00**
Platter, oval, 12¾" l . . . . . . . . . . . . . . . . **8.00**
Salt and Pepper Shakers, pr . . . . . . . . . . **12.00**
Sauce Boat, 5" l . . . . . . . . . . . . . . . . . . . . **6.00**
Soup, lug handle . . . . . . . . . . . . . . . . . . . **18.00**
Sugar, cov . . . . . . . . . . . . . . . . . . . . . . . . . **5.00**
Teapot . . . . . . . . . . . . . . . . . . . . . . . . . . . **45.00**
Tidbit Tray, 2 tiers . . . . . . . . . . . . . . . . . . **22.00**

**TAM O'SHANTER.** Montecito shape. Chartreuse, green, and rust plaid with green border, 1949–1958.

Eggcup . . . . . . . . . . . . . . . . . . . . . . . . . . . **28.00**
Pitcher, 2 qt, ice lip . . . . . . . . . . . . . . . . **32.00**
Platter, oval, 12" l . . . . . . . . . . . . . . . . . . **16.50**
Tidbit Tray, 3 tiers, wood handle . . . . . **37.50**
Tumbler, 14 oz . . . . . . . . . . . . . . . . . . . . **12.00**
Vegetable Bowl, oval, divided, 11½" l **25.00**

**TWEED.** Montecito shape. Gray and yellow plaid, 1950–1954.

Plate
7" d, salad . . . . . . . . . . . . . . . . . . . . . . **4.50**
9½" d, luncheon . . . . . . . . . . . . . . . . . **6.00**
Saucer . . . . . . . . . . . . . . . . . . . . . . . . . . . **1.25**
Soup, flat . . . . . . . . . . . . . . . . . . . . . . . . . **8.00**

**WINCHESTER '73.** Western scene transfer with hand tinted accents on cream colored ground, 1950.

Demitasse Cup and Saucer . . . . . . . . . . **60.00**
Pitcher . . . . . . . . . . . . . . . . . . . . . . . . . . . **38.00**
Plate, 14" d, chop . . . . . . . . . . . . . . . . . . **195.00**
Platter, 16" l . . . . . . . . . . . . . . . . . . . . . . . **48.00**
Tumbler . . . . . . . . . . . . . . . . . . . . . . . . . . **40.00**

**WINGED NYMPH.** Available in a bowl and vase which complement the Walt Disney dinnerware pattern "Fantasia." Pieces are marked "Designed by Walt Disney, Copyright 1940," and "Vernon Kilns, Made in U.S.A."

Bowl, #122, 12" d at base, 2½" h, pink **225.00**

**SOUVENIR ITEMS.**

Ashtray, Santa Fe, red . . . . . . . . . . . . . . . **18.00**
Plate, 10½" d
California, blue . . . . . . . . . . . . . . . . . . **15.00**
Colonial Annapolis, brown . . . . . . . . **15.00**
Eisenhower, red . . . . . . . . . . . . . . . . . . **18.00**
Kentucky, red . . . . . . . . . . . . . . . . . . . . **12.00**
Massachusetts, red . . . . . . . . . . . . . . . **12.00**
Pennsylvania, multicolored . . . . . . . . **12.00**
Vermont, red . . . . . . . . . . . . . . . . . . . . **12.00**

# VETERINARY COLLECTIBLES

**Collecting Hints:** Individuals collect veterinary items for a variety of reasons. Many prefer to collect items which pertain to the pet which is currently in residence within their home or which was a devoted companion during childhood. Veterinarians often decorate their offices with a variety of antique veterinary items.

**History:** Iowa State established the first veterinary college in the United States in 1879. By 1900 many additional veterinary colleges were founded. Veterinary research advanced. Pharmaceutical companies began developing medical products strictly for veterinary use.

Following World War II, there was an acute shortage of veterinarians. The period from 1945–1984 is the "golden age" of veterinary education.

Interest in veterinary products ranges from the farm to the city. 4–H projects introduce farm youngsters to the proper use of veterinary products. Studies have shown that individuals with pets are less likely to suffer from stress. Recently, cats surpassed dogs as the most common form of household pet. Specialty cat and dog catalogs are part of the mail order business. Individuals in limited accommodations often chose fish or birds as pets. Of course, there are always those individuals who focus on the exotic.

**References:** PEW National Veterinary Education Program, *Future Directions for Veterinary Medicine*, Institute of Policy Sciences and Public Affairs, Duke University, 1988; Jack J. Stockton, *A Century of Service, Veterinary in Indiana, 1884–1984*, Purdue University.

**Advisor:** Patricia McDaniel.

## BIRDS

American Bird Food Mfg Corp, Chicago, IL, 3 Vees Moulting Food, clear glass jar, green and yellow label, red and black lettering, 4½ x 2", 3 oz ...... **6.00**

Hartz Mountain Products Corp, New York, NY

- Chlorophyll Gravel, clear plastic bag, orange and white printed label, black lettering, 8½ x 6 x 1", 1 lb 4 oz ...... **6.00**
- Parakeet Biscuits, four biscuits in individual metal pans, white, yellow, and orange cardboard box, black lettering, ⅝ x 3¾ x 2½", 1¼ oz .. **7.50**

House of Huston, Inc, Miami, FL, Song Feast Canary Treat, clear glass jar, light green and white label, red and black lettering, 4½ x 2, 3¼" oz .... **6.00**

Lustar, feeder, 8" glass tube, red and white cardboard box, blue lettering, 1¼ x 8¾ x 2⅜" ...... **6.75**

The R T French Co, Rochester, NY, French's Song Food, red metal tin, white and black lettering, 1¾ x 2¼ x 1¼", 1¼ oz ...... **3.50**

William Cooper & Nephews, Inc, Chicago, IL, Pulvex Bird Powder, red, white, yellow, and black cardboard cylinder, metal shaker top, 2⅞ x 1¾", 1 oz ...... **6.00**

**Tin, Lee's Tonax, poultry conditioner, blue, yellow, and red label, 6" h, 3" d, $11.00.**

## COWS

Cenol Co, Chicago, IL, Udder Balm, orange, white, and blue metal tube in matching cardboard box, 7⅞ x 1¾ x 1¾", 5½ oz ...... **10.00**

Dairy Association Co, Inc, Lyndonville, VT

- Bag Balm Dilators, green and red tin box, 1¾ x 2⅜ x 1½" ...... **7.25**
- Kow–Kare, orange, black, and white cardboard and metal canister, 6 x 4¼", 1¼ lbs ...... **8.00**

Dr L D LeGear Medicine Co, St Louis, MO, Cow Prescription Concentrated, gray cardboard box, red, yellow, black, and white paper wrapper, 6¾ x 4½ x 2⅛", 1 lb, 14 oz ...... **10.00**

Globe Laboratories, Fort Worth, TX

- A–B–C Powder, yellow plastic cylinder, red and blue printing, 6⅝ x 1⅞", 4 oz ...... **8.75**
- Frye–Les Branding Fluid, metal can, yellow, red, and blue paper label, 3⅞ x 3⅜", 1 pt ...... **8.75**
- Udder Tone, clear glass jar, red, yellow, and blue label, 3¼ x 2⅛", 4 oz ...... **7.50**

Johnson & Johnson, Filter Products Div, Chicago, IL, Animal Antiseptic Ointment, white plastic tube, blue and brown lettering, 7½ x 2½" ...... **10.00**

McGraw–Edison Co, Boonville, MO, Crown Weaning Ring, white cardboard box, brown lettering, 2¾ x 2¾ x 1⅜" ...... **4.75**

Parke, Davis & Co, Detroit, MI, Kresco Dip No. 1, yellow metal can, red and black lettering, 6¾ x 4½ x 2⅛", 1 qt **12.00**

## DOGS

Bacon Products, Chattanooga, TN, Flipo Worm Syrup, clear glass bottle, white label, blue and red lettering, 3¼ x 1⅞ x 1⅛", 2 oz ...... **8.00**

Dr A C Daniels, Inc, Boston, MA, Dog Soap, red cardboard box, black lettering, 3⅜ x 2⅜ x 1¼" ...... **15.00**

Dr L D LeGear Medicine Co, St Louis, MO, Round Worm and Hook Worm Capsules, white and red cardboard box, black lettering, 2⅞ x 1¾ x 1" . **10.00**

Globe Laboratories, Fort Worth, TX, Cough Syrup For Dogs & Puppies, clear glass bottle, yellow and red label, blue lettering, 4½ x 1⅞", 4 oz . **8.00**

H Clay Glover Co, Inc, Toms River, NJ, Kotekare Pressurized Foam Bath, metal spray can, white label, red and blue lettering, 6¾ x 2", 7 oz ...... **9.00**

Pet'm Laboratories, Philadelphia, PA, Pet'm Shampoo Kit, green cardboard box, 5 x 4 x 2" ...... **12.00**

The Pfeiffer Co, St Louis, MO, Lynn's Worm Syrup, clear glass bottle, white label, red, yellow, and blue lettering, white, red, yellow, and blue cardboard box, 4 x 2 x 1⅛", 2 oz ...... **9.00**

Polk Miller Products Corp, Sergent's Sedative Tablets, cellophane wrapped, white tablets, red, black, and white cardboard box, 2¾ x 2 x 1½" .......... **9.00**

Sudbury Laboratory, Sudbury, MA, Chaperone, cone shaped metal and cardboard container, gold and white label, red and black lettering, 6⅞ x 2¾", 3 oz .......... **8.00**

Wilke K–9 Products, St Louis, MO, Scabisol, brown glass bottle, orange and white label, black lettering, 6⅜ x 2⅛", 8 oz .......... **11.00**

## FISH

Grassyfork Fisheries, Martinsville, IN, Fungus Remedy, gray cardboard cylinder, white label, green lettering, 2⅝ x 1⅝" .......... **4.50**

Hartz Mountain Corp, Harrison, NJ, Goldfish Food, yellow cardboard box, red and black lettering, 3 x 2¼ x 1⅛", 2 oz .......... **4.75**

## HOG

The Avalon Farms Company, Chicago, IL, Special Hog Physic Boluses, cellophane wrapped white cardboard box, black lettering, ¾ x 3 x 2" .......... **7.50**

Flohr Hog Ring Mfg, Co, Bucyrus, OH, Blair Hog Rings, purple cardboard box, black lettering, 3 x 2¼ x 1⅜" . **6.50**

Stewart Hog Ring Co, Inc, Paris, IL, Bartype Shoat Ring, blue cardboard box, white lettering, 3 x 2½ x 1¼", box of 20 .......... **6.75**

## HORSE

Bickmore, Inc, Evanston, IL, Galls Salve, round metal tin, yellow label, black lettering, ⅞ x 2½", 2 oz .......... **14.00**

Dr Hess & Clark Inc, Ashland, OH, Dr Hess Medicated Powder, cardboard cylinder, blue and yellow label, white and blue lettering, 4½ x 2⅛", 4 oz . **15.00**

Globe Laboratories, Fort Worth, TX, Equi–Dine, clear glass bottle, yellow, pink, and blue label, 4¾ x 1⅞", 4 oz **6.50**

Wells Medicine Co, Lafayette, IN, Craft's Medicine, brown glass bottle, white cardboard box with black lettering, 5¼ x 2 x 1¼", 2.5 oz .......... **7.00**

## MISCELLANEOUS

Allied Drug Products Co, Chattanooga, TN, Allied Brand Lice Killer, brown cardboard cylinder, white label, red and blue lettering, metal spout on top, 4½ x 2⅞", 8 oz .......... **8.00**

Anchor Serum Company, Indianapolis, IN, Anti–Ferment, brown glass bottle, white label, blue lettering, 6½ x 2¾", 1 pt .......... **7.75**

Dr Hess & Clark Inc, Ashland, OH, Liqui–Rid Drinking Water Wormer, brown glass bottle, red and yellow label, black lettering, 5½ x 2¼", 8 oz **7.00**

Dr L D LeGear Medicine Co, St Louis, MO, Antiseptic Oil, clear glass bottle, yellow label, black lettering, yellow cardboard box, red and blue lettering, 4¾ x 2 x 1", 2 oz .......... **9.00**

Globe Laboratories, Fort Worth, Tx, Phenothiazine, red, yellow, and blue cardboard and metal canister, 5¾ x 3⅜", 1 lb .......... **5.50**

Pfeiffer Chemical Company, New York, NY, Hobson's Sarcoptic Mange Treatment, clear glass bottle, yellow label, brown lettering, instructions sheet, corrugated cardboard wrapper, yellow cardboard box, brown lettering, 7¼ x 2½ x 1½", 5 oz .......... **15.00**

Standard Medicine Co, St Louis, MO, Duncan's Allstock Antiseptic Dressing, clear glass bottle, red, white, and black lettering, 5¼ x 2", 6 oz ...... **6.00**

## POULTRY

American Cyanamid Company, Agricultural Division, Princeton, NJ, Enheptin Soluble, brown glass jar, white and green label, black and red lettering, 5¾ x 3", ½ lb .......... **6.00**

Burrell–Dugger Co, Indianapolis, IN, Don Sung Feed Supplement for Hens, tan cardboard box, red lettering, 3½ x 2⅝ x ⅞", 2¼ oz .......... **12.00**

Cenol Company, Chicago, IL, Roost paint, brown glass bottle, white, orange, and blue label, 6⅛ x 2¼", 8 oz **8.00**

Clark Remedies Co, Kokomo, IN, No. 3 and 4 Powder, cardboard and metal canister, green label, red and black lettering, 4½ x 2⅞", 10 oz .......... **10.00**

Geo H Lee Co, Omaha, NE, Lee's Gizzard Capsule, red, white, yellow, and black paper envelope, 4¼ x 2½", trial package, 10 capsules .......... **6.00**

Pratt Food Co, Philadelphia, PA, N–K Capsules, brown paper bags, red and black lettering, yellow and red cardboard box, black lettering, 8½ x 4½ x 3¾" .......... **35.00**

The Germo Manufacturing Co, St Louis, MO, Germo–Form 4X Concentrate, clear glass bottle, yellow and red label, blue lettering, 8 x 3⅛ x 2⅛", 1 pt .......... **7.00**

The Quaker Oats Company, Chicago,

IL, *Ful–O–Pep Poultry Book for 1925,* 8th annual edition, paperback booklet, chicken and girl carrying basket illus on cov, 8⅜ x 5½", 48 pgs .... **10.00**

## VETERINARY INSTRUMENTS

Bestmake, syringe, metal barrel, turned wood handle, tan cardboard box, white label, black lettering, 1½ x 9 x 1⅝" .... **18.00**

Davol Rubber Company, Providence, RI, Lambs Nipples, Pure–Gum, No. 97, swan's bill shape, orange cardboard box, blue lettering, 2 x 4½ x 2¾" .... **6.00**

Ideal Instrument Mfg Co, Chicago, IL

- Ideal–Vasco, syringe, 6¼ x ¾" .... **8.50**
- Milk Tubes, olive green and tan cardboard box, tan label, black lettering, ½ x 4⅛ x 4⅛" .... **2.50**

Parke, Davis & Company, Detroit, MI, Nema Mouth Spreader, olive green cardboard box, white label, black lettering, instruction sheet, ⅝ x 10¾ x 4⅝" .... **12.00**

# VIEW–MASTER PRODUCTS

**Collecting Hints:** Condition is the key in determining price. In most cases because of relative newness of this collecting category and quantities of material made, viewers and reels in mint or near new condition may still be found.

Original packaging is sought by collectors. Many viewers and reels were removed from boxes and envelopes and became subject to damage and excessive wear.

**History:** The first View–Master viewers and reels were made available in 1939. Invented by William Gruber, View–Master products were manufactured and sold by Sawyer's, Inc., of Portland, Oregon. The sudden growth of View–Master was cut short by World War II. Shortages of film, plastic, and paper would have crippled the operation and possibly ended the existence of View–Master had not the Army and Navy recognized the visual training potential of this product. Between 1942 and the war's end, about 100,000 viewers and 5 to 6 million reels were ordered by the military.

After the war, public demand for View–Master products soared. Production barely satisfied the needs of the original 1,000 dealer network. 1946 saw the introduction of the Model C viewer which was practically indestructible, thus making it the most common viewer found by collectors today.

In October 1966, General Aniline & Film Corporation (GAF) bought Sawyer's and revamped the View–Master line. GAF introduced new 2–D projectors and 3–D Talking View–Master.

In late 1980 GAF sold the View–Master portion of their company to a limited partnership headed by businessman Arnold Thaler. Further acquisition resulted in the purchase of Ideal Toys. Today the 3–D viewers and reels are manufactured by View– Master Ideal, Inc.

**References:** Roger T. Nazeley's *View–Master Single Reels, Volume I,* published by author, 1987; John Waldsmith, *Stereo Views: An Illustrated History And Price Guide,* Wallace–Homestead, 1991.

**Collectors' Club:** Many View–Master collectors are members of the National Stereoscopic Association, P. O. Box 14801, Columbus, OH 43214.

**Advisor:** John S. Waldsmith.

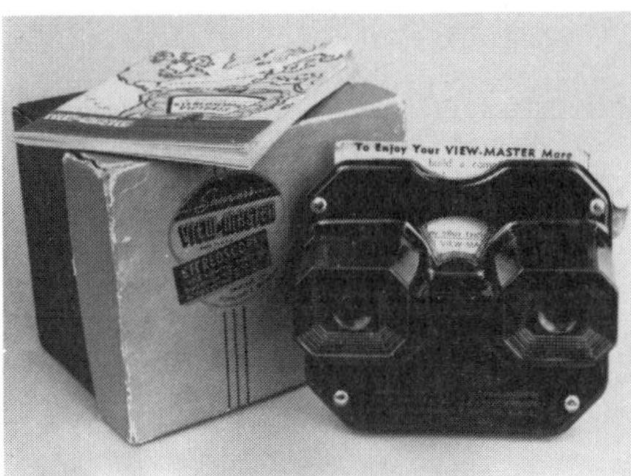


**Sawyer's De Luxe Stereoscope, black Bakelite, 4¼" w, orig brown and silver box, instruction card and catalog, 1948, $25.00.**

## VIEWER

Model C, black Bakelite, insert in top, light attachment, batteries, no corrosion, 1946–56 .... **23.00**

Model D, focuses, orig box .... **85.00**

Model F, lighted, dark brown plastic, pressure bar on top .... **18.00**

Model H, lighted, round bottom, GAF logo on front, 1967–81 .... **13.00**

Modern Viewers .... **1.50**

## PROJECTOR

S–1, metal, brown, single lens, carrying case .... **48.00**

Sawyer's, plastic, single lens .... **10.00**

Stereomatic 500, 3–D, two lens, carrying case .... **250.00**

## CAMERA

Personal 3–D, custom film cutter ..... **175.00**
Mark II, film cutter, made in Europe .. **200.00**

## REEL, SINGLE

Early hand–lettered, white reel, blue and white envelopes
- 26, Grand Canyon, AZ ........... **2.00**
- 58, Golden Gate Exposition, Flowers and Landscaping ............... **14.00**
- 62, Hawaiian Hula Dancers ....... **3.00**
- 76, Mount Vernon, VA ............ **10.00**
- 92, Oregon Caves National Monument ......................... **2.00**
- 101, Rocky Mountain National Park, CO ........................... **2.00**
- 129, Yellowstone National Park, Geysers and Pools ................. **4.00**
- 137, Washington DC ............. **3.00**
- 145, Sanctuary of Our Sorrowful Mother, Portland, OR ........... **10.00**
- 152, Water Falls along Columbia Highway ...................... **5.00**
- 167, Marine Studios, St Augustine .. **5.00**
- 181, Colonial Williamsburg, VA .... **10.00**
- 189, Mission San Juan Capistrano .. **2.00**
- 203, The Black Hills, SD .......... **2.00**
- 236, The Million Dollar Highway .. **4.00**
- 253, Carlsbad Caverns National Park **4.00**
- 267, Cranmore Mt Skimobile Tramway, White Mountains .......... **8.00**
- 284, Death Valley National Monument ......................... **5.00**
- 295, St Louis Zoological Park ...... **3.00**
- 339, Mammoth Cave National Park . **6.00**
- 348, Gettysburg National Military Monument, PA, II .............. **10.00**
- 501, Mexico City and Vicinity ..... **3.00**
- 510, Lake Patzcuaro and Paricutin Volcano ...................... **6.50**
- 515, Typical Scenes in Mexico ..... **4.00**
- 623, Ruins of Pachacamac, near Lima, Peru .................... **21.00**
- 667, La Plata, Argentina .......... **4.00**
- C–1, Morphology of Succulents .... **8.00**

Standard white reels, printed titles, blue and white envelopes
- 14, Reno, "Biggest Little City in the World" ....................... **8.00**
- 43, Grand Teton National Park III, WY .......................... **5.00**
- 51, Garden of the Gods, Colorado . **1.00**
- 72, Island of Kuai, HI ............. **6.00**
- 86, Franklin D Roosevelt's Home, Hyde Park, New York, 1950 ..... **2.00**
- 118, Kings Canyon National Park, CA **2.00**
- 151, Columbia River Highway, OR . **1.00**
- 181, Colonial Williamsburg, VA, 1948 ......................... **1.00**
- 196, Grand Coulee Dam, Washington, 1949 ..................... **2.00**
- 198, San Francisco, CA, 1948 ..... **1.00**
- 222, Tournament of Roses, Pasadena, CA, 1953 ..................... **10.00**
- 253, Carlsbad Caverns National Park, NM, III ....................... **1.00**
- 299, Hot Springs National Park, AR **1.00**
- 332, The Mardi Gras, New Orleans, LA, 1949 ...................... **3.00**
- 338, Lookout Mountain, Chattanooga, TN .................... **1.00**
- 342, Race Horses of the Bluegrass Country, KY, 1952 .............. **3.00**
- 343, Roosevelt's Little White House, Warm Springs, GA, 1949 ........ **1.00**
- 349, Amish Country, PA, 1951 ..... **1.00**
- 360, Historic Charleston, SC, 1950 . **1.00**
- 400, The Inauguration of President Dwight D Eisenhower, 1953 ..... **10.00**
- 641, Santiago, Chile, 1946 ........ **2.00**
- 702, A Day at the Circus II, Ringling Bros and Barnum & Bailey ...... **2.00**
- 742, Movie Stars, Hollywood III .... **15.00**
- 810, Tom and Jerry in The Cat Trapper, 1951 ..................... **2.00**
- 820, Woody Woodpecker in the Pony Express Ride, 1951 ............. **2.00**
- 942, Life with the Cowboys, 1951 .. **2.00**
- 1075, Scarborough, Yorkshire, England .......................... **15.00**

**Mickey Look Viewer Gift Set, plastic, six story reels, orig box, 1989, $8.00.**

- 1420, battlefields of World War II, Normandy, France, 1950 ........ **3.00**
- 1705, The Alhambra Palace, Granada, Spain, 1953 ............... **2.00**
- 2014, Lucerne, Switzerland, 1948 .. **1.00**
- 3100, Victoria Falls, Southern Rhodesia, Africa, 1948 ............. **2.00**
- 3308, People of the Nile Valley, Egypt, 1950 ................... **3.00**
- 4017, Wilderness of Judea, Palestine, 1949 ......................... **2.00**
- 4300, The Taj Mahal and Red Fort, Agra, India, 1949 ............. **3.00**

4820, Buddhist Temples of Bangkok, Siam, 1949 .... **2.00**
5261, The Maoris, Natives of New Zealand, 1950 .... **2.00**
9055, Prehistoric Cliff Dwellers of Mesa Verde, CO, 1950 .... **5.00**
C–18, Euphorbiacease, 1945 .... **8.00**
FT–3, Jack and The Beanstalk, 1951 **1.00**
MG–1, Miss Muffet to Jack and Jill, booklet .... **1.50**
SAM–1, Adventures of Sam Sawyer, Sam Flies to the Moon, booklet .. **4.00**
SP–305, Sitka, AK, 1950 .... **8.00**
SP–9034, Sea Lion Caves, Florence, OR, 1948 .... **1.00**
SP–9039, San Diego, CA, 1949 .... **1.00**
SP–9062, Boys Town, NE, 1951 ... **1.00**

### 3–REEL PACKETS

Values are for complete near new packets. In most cases the 3–reel packets came with story booklets. Sawyer issues (SAW) 1953–1966, GAF issues (GAF) 1967–1981, and View–Master International (VMI) 1981–1982.

Arabian Nights, FT–50 A, B, and C, SAW .... **11.00**
Birth of Jesus, CH–6A, B and C, booklet **3.00**
Buffalo Bill, Jr, 965–A, B and C .... **25.00**
Christmas Carol, FT–31A, B and C ... **3.00**
Cowboy Star Adventures, 946, 951, and 956 .... **10.00**
Dale Evans, Queen of the West, 944–A, B, and C .... **25.00**
Easter Story, EA–1, 2, and 3 .... **4.00**
Garden Flowers, 980, 981, and 982 .. **10.00**
A–085, Iceland, Nations of the World Series .... **18.00**
A–102, Eskimos of Alaska .... **8.00**
A–163, Yosemite National Park, Packet No 2 .... **9.00**
A–181, Los Angeles, CA, edition B ... **6.00**
A–219, San Francisco, Tour No 3 .... **6.00**
A–321, Pikes Peak, Garden of the Gods, Cave of the Winds, CO .... **6.00**
A–360, AZ, State Tour Series .... **6.00**
A–376, Carlsbad Caverns National Park **6.00**
A–635, Historic Philadelphia, edition A **12.00**
A–798, The Restored Ford's Theatre and Lincoln Museum, edition A .... **12.00**
A–818, Arlington National Cemetery, edition A .... **6.00**
A–949, Walt Disney World, Adventureland .... **6.00**
B–146, Castles of Europe .... **10.00**
B–215, Grand Tour of Asia .... **15.00**
B–343, Mark Twain's Huckleberry Finn **30.00**
B–406, Raggedy Ann and Andy .... **6.00**
B–444, Tarzan of the Apes, edition A . **30.00**
B–503, Dark Shadows, edition A, 1968 **20.00**
B–576, Barbie's Great American Photo Race .... **10.00**
B–610, Butterflies of North America .. **6.00**
B–750, Royal Canadian Mounted Police **12.00**
B–811, Forging A Nation, America's Bicentennial Celebration .... **8.00**
BB–432, Treasure Island .... **6.00**
BB–452, The Rookies .... **10.00**
H–19, Disney World, Tomorrowland, VMI .... **4.00**
J–32, Thailand, GAF .... **6.00**
K–57, Star Trek, The Motion Picture, GAF, 1979 .... **4.00**

# WATCH FOBS

**Collecting Hints:** The most popular fobs are those relating to old machinery, either farm, construction or industrial. Advertising fobs are the next most popular group.

The back of a fob is helpful in identifying a genuine fob from a reproduction or restrike. Genuine fobs frequently have advertising or a union trademark on the back. Some genuine fobs do have blank backs; but a blank back should be a warning to be cautious.

**History:** A watch fob is a useful and decorative item attached to a man's pocket watch by a strap. It assists him in removing the watch from his pocket. Fobs became popular during the last quarter of the 19th century. Companies such as The Greenduck Co. in Chicago, Schwabb in Milwaukee, and Metal Arts in Rochester produced fobs for companies who wished to advertise their products or to commemorate an event, individual, or group.

Most fobs are made of metal and are struck from a steel die. Enamel fobs are scarce and sought after by collectors. If a fob was popular, a company would order restrikes. As a result, some fobs were issued for a period of twenty–five years or more. Watch fobs still are used today in promoting heavy industrial equipment.

**Reference:** John M. Kaduck, *Collecting Watch Fobs,* Wallace–Homestead, 1973.

**Collectors' Club:** International Watch Fob Association, Inc., 6613 Elmer Drive, Toledo, OH 43615.

**REPRODUCTION ALERT**

Advertising
Adamant Suit, Rosenthal Bros, NY, boy holding knickers, sitting on box holding extra pants .... **25.00**
Allis Chalmers Monarch Tractors ... **85.00**
Banigan Rubbers, brass, emb lion .. **24.00**
Biston's Golden Grain Coffee, brass, coffee bean shape .... **100.00**

Brown Gin and Liquors, 1½", brass, raised moose head, reverse "Sold by H Obernauer & Co, Pittsburgh, PA" .......... 40.00
Chapman Drug Co, White Lion Drugs, Knoxville, silvered metal .. 25.00
Engeman–Matthew Range, round, diecut range .......... 65.00
Evening Gazette, baseball shape, scorecard back, 1912 .......... 75.00
Fleck Bros Co Plumbing & Heating, 1½", silvered brass, Indian portrait 15.00
Gold Medal Foods, 1½", white metal, ⅞" celluloid insert, black, white, and orange logo, inscribed "Gold Medal Foods," c1900s .......... 35.00
Green River Whiskey, 1¾", silvered brass, .......... 30.00
Hauser Packing Co, 1¾ x 2", white metal, raised western scene, back inscribed "Producers of Angelus Brand Hams, Bacons, and Lard" . 35.00
Huntington Pianos, dark white metal, ⅞" black, white, blue, and gold celluloid with Paderewski, inscription "Paderewski Bought One," early 1900s .......... 35.00
Jersey–Creme/The Perfect Drink, 1 x 1⅞", brass, F H Nobel Co, Chicago, 1920s .......... 25.00
Kelloggs Toasted Corn Flakes, cereal box shape, enameled letters ..... 65.00
Kelly Springfield Tires, 2", white metal, raised illus of female motorist, "Kelly Springfield Hand Made Tires" on back .......... 45.00
Martin–Senour Paints, 1½", silvered brass, 1" multicolored celluloid insert with hand holding dripping paint brush, text on back .......... 40.00
Massey–Harris Tractors .......... 40.00
Monito Hosiery, 2", brass, portrait center, inscribed "Moorehead Knitting Company/Monito Hosiery/Harrisburg, PA," early 1900s .......... 28.00
Northwestern Mutual Life Insurance, brass, figural, green enameled trees 10.00
Oh–Sa–Kist, 1½", silvered brass, inscribed "Presented By John L Mosser/Franklin Hotel/Bethlehem, PA," early 1900s .......... 30.00
Old Dutch Cleanser, porcelain center with Dutch lady .......... 65.00
Oxolin, metal, 1" celluloid inset with lady, adv on reverse .......... 10.00
Porter Hay Carrier, scrolled shield .. 140.00
Quaker City Rubber Co, 1¼ x 1¾", copper colored brass over nickel, raised illus of William Penn, c1920 35.00
Red Goose Shoes, red enameled goose .......... 85.00
Red Owl Coal, enamel, nickel over brass, oval, porcelain center with owl .......... 85.00
Regal Shoes, 1½", oval, copper colored brass, dress boot illus ...... 40.00
Rumsey & Company, Board of Trade, Chicago, 1½ x 2", diecut, silvered brass, cavorting bull and bear, early 1900s .......... 65.00
Tomlinson Quality, 1¼ x 1½", brass, emb, chair image, early 1900s ... 25.00
Twinkies Shoes, 1 x 1½", brass, elf like youngster, 1920s .......... 30.00
Ward's Fine Cakes, white porcelain, bluebird, silvered beaded rim .... 15.00
Zeno Means Good Chewing Gum, brass, high relief .......... 85.00

Automobile

Cadillac, brass, red, white, and blue enamel .......... 80.00
Ford/The Universal Car, silvered and enameled brass, blue and white accents, Ford emblem, c1920 ...... 100.00
Maxwell, 1 x 1¼", enameled metal, red, white, and blue shield, 1910–25 .......... 25.00
REO Motor Car Co, 1¼", enameled metal, pale blue, black, and white, c1920 .......... 75.00
Studebaker, enameled tire design ... 37.50

Fraternal

Fraternal Order of Eagles, bronze, "FOE, Liberty, Truth, Justice, Equality," 1918 .......... 5.00
Knights of Pythias, bronze, 1906 ... 8.00
Masonic, 1¼", brass, Mason Lodge symbol, blue enamel accent, initials "VOA," engraved back, early 1900s .......... 40.00

**Miniature Lathe, brass, hanging ring, 1½" l, ¾" h, $30.00.**

Miscellaneous

American Legion, brass, diecut, Cleveland State Convention, 1946 10.00
Davenport High School, 1904 ..... 42.00
Lone Wolf Tribe .......... 25.00
National Rifle Association, marksman, snakeskin strap .......... 25.00
Princeton University, brass, 1908 ... 20.00
Tom Mix .......... 45.00

Political
- Bryan–Kern, brass, red, white, and blue enamel, spread wing eagle center, 1908 .................. **35.00**
- Republican National Convention, brass, 1920, bust of Lincoln ..... **25.00**
- Taft, 7/8", metal, full color celluloid portrait center, dark silver finish, Bastian Bros adv on reverse, 1908 **50.00**
- To Washington/Roosevelt And Fairbanks, 1904, 1½", brass ........ **15.00**

Sports
- Baseball Bat and Glove, SS, 1920s . **75.00**
- Race Horse, 1½", brass, diecut, raised image, c1930 ............ **20.00**
- World Championship Rodeo Contest, Chicago ...................... **25.00**

World's Fair
- Century of Progress, Chicago, 1933 . **25.00**
- Jamestown, 1907, 1½ x 1¾", silvered brass ........................ **40.00**
- Louisiana Purchase Exposition, 1904, brass, raised relief symbol, Palace Of Arts, and Palace of Mines .... **60.00**
- Panama–Pacific International Exposition, 1915, leather, black, diecut brass poinsettia ................ **75.00**

# WATT POTTERY

**Collecting Hints:** Since Watt pottery was hand painted, there is a great deal of variation in patterns. Look for pieces with designs that are aesthetically pleasing and bright and cheerful.

Watt had strong regional sales in New England, where it sold over 50% of its product. Little made its way west. The balance was sold in the Midwest, Northwest, and South. Beware of placing too much emphasis on availability as a price consideration when buying outside of New England.

Watt made experimental and specialty advertising pieces. These are eagerly sought by collectors. In addition, Watt made pieces to be sold exclusively by other distributors, e.g., Ravarino & Freschi Company which used an "R–F Spaghetti" mark.

**History:** Watt Pottery's roots go back to W. J. Watt who founded the Brilliant Stoneware Company in 1886 in Rose Farm, Ohio. Watt sold his stoneware company in 1897. Between 1903 and 1921 W. J. Watt worked at the Ransbottom Brothers Pottery owned by his brothers–in–law.

In 1921 W. J. Watt purchased the Globe Stoneware Company (known as the Zane W. Burley Pottery between 1919 and 1921) in Crooksville, Ohio, and renamed it Watt Pottery Company. Watt was assisted by Harry and Thomas, his sons, C. L. Dawson, his son–in–law, Marion Watt, his daughter, and numerous other relatives.

Between 1922 and 1935 the company produced a line of stoneware products manufactured from clay in the Crooksville area. The company prospered, exporting some of its wares to Canada.

In the mid–1930s Watt introduced a kitchenware line. The background color consisted of earth tones of off–white and light tan. The overall feel of this new ware was similar to dinnerware patterns made by Pennsbury, Pfaltzgraff, and Purinton. English Torquay is another possible comparison.

Most Watt dinnerware featured an underglaze decoration. Prior to 1950 decoration was relatively simple, e.g., blue and white banding. Starting in 1950 patterns were introduced. A pansy motif was the first. Red Apple began in 1952 and Rooster in 1955. Floral series such as Starflower and Tulip variations were made. New patterns were introduced yearly.

Watt sold its pottery through large chain stores such as Kroger's, Safeway, and Woolworth as well as through other retail merchants. In the early 1960s Watt was grossing over three–quarters of a million dollars. Future prospects were promising. On October 4, 1965, fire destroyed the factory and warehouse. The company never recovered; the pottery was never rebuilt.

**References:** Harvey Duke, *The Official Identification and Price Guide to Pottery and Porcelain, Seventh Edition*, House of Collectibles, 1989; Sue and Dave Morris, *Watt Pottery: An Identification and Value Guide*, Collector Books, 1993.

**Periodical:** *Watt's News*, P. O. Box 708, Mason City, IA 50401.

**Reproduction Alert:** A Japanese copy of a large spaghetti bowl marked simply "U.S.A." is known. The Watt example bear "Peeddeeco" and "U.S.A." marks.

## APPLE

- Bean Pot, #76 ..................... **95.00**
- Bowl
  - #6, adv, ribbed .................. **60.00**
  - #7, adv ........................ **40.00**
  - #8 ............................ **50.00**
  - #63 ........................... **55.00**
  - #66 ........................... **85.00**
- Canister, cov, #72 ................ **250.00**
- Casserole, cov, #67 ............... **120.00**
- Cereal Bowl ....................... **24.00**
- Cookie Jar, #503 .................. **365.00**
- Creamer, #62 ...................... **75.00**
- Mixing Bowl, ribbed
  - #5 ............................ **55.00**
  - #6 ............................ **65.00**
  - #9 ............................ **125.00**
- Mug ............................... **65.00**
- Pie Plate ......................... **65.00**

Pitcher
- #15, adv .......... **80.00**
- #16 .......... **100.00**
- #62 .......... **65.00**

Salad Bowl, #73 .......... **60.00**
Spaghetti Bowl, #39 .......... **150.00**
Vegetable Bowl, cov .......... **48.00**

## BLEEDING HEART

Bean Pot .......... **125.00**
Bowl, #7 .......... **30.00**
Creamer .......... **70.00**
Pitcher, #15 .......... **50.00**

## CHERRY

Berry Bowl, #4 .......... **25.00**
Pitcher, #15 .......... **55.00**
Platter .......... **145.00**
Salt Shaker .......... **50.00**
Spaghetti Bowl, #39 .......... **48.00**

## PANSY

Pie Plate, #33, adv .......... **60.00**
Pizza Plate .......... **275.00**
Spaghetti Bowl
- #11 .......... **100.00**
- #39 .......... **75.00**

## ROOSTER

Bowl, adv .......... **50.00**
Creamer, #62 .......... **95.00**
Ice Bucket .......... **125.00**
Pitcher, adv .......... **48.00**
Salt Shaker, adv .......... **50.00**
Vegetable Bowl, adv .......... **50.00**

## STARFLOWER

Bowl, #55 .......... **60.00**
Casserole, cov
- #67 .......... **100.00**
- Individual .......... **75.00**

Mixing Bowls, nesting set of four, #4, #5, #6, and #7 .......... **175.00**
Mug, #501 .......... **85.00**
Pitcher, #15 .......... **40.00**
Salt and Pepper Shakers, pr, barrel .......... **150.00**
Spaghetti Bowl, #39 .......... **95.00**
Tumbler .......... **300.00**

## TEAR DROP

Bowl, #66, 7″ d .......... **45.00**
Casserole, cov, square, 8″ w, 6″ h .......... **275.00**
Mixing Bowl, #07, ribbed, 7″ d .......... **40.00**
Pitcher, #16, 6½″ h .......... **75.00**
Salt and Pepper Shakers, pr, barrel shape, 4″ h .......... **150.00**

**Tear Drop, bean pot, cov, red and green leaves, cream ground, marked "Watt 76 Oven Ware USA," 8″ w, 5½″ h, $95.00.**

## TULIP

Bowl, #73 .......... **110.00**
Casserole, cov, #600 .......... **125.00**
Cookie Jar, #503 .......... **375.00**
Mixing Bowl
- #63 .......... **60.00**
- #602 .......... **65.00**

Pitcher, #17 .......... **285.00**

# WELLER POTTERY

**Collecting Hints:** Because of the availability of large numbers of pieces in Weller's commercial ware, prices are stable and unlikely to rise rapidly. Forest, Glendale, and Woodcraft are the popular patterns in the middle price range. The Novelty Line is most popular in the lower priced items.

Novice collectors are advised to look to figurals as a starting point. There are over fifty variations of frogs in the figural area. Many other animal shapes also are available.

Pieces in the middle range tend to be marked with an impressed "Weller" in block letters or a half circle ink stamp with the words "Weller Pottery." Late pieces are marked with a script "Weller" or "Weller Pottery." Many new collectors see this dated mark and incorrectly think the piece is old.

There are well over a hundred Weller patterns. New collectors should visit other collectors, talk with dealers, and look at a large range of pieces to determine which patterns they like and want to collect. It is pattern, not shape or type, by which most collections are organized.

**History:** In 1872 Samuel A. Weller opened a small factory in Fultonham, near Zanesville, Ohio, to produce utilitarian stoneware, such as milk pans and sewer tile. In 1882 he moved his facilities to Zanesville. In 1890 Weller built a new plant in the Putnam section of Zanesville along the tracks of the Cincinnati and Muskingum Railway. Additions followed in 1892 and 1894.

In 1894 Weller entered into an agreement with William A. Long to purchase the Lohnuda Faience Company, which had developed an art pottery line under the guidance of Laura A. Fry, formerly of Rookwood. Long left in 1895 but Weller continued to produce Lonhuda under a new name, Louwelsa. This shaded brown pottery with hand decoration under glaze was produced in over 500 different shapes. Replacing Long as art director was Charles Babcock Upjohn. He, along with Jacques Sicard, Frederick Hurten Rhead and Gazo Fudji, developed Weller's art pottery lines.

At the end of World War I, many prestige lines were discontinued and Weller concentrated on commercial wares. Rudolph Lorber joined the staff and designed lines such as Roma, Forest and Knifewood. In 1920 Weller purchased the plant of the Zanesville Art Pottery. Weller claimed to be the largest pottery in the country.

Art pottery enjoyed a revival when the Hudson Line was introduced in the early 1920s. The 1930s saw Coopertone and Graystone Garden ware added. However, the Depression forced the closing of a Putnam plant and one on Marietta Street in Zanesville. After World War II inexpensive Japanese imports took over Weller's market. In 1947 Essex Wire Company of Detroit bought the controlling stock. Early in 1948 operations ceased.

**References:** Sharon and Bob Huxford, *The Collectors Encyclopedia of Weller Pottery,* Collector Books, 1979, 1992 value update; Ann Gilbert McDonald, *All About Weller: A History and Collectors Guide To Weller Pottery, Zanesville, OH,* Antique Publications, 1989.

**Collectors' Club:** American Art Pottery Association, 125 E. Rose Ave., St. Louis, MO 63119.

**Note:** For pieces in the middle and upper price range see *Warman's Antiques And Their Prices.*

Ashtray
- Baying Dog, brown, 5″ w ......... **60.00**
- Three Pigs, brown, 4″ w .......... **80.00**

Bowl
- Blossom, green, ftd, 8″ l .......... **25.00**
- Flemish, squirrel, 8½″ d ........... **70.00**
- Hobart, 150/3/1, 9″ d, 3″ h, with boy with goose flower frog, 279/1/2, 6″ h ............................ **135.00**

Candle Holder
- Paragon, 2″ h .................... **95.00**
- Sydonia, double, green ........... **20.00**

Candlestick, Lustre, 8″ h ............ **25.00**
Child's Feeding Dish, ducks ......... **65.00**
Console, Roma, 129–3–3 ........... **135.00**
Cookie Jar, cov, Pierre, green, 10″ h .. **70.00**
Ewer, Cameo, blue, 10″ h ........... **30.00**
Flower Frog ....................... **75.00**
Flowerpot, liner, Klyro, 6″ h ......... **15.00**
Garden Ornament, Fisher Boy, 21″ h, ink stamp ...................... **1,200.00**
Hanging Basket, Softone, 10″ h ...... **50.00**

**Jardiniere, molded, matte glaze, 6⅝″ h, 8⅛″ d, imp mark, $90.00.**

Mug, Eocean, mushrooms, 5¾″ h .... **145.00**

Pitcher
- Marvo, unmarked ................ **100.00**
- Zona, cobalt blue, apple dec ...... **70.00**

Planter
- Pastel, 8″ l, 4″ h, #P–5 ........... **28.00**
- Softone, oval, ftd, blue, 4 x 8″ ..... **35.00**

Plaque, LPE, 1904
- Butterfly, large ................... **150.00**
- Flower, emb ..................... **100.00**
- Indian Head, emb ................ **200.00**

Stein, Louwelsa, long stemmed flowers, 11½″ h ......................... **250.00**

Teapot
- Forest, glazed .................... **250.00**
- Utility Ware, pineapple 6½″ h ..... **125.00**

Urn, Seneca, 8½″ h ................ **25.00**

Vase
- Bonito, handled, 6″ h ............. **80.00**
- Bouquet, double, green, 4″ h ...... **10.00**
- Darsie, aqua, 7″ h ................ **40.00**
- Eocean, raspberries, 8½″ h ........ **200.00**
- Floretta, flask, B33, 8″ h .......... **100.00**
- Forest, 169/4/3, 12″ h ............ **175.00**
- Hudson, black, white floral dec, urn shape, 6″ h .................... **200.00**
- Knifewood, 197/4/1, 7″ h ......... **175.00**
- Louwelsa
  - 7″ h, pansies, circle seal ........ **95.00**
  - 10½″ h, blue, floral ............ **750.00**
- Malvern, burgundy and yellow, 13½″ h ........................... **120.00**
- Roma, triple bud, 7½″ h .......... **80.00**
- Woodcraft, 157/3/3, 9″ h .......... **125.00**

Wall Pocket
- Fairfield, 10″ h ................... **135.00**
- Squirrel .......................... **130.00**

Window box, Warwick, 12½ x 3½″ .. **225.00**

# WESTERN AMERICANA

**Collecting Hints:** Western Americana is a relatively new field. The initial emphasis has been on books, prints, and paper products. The barbed wire craze of the early 1970s drew attention to three dimensional objects.

Texas material is the most sought after. All collectors tend to focus on the 19th century, rather than modern material. Within the last decade, Indian materials have moved into the level of sophisticated antique collecting.

Collectors should pick a theme or subject. The military west, exploration accounts and maps, and early photography are a few of the more popular focuses. The collecting field now has progressed to the point where there are over a half dozen dealers specializing solely in western materials.

**History:** From the Great Plains to the Golden West, the American west was viewed as the land of opportunity by settlers from the mid–19th century to the early 20th century. Key events caused cataclysmic changes—the 1848 Gold Rush, the opening of the Transcontinental railroad, the silver strikes in Nevada, the Indian massacres, and the Oklahoma land rush. By 1890 the west of the cowboy and cattle was dead; Indians had been relocated onto reservations.

The romance did not die. Novels, movies and television, whether through the Ponderosa or Southfork, keep the romance of the west alive. Oil may have replaced cattle, but the legend remains.

**References:** Warren R. Anderson, *Owning Western History: A Guide To Collecting Rare Documents, Historical Letters And Valuable Autographs From The Old West,* Mountain Press Publishing, 1993; Robert W. D. Ball and Edward Vebell, *Cowboy Collectibles And Western Memorabilia,* Schiffer Publishing, Ltd., 1991, 1993 value update; Robert T. Clifton, *Barbs, Prongs, Points, Prickers & Stickers: A Complete and Illustrated Catalogue of Antique Barb Wire,* University of Oklahoma Press, 1970; Michael Friedman, *Cowboy Culture: The Last Frontier Of American Antiques,* Schiffer Publishing, Ltd., 1992; William C. Ketchum, Jr., *Collecting The West,* Crown Publishing Group, 1993; Bill Macklin, *Cowboy and Gunfighter Collectibles,* Mountain Press Publishing, 1989; Norman E. Martinus and Harry L. Rinker, *Warman's Paper,* Wallace–Homestead, 1993.

**Periodical:** *The Spur,* P. O. Box 3098, Colorado Springs, CO 80934.

**Collectors' Club:** Western American Collectors Society, P. O. Box 620417, Woodside, CA 94062.

**Museum:** Gene Autry Western Heritage Museum, Los Angeles, CA.

Advertising
- Bill Hanger, Austex Mexican Foods Products .......... **37.50**
- Booklet, History of Wells Fargo, illus, 32 pgs .......... **10.00**
- Pinback Button, Wilson Brothers Jewelers, black, white, brown, and red, Indian riding unicycle .......... **7.50**
- Salt and Pepper Shakers, pr, Rod's Steak House, Williams, Arizona .. **35.00**
- Sharpening Stone, Raw Furs, Wool–Hides, and Pelts, EA Stephens & Co, Denver, CO .......... **35.00**
- Sign, Golden West Oil Co, metal, oval .......... **85.00**
- Trade Card, 9½ x 5", Never Rip Nonpariel, blue jeans, San Francisco dry goods store, c1890 .......... **8.50**

Ashtray, hp, covered wagon, c1950 .. **22.00**

Badge
- Sheriff, Lancaster County, NE, eagle top, 1942, photo accompanies with Sheriff Myles Holloway, 1942 .... **175.00**
- US Post Office, Topeka, Kansas .... **30.00**
- Wells Fargo Services .......... **40.00**

Bear Trap
- Kodiak No. 6, H in pan, 42" l ..... **260.00**
- MacKensie District Fur Co, No. 15, 1886 .......... **230.00**

Better Little Book, *2–Gun Montana,* 1939 .......... **9.00**

Book
- Douglas G Brewerton, *The War In Kansas, A Rough Trip To The Border,* New York, 1856, 400 pgs, hard cover .......... **75.00**
- Frank J Dobie, *Apache Gold And Yanqui Silver,* New York, 1939, 384 pgs, illus by Tom Lea .......... **25.00**
- Jay Monaghan, *The Overland Trail,* Indianapolis, 1947, 432 pgs, plates, maps .......... **40.00**

Bookends, pr, Indians, cast iron ...... **85.00**

Bootjack
- Metal, Superior Foundry, Cleveland . **42.50**
- Wood, Lee Rivers .......... **42.50**

Boots, miniature, 5" h, marked "Boots by Fisher" .......... **75.00**

Buckle, Renalde, horse and rider ..... **45.00**

Cabinet Card, 5 x 8", Hop Pickers, Puyallup, WA, group with rakes and other equipment standing in front of their crops and horses .......... **12.00**

Catalog, RT Frazier Saddlery, #37, 136 pages .......... **155.00**

Check
- Gould and Curry Silver Mining Company, Virginia City, NV, 8 x 3", Nov

1876, IRS stamp and Nevada State Revenue stamp ................ **25.00**
Wells Fargo, 7¾ x 3", San Francisco, 1972, ornate .................. **65.00**
Clock, metal, figural cowboy, twirling lariat, United Metal ............... **195.00**
Coaster, paper, Till Goodan, bronco buster, orig packaging ............ **85.00**
Compact, 2¾" d, wood top, cowboy dec, imitation leather back ........ **15.00**
Ledger Book, City Payroll, Waco, Texas, 1904–06, leather bound .......... **145.00**
Lobby Card
Eyes of the Forest, Tom Mix, brown tone, 1923 .................... **100.00**
Gold & The Girl, Buck Jones, blue tone, 1925 .................... **50.00**
Roarin Broncs, Buffalo Bill Jr, color, 1927 ......................... **45.00**
The Timber Wolf, Buck Jones, green tone ......................... **35.00**
Magazine Article, *TV Guide*, Paladin, May 10, 1958, cov with full color photo of Richard Boone ........... **10.00**
Magazine Cover, *Harper's Weekly*, Jan 1849, Elk Hunting in The Bandlands of the Upper Missouri, W M Cary, artist, 11 x 16" .................. **20.00**
Map
Cherokee Nation, Indian Territory, Dept of Interior, Commission to the Five Civilized Tribes, 1900, issued folded, 37 x 27" .............. **75.00**
Mitchell's National Map American Republic, 1844, twenty eight eastern states, Indian Territory listing tribes and tribal claims, population charts, historical info, 41 x 49" ... **140.00**
Nevada Pony Express Map, 1860–1960, published by the Nevada Pony Express Centennial Committee, chromolithograph, 23 x 17", framed ....................... **250.00**
Matchbook, Silver Spur Bar, Rawlings, WY ........................... **6.00**

**Lamp, table, figural cowboy, plaster, glass eyes, 23½" h, 1960s, $375.00.**

**Poster, World Championship Rodeo, Allentown Fair Grounds, cardboard, black and white photos, red lettering, yellow ground, 14 x 22", $25.00.**

Medal
Chicago Fat Stock Show, horns, 1886 **85.00**
Ohio Horseshoer's Ribbon, 1917 ... **57.50**
Paper Epherema
Money Receipt, Wells Fargo, 1885 . **28.00**
Reward Notice, hand written, Jan 25, 1886, by Gov Blasdel of Nevada . **350.00**
Paperweight, brass, Arrowhead brand . **55.00**
Photograph
Cowboys, three riding horseback, 8 x 10" .......................... **20.00**
Dakota Territory tornado, 1885 .... **25.00**
Pinball Game, cowboy, table size .... **125.00**
Plaque, collection of fifty eight tobacco tags .......................... **90.00**
Poster
14 x 36", Outlaws Of Texas, 1950 Monogram Pictures, Whip Wilson and Andy Clyde, minor creasing . **15.00**
27 x 22", Tim McCoy Six Gun Trail, color, 1938 ................... **100.00**
27 x 41", Along The Rio Grande, 1941 RKO Radio Film, Tim Holt . **50.00**
30 x 40", Rodeo Parade In The Montana–Wyoming Dude Ranch Country, Edward P Brewer, c1935, Northern Pacific Railway adv, full color litho, Indian chief leading parade of cowboys .............. **275.00**
Print, Grant In The Wilderness, HA Ogden artist, Knight & Brown publishers, 1897, framed .................... **115.00**
Radio Premium Kit, "Wild West Rodeo," General Electric, 15 x 16", red, white, and blue envelope, punchout sheets, 1952 ..................... **25.00**
Restaurant China
Mayer China, plate, 10" d, scratches **35.00**
Tepco Western Traveller, Wells Fargo

Chili Bowl, 5″ d ................ **18.00**
Cup and Saucer ................ **20.00**
Fruit Bowl, 4¾″ d .............. **14.00**
Oatmeal Bowl, 6½″ d .......... **18.00**
Plate
7½″ d ...................... **22.00**
9½″ d ...................... **35.00**
Wellsville Cowboys
Cup and Saucer ................ **20.00**
Fruit Bowl, 4¾″ d .............. **12.00**
Plate
6¼″ d ...................... **12.00**
9″ d ....................... **25.00**
Wallace Rodeo, Westward Ho, cup and saucer, brands only ......... **40.00**
Saddle Fob
Bronc Rider ..................... **30.00**
El Paso Saddlery, 1889 ............ **140.00**
Hamley's Roundup ............... **175.00**
Los Angeles Saddlery ............. **135.00**
RT Frazer ....................... **150.00**
Van Patters Flying Vee EFF Ranch ... **140.00**
Spurs
Drop Shank
1⅝″ rowels .................... **85.00**
1¾″ rowels, chasing ............ **127.50**
Regulation officer's .............. **40.00**
Straight Shank, 1″ rowels .......... **67.50**
Strong Box, cast iron, weighs 42 lbs, orig maroon paint, 13 x 9″ ........ **445.00**
Tie Bar, Life Time Gate Mineral Wells, TX ............................ **32.50**
Timetable, Nevada Pony Express, 1960 Centennial Re–Run, offset litho, 22 x 14″, framed .................... **75.00**
Watch Chain, Silver Gents, horses slide **157.00**
Watch Fob
Baker's Steam Tractor ............ **75.00**
Bates Steel Mule ................. **85.00**
Cast Steam Tractor .............. **165.00**
Kansas Pacific Railway, longhorn ... **65.00**
Miller Ride 'Em Cowboy Denver, saddle .......................... **60.00**
St Louis Implement Mfg, 1910 ..... **42.50**
Watch, Pocket, 18s
Buffalo Elgin, 1909 ............... **325.00**
Butterfield Overland Mail Coach, Elgin, 1876 ..................... **850.00**
Longhorn, Elgin, 1893 ........... **325.00**
Poker, full house, Lady Luck, Elgin, 1911 ........................ **295.00**
Steer, side view, Elgin, 1897 ....... **295.00**

# WESTMORELAND GLASS COMPANY

**Collecting Hints:** The collector should become familiar with the many lines of tableware produced. English Hobnail made from the 1920s to 1960s is popular. Colonial designs were reproduced frequently, and accessories with dolphin pedestals are distinctive.

The trademark, an interwined "W" and "G", was imprinted on glass since 1949. After January, 1983, the full name "Westmoreland" is on all glass. Early molds were reintroduced. Numbered, signed, dated "Limited Editions" were offered.

**History:** The Westmoreland Glass Company was founded in October, 1899, at Grapeville, Pennsylvania. From the beginning, Westmoreland made handcrafted high quality glassware. In early years the company processed mustard, baking powder, and condiments to fill its containers. During World War I candy–filled glass novelties were popular.

Although Westmoreland is famous for its milk glass, large amounts of other glass were produced. During the 1920s, Westmoreland made reproductions and decorated wares. Color and tableware appeared in the 30s; but, as with other companies, 1935 saw the return to mainly crystal productions. In the 1940s to 1960s, black, ruby, and amber colors were made.

In May 1982 the factory closed. Reorganization brought a reopening in July, 1982. The Grapeville plant closed again in 1984.

**References:** Lorraine Kovar, *Westmoreland Glass, 1950–1984,* Antique Publications, 1991; Lorraine Kovar, *Westmoreland Glass, 1950–1984, Volume II,* Antique Publications, 1991; Ellen Tischbein Schroy, *Warman's Glass,* Wallace–Homestead, 1992; Hazel Marie Weatherman, *Colored Glassware of the Depression Era, Book 2,* Glassbooks, Inc., 1982.

**Collectors' Clubs:** National Westmoreland Glass Collectors Club, P. O. Box 372, Export, PA 15632; Westmoreland Glass Society, 2712 Glenwood, Independence, MO 64052.

Appetizer Set, Paneled Grape, white milk glass ....................... **45.00**
Ashtray, Beaded Grape, white milk glass, 6½″ sq .................... **15.00**
Basket, Paneled Grape, white milk glass 6½″ h, oval .................... **22.50**
Bowl
Beaded Grape, white milk glass
9″ d, cov ...................... **25.00**
9″ w, sq, ftd ................... **25.00**
Old Quilt, white milk glass, 9″ d, ftd, crimped ...................... **45.00**
Paneled Grape, white milk glass
6″ d, ftd, ruffled ................ **40.00**
6½″ l, oval .................... **18.00**
8″ d, bell shape ................ **42.00**
Butter Dish, cov
Old Quilt, white milk glass, ¼ lb .. **25.00**
Paneled Grape, white milk glass, 9″ d **50.00**

Cake Salver
- Beaded Grape, white milk glass, skirted base .......... **65.00**
- Old Quilt, white milk glass, skirted . **85.00**
- Paneled Grape, white milk glass, 11″ d, skirted base .......... **85.00**
- Ring and Petal, white milk glass, low, ftd .......... **45.00**

Canape Set, Paneled Grape, white milk glass .......... **100.00**

Candlesticks, pr
- Beaded Grape, white milk glass, 4″ h **20.00**
- Old Quilt, white milk glass, 4″ h ... **20.00**
- Paneled Grape, white milk glass, 4″ h, skirt base .......... **20.00**
- Ring and Petal, white milk glass, 3½″ h .......... **18.00**

Candy Dish, cov, Paneled Grape, white milk glass, ftd .......... **35.00**

Celery Vase
- Old Quilt, white milk glass, 6½″ h, ftd .......... **15.00**
- Paneled Grape, white milk glass ... **45.00**

Chocolate Box, cov, Paneled Grape, white milk glass .......... **40.00**

Cigarette Box, cov, Beaded Grape, white milk glass .......... **30.00**

Compote, cov, Paneled Grape, white milk glass, 7″ h .......... **22.00**

Creamer and Sugar, price for pair
- Beaded Grape, white milk glass .... **16.00**
- Della Robia
  - Crystal, colored dec .......... **32.00**
  - White milk glass .......... **23.00**
- Old Quilt, white milk glass, large .. **30.00**
- Paneled Grape, white milk glass ... **20.00**

Cruet, Paneled Grape, white milk glass **20.00**

Cup and Saucer
- English Hobnail, white milk glass ... **15.00**
- Paneled Grape, white milk glass ... **20.00**

Decanter, Paneled Grape, white milk glass, orig stopper .......... **125.00**

Dish, cov
- Rooster, standing .......... **40.00**
- Santa, sleigh base .......... **30.00**

Dresser Jar, Roses and Bows, decorated **375.00**

Epergne, Paneled Grape, white milk glass
- 9″ d, patterned bowl .......... **175.00**
- 11″ h, two pieces .......... **160.00**

Fruit Cocktail, Paneled Grape, white milk glass, orig underplate .......... **20.00**

Goblet, water
- Della Robia, white milk glass ...... **20.00**
- English Hobnail, white milk glass ... **14.00**
- Paneled Grape, white milk glass ... **20.00**

Honey, cov
- Beaded Grape, white milk glass .... **20.00**
- Roses and Bows, decorated ........ **40.00**

Iced Tea Tumbler, Della Robia, ftd, white milk glass .......... **22.00**

Ivy Ball, Paneled Grape, white milk glass .......... **45.00**

Jardiniere, Paneled Grape, white milk glass, 5″ h .......... **22.00**

Juice Tumbler, Paneled Grape, white milk glass .......... **24.00**

Mayonnaise, Beaded Grape, white milk glass, lipped, crimped .......... **15.00**

Pitcher, Paneled Grape, white milk glass
- Footed .......... **30.00**
- Pint .......... **40.00**
- Quart .......... **25.00**

Plate
- Della Robia, 14″ d, crystal ........ **50.00**
- Paneled Grape, white milk glass
  - 8½″ d .......... **20.00**
  - 10½″ d .......... **35.00**

**Plate, milk glass, Ring & Petal, No. 1875, 8¼″ d, $12.50.**

Punch Set, Three Fruits, white milk glass, price for fifteen piece set ..... **375.00**

Relish, Old Quilt, white milk glass, three part .......... **45.00**

Rose Bowl, Maple Leaf, white milk glass, 1923 .......... **25.00**

Salt and Pepper Shakers, pr
- Beaded Grape, white milk glass, price for pair .......... **25.00**
- Old Quilt, white milk glass ........ **25.00**
- Paneled Grape, white milk glass ... **21.00**

Spooner, Paneled Grape, white milk glass .......... **45.00**

Tumbler, Paneled Grape, white milk glass, 8 oz .......... **18.00**

Vase
- Old Quilt, white milk glass, 9″ h, fan **22.00**
- Paneled Grape, white milk glass
  - 6″ h, bell shaped rim .......... **18.00**
  - 8¼″ h, ftd, bell shaped rim ...... **18.00**
  - 9″ h, ftd, bell shaped rim ........ **18.00**
  - 14″ h, swung .......... **12.00**

Wedding Bowl, cov, Roses and Bows, decorated .......... **75.00**

Wine, Paneled Grape, white milk glass **25.00**

# WHISKEY BOTTLES, COLLECTORS' SPECIAL EDITIONS

**Collecting Hints:** Beginning collectors are advised to focus on bottles of a single manufacturer or collect around a central theme, e.g., birds, trains, western, etc. Make certain to buy bottles whose finish is very good (almost no sign of wear), with no chips, and with the original labels intact.

A major collection still can be built for a modest investment, although some bottles now command over $1,000, such as the Beam Red Coat Fox. Don't overlook miniatures if you are on a restricted budget.

Finally, it is common practice to find bottles empty. In many states it is against the law to sell liquor without a license; hence, collectors tend to focus on the empty bottle.

**History:** The Jim Beam Distillery began the practice of issuing novelty (collectors' special edition) bottles for the 1953 Christmas trade. By the late 1960s over one hundred other distillers and wine manufacturers followed suit.

The Jim Beam Distillery remains the most prolific of the bottle issuers. Lionstone, McCormick and Ski Country are the other principal suppliers today. One dealer, Jon–Sol, Inc., has distributed his own line of collector bottles.

The "Golden Age" of the special edition bottle was the early 1970s. Interest waned in the late 1970s and early 1980s as the market was saturated by companies trying to join the craze. Prices fell from record highs. Many manufacturers dropped special edition bottle production altogether.

A number of serious collectors, clubs, and dealers have brought stability to the market. Realizing that instant antiques cannot be created by demand alone, they have begun to study and classify their bottles. H. F. Montague deserves special recognition for his classification work. Most importantly, collectors have focused on those special edition bottles which show quality of workmanship and design and which have true limited editions.

**References:** Ralph and Terry Kovel, *The Kovels' Bottle Price List, Ninth Edition,* Crown Publishers, Inc., 1992; H. F. Montague, *Montague's Modern Bottle Identification and Price Guide, Third Edition,* H. F. Montague Enterprises, Inc., 1984.

**Collectors' Clubs:** International Association of Jim Beam Bottle & Specialties Clubs, 5013 Chase Ave., Downers Grove, IL 60515; Michter's National Collectors Society, P.O. Box 481, Schaefferstown, PA 17088; National Ski Country Bottle Club, 1224 Washington Ave., Golden, CO 80401.

**Museum:** American Outpost, James B. Beam Distillery, Clermont, KY.

## JIM BEAM

Beam Clubs and Conventions
- Cherry Hills Country Club, 1973 ... **8.00**
- Conventions
  - Fifth, Sacramento, 1975 ... **15.00**
  - Ninth, Houston, 1979 ... **70.00**
  - Thirteenth, St Louis, 1983 ... **50.00**
- Evergreen State Club, 1974 ... **15.00**
- Foxes, Surfer, 1975 ... **20.00**
- Gem City Club, 1983 ... **65.00**
- Twin Bridges Club, 1971 ... **50.00**

Beam on Wheels
- Cable car, 1983 ... **65.00**
- Fire Engine 1867, 1978 ... **85.00**
- Stutz Bearcat, yellow, 1977 ... **40.00**
- Train
  - Caboose, 1980 ... **40.00**
  - Engine, Turner, 1982 ... **55.00**
  - Tender, coal, Grant, 1979 ... **25.00**

Casino Series
- Golden Nugget, 1969 ... **55.00**
- Harolds Club, Man in Barrel #1, 1957 ... **475.00**
- Harvey Hotel Glass, 1969 ... **8.00**

Centennial Series, First Issued, 1960
- Alaska Purchase, 1966 ... **8.00**
- Civil War, 1961, South ... **55.00**
- Hawaii, 200th, 1978 ... **20.00**
- Reidsville, 1973 ... **8.00**
- San Diego, 1968 ... **7.00**
- Washington Bicentennial, 1976 ... **18.00**

Clubs and Organizations
- B.P.O. Does, 1971 ... **6.00**
- Ducks Unlimited
  - #5, 1979 ... **20.00**
  - #10, 1984 ... **45.00**
- Homebuilder's Association, 1979 ... **25.00**
- Pennsylvania Dutch Club, 1974 ... **12.00**
- Shriners
  - Moila, 1972 ... **35.00**
  - Western Association, 1980 ... **30.00**
- Wolverine Club, 1975 ... **15.00**

Customer Specialties
- Bohemian Girl, 1974 ... **18.00**
- Katz Cat, black, 1968 ... **12.00**
- Ralph's Market, 1973 ... **14.00**
- Richard's New Mexico, 1967 ... **5.00**
- Zimmerman, vase, brown, 1972 ... **18.00**

Executive Series, First Issue, 1955
- 1957, Royal DiMonte ... **75.00**
- 1960, Blue Cherub ... **125.00**
- 1964, Royal Gold Diamond ... **50.00**
- 1969, Sovereign ... **12.00**
- 1972, Regency ... **12.00**
- 1975, Reflections In Gold ... **15.00**
- 1980, Titian ... **18.00**

Foreign Countries
- Australia, Tigers, 1977 ... **22.00**

- Thailand, 1969 — **6.00**

Glass Series, First Issue, 1952
- Coffee Warmer, black handle, stand, 1956 — **8.00**
- Crystal Pressed, 1971, blue — **8.00**
- Delft Rose, 1963 — **8.00**
- Oriental Jade, 1972 — **6.00**
- Royal Opal, 1957 — **8.00**

People Series
- Cowboy, 1981 — **15.00**
- John Henry, 1972 — **70.00**
- Paul Bunyan, 1970 — **8.00**
- Viking, 1973 — **12.00**

Political Series
- Boxer Elephant, 1964 — **18.00**
- Kansas City Convention Elephant, 1976 — **15.00**
- Spiro Agnew Elephant, 1970 — **2,200.00**

Regal China Series
- Bonded, silver, 1975 — **6.00**
- Green China Jug, 1965 — **7.00**
- Las Vegas, 1969 — **6.00**
- New Hampshire Golden Eagle, 1971 — **45.00**
- Submarine–Redfin, 1970 — **8.00**

Sports Series
- Fiesta Bowl, 1970 — **15.00**
- Hawaiian Open, Golf Ball, 1973 — **12.00**
- Louisiana Superdome, 1975 — **10.00**
- Mint 400, 6th, 1973 — **10.00**

States Series
- Colorado, 1959 — **35.00**
- Idaho, 1963 — **55.00**
- New Hampshire, 1968 — **8.00**
- South Carolina, 1970 — **8.00**

**Jim Beam, State Series, Arizona, 1968, $8.00.**

Trophy Series
- Bird, pheasant, 1960 — **28.00**
- Dog, Poodle, gray, 1970 — **8.00**
- Fish
  - Salmon, Coho, 1976 — **12.00**
  - Walleye Pike, 1977 — **12.00**
- Horse, brown, 1967–68 — **20.00**

## EZRA BROOKS

Animal Series
- Hereford, 1971 — **15.00**
- Lion, African, 1980 — **50.00**
- Panda, 1972 — **18.00**

Automotive/Transportation Series
- Ford Thunderbird, 1956, blue, 1976 — **64.00**
- Ontario Racer, #10, 1970 — **20.00**
- Train, Iron Horse, 1969 — **12.00**

Bird Series, owl, Scops #4, 1980 — **55.00**

Heritage China Series
- Pot Belly Stove, 1968 — **12.00**
- Silver Dollar, black base, 1969 — **8.00**

Institutional Series
- Club Bottle #1, Distillery, 1970 — **12.00**
- Iowa Farmers Elevator, 1978 — **35.00**
- Liquor Square, 1972 — **8.00**
- Wichita Centennial, 1970 — **8.00**

People Series
- Clown with balloons, 1973 — **20.00**
- Iowa Farmer, 1977 — **75.00**
- Max "The Hat" Zimmerman, 1976 — **30.00**
- Oliver Hardy, 1976 — **18.00**
- Stonewall Jackson, 1974 — **32.00**

Sports Series
- Basketball Players, 1974 — **10.00**
- Go Big Red #3, Rooter, 1972 — **15.00**
- Greensboro Open, Cup, 1975 — **50.00**
- Trojan, USC, 1973 — **20.00**

## CYRUS NOBLE

Animal Series
- Buffalo Cow & Calf, Nevada edition, 1977 — **90.00**
- Moose & Calf, 2nd Edition, 1977 — **85.00**

Carousel Series, Pipe Organ, 1980 — **45.00**

Mine Series
- Gold Miner, 1974 — **18.00**
- Mine Shaft, 1978 — **35.00**

Sea Animals
- Harp Seal, 1979 — **50.00**
- Sea Turtle, 1979 — **50.00**

## J. W. DANT

Field Birds, 1969
- #4, Mountain Quail — **10.00**
- #7, Bob White — **10.00**

Patrick Henry, 1969 — **6.00**

## DOUBLE SPRINGS

Bicentennial Series
- Missouri — **18.00**
- Washington, DC — **12.00**

Car Series
- Mercedes Benz, 1975 — **30.00**
- Rolls Royce, 1971 — **40.00**

## EARLY TIMES, 1976

Cannon Fire, Delaware ............ **25.00**
Nevada ............ **22.00**
New Mexico ............ **28.00**
Drum and Fife
Hawaii ............ **30.00**
Kansas ............ **22.00**
Minuteman
Alaska ............ **35.00**
Oklahoma ............ **25.00**
Washington Crossing the Delaware, South Dakota ............ **18.00**

## FAMOUS FIRSTS

Airplane Series
Spirit of St Louis, medium, 1972 ... **65.00**
Winnie Mae, large, 1972 ............ **90.00**
Animal Series
Bears, miniature, 1981 ............ **35.00**
Hippo, baby, 1980 ............ **55.00**
Rooster, Richardo, 1973 ............ **18.00**
Car/Transportation Series
Balloon, 1971 ............ **65.00**
Corvette, 1963 Stingray, white, miniature 1979 ............ **15.00**
Locomotive, 1969 ............ **48.00**
Porsche Targa, 1979 ............ **45.00**
Yacht America, miniature, 1978 .... **15.00**
Miscellaneous
Fireman, 1980 ............ **55.00**
Phonograph, 1969 ............ **35.00**
Sewing Machine, 1979 ............ **35.00**

## GRENADIER

American Revolution Series
First Pennsylvania, 1970 ............ **38.00**
Third New York, 1970 ............ **20.00**
Bicentennial Series, 1976, 10th, 13 types, each ............ **15.00**
British Army Series, Kings African Rifle Corps, 5th, 1970 ............ **20.00**
Civil War Series
General Robert E Lee, ½ gallon, 1977 **145.00**
Soldier, series, miniature, 10 types, 1975, each ............ **18.00**
Miscellaneous
Fire Chief, 1973 ............ **85.00**
Jester Mirth King, 1977 ............ **55.00**
San Fernando Electric Mfg Co, 1976 **65.00**
Texas Ranger, 1977 ............ **25.00**

## HOFFMAN

Aesop Fables Series, music, six types, 1978 ............ **28.00**
Band Series, miniature
Accordion Player, 1987 ............ **15.00**
Drummer, 1979 ............ **18.00**
Bird Series
Eagle, open wing, miniature, 1979 . **20.00**
Love Birds, ½ pint, 1979 ............ **18.00**
Cheerleaders, Dallas, 1979 ............ **25.00**
Horse Series, 6 types, miniature, 1979, each ............ **12.00**
Mr Lucky Series, music
Barber, 1980 ............ **40.00**
Fiddler, 1974 ............ **26.00**
Mailman, miniature, 1976 ............ **12.00**
Rodeo Series, 6 types, 1978, each .... **30.00**
School Series, Kentucky Wildcats, Football, 1979 ............ **35.00**
Wildlife Series
Doe & Fawn, 1975 ............ **50.00**
Eagle & Fox, 1978 ............ **35.00**

## JAPANESE FIRMS

House of Koshu
Geisha, chrysanthemum, 1969 ..... **24.00**
Maiden, 1970 ............ **18.00**
Sake God, white, 1969 ............ **12.00**
Kamotsuru
God #6, Bishamon (God Military), 1965 ............ **15.00**
Treasure Tower, 1966 ............ **18.00**
Kikukawa
Haru ............ **6.00**
Royal Couple, pr ............ **30.00**

## LEWIS AND CLARK

Clark, miniature, 1971 ............ **15.00**
Lewis, 1971 ............ **85.00**
Troll Family, Grandmother Troll, 1979 **30.00**

## LIONSTONE

Bicentennial Series, Valley Forge, 1975 **25.00**
Bird Series
Dove of Peace, 1977 ............ **38.00**
Roadrunner, miniature, 1969 ...... **12.00**
Car/Transportation Series
Mercedes, miniature, 1978 ............ **15.00**
Stutz Bearcat, miniature, 1978 ..... **15.00**
Clown Series
#3, Say it with Music, 1978 ....... **32.00**
#6, Lampy, 1979 ............ **35.00**
Firefighter Series
Fire Equipment Set, miniature, 1976 **38.00**
Fireman, #8, Fire Alarm Box, 1983 **55.00**
Old West Series
Bartender, 1969 ............ **30.00**
Dancehall Girl, 1973 ............ **65.00**
Gambler, miniature, 1970 ............ **12.00**
Indian, Squaw, 1973 ............ **26.00**
Riverboat Captain, 1969 ............ **12.00**
Wells Fargo Man, 1969 ............ **15.00**
Sports Series
Baseball Players, 1974 ............ **25.00**

Hockey Players, 1974 .......... **20.00**
Tennis Player, male, 1980 .......... **45.00**

## LUXARDO

Babylon, 1960 .......... **18.00**
Calypso Girl, 1962 .......... **15.00**
Frog, miniature .......... **15.00**
Medieval Palace, 1970 .......... **8.00**
Tower of Flowers, 1968 .......... **20.00**
Zodiac, 1970 .......... **32.00**

## McCORMICK

Bicentennial Series, miniature
Betsy Ross, 1976 .......... **50.00**
Paul Revere, 1976 .......... **50.00**
Bull Series
Black Angus, miniature, 1975 .......... **20.00**
Texas Longhorn, 1974 .......... **35.00**
Football Mascots
Drake Bulldogs, 1974 .......... **25.00**
Indiana Hoosiers, 1974 .......... **18.00**
Texas Tech Raiders, 1972 .......... **30.00**
Frontiersman Series, 1975
Daniel Boone .......... **28.00**
Kit Carson .......... **15.00**
Great American Series
Grant, Ulysses S, 1976 .......... **28.00**
Peary, Robert E, 1977 .......... **30.00**
Twain, Mark, 1977 .......... **32.00**
Miscellaneous
Car, Packard, cream, 1980 .......... **65.00**
Woman Feeding Chickens, 1980 .......... **45.00**
Sports Series
Air Race Pylon, 1970 .......... **12.00**
Nebraska Football Player, 1972 .......... **25.00**
Train Series, wood tender, 1969 .......... **20.00**
Warrior Series, 1969
Centurion .......... **20.00**
Napoleon .......... **25.00**

## MICHTER'S

American Legion, Doughboy, 1979 .......... **40.00**
Car, Fleetwood Packard, 1979 .......... **30.00**
Liberty Bell, brown, 1969 .......... **45.00**
Shrine, King Tut, white, 1978 .......... **350.00**

## MISCELLANEOUS

Aesthetic Specialties, Inc
Chevrolet, 1912, black, 1979 .......... **40.00**
World's Greatest Hunter, 1979 .......... **35.00**
ALPA, Warner Bros Characters
Bugs Bunny, 1977 .......... **8.00**
Tweety Bird, 1978 .......... **20.00**
Anniversary
Lincoln, 1973 .......... **15.00**
Thomas Edison, 1972 .......... **25.00**
Ballantine
Golf Bag, 1969 .......... **8.00**
Mallard, 1969 .......... **18.00**
Zebra, 1970 .......... **15.00**
Beneagle
Barrel, thistle .......... **5.00**
Chess Pawn, John Knox, black, miniature .......... **12.00**
Loch Ness Monster wearing tam, 1960 .......... **8.00**
Bischoff
Chinese Boy, 1962 .......... **35.00**
Grecian Vase, 1969 .......... **15.00**
Pirate .......... **20.00**
Collector's Art
Bird Series, miniature, cardinal .......... **32.00**
Cattle Series
Black Angus, miniature, 1975 .......... **20.00**
Texas Longhorn, 1974 .......... **35.00**
Dog Series, miniature
Basset Hound .......... **25.00**
Poodle, white .......... **20.00**
Garnier (France)
Bouquet, 1966 .......... **20.00**
Christmas Tree, 1956 .......... **65.00**
Locomotive, 1969 .......... **15.00**
Paris Mountains .......... **25.00**
Soccer Shoe, 1962 .......... **35.00**
Watering Can, 1958 .......... **15.00**
Kentucky Gentleman
Confederate Soldier, 1969 .......... **12.00**
Pink Lady .......... **25.00**
Union Soldier, 1969 .......... **12.00**
W A Lacey
Harold's Club, 1970 .......... **20.00**
Log Animal, raccoon, miniature, 1980 .......... **20.00**
Tun Tavern, 1975 .......... **15.00**
OBR
Caboose, 1973 .......... **20.00**
River Queen, 1967 .......... **10.00**
W C Fields, top hat, 1976 .......... **15.00**
Old Bardstown
Bull Dog, 1980 .......... **80.00**
Stanley Steamer, 1978 .......... **50.00**
Old Crow
Chess Series, Bishop .......... **12.00**
Crow, 1974 .......... **15.00**
Pancho Villa, Pancho Villa on horse, 1975 .......... **38.00**
Potters
Clydesdale, miniature, 1978 .......... **20.00**
Pirate, 1973 .......... **50.00**
Rutherford
Jug, crest, miniature, 1978 .......... **8.00**
Picture Frame, MacLachlan, miniature .......... **12.00**

## OLD COMMONWEALTH

Apothecary Series, North Carolina University, 1979 .......... **30.00**
Coal Miners
#3, with shovel, 1977 .......... **40.00**
#5, coal shooter, 1983 .......... **45.00**

Fireman Series, Modern
#1, Hero, 1982 .................. **58.00**
#5, Lifesaver, 1983 .............. **75.00**
Miscellaneous
Lumberjack, Old Time, 1979 ...... **20.00**
Kentucky Thoroughbreds, 1977 .... **40.00**

## OLD FITZGERALD

Blarney, Irish Toast, 1970 ........... **15.00**
Davidson, NC, 1972 ............... **38.00**
Gold Coaster, 1954 ................. **15.00**
Hospitality, 1958 ................... **8.00**
Monticello, 1968 ................... **6.00**
Rip Van Winkle, 1971 .............. **35.00**
Texas University, 1971 .............. **18.00**
West Virginia Forest Festival, 1973 ... **22.00**

## OLD MR. BOSTON

Bektash Temple, 1976 .............. **25.00**
Concord Coach, 1976 .............. **18.00**
Deadwood, SD, 1975 .............. **15.00**
Hawk, 1975 ....................... **18.00**
Lincoln Horseback, 1972 ............ **10.00**
Nebraska, #1, gold, 1970 ........... **22.00**
Paul Revere, 1975 .................. **15.00**
Town Crier, 1976 .................. **12.00**

## PACESETTER

Camaro, Z28, yellow, 1982 ......... **40.00**
Tractor Series, No. 2, Big Green Machine, International Harvester, 1983 **65.00**
Vokovich, #2, 1974 ................ **30.00**

## SKI COUNTRY

Christmas Series
Ebenezer Scrooge, miniature, 1979 . **25.00**
Mrs Cratchit, 1978 ............... **58.00**
Circus Series
Clown, bust, miniature, 1974 ...... **18.00**
Ringmaster, miniature, 1975 ....... **25.00**
Wagon, 1977 .................... **45.00**
Customer Specialties
Eagle, paperweight ............... **185.00**
Mill River Country Club, 1977 ..... **45.00**
Political, Donkey or Elephant, 1976 **35.00**
Submarine, miniature, 1976 ....... **30.00**
Domestic Animal Series, Labrador Dog with mallard, miniature, 1977 ..... **38.00**
Indian Series
Cigar Store Indian, 1974 .......... **40.00**
Dancer, Ceremonial Buffalo, 1975 .. **125.00**
North American Tribe, set of 6, miniature, 1977 ................... **90.00**
Waterfowl Series, duck, mallard, miniature, 1973 ...................... **38.00**
Wildlife Series
Antelope, Pronghorn .............. **70.00**
Jaguar, miniature ................. **34.00**
Koala, 1973 ..................... **40.00**
Mountain Lion, miniature, 1973 .... **30.00**
Polar Bear, miniature ............. **30.00**
Raccoon, 1974 .................. **60.00**
Woodpecker, ivory bill, 1974 ...... **65.00**

## WILD TURKEY

Crystal Anniversary, 1955 .......... **2,000.00**
Mack Truck ....................... **15.00**
Series #1
2, Female, 1972 ................. **165.00**
5, With Flags, 1975 .............. **40.00**
8, Strutting, 1978 ................ **48.00**
Turkey Lore Series
2, 1980 ......................... **38.00**
4, 1982 ......................... **50.00**

# WORLD'S FAIRS AND EXPOSITIONS

**Collecting Hints:** Familiarize yourself with the main buildings and features of the early World's Fairs and Expositions. Many of the choicest china and textiles pictured an identified building, assuming the buyer was aware of the significance. Many exposition buildings remained standing long after the fair was over, and souvenirs proliferated. Prices almost always are higher in the city or area where an exposition was held.

There have been hundreds of local fairs, state fairs, etc., in the last hundred years. These events generally produced items of little value except to local collectors.

**History:** The Great Exhibition of 1851 in London marked the beginning of the World's Fair and Exposition movement. The fairs generally feature exhibitions from nations around the world displaying the best of their industrial and scientific achievements.

Many important technological advances have been introduced at world's fairs. Examples include the airplane, telephone, and electric light. The ice cream cone, hot dog, and iced tea were products of vendors at fairs. Art movements often were closely connected to fairs with the Paris Exhibition of 1900 generally considered to have assembled the best of the works of the Art Nouveau artists.

**References:** *American Art, New York World's Fair, 1939,* Apollo Books, 1987; Carl Abbott, *The Great Extravaganza: Portland and the Lewis and Clark Exposition*, Oregon Historical Society, 1981; S. Applebaum, *The New York World's Fair 1939–40*, Dover Pub., 1977; Patricia F. Carpenter and Paul Totah, *The San Francisco Fair, Treasure Island, 1939–40,* Scottwall Associates, 1989; Richard Friz, *World's Fair Memorabilia,* Collector Books, 1989, out–of–print; Kurt Krueger, *Meet Me In St. Louis—The Exonumia of the 1904 World's Fair,* Krause Publications, 1979; Howard Rossen and John Kaduck, *Columbia World's Fair Collectibles,* Wallace–Homestead, 1976, revised price list 1982, out–of–print; Norman E. Martinus and Harry L. Rinker, *Warman's Paper,* Wallace–Homestead, 1993; Frederick and Mary Megson, *American Exposition Postcards, 1870–1920: A Catalog And Price Guide,* The Postcard Lovers, 1992; Larry Zim, Mel Lerner, and Herbert Rolfes, *The World Of Tomorrow: The 1939 New York World's Fair,* Main Street Press Book, Harper & Row, 1988.

**Periodical:** *World's Fair,* P. O. Box 339, Corte Madera, CA 94976.

**Collectors' Club:** World's Fair Collectors' Society, Inc., P. O. Box 20806, Sarasota, FL 34276.

1893, Chicago, Columbia Exposition
- Bone Dish ........ **25.00**
- Booklet, Acorn Stoves ........ **20.00**
- Charm, Heinz Pickle ........ **35.00**
- Crumb Tray and Scraper, silverplated **25.00**
- Guide Book, Official Guide To Columbian Expo, 1893, 194 photos . **25.00**
- Paperweight, stack coin ........ **45.00**
- Playing Cards ........ **65.00**
- Rose Bowl, peachblow, New England Glass Co ........ **300.00**
- Souvenir Plate, Wedgwood ........ **30.00**
- Sword ........ **185.00**

1901, Pan American Exposition, Buffalo
- Bandana, 20" sq, silk, Electrical Tower ........ **40.00**
- Match Holder, hanging ........ **15.00**
- Playing Cards ........ **65.00**
- Souvenir Spoon, Indian, demitasse size ........ **45.00**
- Teaspoon, sterling ........ **20.00**

1904, St Louis, Louisiana Purchase Exposition
- Bowl, Grant log cabin ........ **150.00**
- Coffee Tin, Hanley & Kinsella ........ **22.00**
- Letter Opener, emb buildings on handle ........ **28.00**
- Sword, Jefferson Guard ........ **300.00**

1915, San Francisco, Panama–Pacific International Exposition
- Guide Book, *Official Guidebook,* 168 pgs, black and white photos ..... **25.00**
- Tray, 3½ x 5½", hammered metal, bear figural, emb "Tower of Jewels, Panama Pacific Internation/San Francisco, Cal 1915," dark finish . **40.00**
- Watch Fob, brass, black leather strap **75.00**

1926, Philadelphia, Sesquicentennial Exposition
- Lapel Stud, ⅝" d, brass, Liberty Bell flanked by '76 and '26, lettering on rim with lime green enamel accents **10.00**
- Pin, ⅝" d, diecut, bronze colored, Liberty Bell inscribed with "1776" inside inscribed horseshoe ........ **12.00**
- Tape Measure, 1½" d, celluloid, multicolored scene on top ....... **25.00**

**1926 Philadelphia Sesqui-Centennial International Exposition, booklet, The Broadway of America's Transportation System, PA RR giveaway, 20 pgs, foldout exhibit photo, 3½ x 6", $15.00.**

1934, Chicago, Century of Progress
- Automobile, rear view mirror, no glare, orig box ........ **75.00**
- Bracelet, copper, scenic ........ **20.00**
- Camera, 3 x 4 x 5½", box style, metal and cardboard, metal title plate, Agfa B–2 Plenachrome Film paper sticker ........ **75.00**
- Cigarette Lighter, camel ........ **30.00**
- Game, Bambino Baseball, orig box . **265.00**
- Guide Book, *Official Guide Book,* 5½ x 8½", 192 pgs ........ **25.00**
- Handkerchief, silk ........ **12.00**
- Jackknife, marbleized plastic ....... **20.00**
- Key, Key to Fair, paint peeling, orig box ........ **25.00**
- Lamp, brass, marked "Century of Progress 1934" ........ **45.00**
- Letter Opener ........ **28.00**
- Magazine, *Marshall Field & Co,* 9½ x 13", 44 pgs, photos and articles .. **18.00**
- Medal
  - American Legion ........ **25.00**
  - Male figure symbol of Research/Industry and "1833–1933" on front, aerial view on back, rim inscription, 1½" d ........ **25.00**
  - Youthful figure symbolizing Research and Industry, bronze display box and leaflet, 2⅜" d .... **40.00**
- Mirror, pocket ........ **20.00**
- Mug, coffee, Stewarts ........ **45.00**
- Pillow, leather, scenic, large ....... **75.00**
- Pin, 1½" d, metal, official symbol with black enamel accents and skyscrapers, raised relief center scenes ........ **20.00**
- Playing Cards, gold leaf, orig red leather case ........ **20.00**

**1934 Century of Progress, Chicago, mesh purse, silver frame, green and white enameled mesh front with "1934 World's Fair Chicago" and comet logo, white enameled back, 4" w, 6½" h with handle, $125.00.**

Portrait, charcoal, signed by artist, stamped "General Exhibit, Pavilion #2" ..... **55.00**
Shell, cowry, carved ..... **24.00**
Snowglobe ..... **50.00**
Souvenir Book, Official Guide Book of Fair, 1933 ..... **5.00**
Souvenir Key, 3 x 8", metal, copper colored, emb Travel and Transport Building on one side, Hall of Science on other ..... **30.00**
Sunday Comic, full page, sponsored by Reynolds Tobacco, 1934 ..... **15.00**
Tea Infuser, spoon, silver plated ..... **28.00**
Token, Walgreen Drugs, large ..... **20.00**
Tray, Hall of Science, emb buildings, bridge ..... **25.00**
Viewbook, 7 x 10", 64 pgs, black and white photos ..... **25.00**

1936, Cleveland, Great Lakes Expo
Bank, 3½" h, waxed cardboard, milk carton, red and blue design on white background, Dairymens Milk Co, Cleveland sponsors ..... **35.00**
Guide Book, 6 x 9", spiral bound, 64 pgs, 1937 ..... **25.00**
Toy, bus, 11" l, cast iron, blue and cream, silver accents, raised Greyhound logo, white "Greyhound Lines/Great Lakes Exposition 1936" on roof, orig box ..... **400.00**

1936, Texas Centennial Exposition, glass, 3½" h, clear, dark blue official seal, reverse with dark blue cowboy on rearing horse ..... **25.00**

1939, New York, New York World's Fair
Ashtray
3 x 3¾" x 4½", metal, dark finish, inscribed "Strikalite" ..... **50.00**
4½ x 3½", jasperware, Japanese . **50.00**
Bank, 2½ x 3¾", cardboard, book form, white, orange and blue Trylon and Perisphere, marked "Dalton–Tumulty Co, Jersey City" ..... **35.00**
Bookends, pr, alabaster, figural, Trylon and Perisphere ..... **95.00**
Bowl, 5½" d, glass, clear, white Trylon and Perisphere, orange inscription ..... **75.00**
Cake Plate ..... **85.00**
Cane, 34" l, wood, blue, round wooden knob, Trylon and Perisphere decal ..... **75.00**
Charm, ⅝" w, book shape, silvered metal, emb Trylon and Perisphere on front ..... **25.00**
Clock, travel, ½ x 1¼ x 1½", chrome silver case, Trylon, Perisphere, and fair buildings on cov with blue and orange enamel accents ..... **125.00**
Clothing, lady's jacket ..... **125.00**
Compact, 2¾" d, metal, full color celluloid insert, ivory white enameling **40.00**
Exhibit Folder
GM ..... **3.00**
Your World of Tomorrow ..... **5.00**
Guide Book, 1940, 168 pages ..... **35.00**
Hat, employee, wool, navy, orange Trylon and Perisphere and "1940" on front ..... **40.00**
Hearing Test, Bell Telephone Exhibit **3.00**
Jewelry, tie bar ..... **12.00**
Mirror
Hand, 12½" h, metal, celluloid panel, brass finish ..... **125.00**
Purse ..... **20.00**

**1939 World's Fair, radio, RCA Victor, table model, dark brown syroco and wood case, molded front with Trylon and Perisphere, 9 x 6 x 6", $80.00.**

Night Light, ceramic, oval base with Trylon and Perisphere, ivory white finish, gold accents ..... **100.00**
Picture, framed, Perisphere, thermometer, adv for North Dakota Grain Elevator ..... **25.00**
Pin
Six Pointed Star, silvered metal, orange and blue enameled raised

Trylon and Perisphere, back with Star of David ... **15.00**
Three discs ... **30.00**
Plate, 10½" d, china, Shelter Building illus, leaf pattern border, made by Spode of England for Abraham & Strauss Inc, Brooklyn ... **50.00**
Playing Cards, two decks, orig box, US Playing Card Co ... **50.00**
Pocket Watch, 1¾" d, metal, enameled Trylon and Perisphere scene, inscribed "Ingersoll Yankee" ... **200.00**
Pot Holder, 7½ x 8½", woven terrycloth, blue and white design, inscribed "Macy's Pot Holder" ... **50.00**
Program, 9 x 12", Billy Rose's Aquacade, New York State Marine Amphitheatre, 32 pgs ... **25.00**
Scrapbook, Official, clippings, layout diagrams, buildings ... **12.00**
Snow Dome, 4" h, Trylon and Perisphere, black plastic base, orange "New York World's Fair" decal ... **125.00**
Souvenir Plate, George Washington . **65.00**
Souvenir Spoon ... **15.00**
Tape Measure, 2½" w, egg shape, metal, blue finish, bee figure on both sides, orange Trylon and Perisphere on one side, marked "New York World's Fair 1939" ... **50.00**
Thermometer, 8¾" l, key shape, aerial view ... **30.00**
Thermos, 10" h, steel, threaded aluminum cup, orange Trylon and Perisphere, Universal Thermos ... **100.00**
Ticket, 3 x 4", black and white photo, starched black fabric holder ... **50.00**
Tie Clip, 2¾" w, brass, raised center emblem of Trylon and Perisphere . **25.00**
Timetable
Around The Grounds, Greyhound **8.00**
NYC transit ... **8.00**
Tray, 18" l, litho tin, blue, white, and orange enamel design ... **75.00**
Valet Holder, clothes brush holder and tie rack, syrocco wood, raised Trylon and Perisphere, orig brush **50.00**
Vase, 3¾" h, clear glass, ruby flashed, inscribed "New York World's Fair 1940" in gold ... **20.00**

1939, San Francisco, Golden Gate International Exposition
Coin, 1¼" d, aluminum, emb, rim inscriptions on back ... **10.00**
Matchbook Cover, Golden Gate Bridge scenes, pr ... **25.00**
Pinback Button, 1¼" d, yellow, blue, and white ... **25.00**

1962, Seattle, Century 21 Exposition
Pinback Button, 1¼" d, red, white, and blue, Space Needle scene ... **15.00**
Token, gold ... **9.00**
Tray, metal ... **10.00**
Tumbler, frosted, tall, set of seven different views ... **65.00**

1964, New York, New York World's Fair
Advertising Display, Magic Coin Purse, cardboard, holds 24 orig triangular shape vinyl coin purses, Vinylcraft, New York City ... **200.00**
Ashtray, 7½ x 5", colorful, Unisphere and skyline ... **12.00**
Back Pack, vinyl ... **12.50**
Change Tray ... **11.00**
Clothing, jacket, Greyhound Tram .. **95.00**
Coaster, 4" d, set of 4, plastic, white, emb gold Unisphere, title and date **30.00**
Glass, 5½" h, frosted, aqua blue and black Unisphere design, text description on back ... **22.00**
Hat
Beach, fabric, aqua blue, multicolored band with exhibit buildings and Unisphere, title and dates . **30.00**
Safety, adult, hard white plastic, red, white, blue, and yellow sticker ... **25.00**
Mug, 3¼" h, milk glass, inscribed in red ... **15.00**
Nodder, 4" h, composition, Unisphere, white and blue, base with decal "1964–New York World's Fair–1965" ... **30.00**
Placemats, pr, 11 x 17½", plastic, full color illus, Swiss Sky Ride and Lunar Fountain ... **25.00**
Plate, 10" d, milk glass, Unisphere, Swiss Sky Ride, Monorail, and exhibit buildings, Anchor Hocking .. **15.00**
Post Card, Reddy Kilowatt ... **15.00**
Puzzle, set of 3, Milton Bradley, full color illus scenes, titled "New York World's Fair" ... **50.00**
Salt and Pepper Shakers, figural ... **10.00**
Thermometer, 6 x 6", diamond shape, metal and plastic, full color fair buildings and attractions illus, ... **25.00**
Towel, 17 x 26", terrycloth, Unisphere and four exhibits illus, "Peace Through Understanding" theme ... **40.00**
Tray
10½ x 11½", oval, plastic, raised fair attractions ... **40.00**
12" d, red, Unisphere center with eight fair attractions dec ... **30.00**
Tumbler, Science Hall, 6½" h ... **16.00**

1967, Montreal, Montreal Expo
Lapel Pin, brass, repeated motif around edge, threaded post fastener on back ... **10.00**
Tab, 1½", litho tin, blue and white, US Pavilion, "Compliments of Avis Car Rental" on reverse ... **5.00**

1976, Philadelphia, Bicentennial
- Alarm Clock, [illegible]" h, metal, windup, Declaration of Independence on dial, dark copper–bronze finish, "Commemorative Series Registered Edition" inscription on back ..... **45.00**

1982, Knoxville, World's Fair
- Glass, 5½" h, clear, tapered, Energy Turns The World theme and illus, McDonald's and Coca–Cola trademark ........................ **8.00**
- Sailor Cap, black and red inscription on brim ...................... **5.00**

# WORLD WAR I COLLECTIBLES

**Collecting Hints:** Be careful. Uniforms and equipment from World War I were stockpiled at the end of the war and reissued in the early years of World War II. Know the source of the items that you have received or buy. Scrutinize all unknown materials. Some research and investigation might be necessary to correctly identify an item as an actual war artifact.

Collector clubs and re–enactment groups are one of the best sources for information and identification due to their quest for authenticity. These groups also are very knowledgeable about reproductions, copycats, and fantasy items.

**History:** Power struggles between European countries raged for hundreds of years. As the twentieth century dawned, leading European countries became entangled in a series of complex alliances, many sealed by royal marriages, and a massive arms race. All that was needed to set the powder keg was a fire. The assassination of Austrian Archduke Franz Ferdinand by a Serbian national, June 28, 1914, ignited the fuse. Germany invaded Belgium and moved into France. Russia, England, and Turkey joined the war. Italy and the United States were involved by mid–1917.

In 1918 Germany sued for peace. A settlement was achieved at the Versailles Conference, January–June 1919. The United Sates remained in the background. President Wilson's concept of a League of Nations failed to gain acceptance in his own country, opening the door to the events leading up to World War II.

**References:** Robert Fisch, *Field Equipment of the Infantry 1914–1945,* Greenberg Publishing Company, Inc., 1989; Norman E. Martinus and Harry L. Rinker, *Warman's Paper,* Wallace–Homestead, 1993.

**Periodical:** *Military Collectors News,* P. O. Box 702073, Tulsa, OK 74170.

**Collectors' Clubs:** American Society of Military Insignia Collectors, 526 Lafayette Ave., Palmerton, PA 18701; Association of American Military Uniform Collectors, P.O. Box 1876, Elyria, OH 44036.

Book
- Doyle, Arthur Conan, *The Guards Came Through and Other Poems,* George H Doran, 1920, 76 pages **25.00**
- Hoyt, Edwin P, *The Army Without A Country,* Macmillan, 1967, first edition, 243 pages, dust jacket ..... **15.00**
- Pershing, John J, *My Experiences In The World War,* two volumes, Frederick Stokes, 1931, illus, maps, price for set .................. **25.00**

Canteen, aluminum, brown felt cover, German, expanding rubber stopper, worn leather straps .............. **30.00**

Cartridge Belt, canteen, two medical packs .......................... **35.00**

Cartridge Pouch, leather, triple pocket, "D" rings ..................... **30.00**

Catalog, The Warnock Uniform Co, New York, NY, illus of uniforms and equipment for US Army and National Guard, 1910, 64 pages, 5½ x 7¾" . **45.00**

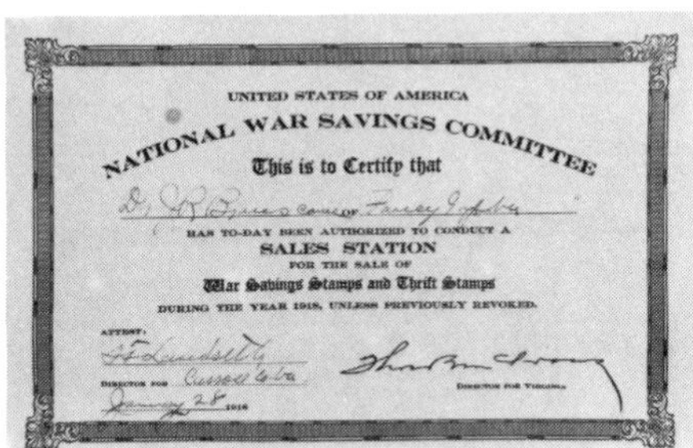
UNITED STATES OF AMERICA
NATIONAL WAR SAVINGS COMMITTEE
This is to Certify that
HAS TO-DAY BEEN AUTHORIZED TO CONDUCT A
SALES STATION
FOR THE SALE OF
War Savings Stamps and Thrift Stamps
DURING THE YEAR 1918, UNLESS PREVIOUSLY REVOKED.

**Certificate, National War Savings Committee, Sales Station authorization, printed, black and white, 1918, 8⅜ x 5¼", $15.00.**

Clothing, uniform, Doughboy, unissued **85.00**

Cup, German, porcelainized steel, gray–green, fixed handle, slightly dented, marked "B & F16" ........ **20.00**

Field Shoes, US, brown leather, marked "Kennedy, St Louis Depot 9A" on soles, heels marked "U. S. Army 9A" **90.00**

Gas Mask, bag, Doughboy
- "307 M. G. Battalion" ............ **33.00**
- "S.R.O.U.S.A.–AEF Cavalry" ...... **33.00**

Helmet, German
- Spiked, gray plate, two lions, crown, left rosette missing .............. **110.00**

Steel, orig liner, no chin strap ...... **55.00**
Knapsack
Austrian, hair, complete, blanket straps, marked "Ott Romer & Co, Wein, 1916" .................. **180.00**
United States, canvas, model 1910, khaki colored, marked "P.B & Co. 4–18" ........................ **20.00**
Lapel Stud, enamel, US Naval Reserve **13.00**
Magazine
Army Pictorial Section of the Home-back, published for soldier patients at Walter Reed Hospital, 1912, 9 x 12", black and white ........... **10.00**
To The Homeward Bound Americans, B Von Vorst, published in France, 32 pages, black and white ....... **6.00**
Map, Official War Map Western Battle Front, bank advertisement on back . **10.00**
Medal
French, "They Shall Not Pass," Verdun .......................... **22.00**
US, Utica, NY, "World War" ...... **12.00**
Medallion, Kaiser Wilhelm, bronze ... **45.00**
Mess Kit, US, Model 1910, aluminum, steel knife, fork, and spoon, marked "U.S.J.W.B.A. 1918" ............. **20.00**
Pennant, 27th Division .............. **24.00**
Photograph, 37 x 22", mounted on wood, enlarged news type photo, German biplane, Lt Gerhart Bessenge, Lt Kempf, and Lt Dr Herman Vallenor in foreground ............ **225.00**
Pin, World War Veteran ............. **10.00**
Poncho, US, dual layer canvas, steel buttons, marked "Hodgman Rubber Co, Contract 47, Philadelphia, PA," slightly worn, small holes, 69 x 53" . **65.00**
Print
"Lt Werner Ross' Plane," Mylogar, colored ....................... **125.00**
"True Blue," black soldier ......... **50.00**
Sea Bag, Navy, American issue, unit marked ......................... **15.00**
Sheet Music, patriotic pictorial cov
*Break The News To Mother* ........ **7.50**
*For Your Boy & My Boy* ........... **5.00**
*Good–Bye Broadway, Hello France* . **7.50**
*In The Navy* ..................... **5.00**
*Send Me Away With A Smile* ...... **7.50**
*The Girls We Leave Behind* ........ **5.00**
*The Red, White & Blue Is Calling You* **5.00**
*When Sammy Goes Over The Top* .. **5.00**
Shelter Half, US, canvas, brass buttons, two sections, 66 x 57" rectangular, 51 x 56" triangular, five steel pegs, three wooden poles, marked "U.S." ..... **60.00**
Swagger Stick, officer ............... **11.00**
Tunic, Canadian, moth damage ...... **57.00**
Watch Fob, Order of Cootie ......... **18.00**

# WORLD WAR II COLLECTIBLES

**Collecting Hints:** To the victors go the spoils or so WWII collectors would like to think. Now that the Soviet Bloc has fallen, a large number of dealers are making efforts to import Soviet Bloc WWII collectibles into the United States. Be careful when buying anything that has a new or unused appearance. Many Soviet countries continued to use stockpiled WWII equipment and still manufacture new goods based on WWII designs.

The Korean Conflict occurred shortly after WWII. The United States and other armed forces in the conflict used equipment and uniforms similar to those manufactured during WWII. Familiarize yourself with model styles, dates of manufacture, and your buying sources.

If you locate a WWII item, make certain to record all personal history associated with the item. This is extremely important. Collectors demand this documentation. If possible, secure additional information on the history of the unit and the battles in which it was engaged. Also make certain to obtain any extras such as insignia or a second set of buttons.

**History:** With the rise of the German Third Reich, European nations once again engaged in a massive arms race. The 1930s Depression compounded the situation.

After numerous compromises to German expansionism, war was declared in 1939 following Germany's Blitzkrieg invasion of Poland. Allied and Axis alliances were formed.

America's neutrality was heavily supportive of the Allied cause. The December 7, 1941, Japanese attack on the U. S. Naval Station at Pearl Harbor, Hawaii, forced America into the war. It immediately adopted a two front strategy.

During 1942 to 1945 the entire world was directly or indirectly involved in the war. Virtually all industrial activity was war related. The technological advances guaranteed that life after the war would be far different than before the war.

Germany surrendered May 7, 1945. Japan surrendered on August 14, 1945, after the atomic bombing of Hiroshima on August 6, 1945, and Nagasaki on August 9, 1945.

**References:** Thomas Berndt, *Standard Catalog of U. S. Military Vehicles: 1940–1965,* Krause Publications, 1993; Stan Cohen, *V For Victory: America's Home Front During World War II,* Pictorial Histories Publishing Company, Inc., 1991; Robert Fisch, *Field Equipment of the Infantry 1914–1945,* Greenberg Publishing Company, Inc., 1989; Norman E. Martinus and Harry L. Rinker, *Warman's Paper,* Wallace–Homestead, 1993; Walton Rawls, *Disney Dons Dogtags: The*

*Best of Disney Military Insignia from World War II,* Abbeville Publishing, 1992.

**Periodical:** *Military Collectors News,* P. O. Box 702073, Tulsa, OK 74170.

**Collectors' Clubs:** American Society of Military Insignia Collectors, 526 Lafayette Ave., Palmerton, PA 18701; Association of American Military Uniform Collectors, P. O. Box 1876, Elyria, OH 44035.

**Advisor:** Harry L. Rinker, Jr.

**Arm Band, worn by D-Day Invasion paratrooper, $15.00.**

Admiralty Charts, fold out photos, packet, "France: North Coast, Feb 1944, Coastal Recognition," very detailed .......... **60.00**
Award, Russian Official Order of the Red Star, silver and red enamel, serial number on back .......... **50.00**
Banner, crocheted, German Labor, attributed to Imperial, 26 x 20" .......... **55.00**
Bayonet
- 13½" l, leather belt holders, scabbards, matching pair .......... **60.00**
- 18" l, no scabbard .......... **21.00**

Belt Buckle, Nazi .......... **25.00**
Book
- *Abbott Hall USNR,* Naval Reserve School, Northwestern Univ, 1940–45, 170 pages, illus, hard cover .. **20.00**
- *A Pictorial Record Of The 4th Infantry Division,* Army and Navy Publication, 1945, 132 pages, illus, maps **100.00**
- Carter, Ross S, *Those Devils In Baggy Pants,* Appleton Century Crofts, first ed, 299 pages .......... **40.00**
- D'Este, Carlo, *Bitter Victory, The Battle For Sicily,* Dutton, 1943, illus, maps, 666 pages, dust jacket .... **15.00**
- Driscoll, Joseph, *War Discovers Alaska,* Lippincott, 1943, illus, maps, 352 pages .......... **25.00**
- Smedley, Agnes, *China Fights Back,* Vanguard Press, 1938, illus, 282 pgs .......... **15.00**

Canteen
- Japanese, aluminum, cork stopper, painted brown .......... **40.00**
- United States, cover only, 1942 .... **12.00**

Cartridge Belt, web, canteen .......... **20.00**
Chain Saw, Canadian Engineers Montreal Contract Pioneer, leather case, 1944 .......... **33.00**
Chest, war, Captain's, 13th Air Force, decorated blouse jacket, ribbons, battle stars, citations, officer's overcoat, two shirts, dress shirt, tropical jacket, fatigue cap dated 1942, pants, 13th insignia, wool lined flight line tuck field jacket with insignia, cloth Lt. bars, artistically painted flight garment bag .......... **250.00**
Cleaning Kit, K98 8mm Mauser, German, chain, oil can, tin container .. **30.00**
Clothing
- Blouse Jacket, wool, olive, brass buttons, T–3 rank, unit citation, size 39–R .......... **35.00**
- Cap, overseas, unused .......... **7.00**
- Deck Pants, wool, lined, Navy Dept, contract carrier .......... **30.00**
- Dress, Red Cross, seersucker .......... **35.00**
- Hat Cord, Nazi, officer .......... **10.00**
- Hat, Wave
  - Navy .......... **25.00**
  - Seersucker, overseas .......... **12.00**
- Helmet, British, liner, chin strap, netting .......... **40.00**
- Jacket
  - British, R.A.F., green wool, officer's insignia .......... **45.00**
  - United States, bomber type, issue wool, Army .......... **25.00**
- Overcoat, Army, Canadian .......... **55.00**
- Pants
  - Enlisted, man's, US Army, wool, olive, size 34–31 .......... **15.00**
  - WAAC, lady's, field .......... **30.00**
- Parka Cover, ski troops, white/olive, reversible .......... **120.00**
- Shirt, wool, olive, T–3 rank, three hash, mint .......... **15.00**
- Suit
  - Nurse, Naval .......... **25.00**
  - WAAC, two piece
    - Beige .......... **65.00**
    - Green .......... **65.00**

Command Set Transmitter, P–39 cockpit, marked "Signal Corps US Army" **55.00**
Cruise Book, *USS Henley* destroyer, 1953 .......... **15.00**
Dagger
- Nazi, enlisted SS .......... **875.00**
- Russian Air Force .......... **225.00**

Entrenching Tool and Carrier, US, painted olive green, stamped "U. S. Ames 1945" .......... **25.00**
First Aid Steel Packet, US, painted olive green, stamped "First Aid Packet, U. S. Gov't/Carlisle Model" .......... **6.00**

Garment Bag, flight, Army Air Force, stuck zipper ..................... **30.00**
Gas Mask, Nazi, swastika mask ...... **20.00**
Handbook English Channel, London Admiralty, April 18, 1944, restricted invasion item .................... **100.00**
Identification Tag (Dog Tag), US, stainless steel, round ended, rectangular, bead chain ...................... **8.00**
Insignia Guide, Wonder Bread premium, mechanical, disk turns to show comparison of army and navy ranks, 4" h, 5¼" d disk, cardboard, red, white, gold, and black ............ **12.00**
Magazine
Our Fighting Forces, US and enemy's uniforms, 1943 ................ **25.00**
War Stories From The Front, 1944 .. **15.00**
Manual, Recognition Pictorial Manual, April 1943, War/Navy Dept, Espionage Act 50, used to recognize Allied/Axis war planes .................. **50.00**
Mess Tin, British, two parts, one with steel wire folding handle, marked, dated, broad arrow ............... **30.00**
Mortar Shell, German, 80 mm, de–activated, lightly rusted ............. **25.00**
Photo Album, American Navy, 1943, 49th Seabee Battalion, large company photo, names, autographs, snap shots **140.00**
Photo, studio portrait, SS officer ...... **25.00**

**Pillow Cover, silk, Army Air Forces, Traux Army Air Field, Madison, WI, flocked planes and banner, dark blue ground, red fringe border, 17½" sq, $25.00.**

Plate, Christmas, 1940, Iron Cross in center, given to infantry unit, marked "Villeroy & Boch" ............... **100.00**
Shell Casings, brass, 90 millimeter, 23½" l ......................... **25.00**
Siren, trench/front, hand held, crank, painted olive, carry strap and cover . **100.00**
Spade, entrenching, folding, GI, 1944 **18.00**
Sword, Nazi Luftwaffe Officer, squadron marked to flight unit, complete with hanger ......................... **625.00**

Torpedo Angle Solver–Mark VII–Mod 3, submarine officer's, orig wood case . **50.00**
Vest, emergency sustenance, Type C–1, Army Air Forces .................. **35.00**

# WRIGHT, RUSSEL

**Collecting Hints:** Russel Wright worked for many different companies in addition to creating material under his own label, American Way. Wright's contracts with firms often called for the redesign of pieces which did not produce or sell well. As a result, several lines have the same item in more than one shape.

Wright was totally involved in design. Most collectors focus on his dinnerware; however, he also designed glassware, plastic items, textiles, furniture, and metal objects. Bleached and blonde furniture were part of his contributions. His early work in spun aluminum often is overlooked as is his later work in plastic for the Northern Industrial Chemical Company.

**History:** Russel Wright was an American industrial engineer with a design passion for domestic efficiency through simple lines. His streamlined influence is found in all aspects of living. Wright and his wife, Mary Small Einstein, wrote *A Guide To Easier Living* to explain the concepts.

Russel Wright was born in 1904 in Lebanon, Ohio. His first jobs included set designer and stage manager under the direction of Norman Bel Geddes. He later used this theatrical flair for his industrial designs, stressing simple clean lines. Some of his earliest designs were executed in polished spun aluminum. These pieces, designed in the mid–1930s, included trays, vases, teapots, and other items. Wright received awards from the Museum of Modern Art in 1950 and 1953. His designs garnered many other awards.

Among the companies for which Russel Wright did design work are Chase Brass and Copper, General Electric, Imperial Glass, National Silver Co., Shenango, and Steubenville Pottery Company. In 1983 a major exhibition of Wright's designs was held at the Hudson River Museum in Yonkers, New York, and at the Smithsonian's Renwick Gallery in Washington, D.C.

**References:** Ann Kerr, *The Collector's Encyclopedia of Russel Wright Designs,* Collector Books, 1990, 1993 value update; Dana Gehman Morykan and Harry L. Rinker, *Warman's Country Antiques & Collectibles,* Wallace–Homestead, 1992.

## ALUMINUM WARE

Bun Warmer, liner .................. **50.00**
Punch Set, spun aluminum, bowl, platter, ladle, eight cups, price for 11 pc set ........................... **650.00**

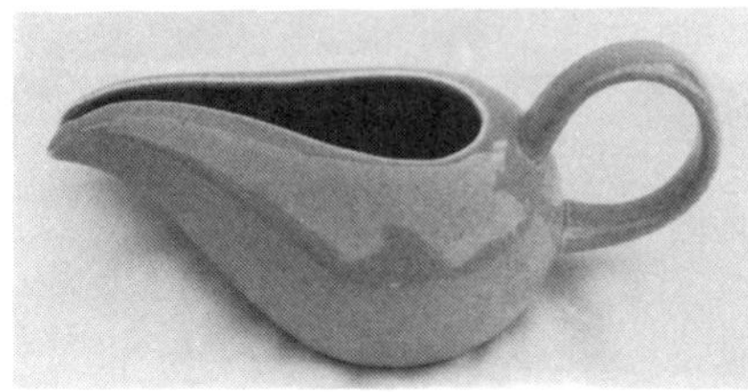

**American Modern, creamer, Coral, $12.00.**

## DINNERWARE

American Modern. Made by the Steubenville Pottery Company, 1939–59. Originally issued in Bean Brown, Chartreuse Curry, Coral, Granite Grey, Seafoam Blue, and White. Later color additions were Black Chutney, Cedar Green, Canteloupe, Glacier Blue, and Steubenville Blue. The Ideal Toy Company made a set of miniature dishes, which was distributed by Sears, Roebuck.

- Baker, Coral .......... **45.00**
- Bowl, 5¼" d, Granite Grey .......... **9.00**
- Butter Dish, cov, Black Chutney .......... **300.00**
- Carafe, Granite Grey .......... **165.00**
- Casserole, lug handle, Seafoam Blue **45.00**
- Celery
  - Bean Brown .......... **45.00**
  - Chartreuse Curry .......... **10.00**
  - White .......... **50.00**
- Chop Plate
  - Coral .......... **35.00**
  - Seafoam Blue .......... **15.00**
- Coaster, Black Chutney .......... **22.00**
- Coffeepot, after dinner, Chartreuse Curry .......... **72.00**
- Creamer
  - Chartreuse Curry .......... **12.00**
  - White .......... **20.00**
- Cup and Saucer
  - Black Chutney .......... **6.00**
  - Cedar Green .......... **9.00**
- Demitasse Cup and Saucer
  - Coral .......... **16.00**
  - Granite Grey .......... **20.00**
- Fruit Bowl, lug handle, Black Chutney **9.00**
- Gravy, Cedar Green .......... **15.00**
- Pickle Dish, Coral .......... **14.00**
- Pitcher, water
  - Cedar Green .......... **80.00**
  - Granite Grey .......... **70.00**
  - Seafoam Blue .......... **70.00**
- Plate
  - 6" d, bread and butter, Granite Grey .......... **4.00**
  - 8" d, salad
    - Granite Grey .......... **18.00**
    - White .......... **28.00**
  - 10" d, dinner
    - Black Chutney .......... **25.00**
    - Granite Grey .......... **5.00**
    - Steubenville Blue .......... **20.00**
- Platter, Cedar Green .......... **35.00**
- Relish Dish, divided, Granite Grey . **160.00**
- Salad Bowl, Coral .......... **50.00**
- Salt and Pepper Shakers, pr
  - Bean Brown .......... **40.00**
  - Granite Grey .......... **18.00**
- Sauce Boat, Chartreuse .......... **22.00**
- Soup Bowl, lug handle, Black Chutney .......... **9.00**
- Sugar, cov, Cedar Green .......... **10.00**
- Teapot, Granite Grey .......... **100.00**
- Tumbler, Black Chutney .......... **65.00**
- Vegetable Bowl, divided
  - Cedar Green .......... **50.00**
  - Chartreuse Curry .......... **35.00**

Iroquois Casual. Made by the Iroquoise China Company and distributed by Garrison Products, 1946–60s. Initially issued in Ice Blue, Lemon Yellow, and Sugar White. Later colors produced were Aqua, Avocado Yellow, Brick Red, Canteloupe, Charcoal, Lettuce Green, Oyster, Nutmeg Brown, Parsley Green (later called Forest Green,) Pink Sherbet, and Ripe Apricot.

- Butter, cov, Avocado Yellow .......... **55.00**
- Carafe, Ice Blue .......... **125.00**
- Casserole, cov, 8" l, 2 qt
  - Lettuce Green .......... **60.00**
  - Ripe Apricot .......... **45.00**
- Cereal Bowl, 6" d
  - Avocado Yellow .......... **6.00**
  - Nutmeg Brown .......... **8.00**
  - Ripe Apricot .......... **14.00**
- Chop Plate, Ice Blue .......... **25.00**
- Coffeepot, Ice Blue .......... **95.00**
- Creamer, stacking, Nutmeg Brown .. **12.00**
- Creamer and Sugar, cov, stacked, Ice Blue .......... **20.00**
- Cup and Saucer
  - Parsley Green .......... **18.00**
  - Sugar White .......... **20.00**
- Demitasse Cup and Saucer
  - Charcoal .......... **24.00**
  - Lemon Yellow .......... **15.00**
  - Oyster .......... **18.00**
- Fruit Bowl, 5" d
  - Aqua .......... **35.00**
  - Ripe Apricot .......... **13.00**
- Gravy, attached underplate, 16 oz, Ripe Apricot .......... **12.00**
- Gumbo Bowl, Avocado Yellow .......... **15.00**
- Mug, 13 oz, Pink Sherbet .......... **28.00**
- Nappy, 8" d, Sugar White .......... **30.00**
- Plate
  - 6½" d, bread and butter
    - Avocado Yellow .......... **3.00**
    - Pink Sherbet .......... **6.00**
  - 7½" d, salad
    - Lettuce Green .......... **5.00**
    - Nutmeg Brown .......... **4.00**
  - 9½" d, luncheon, Ice Blue .......... **5.00**

10″ d, dinner
Charcoal .......... **7.00**
Lettuce Green .......... **18.00**
Nutmeg Brown .......... **10.00**
Platter, oval
12¾″ l
Nutmeg Brown .......... **25.00**
Ripe Apricot .......... **30.00**
14½″ l, Nutmeg Brown .......... **20.00**
Salt and Pepper Shakers, pr, stacked, Ripe Apricot .......... **32.00**
Sugar, stacking, Oyster .......... **24.00**
Vegetable Bowl
8¼″ d, open, Oyster .......... **30.00**
10″ l, cov, divided, Avocado Yellow **25.00**

Iroquois Casual, redesigned. In 1959 Iroquois Casual dinnerware was produced in patterns and offered in 45 piece sets. Cookware was another later addition in the redesigned style.

Creamer
Charcoal .......... **54.00**
Lemon Yellow .......... **18.00**
Cup, Canteloupe .......... **24.00**
Fruit Bowl, Ripe Apricot .......... **13.00**
Frying Pan, Ripe Apricot .......... **200.00**
Mug, Lemon Yellow .......... **55.00**
Party Plate, Pink Sherbet .......... **75.00**
Plate, 6″ d, Sugar White .......... **6.00**
Sauce Pan, Ice Blue .......... **200.00**
Saucer, Sugar White .......... **4.50**
Sugar, Lemon Yellow .......... **40.00**
Teapot, Pink Sherbet .......... **100.00**

## FLATWARE

Pinch, Highlight Line, stainless steel, brushed satin finish
Dinner Fork .......... **32.50**
Salad Fork .......... **30.00**
Soup Spoon .......... **35.00**
Teaspoon .......... **30.00**

## GLASSWARE

American Modern, Old Morgantown, compliments American Modern dinnerware, 1951
Dessert Bowl, 4″ d, 1⅞″ h
Seafoam .......... **30.00**
Smoke .......... **30.00**
Stemware
Cocktail, 2½″ h, 3 oz, Seafoam .. **22.00**
Goblet, 4″ h, 10 oz
Seafoam .......... **32.50**
Smoke .......... **35.00**
Sherbet, 2½″ h, 5 oz
Coral .......... **27.50**
Seafoam .......... **20.00**
Wine, 3″ h, 4 oz, Chartreuse .... **17.00**
Tumbler, flat
4″ h, juice, 7 oz
Seafoam .......... **15.00**
Smoke .......... **20.00**
4½″ h, water, 10 oz, Seafoam ... **35.00**

Eclipse, Bartlett Collins, 1957, tumbler
Double Old Fashioned, Blue .......... **22.00**
Ice Tea, Red .......... **17.00**
Water, Blue .......... **15.00**

Pinch, Imperial Glass, complements Iroquoise Casual, 1951, tumbler
6 oz, juice, Chartreuse .......... **30.00**
11 oz, water, Chartreuse .......... **20.00**
14 oz, ice tea, Smoke .......... **22.00**

**Tidbit Tray, two tiers, bamboo handle, $50.00.**

## HOUSEWARES

Clock, General Electric, green face ... **60.00**
Warming Tray, Appleman, glass, electric .......... **125.00**

# INDEX

## - B -

## - D -



## - E -

## - R -

## - S -

## - T -

## - U, V, W -

## - X, Y, Z -